274 SONGS FOR ALL OCCASIONS

The E-Z Play® TODAY Jumbo Songbook has been especially created to offer the widest variety of musical selections for all occasions...and compiled in one convenient, easy-to-read volume.

In addition to the hundreds of pages of music, you'll also find a section in the front of this book devoted to note reading, chord accompaniment, organ registration and automatic rhythm. In the back of the book, for your reference, there is a glossary of music notation, terms, and note values. A chord speller chart for keyboard instruments and a guitar chord chart follow the glossary.

For quick cross-reference, all song arrangements in the E-Z Play TODAY Jumbo Songbook are listed by categories in the front of the book...and listed alphabetically in the back of the book.

For your continued playing enjoyment, dozens of songbooks are available in the E-Z Play TODAY music series. The entire series provides a play-on-sight repertoire filled with musical fun for everyone. A listing of these books can be found in the back of this book. Complete your music library today...see your local music dealer, or write directly to the National Sales Office of Hal Leonard Publishing Corporation.

CONTENTS

HAL LEONARD PUBLISHING CORPORATION
Home Office: 960 East Mark Street Winona MN 55987
National Sales Office: 8112 West Bluemound Road Milwaukee WI 53213

CATEGORICAL INDEX

NOTATION

All songs are written in the exclusive E-Z Play TODAY music notation.

- A STAFF is five lines with spaces between them. Each line or space represents a lettered note.

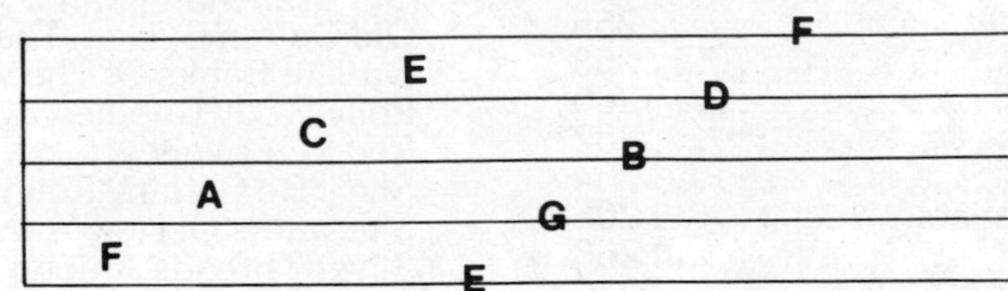

- Sometimes LEDGER LINES are added above or below the staff to accommodate additional notes.

LEDGER LINES

LEDGER LINES

- The lettered notes correspond to lettered keys on the keyboard guide. As notes move down the staff, the corresponding keys move down (to the left) on the keyboard. As the notes move up the staff, they move up (to the right) on the keyboard.

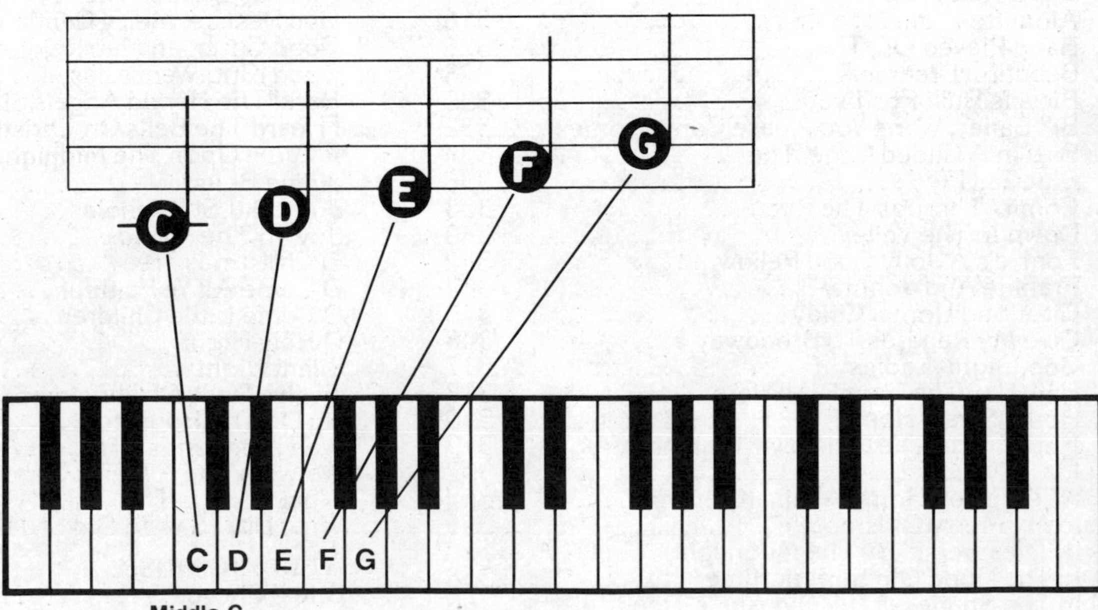

NOTE VALUES

- Each type of note has a specific TIME VALUE which is measured in rhythmic beats.

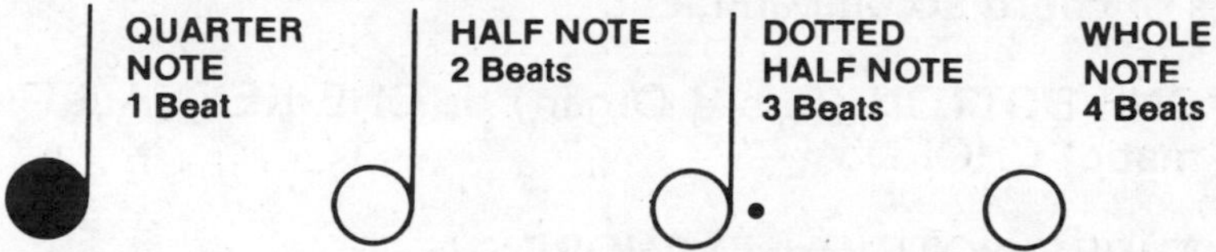

- Each staff is divided by BAR LINES into sections called MEASURES. A DOUBLE BAR indicates the end of a song.

Measure Measure

Bar Line Bar Line Double Bar Line

- A TIME SIGNATURE appears at the beginning of each song after the TREBLE CLEF sign.

The **top number** indicates the number of rhythmic beats in each measure.

The **bottom number** indicates the type of note that receives one beat. 4 indicates a quarter note.

- Sometimes a note or notes appear at the beginning of a song which do not equal the number of beats indicated by the time signature. These are called PICK-UP NOTES, and the missing beats are written at the end of the song.

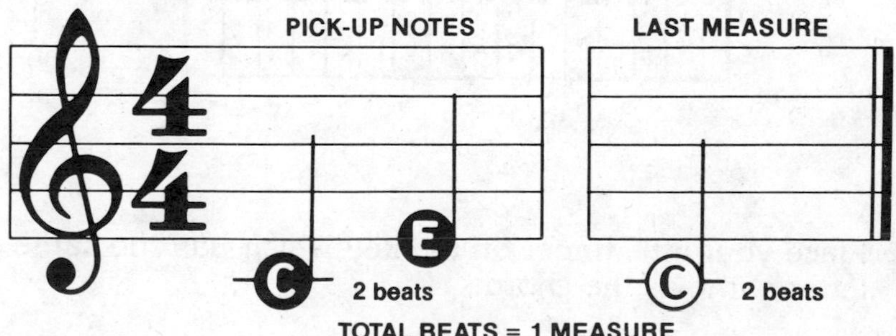

- A TIE is a curved line that connects notes of the same pitch (notes on the same line or space). Play the first note and then hold for the total time of all tied notes.

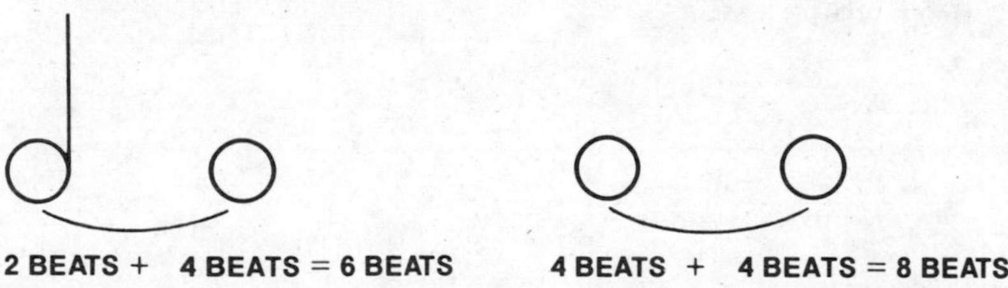

ACCOMPANIMENT

The arrangements in this book have been written for all types of chord accompaniment.

1 ONE BUTTON (Chord Organ) or ONE-KEY (Automatic) CHORDS

2 THREE-NOTE (Triad) CHORDS

3 CONVENTIONAL (Standard) KEYBOARD CHORD POSITIONS

4 GUITAR CHORDS

Chord names, called chord symbols, appear above the melody line as either a boxed symbol [C]

or as an alternate chord (C7)

or both C7 [C]

1 CHORD ORGAN or ONE-KEY AUTOMATIC CHORDS —Play whichever name is on your instrument.

2 THREE-NOTE (Triad) CHORDS—If you've previously learned to play three-note triad chords, or if you wish to learn this system:

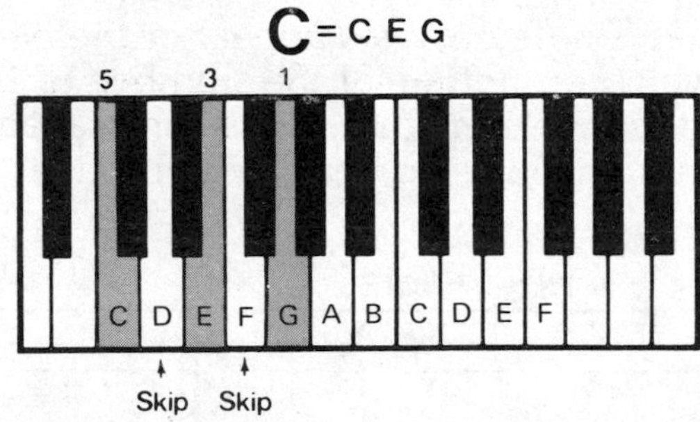

- Place your little finger on the key which has the same letter name as the chord.
- Skip a white key and place your middle finger on the next white key.
- Skip another white key and place your thumb on the next white key.

CHORD SYMBOLS WITH ARROWS

When triad chord symbols are made up of one or more black keys, a special chord notation with arrows is used. The following illustration will help you understand this system.

- Think of a chord as having three sections.
- Each section represents one note of the triad.

The placement of arrows in one or more "sections" to the right or the left of the chord name indicates which of the notes will be raised or lowered one half step. For example:

- Move a chord key **down** one half step when the arrow is placed to the **left** of the chord letter name.

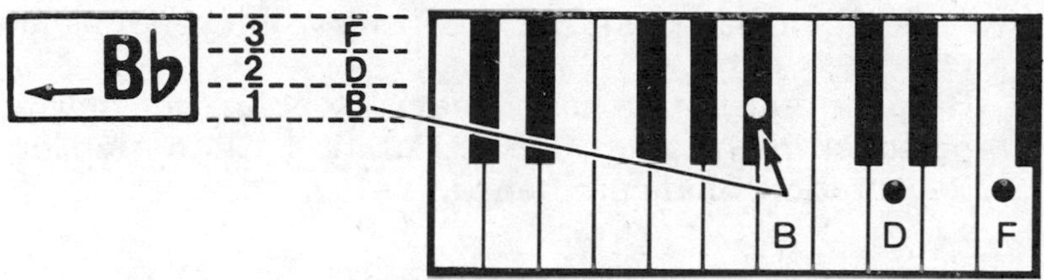

B is lowered one-half step.

- Move a chord key **up** when the arrow is placed to the **right** of the chord letter name.

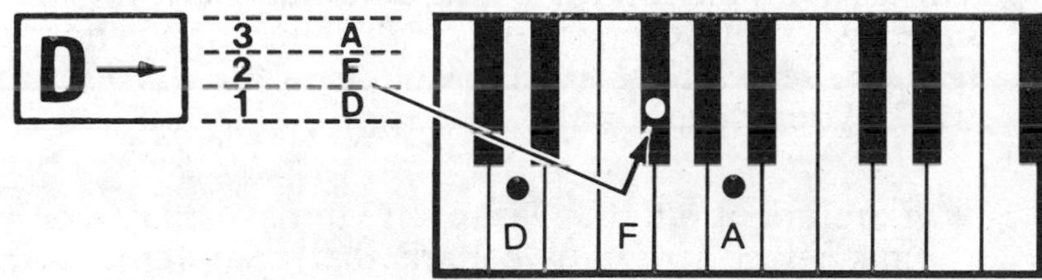

F is raised one-half step.

- If two or three arrows are shown, use the same procedure by altering the number of chord keys according to the direction of the arrows.

3 STANDARD CHORD POSITIONS—When playing standard chord positions, the positions (inversions) of the three-note and four-note chords is strictly a matter of your own choice. Usually, bass pedals are played with standard chord positions.

For your reference, a CHORD SPELLER of commonly used standard chord positions is included at the back of this book.

4 GUITAR CHORDS—Follow the boxed chord symbol, unless an alternate is indicated. Play the alternate chord whenever possible.

REGISTRATION

On most organs or electronic keyboards, there are various tabs or tonebars and/or controls which produce and/or enhance sounds. Some are called voice tabs . . . instrumental voices at different pitches. Some are general controls . . . such as Vibrato or Tremolo. A combination of tabs or tonebars and general controls is called REGISTRATION.

A registration number appears at the beginning of each song in this book.

- Match this number with the same number on the E-Z Play TODAY Registration Guide (opposite page).

- Set the voice tabs or tonebars and controls as indicated.

- If you wish to use special effect registrations such as Banjo or Hawaiian Guitar, consult your Owner's Manual.

Because registration has so many variables, one of which is personal imagination, the registrations suggested on the Registration Guide are generalized.

AUTOMATIC RHYTHM

The excitement created by an automatic rhythm will enhance your music regardless of which left-hand chord system you select. Here are a few hints for the most effective use of your rhythm unit:

- Experiment with the various rhythms available on your unit. Select a rhythm pattern that complements each song. Sometimes it's fun to create unusual or different moods by combining two or more rhythm patterns.

- Most rhythm units have a volume control which regulates the volume level of the percussion instruments. For Latin rhythms, the percussion instruments usually play a more prominent role than they do in a ballad type rhythm; therefore adjust the volume control accordingly.

- Every rhythm unit has a tempo (speed) control which regulates the speed of the selected rhythm pattern. As you first begin to learn a song, adjust the tempo control to a slower speed until you can play the song with ease and accuracy.

- The tempo light flashes at predetermined time intervals. Watch the light for the speed of the rhythm and also to determine when a rhythm pattern begins.

REGISTRATION GUIDE

Instrumental voices can be categorized into three groups: Strings, Reeds, and Horns. The names of these voices vary from one organ model to another. The following chart shows a variety of instrumental voice names listed in each of the categories.

E-Z Play TODAY registrations show instrumental voices by their general catgegory. Select the tabs that most closely resemble the tab names on your organ model.

Strings	Reeds	Horns
Violin	Clarinet	Trumpet
Cello	Oboe	Trombone
Viola	Bassoon	Brass
Violina	Saxophone	Kinura
String	Reed	Tuba
		Horn

E-Z Play TODAY Reg. No.	Tab Model Organs	Tonebar Model Organs
1 Open Flutes	Upper: Flutes (Tibias) 16′, 4′ Lower: Diapason 8′ or Flute 8′ Pedal: 16′, 8′ Vib/Trem: On, Normal	Upper: 80 0800 000 Lower: (00) 7600 000 Pedal: 4(0)5(0) Vib/Trem: On, Normal
2 Full Flutes	Upper: Flutes (Tibias) 16′, 8′, 4′, 2′ Lower: Diapason 8′, Reed 8′ Pedal: 16′, 8′ Vib/Trem: On, Normal	Upper: 80 8808 008 Lower: (00) 7503 000 Pedal: 4(0)6(0) Vib/Trem: On, Normal
3 Flute/String Ensemble	Upper: Flutes (Tibias) 8′, 4′, String 8′ Lower: Diapason 8′ Pedal: 16′, 8′ Vib/Trem: On, Normal	Upper: 40 4555 554 Lower: (00) 7503 333 Pedal: 5(0)5(0) Vib/Trem: On, Normal
4 Flute/Reed Ensemble	Upper: Flutes (Tibias) 8′, 4′, Reed 16′ or 8′ Lower: Flute 8′, Reed 8′ Pedal: 16′, 8′ Vib/Trem: On, Normal	Upper: 80 7766 006 Lower: (00) 7540 000 Pedal: 5(0)6(0) Vib/Trem: On, Normal
5 Flute/Reed/String Ensemble	Upper: Flutes (Tibias) 16′, 8′, 4′, Reed 16′ or 8′, String 8′ Lower: Diapason 8′, String 8′ Pedal: 16′, 8′ Vib/Trem: On, Normal	Upper: 80 8868 553 Lower: (00) 6634 221 Pedal: 5(0)6(0) Vib/Trem: On, Normal
6 Liturgical or Classical	Upper: Flutes (Tibias) 16′, 8′, 4′, Reed 8′, String 8′ Lower: Diapason 8′, Reed 8′ Pedal: 16′ Vib/Trem: Off	Upper: 80 8868 550 Lower: (00) 6604 020 Pedal: 6(0)4(0) Vib/Trem: Off
7 Jazz Ensemble	Upper: Flutes (Tibias) 16′, 8′, 5⅓′, 2⅔′ Lower: Diapason 8′, Flute 8′ Pedal: 8′ or 16′ Vib/Trem: Off or Slow	Upper: 88 5080 000 Lower: (00) 5633 320 Pedal: 4(0)6(0) Vib/Trem: Off or Celeste
8 Piano Solo	Upper: Piano or Flute (Tibia) 8′ Lower: Diapason 8′ Pedal: 8′ or 16′ Vib/Trem: On, Normal (lower only)	Upper: Piano Solo Lower: (00) 4302 010 Pedal: 4(0)3(0) Vib/Trem: On, Normal (lower only)
9 Reed Solo	Upper: Reed 16′ or 8′ Lower: Flute 8′ Pedal: 16′, 8′ Vib/Trem: On, Small	Upper: 00 8080 840 Lower: (00) 5544 331 Pedal: 4(0)4(0) Vib/Trem: On, Small
10 String Solo	Upper: String 8′ Lower: Flute 8′ Pedal: 8′ or 16′ Vib/Trem: On, Small (delay)	Upper: 00 7888 888 Lower: (00) 7765 443 Pedal: 5(0)4(0) Vib/Trem: On, Small (delay)

Boola Boola

Registration 5

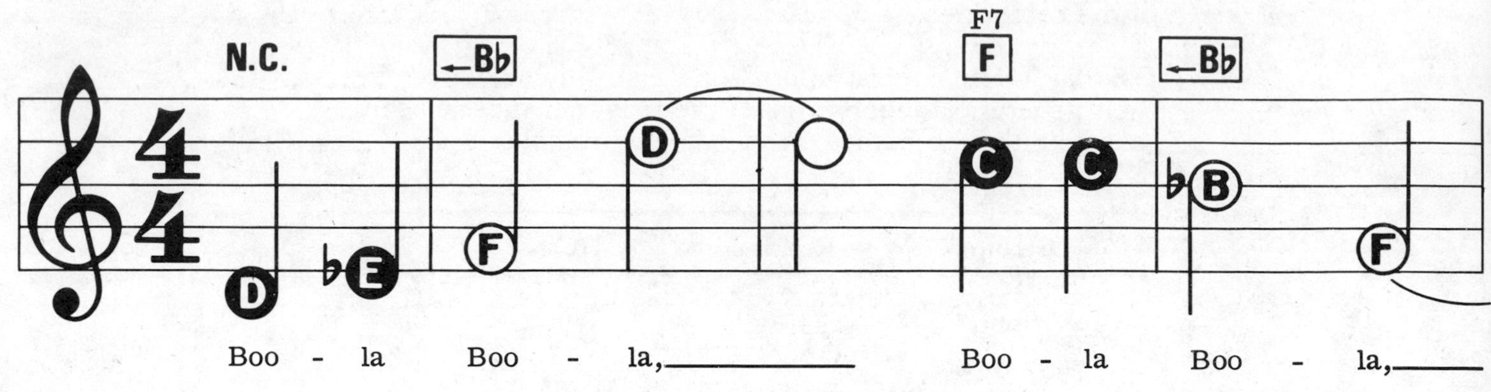

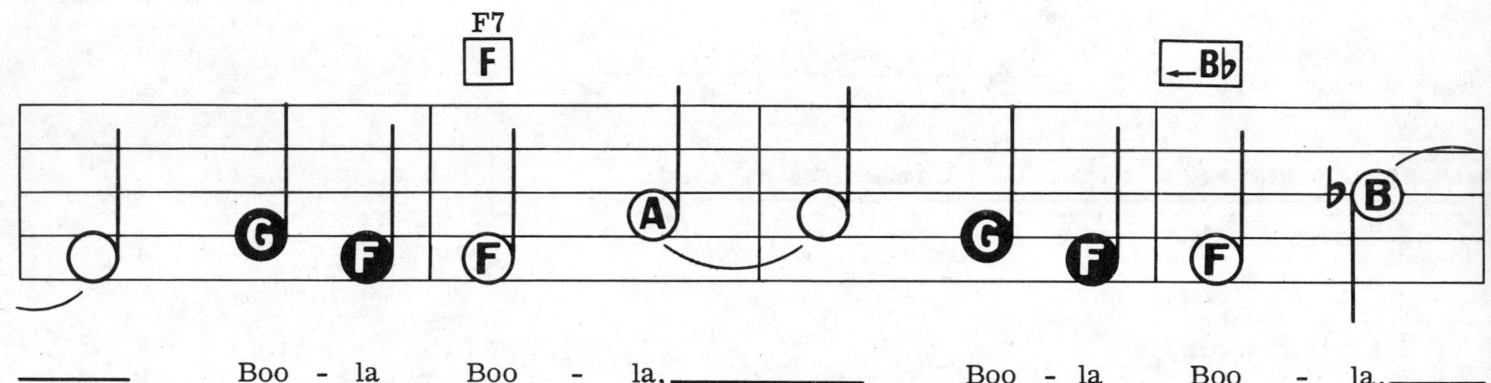

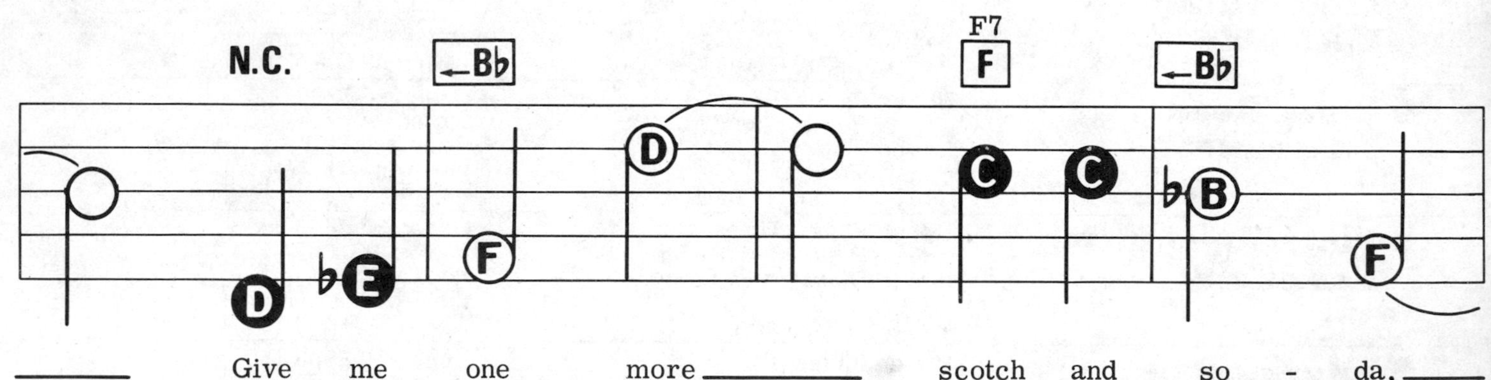

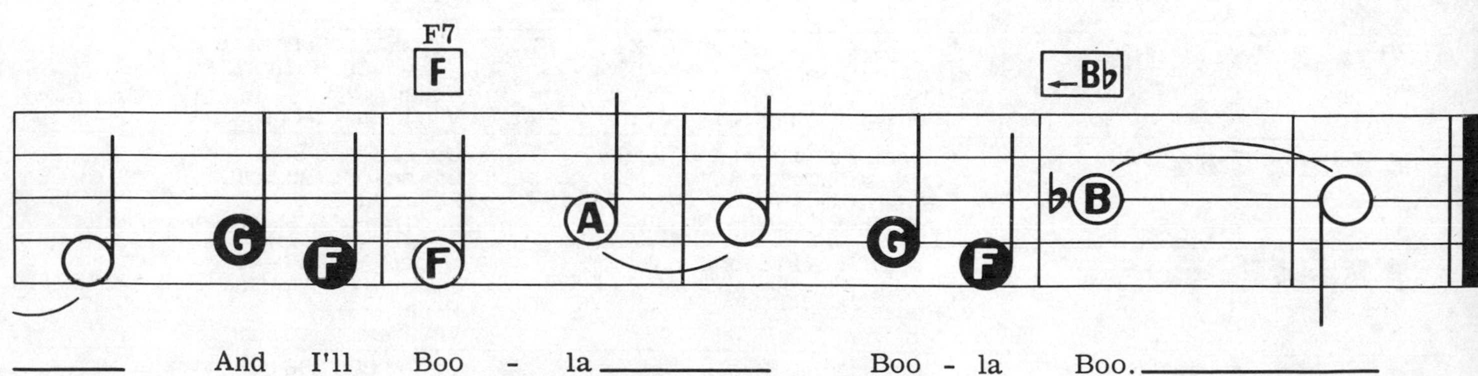

Far Above Cayuga's Waters

Registration 6

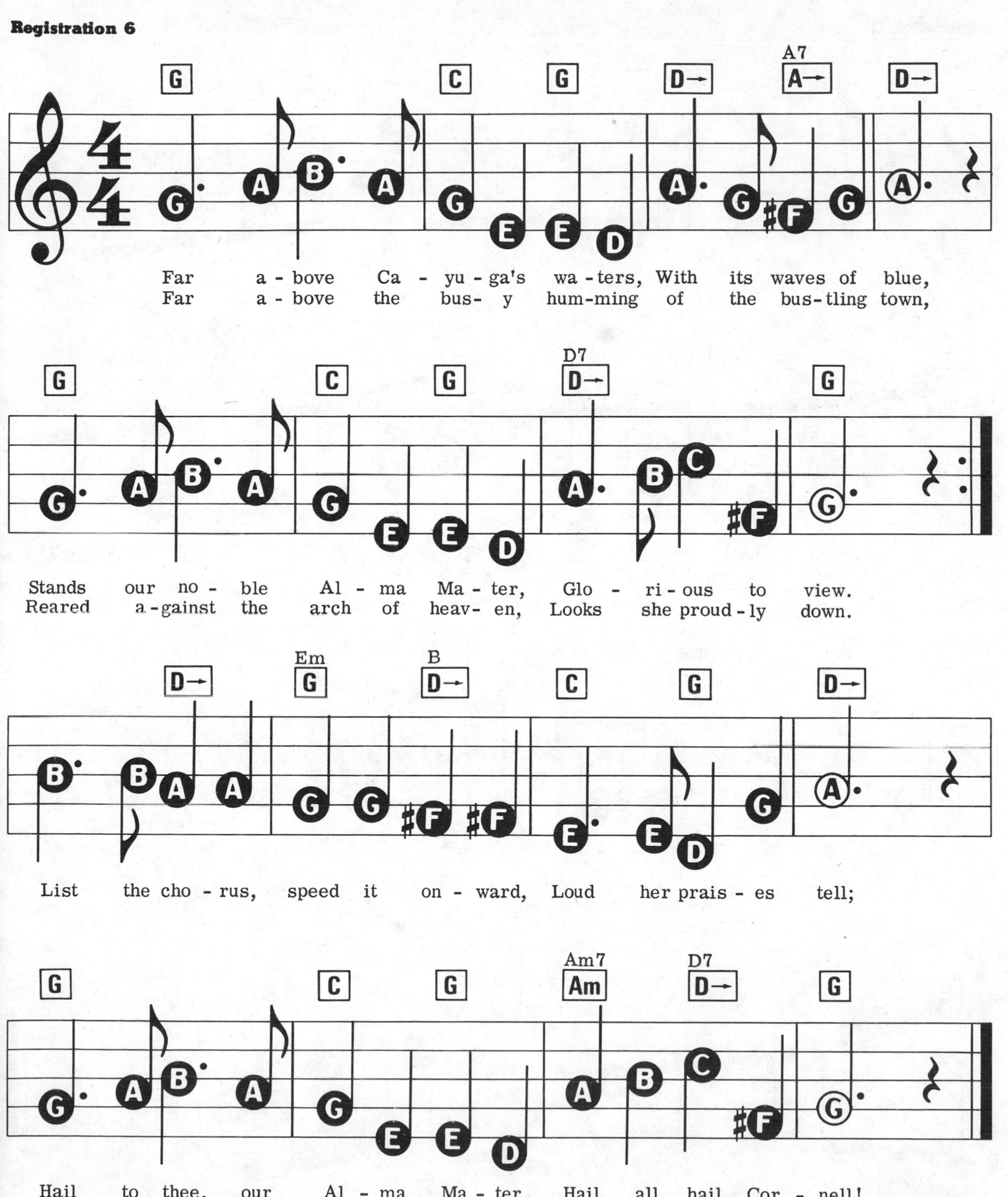

My College Gal

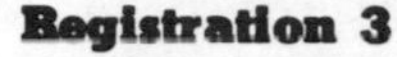

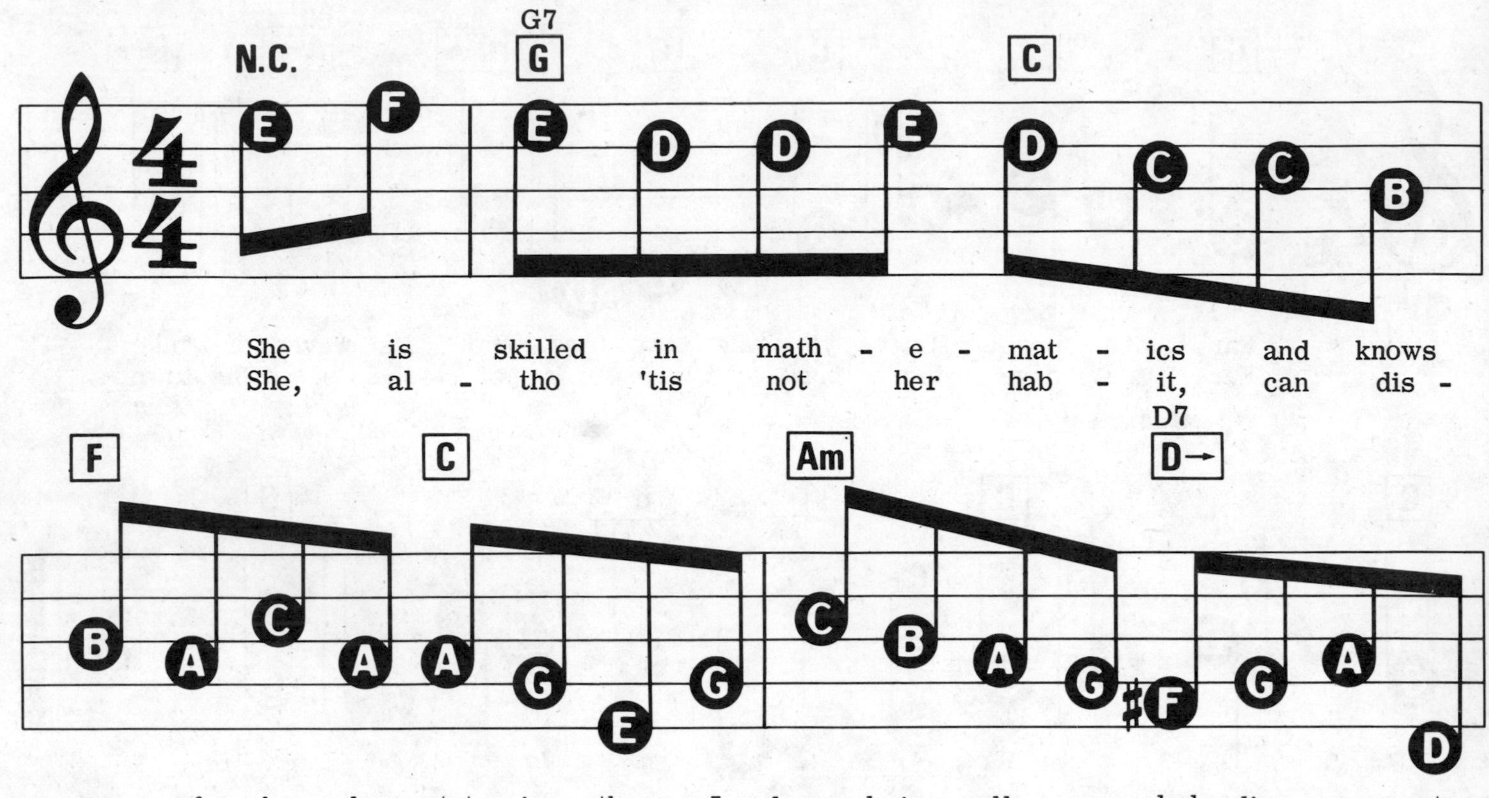

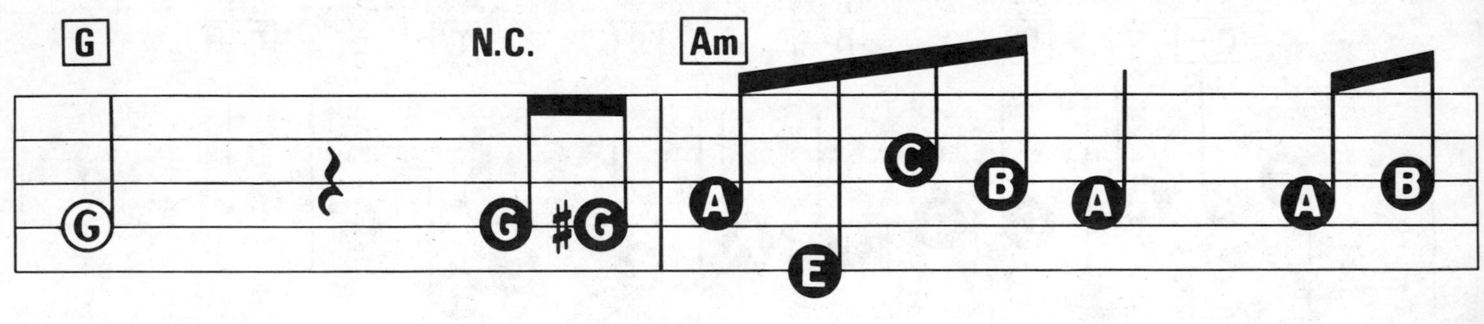

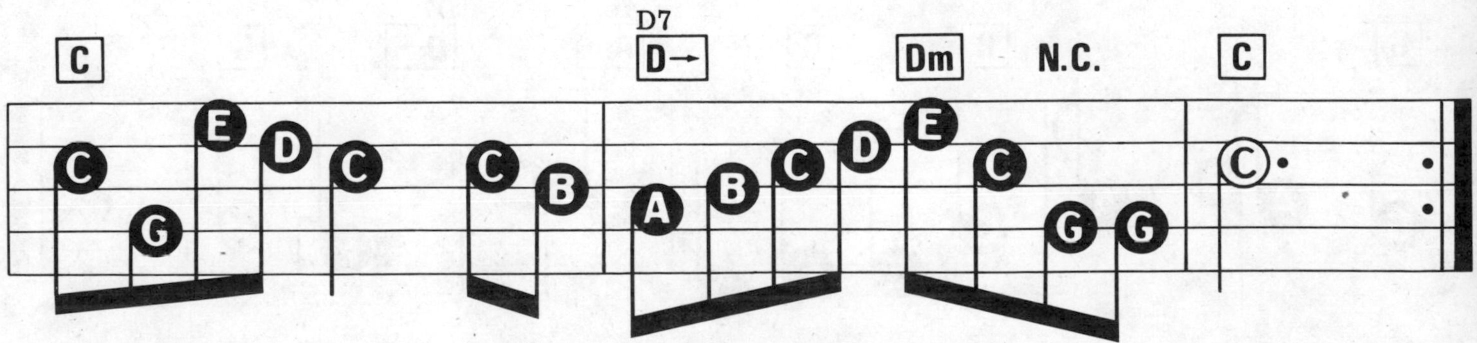

University Of Michigan Song

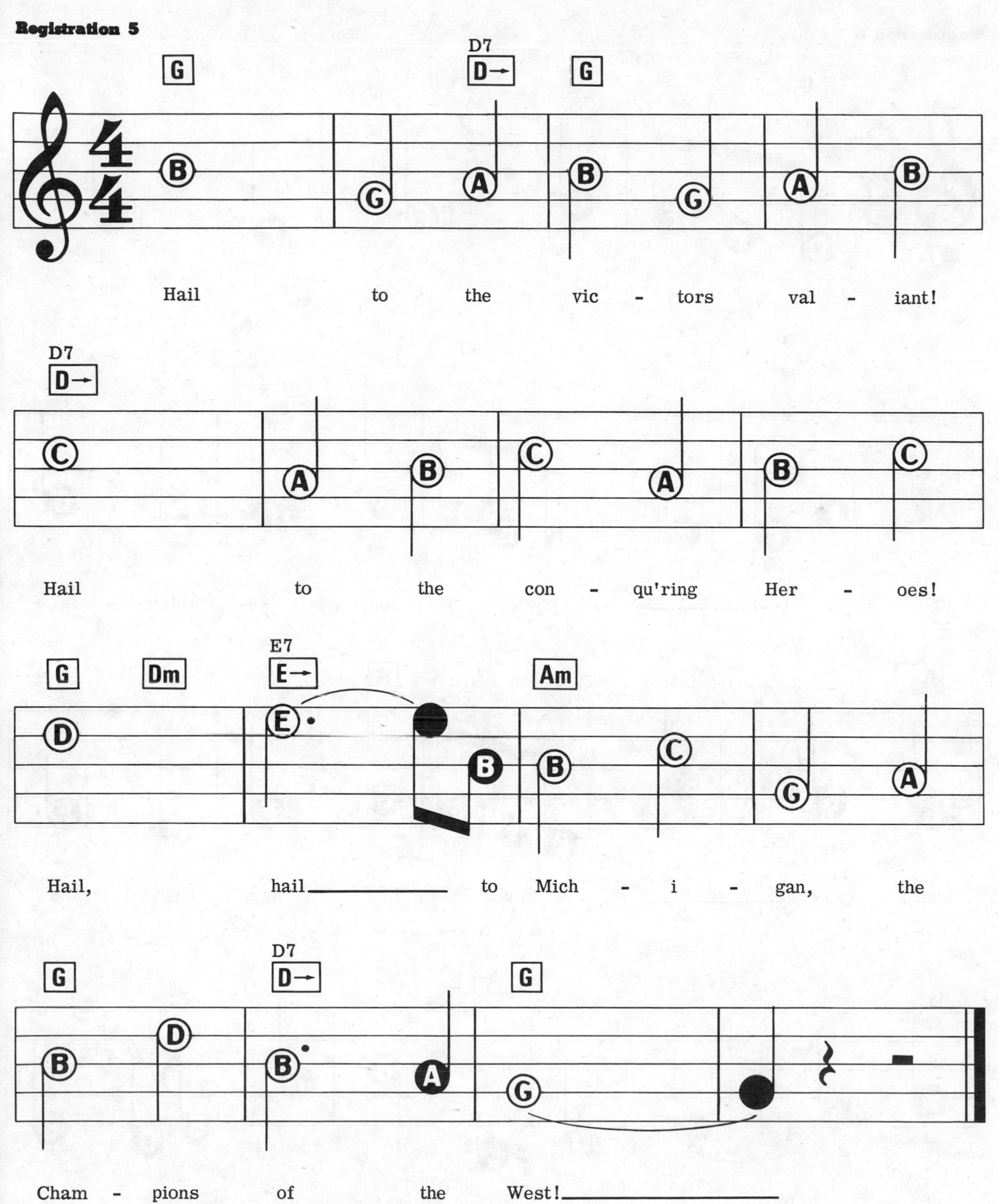

Harvard March

Registration 4

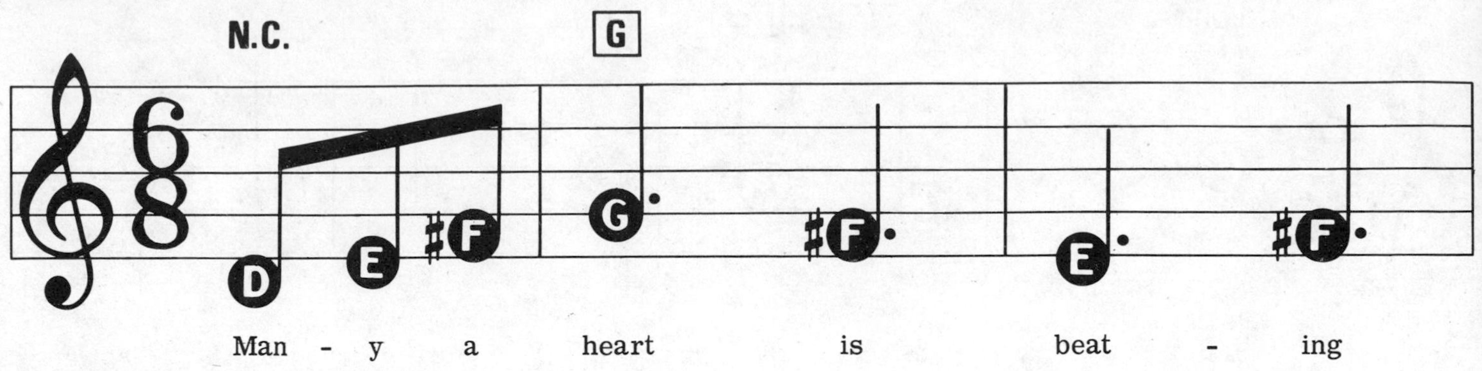

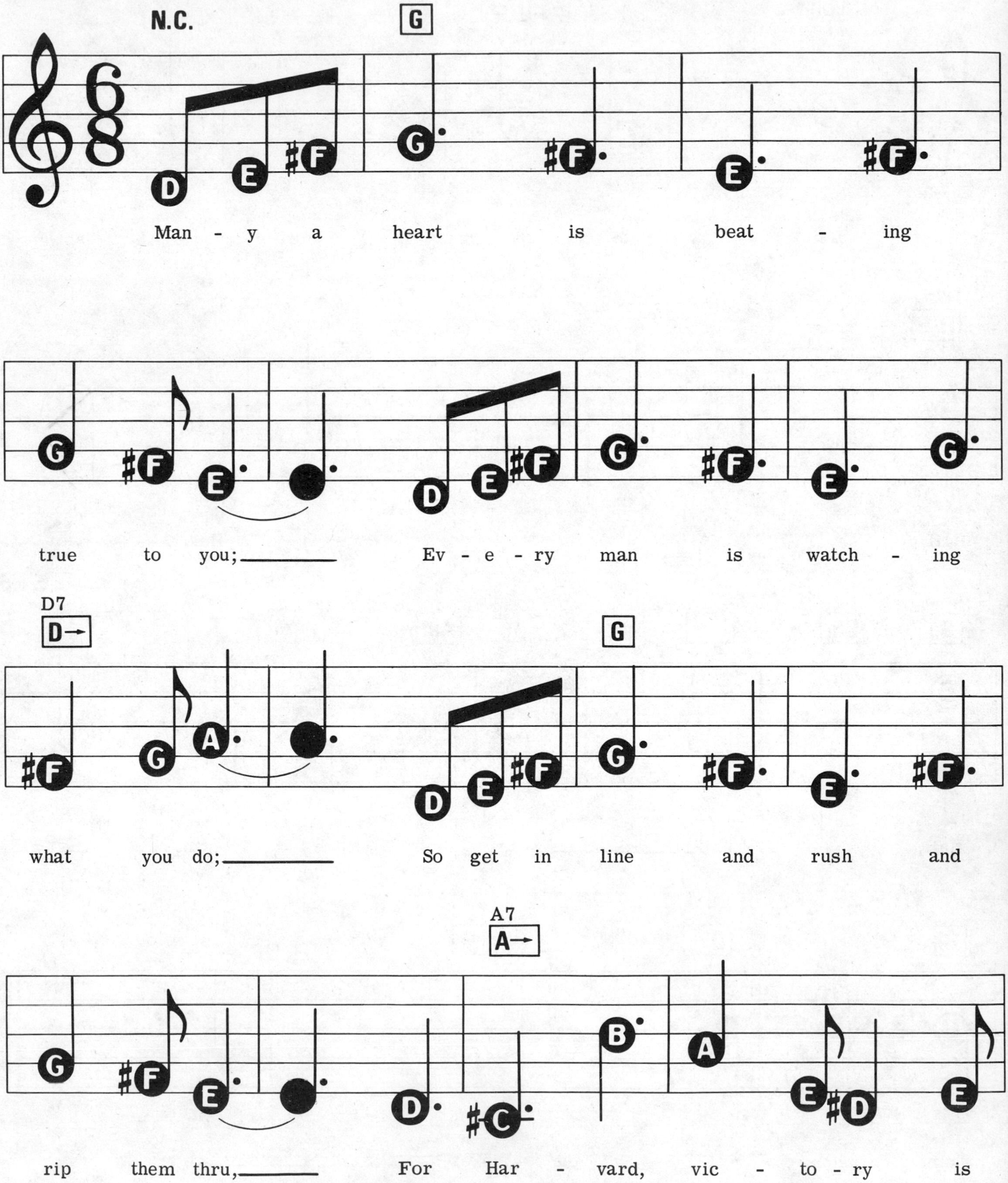

N.C.
G
Man - y a heart is beat - ing
true to you; Ev - e - ry man is watch - ing
D7
G
what you do; So get in line and rush and
A7
rip them thru, For Har - vard, vic - to - ry is

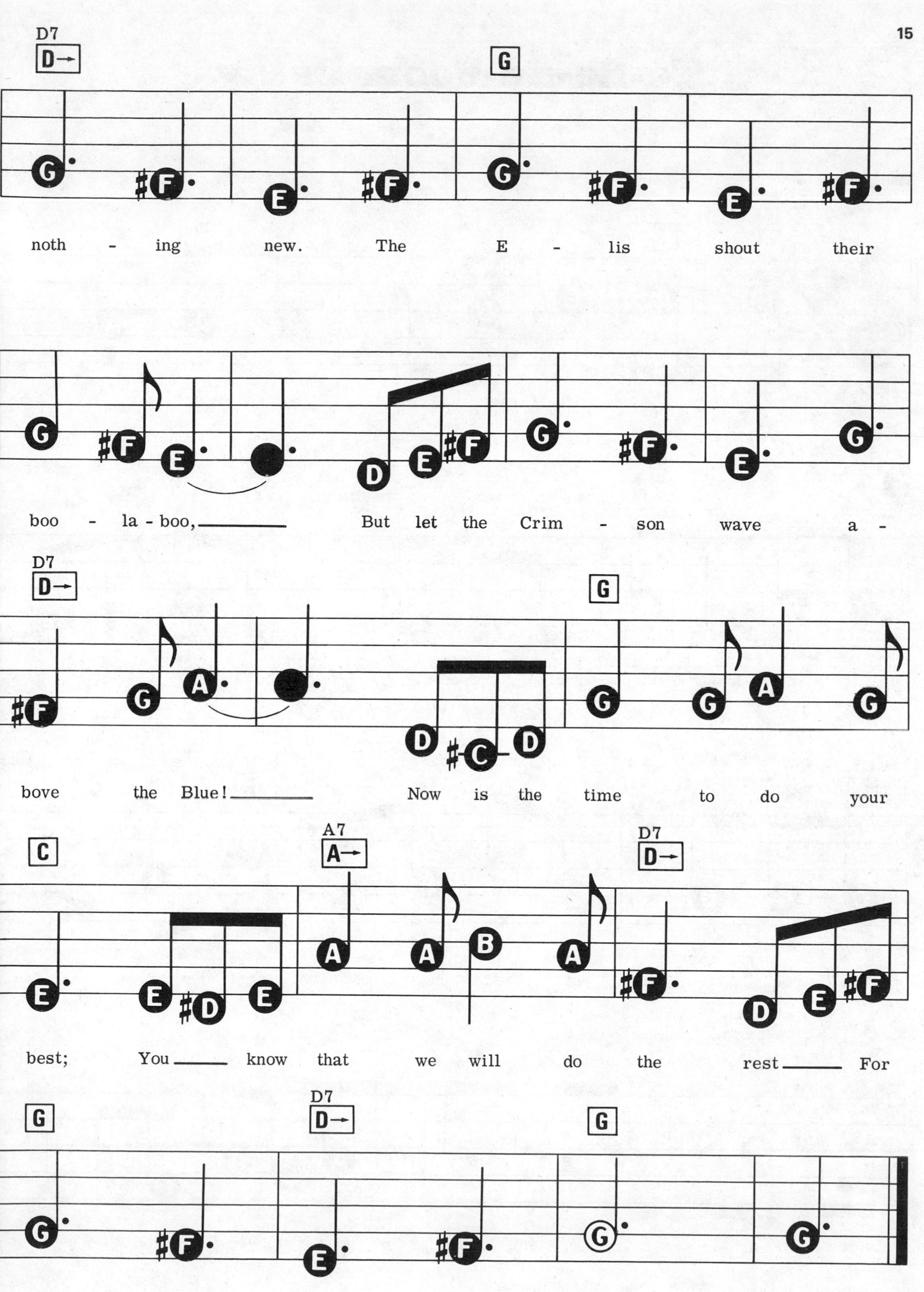
D7 D→ G
noth - ing new. The E - lis shout their
boo - la - boo, But let the Crim - son wave a -
D7 D→ G
bove the Blue! Now is the time to do your
C A7 A→ D7 D→
best; You know that we will do the rest For
G D7 D→ G
Har - vard, Har - vard, Har - vard!

Ta-Ra-Ra-Boom-De-Ay

Registration 5

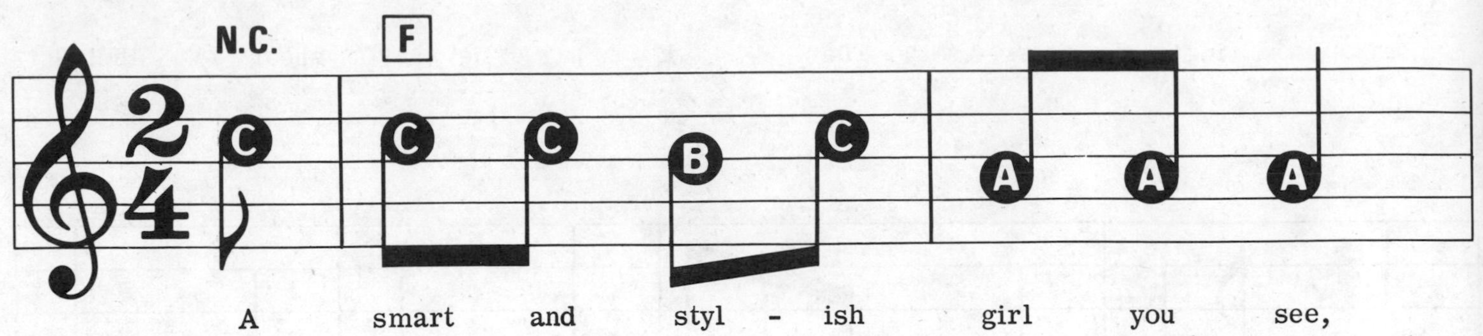

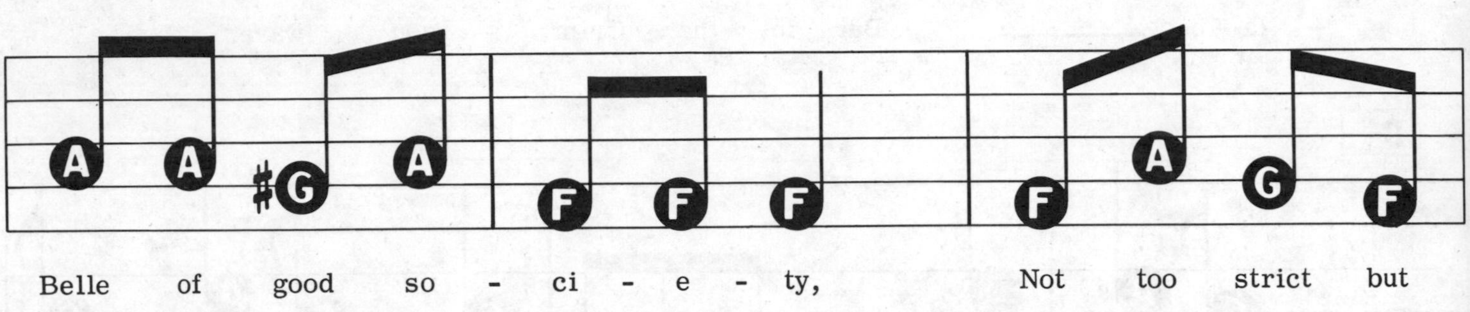

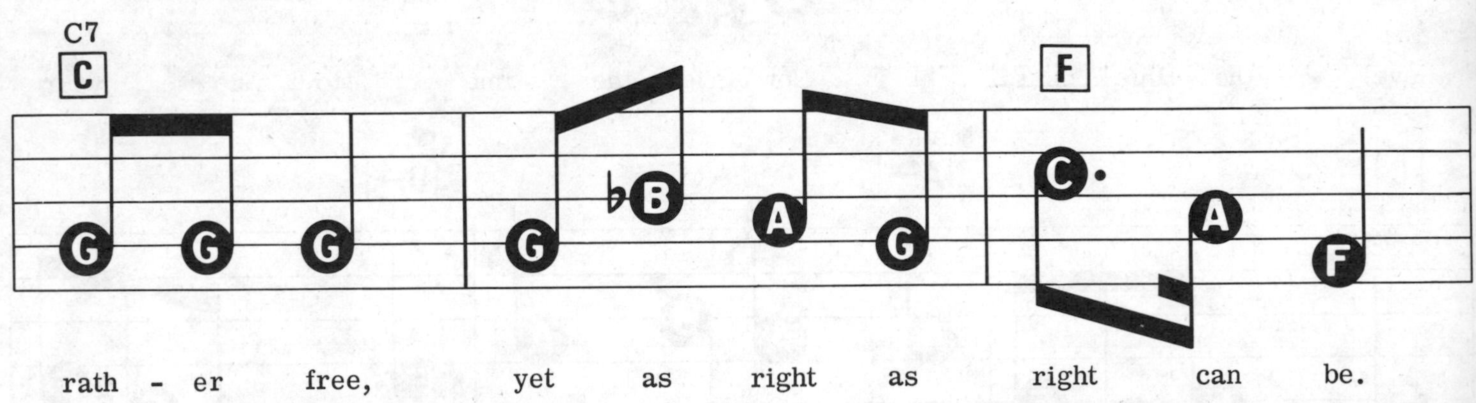

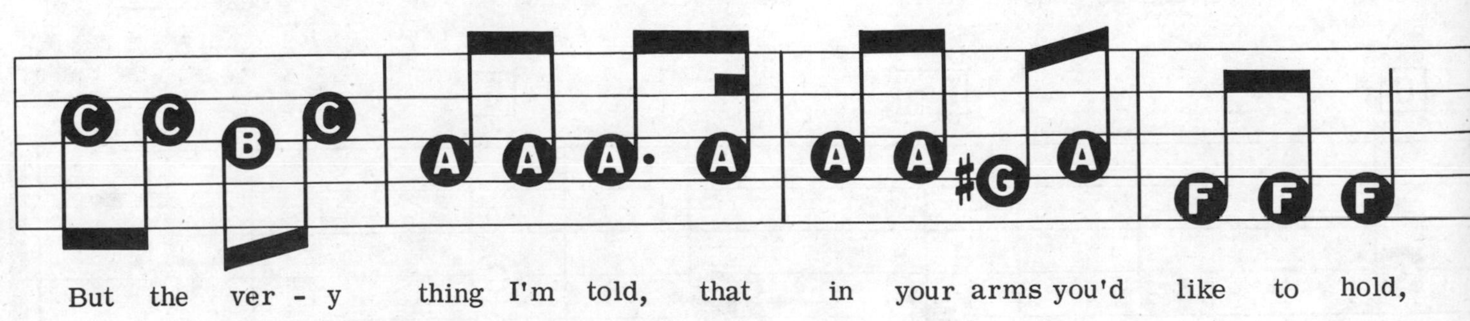

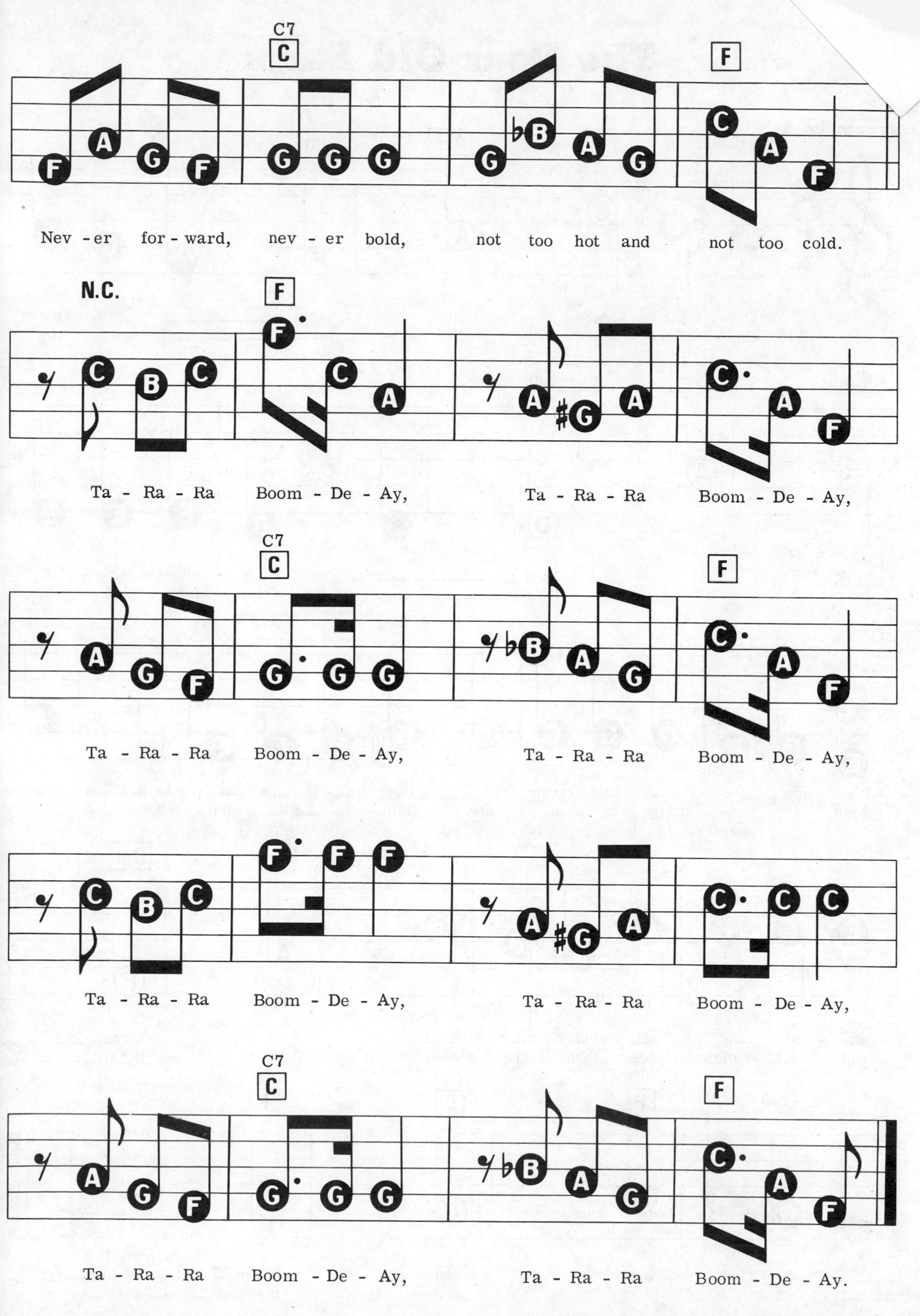
C7
C
F
Nev - er for - ward, nev - er bold, not too hot and not too cold.
N.C.
F
Ta - Ra - Ra Boom - De - Ay, Ta - Ra - Ra Boom - De - Ay,
C7
C
F
Ta - Ra - Ra Boom - De - Ay, Ta - Ra - Ra Boom - De - Ay,
Ta - Ra - Ra Boom - De - Ay, Ta - Ra - Ra Boom - De - Ay,
C7
C
F
Ta - Ra - Ra Boom - De - Ay, Ta - Ra - Ra Boom - De - Ay.

The Dear Old Farm

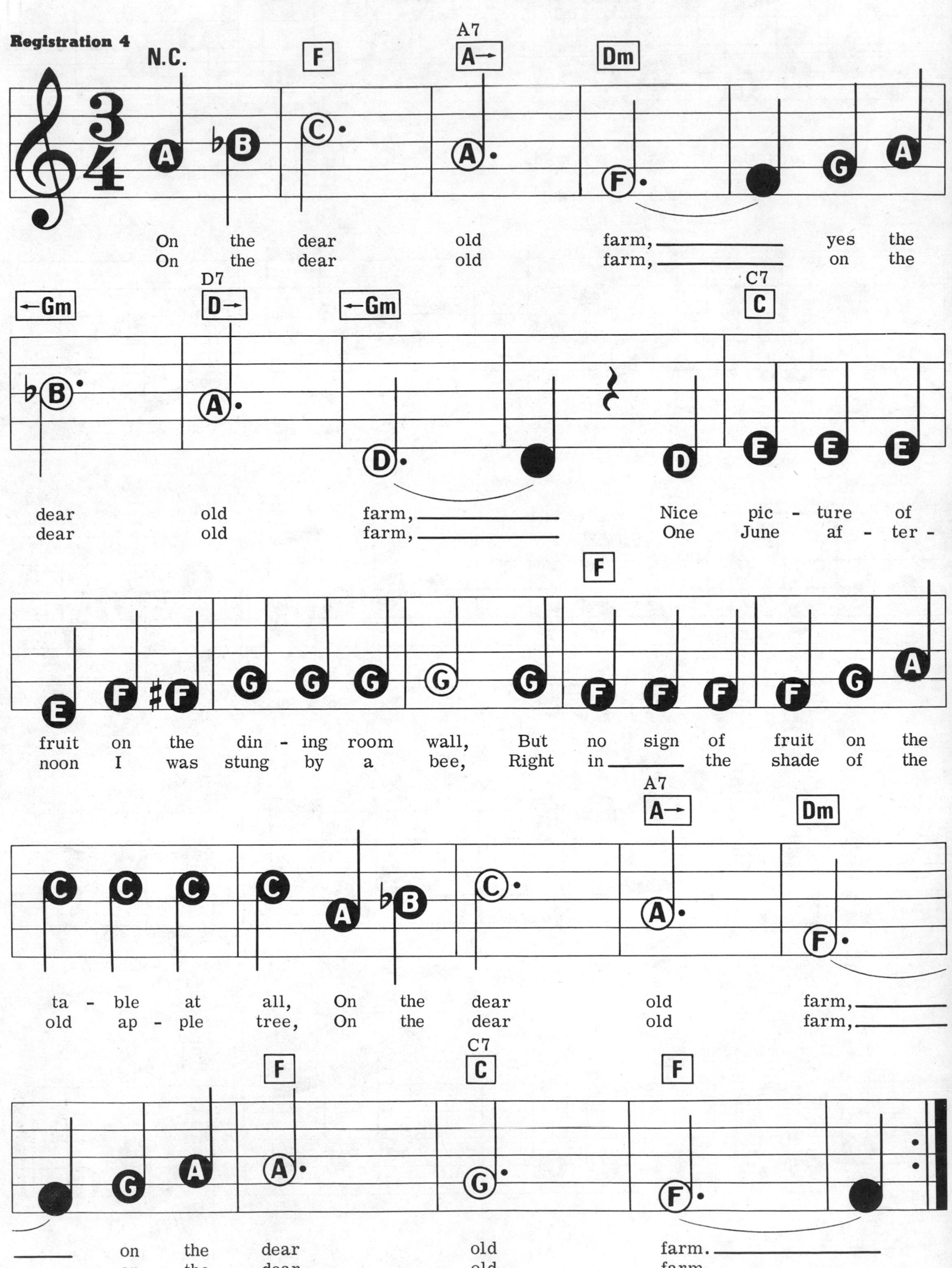

I Don't Mind If I Do

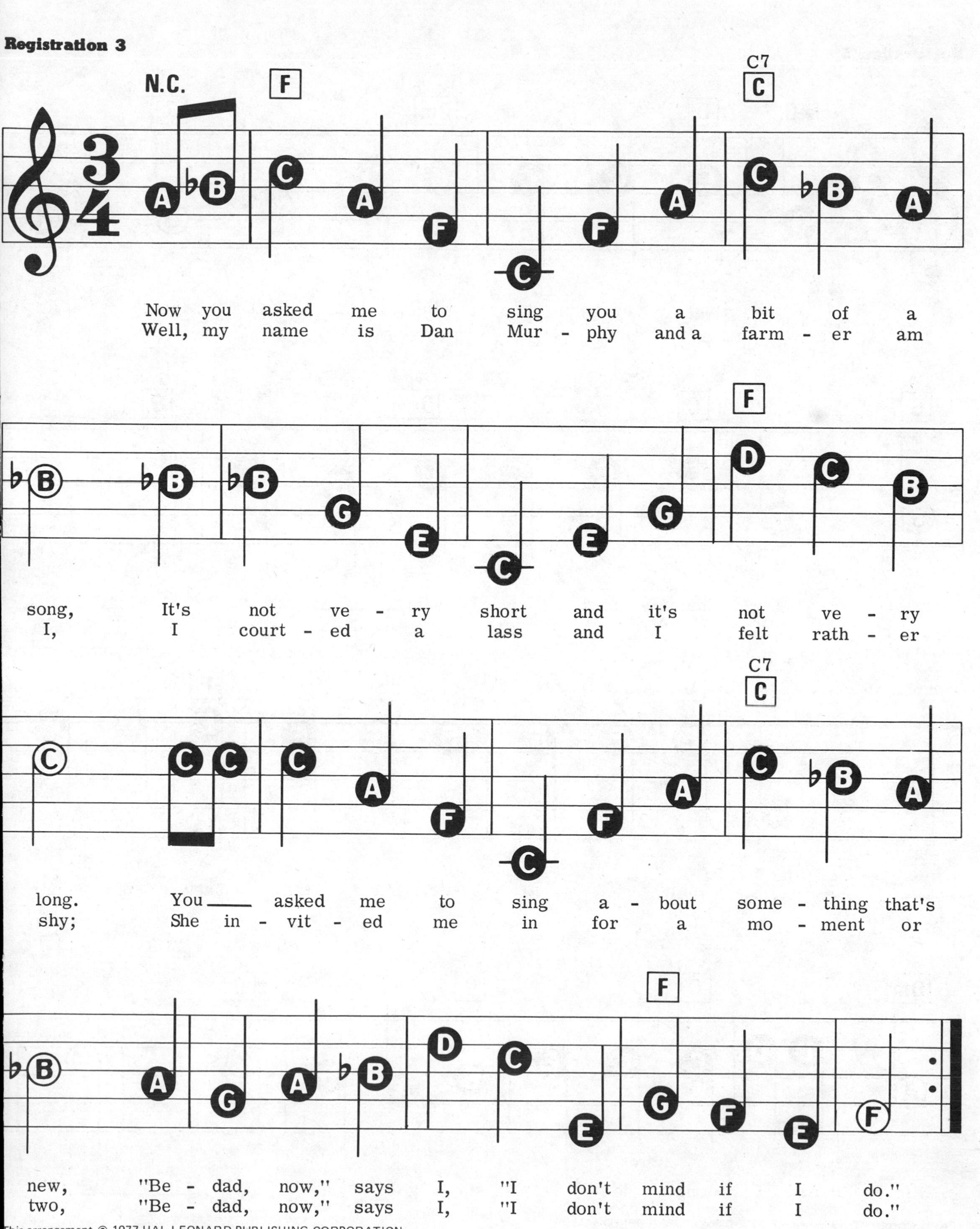

I Married A Wife

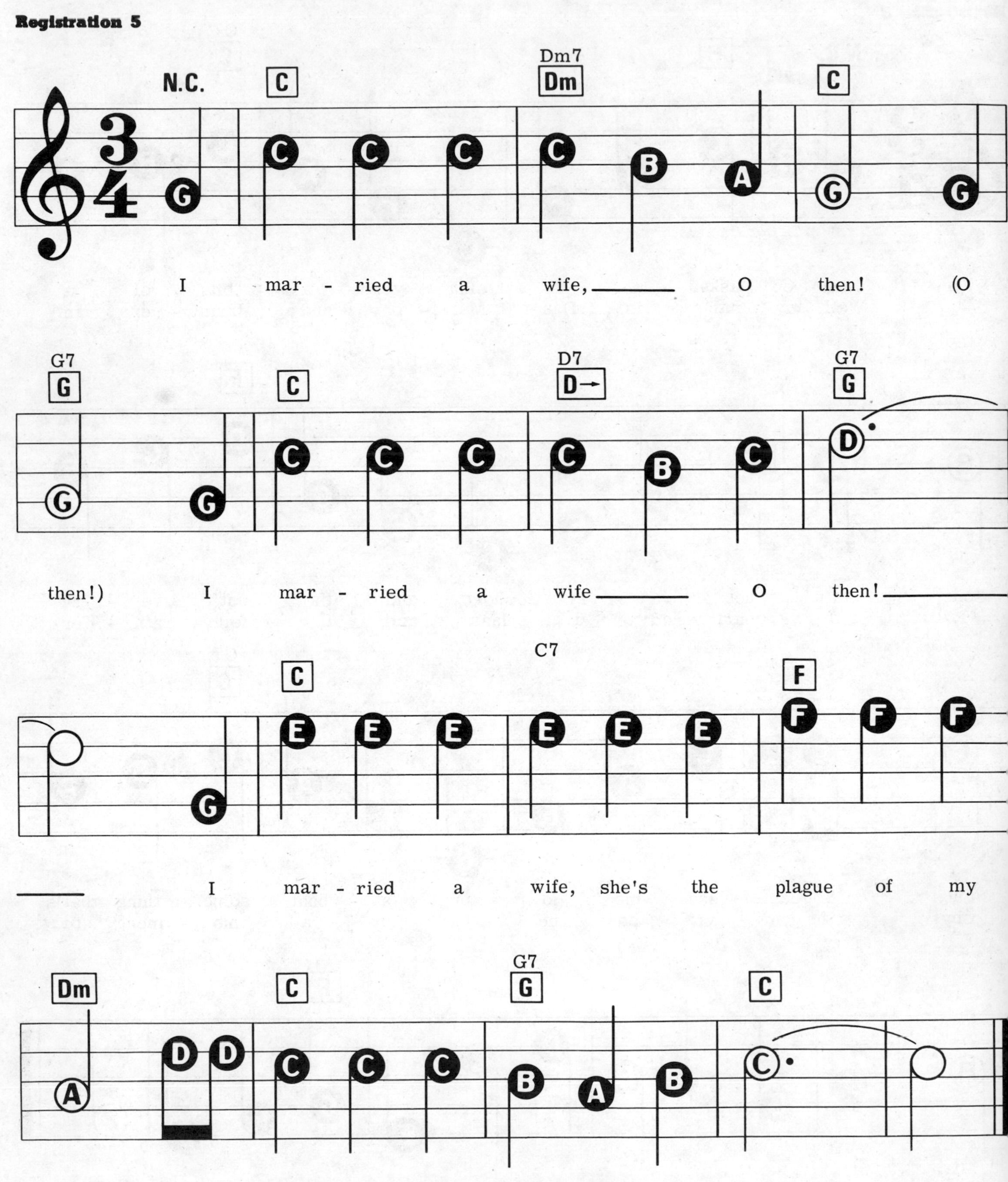

I'm Unlucky

Registration 3

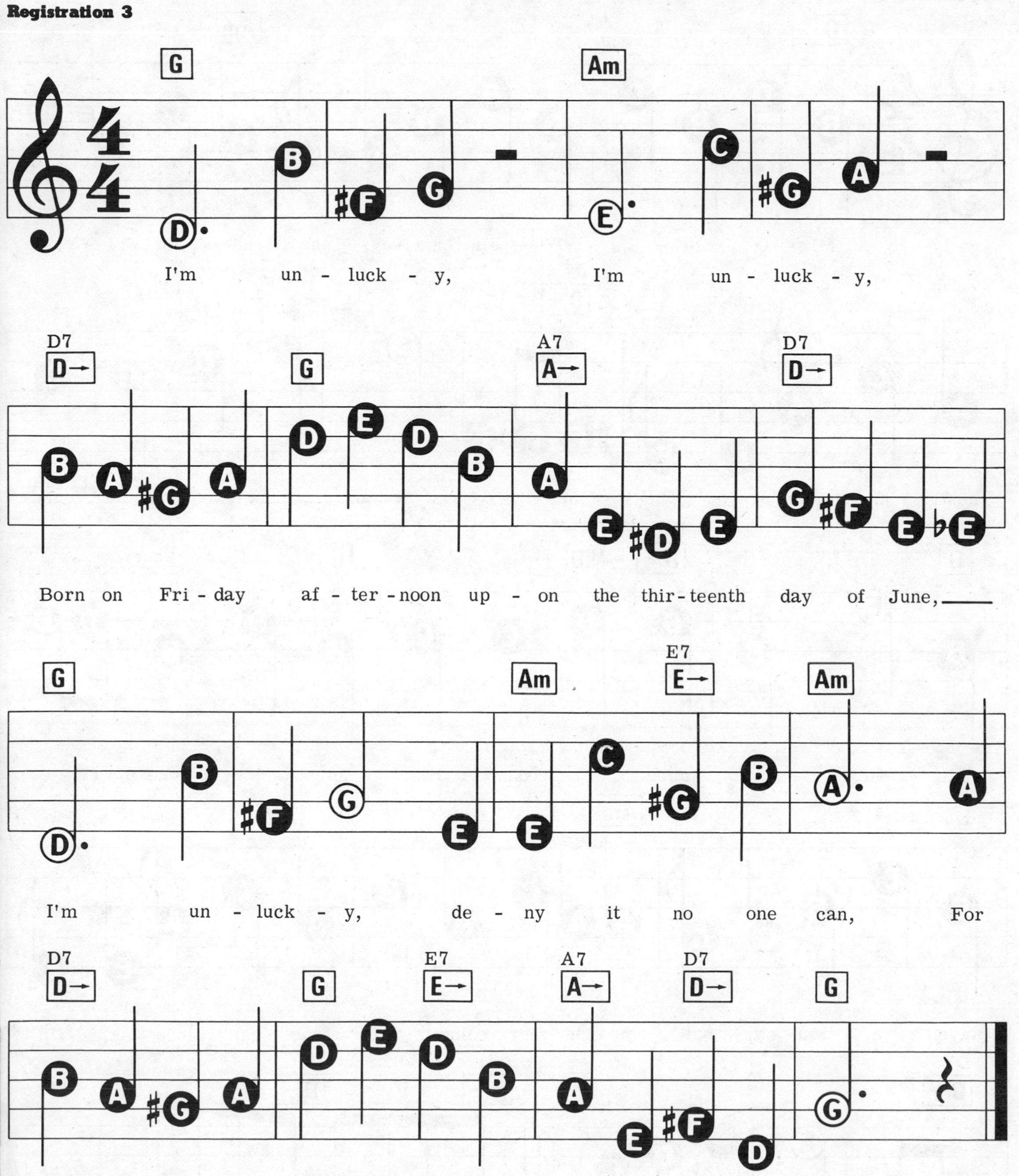

M-O-N-E-Y Spells Money

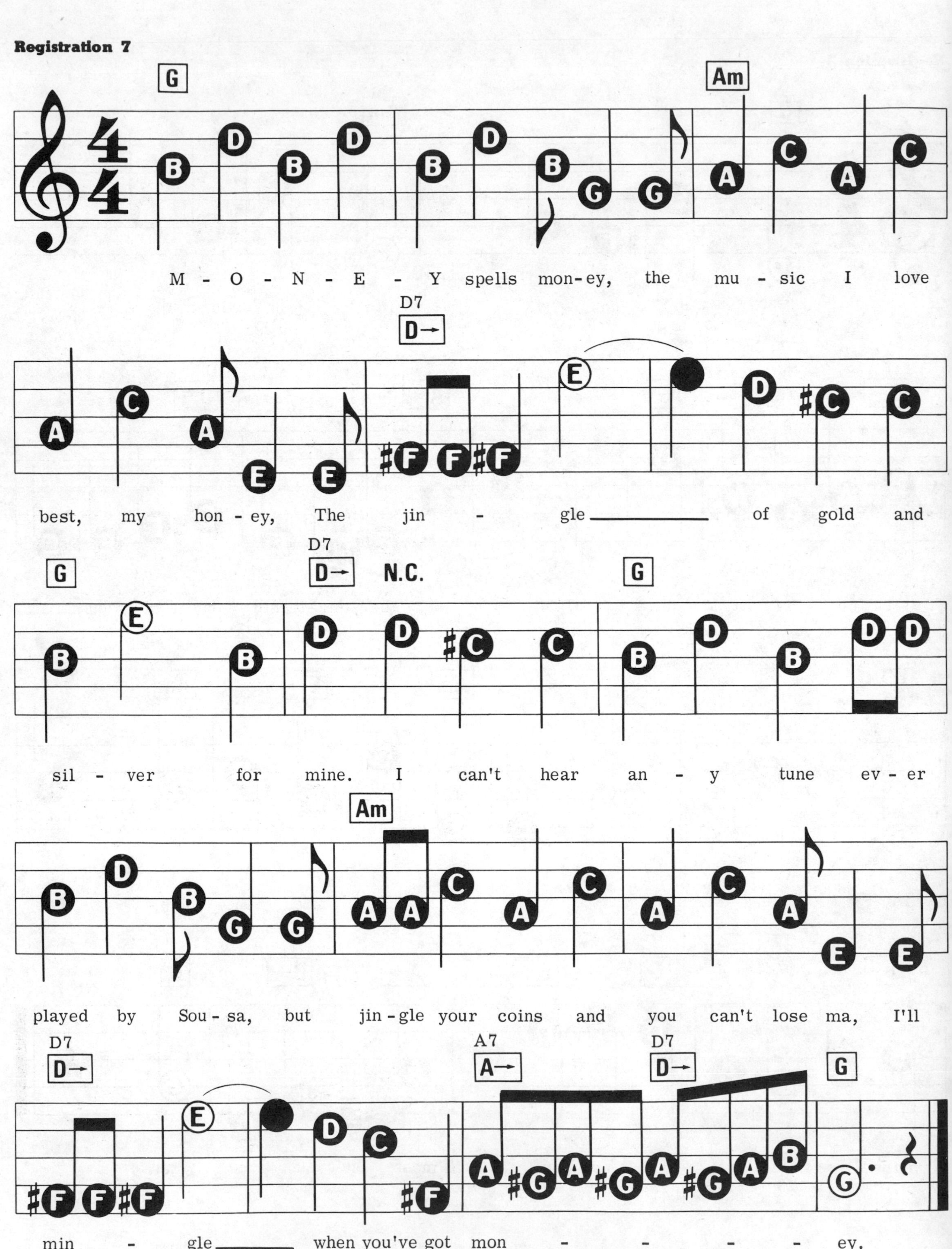

Oh, Dear What Can The Matter Be

Registration 2

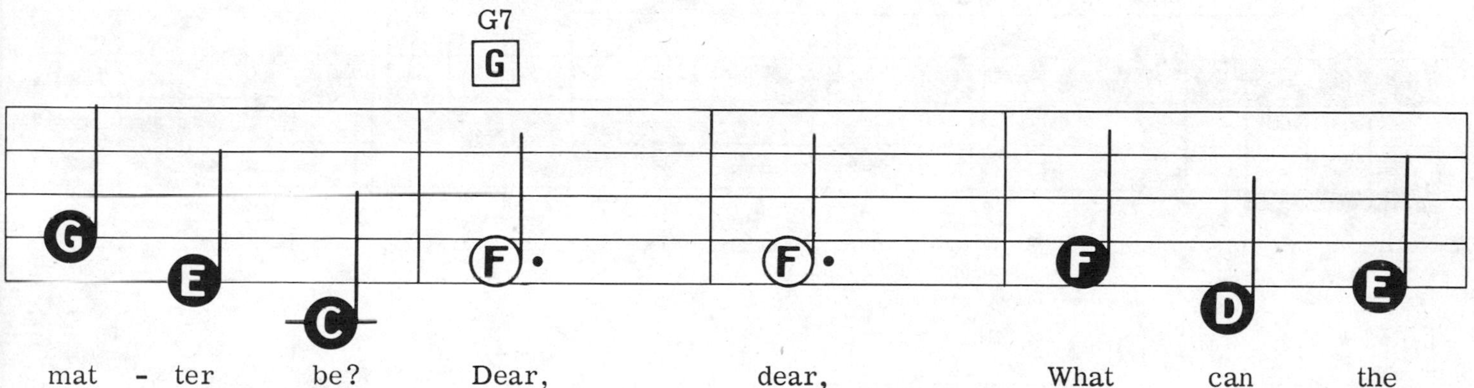

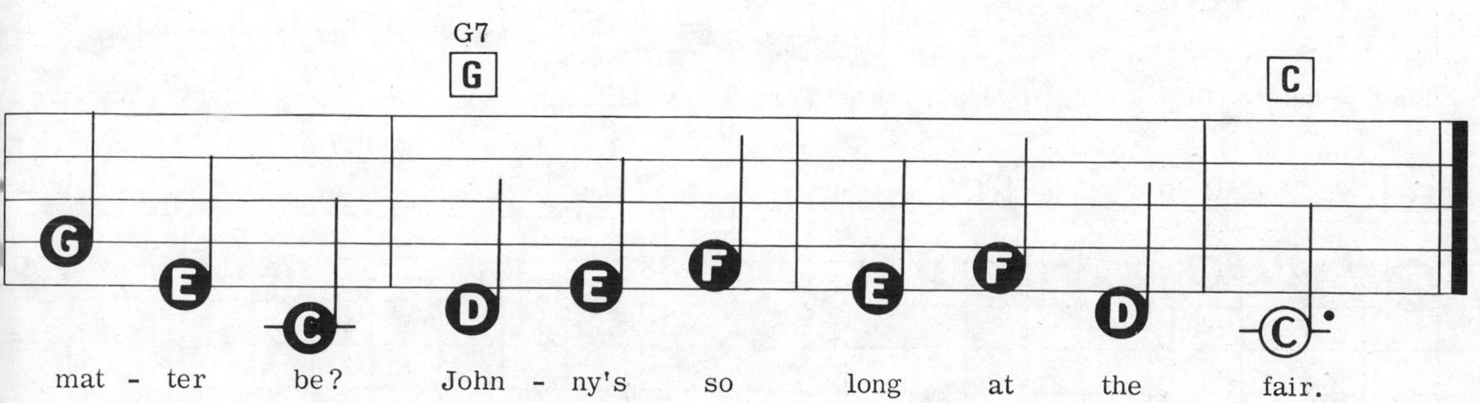

Nothin' From Nothin' Leaves You

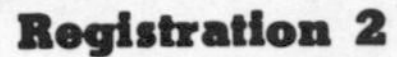

You walk like noth - in' and you talk like noth - in',
Noth- in' seems to be ___ your aim; You look like noth - in' and you act like noth - in',
Noth - in' and you ___ are the same. You can't learn noth - in' 'cause you
don't know noth - in', I've for - got more than you ___ ev - er knew; And the
on - ly way ___ I can fig-ure you out ___ is: Noth -in' from noth - in' leaves you. You

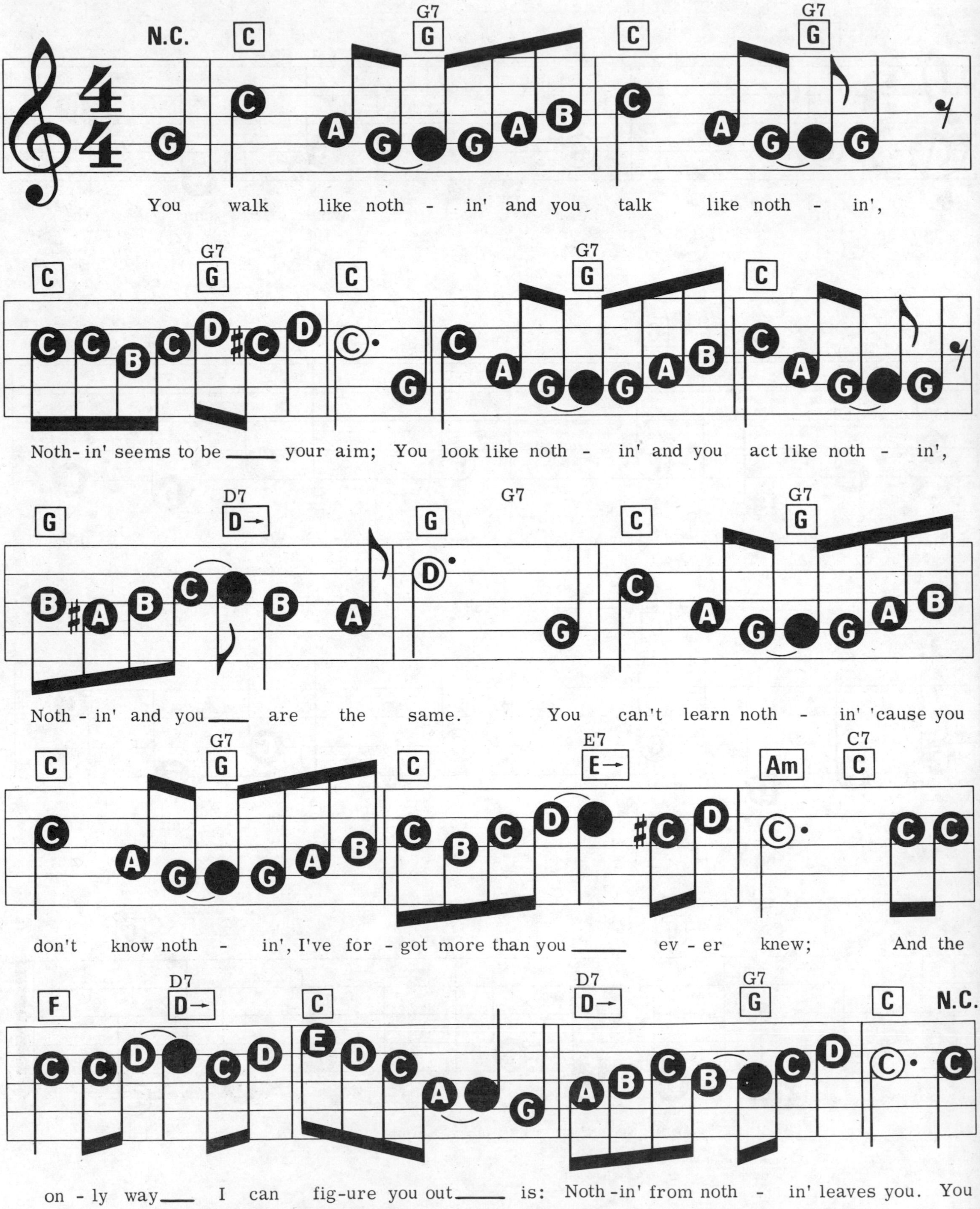

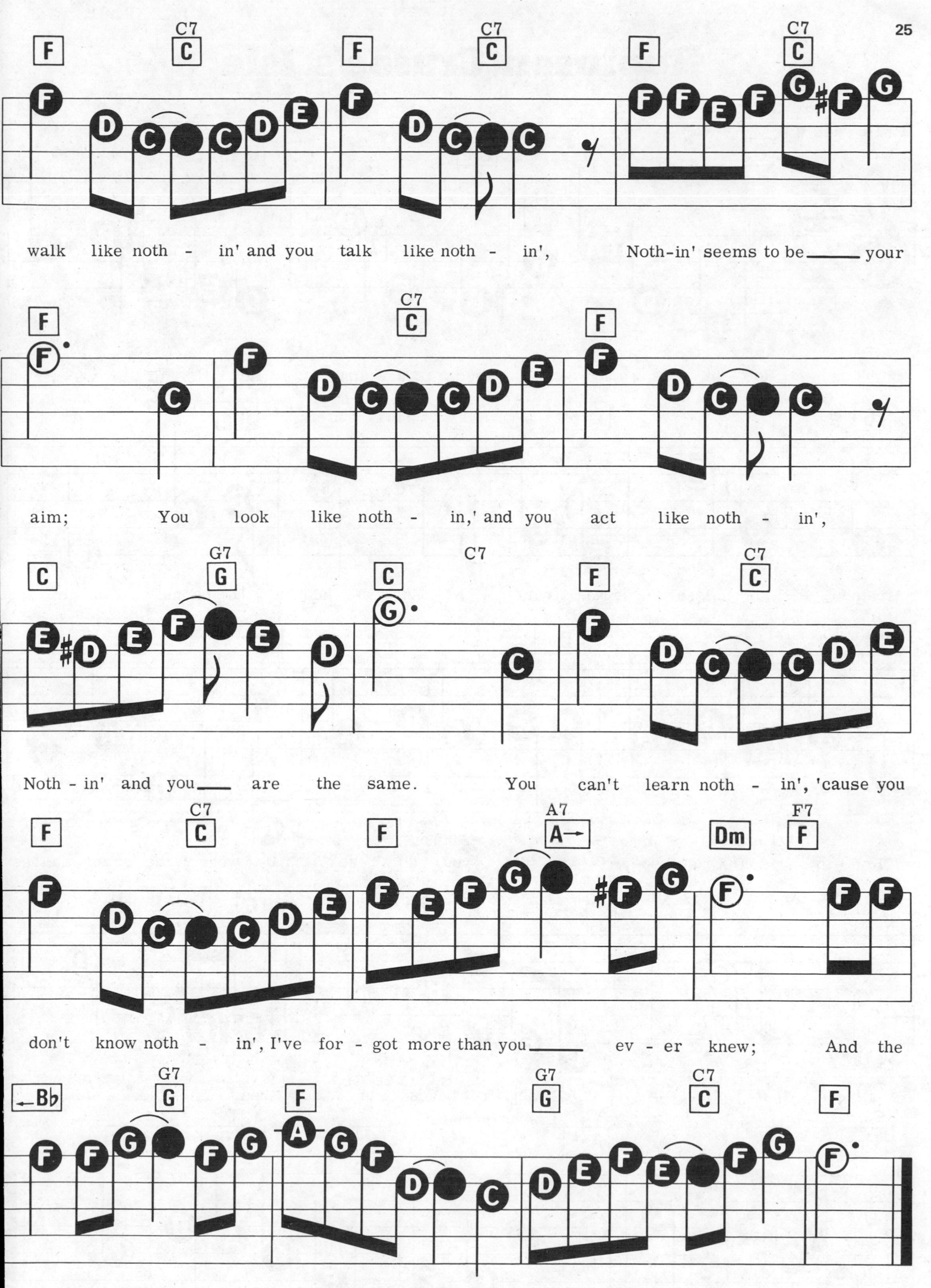
walk like noth - in' and you talk like noth - in', Noth-in' seems to be ___ your
aim; You look like noth - in,' and you act like noth - in',
Noth - in' and you ___ are the same. You can't learn noth - in', 'cause you
don't know noth - in', I've for - got more than you ___ ev - er knew; And the
on - ly way ___ I can fig - ure it out ___ is: Noth - in' from noth - in' leaves you.

Robinson Crusoe's Isle

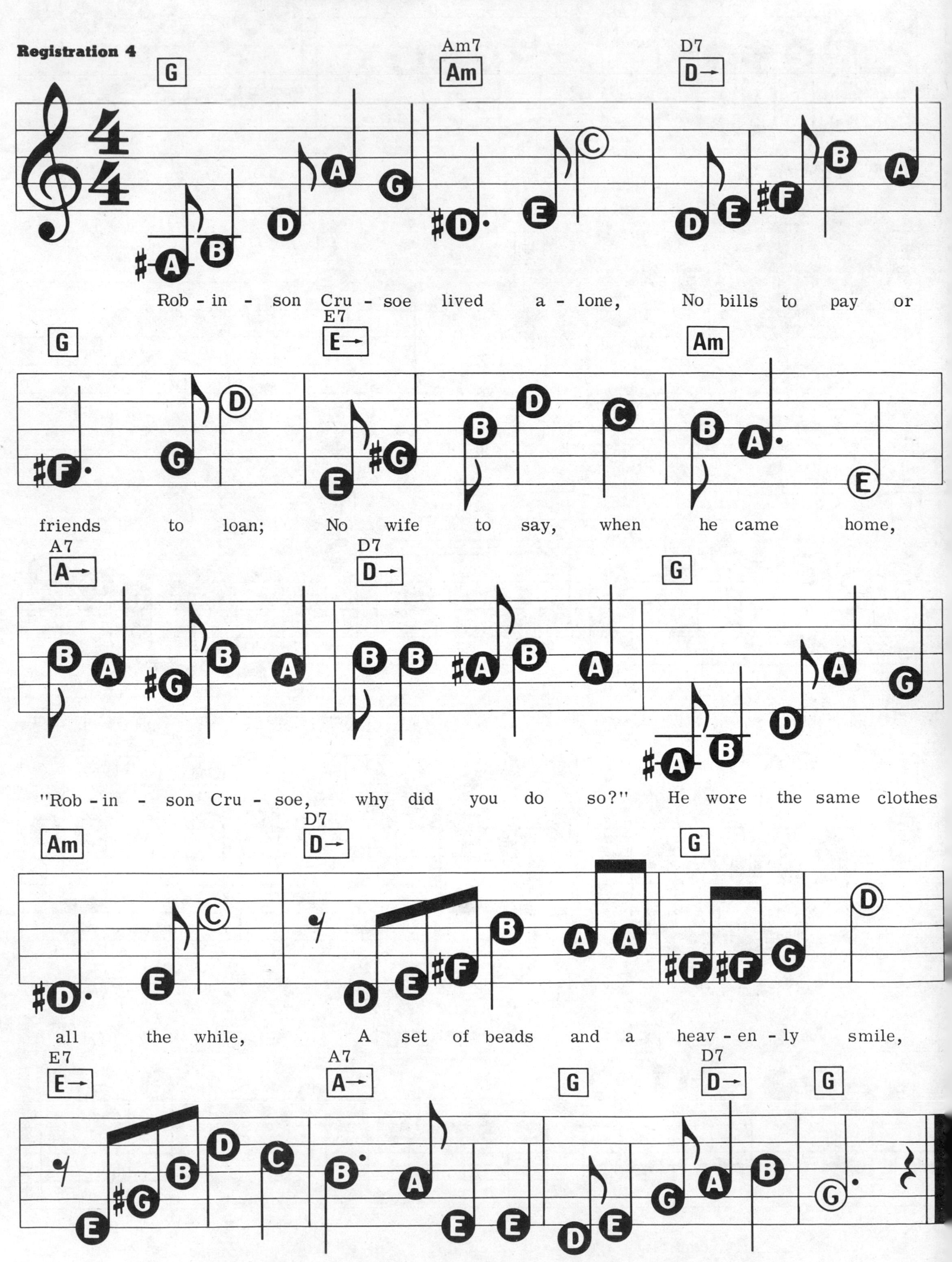

The Girl I Left Behind Me

Registration 4

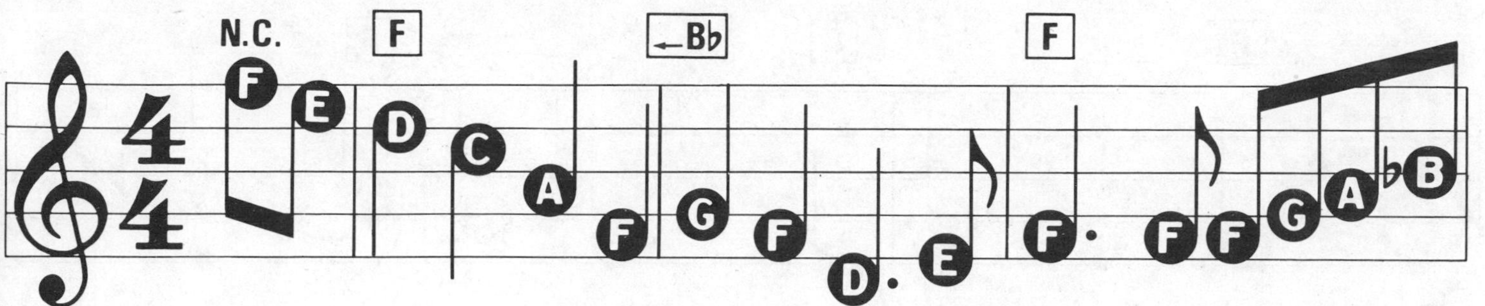

The ___ dames of France are fond and free, and Flem - ish lips ___ are ___

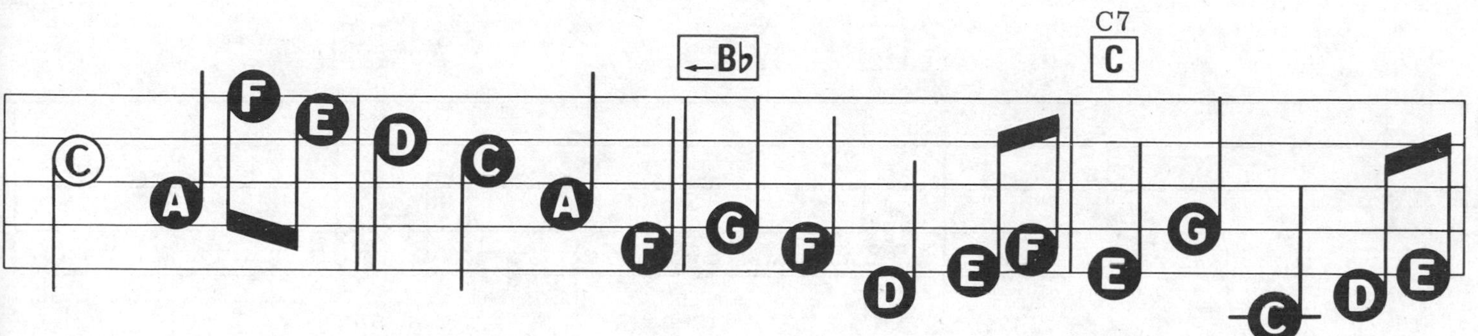

will - ing, and ___ soft the maids of It - a - ly, and ___ Span - ish eyes are ___

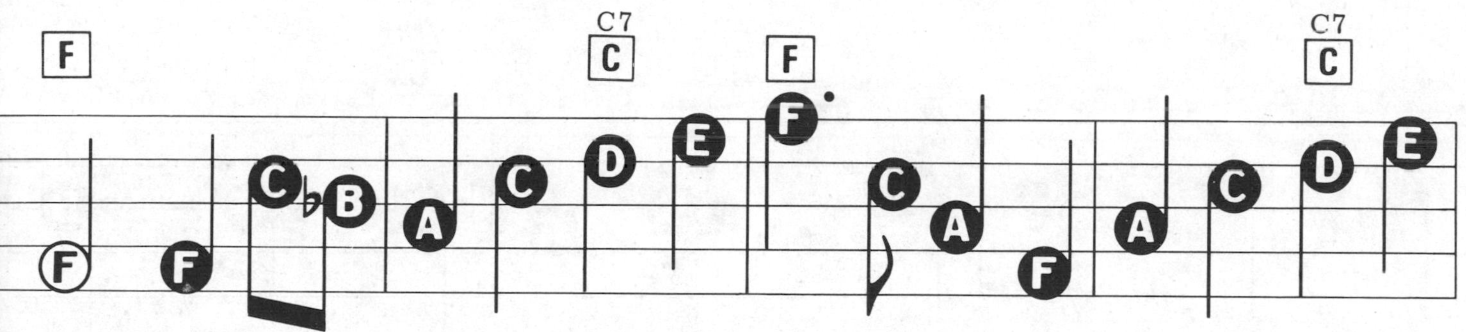

thrill - ing: Still ___ though I bask be - neath their smile, their charms ___ fail to

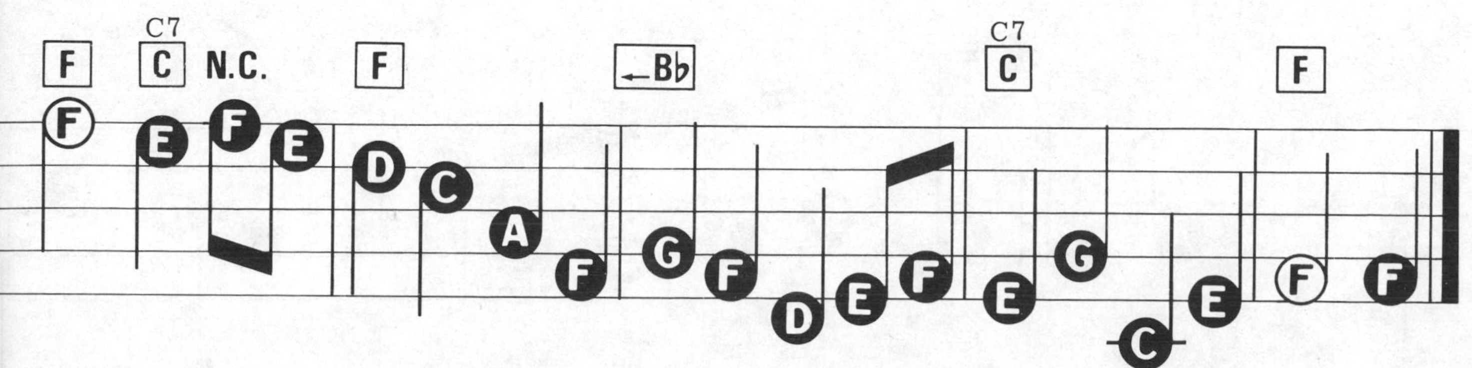

bind me, and my heart falls back to E - rin's Isle to the girl I left be - hind me.

America

Registration 5

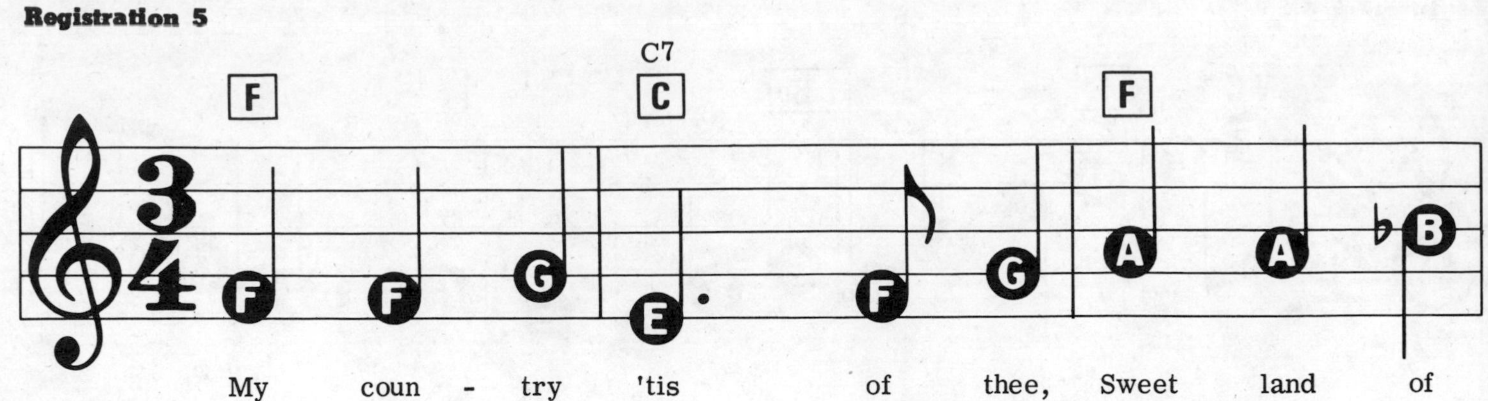

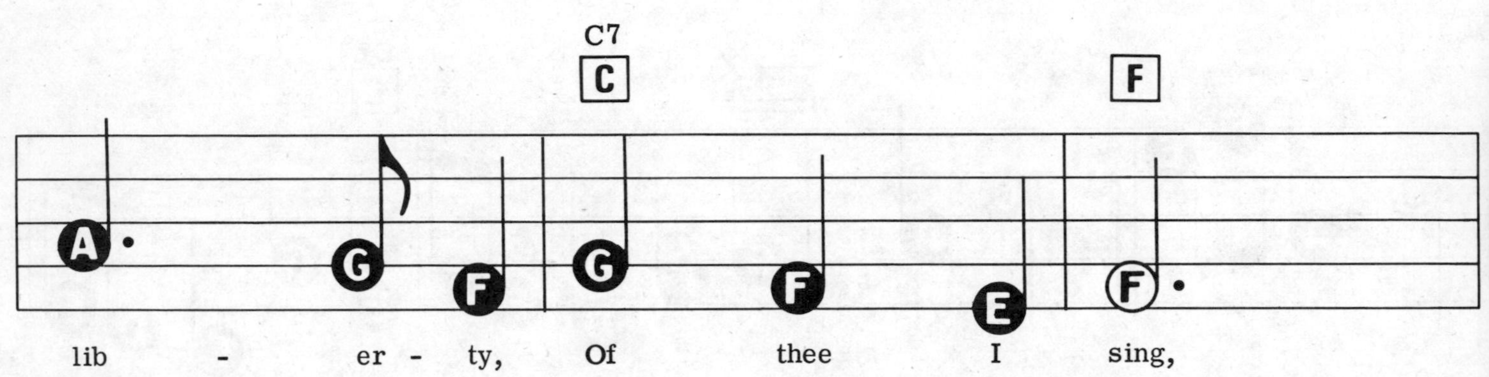

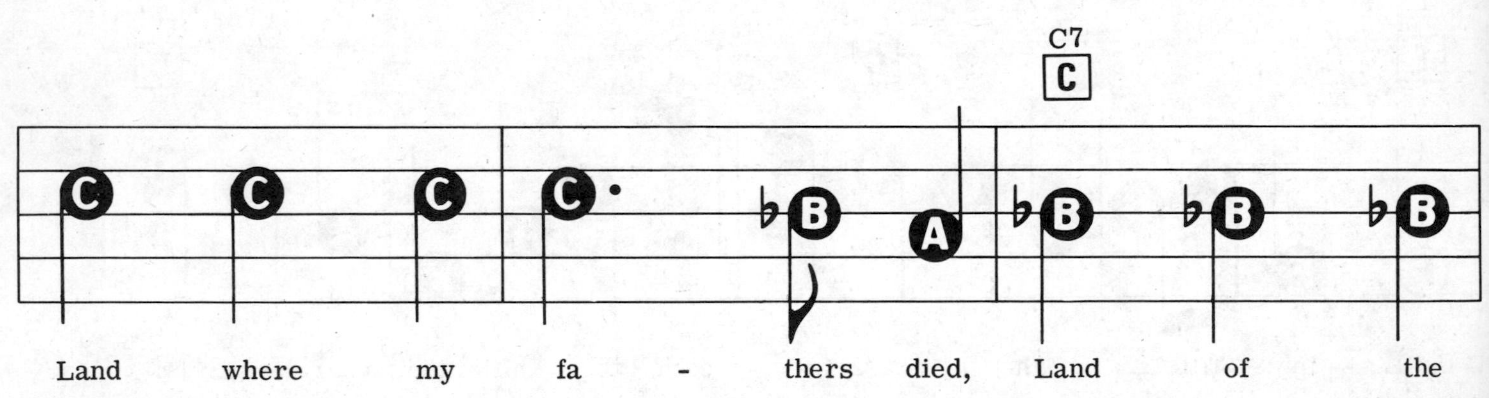

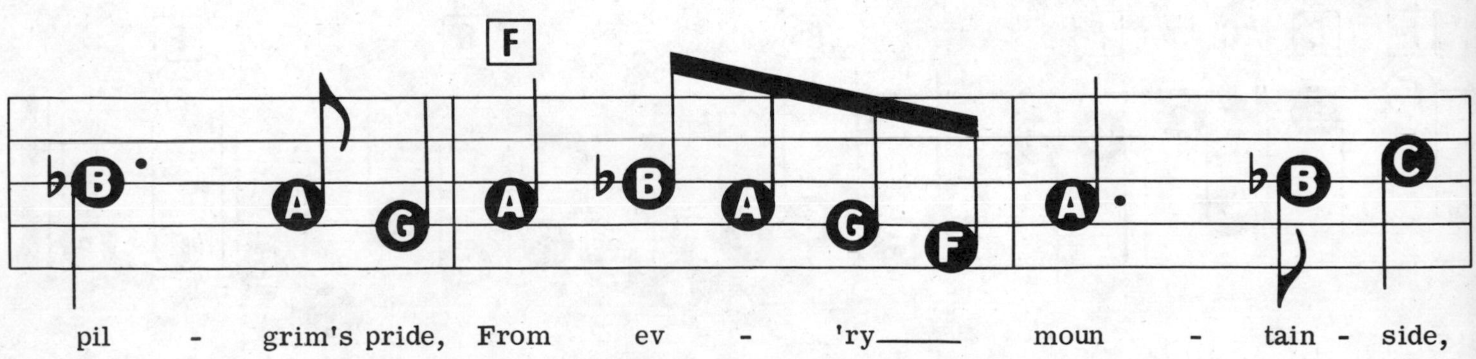

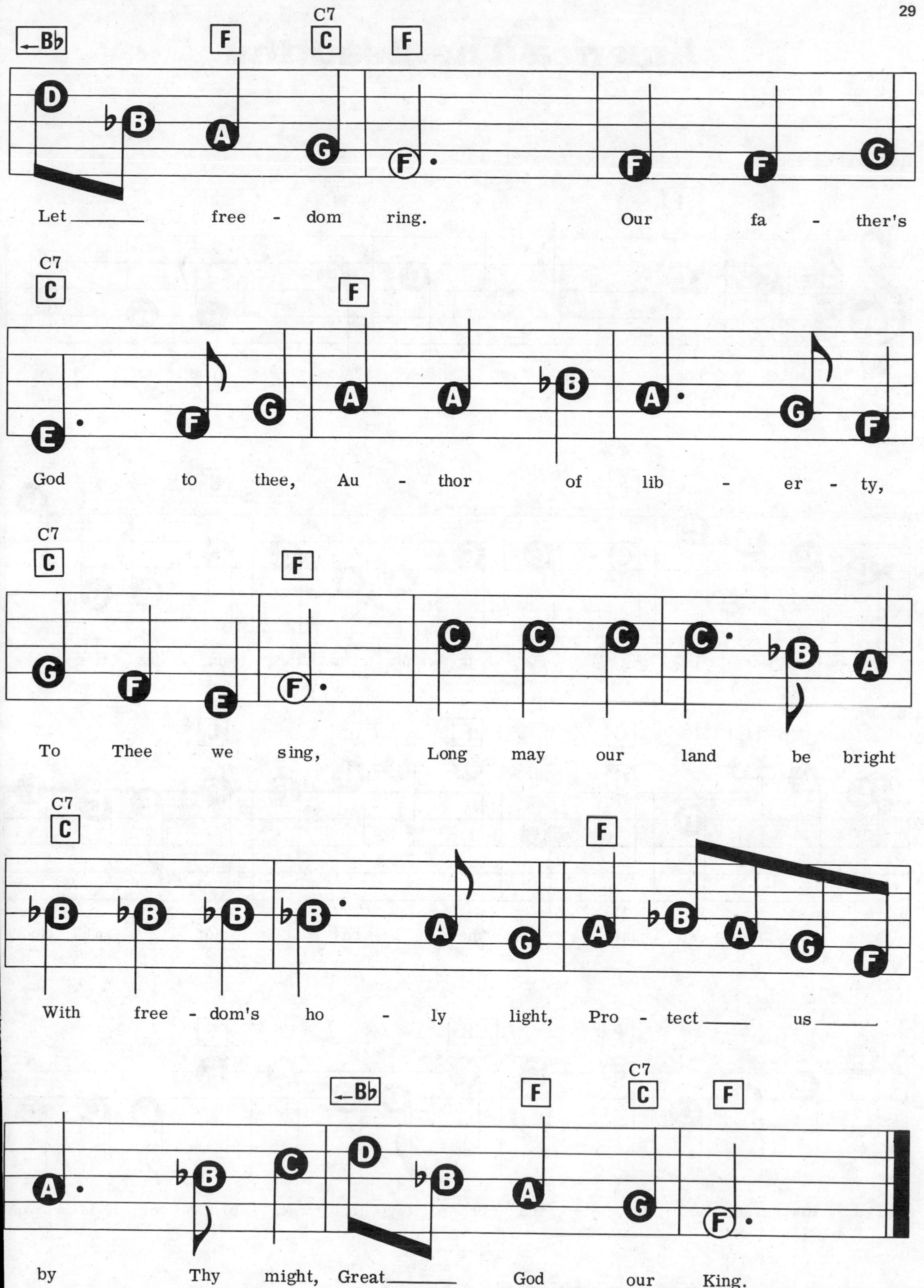
←B♭
F
C7
C
F
D
♭B
A
G
F
F
F
G
Let ____ free - dom ring. Our fa - ther's
C7
C
F
E
F
G
A
A
♭B
A
G
F
God to thee, Au - thor of lib - er - ty,
C7
C
F
G
F
E
F
C
C
C
C
♭B
A
To Thee we sing, Long may our land be bright
C7
C
F
♭B
♭B
♭B
♭B
A
G
A
♭B
A
G
F
With free - dom's ho - ly light, Pro - tect ____ us ____
←B♭
F
C7
C
F
A
♭B
C
D
♭B
A
G
F
by Thy might, Great ____ God our King.

America The Beautiful

Registration 3

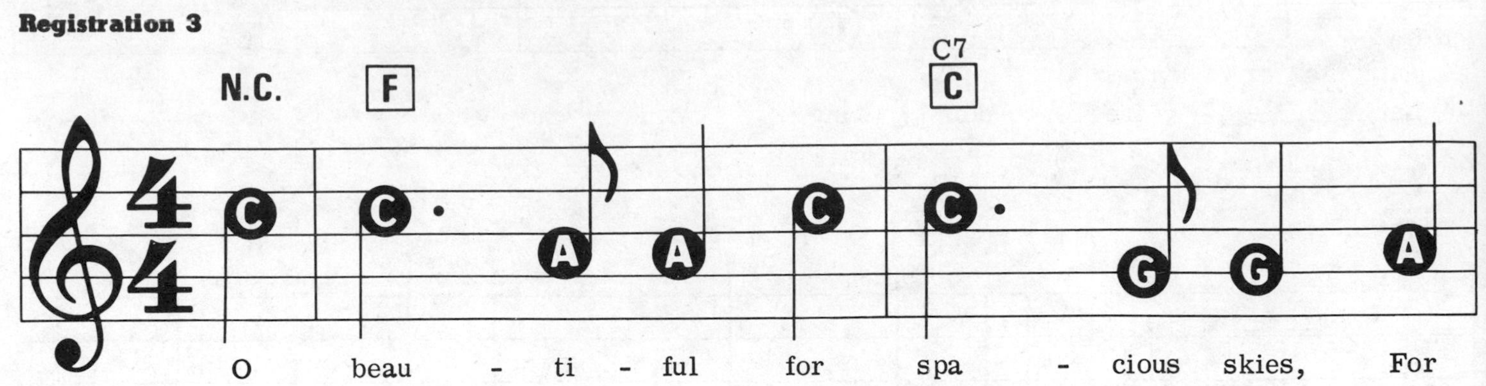

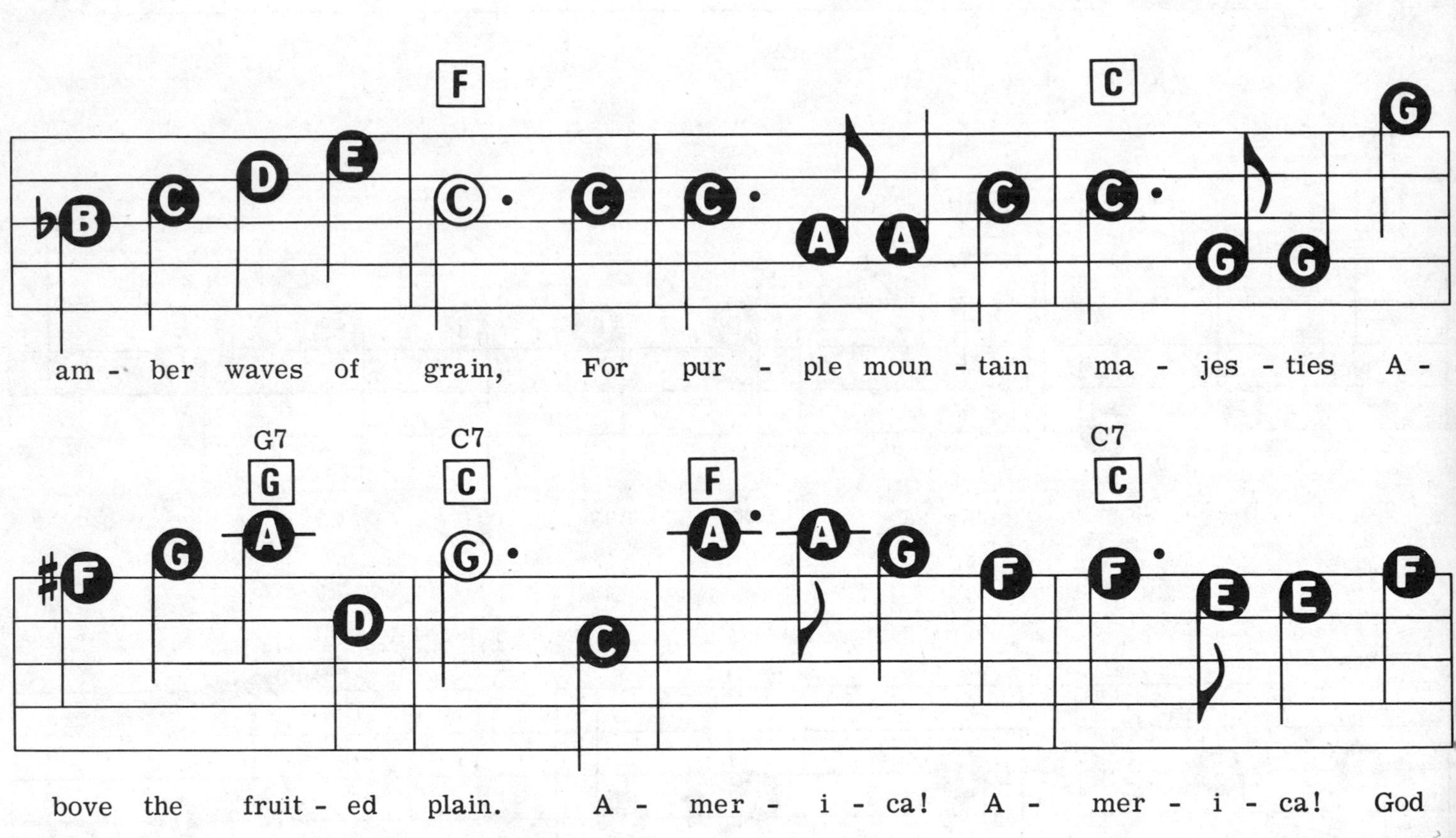

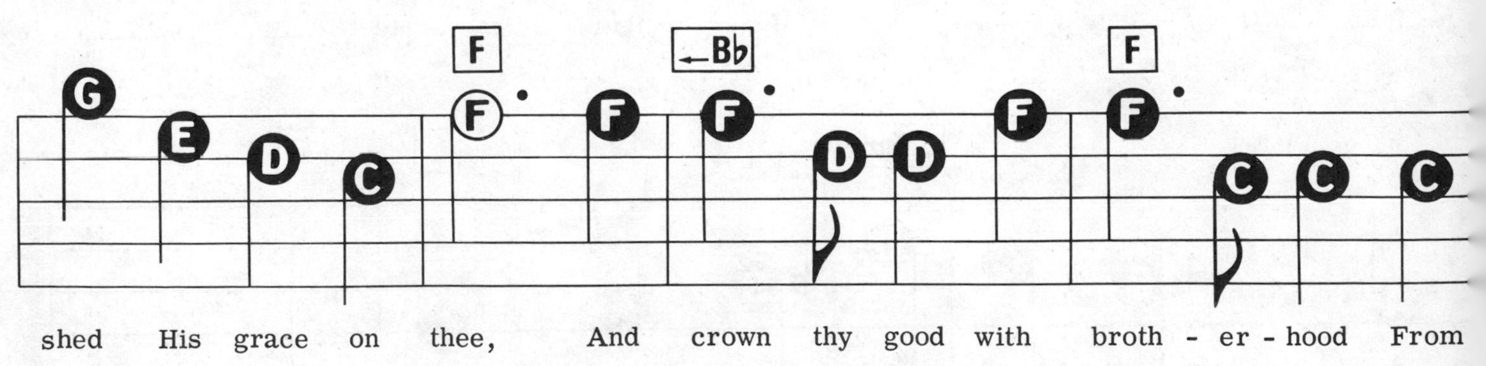

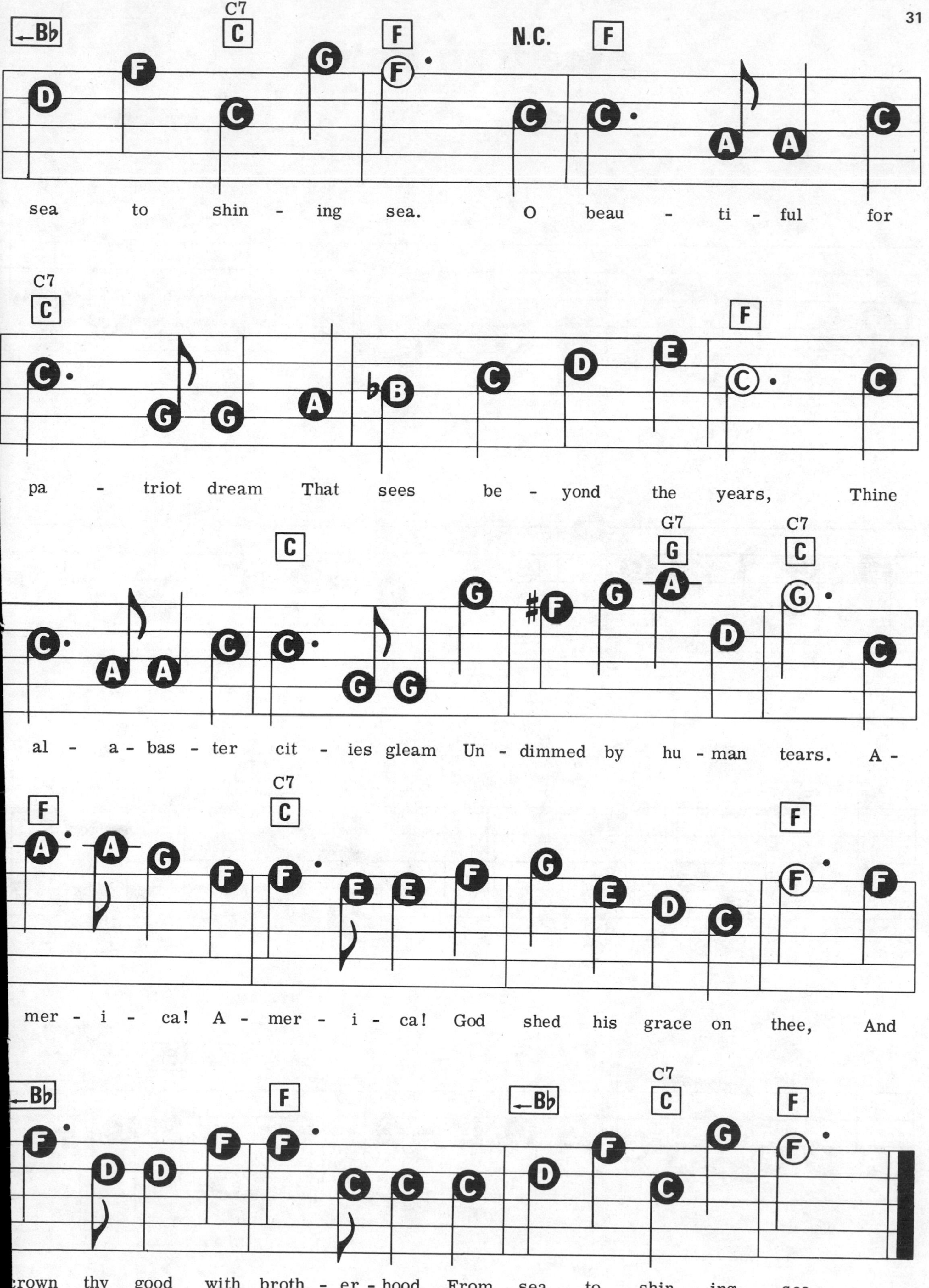
Bb C7 C F N.C. F
sea to shin - ing sea. O beau - ti - ful for
C7 C F
pa - triot dream That sees be - yond the years, Thine
C G7 G C7 C
al - a - bas - ter cit - ies gleam Un - dimmed by hu - man tears. A -
F C7 C F
mer - i - ca! A - mer - i - ca! God shed his grace on thee, And
Bb F Bb C7 C F
crown thy good with broth - er - hood From sea to shin - ing sea.

American Patrol

Registration 4

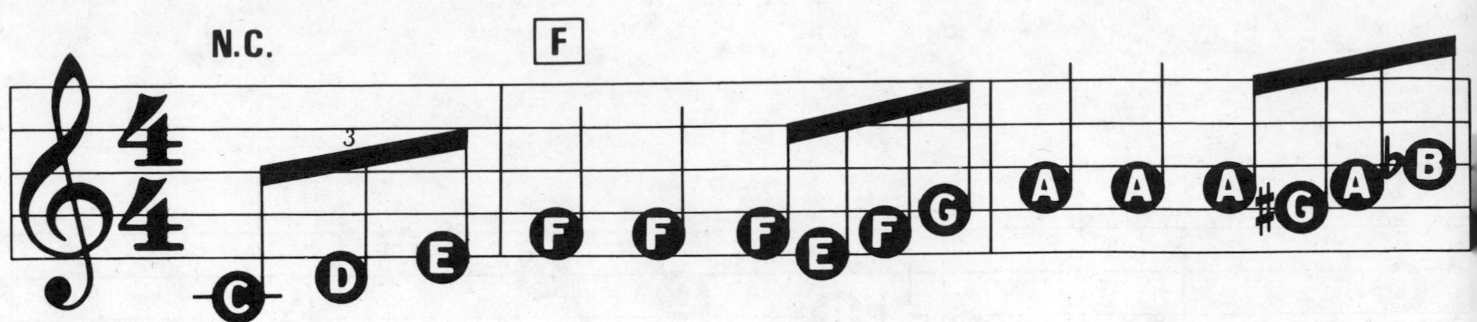

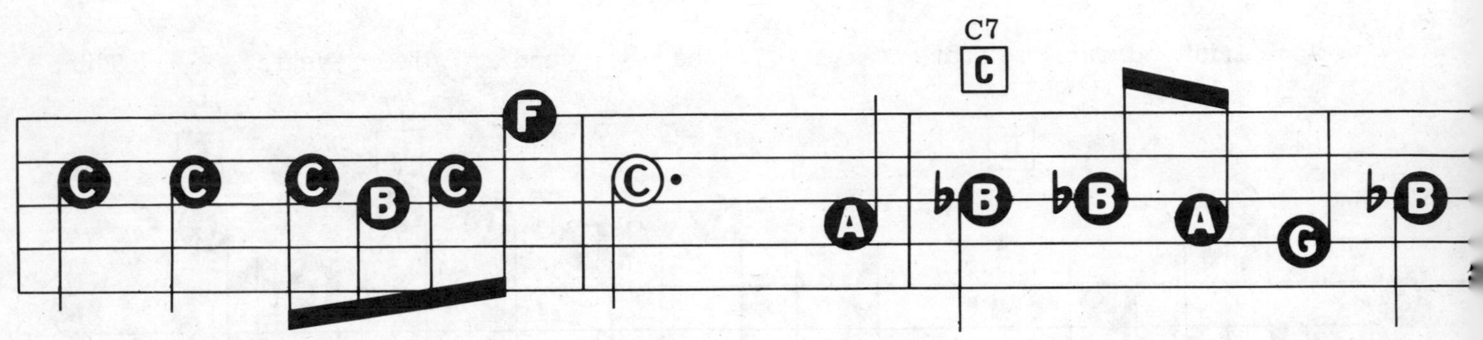

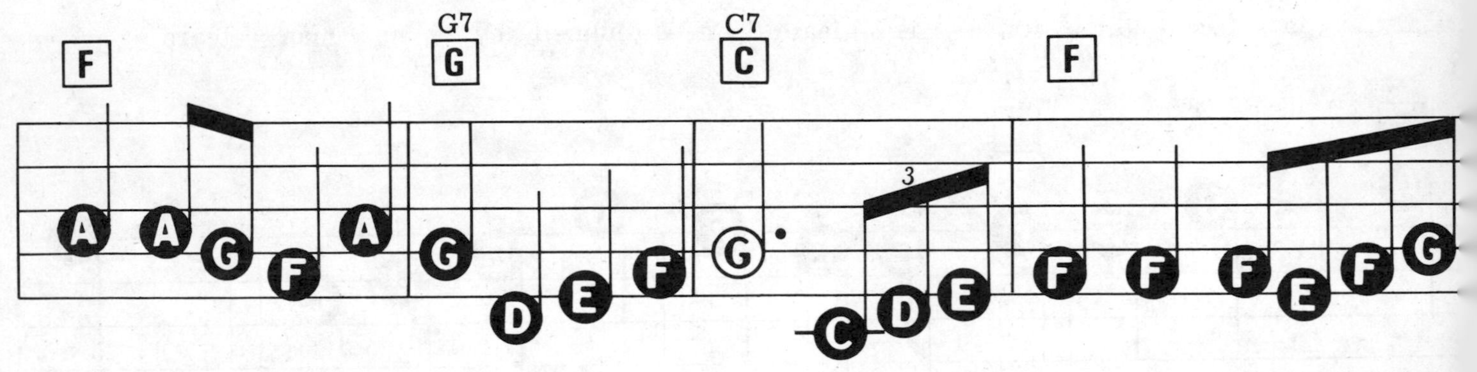

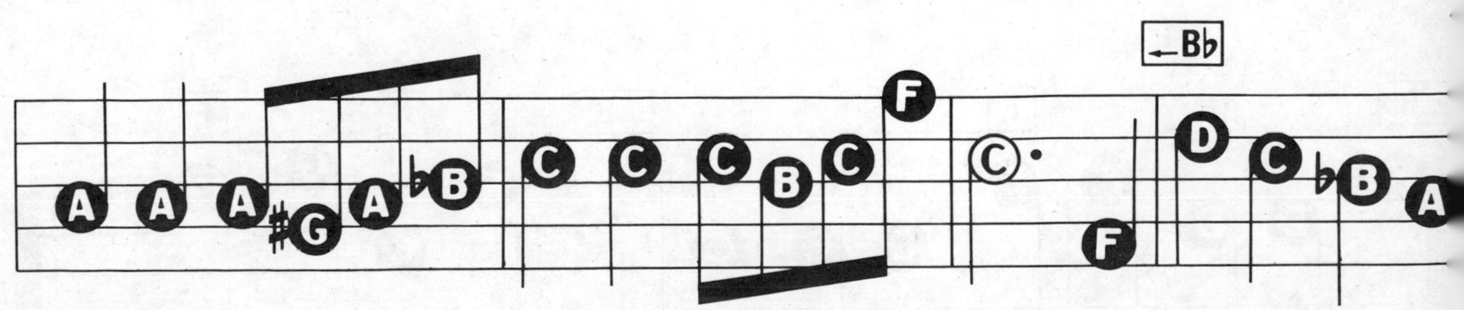

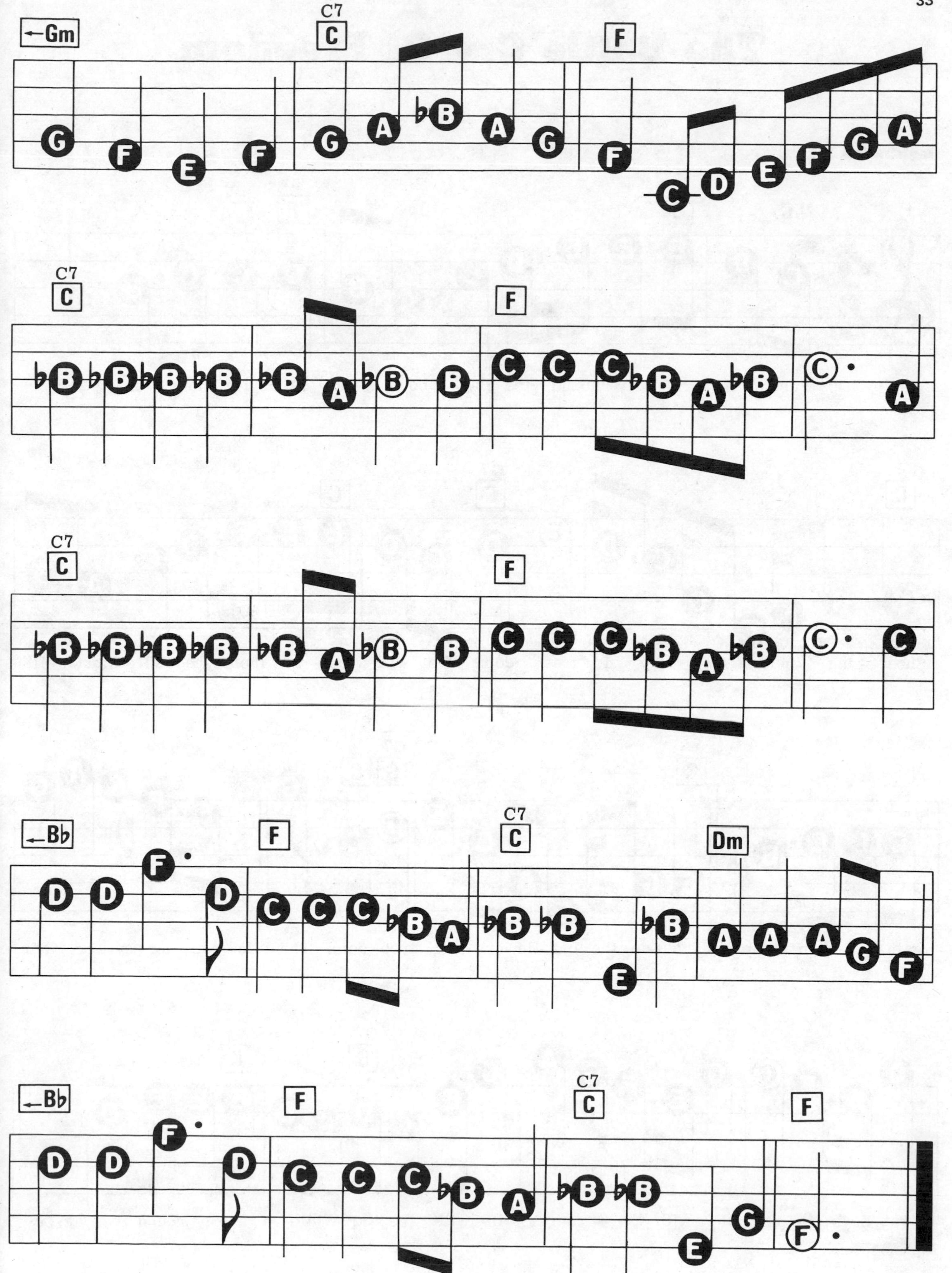

←Gm
C7
C
F
G F E F G A ♭B A G F C D E F G A
C7
C
♭B ♭B ♭B ♭B ♭B A ♭B B
F
C C C ♭B A ♭B C A
C7
C
♭B ♭B ♭B ♭B ♭B A ♭B B
F
C C C ♭B A ♭B C C
←B♭
D D F D
F
C C C ♭B A
C7
C
♭B ♭B E ♭B
Dm
A A A G F
←B♭
D D F D
F
C C C ♭B A
C7
C
♭B ♭B E G
F
F

The Battle Cry Of Freedom

Registration 1

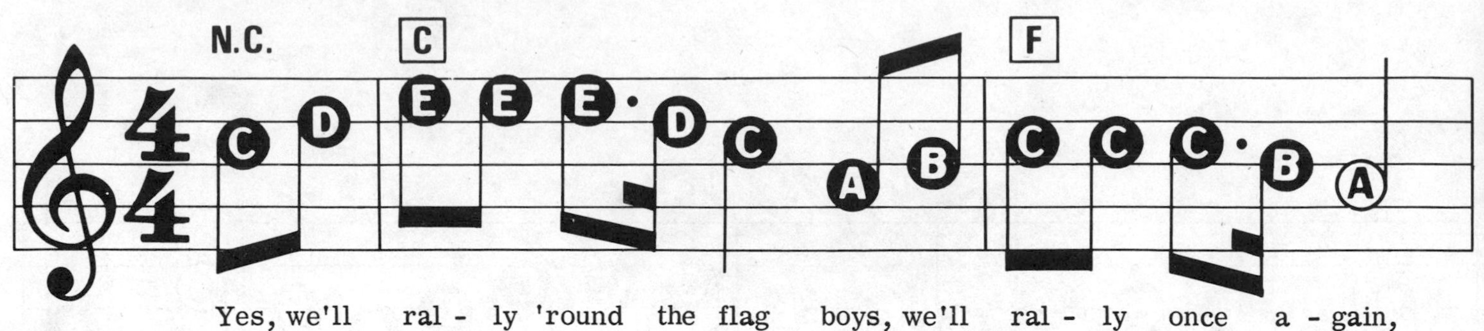

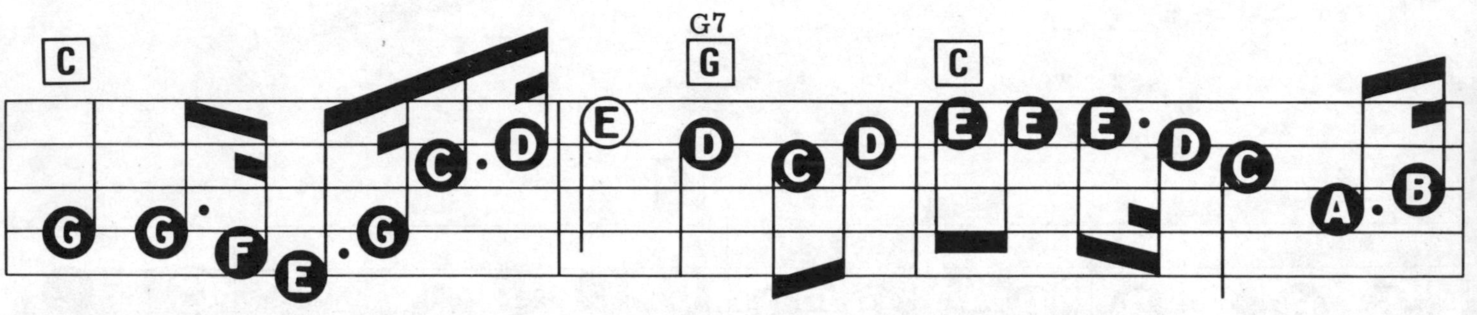

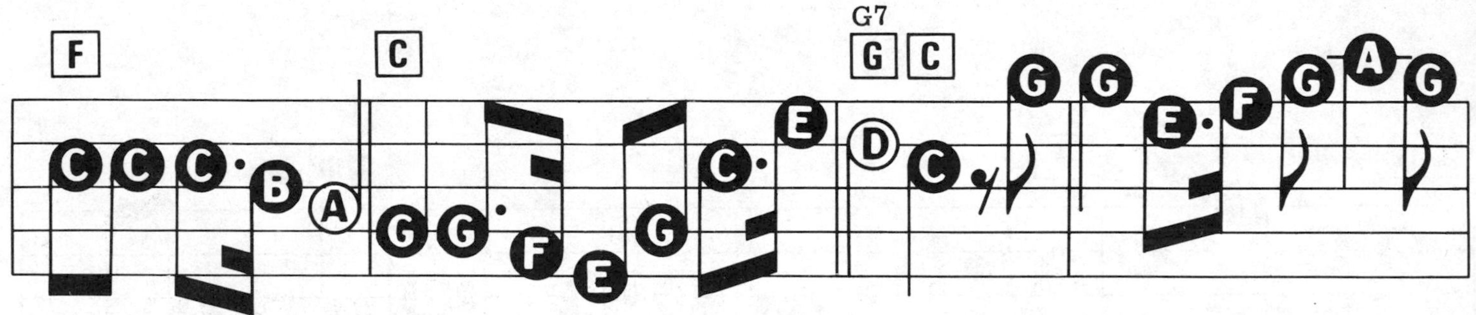

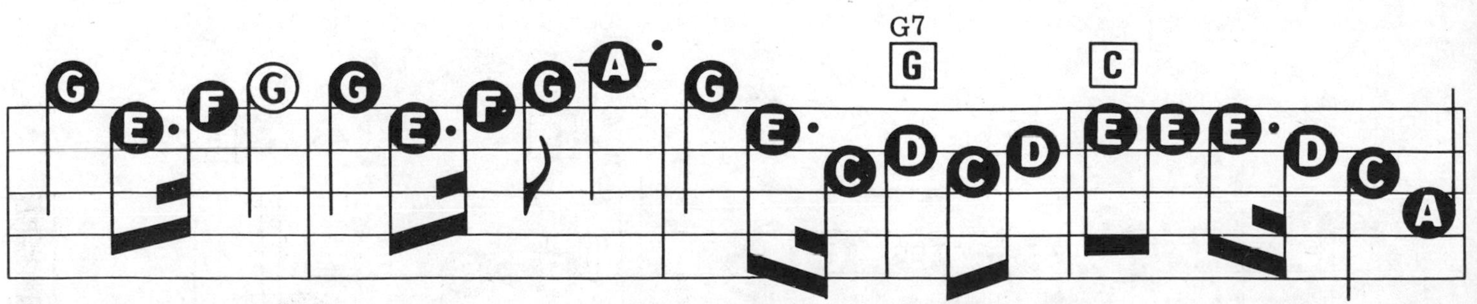

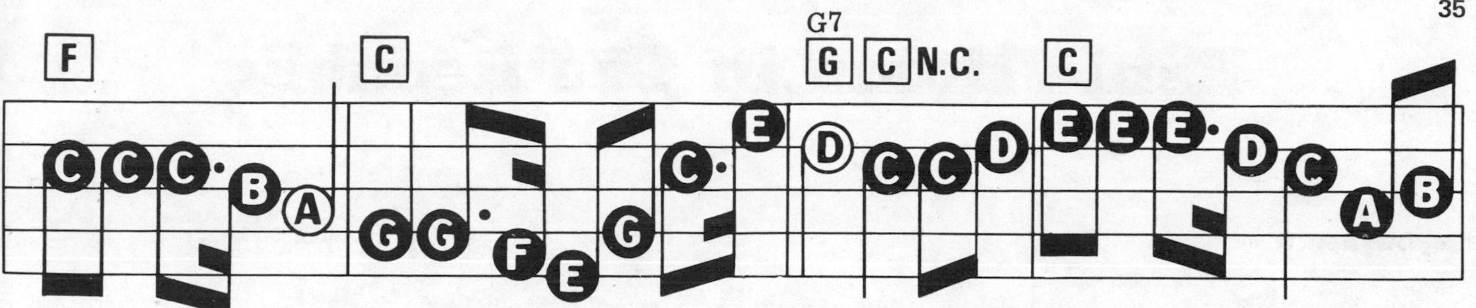
F C G7 G C N.C. C
ral -ly once a-gain, Shout-ing the bat- tle cry of free-dom. We are spring-ing to the call of our

F C G7 G
broth-ers gone be - fore, Shout - ing the bat - tle cry of free - dom; And we'll

C F C G7 G C

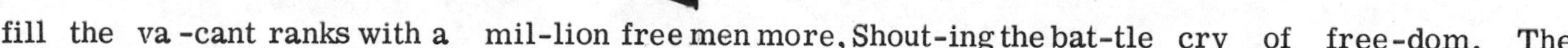
fill the va -cant ranks with a mil-lion free men more, Shout-ing the bat-tle cry of free-dom. The

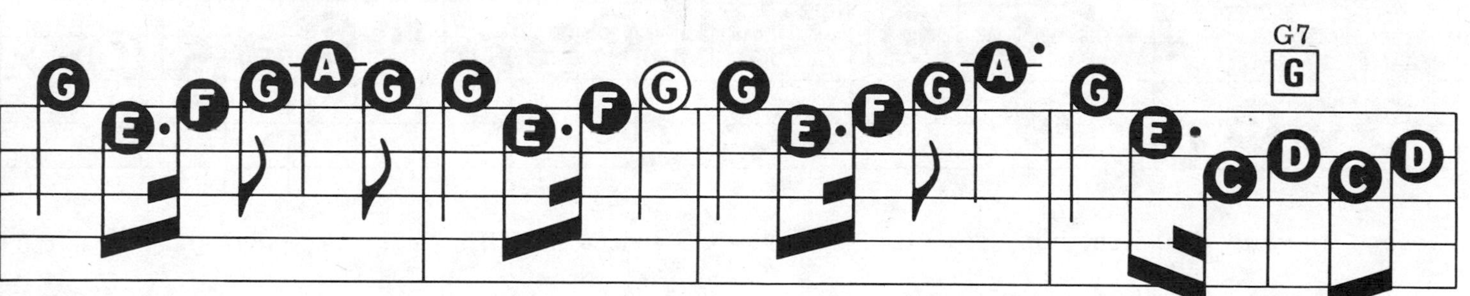
G7 G
Un- ion for - ev - er, hur - rah, boys, hur -rah! Down with the trai-tor, Up with the star; While we

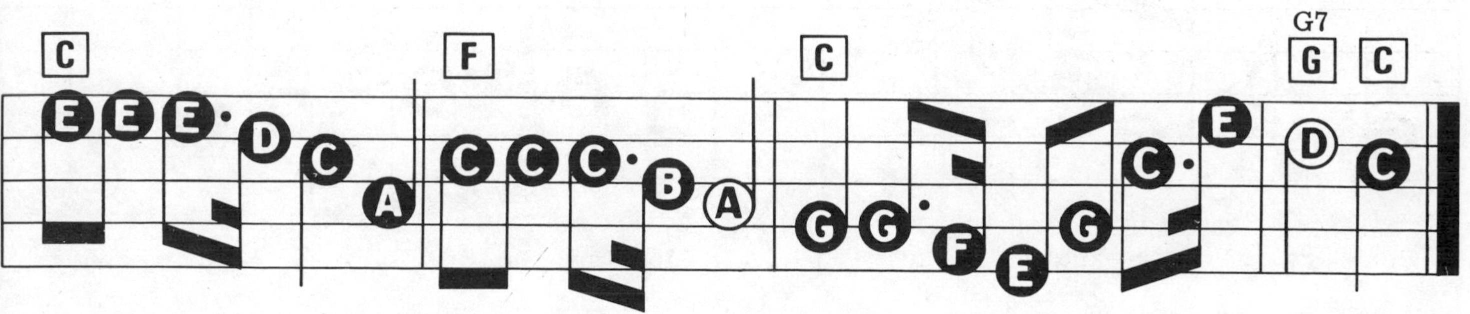
C F C G7 G C
ral -ly 'round the flag, boys, ral - ly once a- gain, Shout-ing the bat -tle cry of free-dom.

Battle Hymn Of The Republic

Registration 5

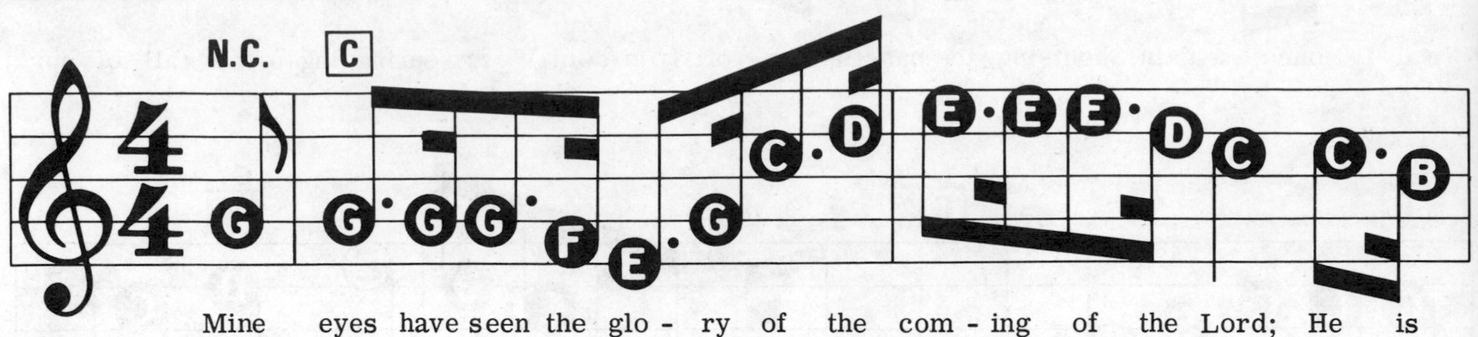

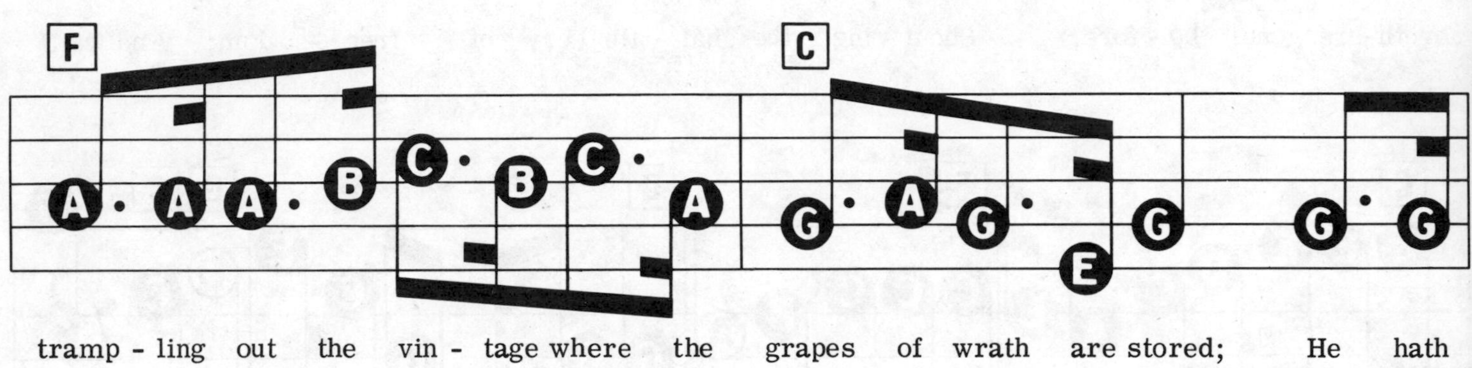

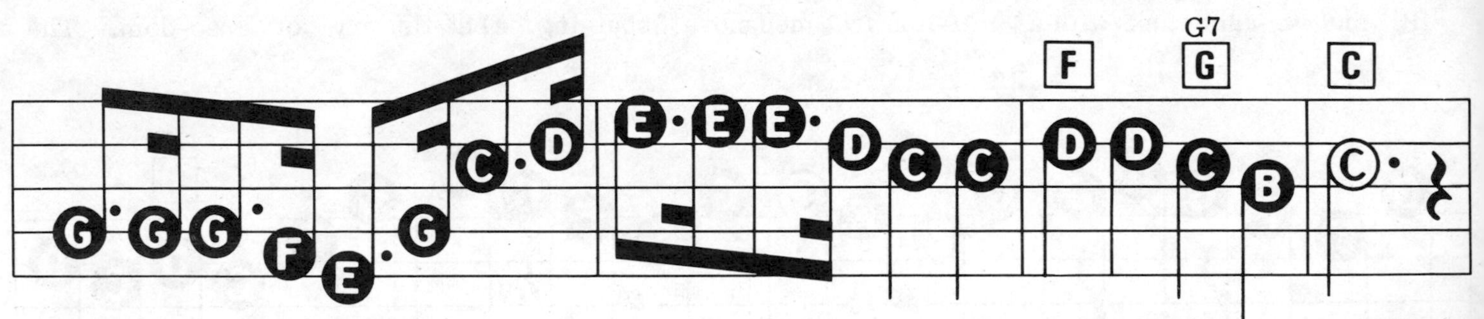

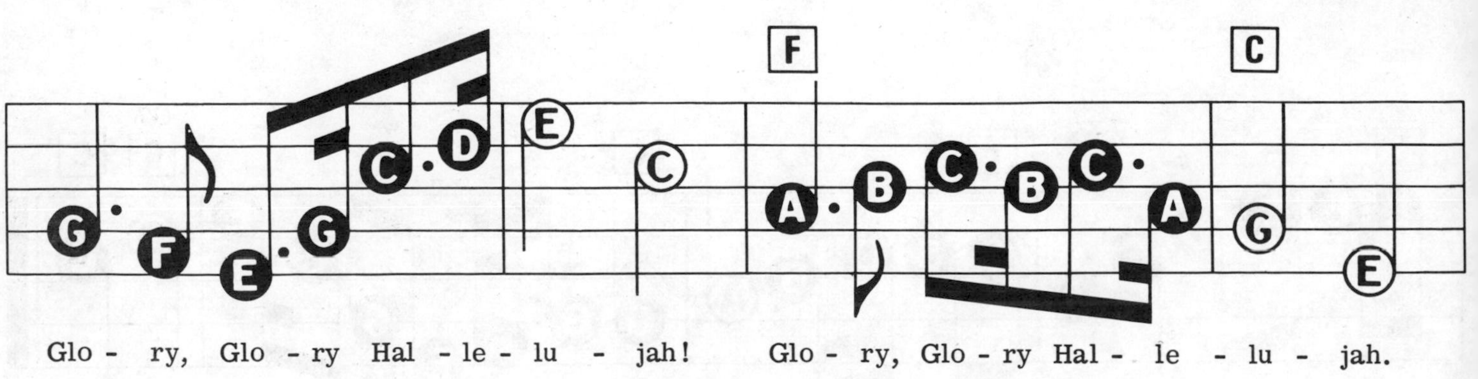

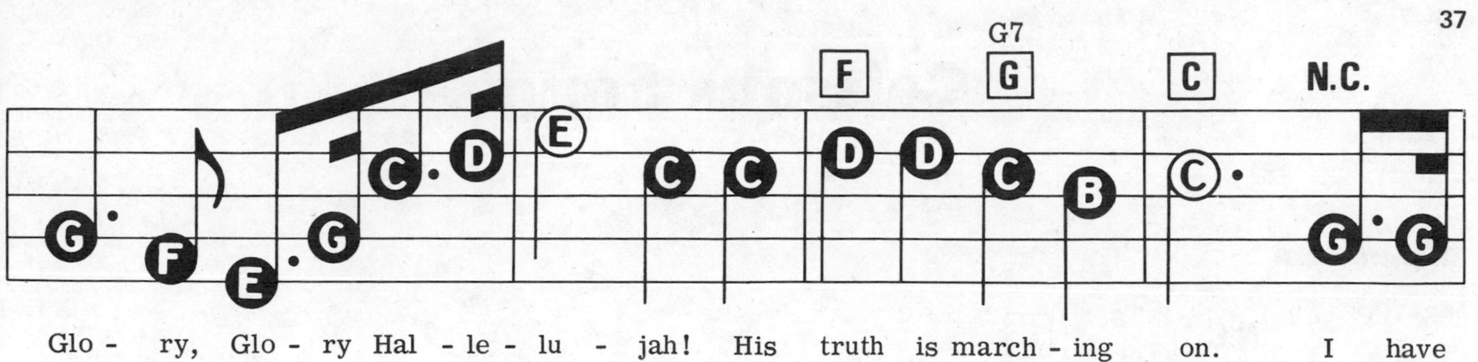
F
G7
G
C
N.C.
Glo - ry, Glo - ry Hal - le - lu - jah! His truth is march - ing on. I have

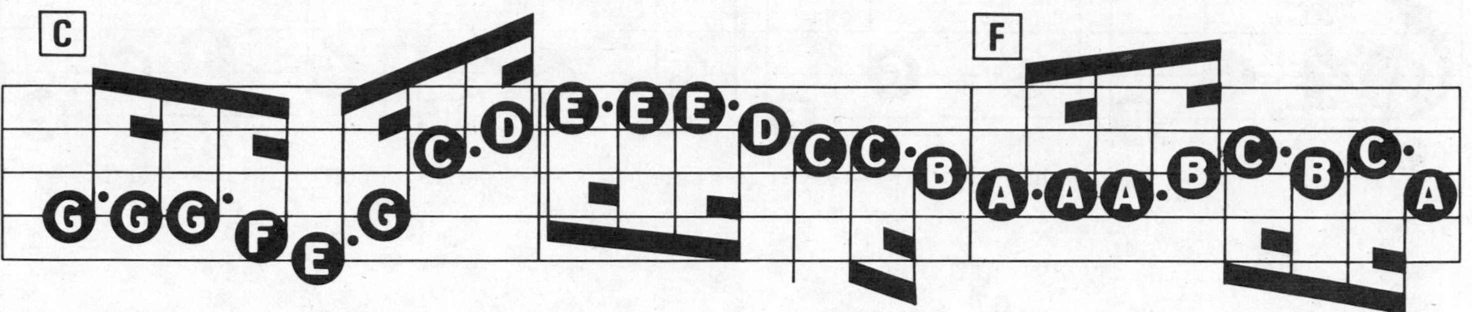
C
F
seen Him in the watch-fires of a hun-dred circ-ling camps, They have build-ed Him an al - tar in the

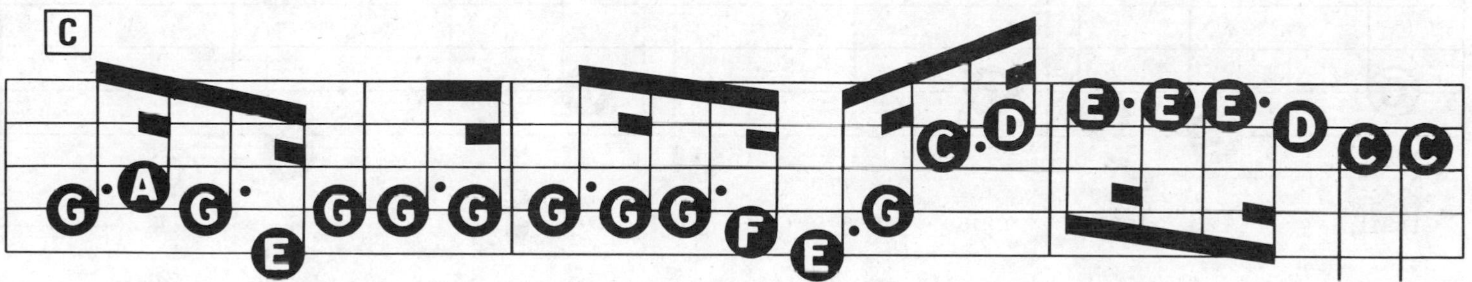
C
eve - ning dews and damps; I can read His right-eous sen-tence by the dim and flar-ing lamps, His

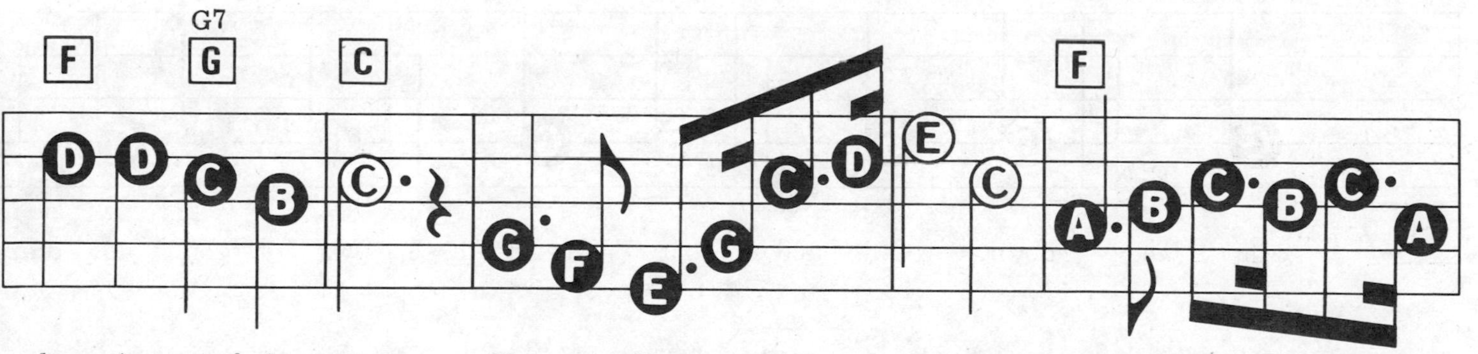
F
G7
G
C
F
day is march-ing on. Glo - ry, Glo - ry Hal - le - lu - jah! Glo - ry, Glo - ry Hal - le -

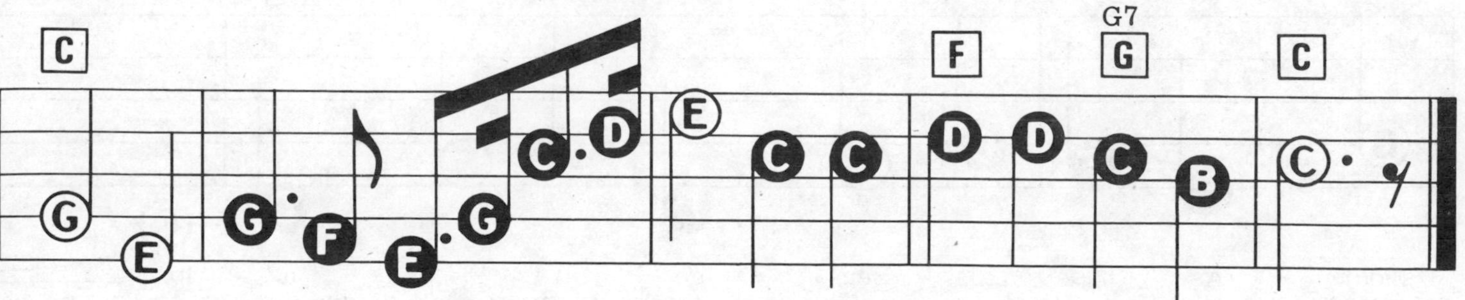
C
F
G7
G
C
lu - jah! Glo - ry, Glo - ry Hal - le - lu - jah! His truth is march - ing on.

Caissons Song

Registration 2

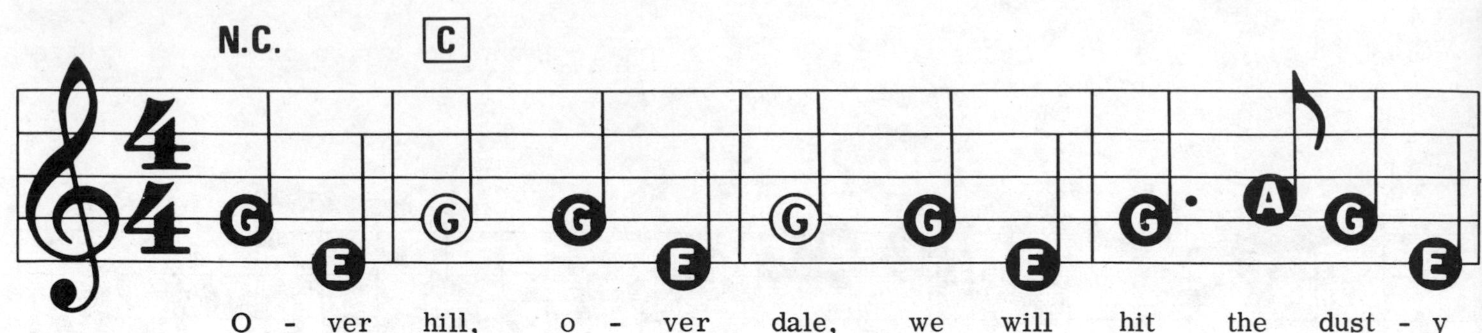

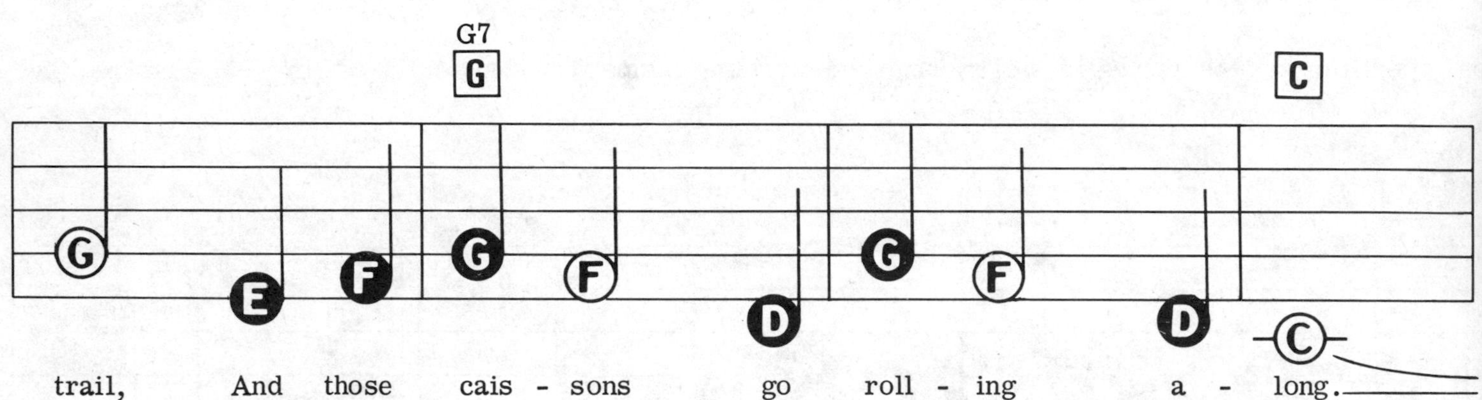

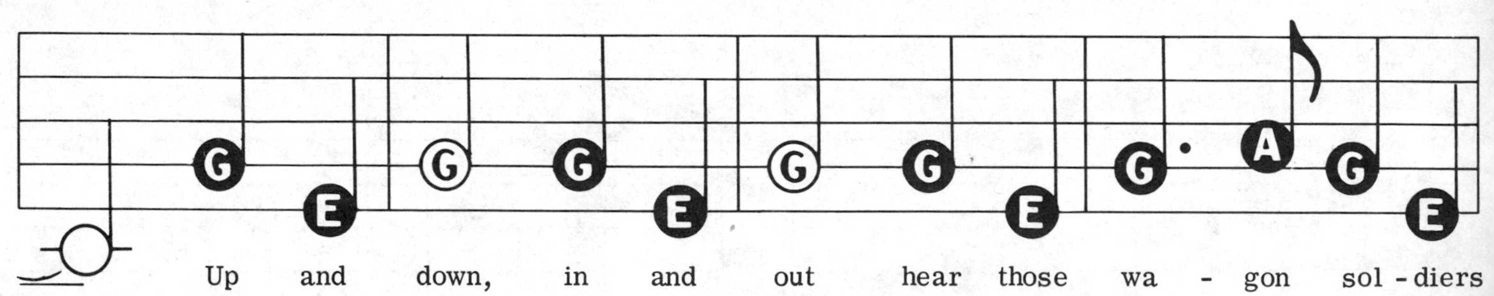

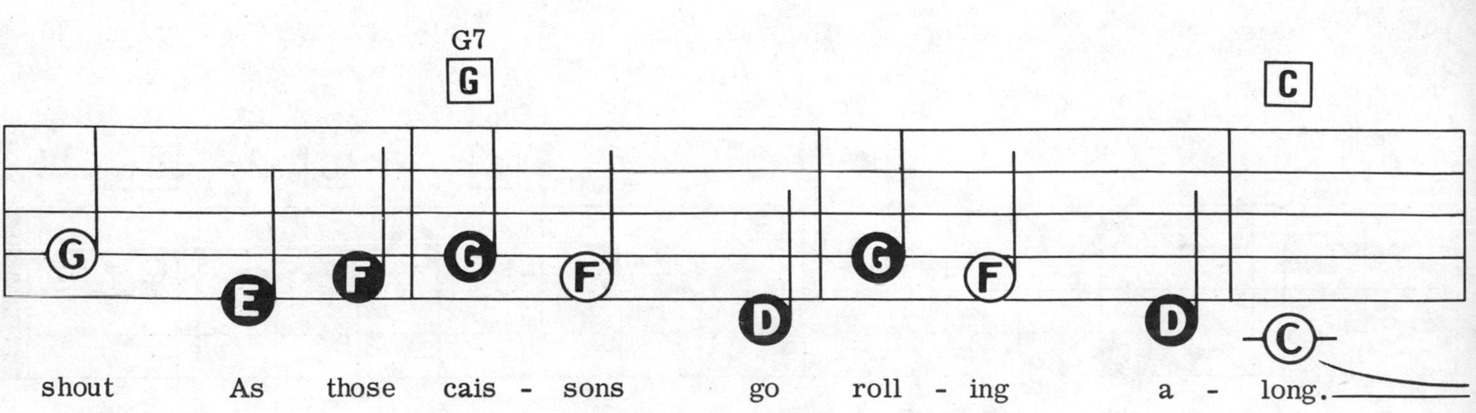

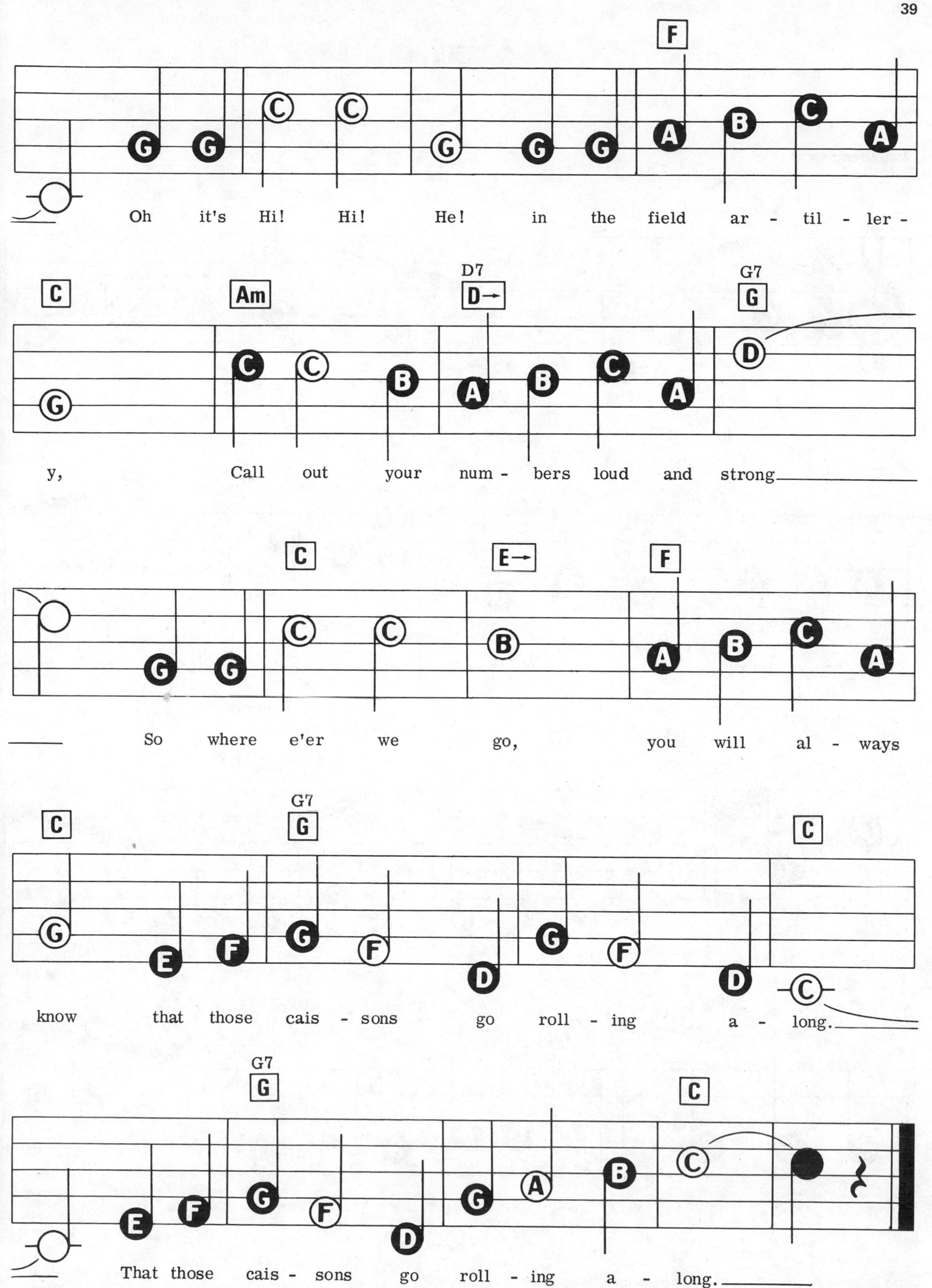
F
Oh it's Hi! Hi! He! in the field ar - til - ler -
C Am D7 D→ G7 G
y, Call out your num - bers loud and strong
C E→ F
So where e'er we go, you will al - ways
C G7 G C
know that those cais - sons go roll - ing a - long.
G7 G C
That those cais - sons go roll - ing a - long.

Dixie

Registration 9

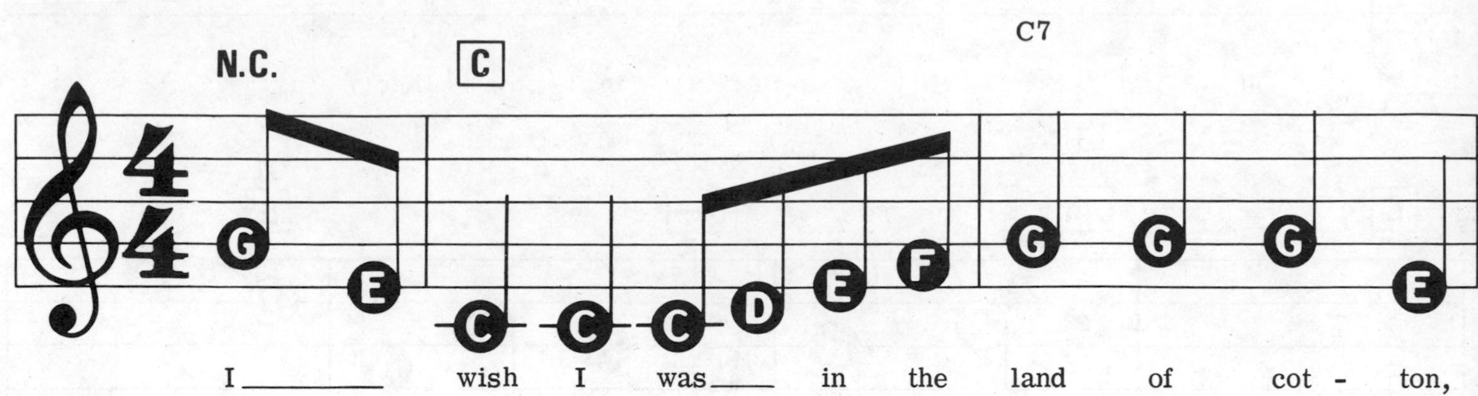
N.C.
C
C7
G E C C C D E F G G G E
I wish I was in the land of cot - ton,

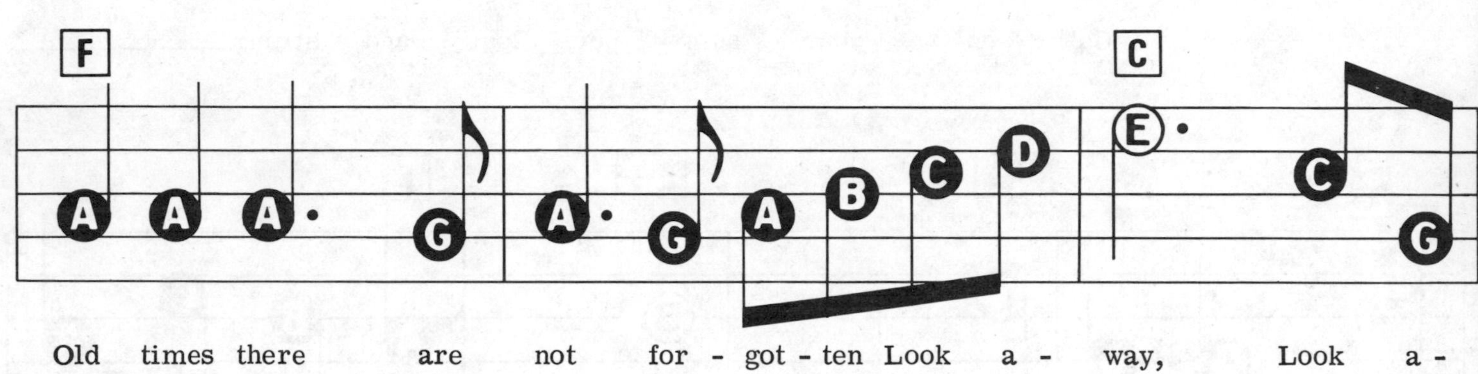
F
C
A A A G A G A B C D E C G
Old times there are not for - got - ten Look a - way, Look a -

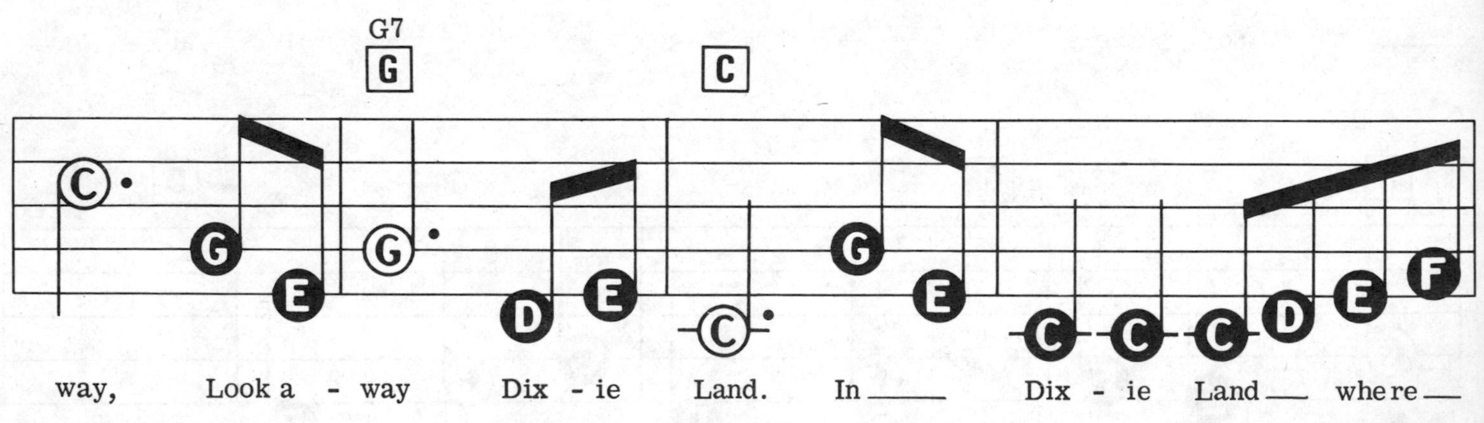
G7
G
C
C G E G D E C G E C C C D E F
way, Look a - way Dix - ie Land. In Dix - ie Land where

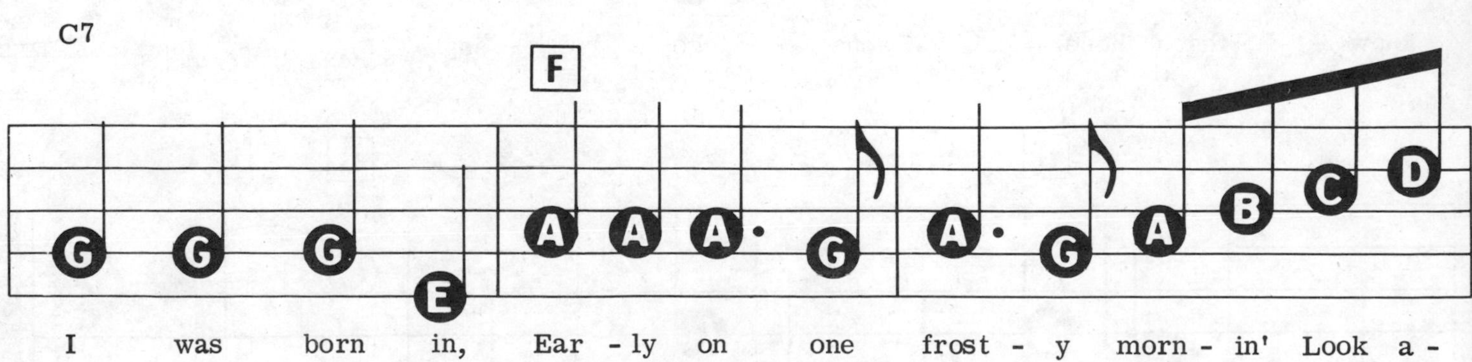
C7
F
G G G E A A A G A G A B C D
I was born in, Ear - ly on one frost - y morn - in' Look a -

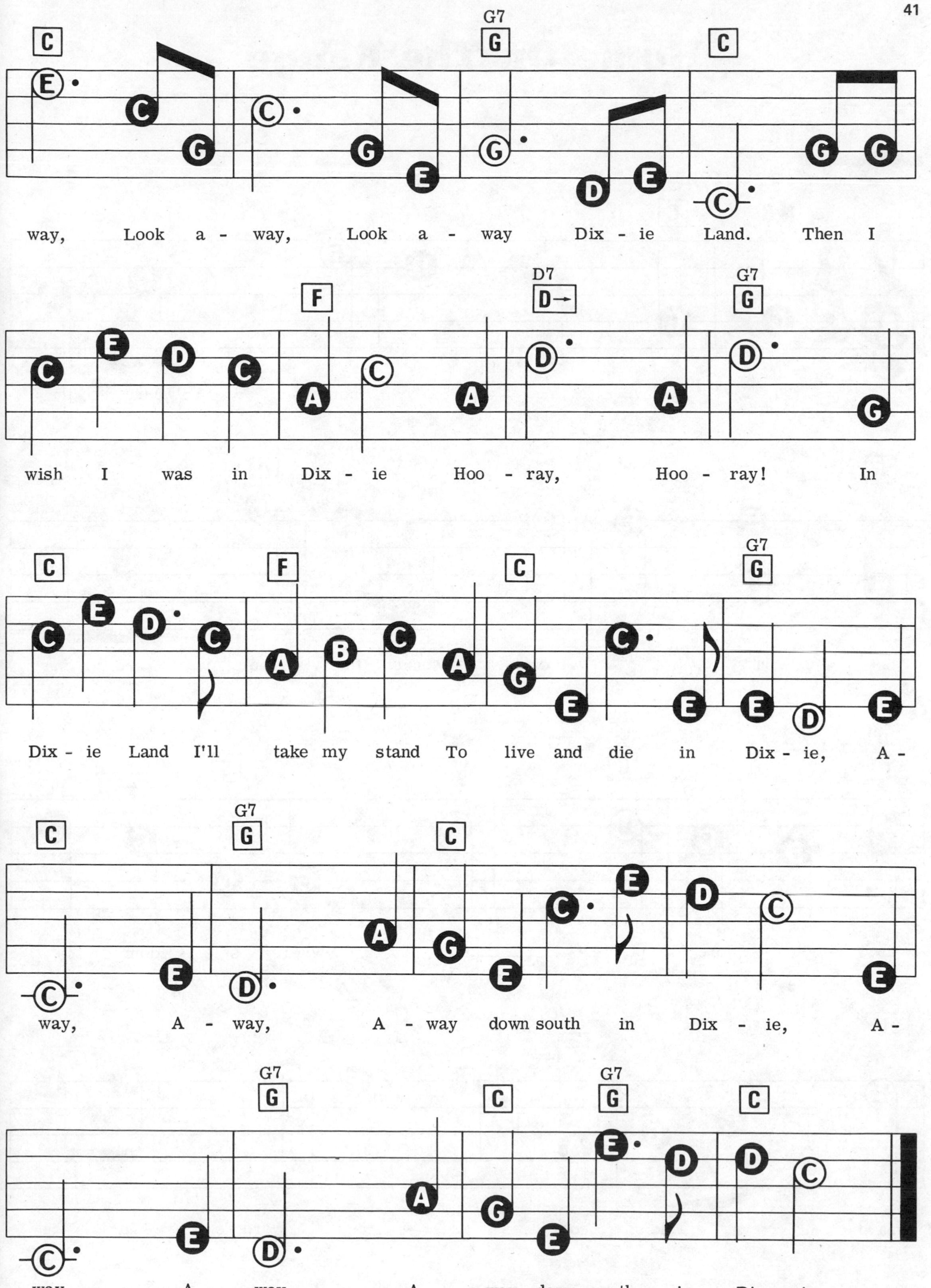
C G7 G C
way, Look a - way, Look a - way Dix - ie Land. Then I
F D7 D→ G7 G
wish I was in Dix - ie Hoo - ray, Hoo - ray! In
C F C G7 G
Dix - ie Land I'll take my stand To live and die in Dix - ie, A -
C G7 G C
way, A - way, A - way down south in Dix - ie, A -
G7 G C G7 G C
way, A - way, A - way down south in Dix - ie.

Home On The Range

Registration 4

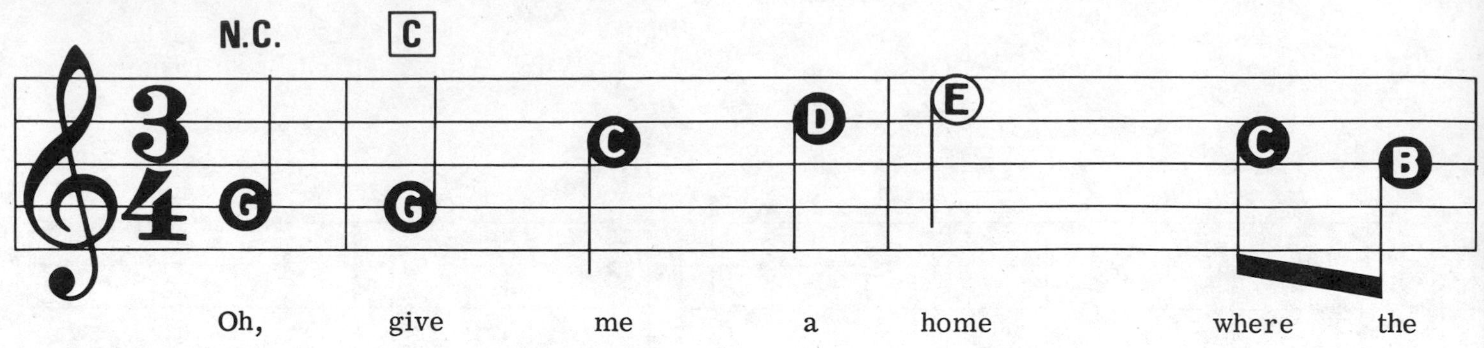

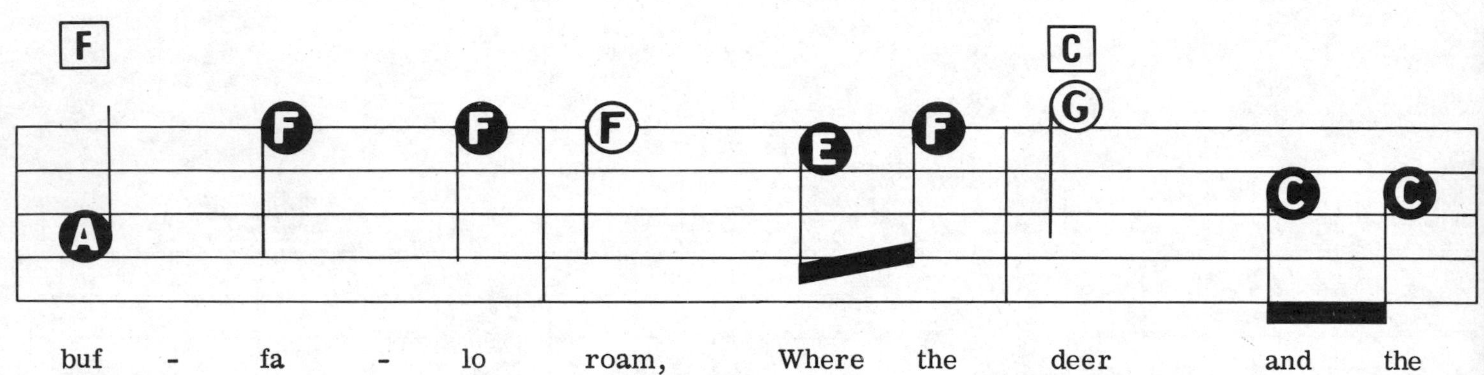

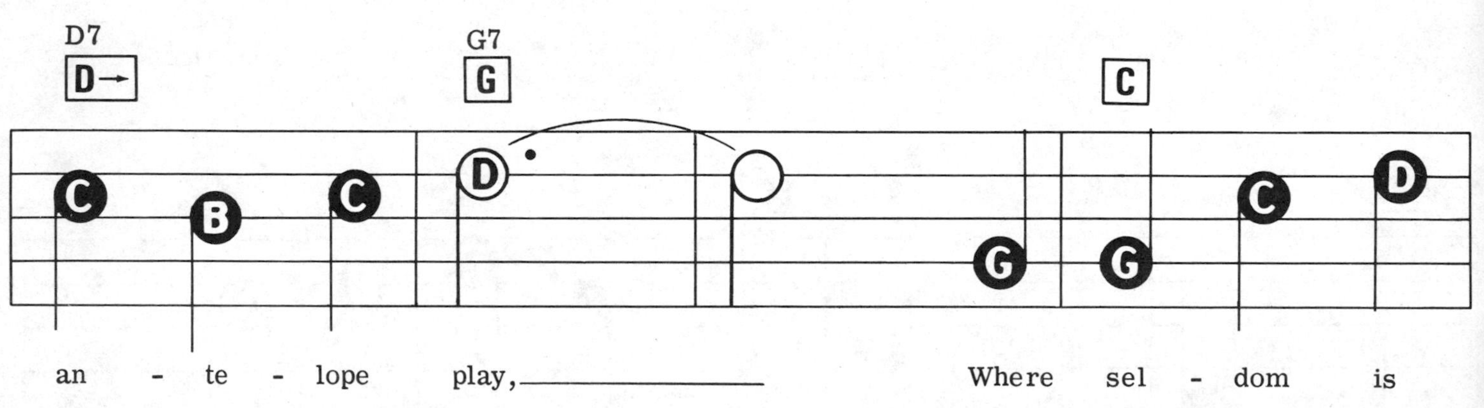

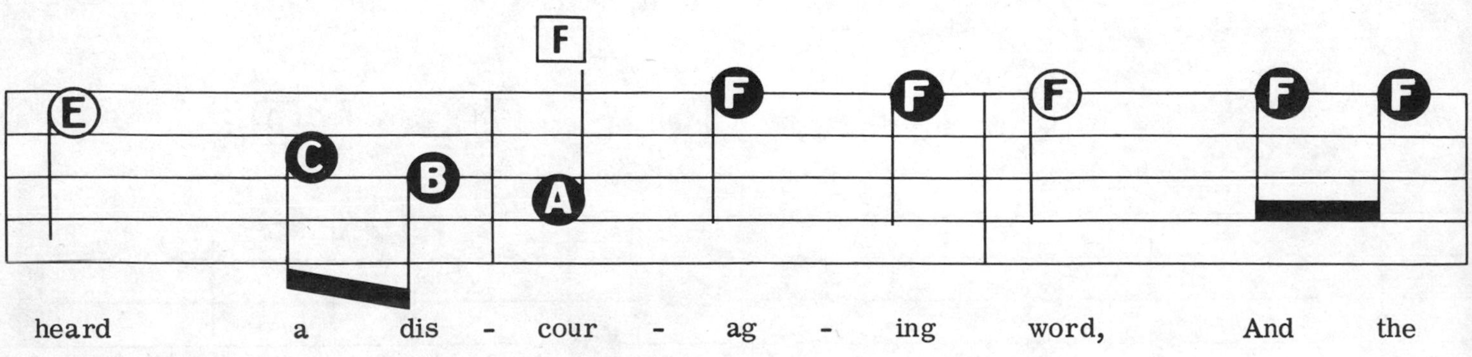

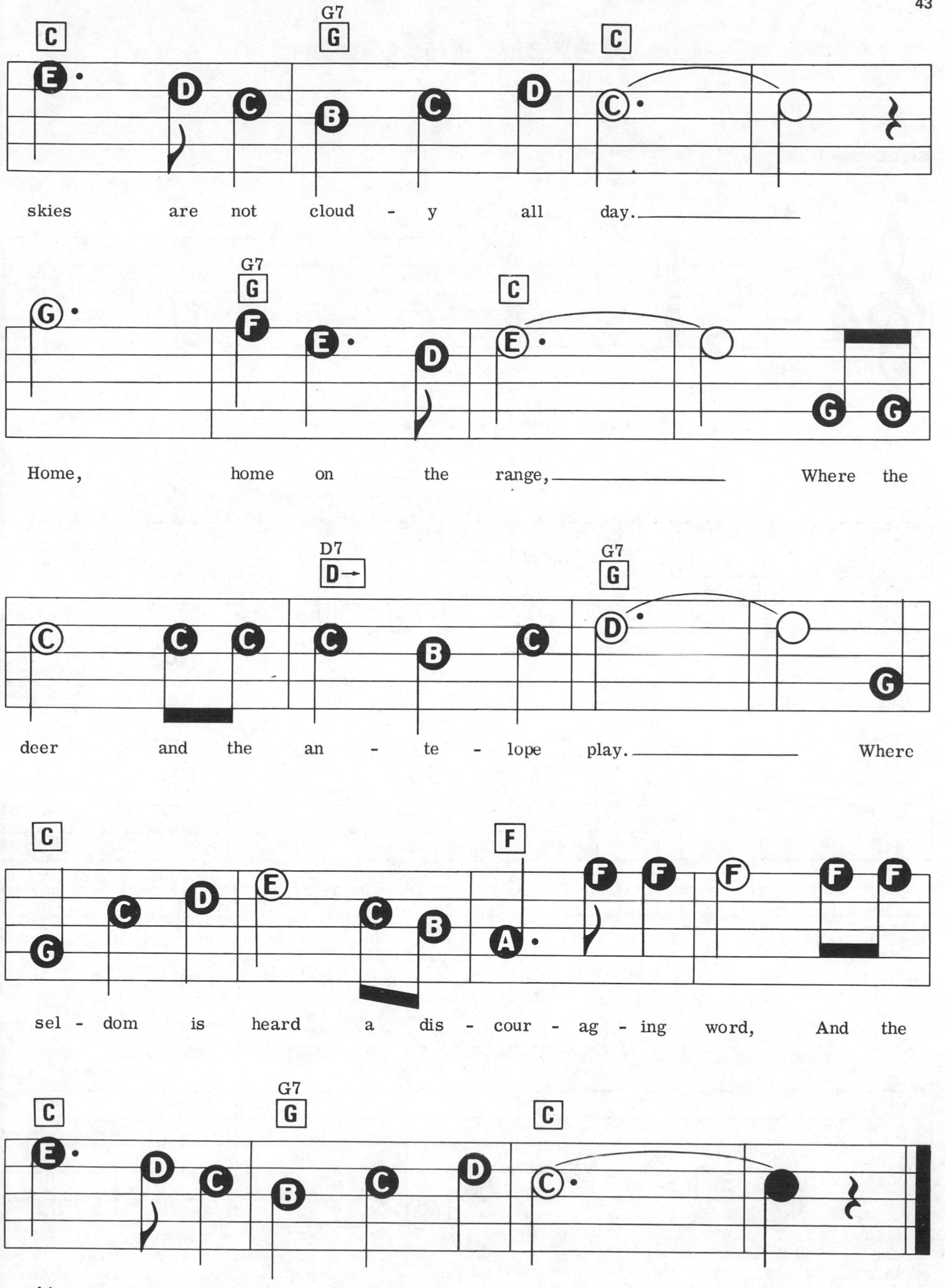
C G7 G C
E D C B C D C C
skies are not cloud - y all day.
G7 G C
G F E D E G G
Home, home on the range, Where the
D7 D→ G7 G
C C C C B C D G
deer and the an - te - lope play. Where
C F
G C D E C B A F F F F F
sel - dom is heard a dis - cour - ag - ing word, And the
C G7 G C
E D C B C D C
skies are not cloud - y all day.

Marine's Hymn

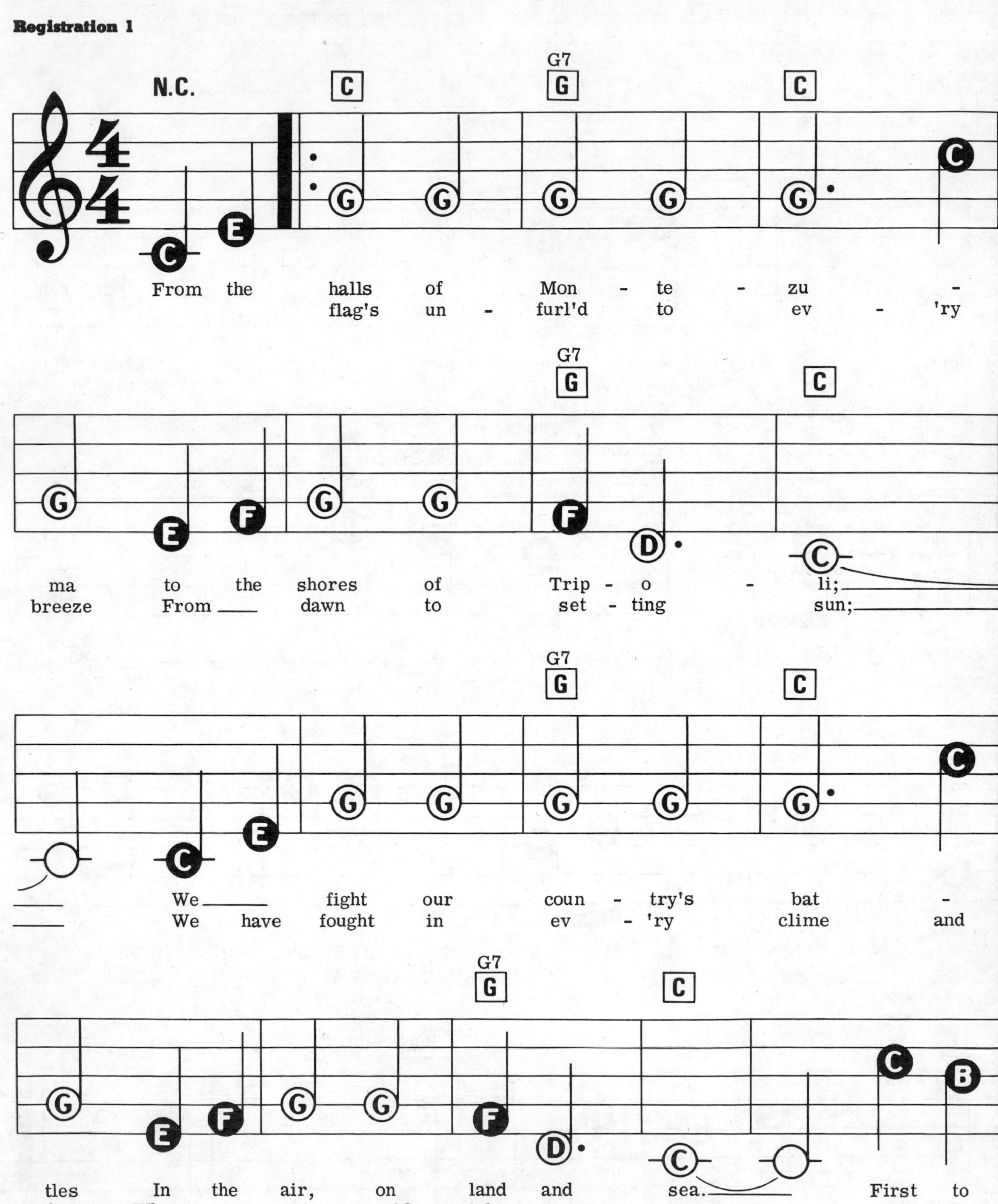

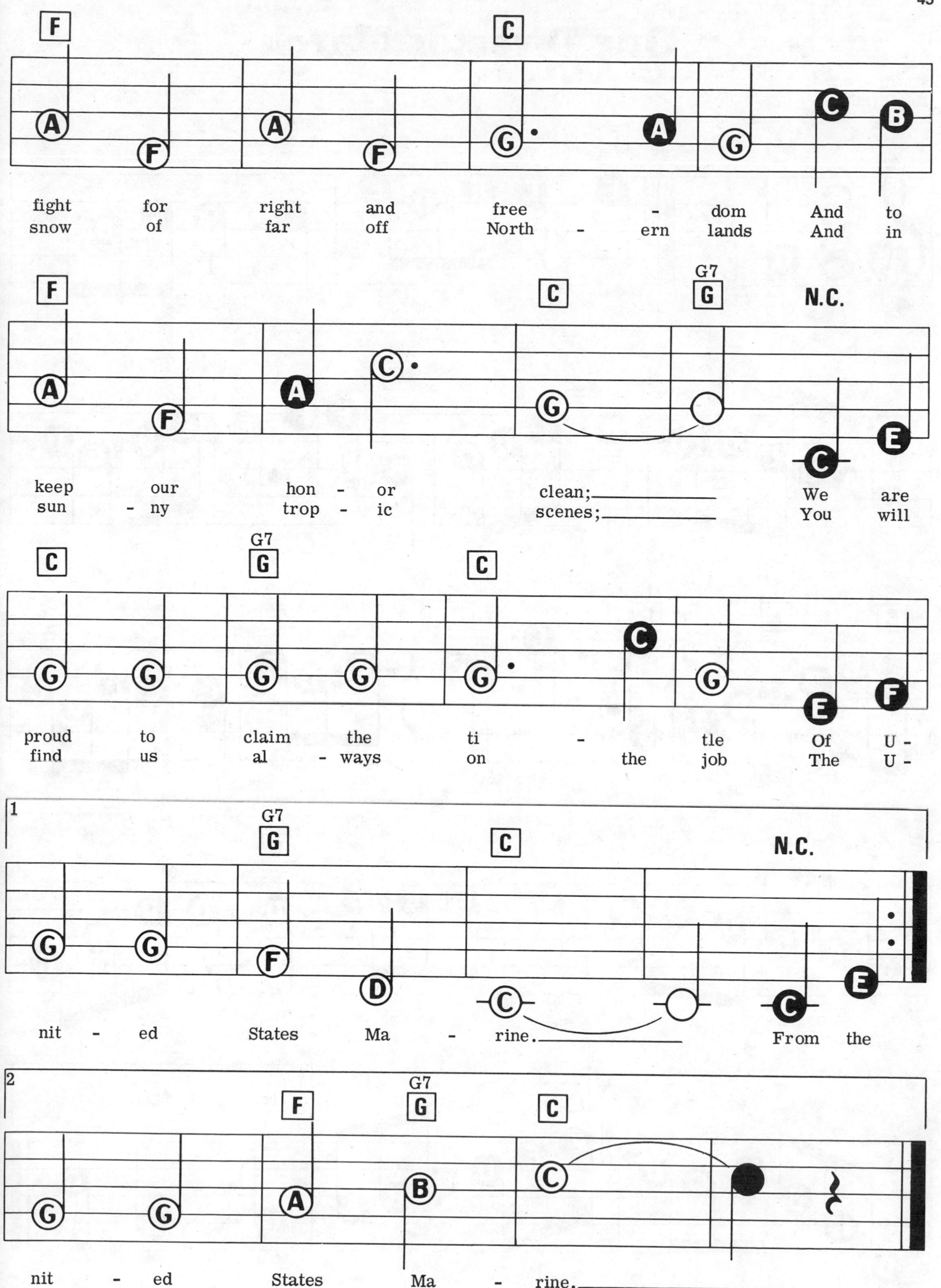
F
C
A
F
A
F
G
A
G
C
B
fight for right and free - dom And to
snow of far off North - ern lands And in
F
C
G7
G
N.C.
A
F
A
C
G
C
E
keep our hon - or clean; We are
sun - ny trop - ic scenes; You will
C
G7
G
C
G
G
G
G
G
C
G
E
F
proud to claim the ti - tle Of U -
find us al - ways on the job The U -
1
G7
G
C
N.C.
G
G
F
D
C
C
E
nit - ed States Ma - rine. From the
2
F
G7
G
C
G
G
A
B
C
nit - ed States Ma - rine.

Our Director March

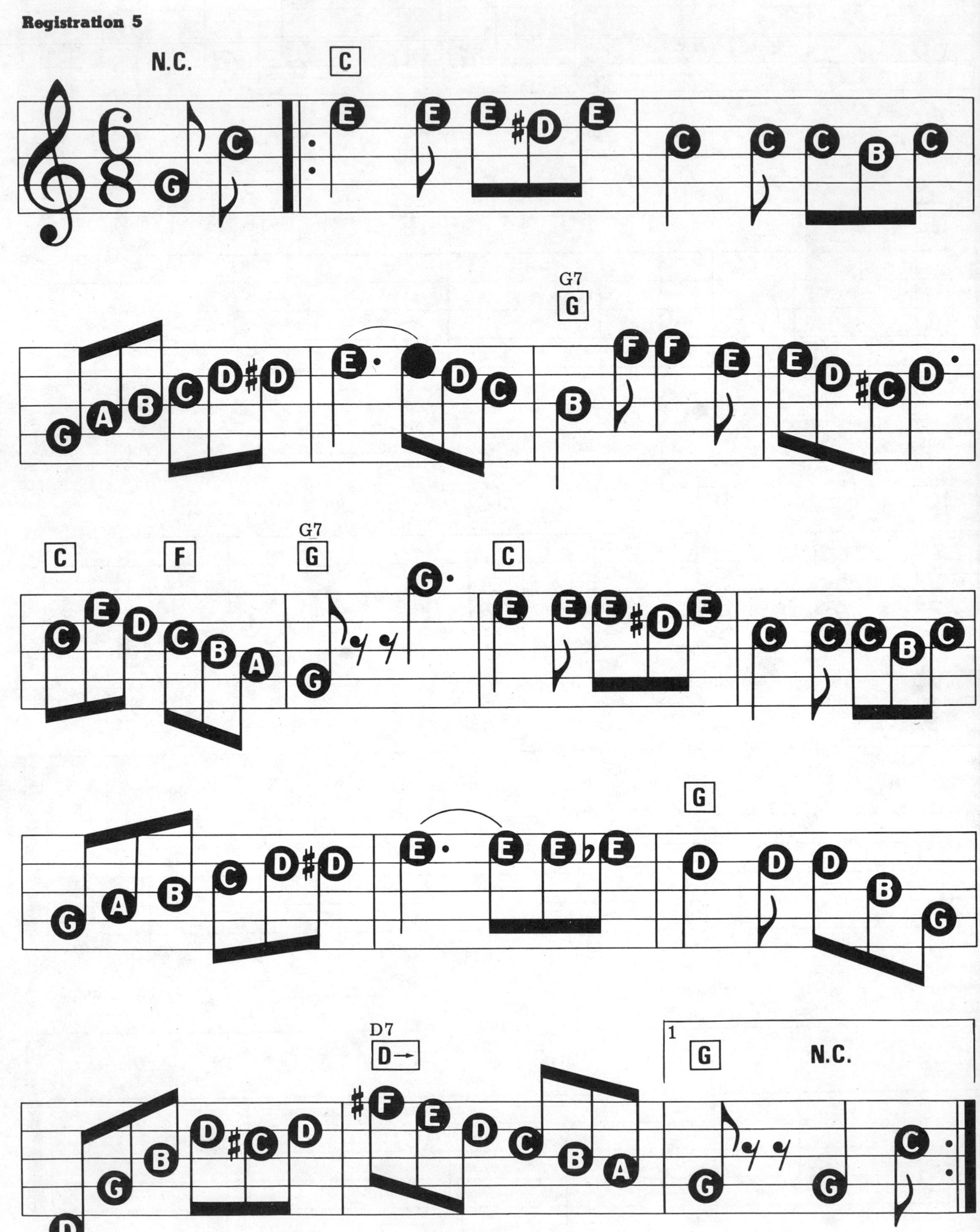

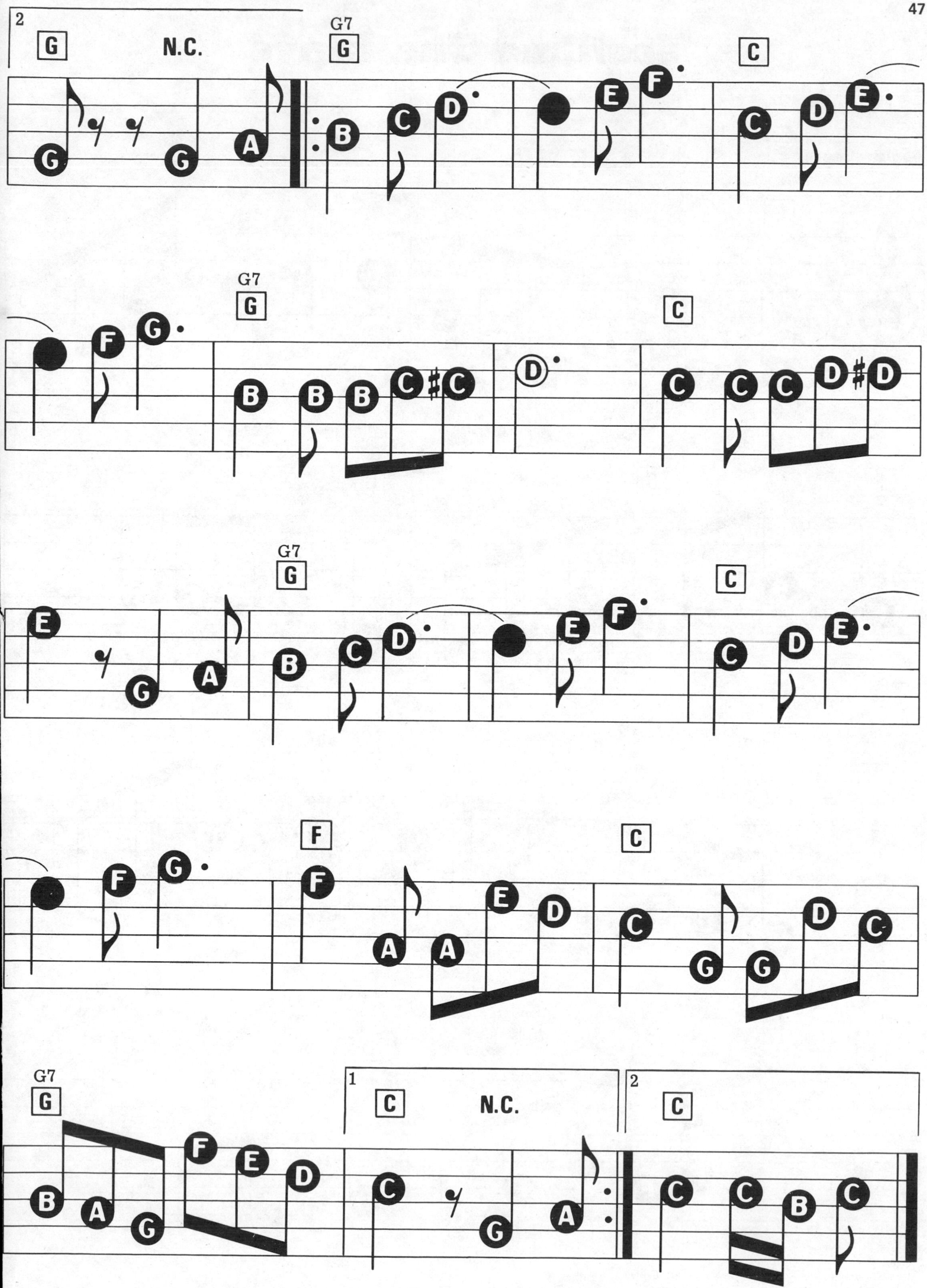
2
G N.C. G7 G C
G G A B C D E F C D E
G7 G C
F G B B B C ♯C D C C C D ♯D
G7 G C
E G A B C D E F C D E
F C
F G F A A E D C G G D C
G7 G 1 C N.C. 2 C
B A G F E D C G A C C B C

Scotland The Brave

Registration 4

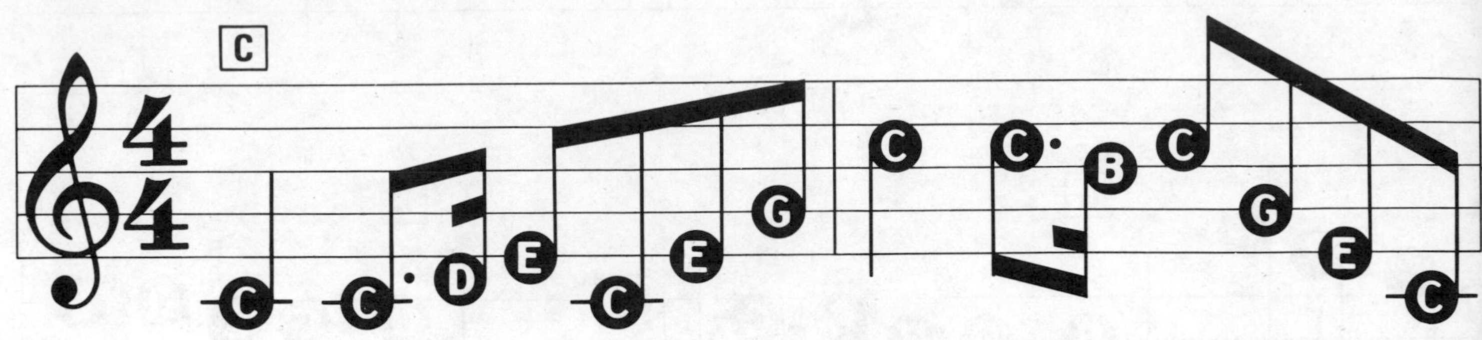

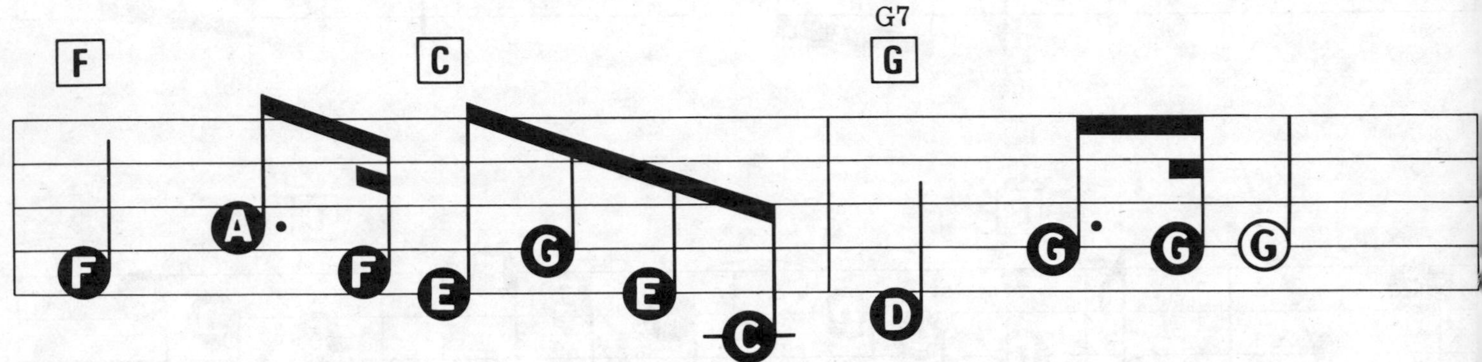

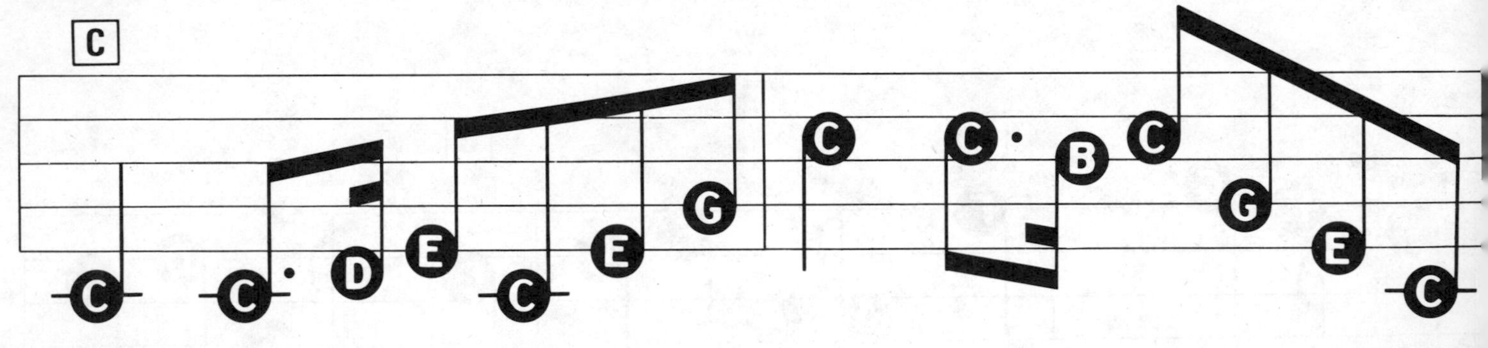

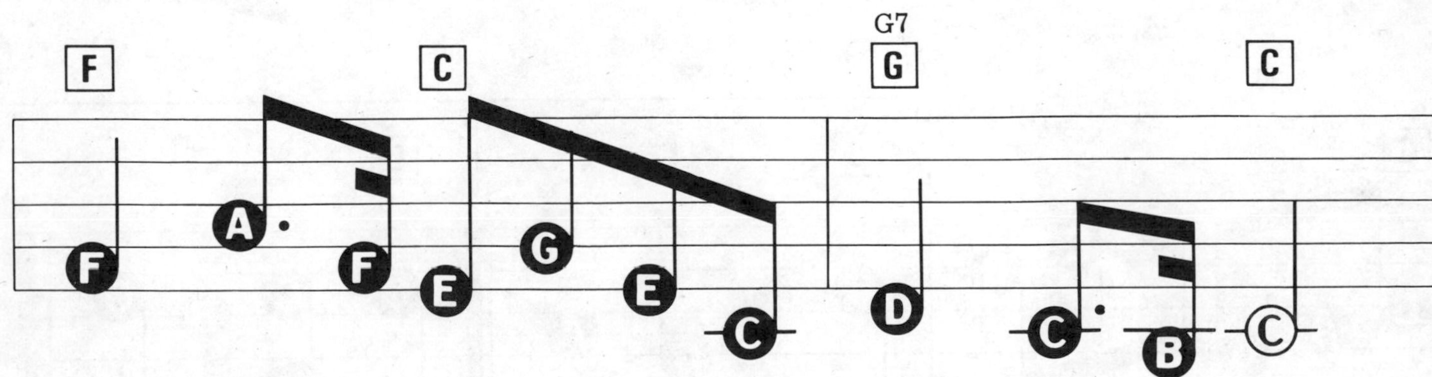

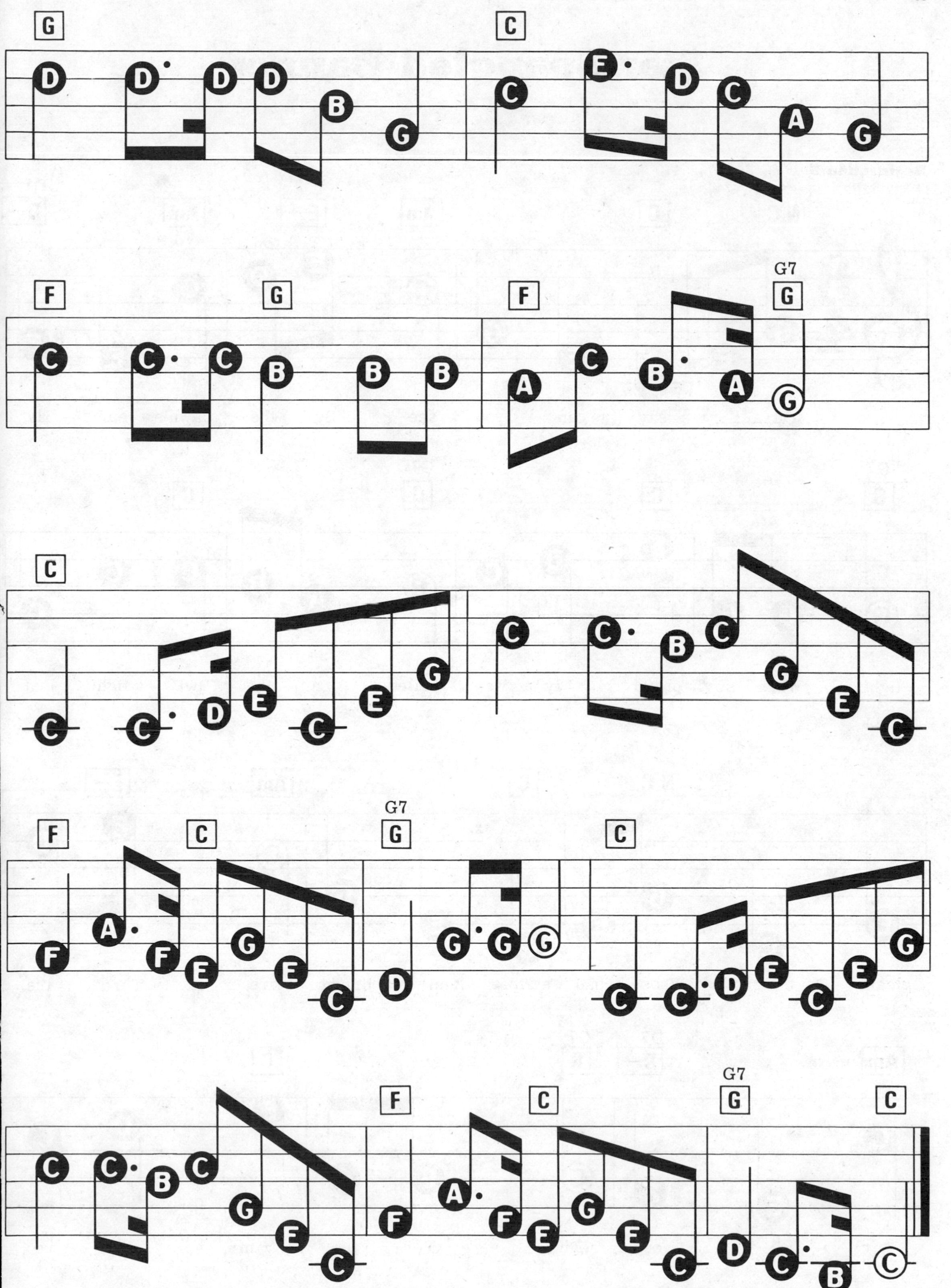
G
D D D D D B G
C
C E D C A G
F
C C C
G
B B B
F
A C B A
G7
G
G
C
C C D E C E G C C B C G E C
F
F A F
C
E G E C
G7
G
D G G G
C
C C D E C E G
C C B C G E C
F
F A F
C
E G E C
G7
G
D C B
C
C

Star Spangled Banner

Registration 5

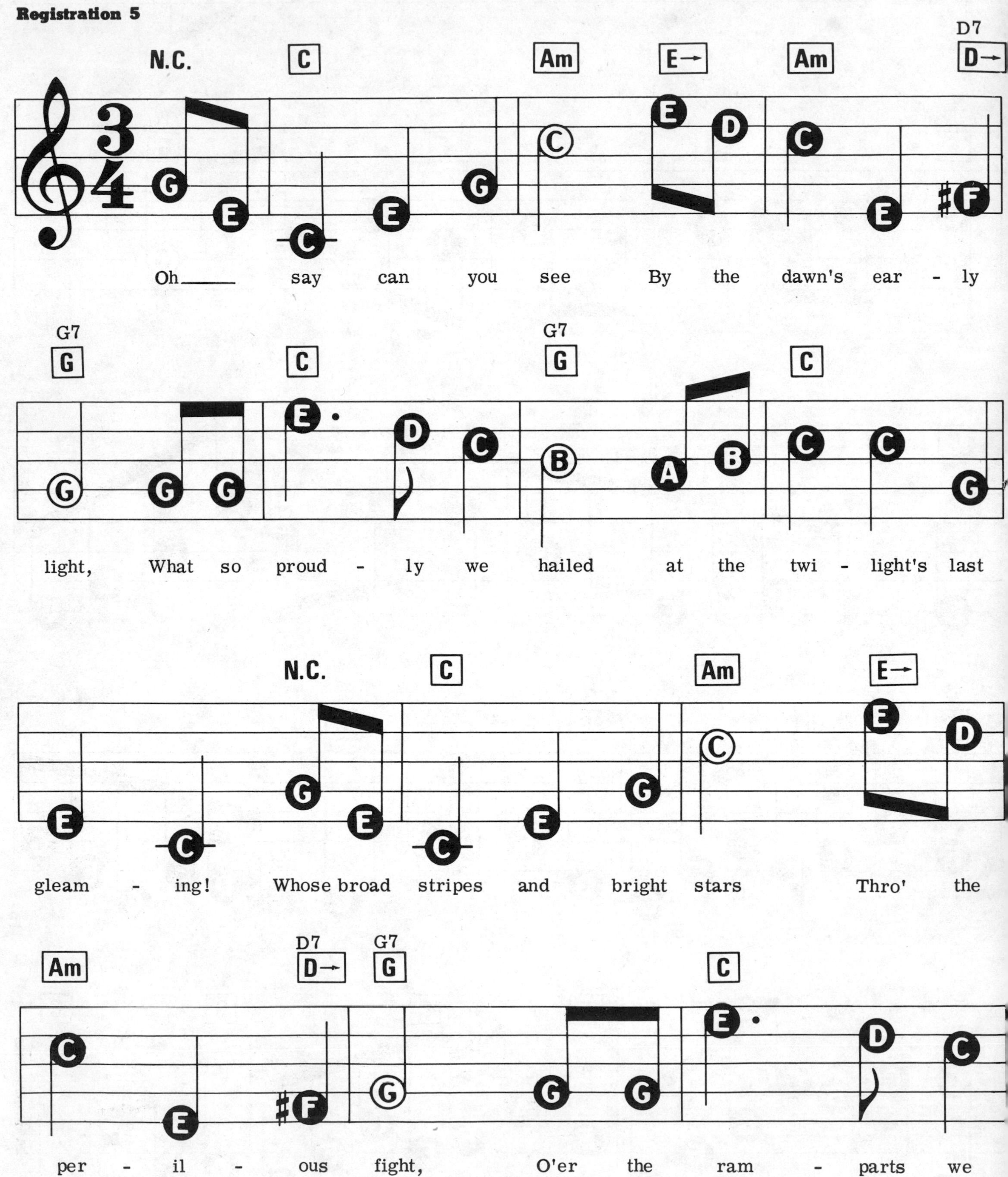

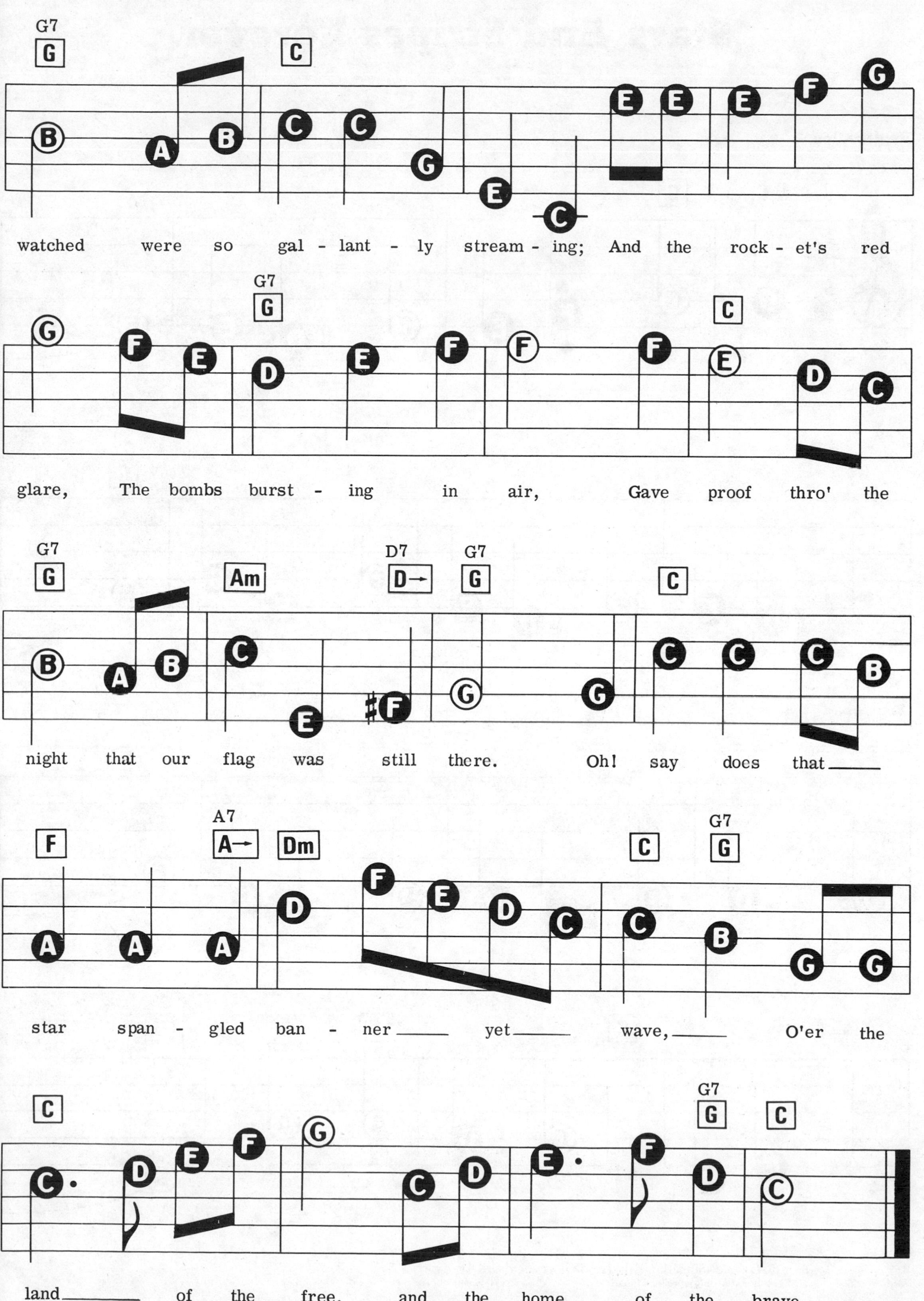
G7
G
C
B A B C C G E C E E E F G
watched were so gal - lant - ly stream - ing; And the rock - et's red
G7
G
C
G F E D E F F F E D C
glare, The bombs burst - ing in air, Gave proof thro' the
G7
G
Am
D7
D→
G7
G
C
B A B C E ♯F G G C C C B
night that our flag was still there. Oh! say does that
F
A7
A→
Dm
C
G7
G
A A A D F E D C C B G G
star span - gled ban - ner yet wave, O'er the
C
G7
G
C
C. D E F G C D E. F D C
land of the free, and the home of the brave.

Stars And Stripes Forever

Registration 2

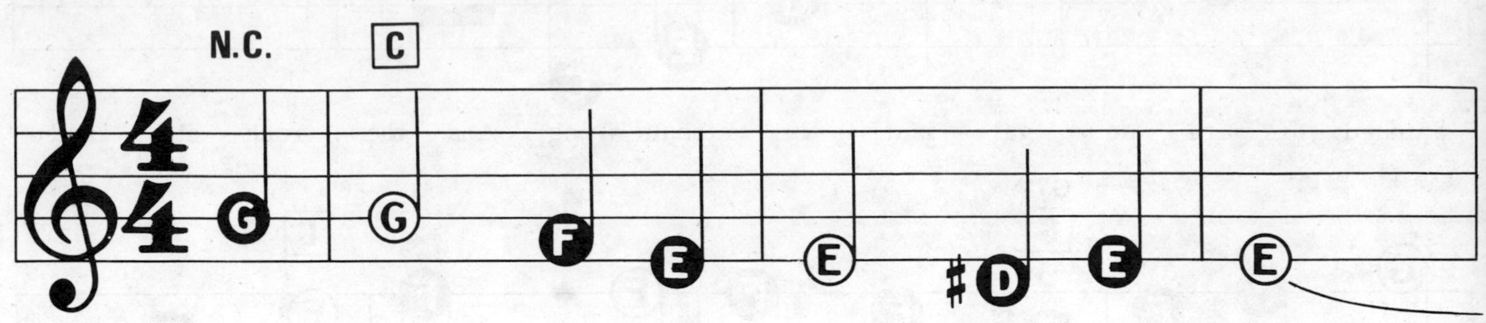

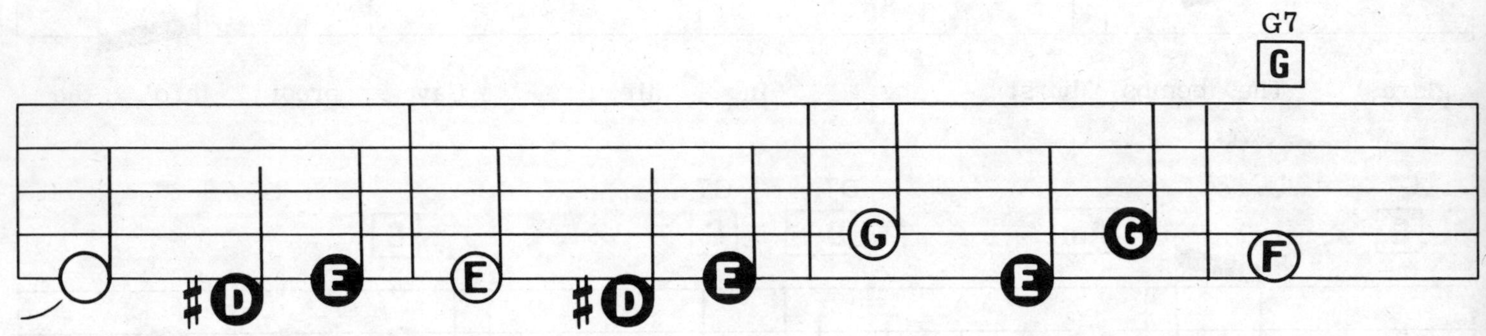

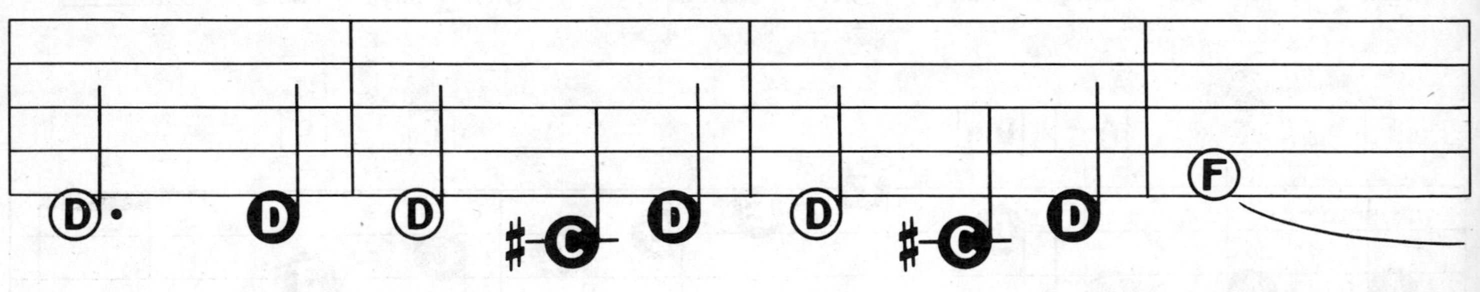

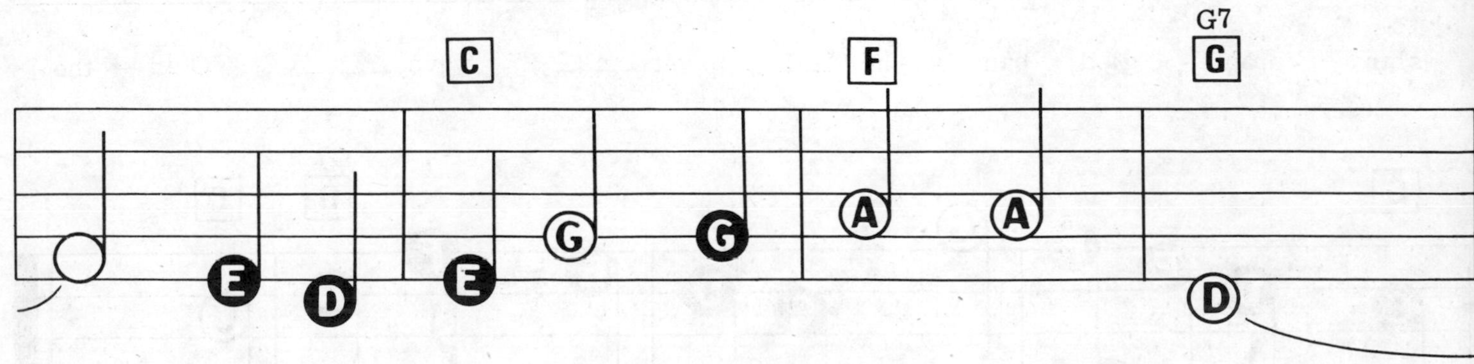

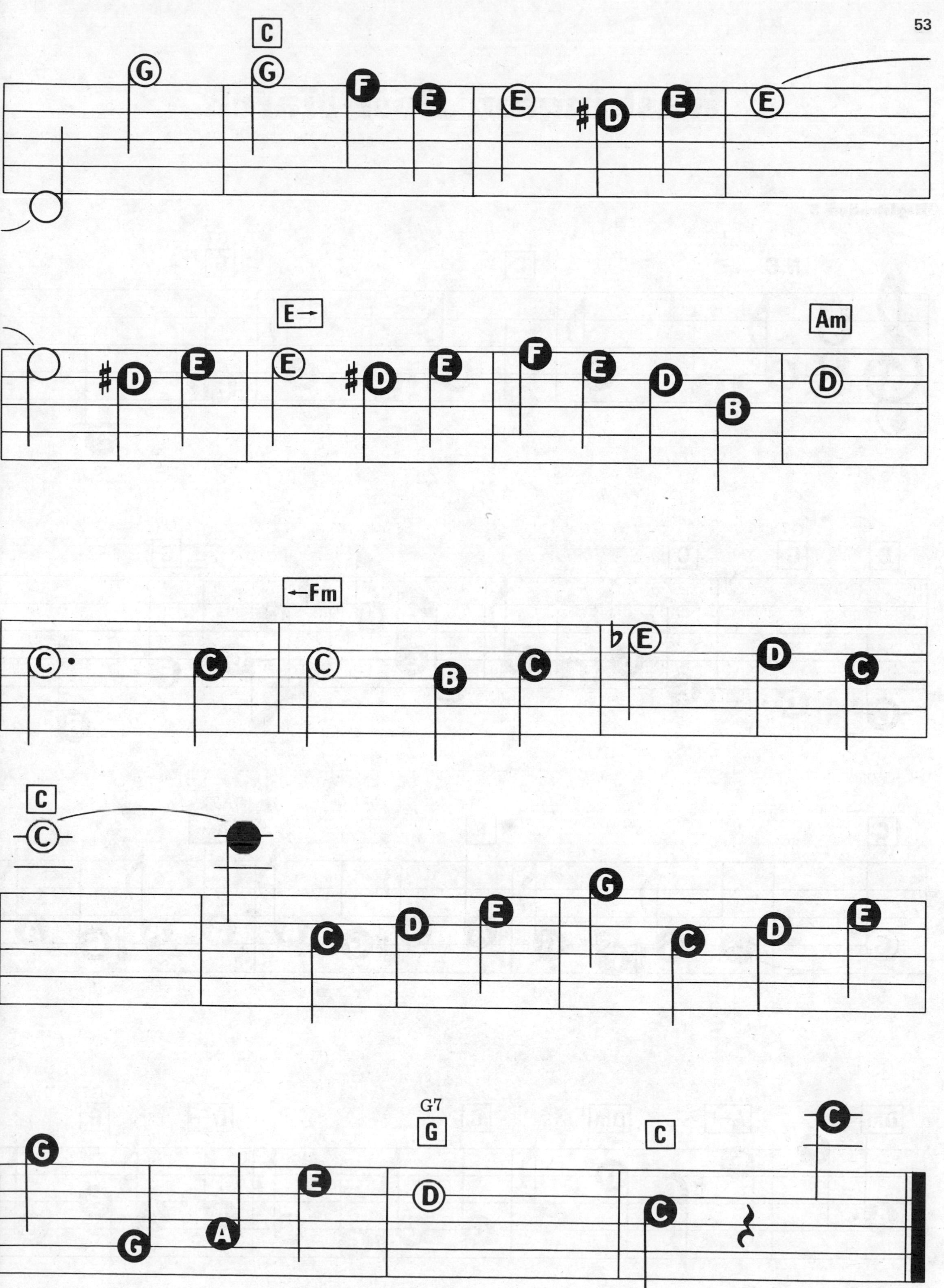
C
G
G
F
E
E
♯D
E
E
E→
E
♯D
E
E
♯D
E
F
E
D
B
Am
D
←Fm
C
C
C
B
C
♭E
D
C
C
C
C
D
E
G
C
D
E
G
G
A
E
G7
G
D
C
C
C

Washington Post March

Registration 5

N.C. C G7 G

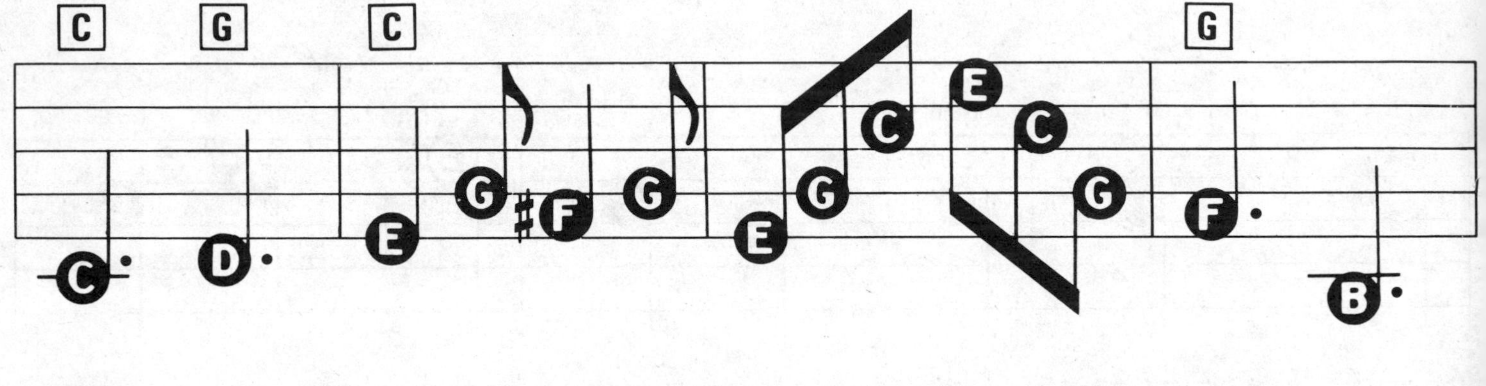

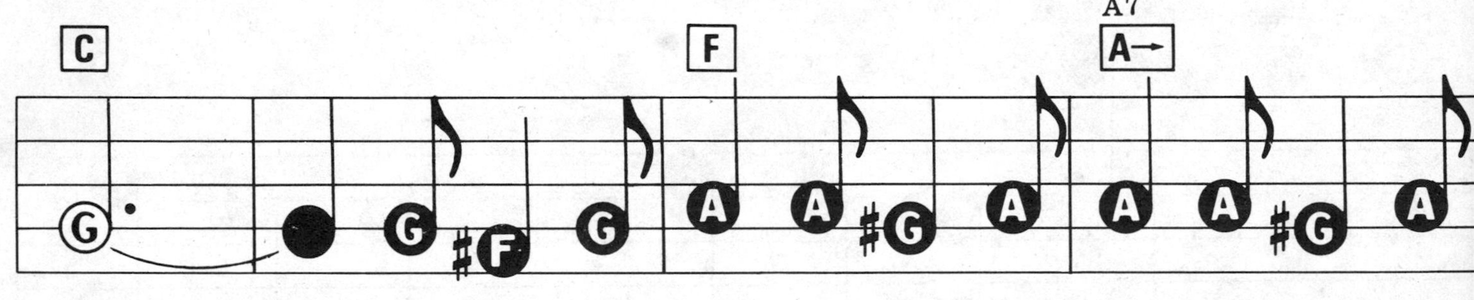

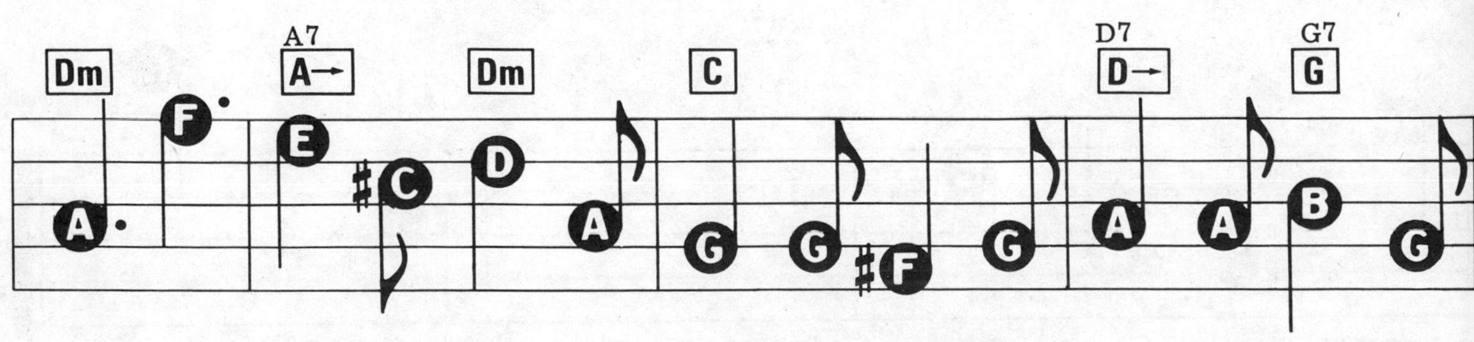

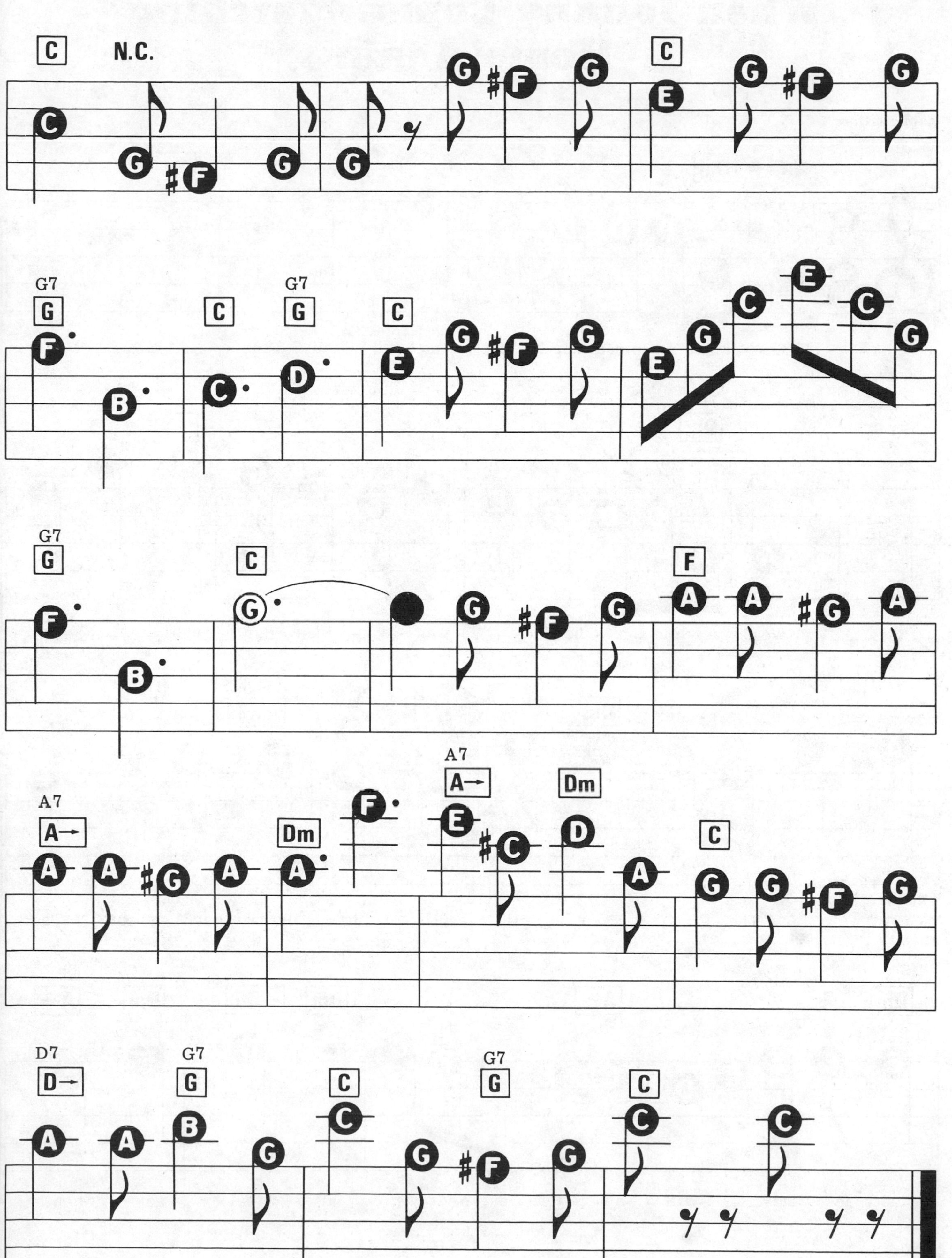
C N.C. C
G7 G C G7 G C
G7 G C F
A7 A→ Dm A7 A→ Dm C
D7 D→ G7 G C G7 G C

When Johnny Comes Marching Home Again

Registration 4

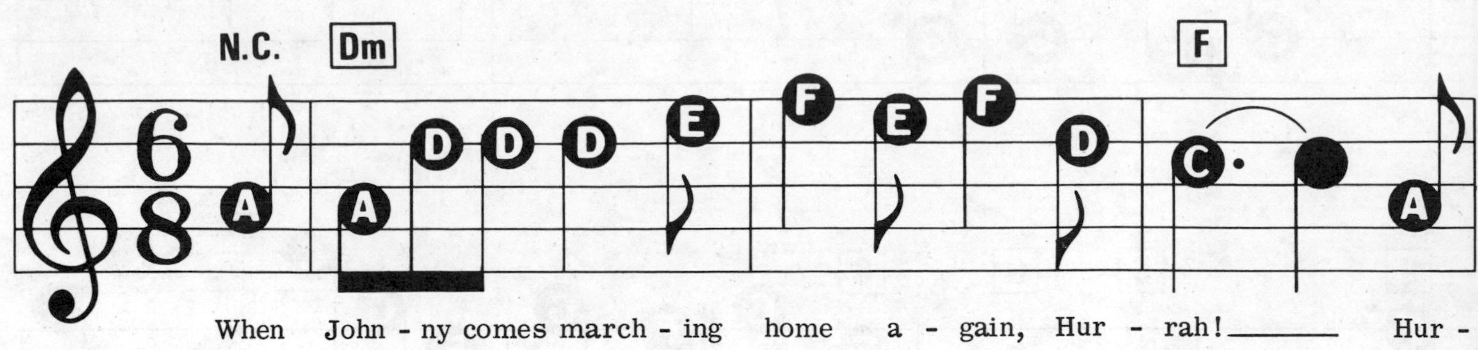

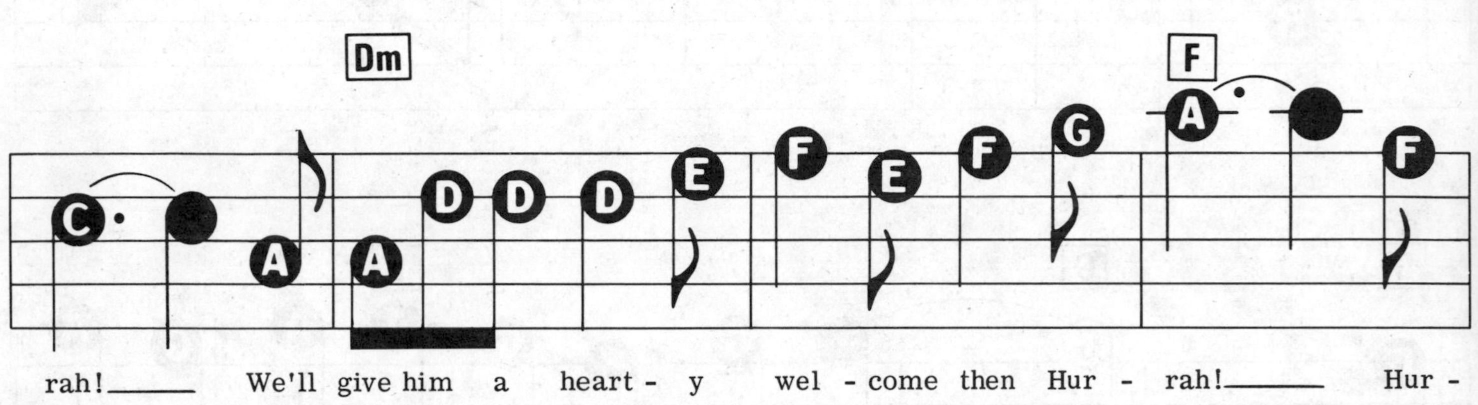

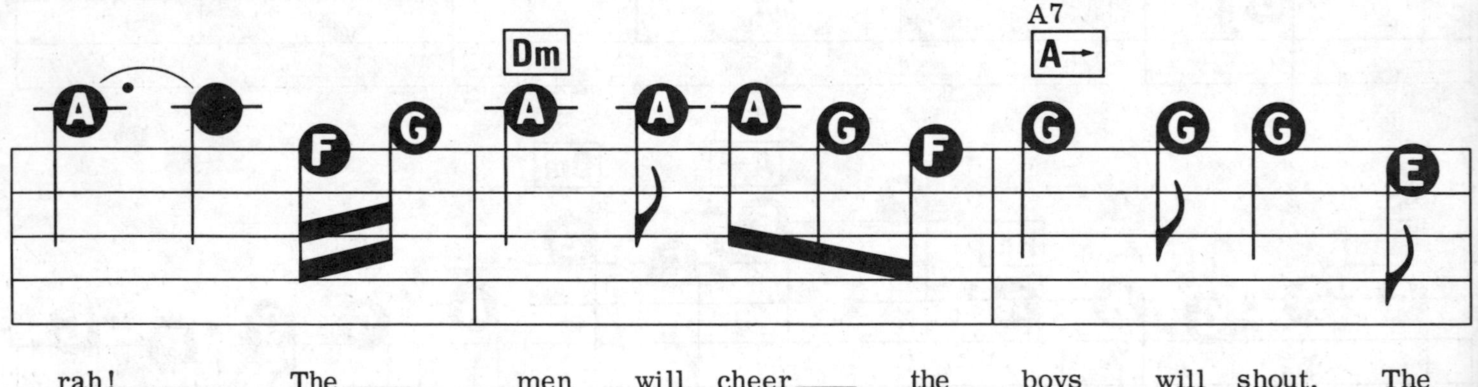

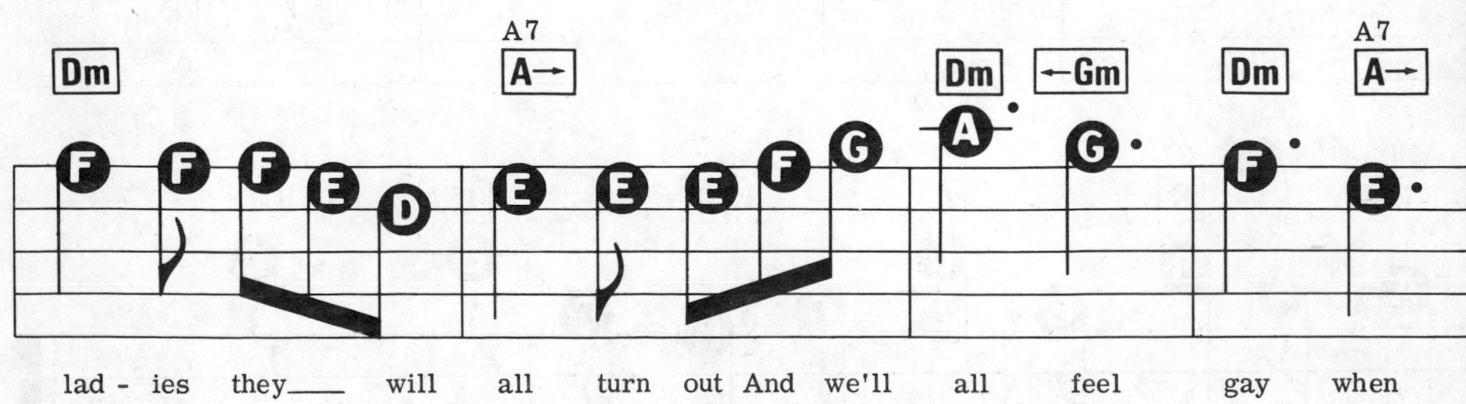

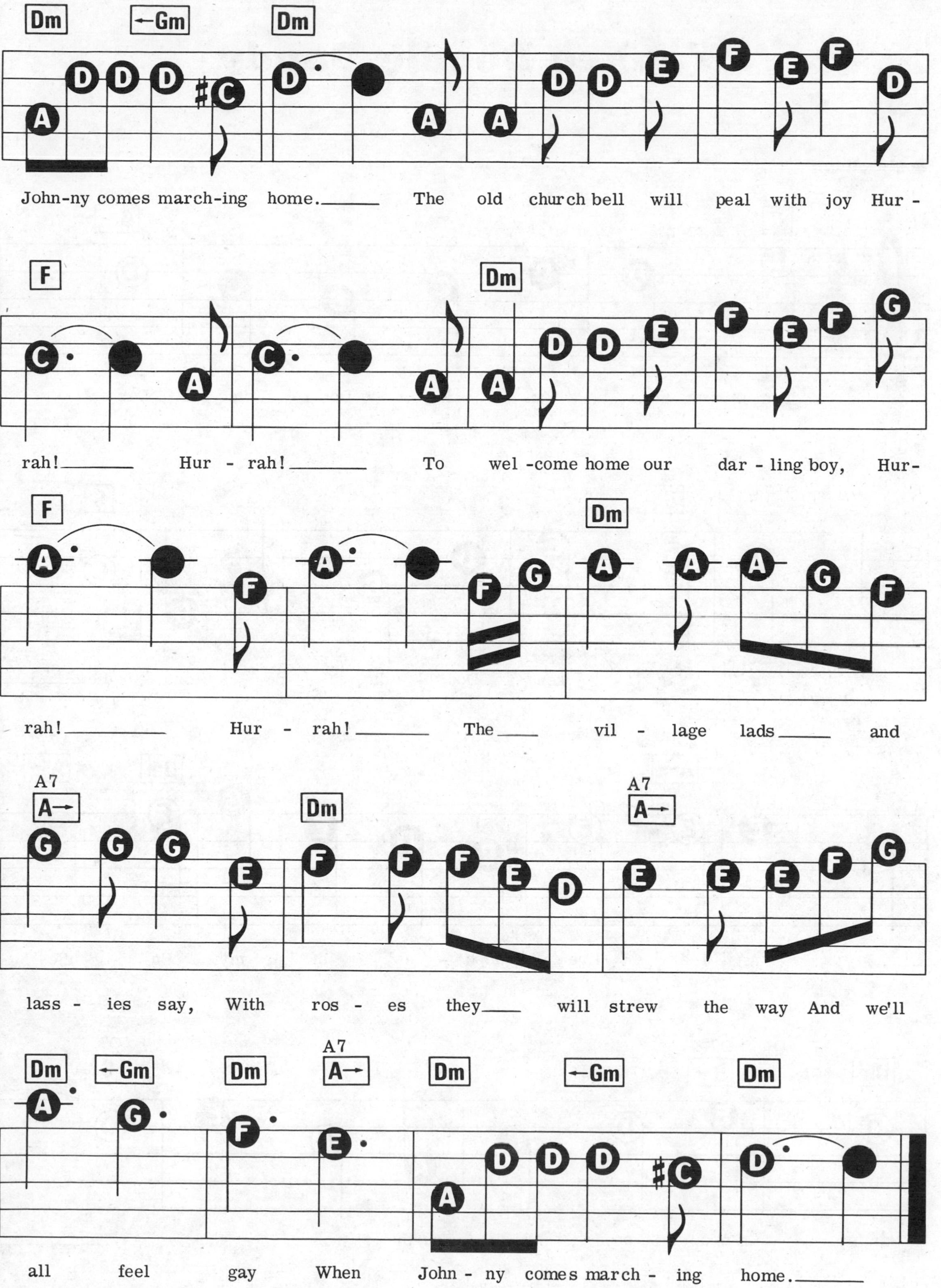
Dm
←Gm
Dm
A D D D D ♯C D A
A D D E F E F D
John-ny comes march-ing home. The old church bell will peal with joy Hur -
F
Dm
C A C A A D D E F E F G
rah! Hur - rah! To wel -come home our dar - ling boy, Hur-
F
Dm
A F A F G A A A G F
rah! Hur - rah! The vil - lage lads and
A7
A→
Dm
A7
A→
G G G E F F F E D E E E F G
lass - ies say, With ros - es they will strew the way And we'll
Dm
←Gm
Dm
A7
A→
Dm
←Gm
Dm
A G F E A D D D ♯C D
all feel gay When John - ny comes march - ing home.

Yankee Doodle Dandy

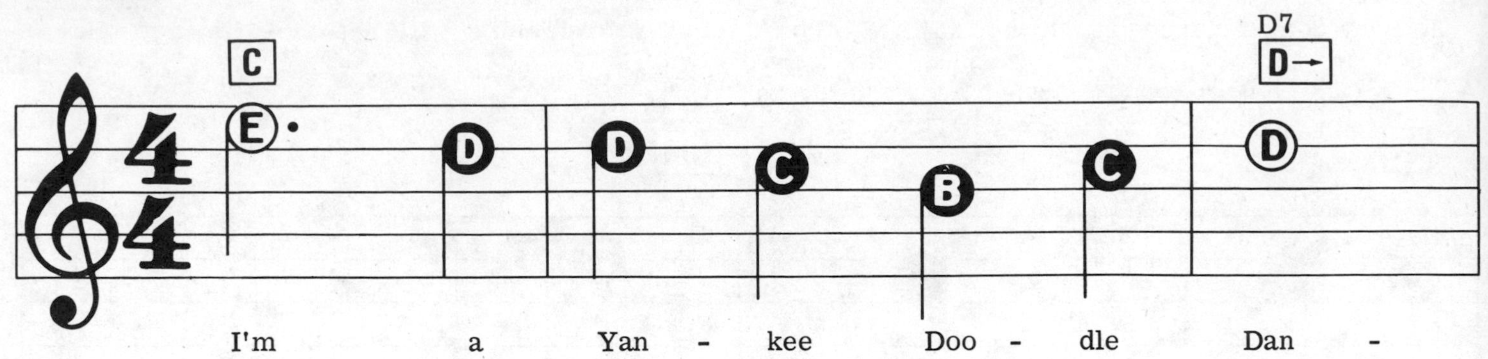

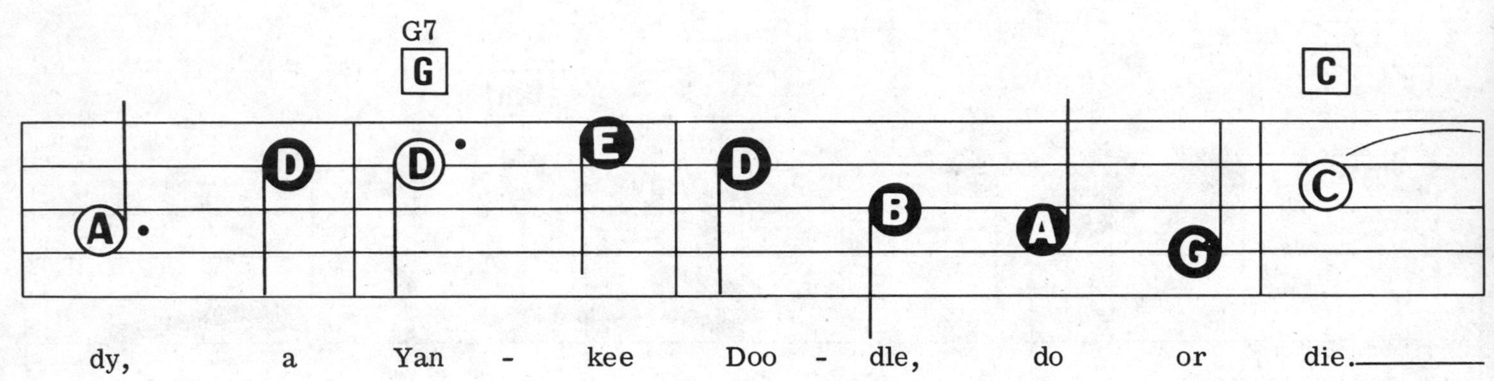

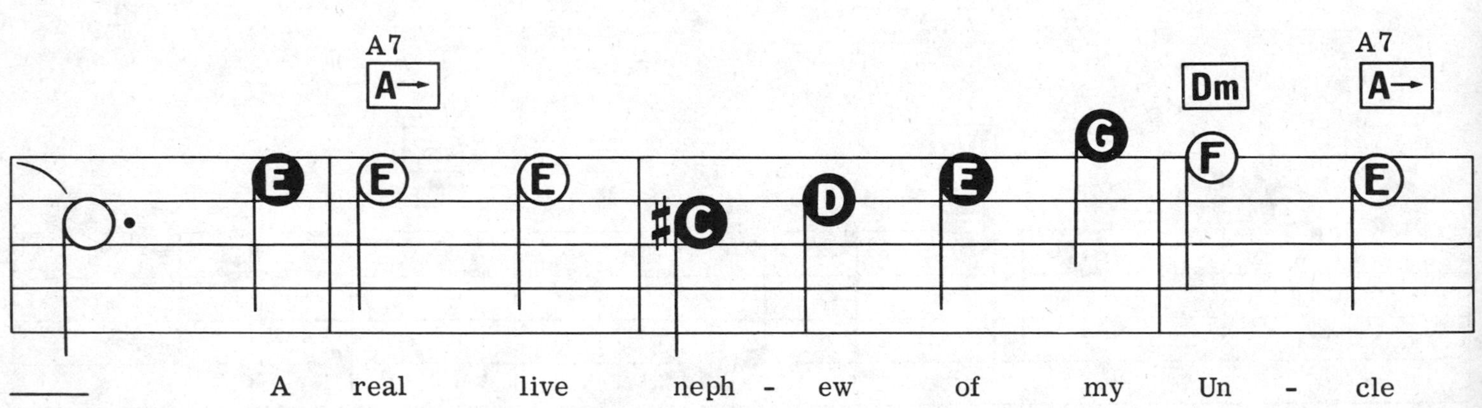

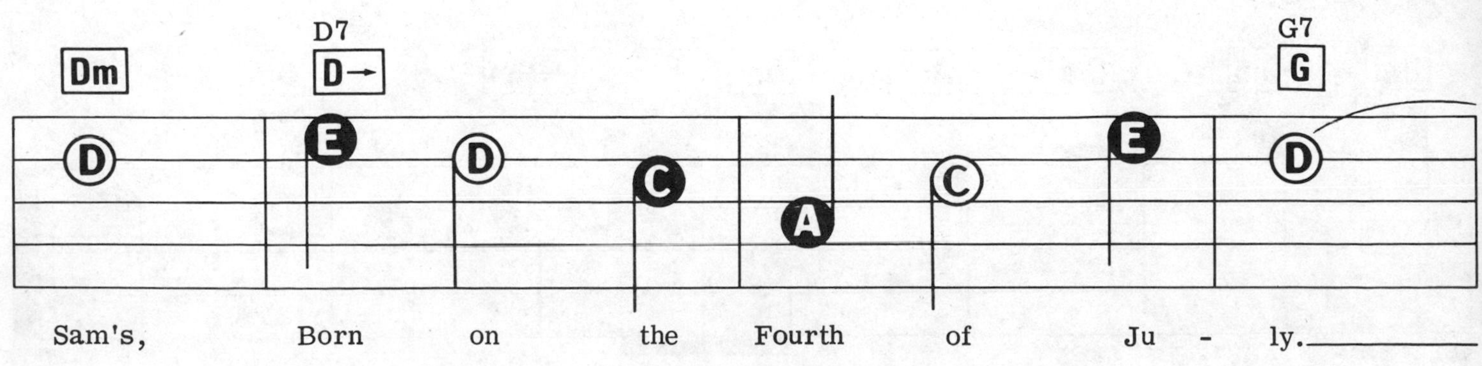

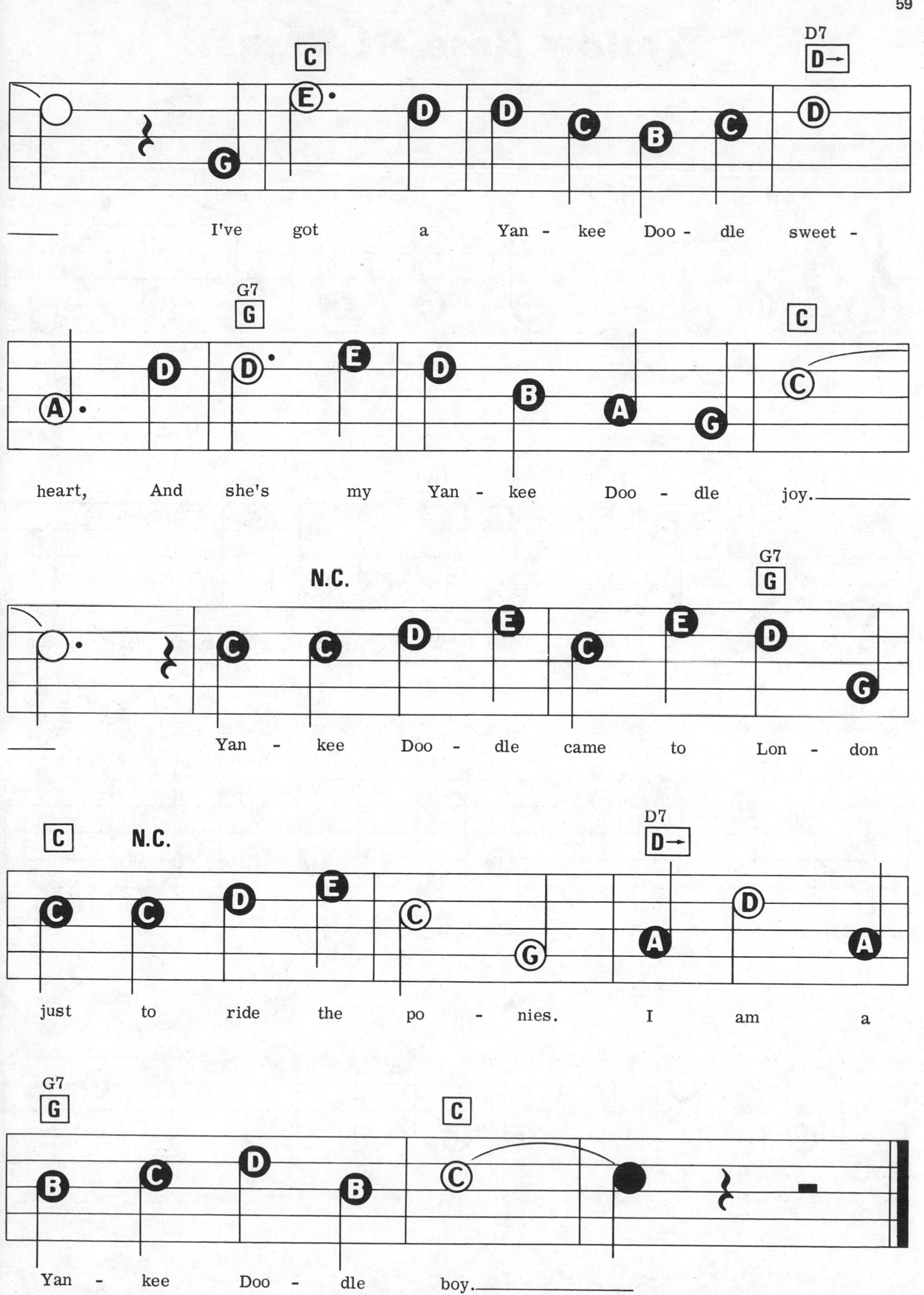

C
D7
D→
I've got a Yan - kee Doo - dle sweet -
G7
G
C
heart, And she's my Yan - kee Doo - dle joy.
N.C.
G7
G
Yan - kee Doo - dle came to Lon - don
C
N.C.
D7
D→
just to ride the po - nies. I am a
G7
G
C
Yan - kee Doo - dle boy.

Yellow Rose Of Texas

Registration 3

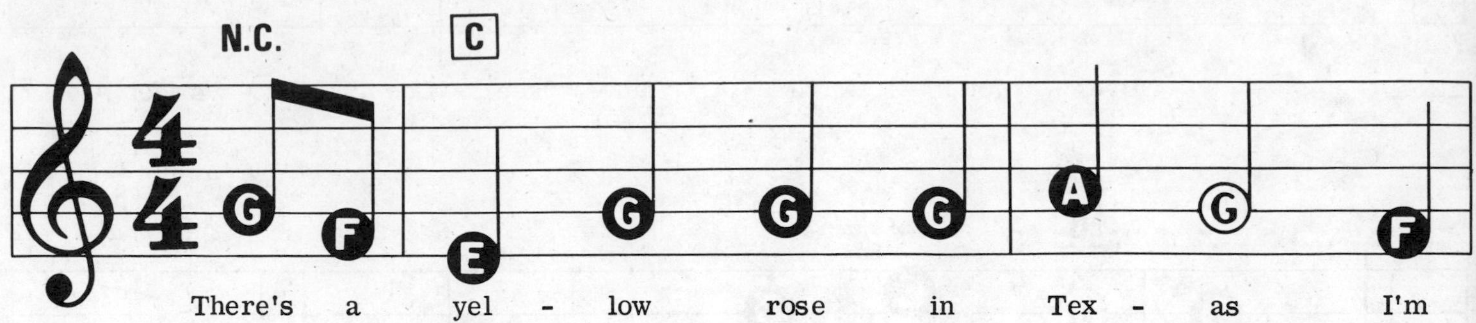

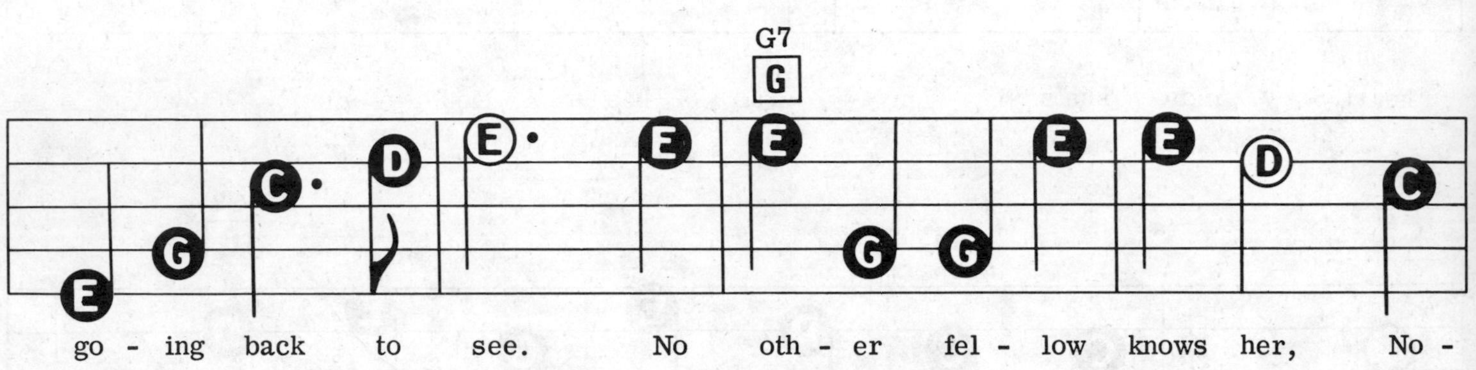

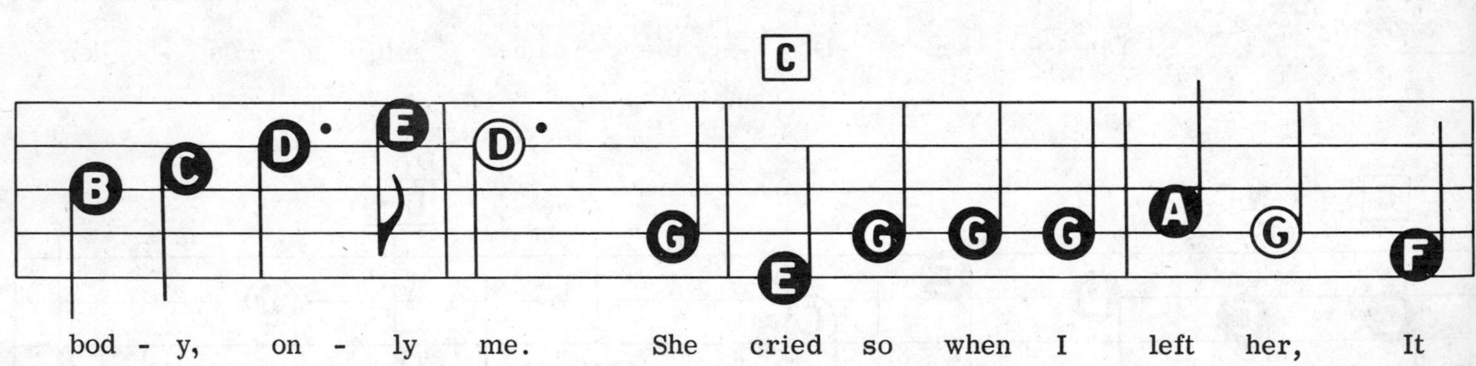

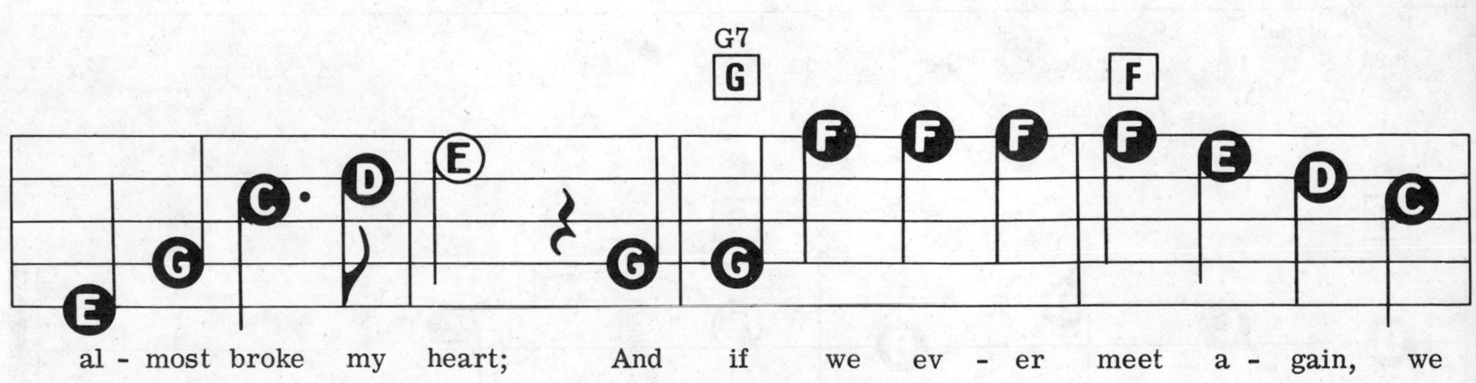

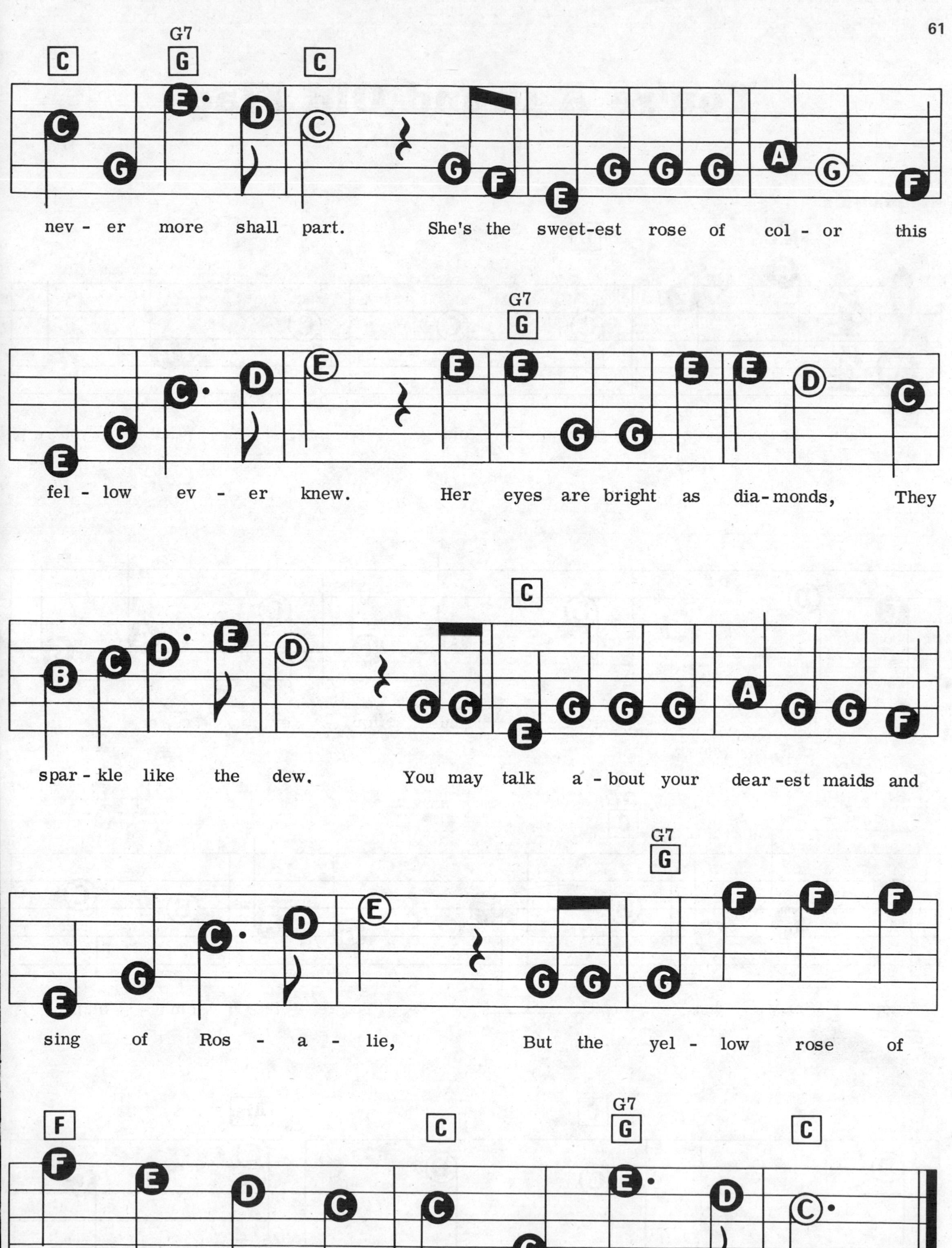
C G7 G C
nev - er more shall part. She's the sweet-est rose of col - or this
G7 G
fel - low ev - er knew. Her eyes are bright as dia-monds, They
C
spar - kle like the dew. You may talk a - bout your dear -est maids and
G7 G
sing of Ros - a - lie, But the yel - low rose of
F C G7 G C
Tex - as beats the belle of Ten - nes - see.

You're A Grand Old Flag

Registration 2

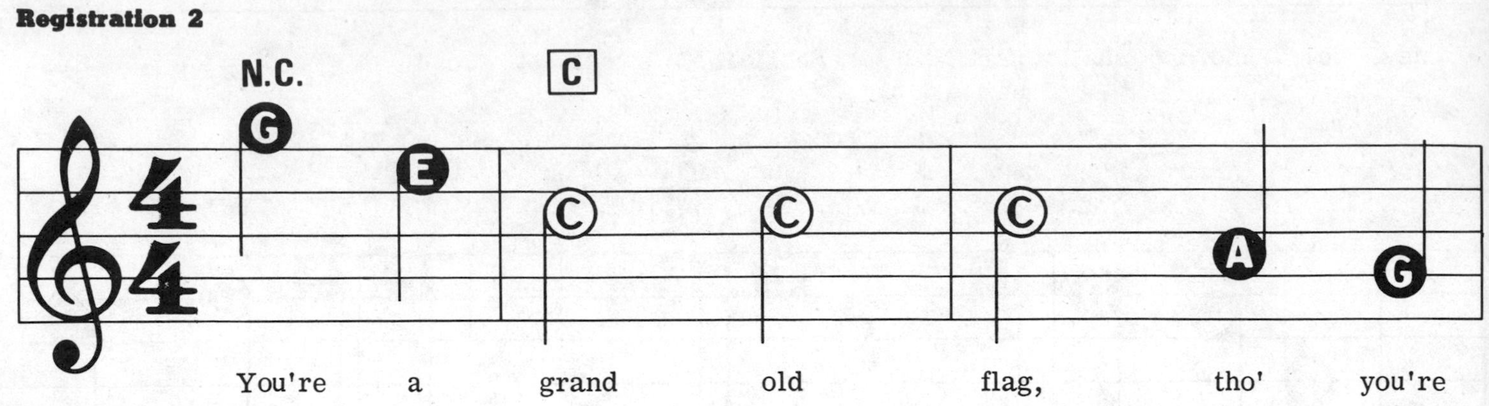

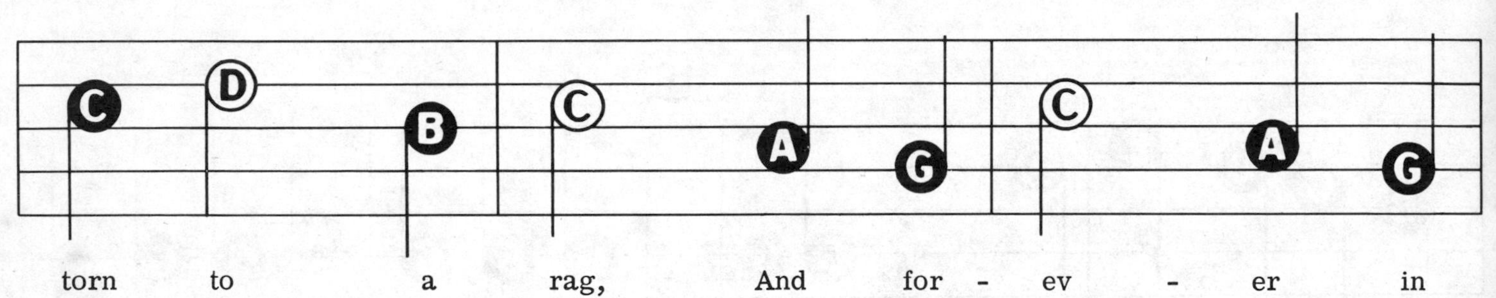

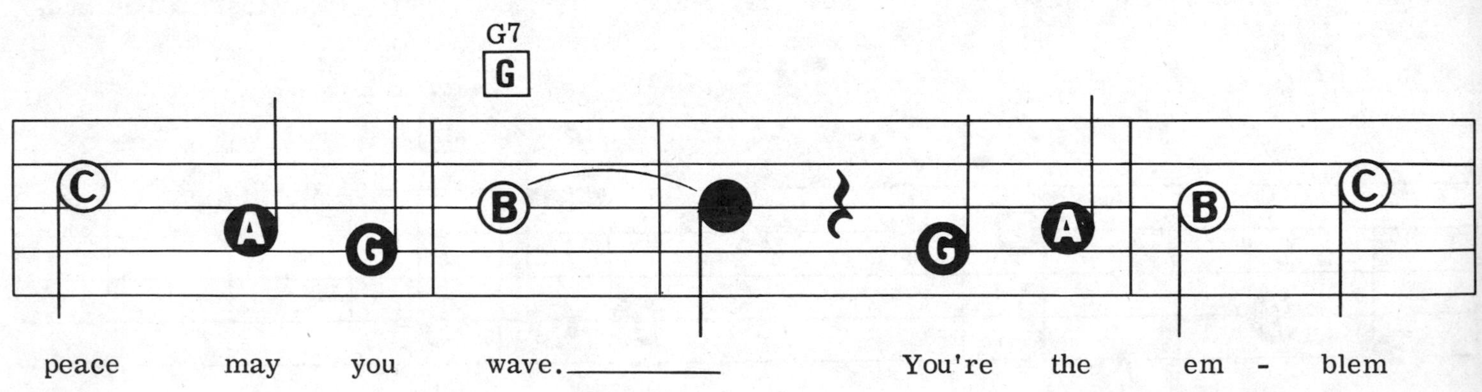

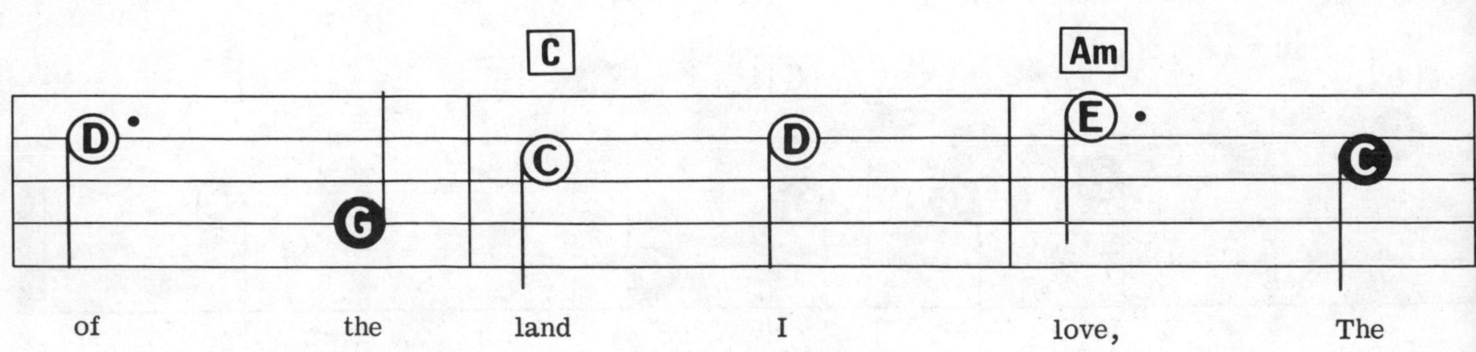

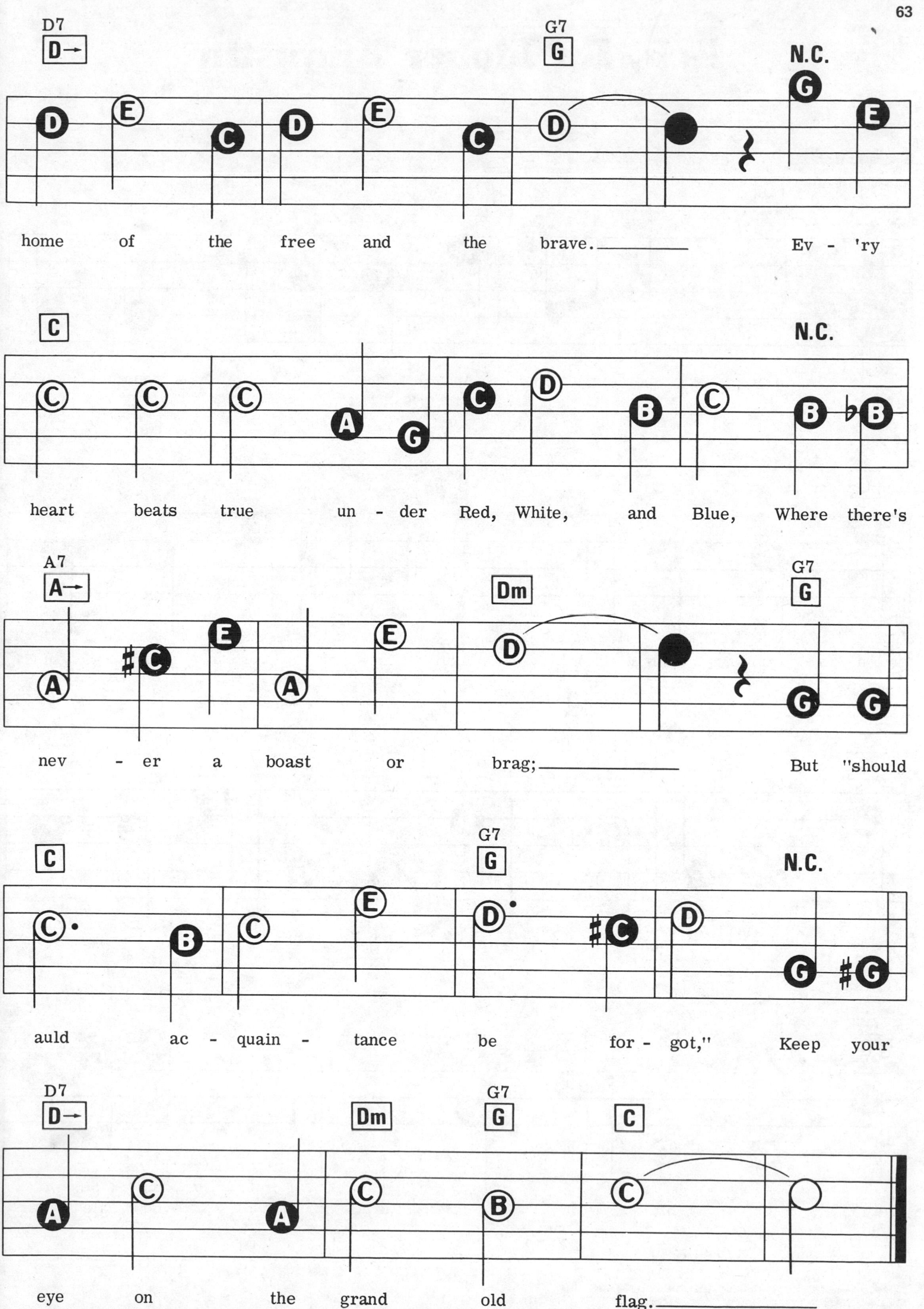
D7
D→
G7
G
N.C.
home of the free and the brave. Ev - 'ry
C
N.C.
heart beats true un - der Red, White, and Blue, Where there's
A7
A→
Dm
G7
G
nev - er a boast or brag; But "should
C
G7
G
N.C.
auld ac - quain - tance be for - got," Keep your
D7
D→
Dm
G7
G
C
eye on the grand old flag.

Ach, Du Lieber Augustin

Registration 4

German

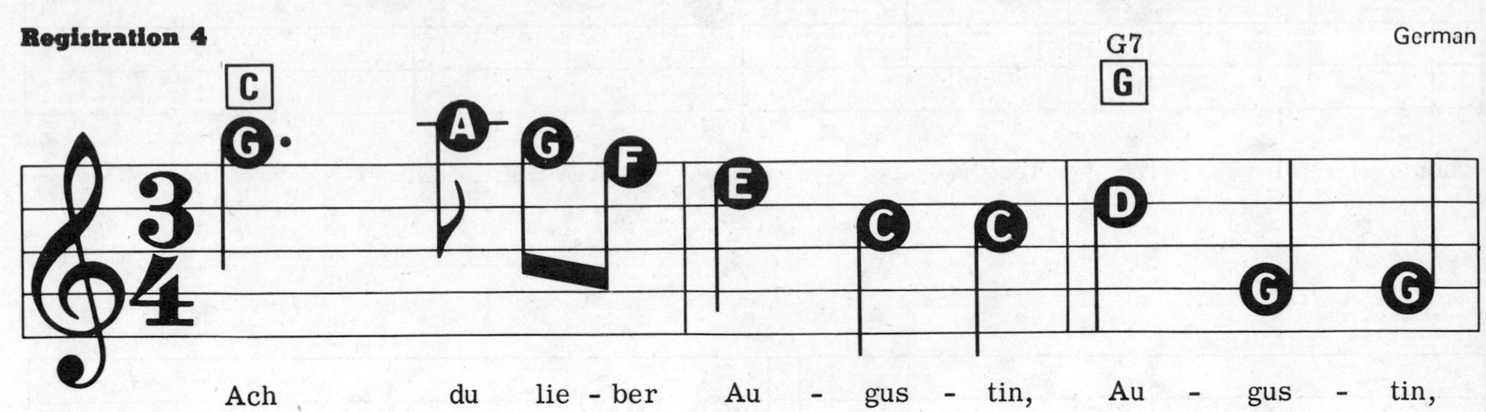

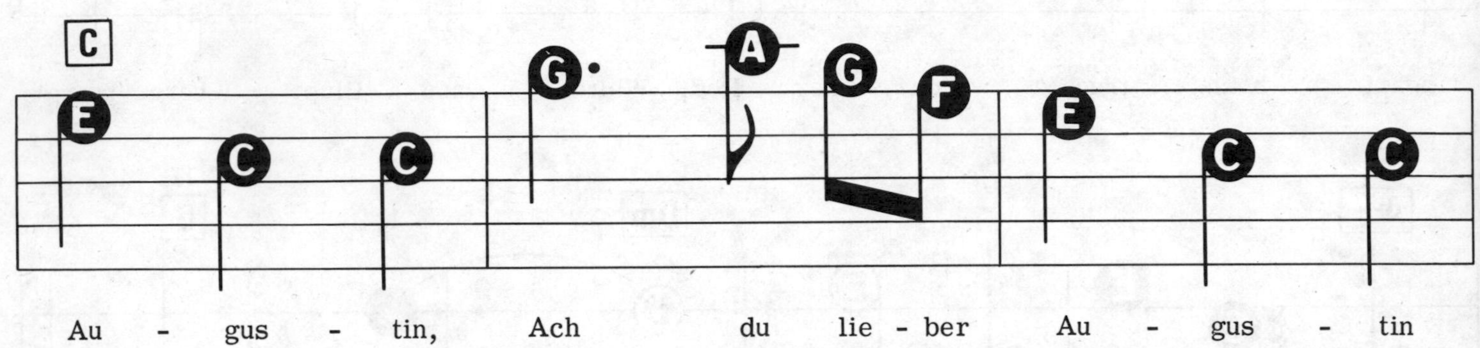

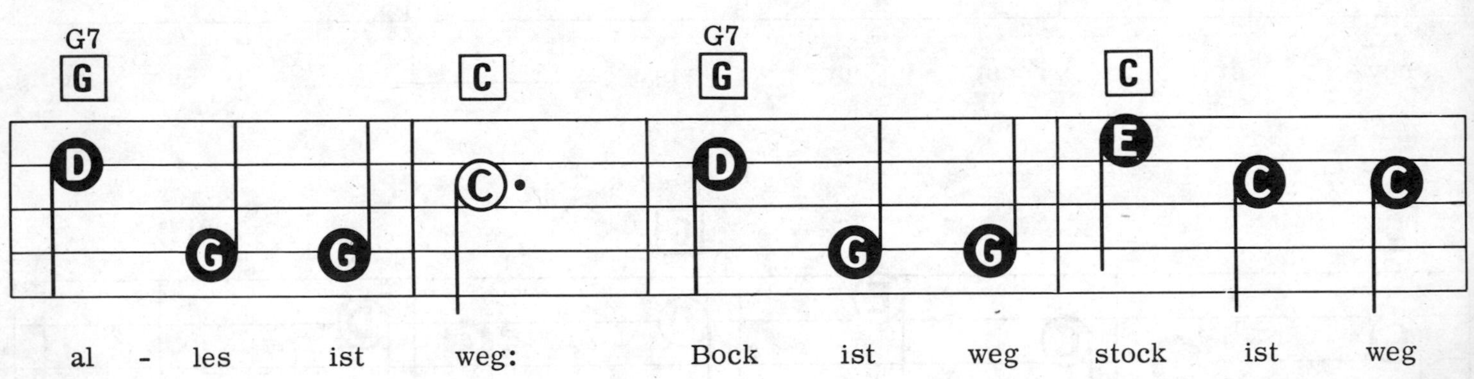

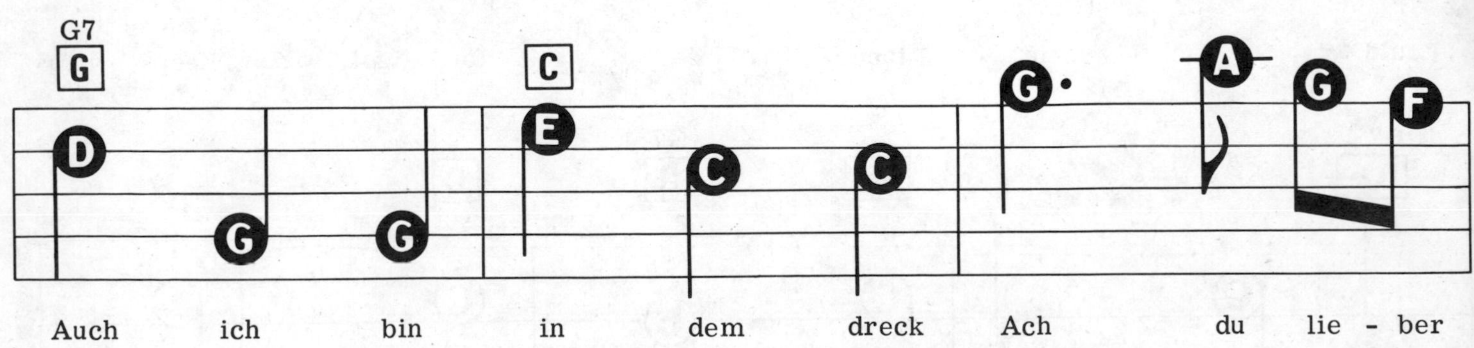

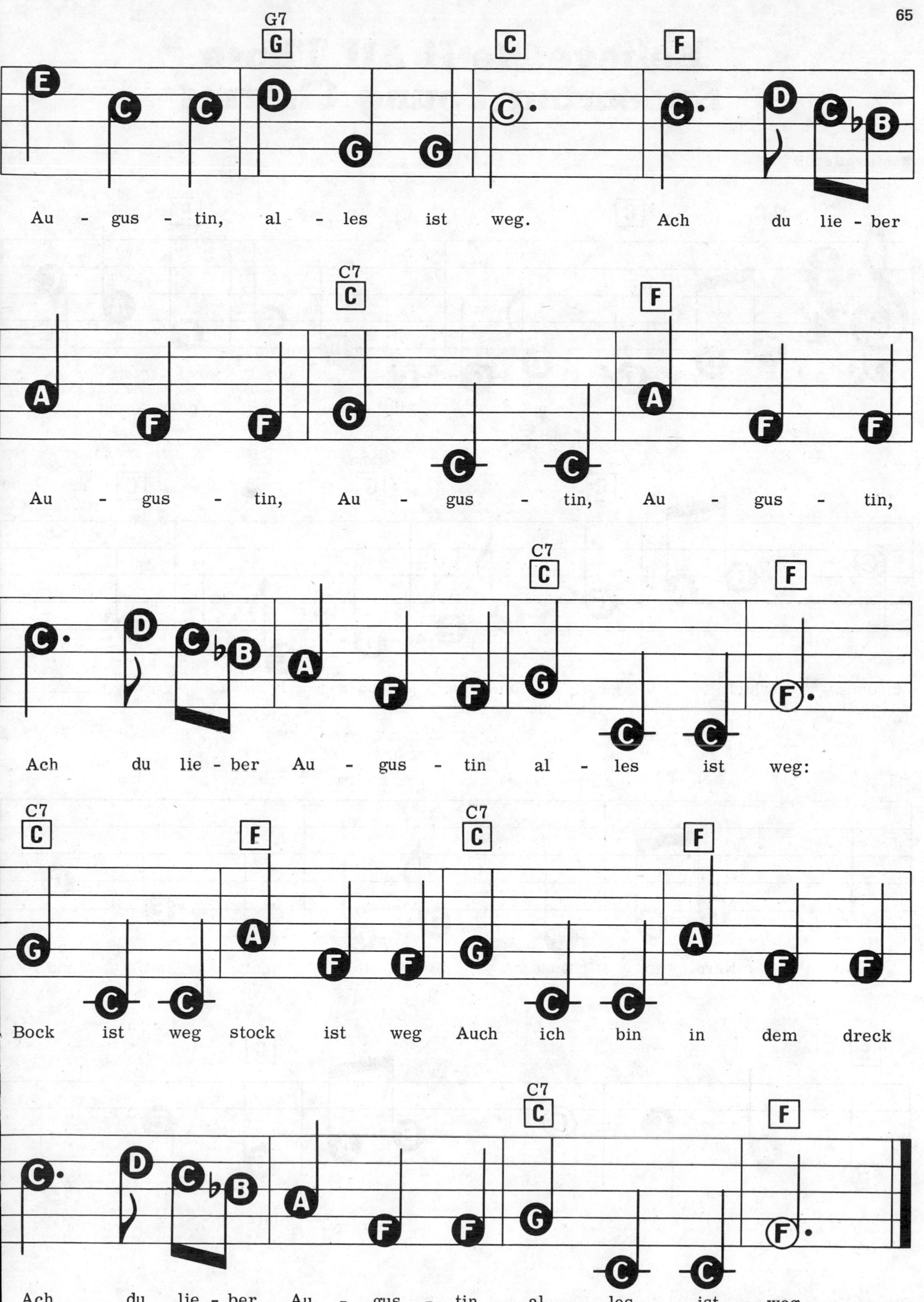
G7
G
C
F
E C C D G G C C D C ♭B
Au - gus - tin, al - les ist weg. Ach du lie - ber
C7
C
F
A F F G C C A F F
Au - gus - tin, Au - gus - tin, Au - gus - tin,
C7
C
F
C D C ♭B A F F G C C F
Ach du lie - ber Au - gus - tin al - les ist weg:
C7
C
F
C7
C
F
G C C A F F G C C A F F
Bock ist weg stock ist weg Auch ich bin in dem dreck
C7
C
F
C D C ♭B A F F G C C F
Ach du lie - ber Au - gus - tin, al - les ist weg.

Believe Me If All Those Endearing Young Charms

Registration 9

Irish

N.C. C F

E D C D C C E G F A C

Be - lieve me, if all those en - dear - ing young

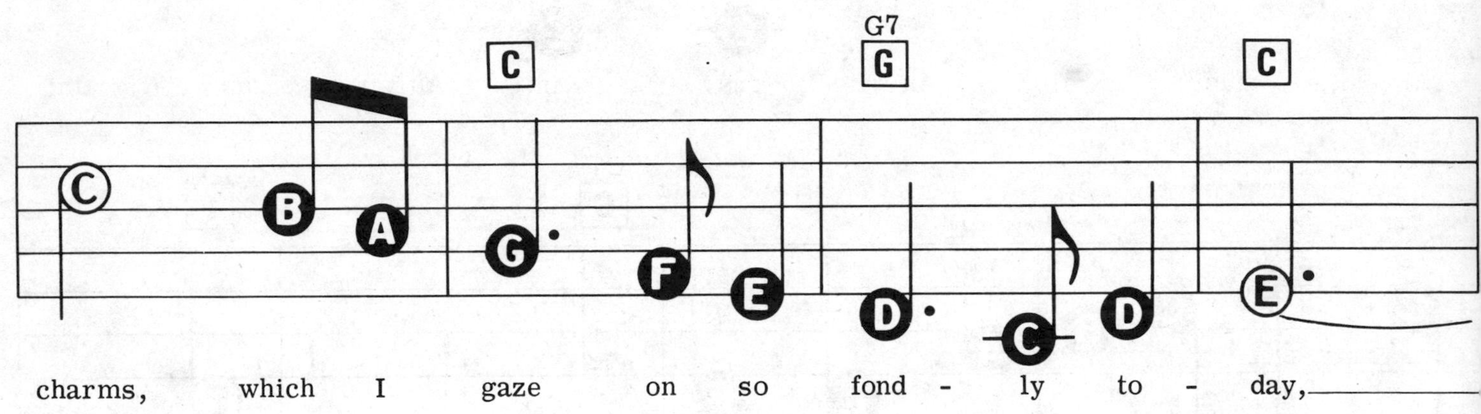

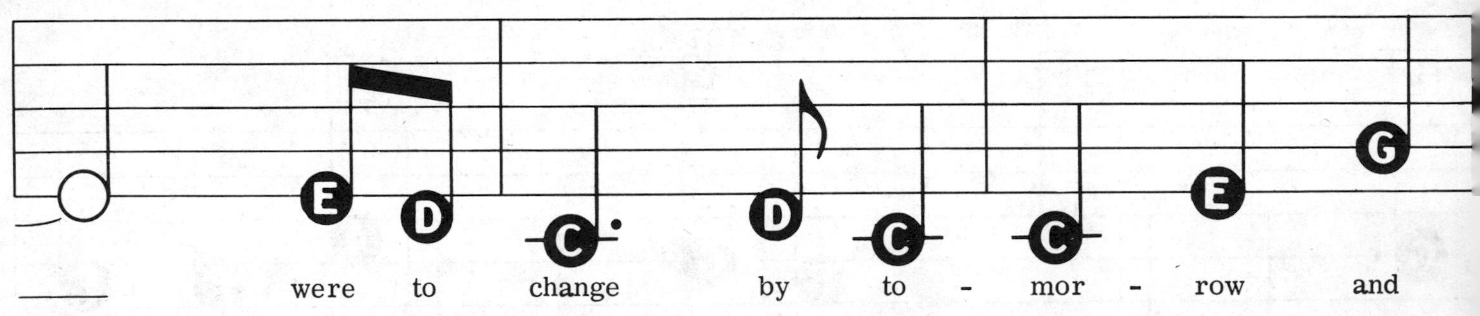

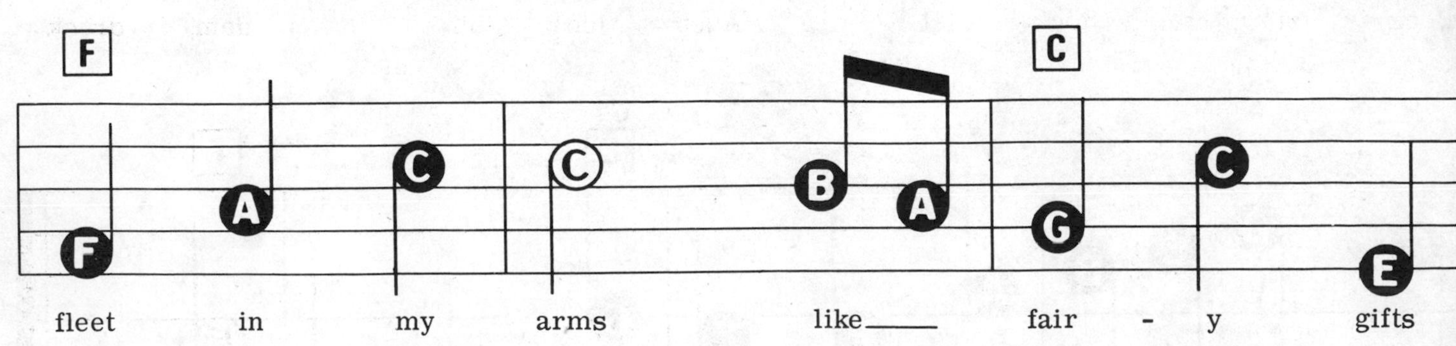

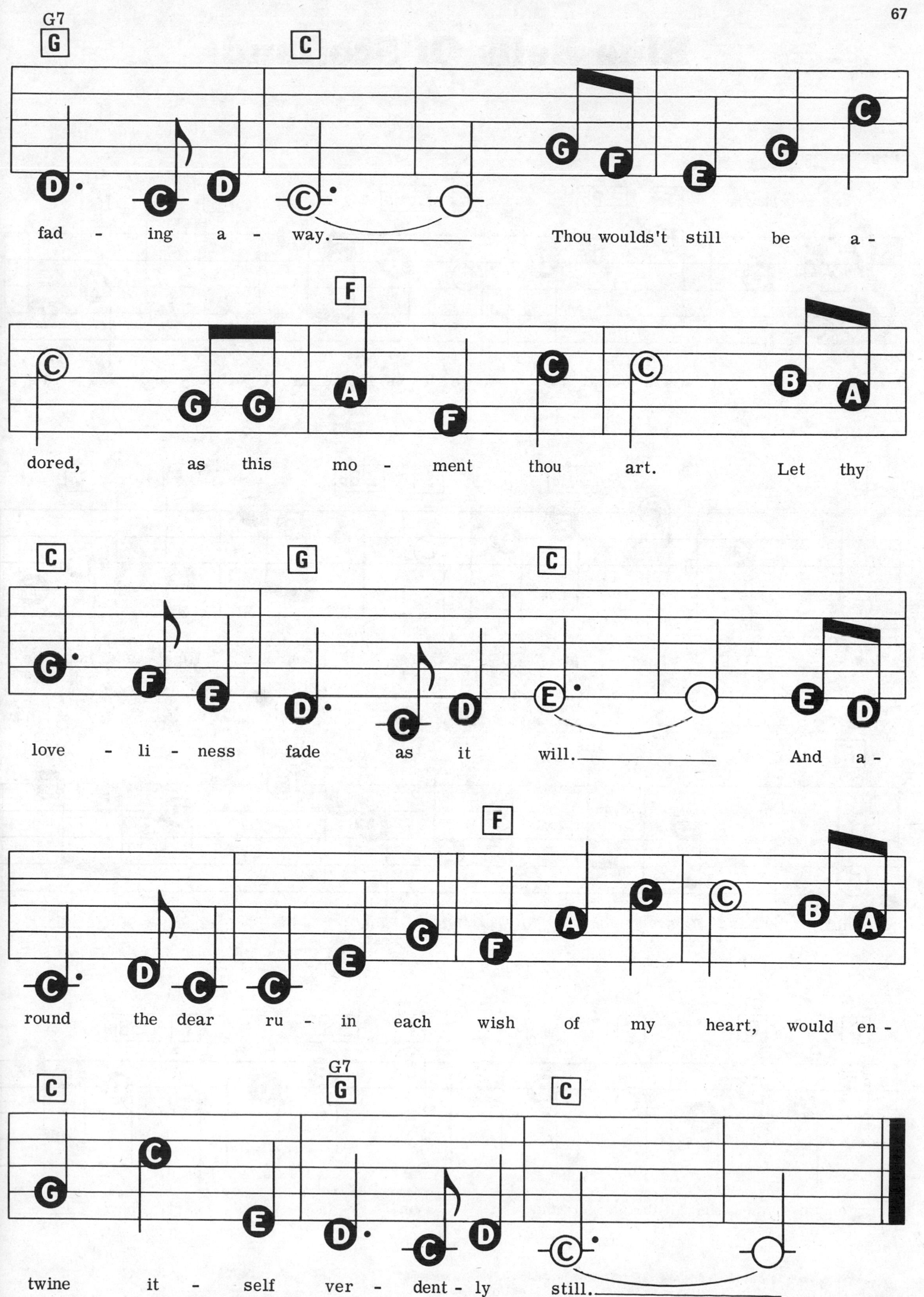
G7
fad - ing a - way.
Thou would's't still be a -
dored, as this mo - ment thou art.
Let thy
love - li - ness fade as it will.
And a -
round the dear ru - in each wish of my heart, would en -
twine it - self ver - dent - ly still.

Blue Bells Of Scotland

Registration 2

Scottish

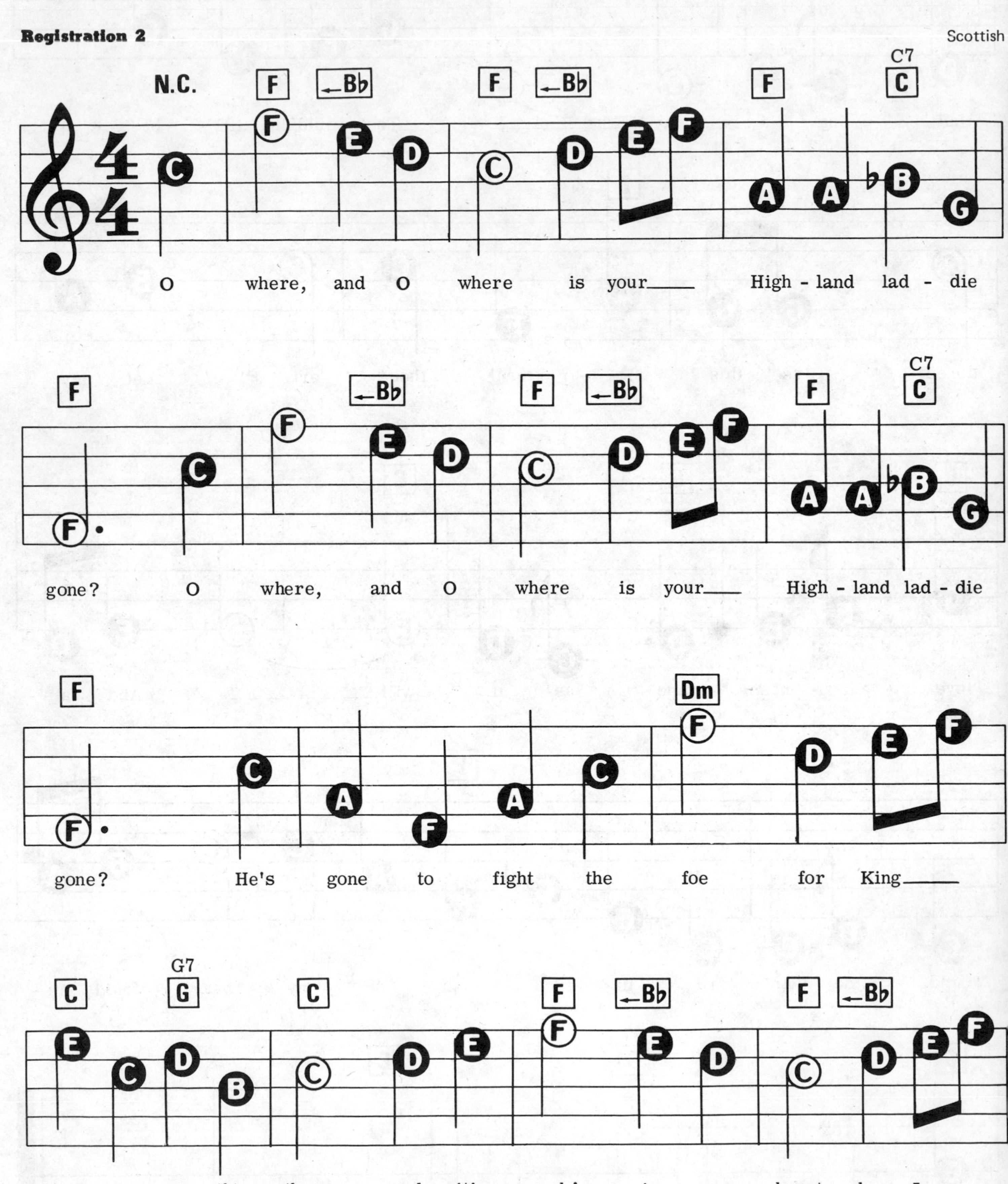

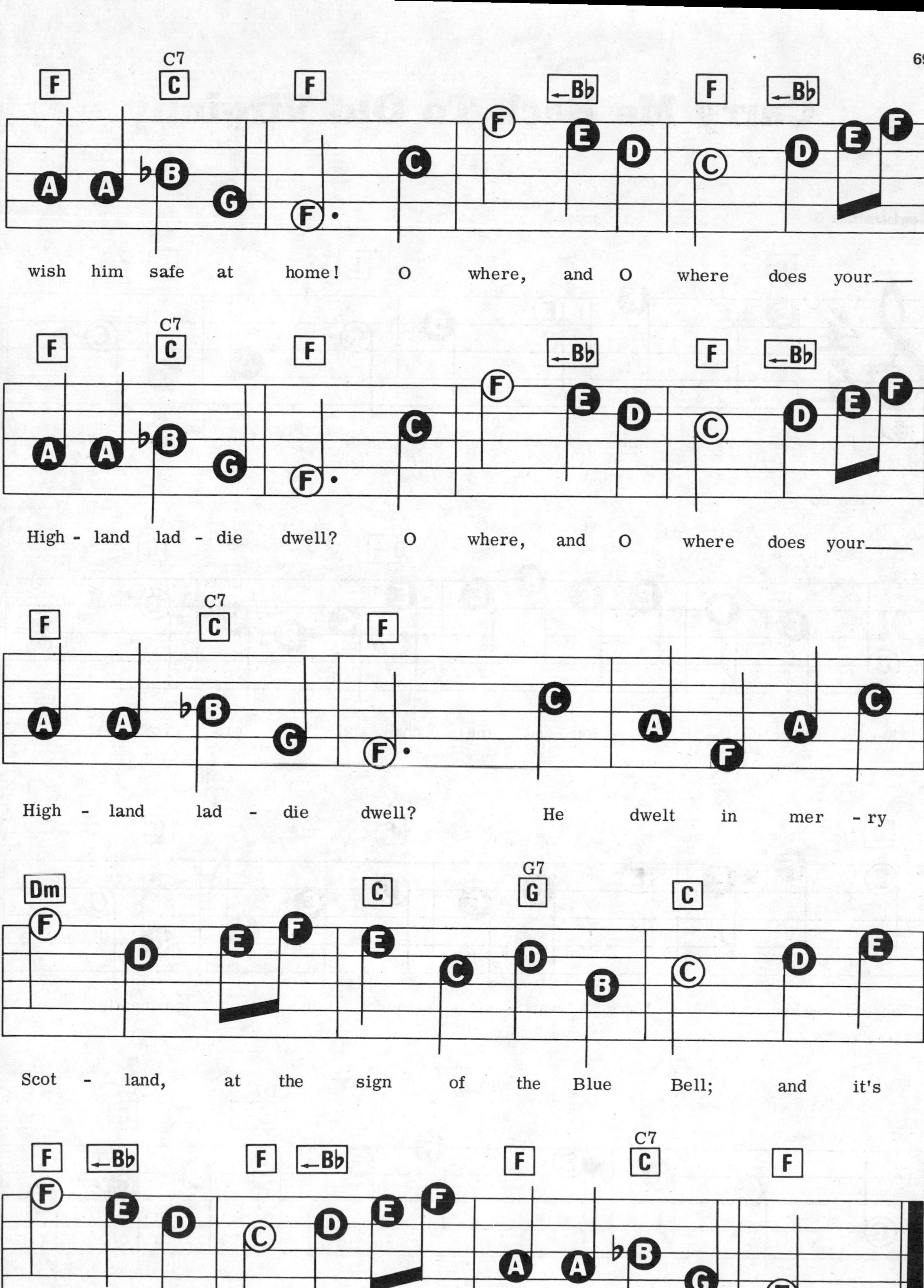
wish him safe at home! O where, and O where does your___
High - land lad - die dwell? O where, and O where does your___
High - land lad - die dwell? He dwelt in mer - ry
Scot - land, at the sign of the Blue Bell; and it's
oh! in my heart that I___ love my lad - die well.

Carry Me Back To Old Virginny

Registration 3

American

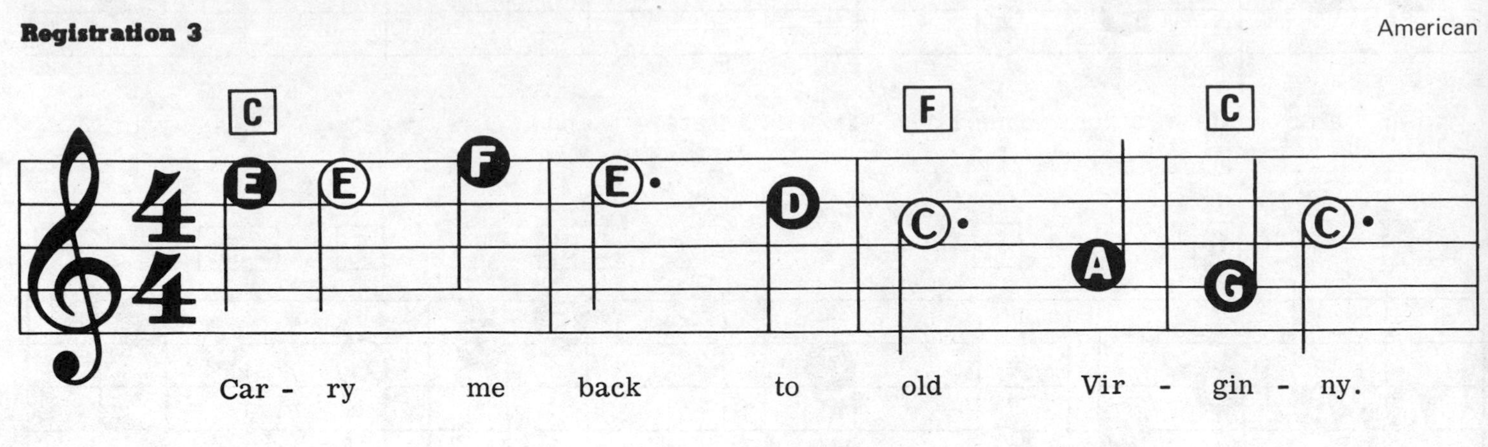

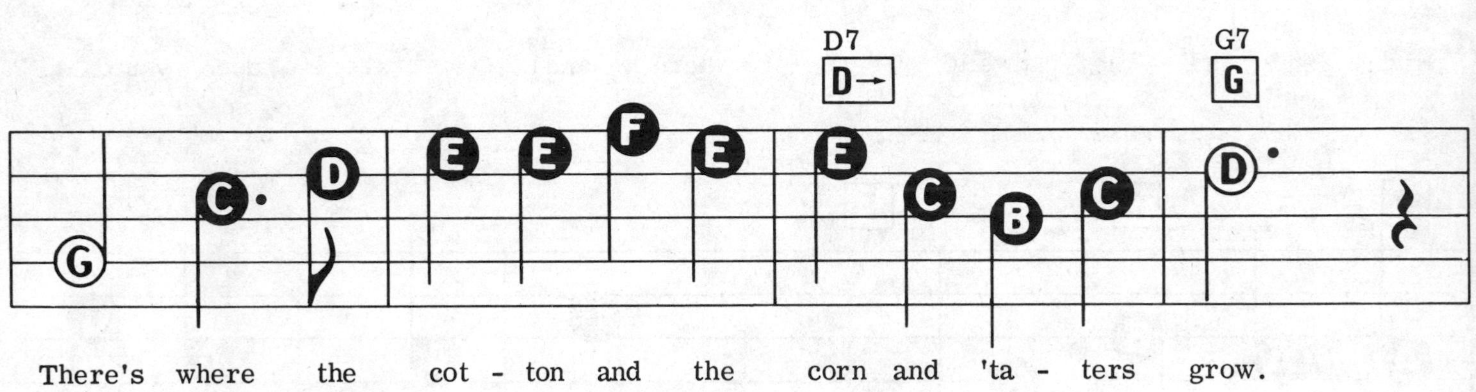

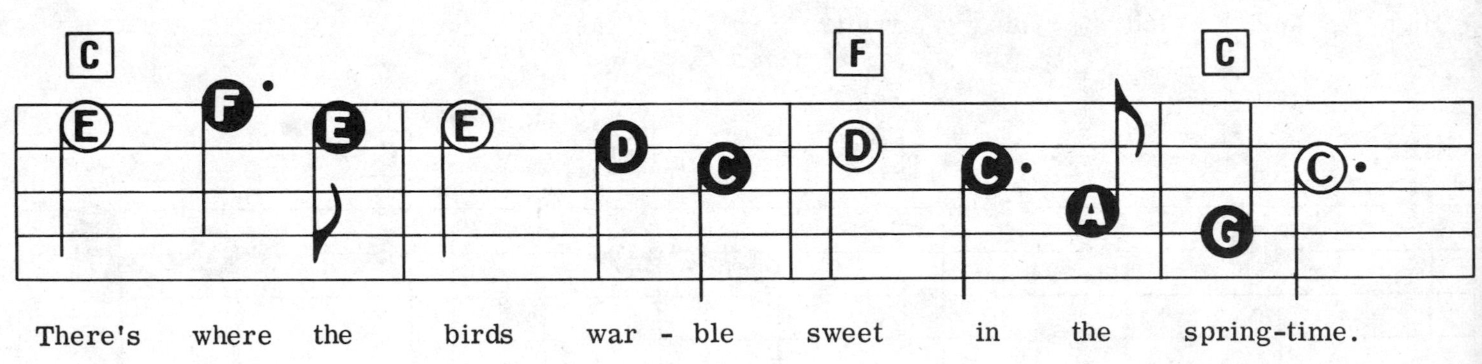

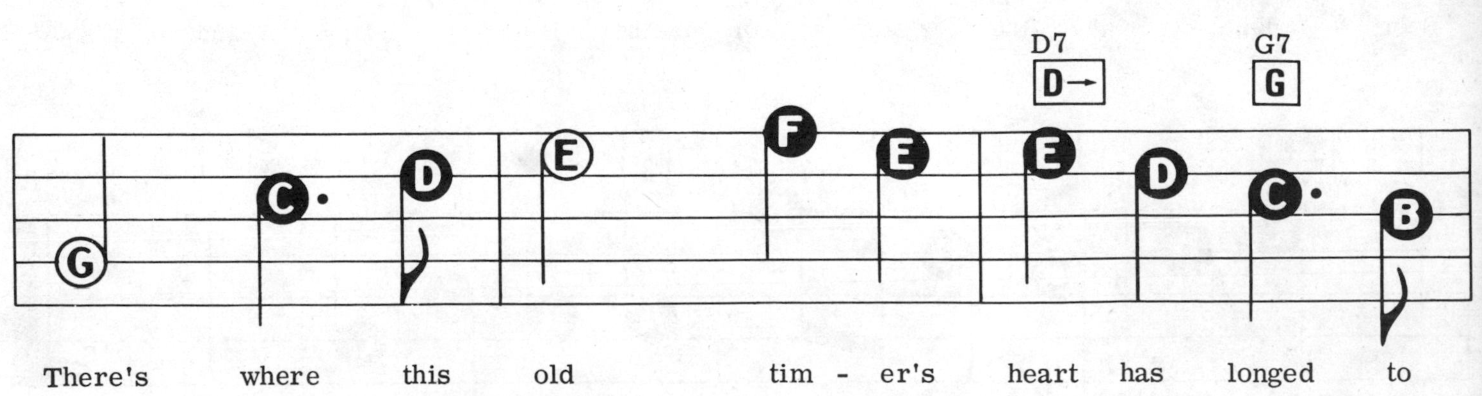

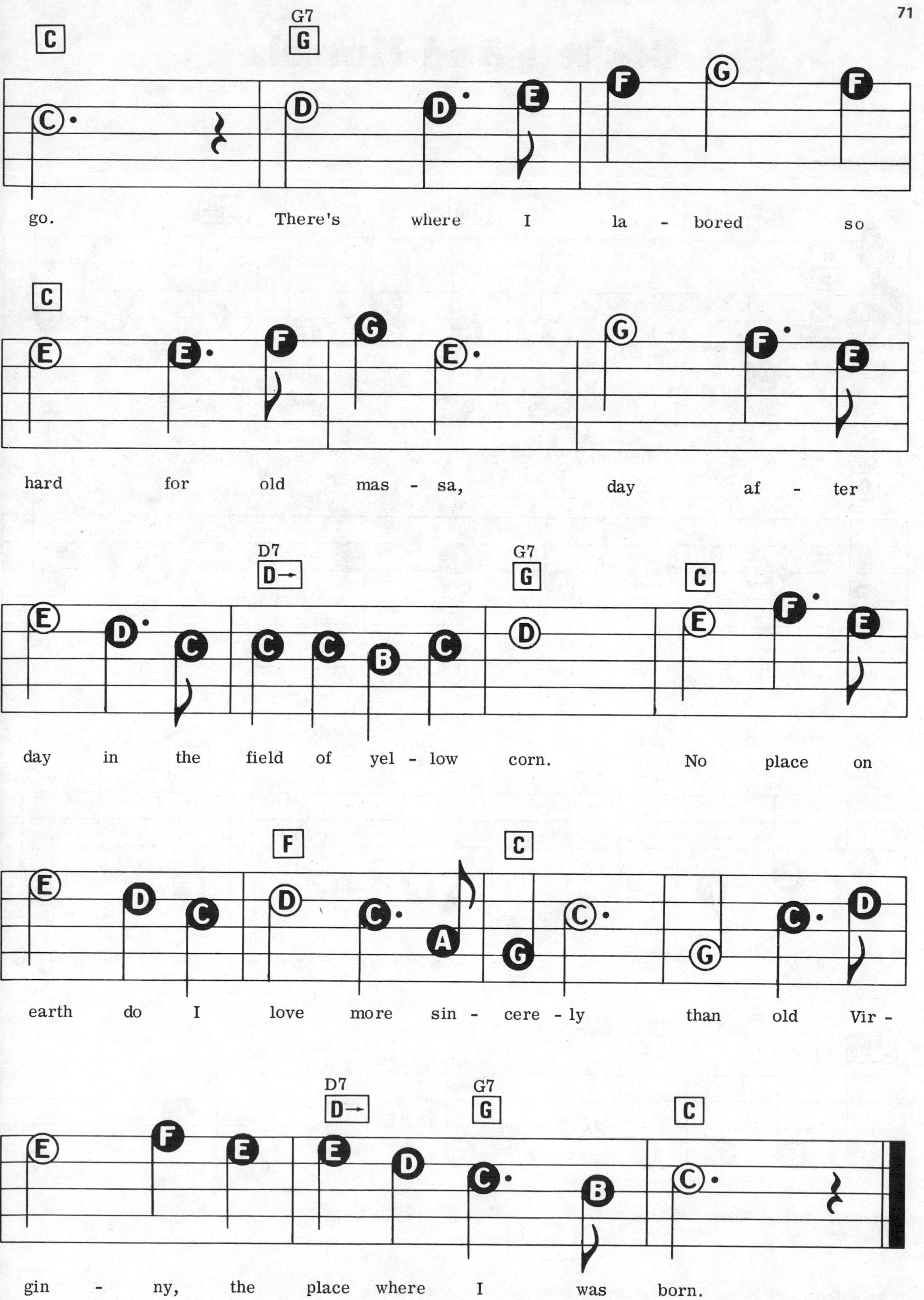
C
G7
G
go. There's where I la - bored so
C
hard for old mas - sa, day af - ter
D7
D→
G7
G
C
day in the field of yel - low corn. No place on
F
C
earth do I love more sin - cere - ly than old Vir -
D7
D→
G7
G
C
gin - ny, the place where I was born.

Cockels And Mussels

Registration 5

Irish

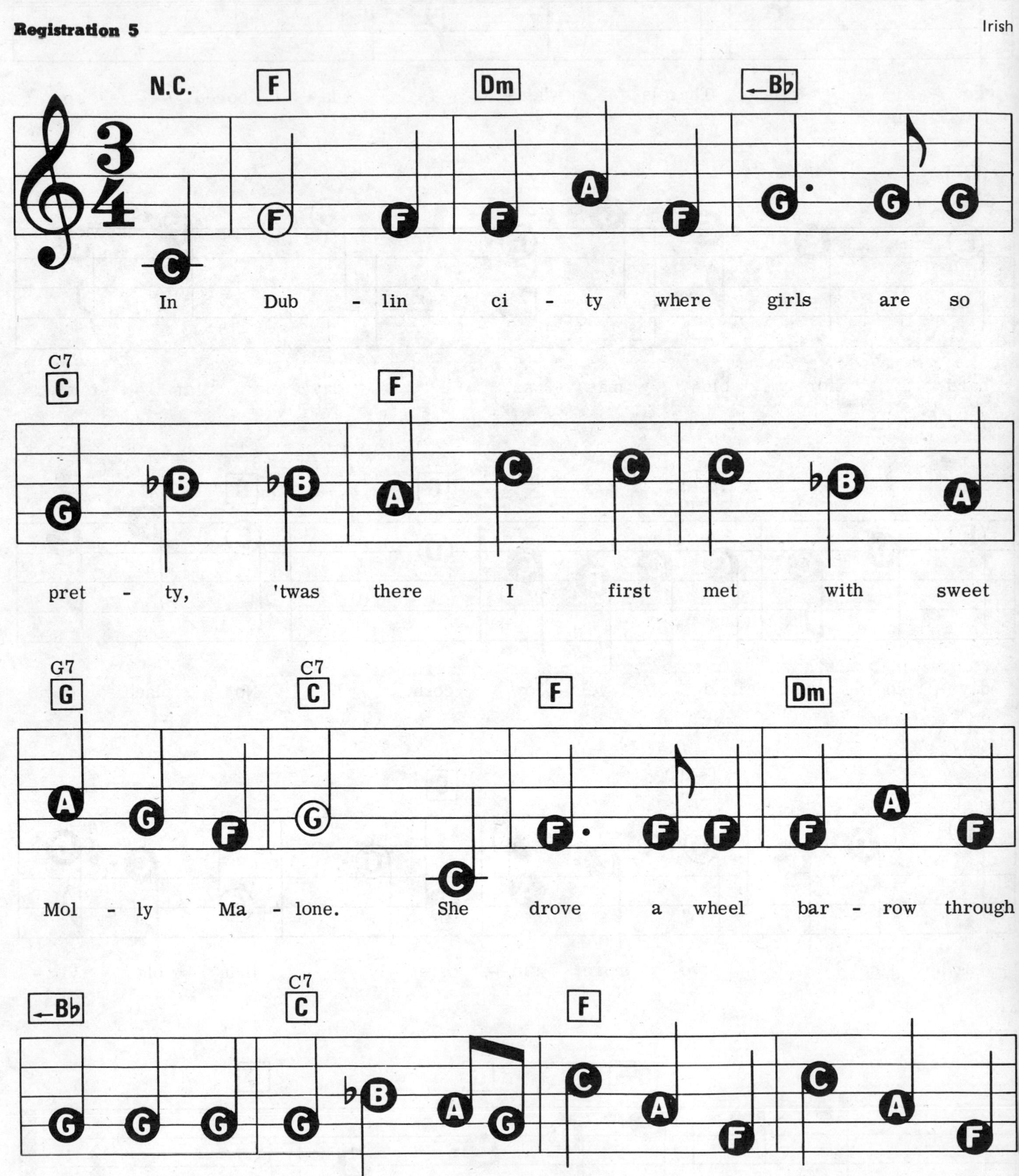

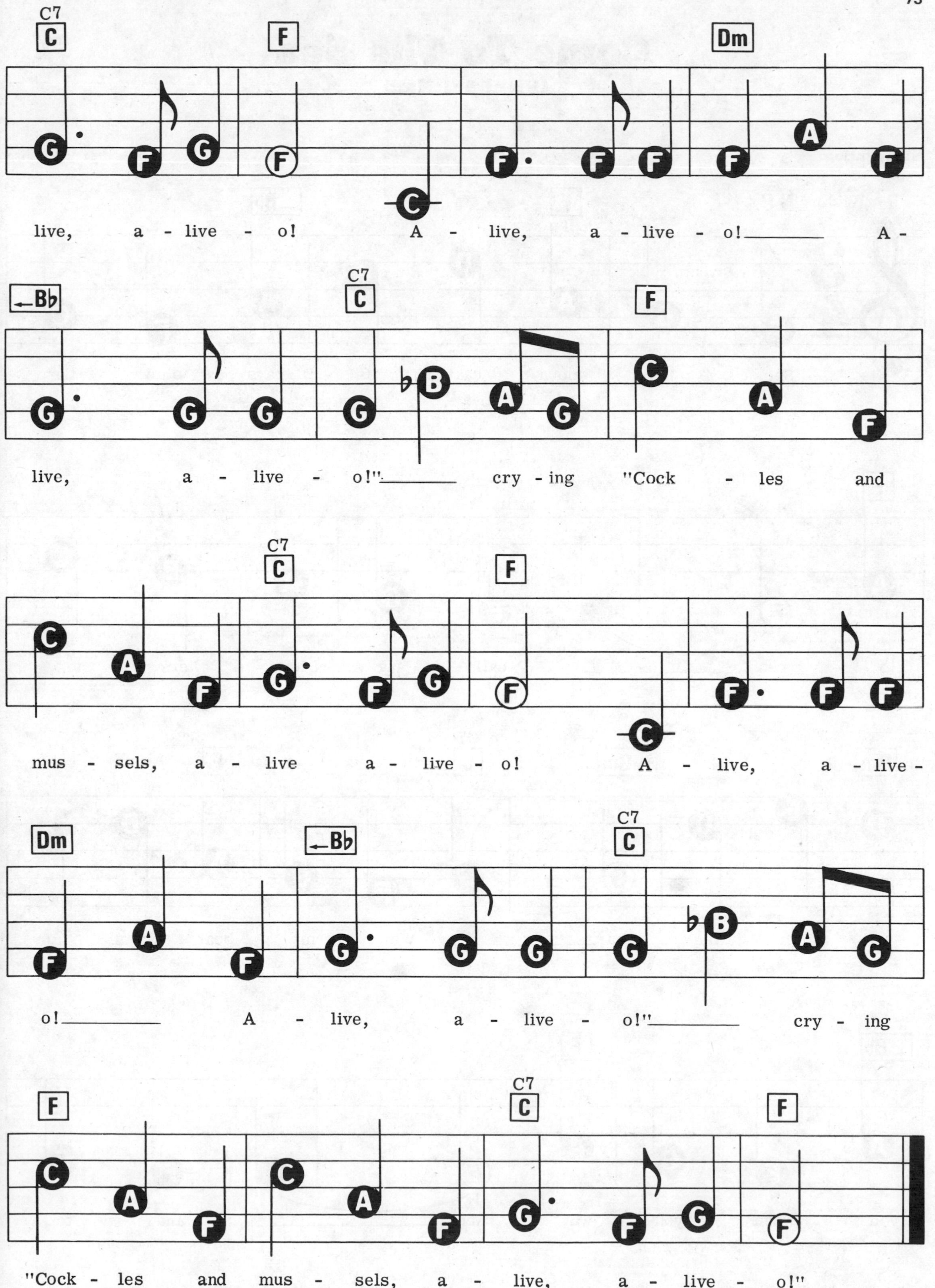
C7 C F Dm
live, a - live - o! A - live, a - live - o! A -
Bb C7 C F
live, a - live - o!" cry - ing "Cock - les and
C7 C F
mus - sels, a - live a - live - o! A - live, a - live -
Dm Bb C7 C
o! A - live, a - live - o!" cry - ing
F C7 C F
"Cock - les and mus - sels, a - live, a - live - o!"

Come To The Sea

(Vieni Sul Mar!)

Italian

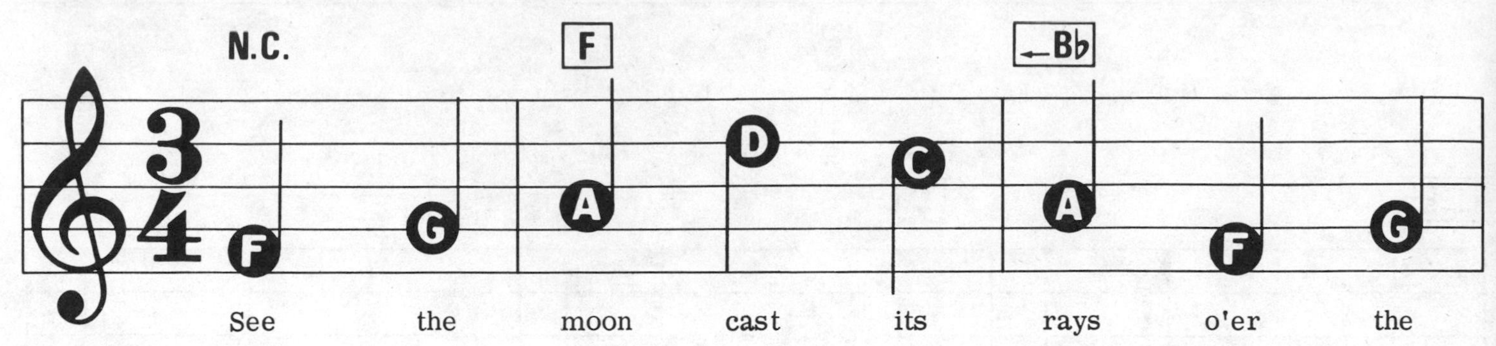

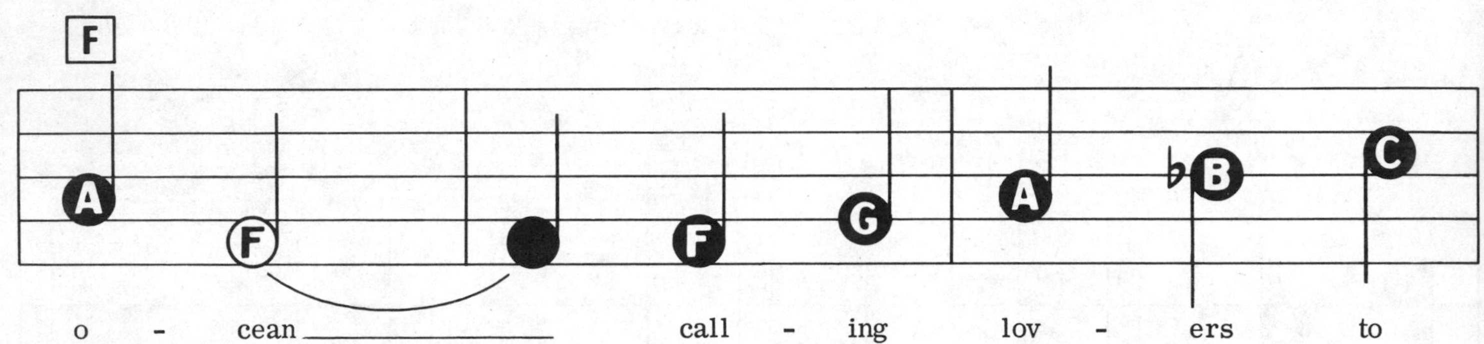

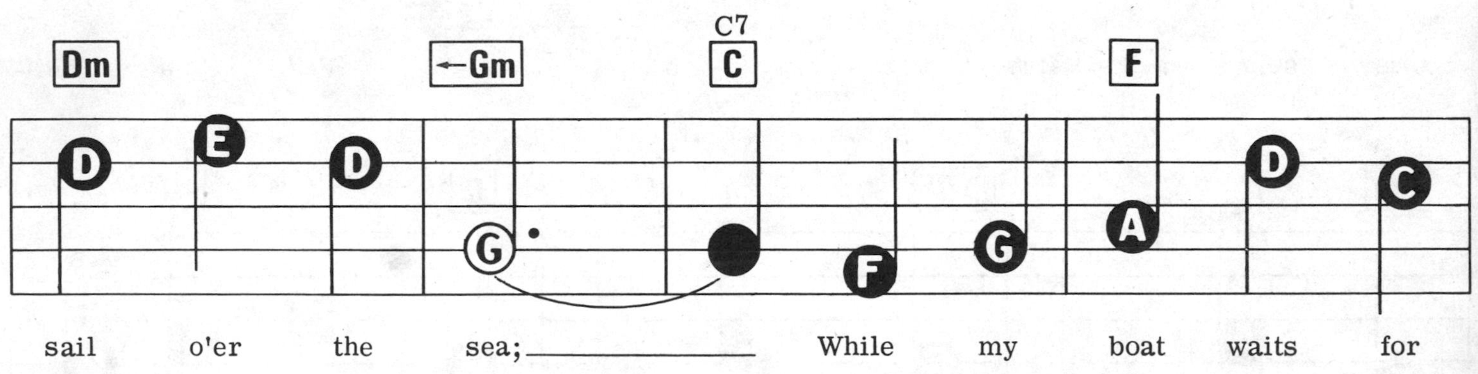

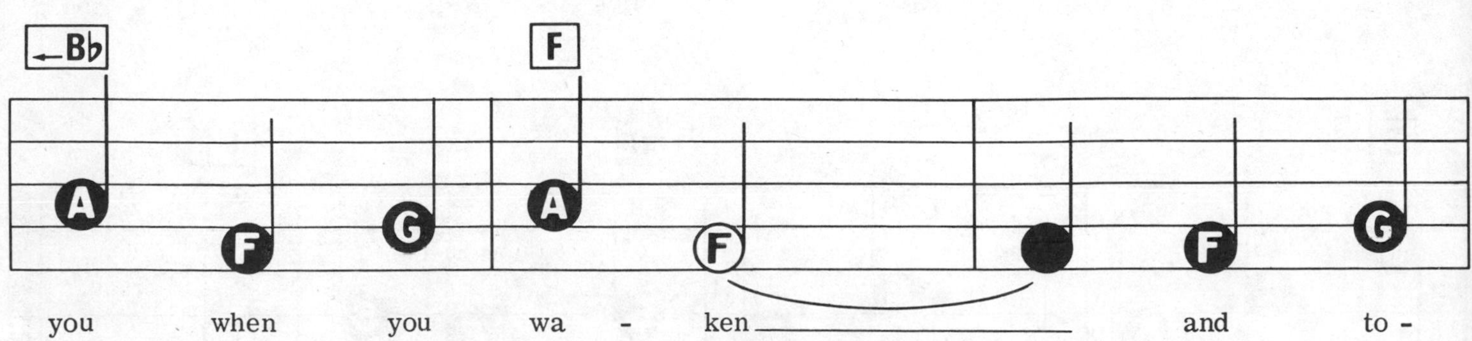

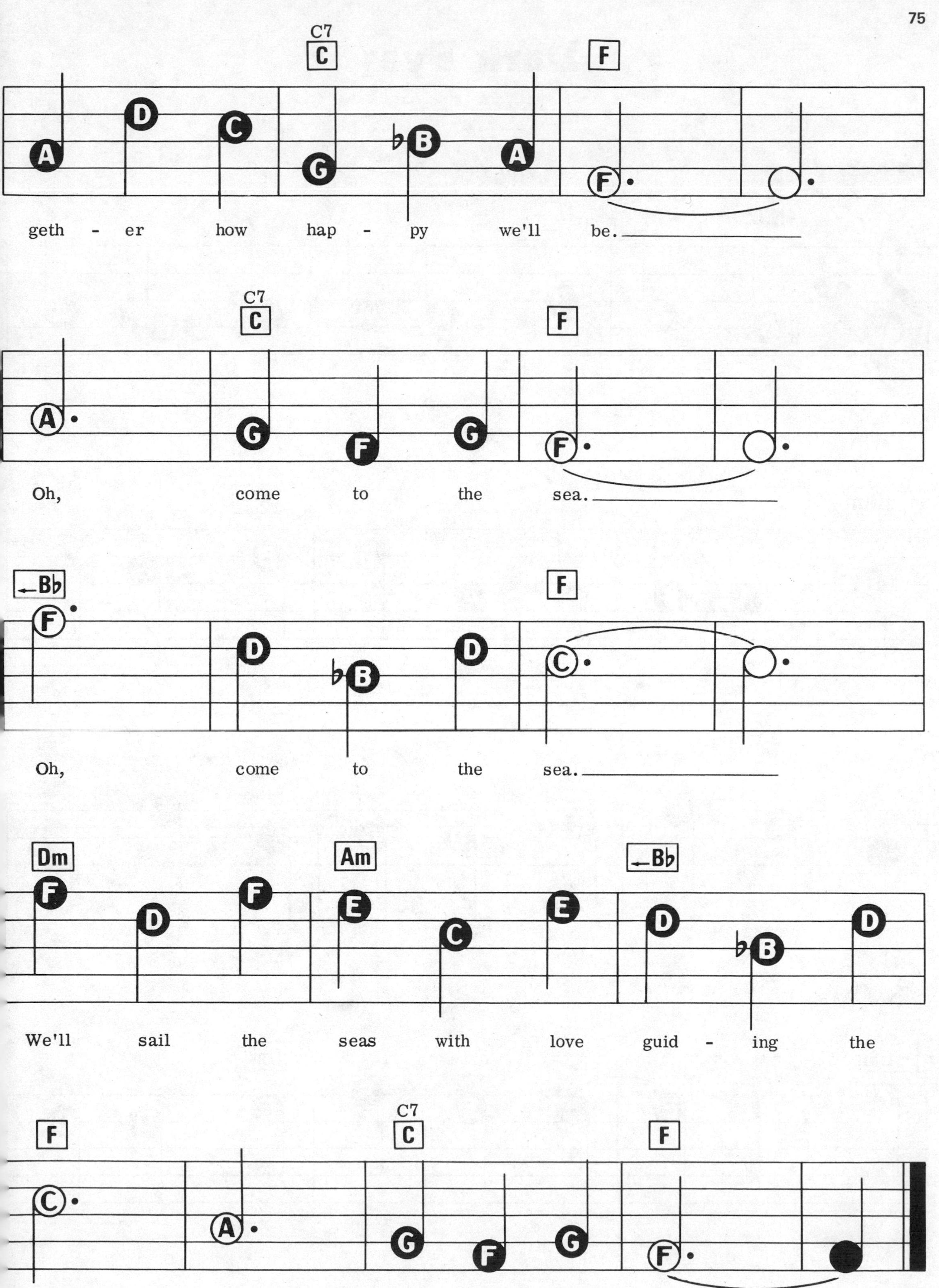
C7
C
F
geth - er how hap - py we'll be.
C7
C
F
Oh, come to the sea.
←B♭
F
Oh, come to the sea.
Dm
Am
←B♭
We'll sail the seas with love guid - ing the
F
C7
C
F
breeze. Oh, come to the sea.

Dark Eyes

Registration 10

Russian

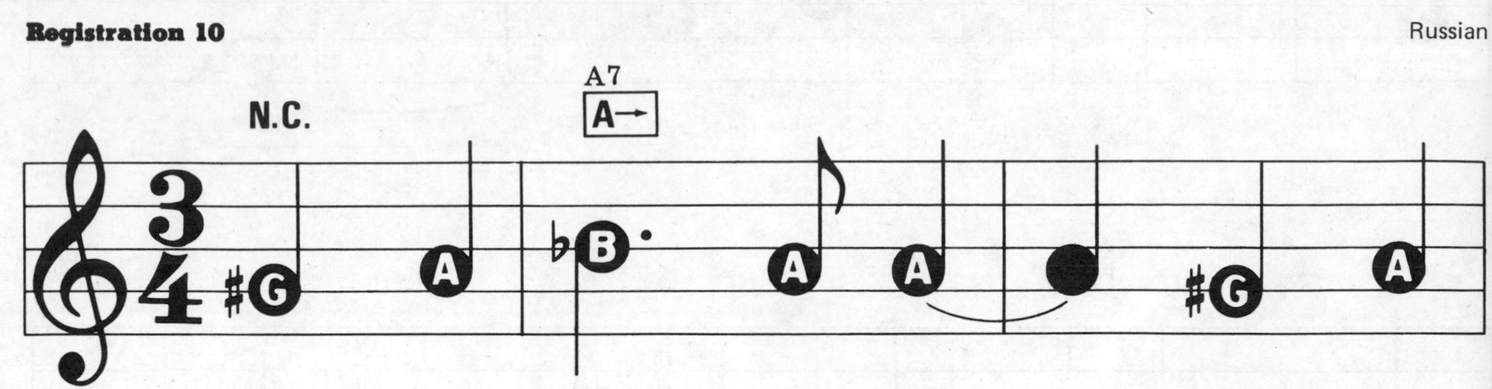

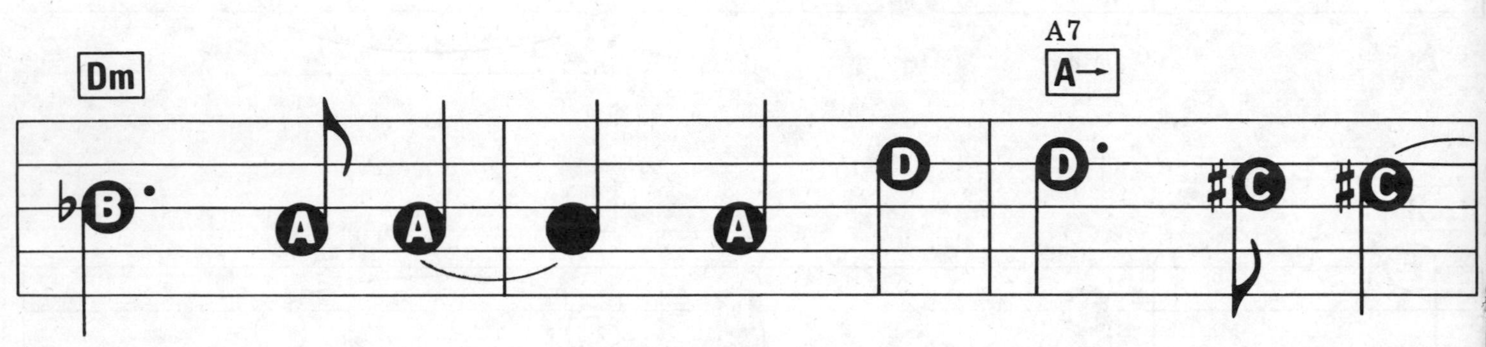

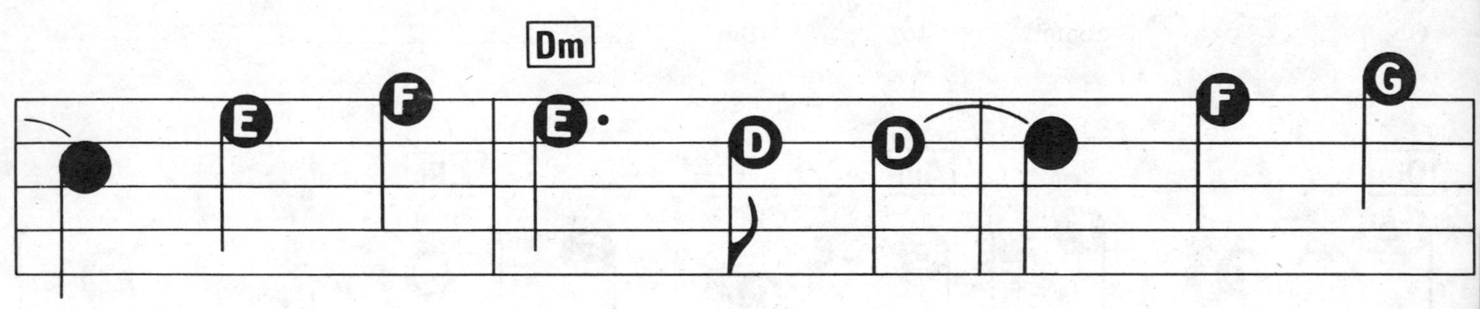

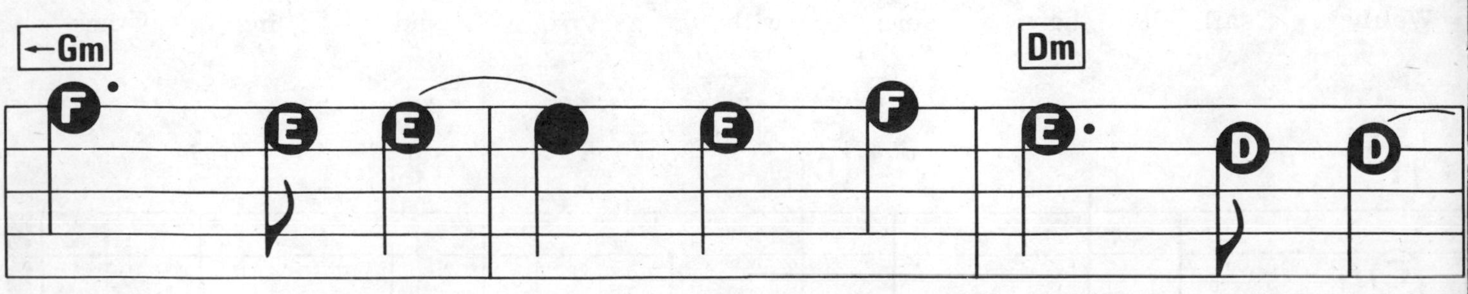

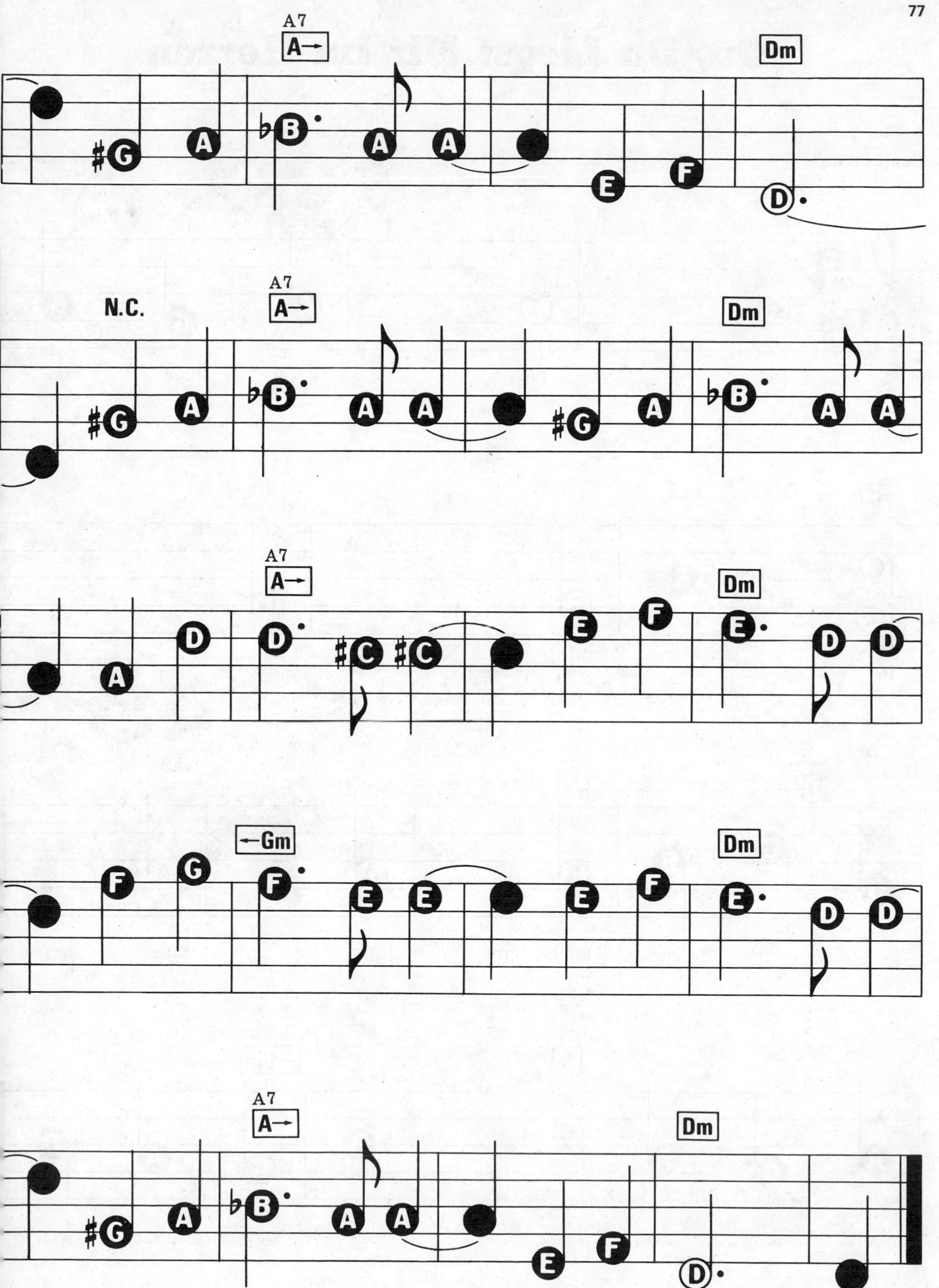
A7
A→
Dm
N.C.
A7
A→
Dm
A7
A→
Dm
←Gm
Dm
A7
A→
Dm

Du, Du Liegst Mir Im Herzen

Registration 4

German

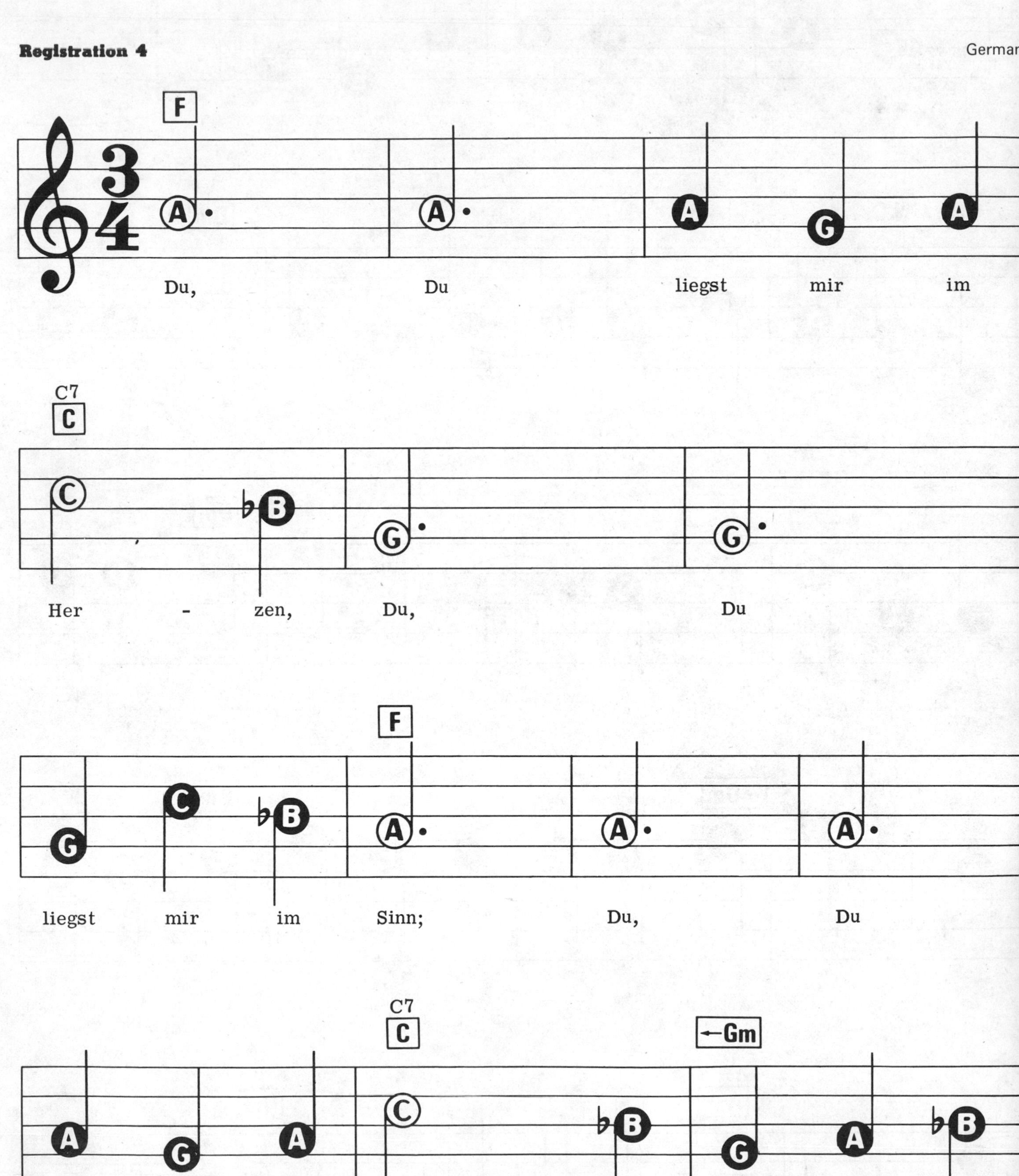

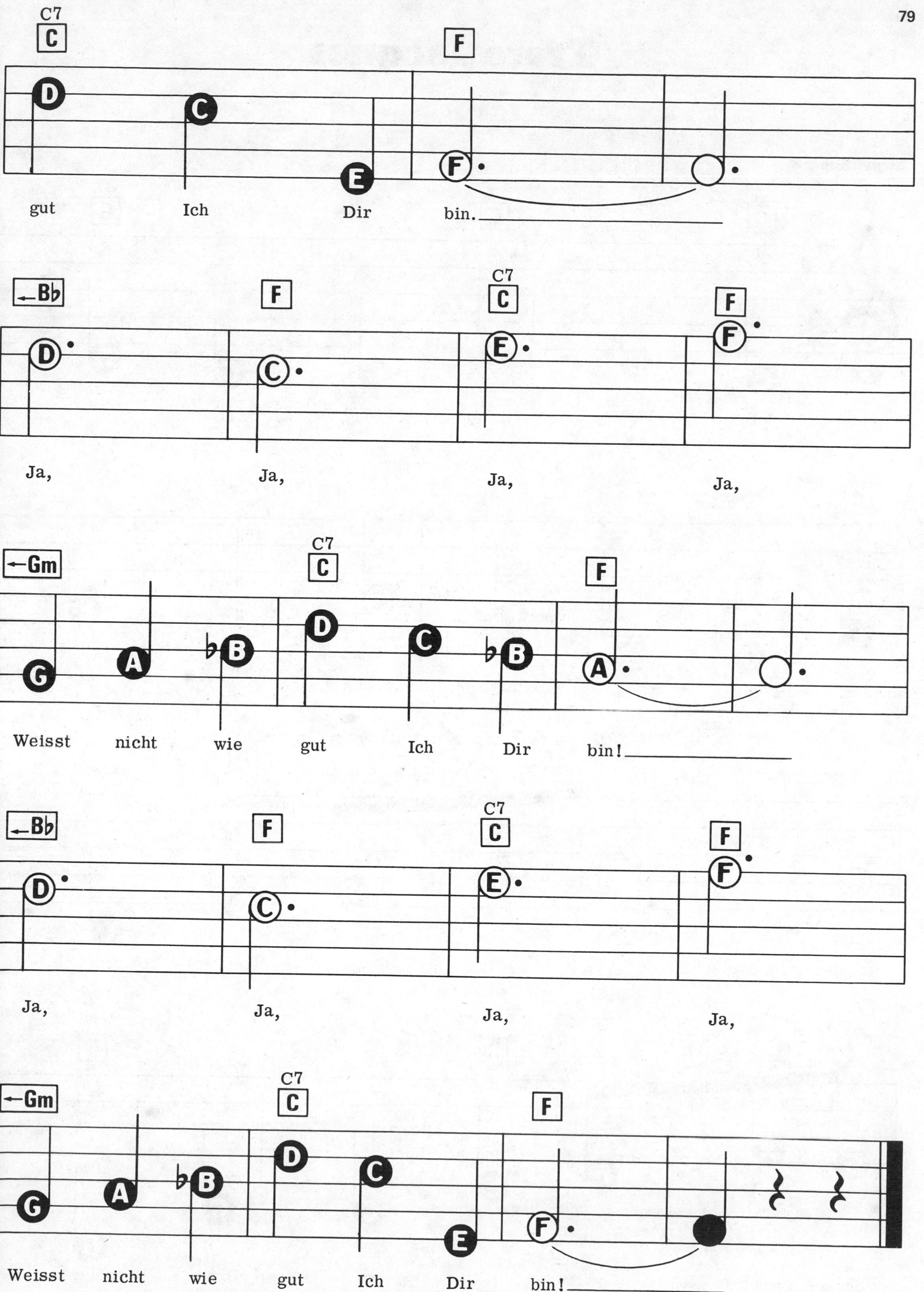
C7 C F
D C E F
gut Ich Dir bin.
←B♭ F C7 C F
D C E F
Ja, Ja, Ja, Ja,
←Gm C7 C F
G A ♭B D C ♭B A
Weisst nicht wie gut Ich Dir bin!
←B♭ F C7 C F
D C E F
Ja, Ja, Ja, Ja,
←Gm C7 C F
G A ♭B D C E F
Weisst nicht wie gut Ich Dir bin!

Frère Jacques

Registration 8

French

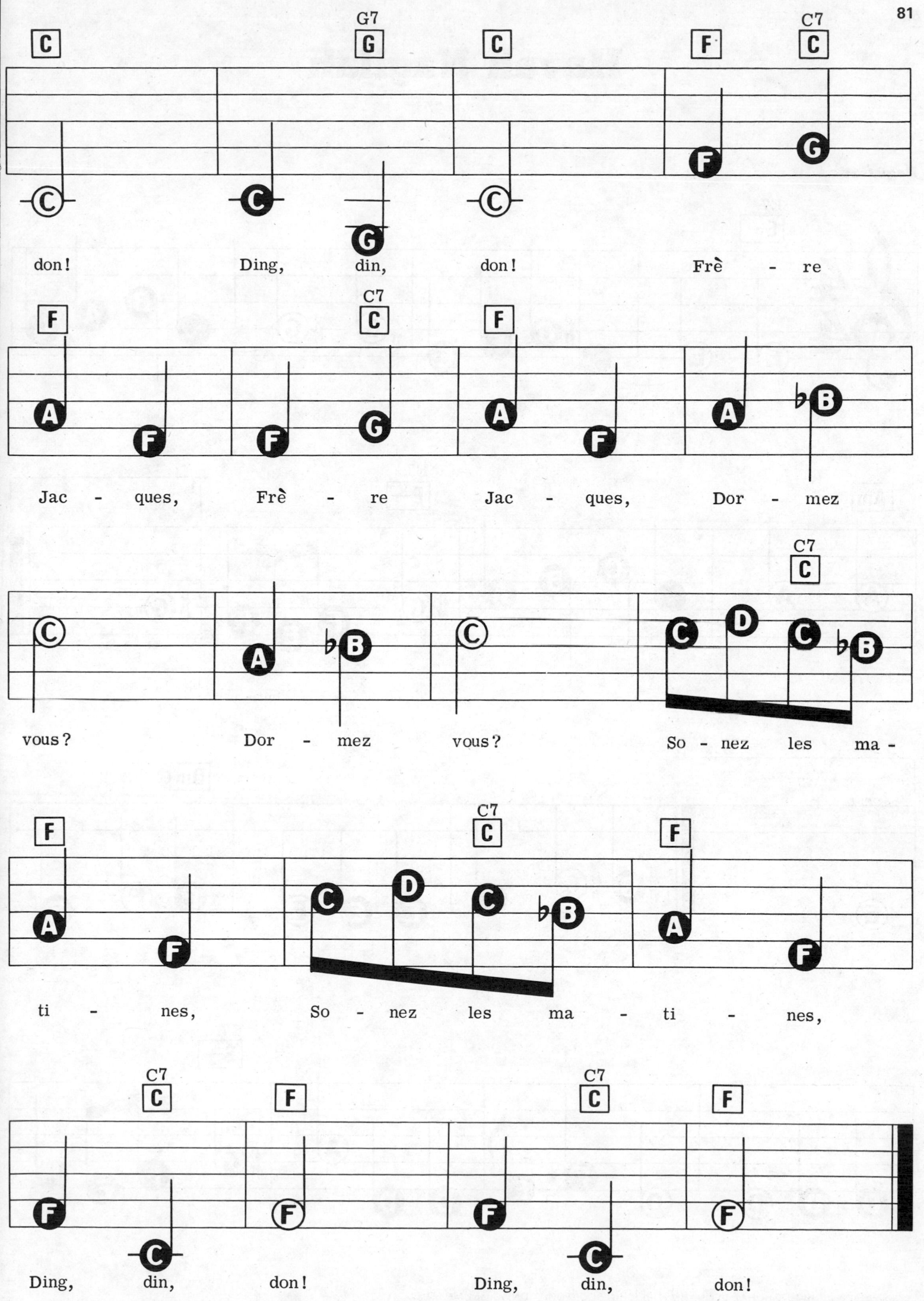
C G7 G C F C7 C
don! Ding, din, don! Frè - re
F C7 C F
Jac - ques, Frè - re Jac - ques, Dor - mez
C7 C
vous? Dor - mez vous? So - nez les ma -
F C7 C F
ti - nes, So - nez les ma - ti - nes,
C7 C F C7 C F
Ding, din, don! Ding, din, don!

Havah Nagilah

Registration 10

Hebrew

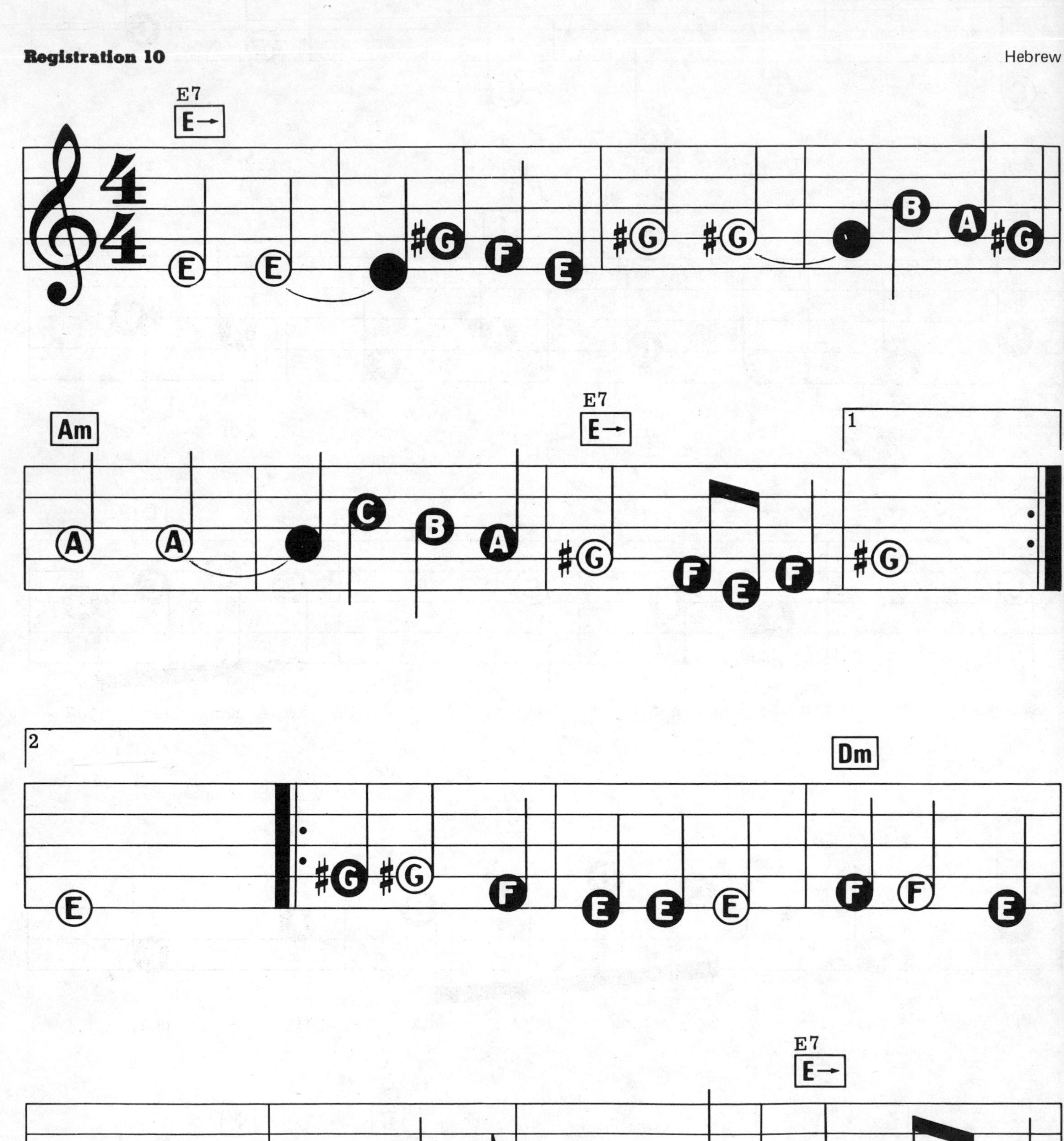

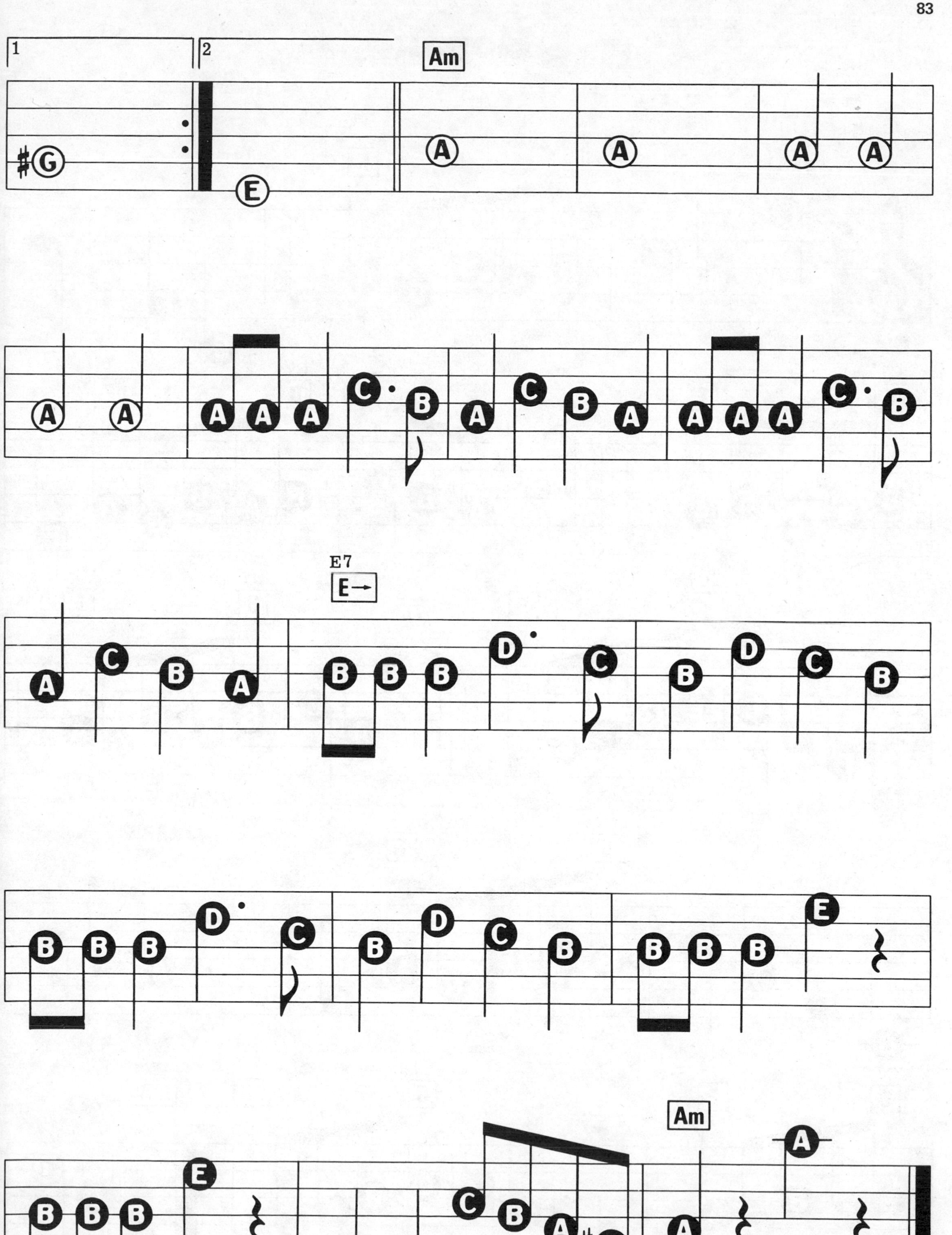
1
2
Am
♯G
E
A A A A
A A
A A A A C B A C B A A A A A C B
E7
E→
A C B A
B B B D C
B D C B
B B B D C
B D C B
B B B E
Am
B B B E
E E C B A ♯G
A A

Hopak

Registration 2

Polish

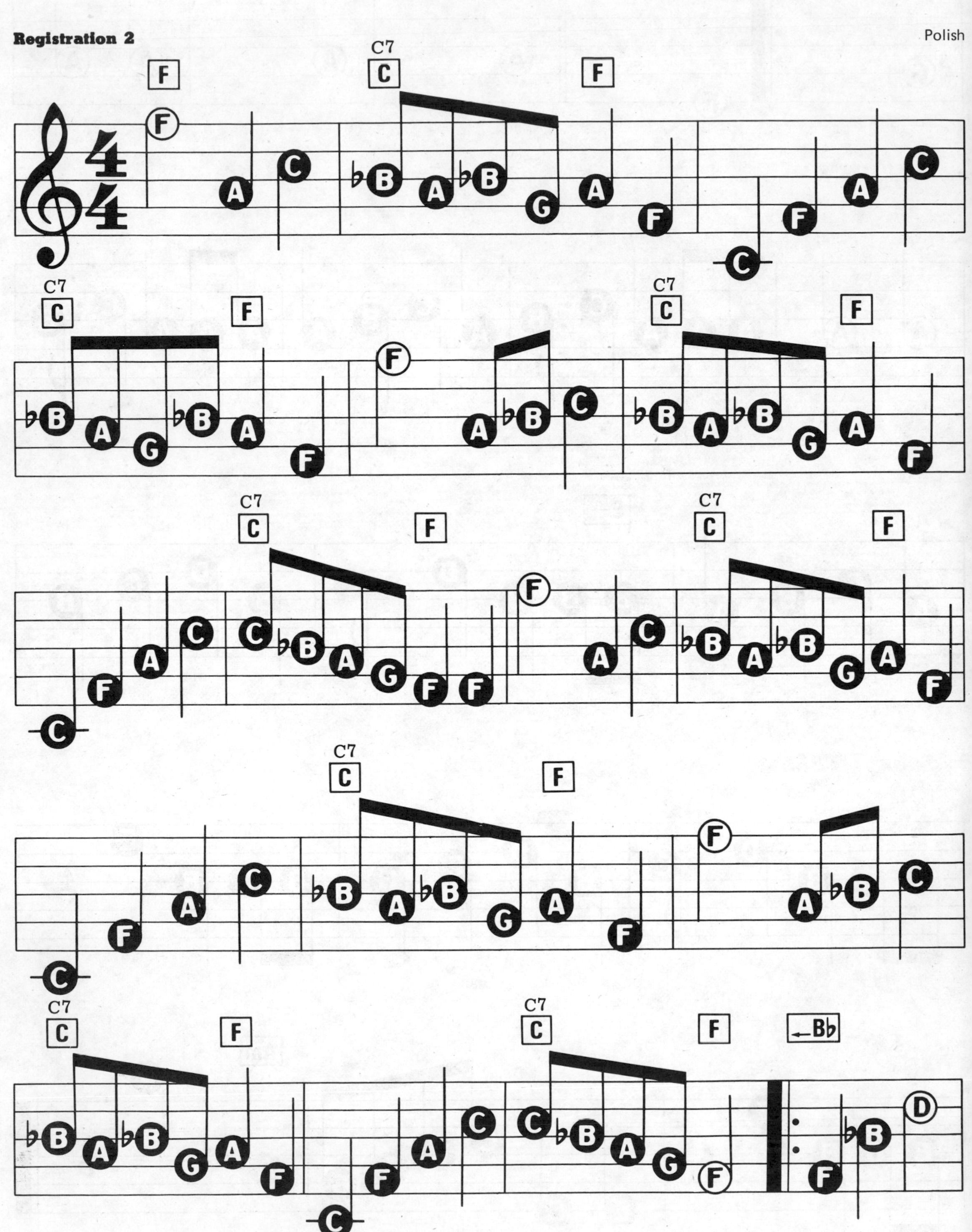

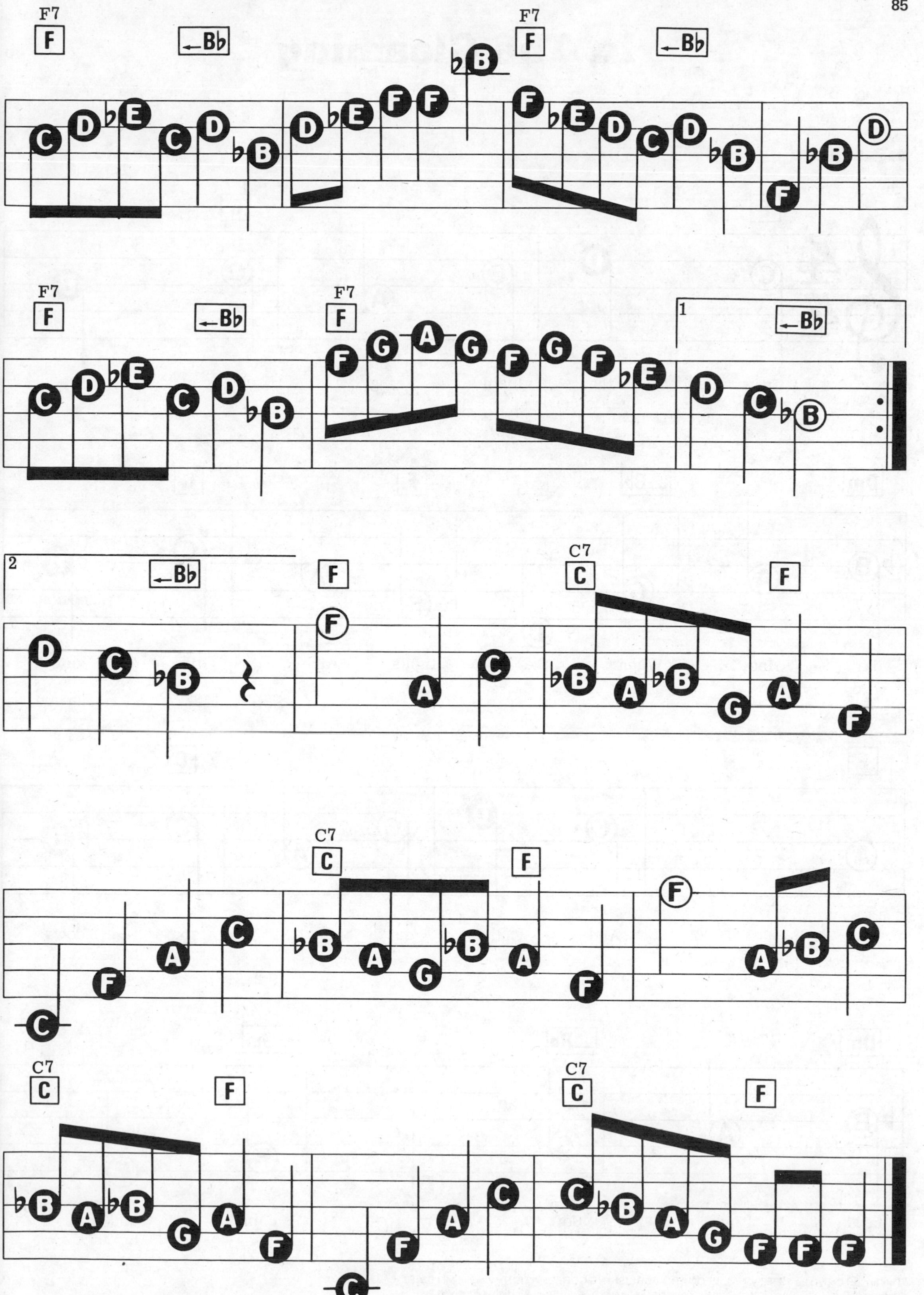
F7
F
←B♭
C D ♭E C D ♭B D ♭E F F ♭B
F7
F
←B♭
F ♭E D C D ♭B F ♭B D
F7
F
←B♭
C D ♭E C D ♭B
F7
F
F G A G F G F ♭E
1
←B♭
D C ♭B
2
←B♭
D C ♭B
F
F A C
C7
C
♭B A ♭B G A
F
F
C F A C
C7
C
♭B A G ♭B A
F
F
F A ♭B C
C7
C
♭B A ♭B G A
F
F
C F A C
C7
C
C ♭B A G
F
F F F

In The Gloaming

Registration 9

Scottish

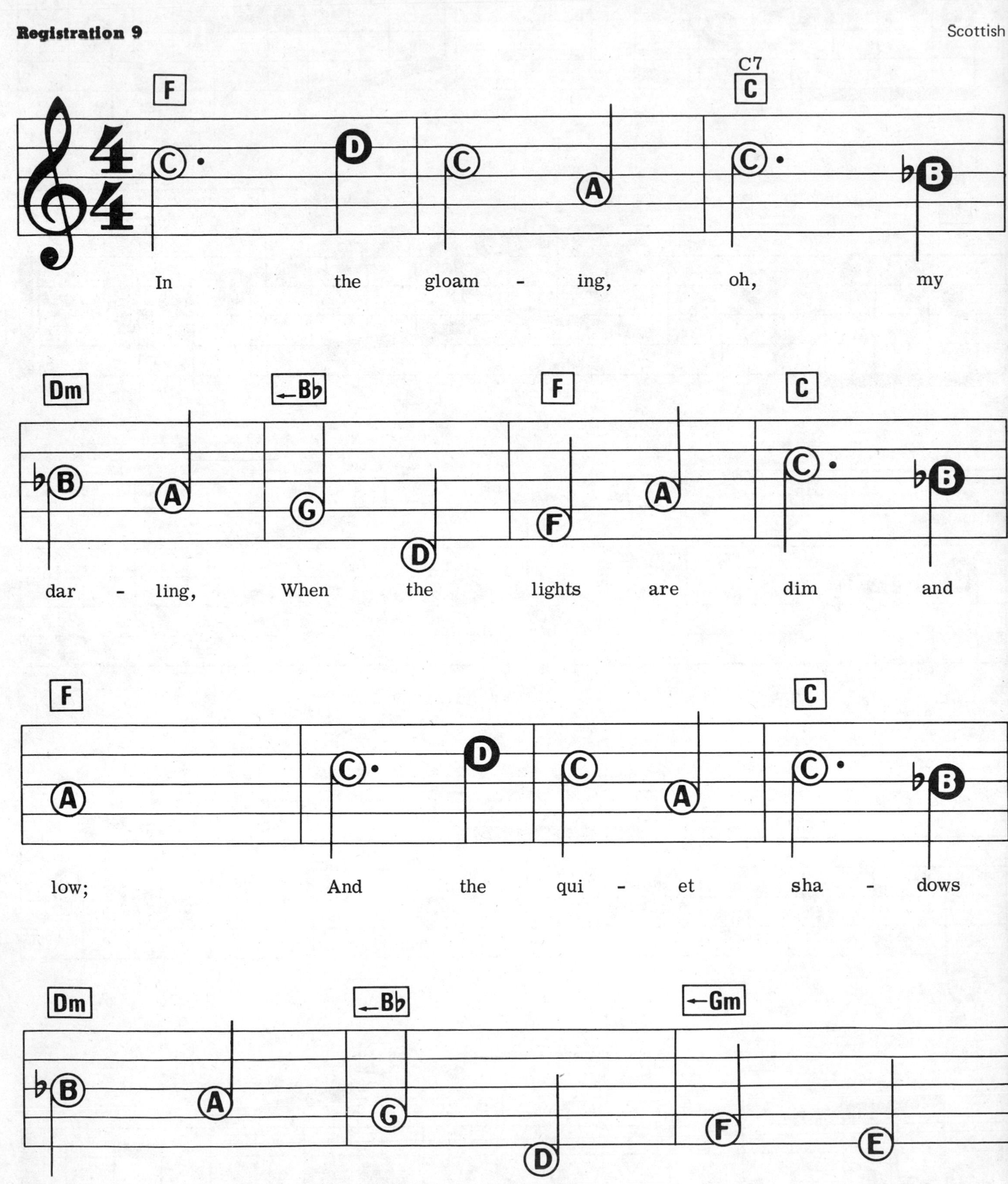

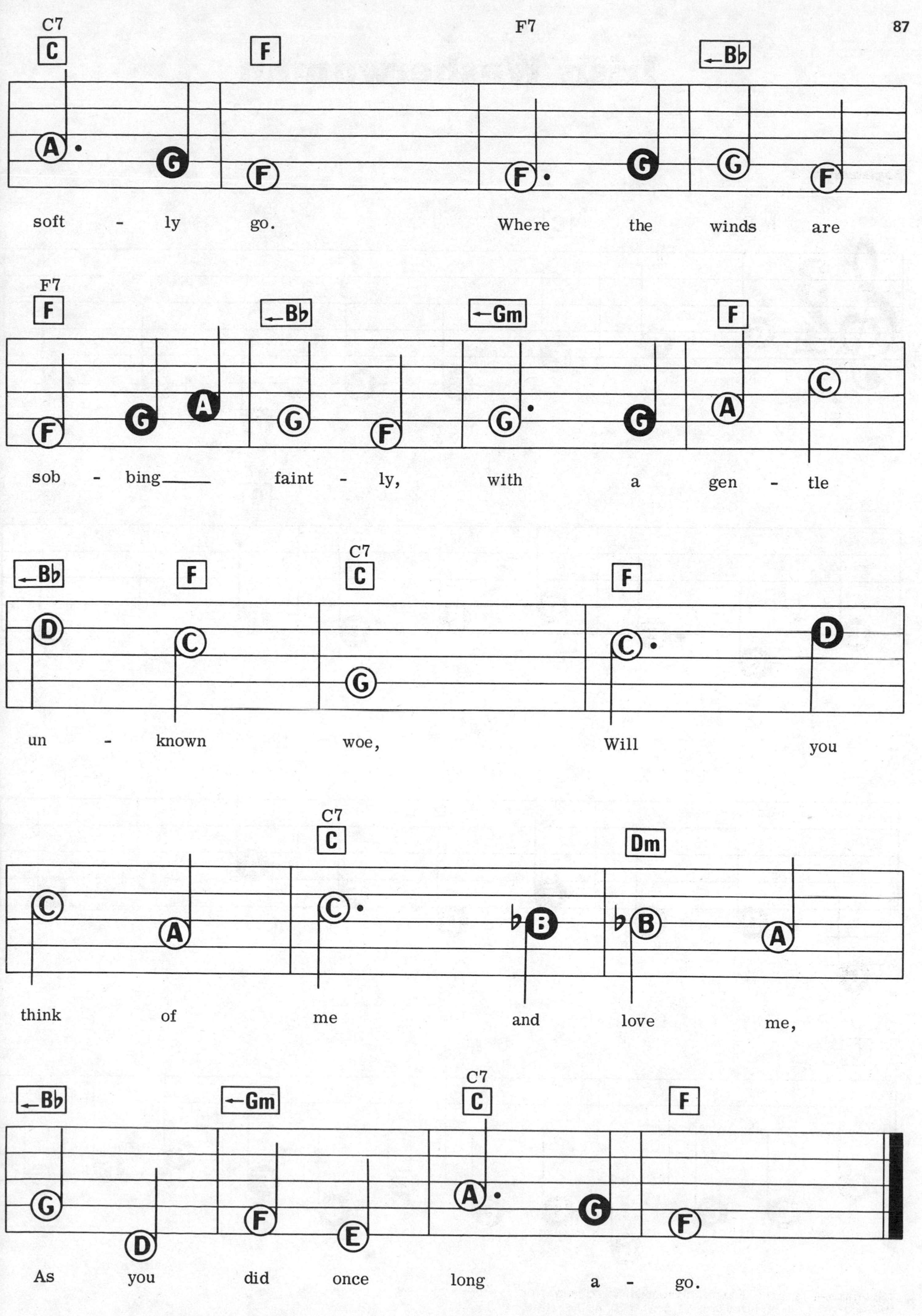
C7 C
F
F7
Bb
soft - ly go. Where the winds are
F7 F
Bb
Gm
F
sob - bing faint - ly, with a gen - tle
Bb
F
C7 C
F
un - known woe, Will you
C7 C
Dm
think of me and love me,
Bb
Gm
C7 C
F
As you did once long a - go.

Irish Washerwoman

Registration 2

Irish

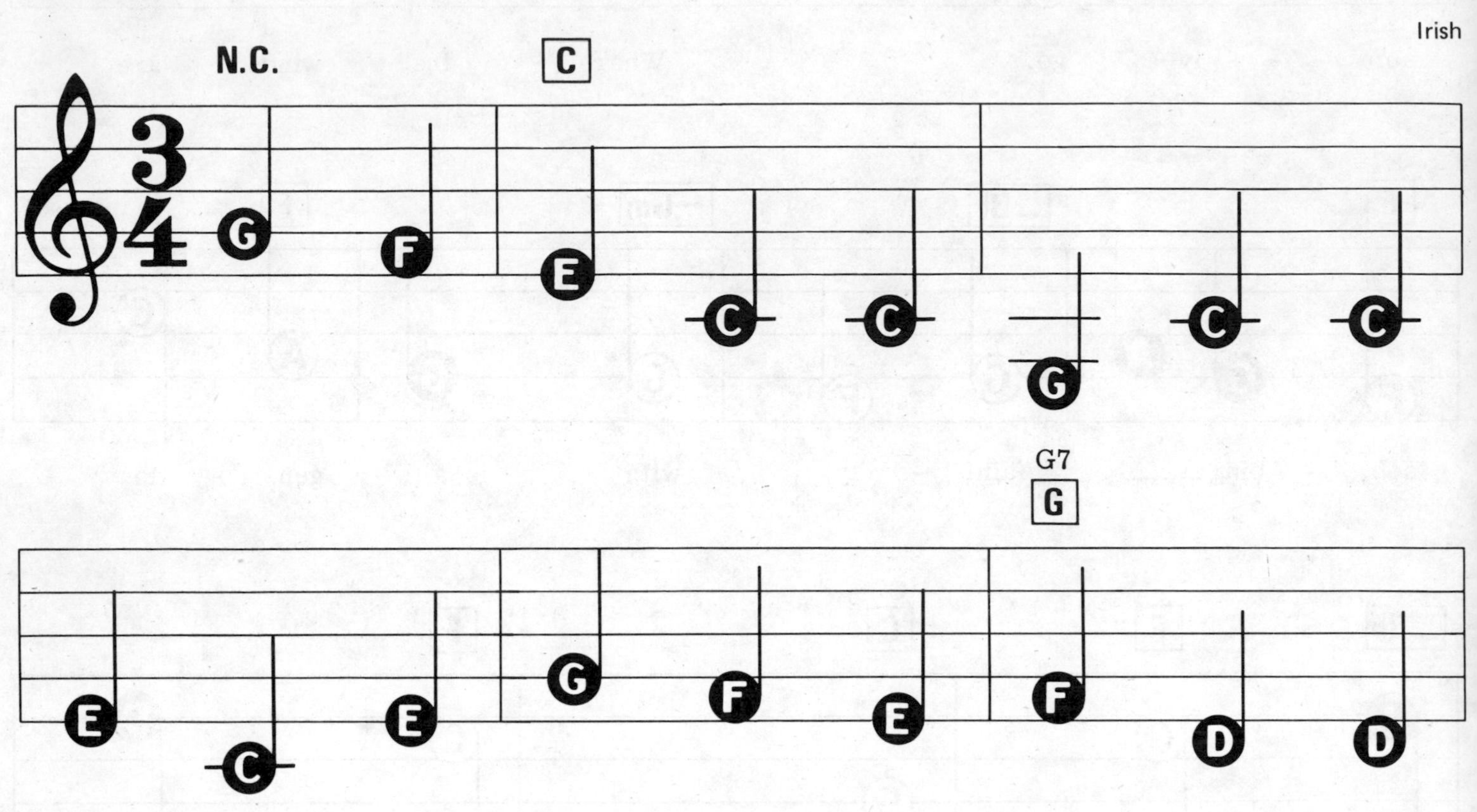

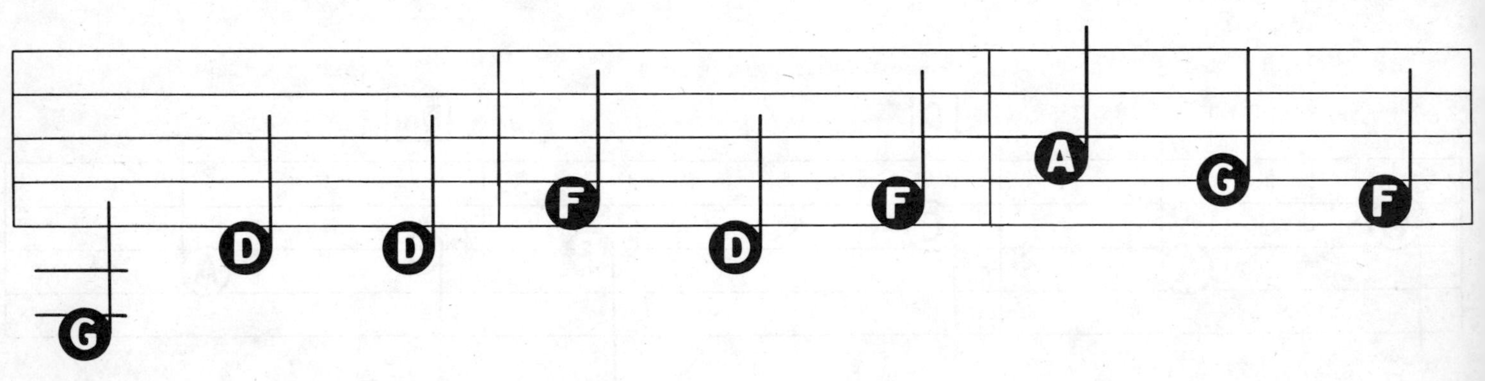

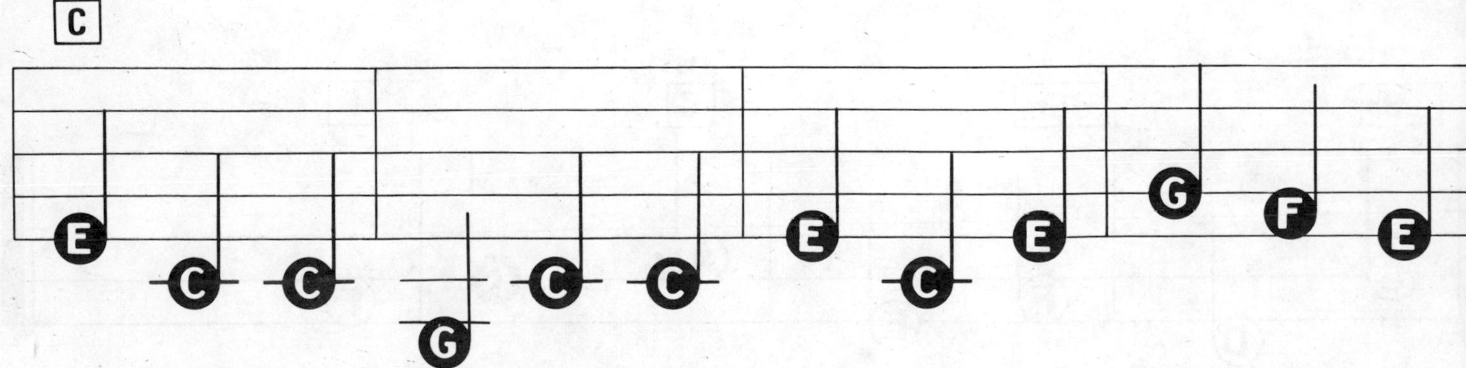

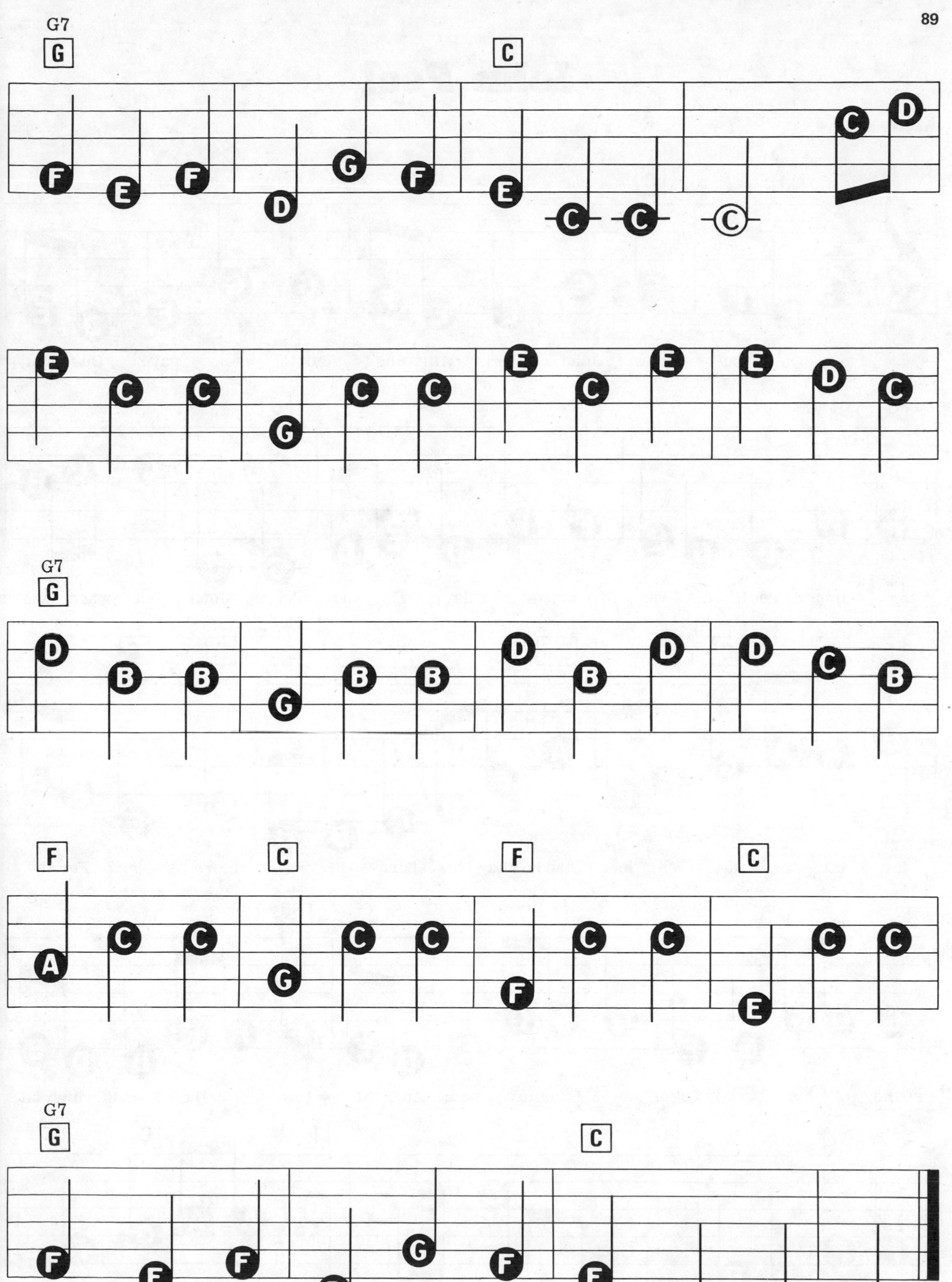
G7
G
C
F
E
F
D
G
F
E
C
C
C
C
D
E
C
C
G
C
C
E
C
E
E
D
C
G7
G
D
B
B
G
B
B
D
B
D
D
C
B
F
C
F
C
A
C
C
G
C
C
F
C
C
E
C
C
G7
G
C
F
E
F
D
G
F
E
C
C
C

John Peel

Registration 4 English

N.C. C

Do you know John Peel with his coat so gay? Do you

G7 C

know John Peel at the break of day, Do you know John Peel when he's

F C Dm G7 C

far, far a - way, With his hands and his horn in the morn - ing? For the

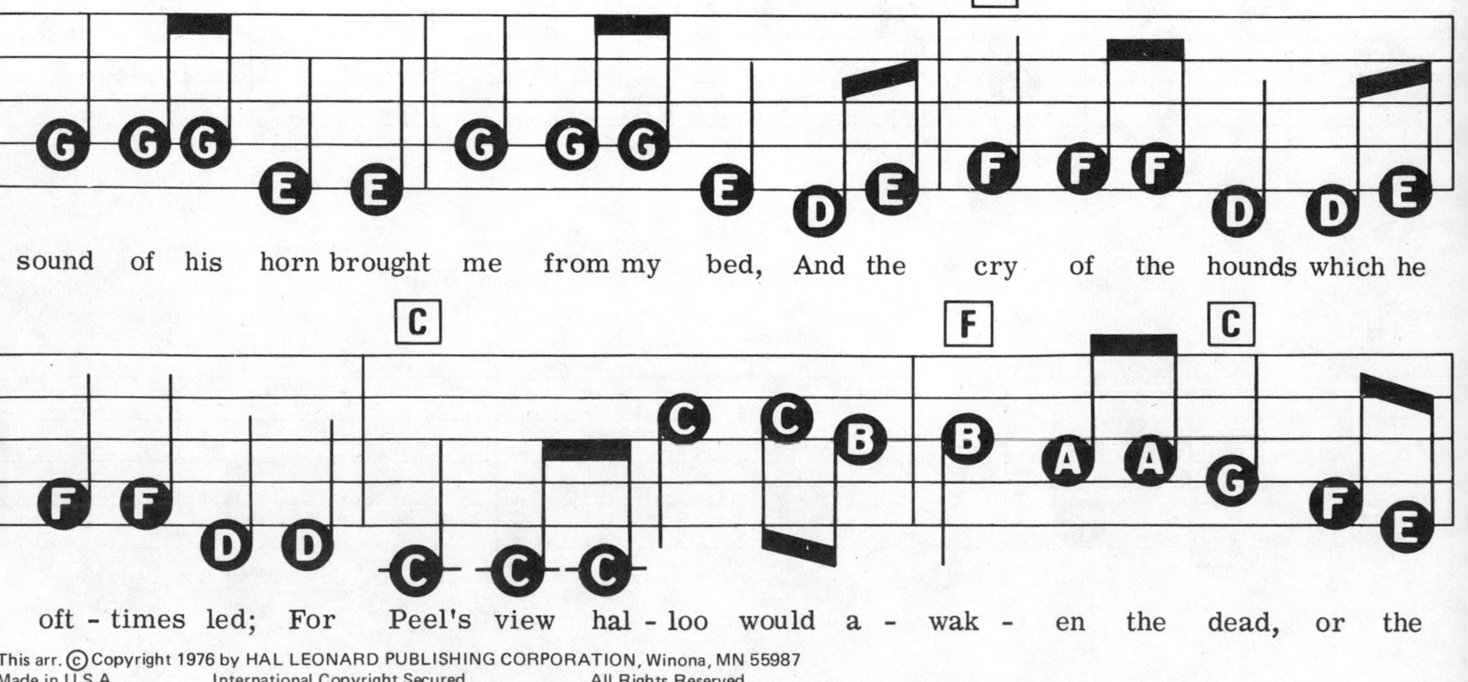

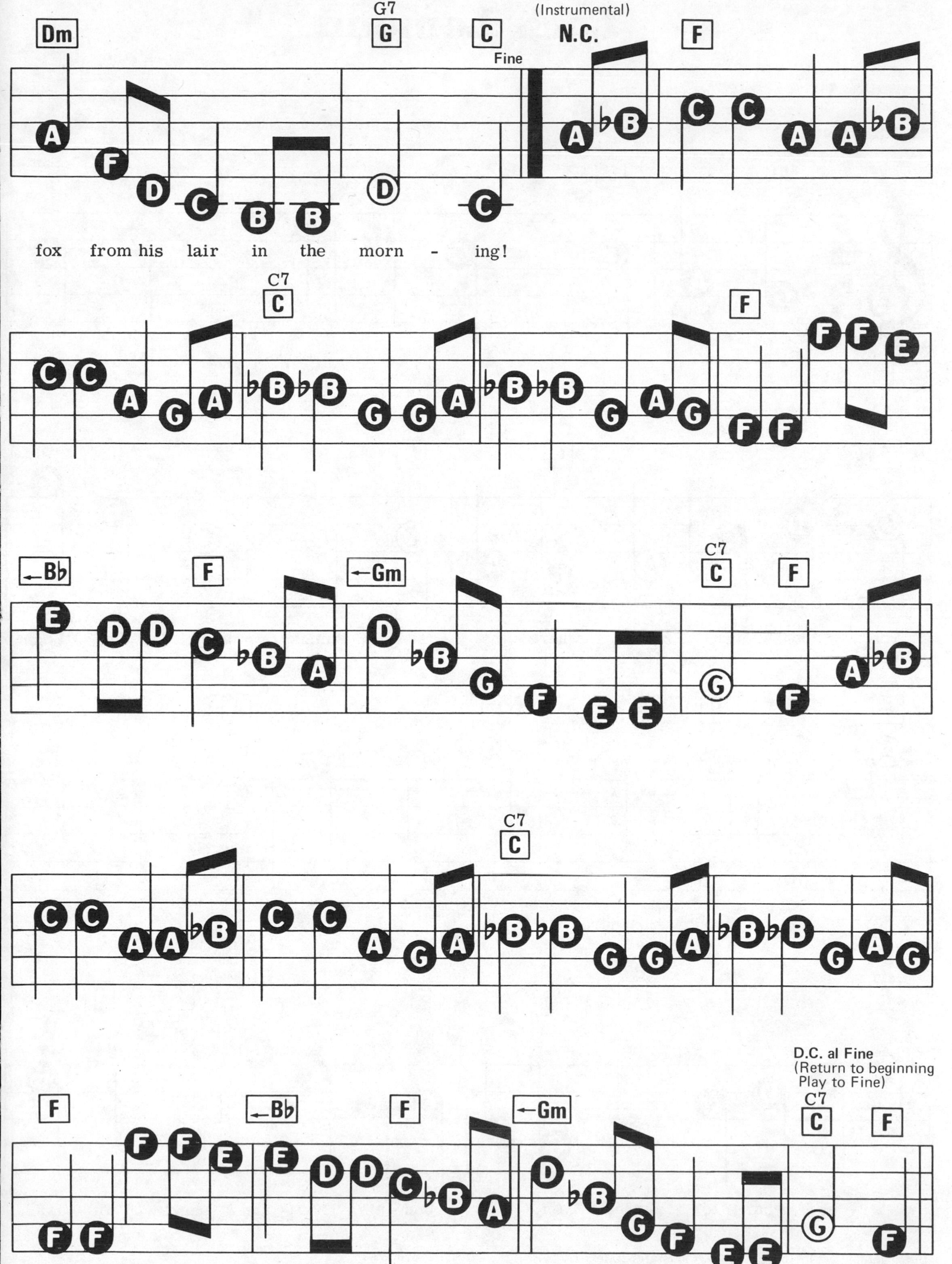
Dm
G7
G
C
Fine
(Instrumental)
N.C.
F
fox from his lair in the morn - ing!
C7
C
F
Bb
F
Gm
C7
C
F
C7
C
F
Bb
F
Gm
D.C. al Fine
(Return to beginning
Play to Fine)
C7
C
F

Loch Lomond

Registration 9

Scottish

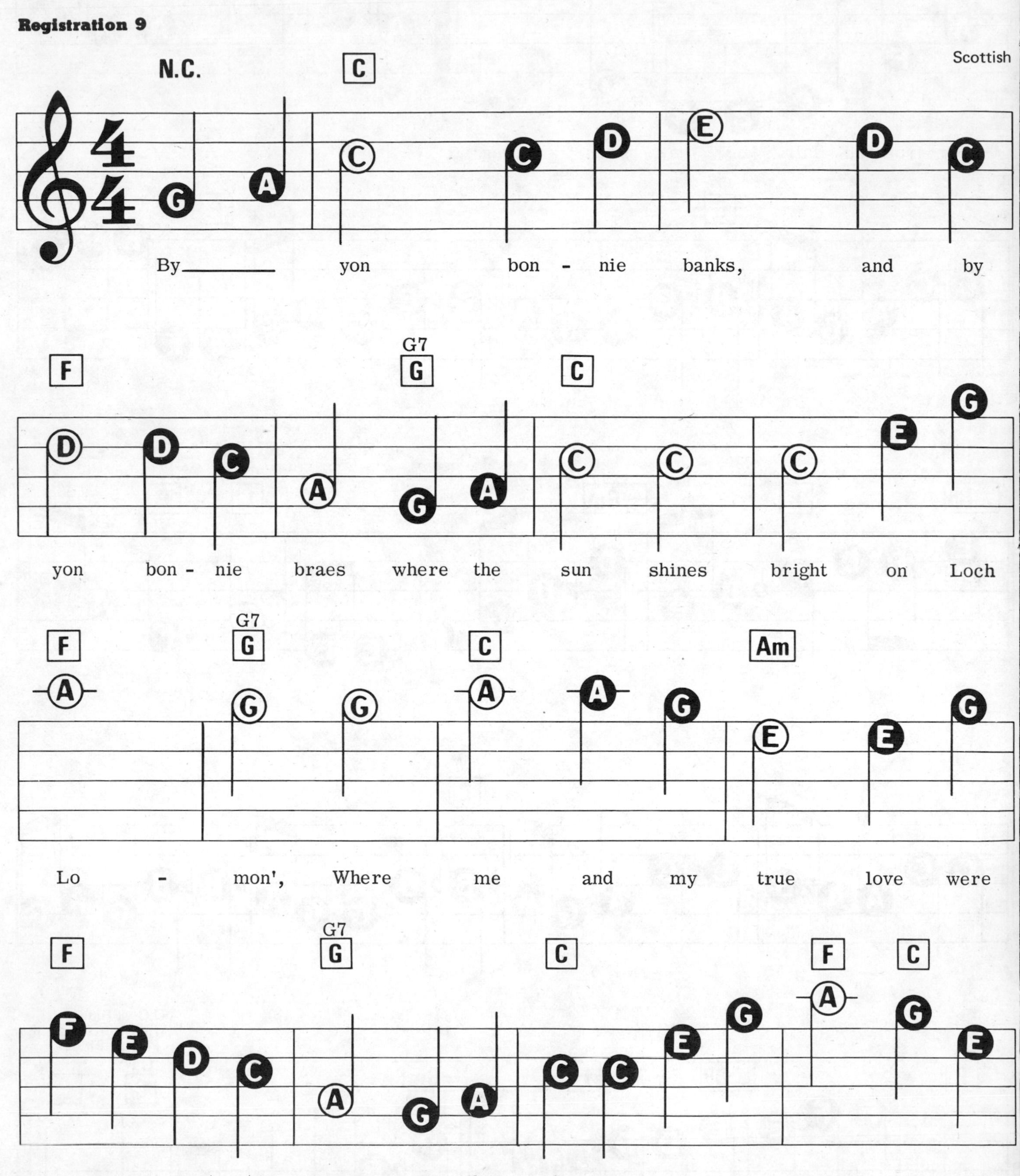

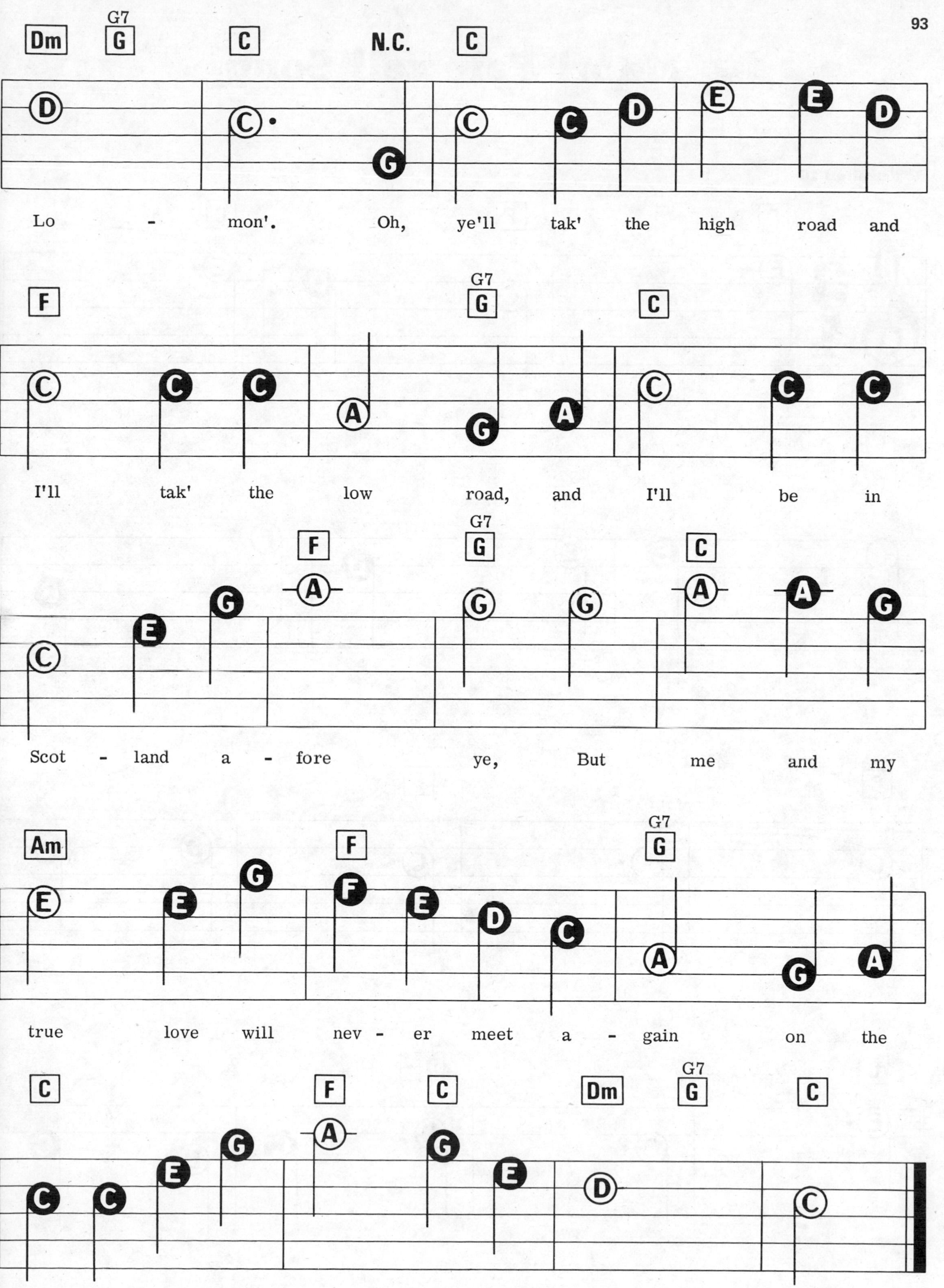
Dm
G7
G
C
N.C.
C
D
C
G
C
C
D
E
E
D
Lo - mon'. Oh, ye'll tak' the high road and
F
G7
G
C
C
C
C
A
G
A
C
C
C
I'll tak' the low road, and I'll be in
F
G7
G
C
C
E
G
A
G
G
A
A
G
Scot - land a - fore ye, But me and my
Am
F
G7
G
E
E
G
F
E
D
C
A
G
A
true love will nev - er meet a - gain on the
C
F
C
Dm
G7
G
C
C
C
E
G
A
G
E
D
C
bon - nie, bon - nie banks of Loch Lo - mond.

Maori Farewell Song

Registration 10

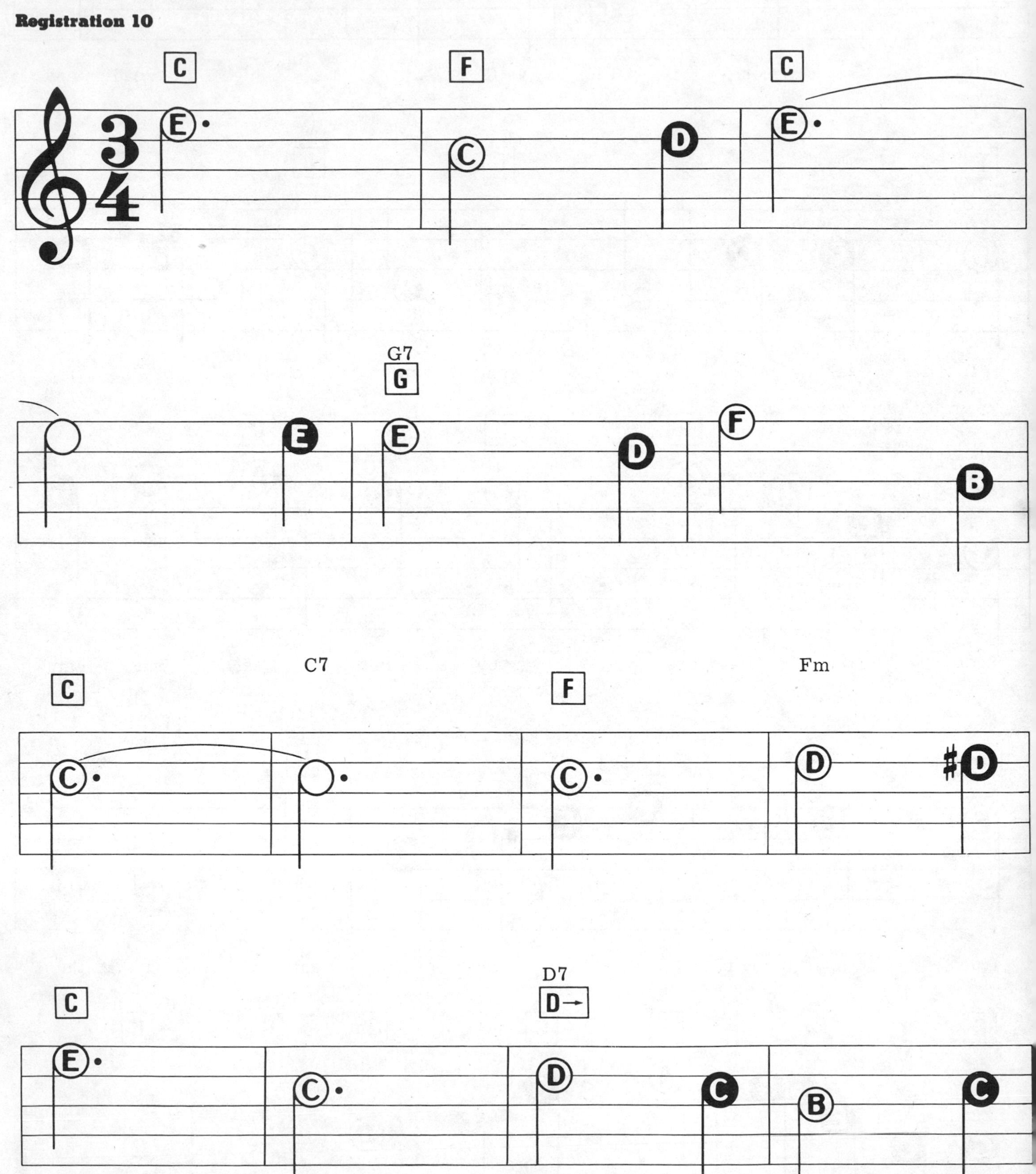

G7
G
C
F
D
G
E
C
D
C
G7
G
E
E
E
D
F
B
C
C7
F
C
C
Fm
C
A7
A
D
D
E
C
F
E
D7
D
G7
G
C
A
B
C

My Old Kentucky Home

Registration 5

American

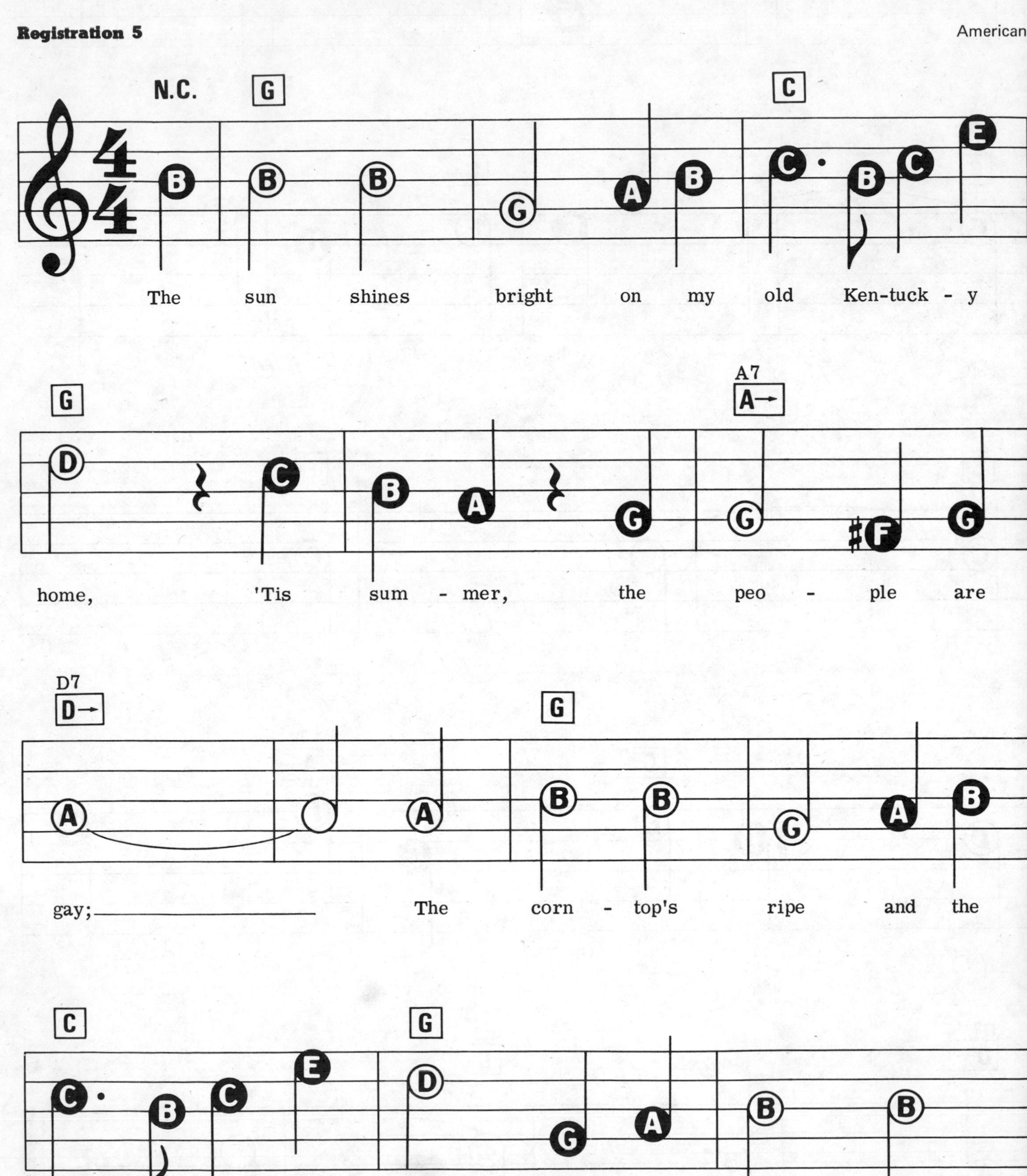

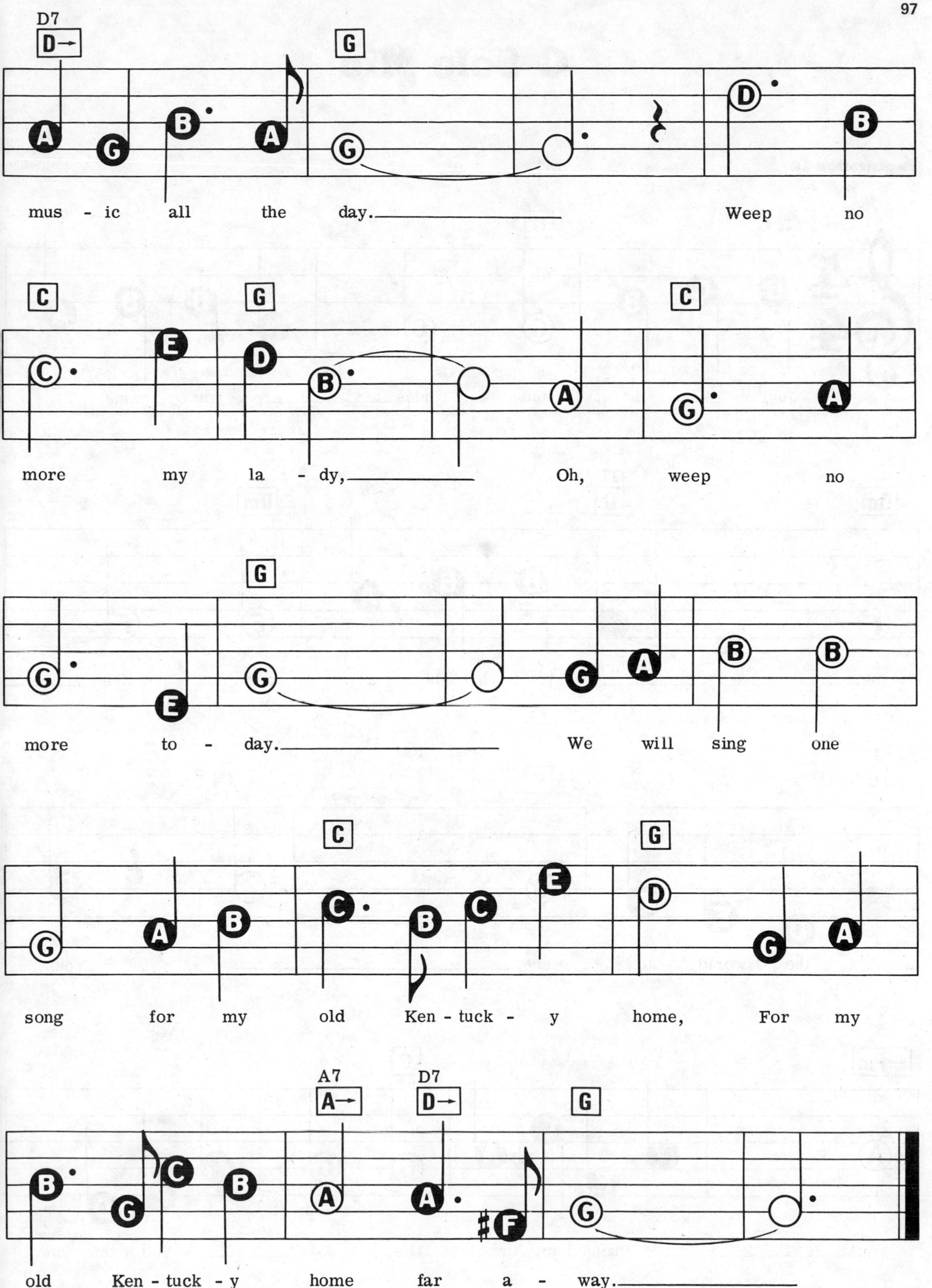

D7
D→
G
A G B A G D B
mus - ic all the day. Weep no
C G C
C E D B A G A
more my la - dy, Oh, weep no
G
G E G G A B B
more to - day. We will sing one
C G
G A B C B C E D G A
song for my old Ken - tuck - y home, For my
A7 D7 G
A→ D→
B G C B A A F G
old Ken - tuck - y home far a - way.

O Sole Mio

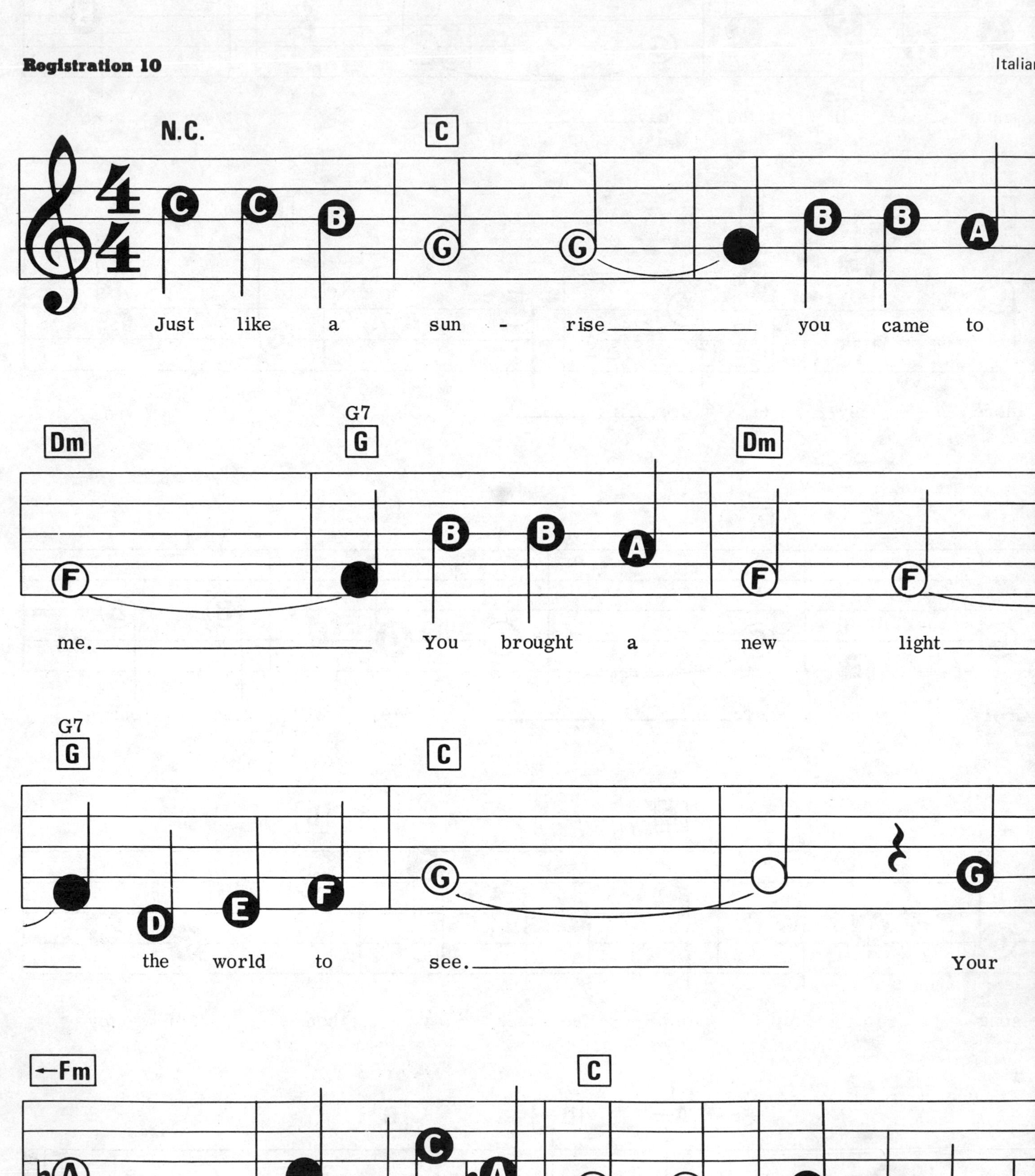
Registration 10
Italian
N.C.
C
Just like a sun - rise you came to
Dm
G7
G
Dm
me. You brought a new light
G7
G
C
the world to see. Your
←Fm
C
smile changed my whole life, dear. You came one

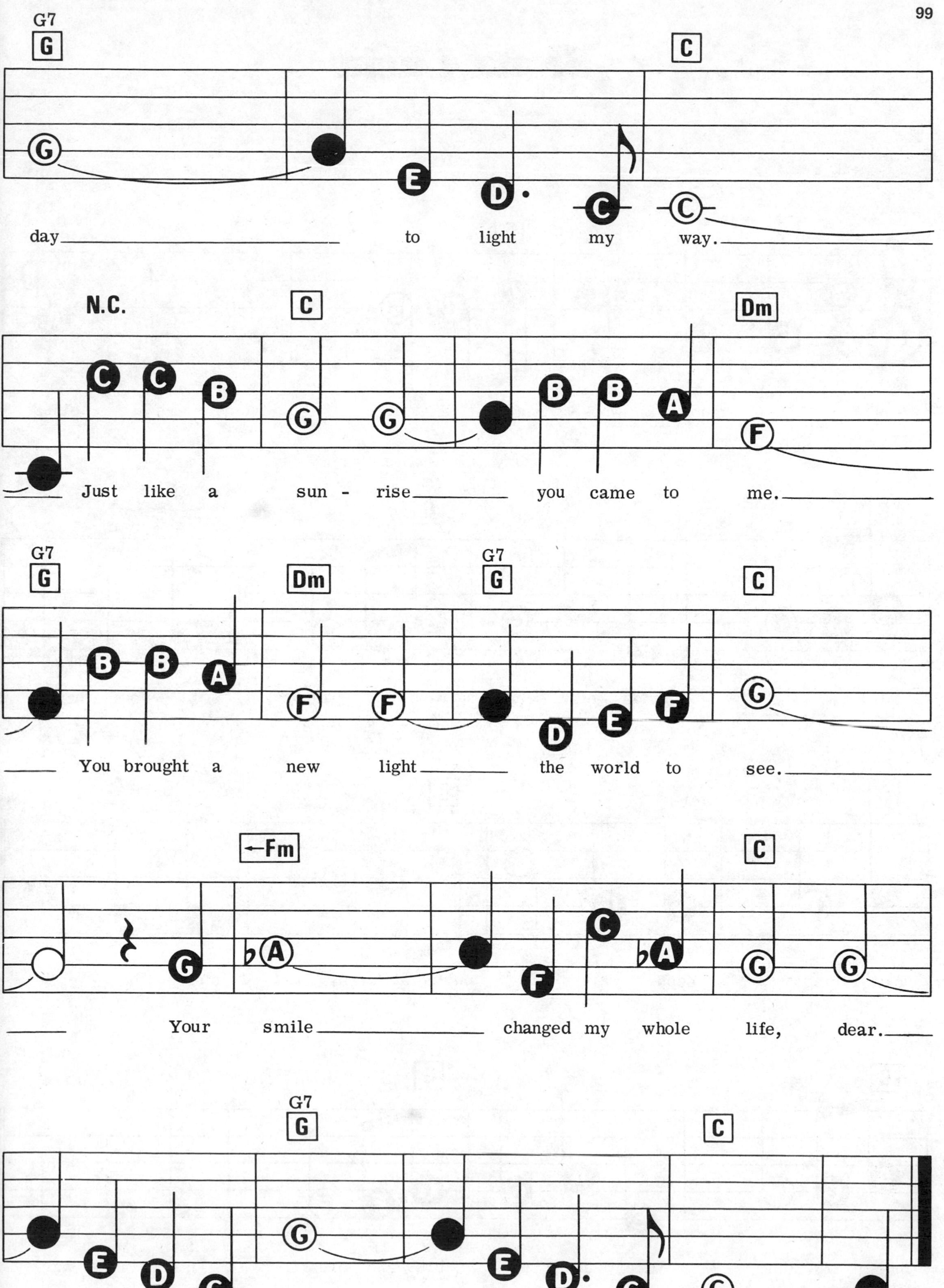
G7
G
C
G
E
D
C
C
day to light my way.
N.C.
C
Dm
C
C
B
G
G
B
B
A
F
Just like a sun - rise you came to me.
G7
G
Dm
G7
G
C
B
B
A
F
F
D
E
F
G
You brought a new light the world to see.
←Fm
C
G
♭A
F
C
♭A
G
G
Your smile changed my whole life, dear.
G7
G
C
E
D
C
G
E
D
C
C
You came one day to light my way.

Santa Lucia

Registration 3

Italian

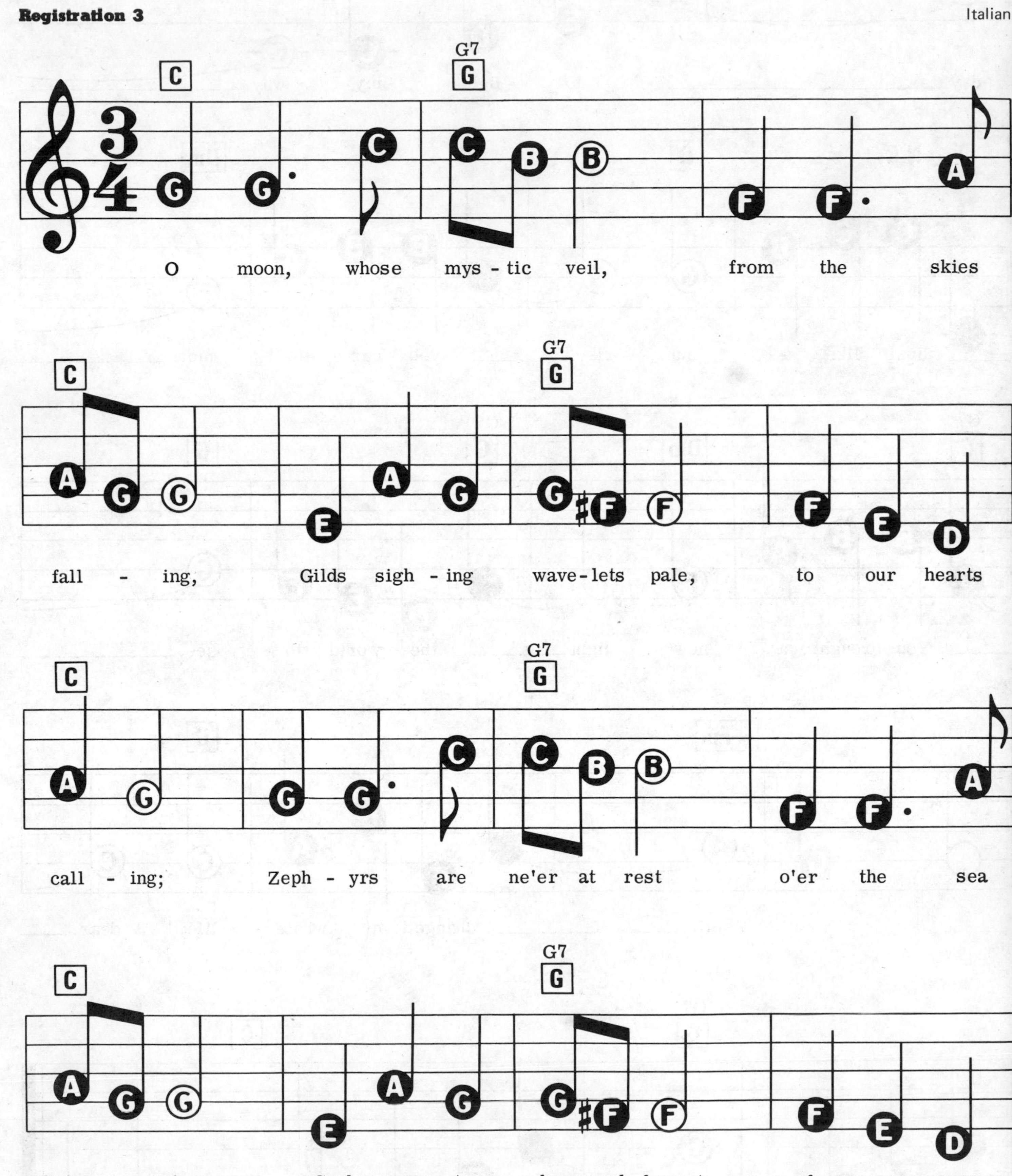

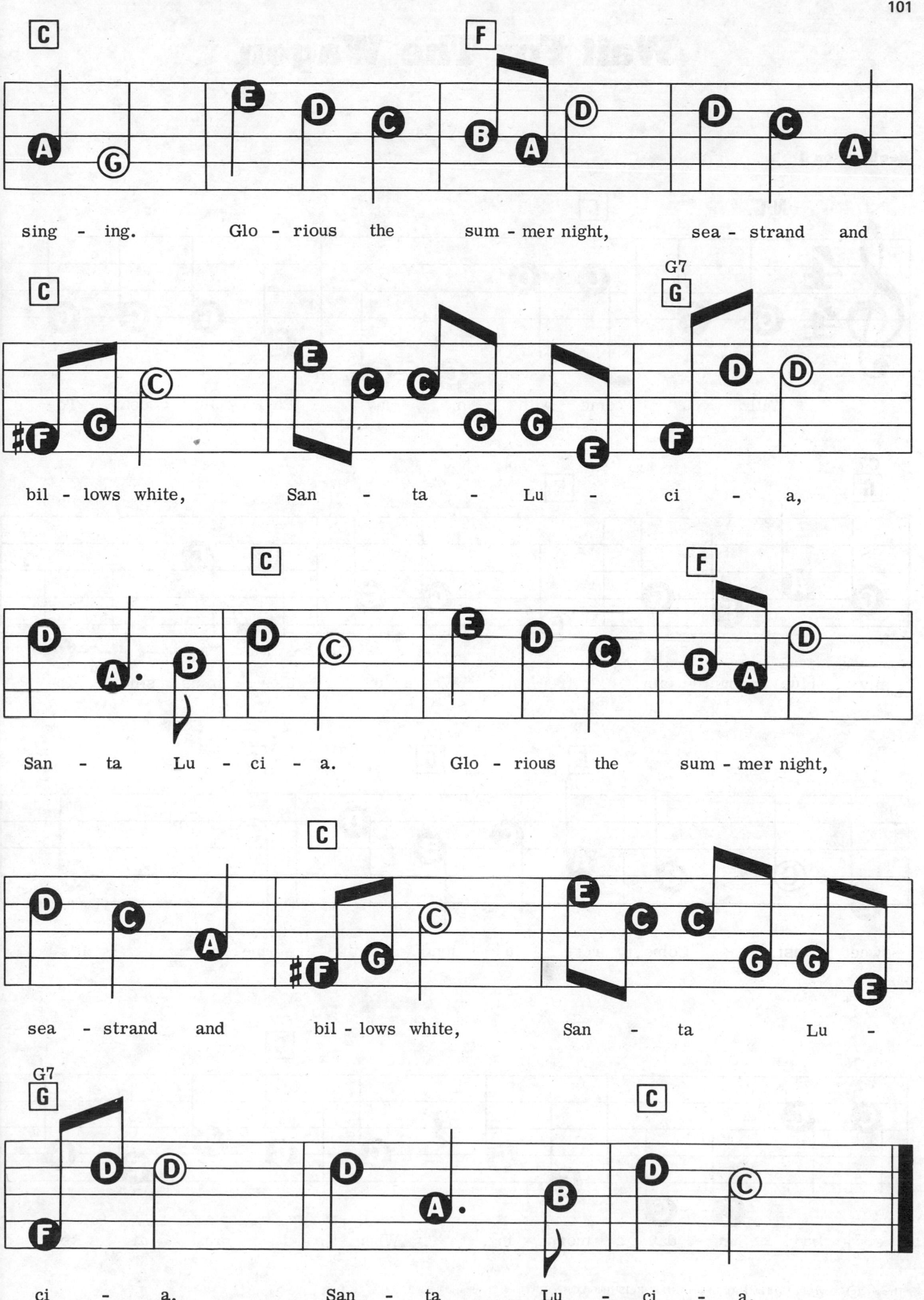
C
F
A G E D C B A D D C A
sing - ing. Glo - rious the sum - mer night, sea - strand and
C
G7
G
F G C E C C G G E F D D
bil - lows white, San - ta - Lu - ci - a,
C
F
D A B D C E D C B A D
San - ta Lu - ci - a. Glo - rious the sum - mer night,
C
D C A F G C E C C G G E
sea - strand and bil - lows white, San - ta Lu -
G7
G
C
F D D D A B D C
ci - a, San - ta Lu - ci - a.

Wait For The Wagon

Registration 1

American

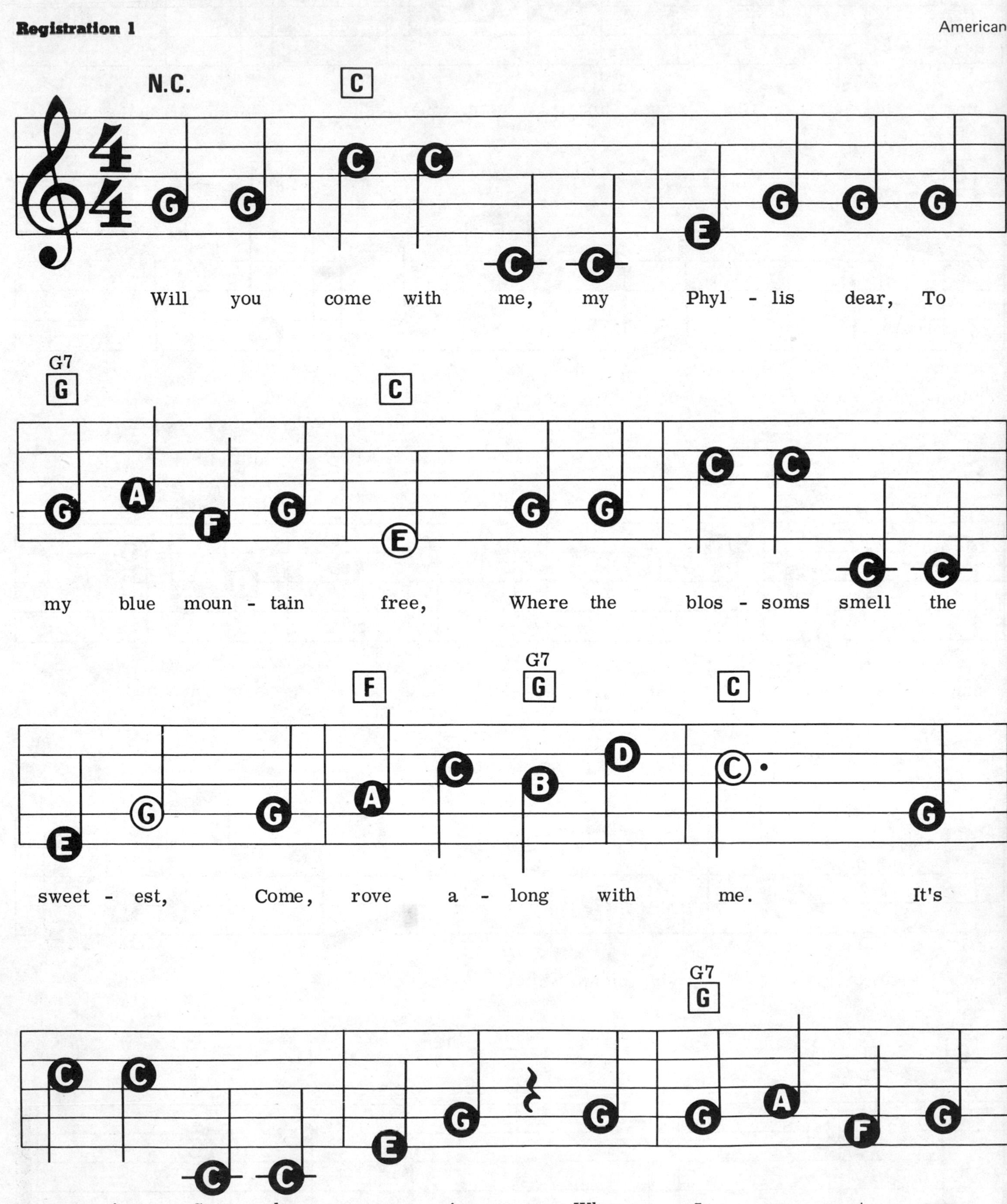

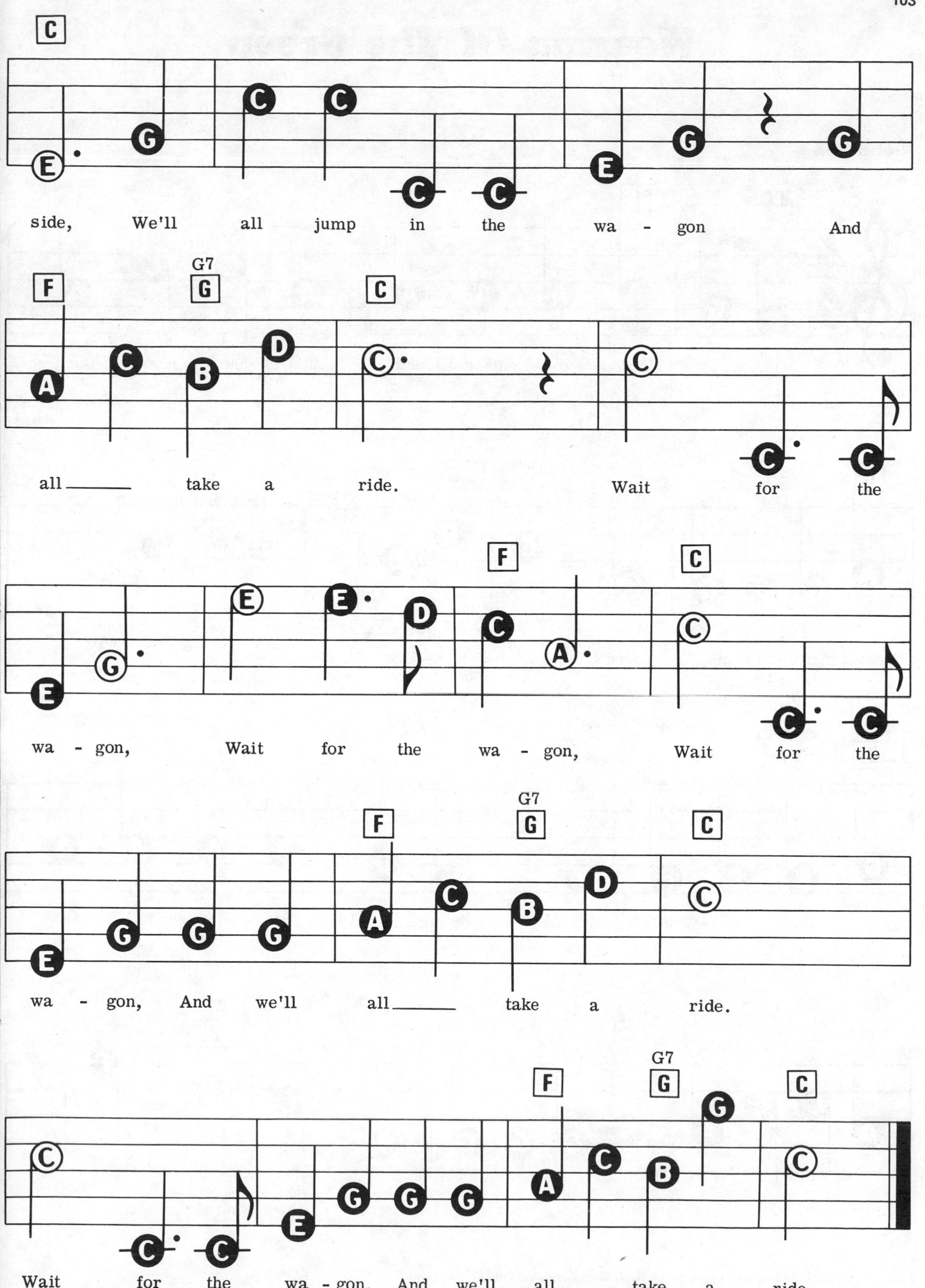
C
E G C C C C E G G
side, We'll all jump in the wa - gon And
F G7 G C
A C B D C C C C
all take a ride. Wait for the
F C
E G E E D C A C C C
wa - gon, Wait for the wa - gon, Wait for the
F G7 G C
E G G G A C B D C
wa - gon, And we'll all take a ride.
F G7 G C
C C C E G G G A C B G C
Wait for the wa - gon, And we'll all take a ride.

Wearing Of The Green

Registration 9 Irish

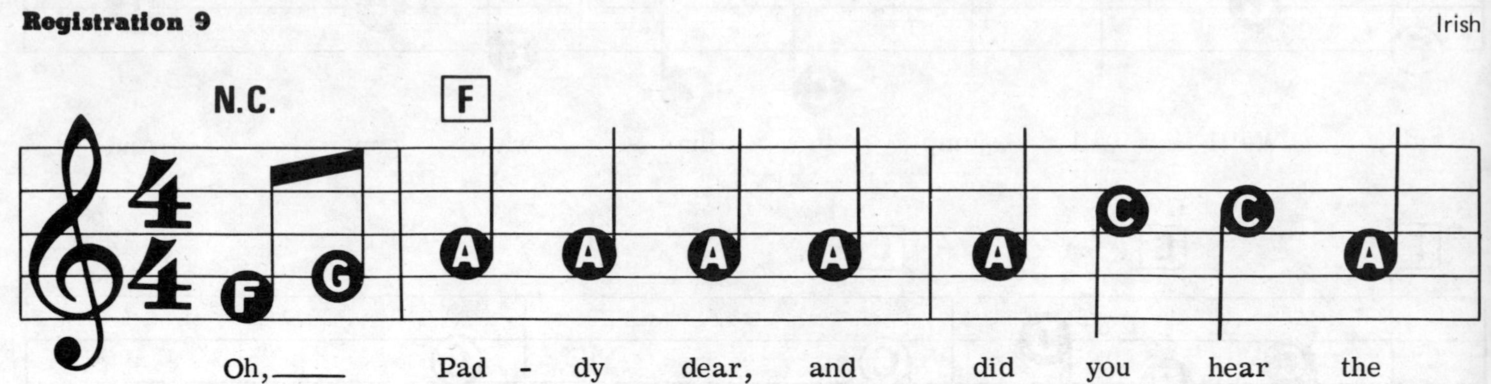

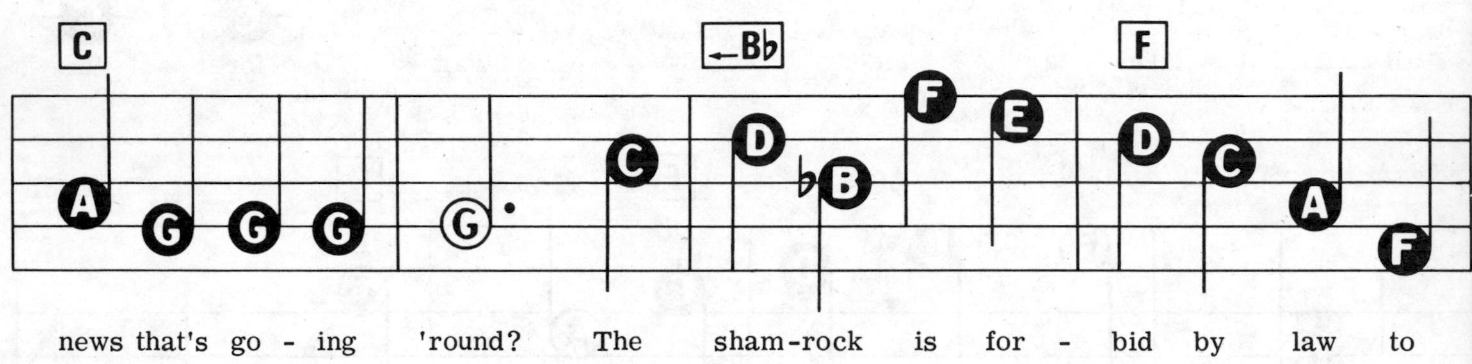

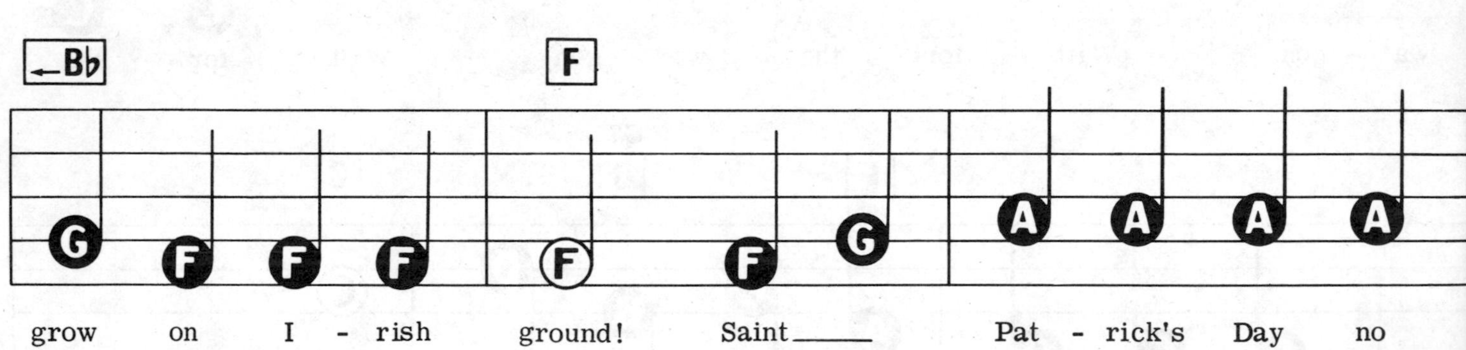

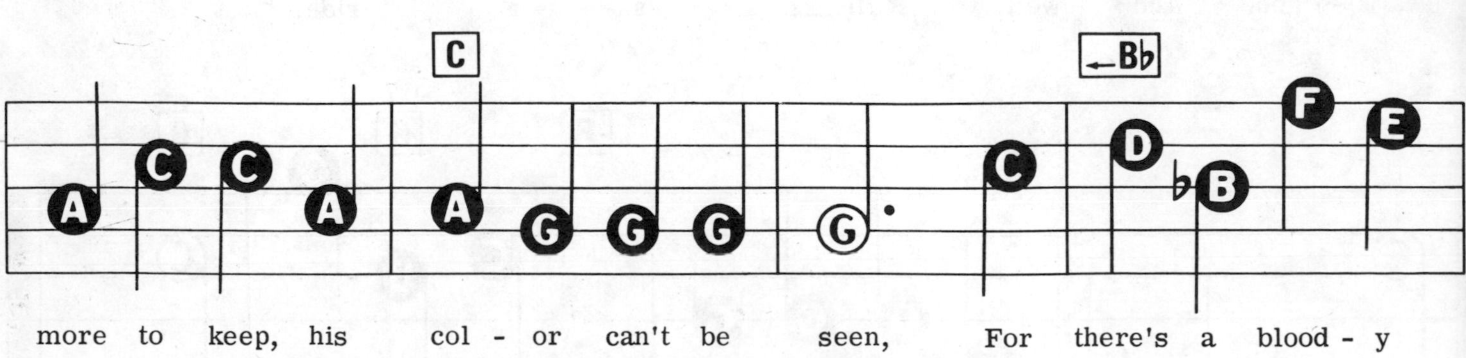

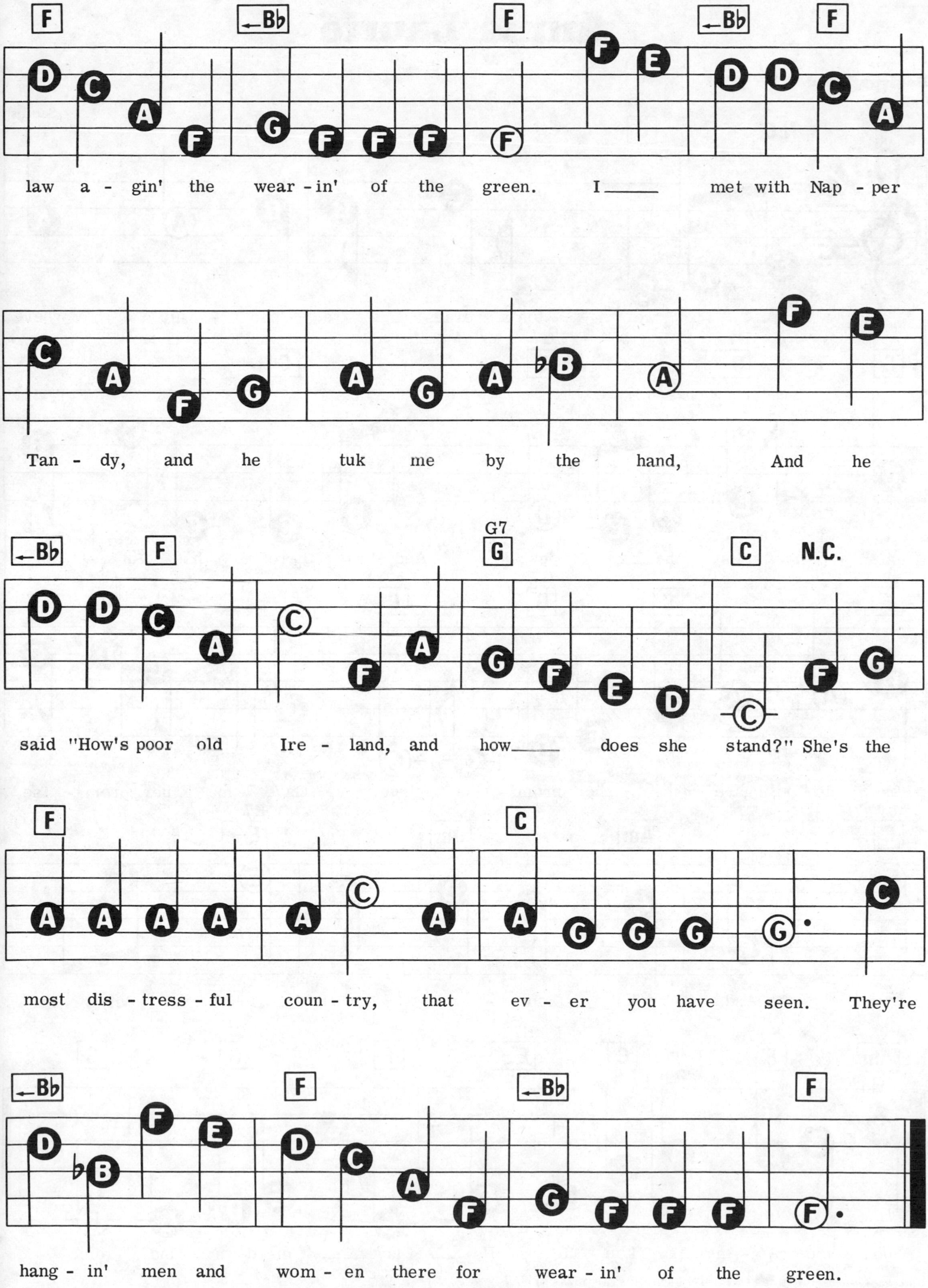

F ←B♭ F ←B♭ F

D C A F G F F F F F E D D C A

law a - gin' the wear - in' of the green. I ____ met with Nap - per

C A F G A G A ♭B A F E

Tan - dy, and he tuk me by the hand, And he

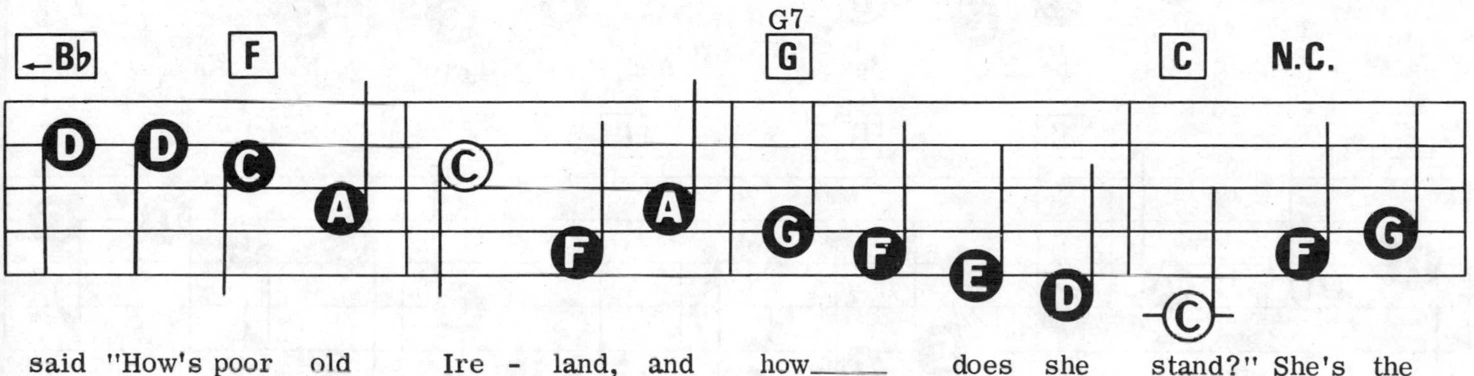

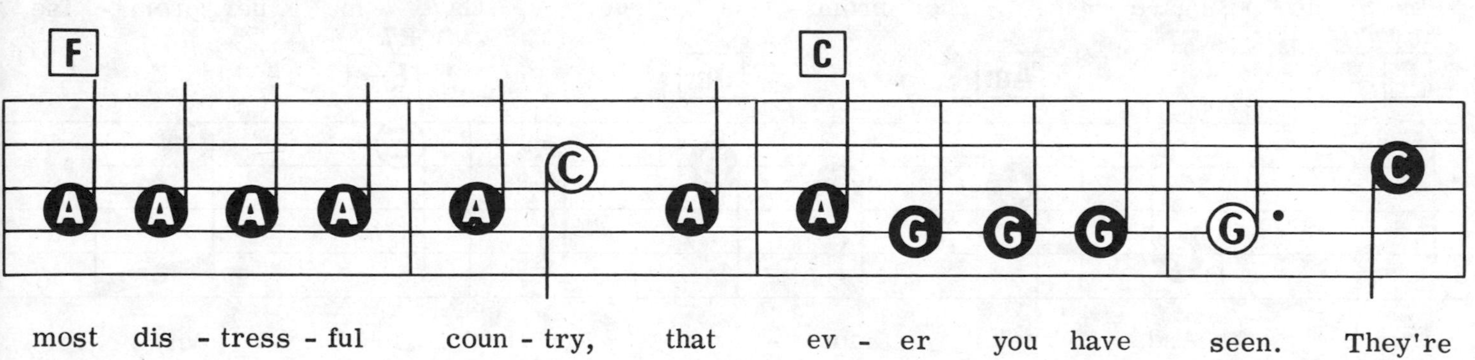

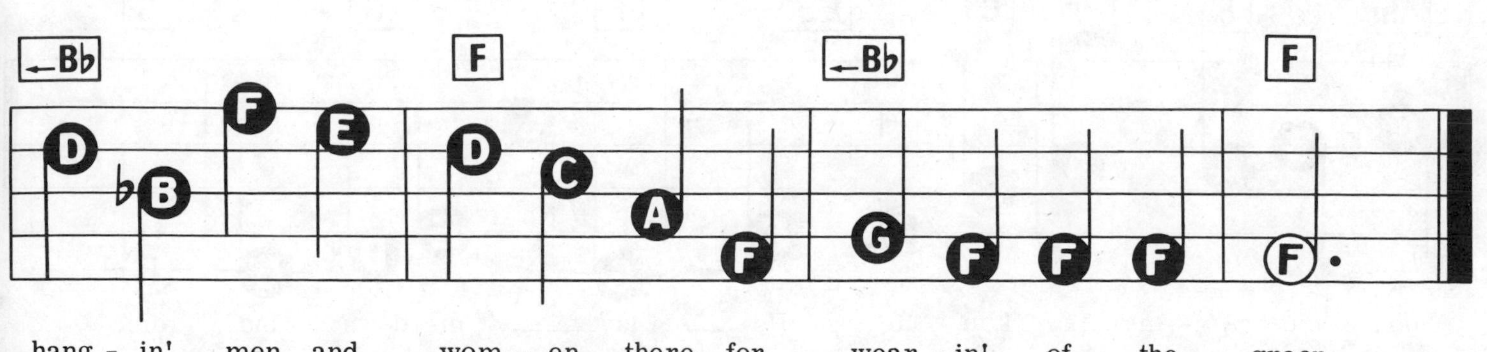

Annie Laurie

Registration 9

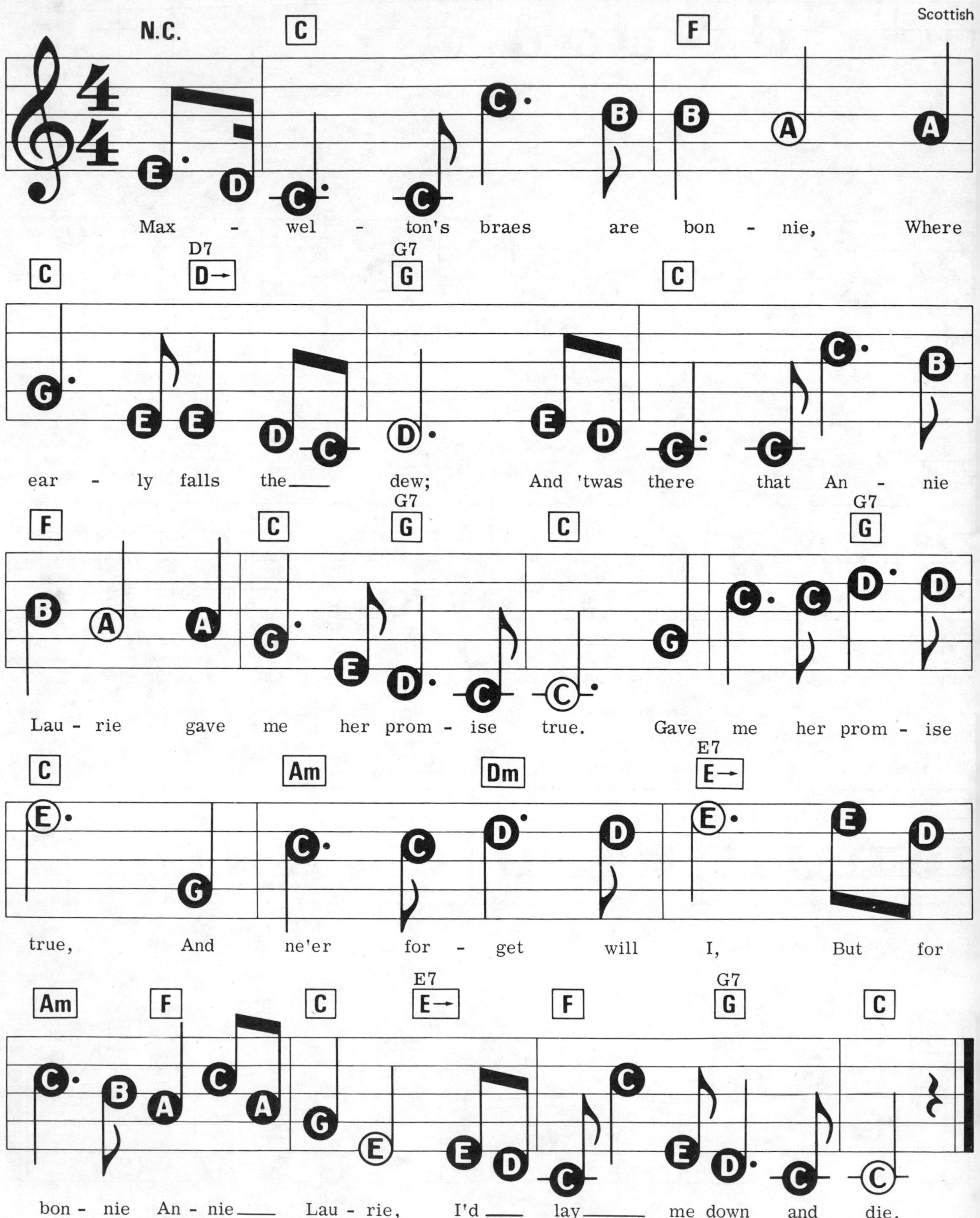

Banana Boat

Registration 4

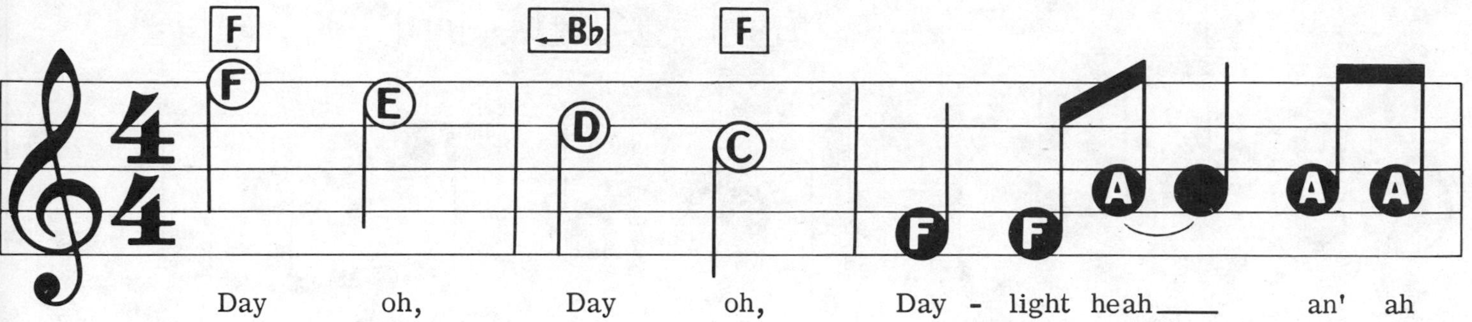
F
←B♭
F
F E D C F F A A A
Day oh, Day oh, Day - light heah___ an' ah

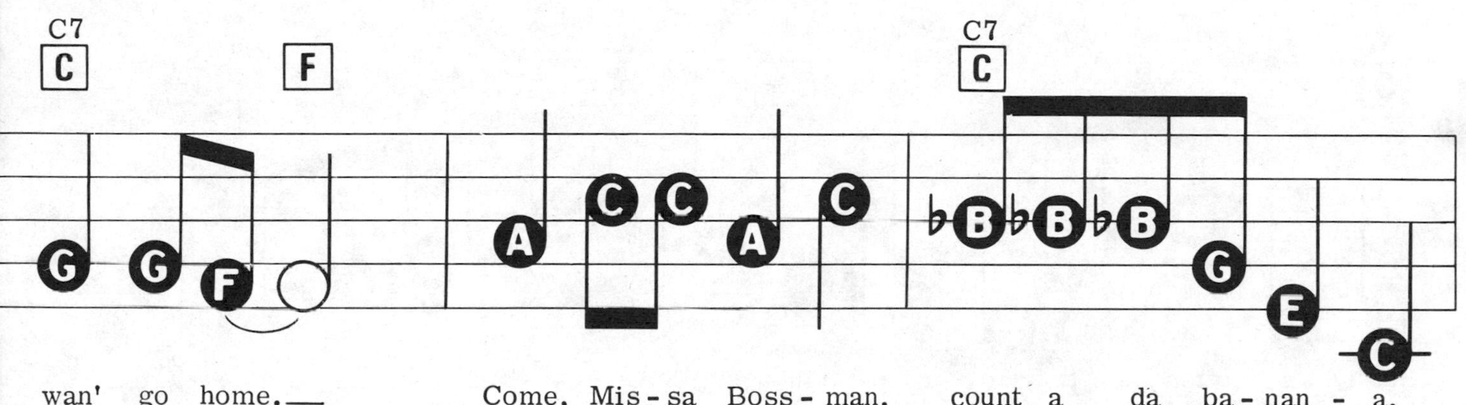
C7
C
F
C7
C
G G F A C C A C B B B G E C
wan' go home.___ Come, Mis - sa Boss - man, count a da ba - nan - a,

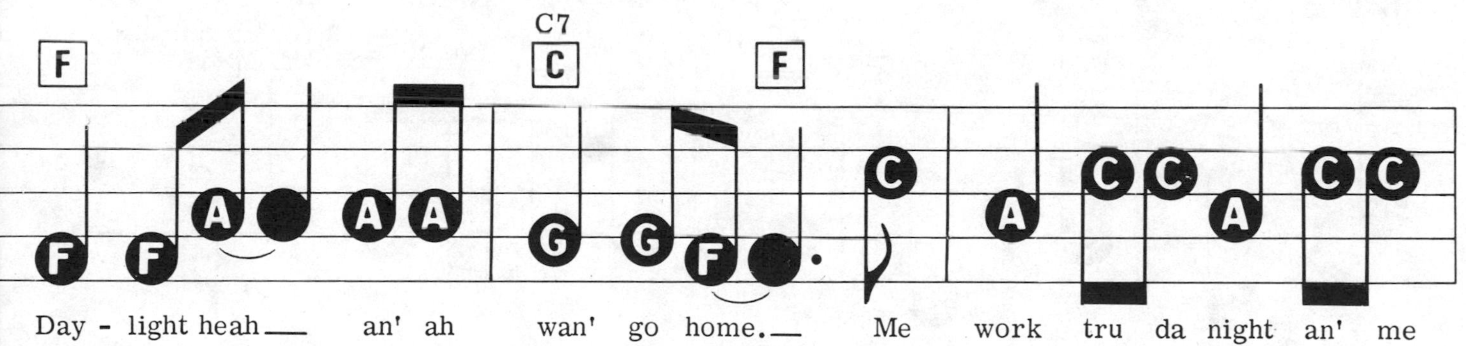
F
C7
C
F
F F A A A G G F C A C C A C C
Day - light heah___ an' ah wan' go home.___ Me work tru da night an' me

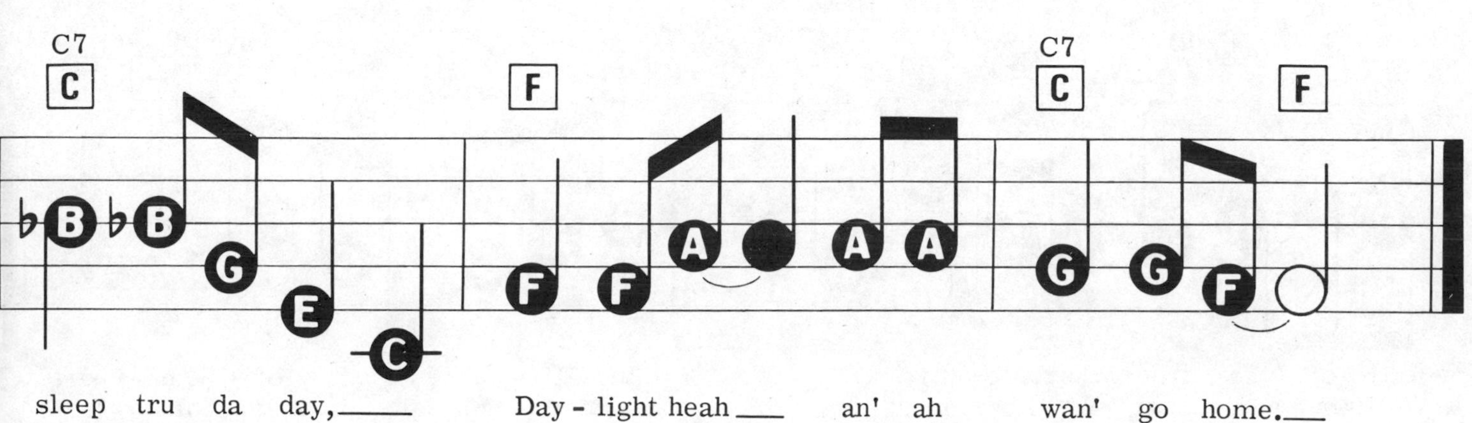
C7
C
F
C7
C
F
B B G E C F F A A A G G F
sleep tru da day,___ Day - light heah___ an' ah wan' go home.___

Beautiful Isle Of Somewhere

Registration 5

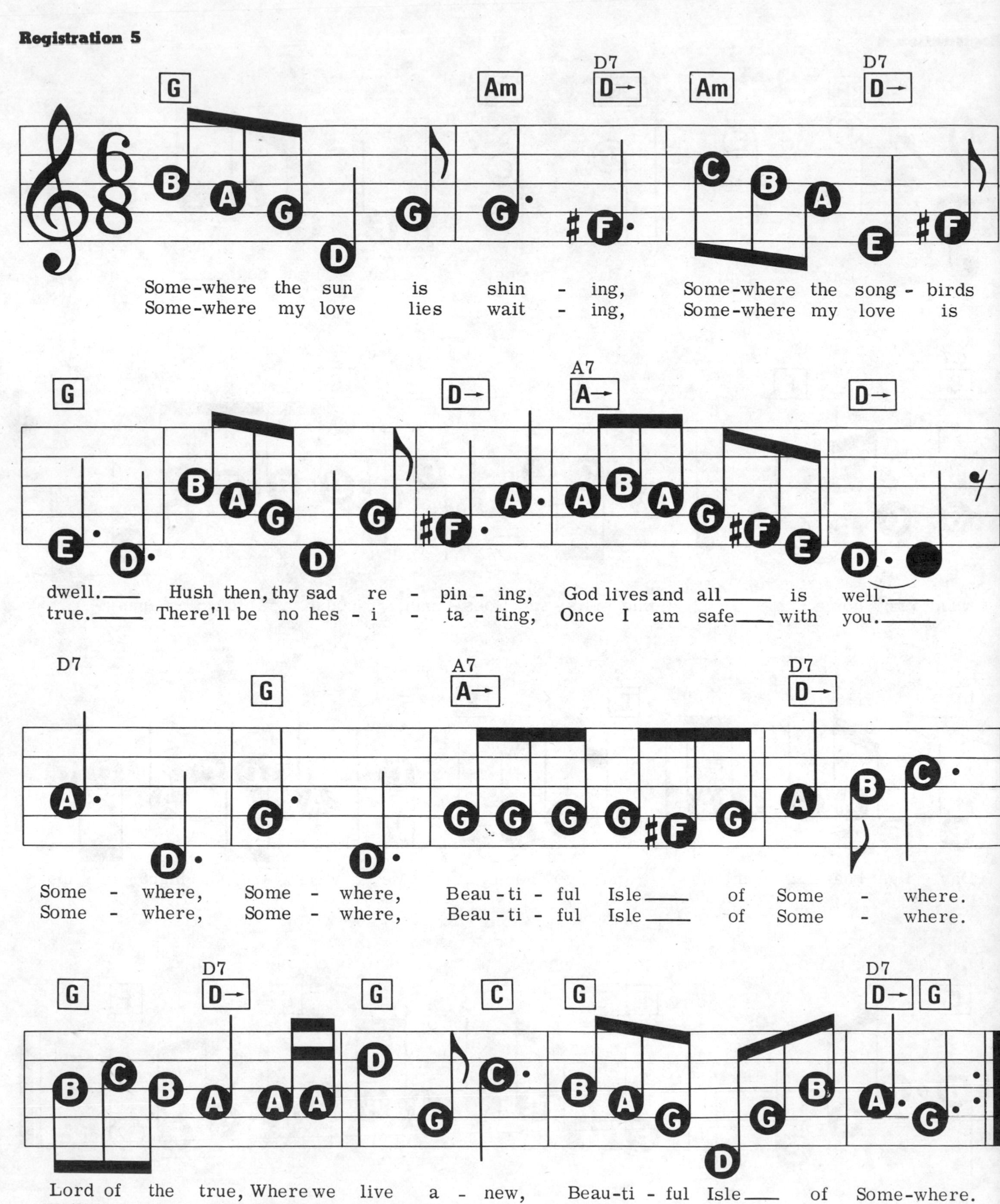

Beautiful Sea

Registration 10

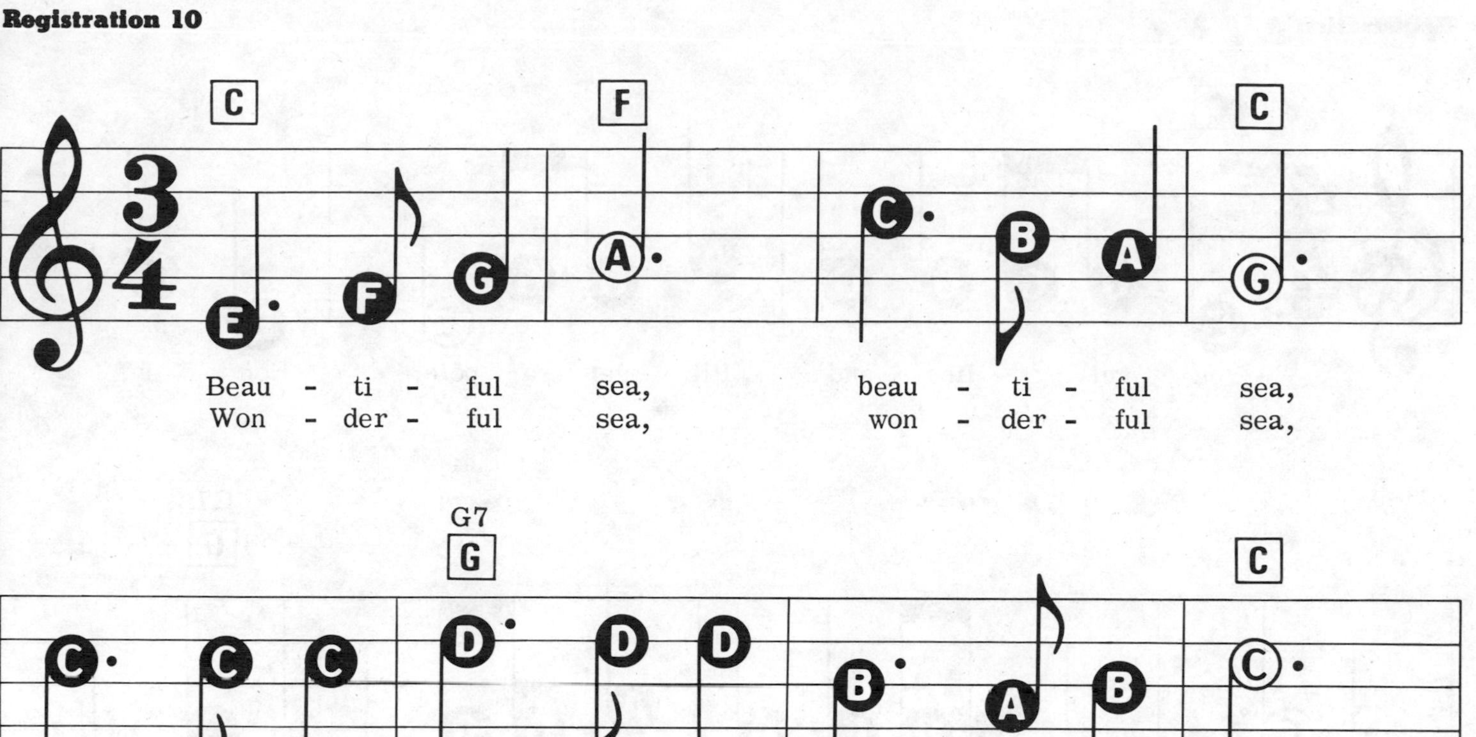

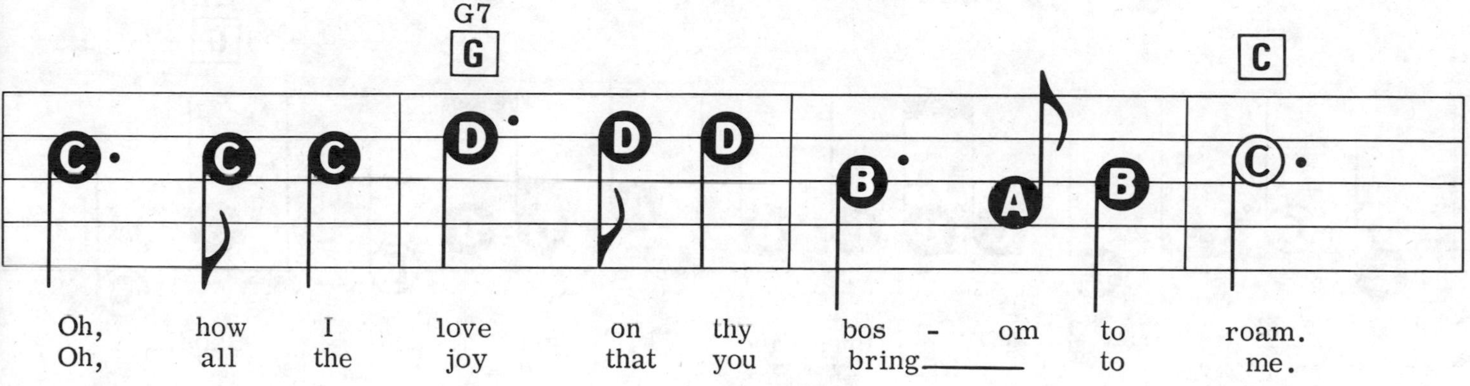

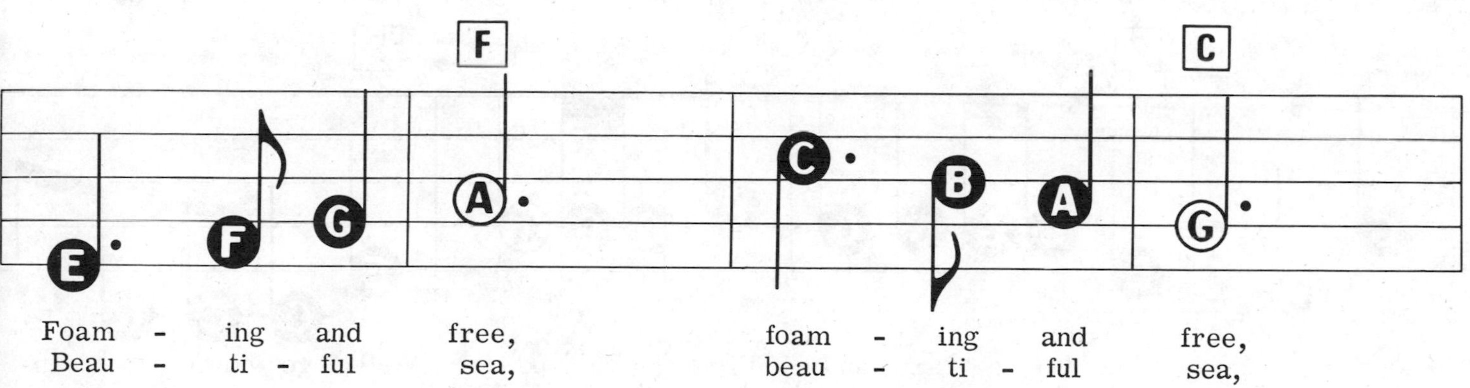

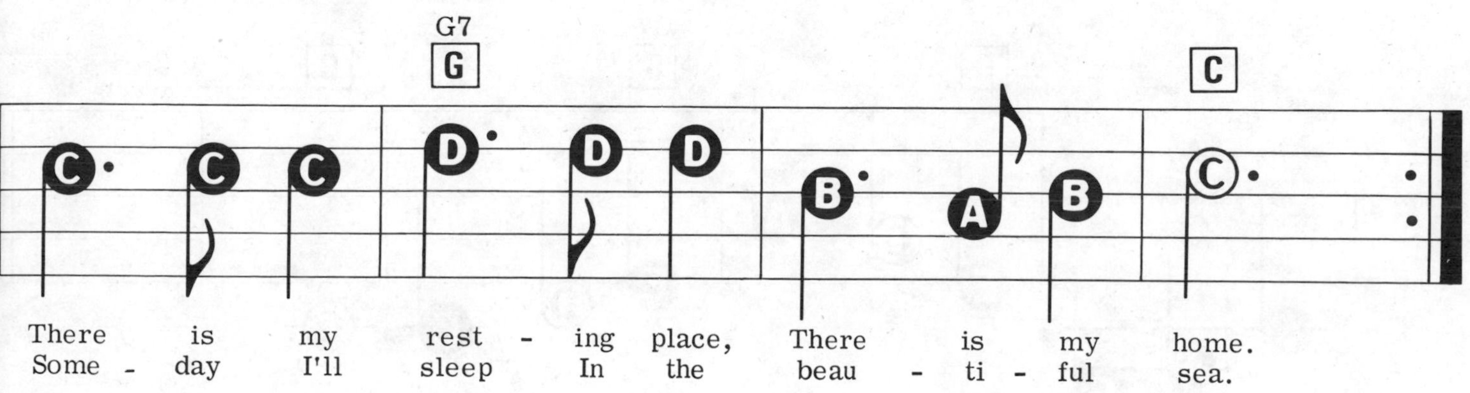

Crawdad Song

Registration 8

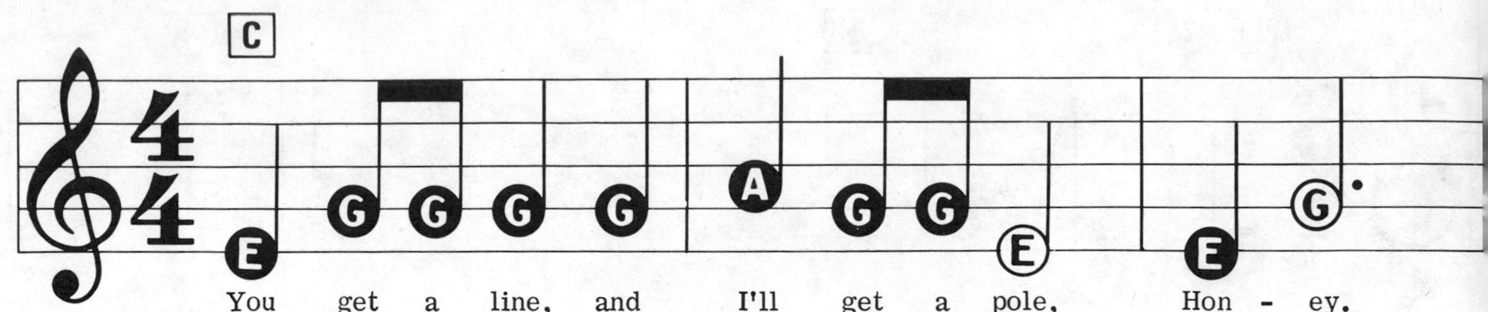

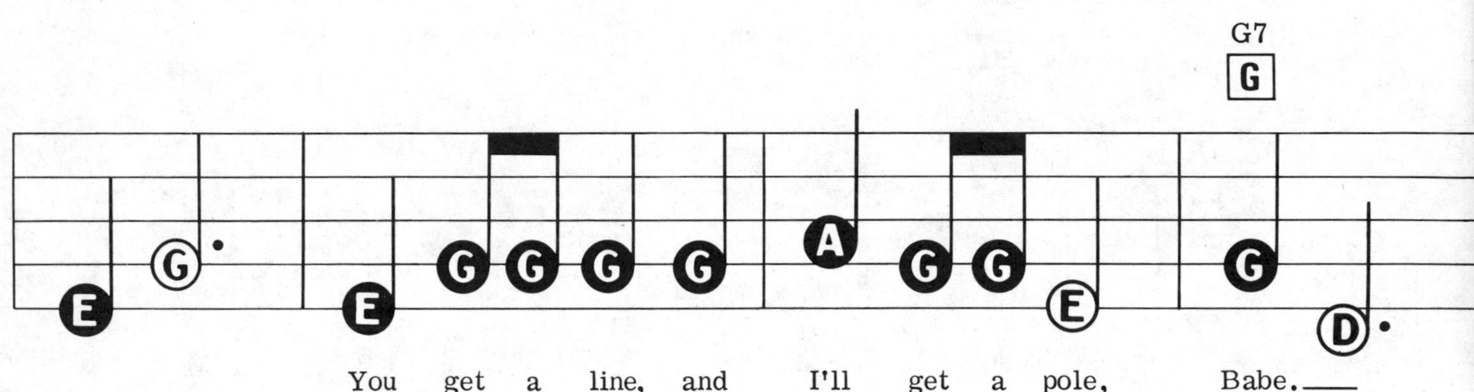

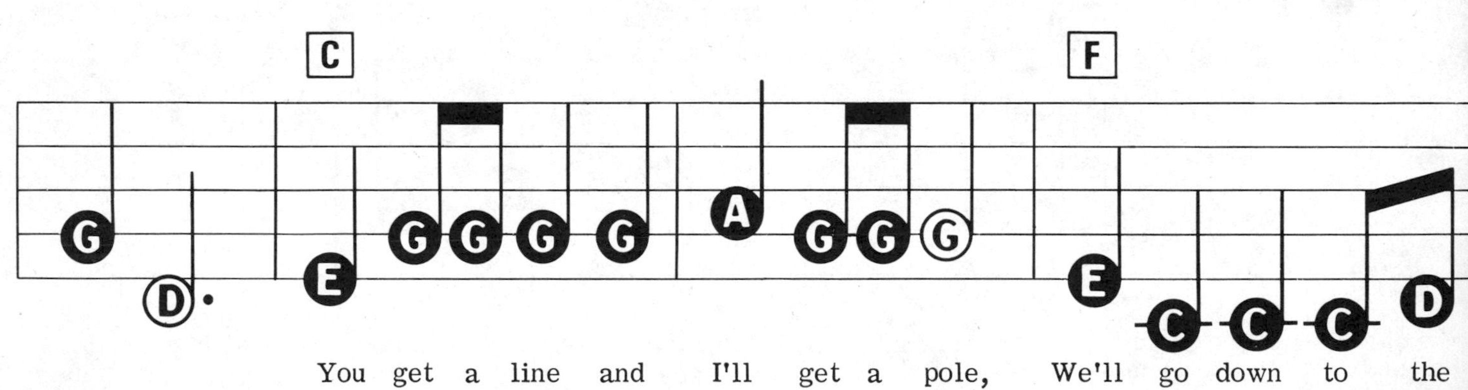

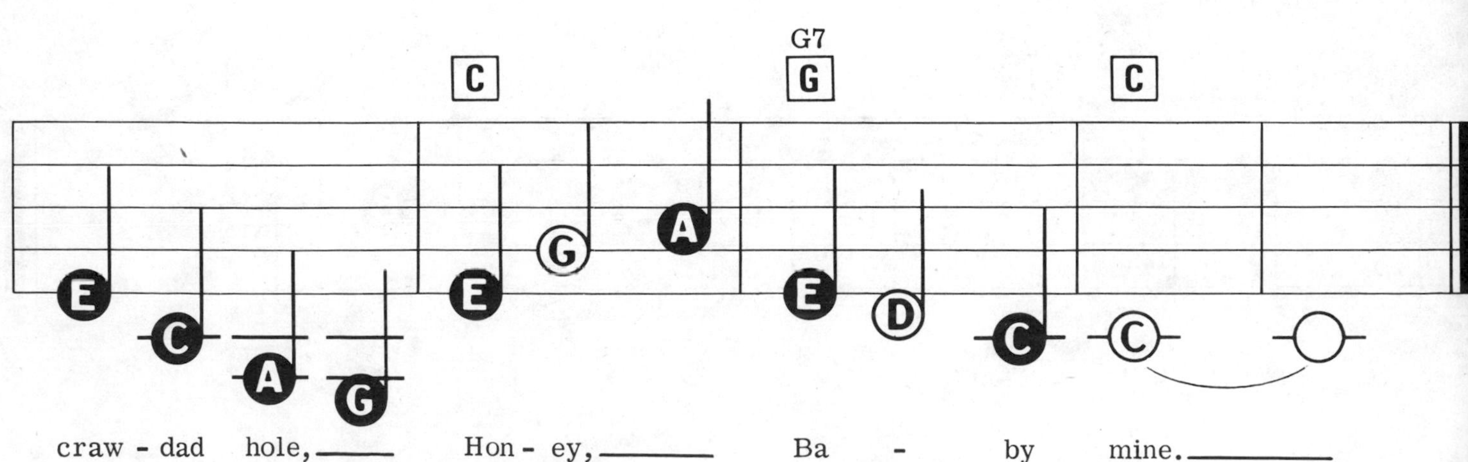

Immer Noch Ein Troepchen

Registration 5

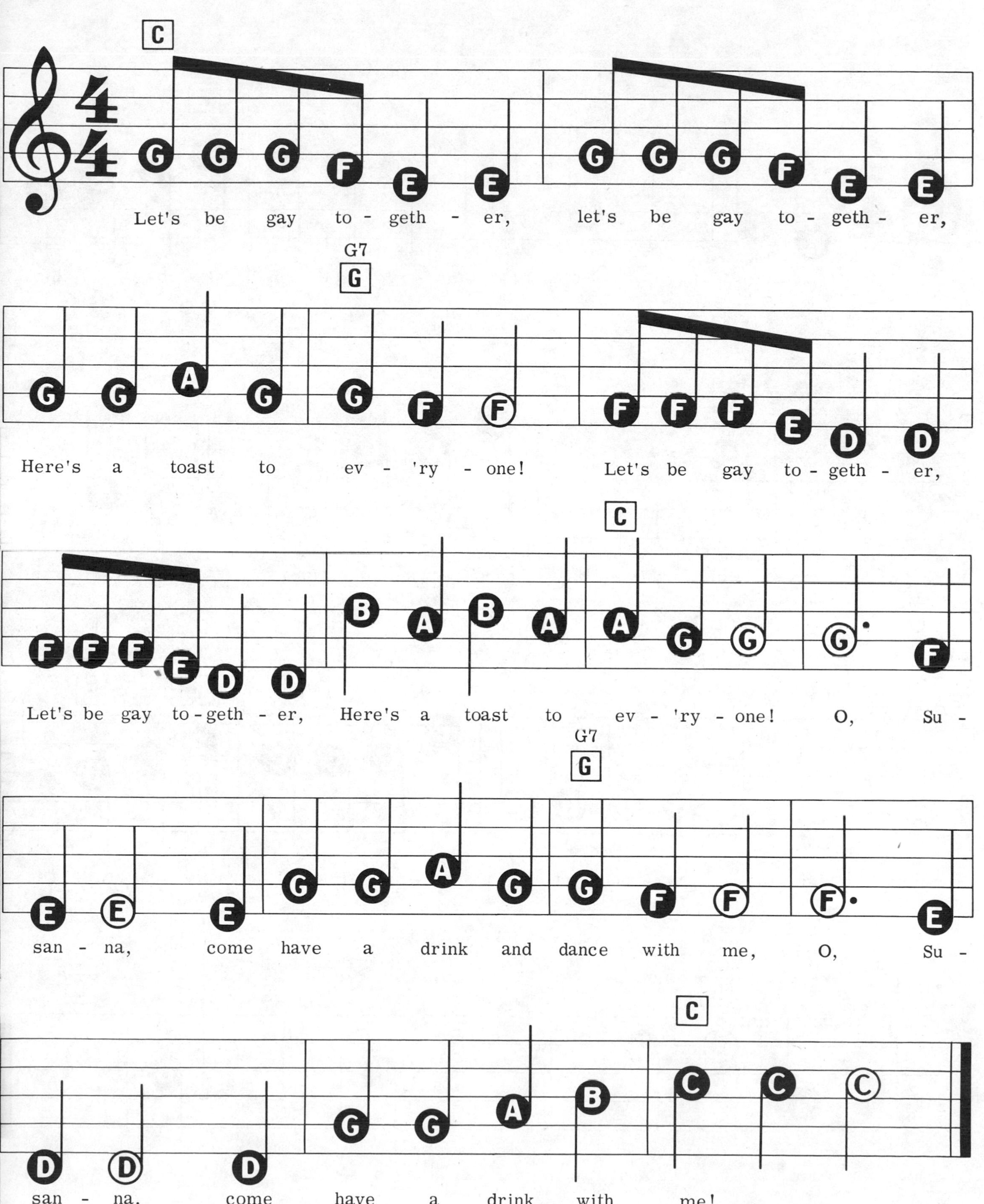

Let Him Go, Let Him Tarry

Registration 5

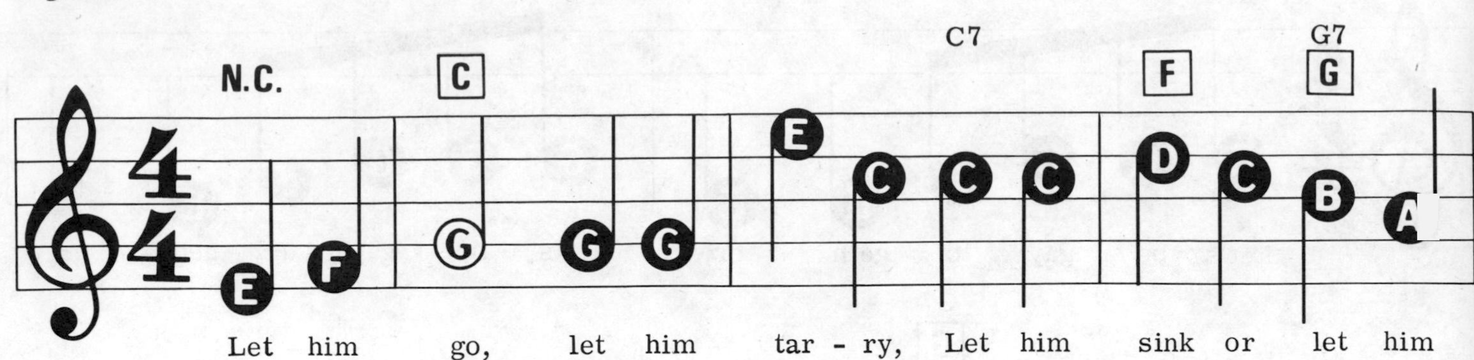

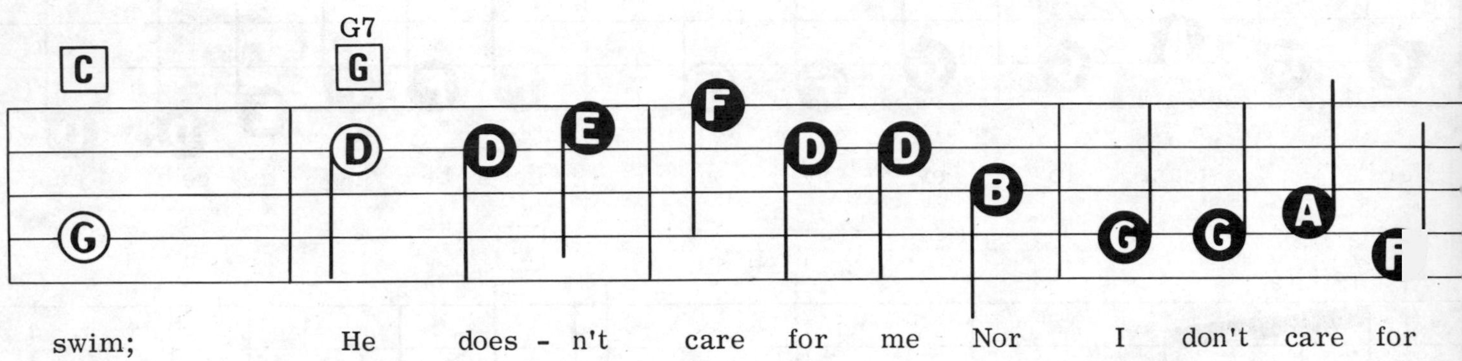

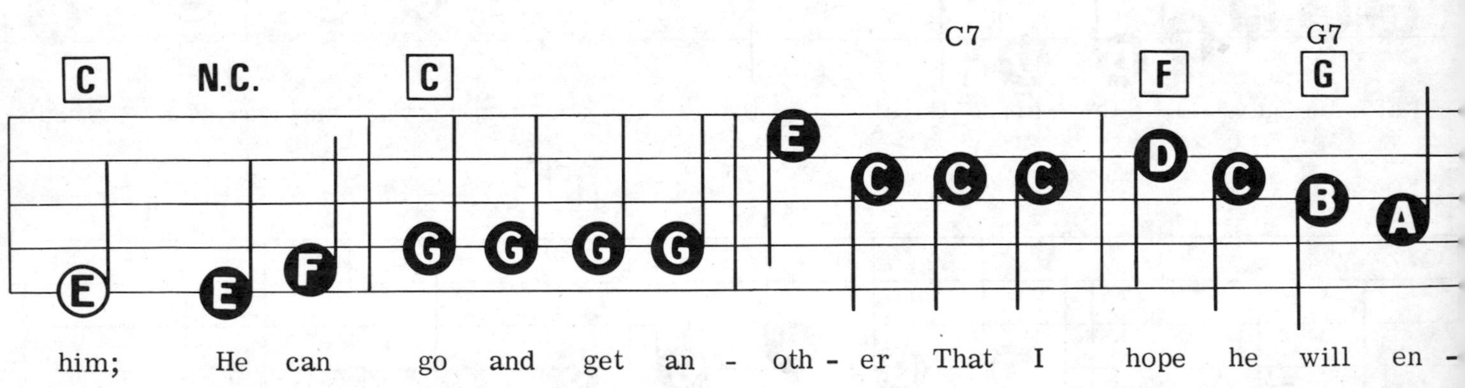

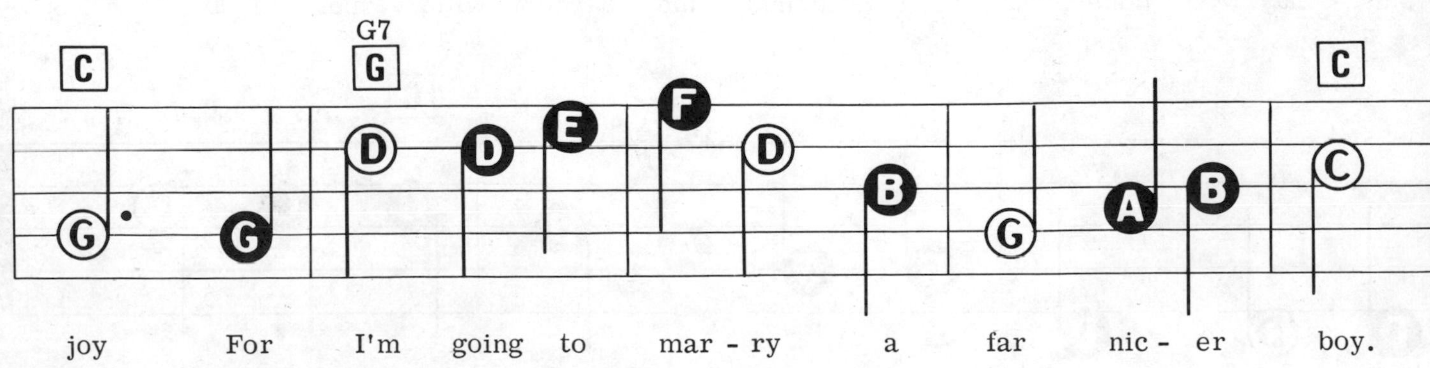

Marianne

Registration 4

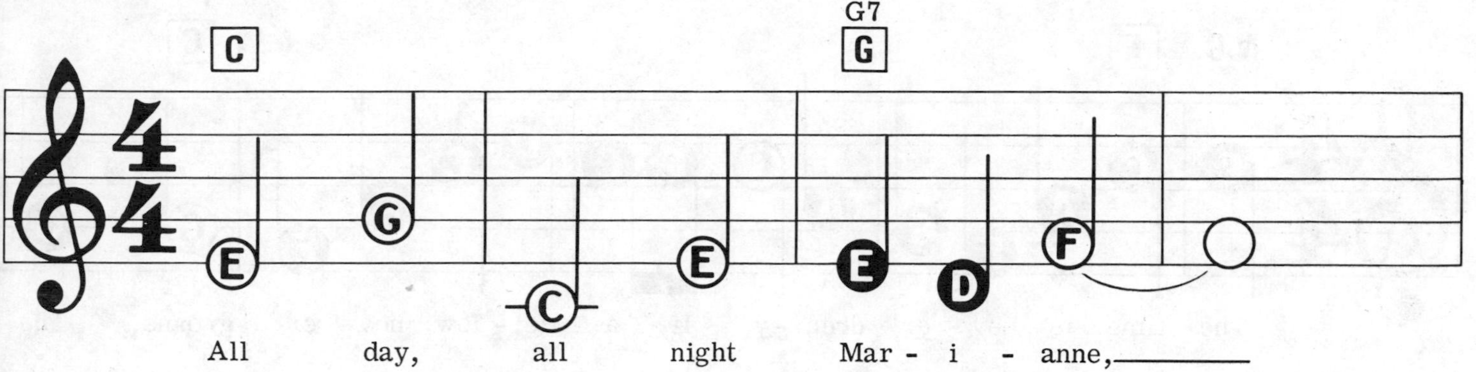

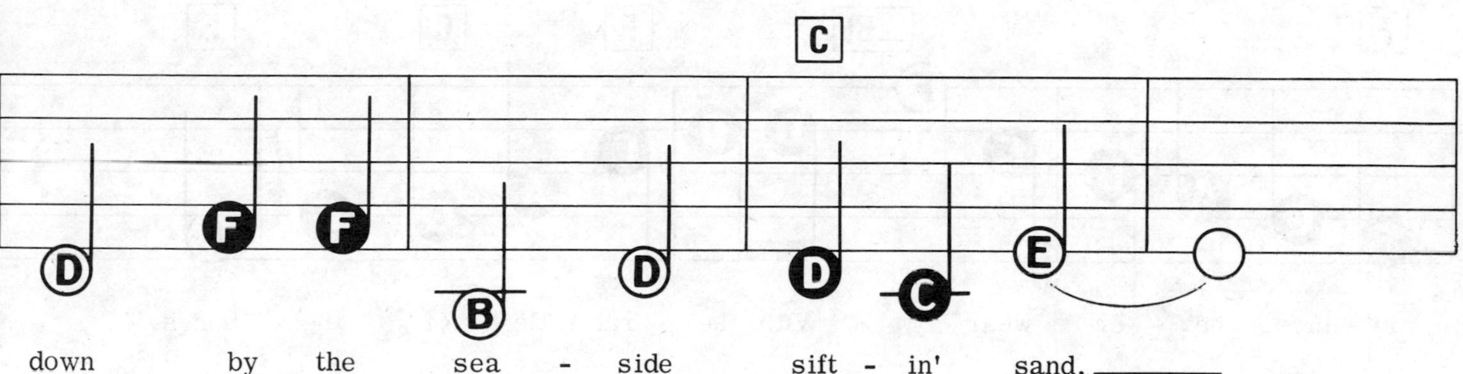

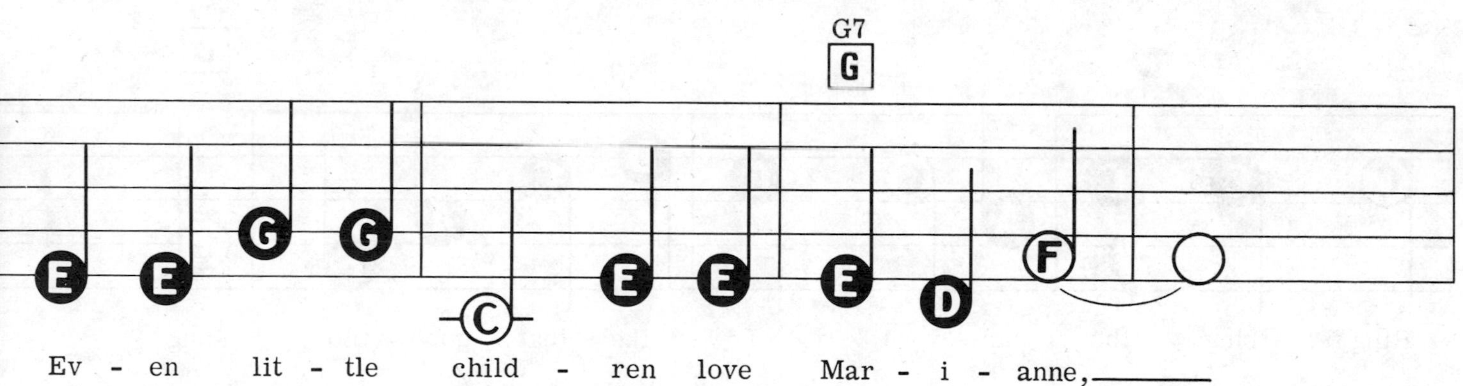

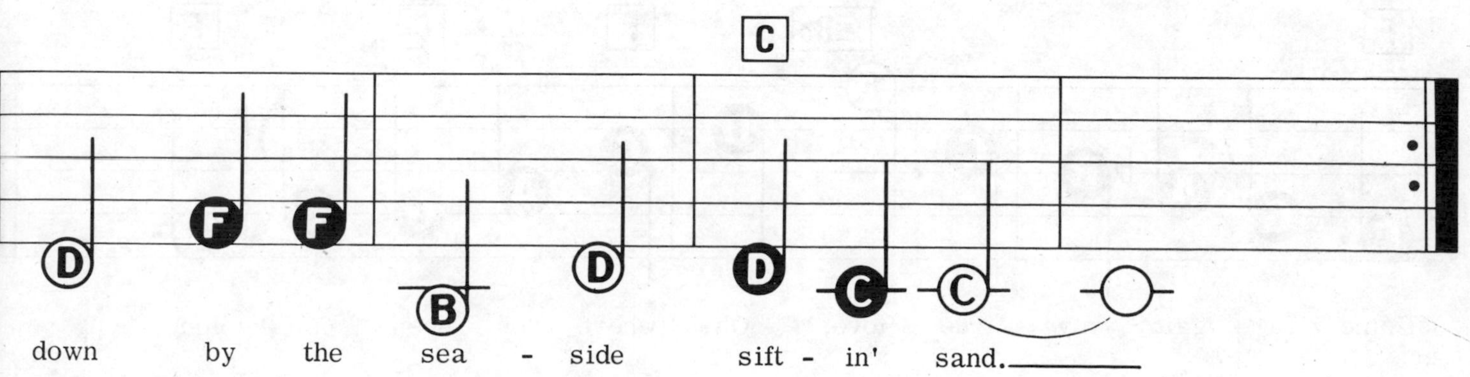

Ring, Ring The Banjo

Registration 3

American

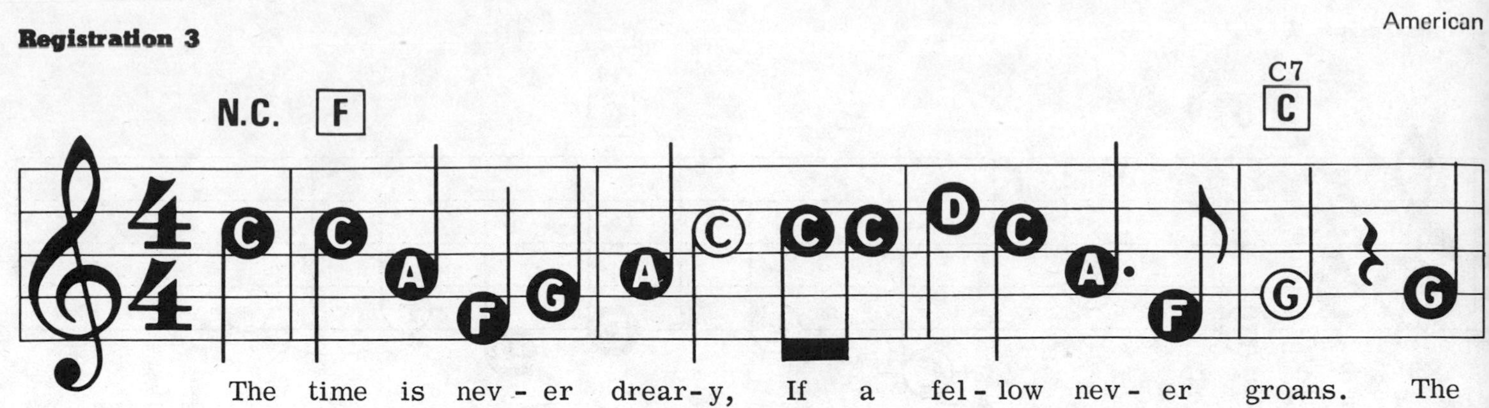

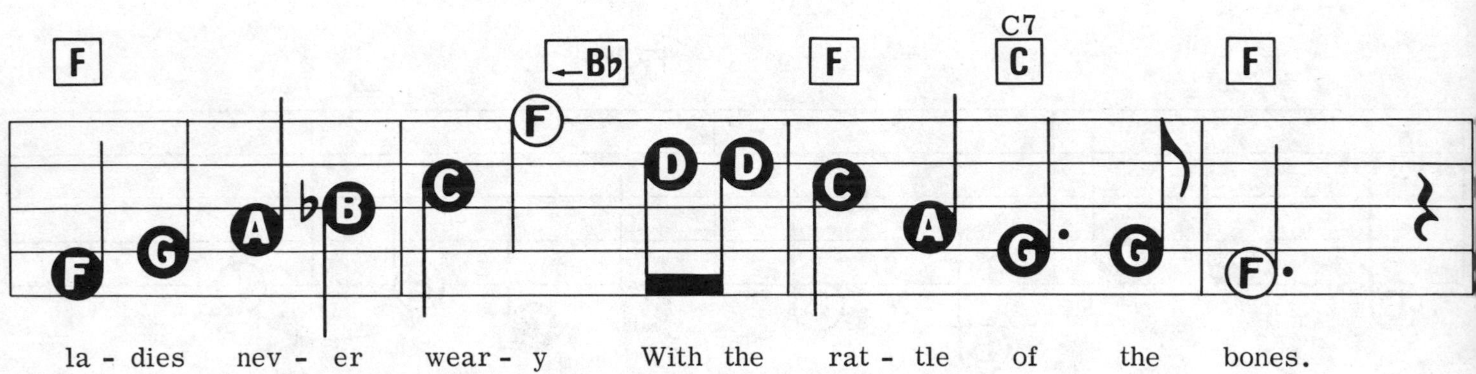

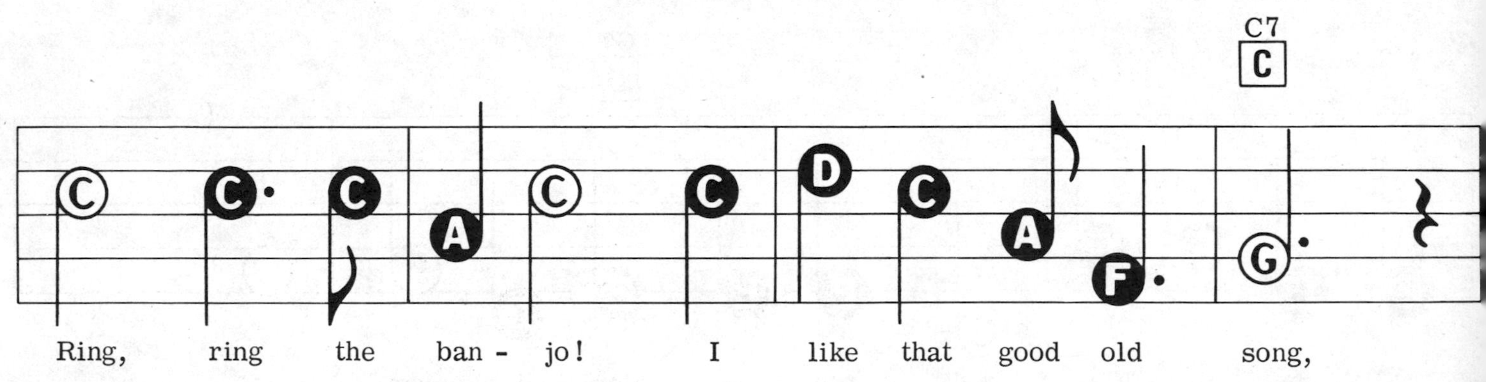

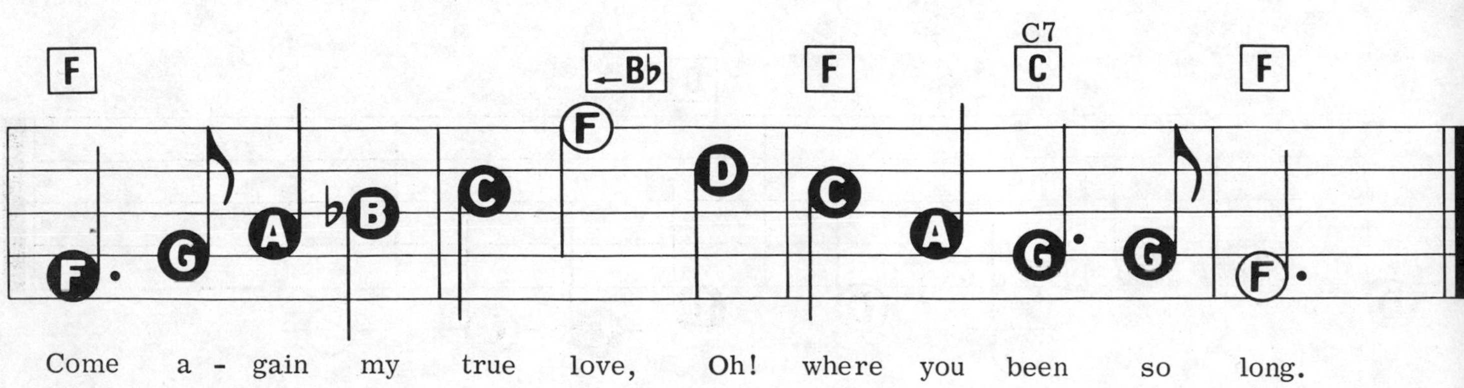

Ballet Music

Registration 3

Franz Schubert

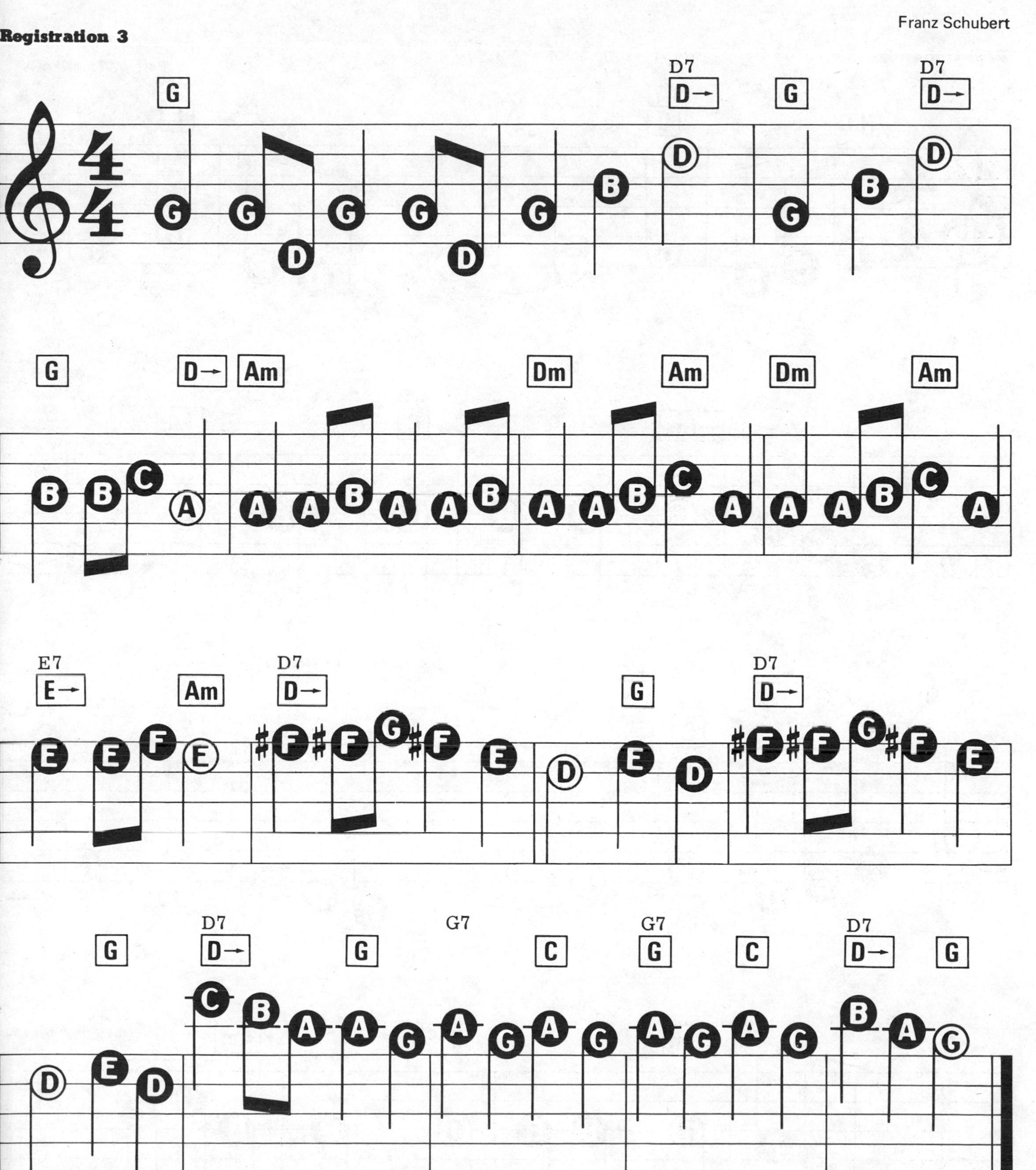

Andante Cantabile

Registration 6

Peter I. Tschaikowsky

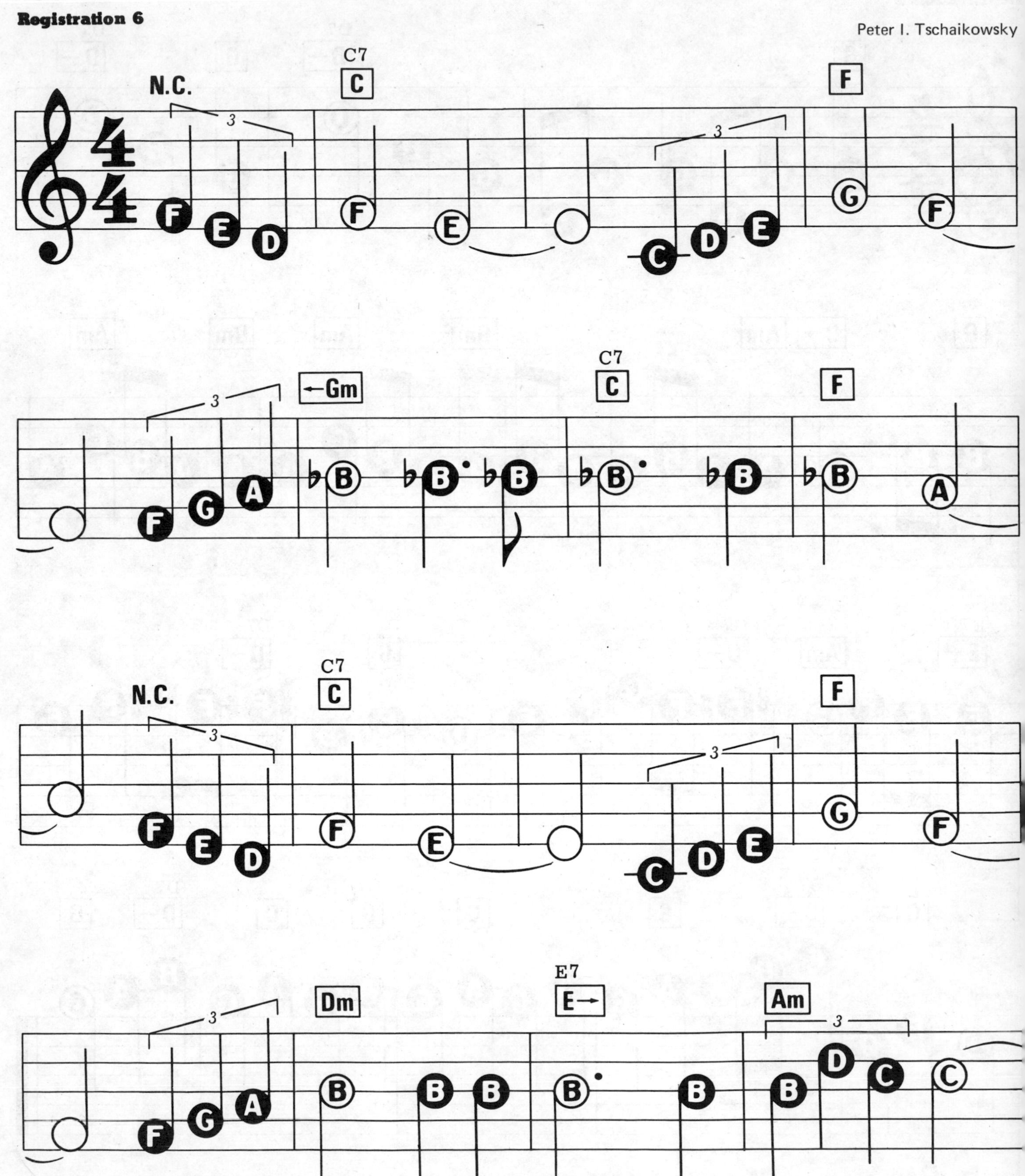

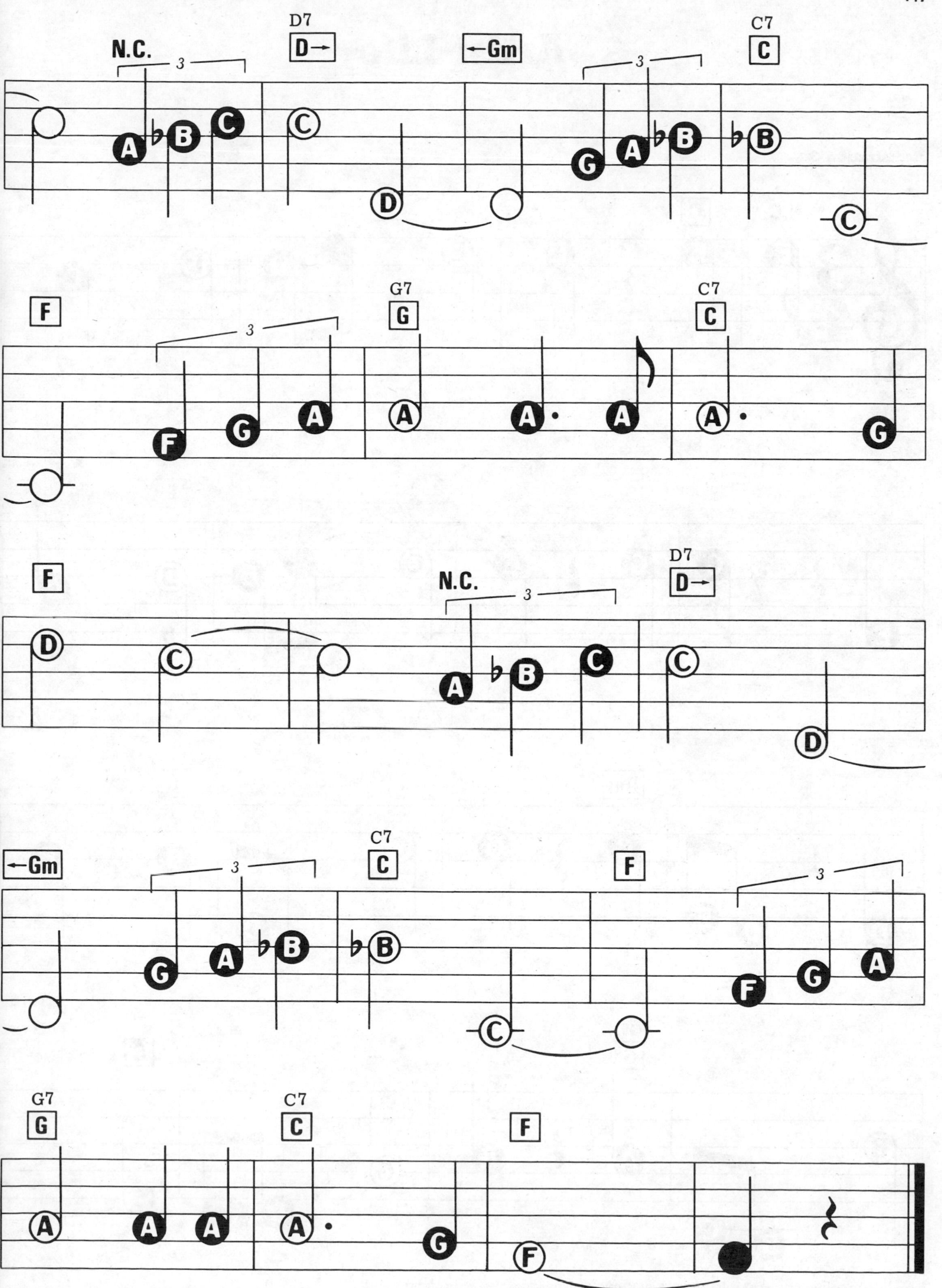
N.C.
D7
D→
←Gm
C7
C
F
G7
G
C7
C
F
N.C.
D7
D→
←Gm
C7
C
F
G7
G
C7
C
F

Artist Life

Registration 3

Johann Strauss

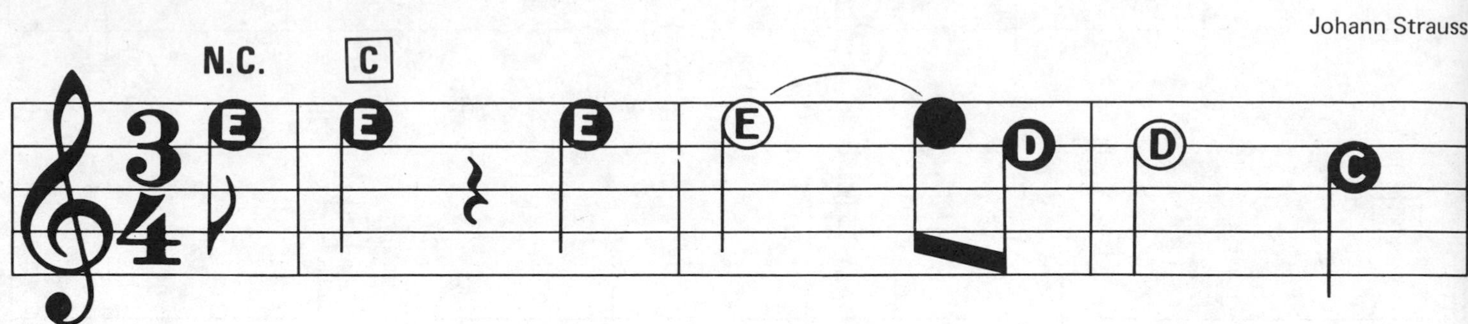

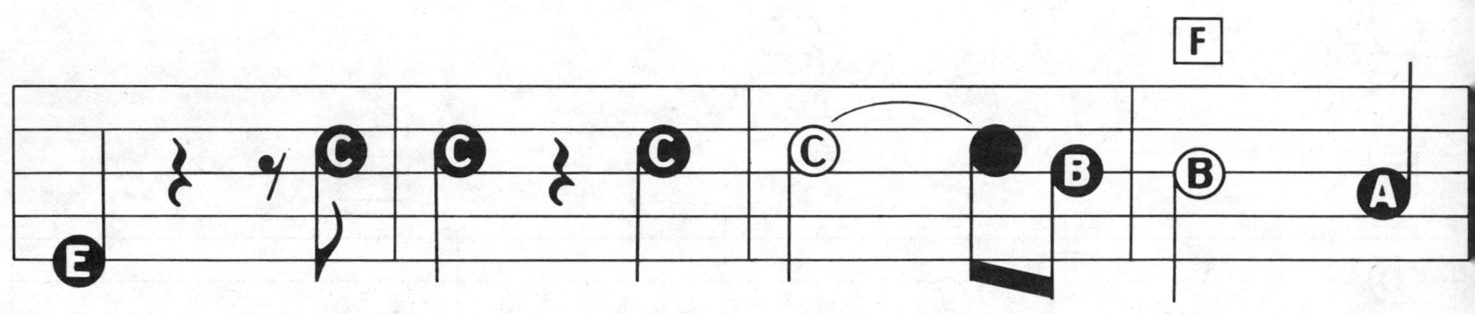

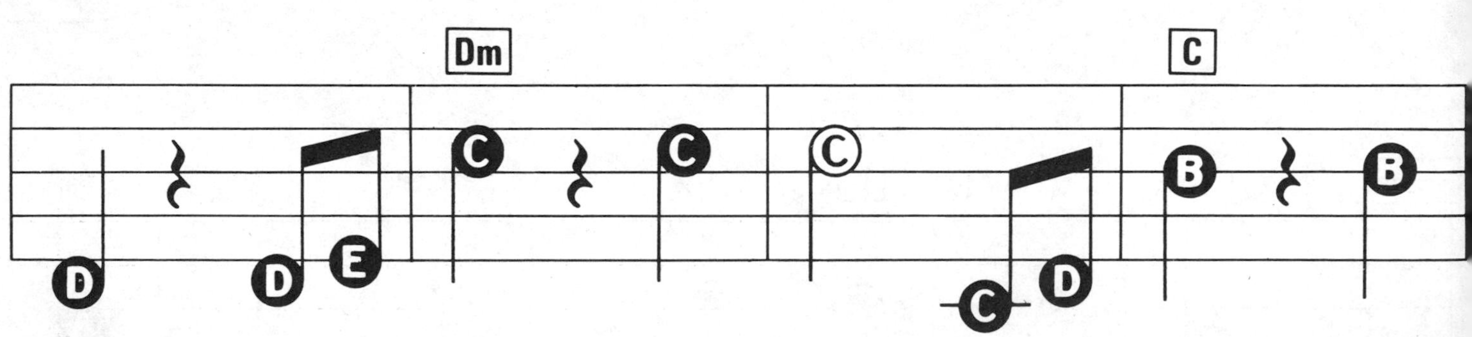

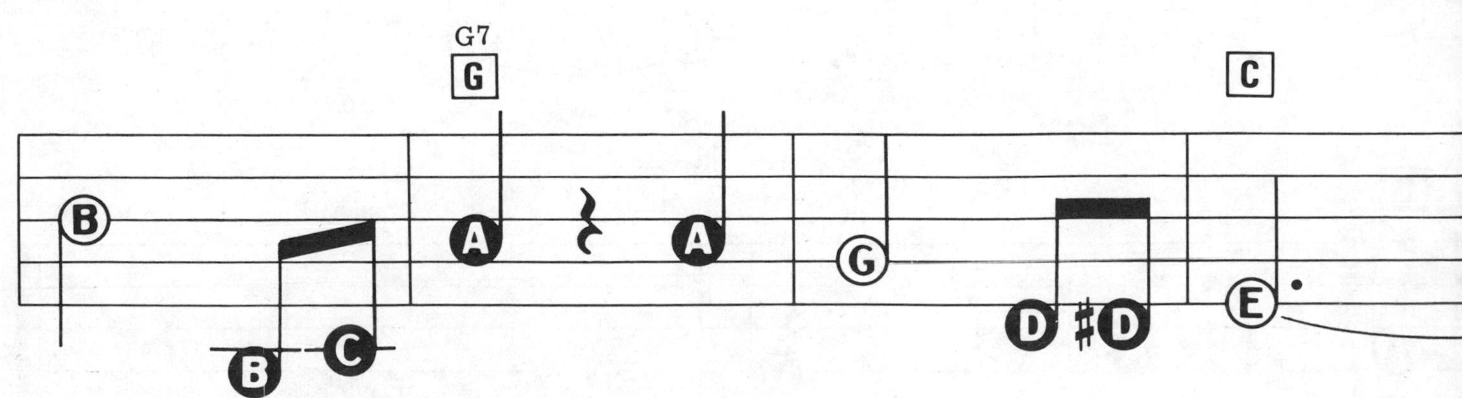

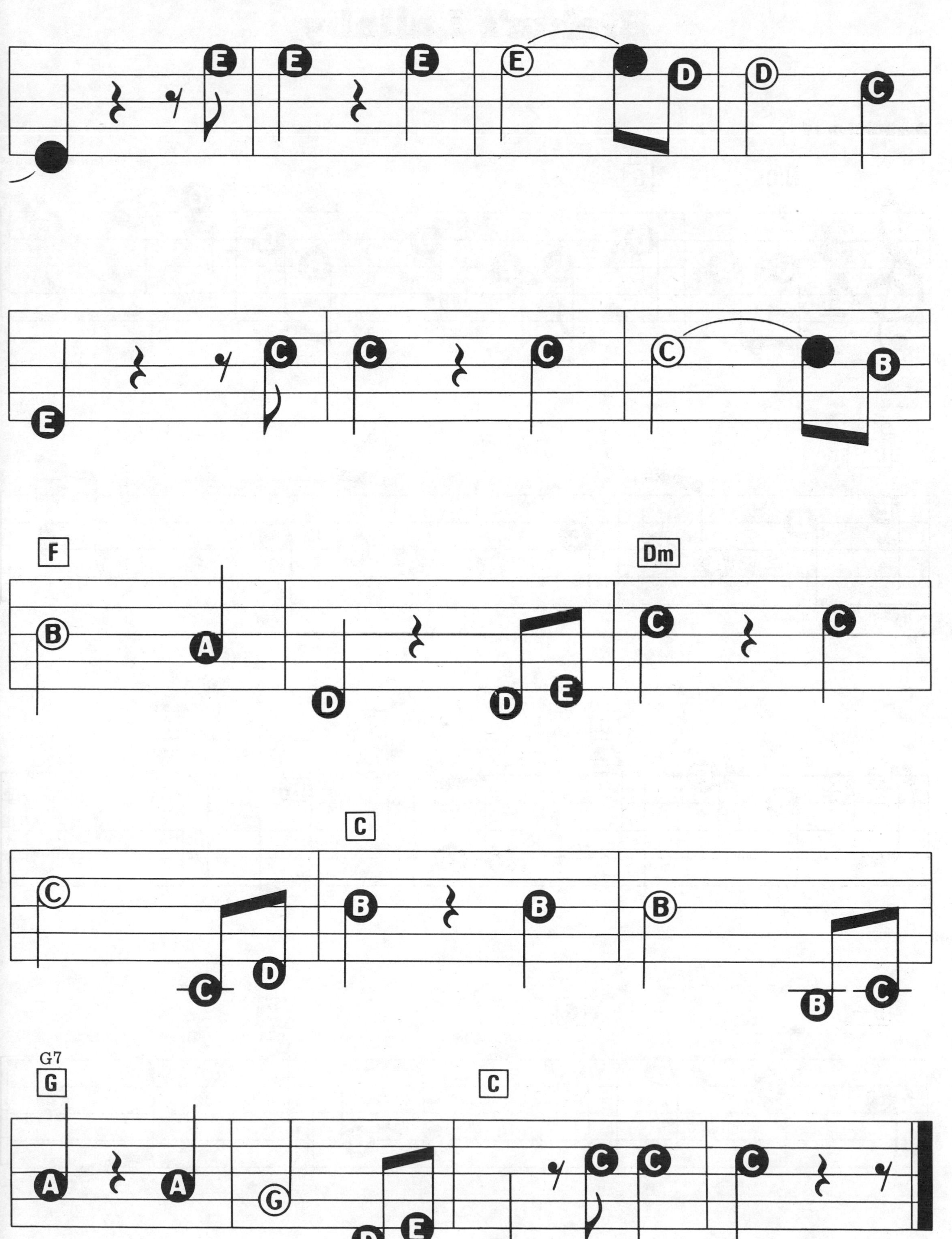
E E E E E D D C
E C C C C B
F
Dm
B A D D E C C
C
C D B B B B C
G7
G
C
A A G D E C C C C

Brahm's Lullaby

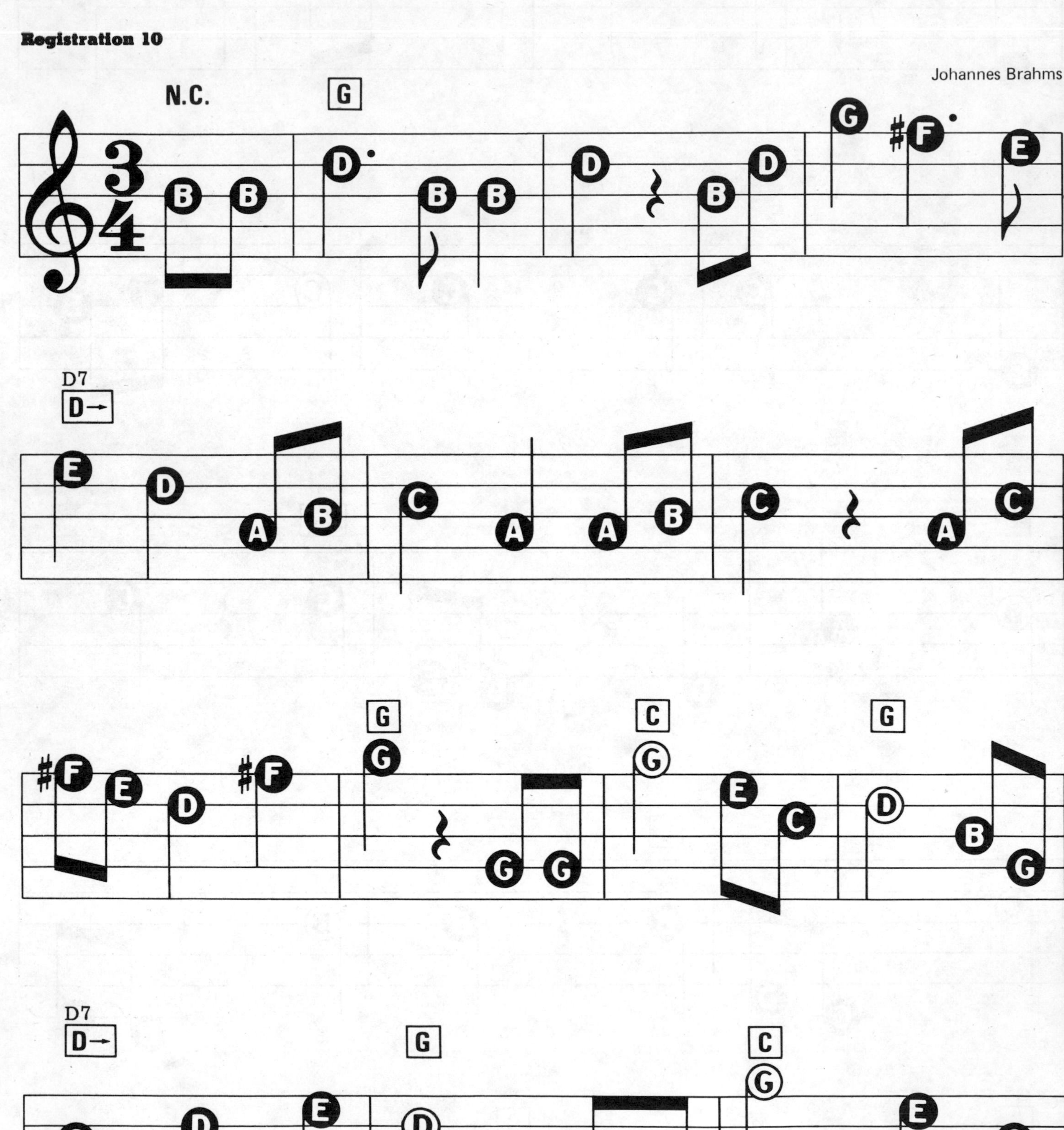

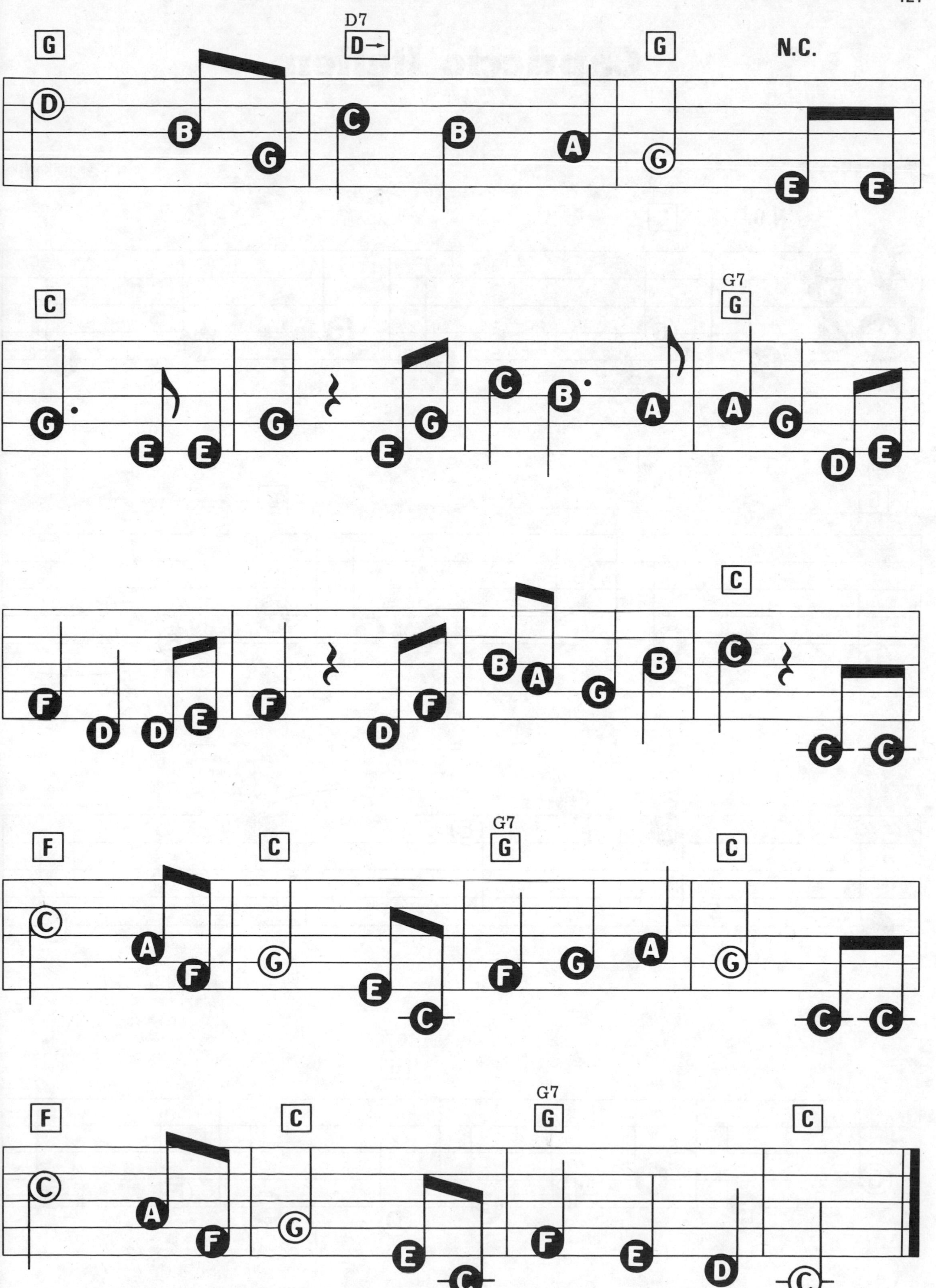
G
D7
D→
G
N.C.
D B G C B A G E E
C
G7
G
G E E G E G C B A A G D E
C
F D D E F D F B A G B C C C
F
C
G7
G
C
C A F G E C F G A G C C
F
C
G7
G
C
C A F G E C F E D C

Capriccio Italien

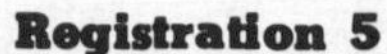

Peter I. Tschaikowsky

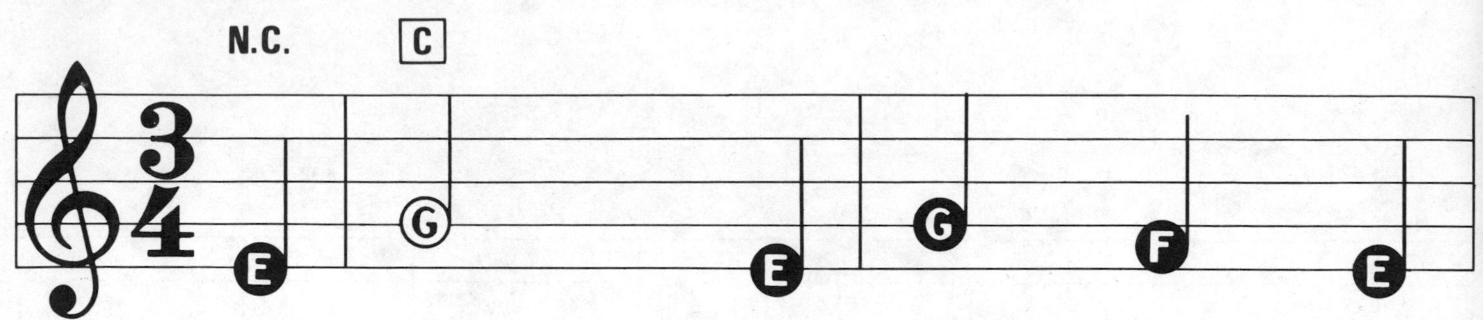

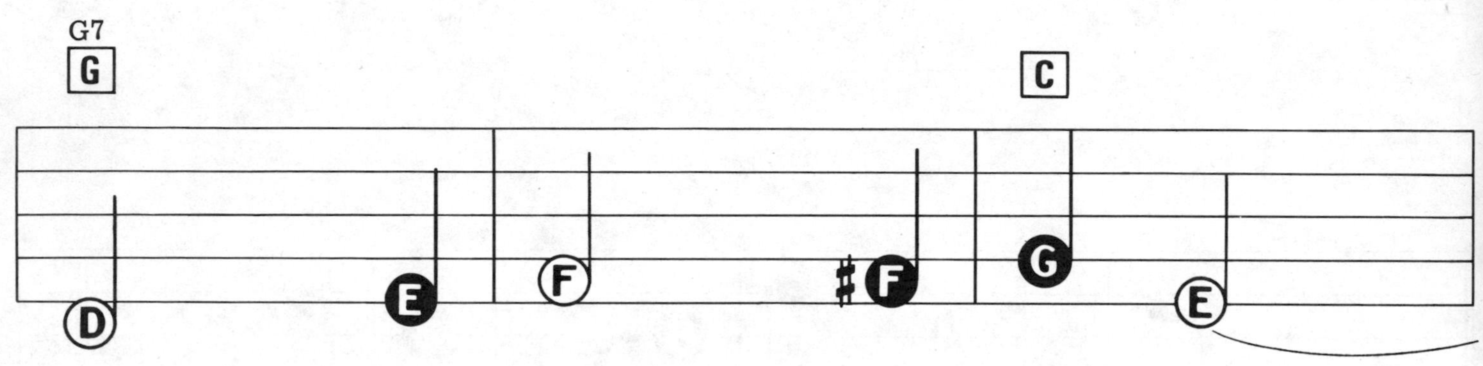

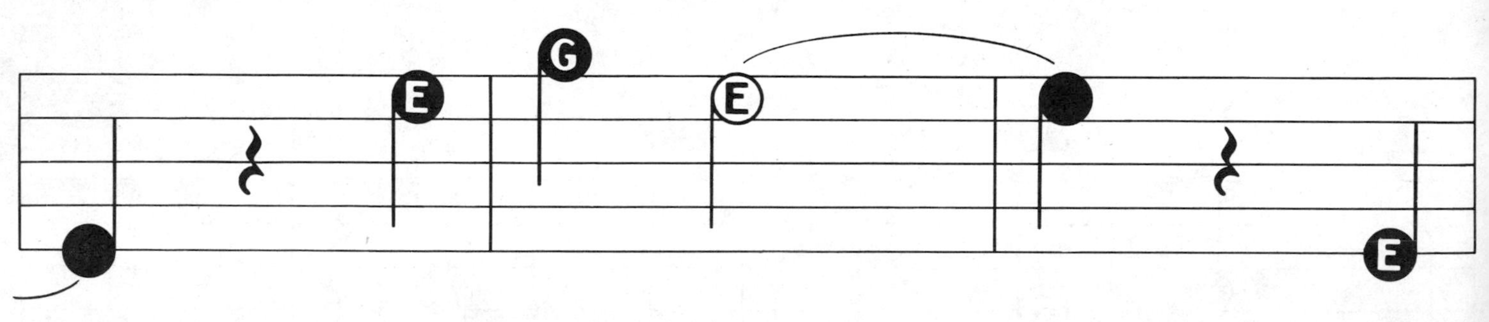

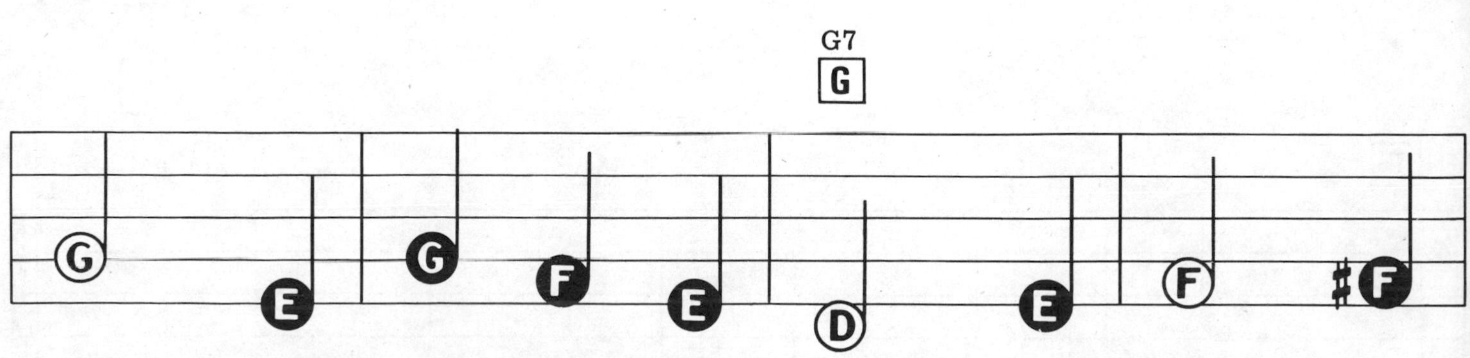

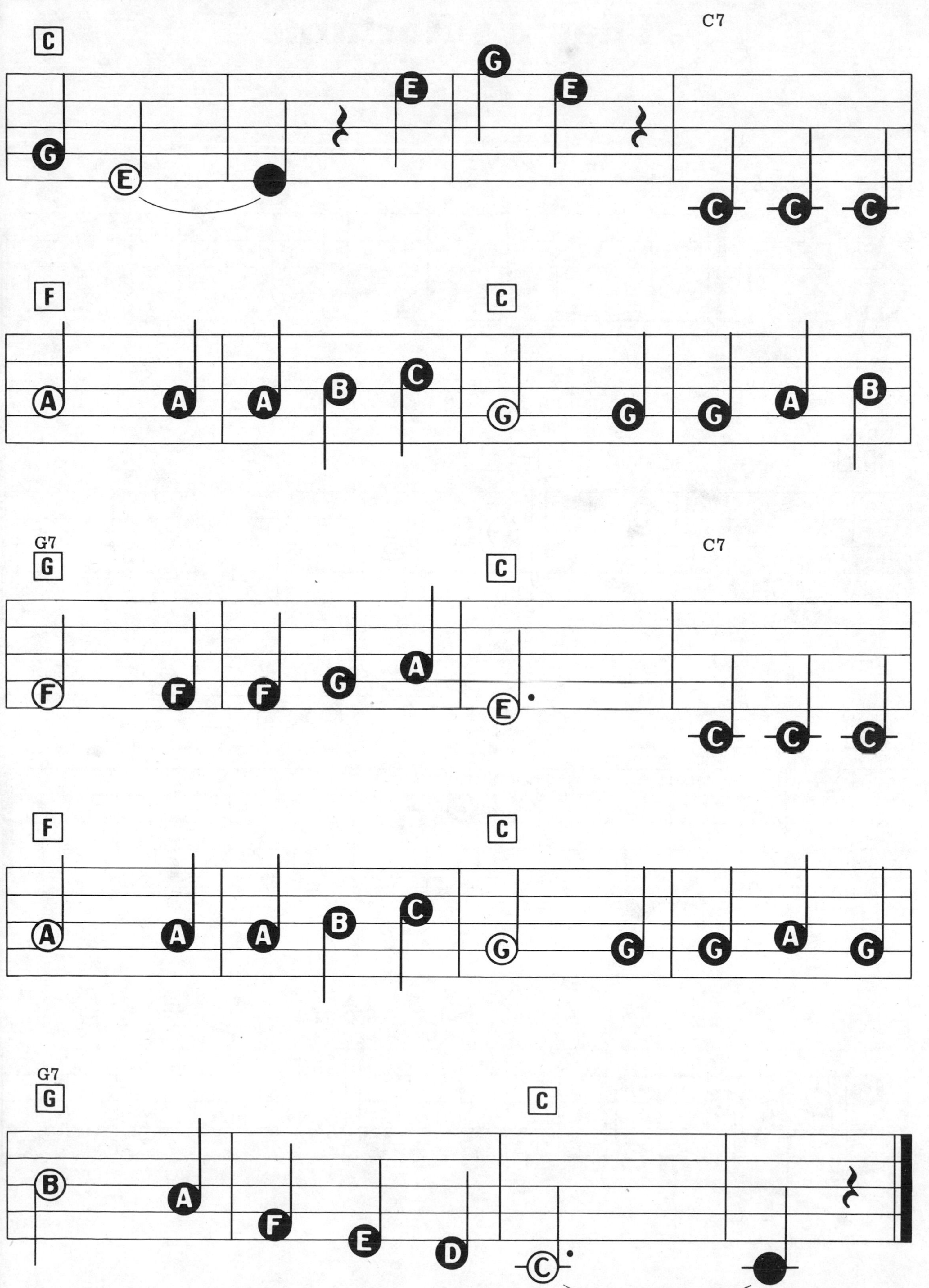
C
C7
G E E G E C C C
F
C
A A A B C G G G A B
G7
G
C
C7
F F F G A E C C C
F
C
A A A B C G G G A G
G7
G
C
B A F E D C

Chopin's Nocturne

Registration 6

Chopin

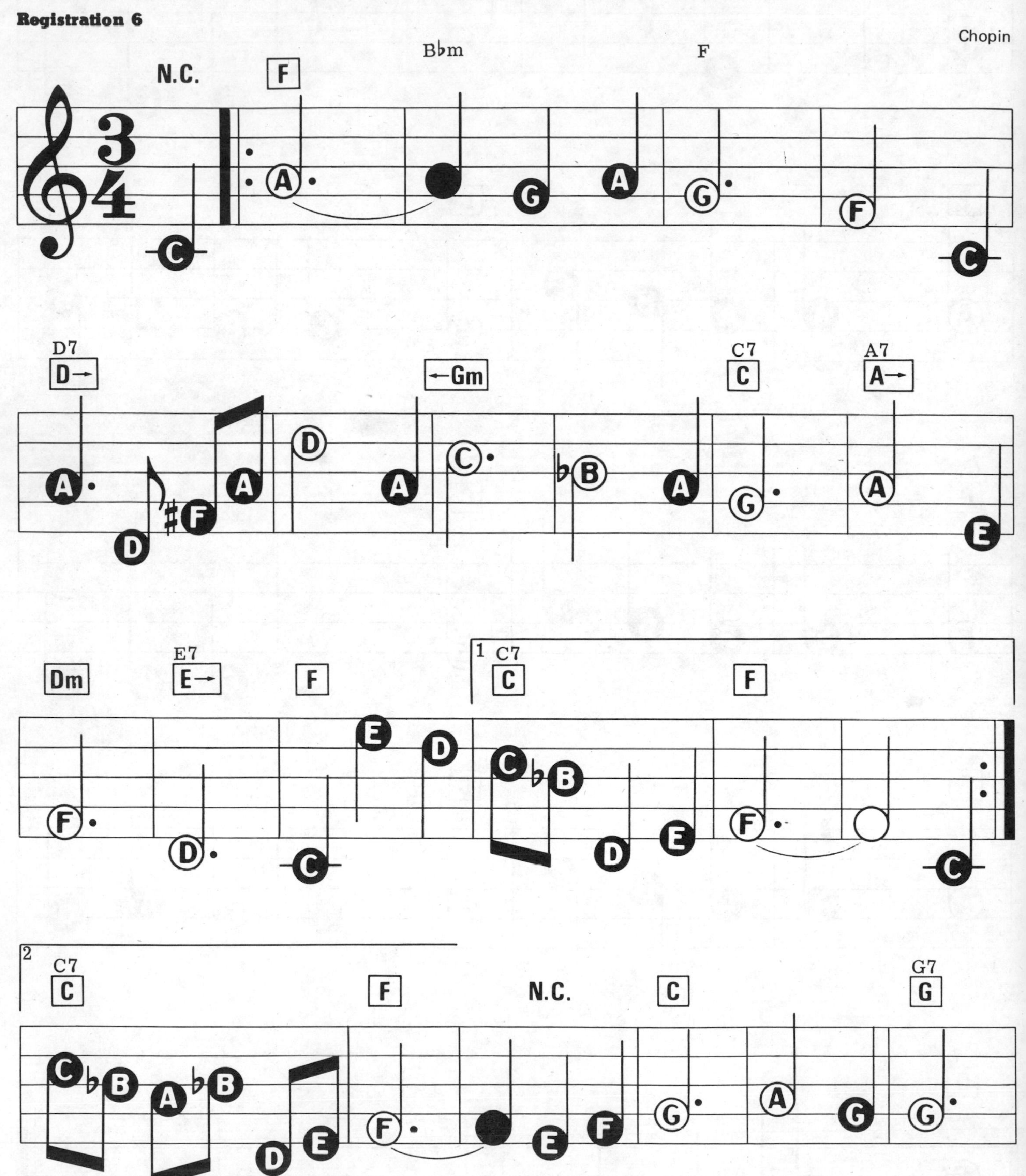

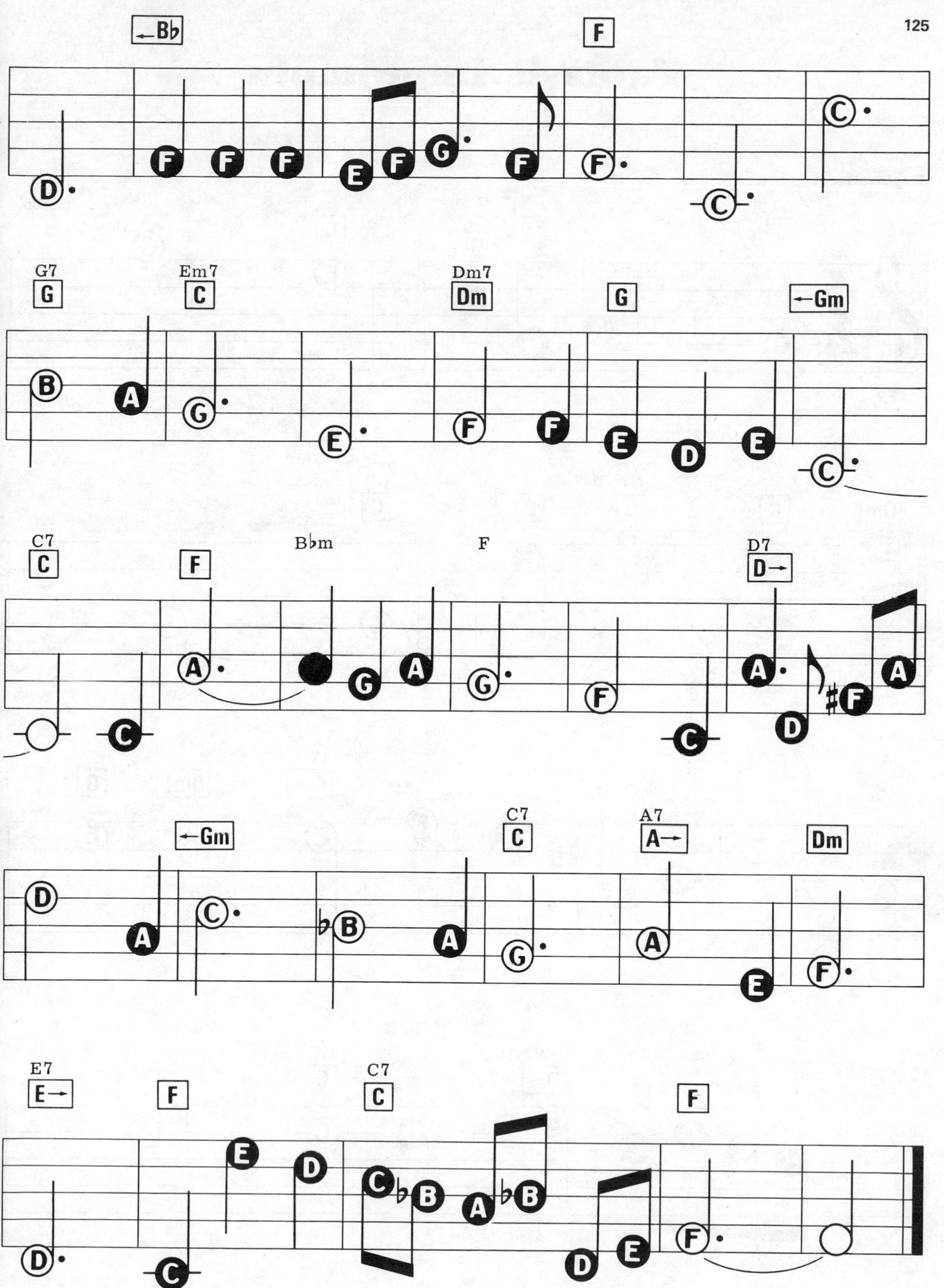
←B♭
F
G7
G
Em7
C
Dm7
Dm
G
←Gm
C7
C
F
B♭m
F
D7
D→
←Gm
C7
C
A7
A→
Dm
E7
E→
F
C7
C
F

Fantasie Impromptu

Registration 1

Frederic Chopin

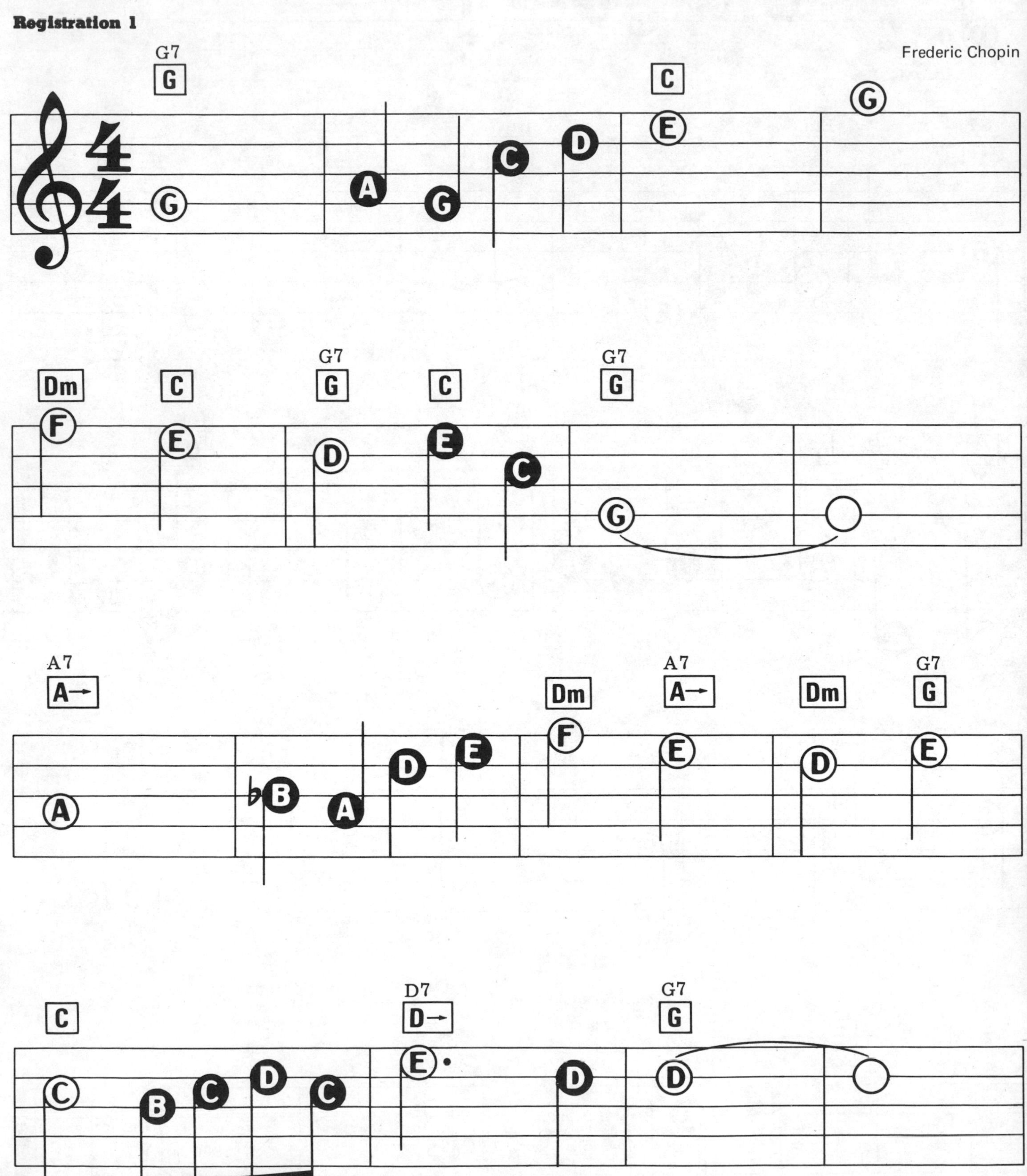

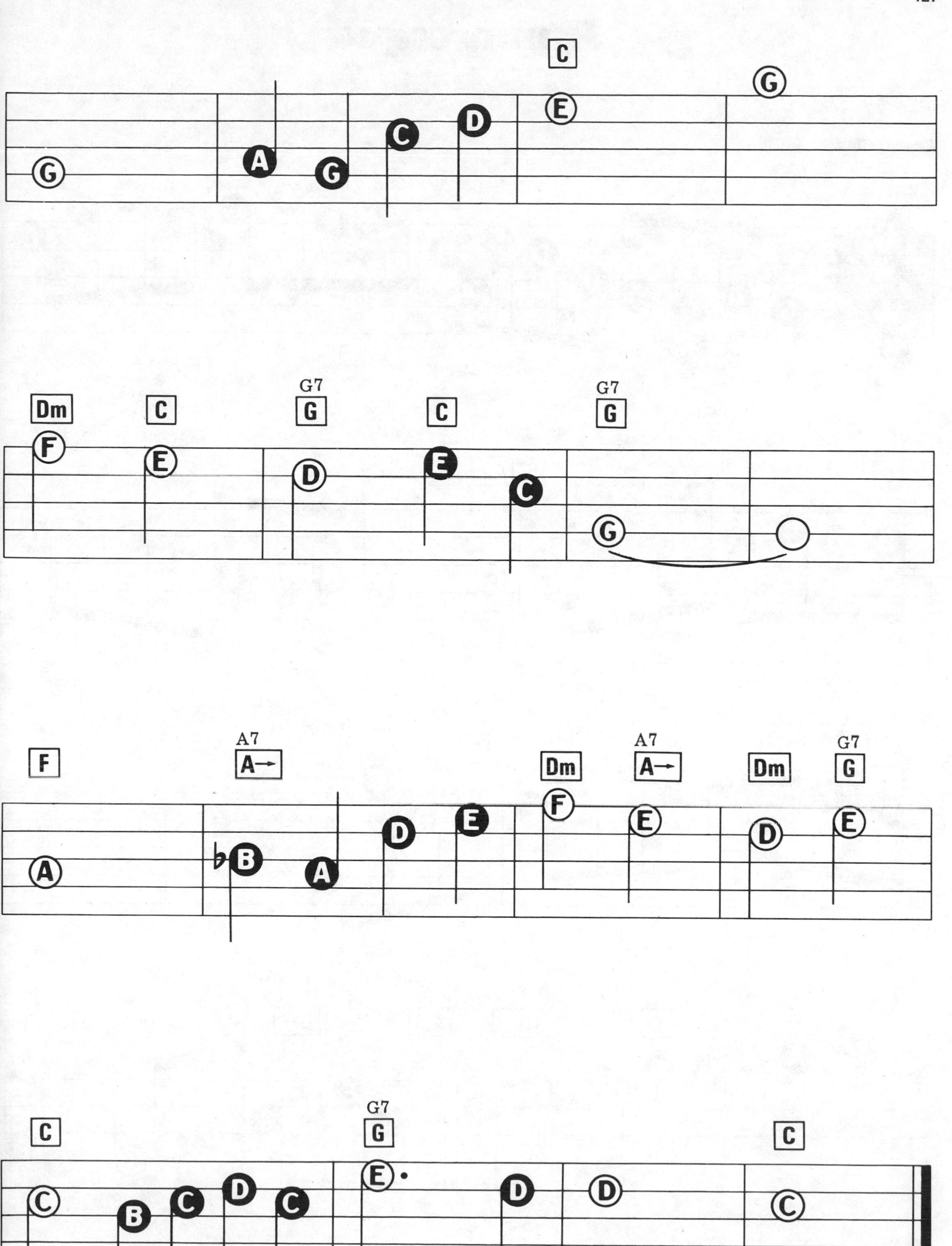
C
G
G A G C D E G
G7
G7
Dm C G C G
F E D E C G
A7
A7
G7
F A Dm A Dm G
A ♭B A D E F E D E
G7
C G C
C B C D C E D D C

Humoresque

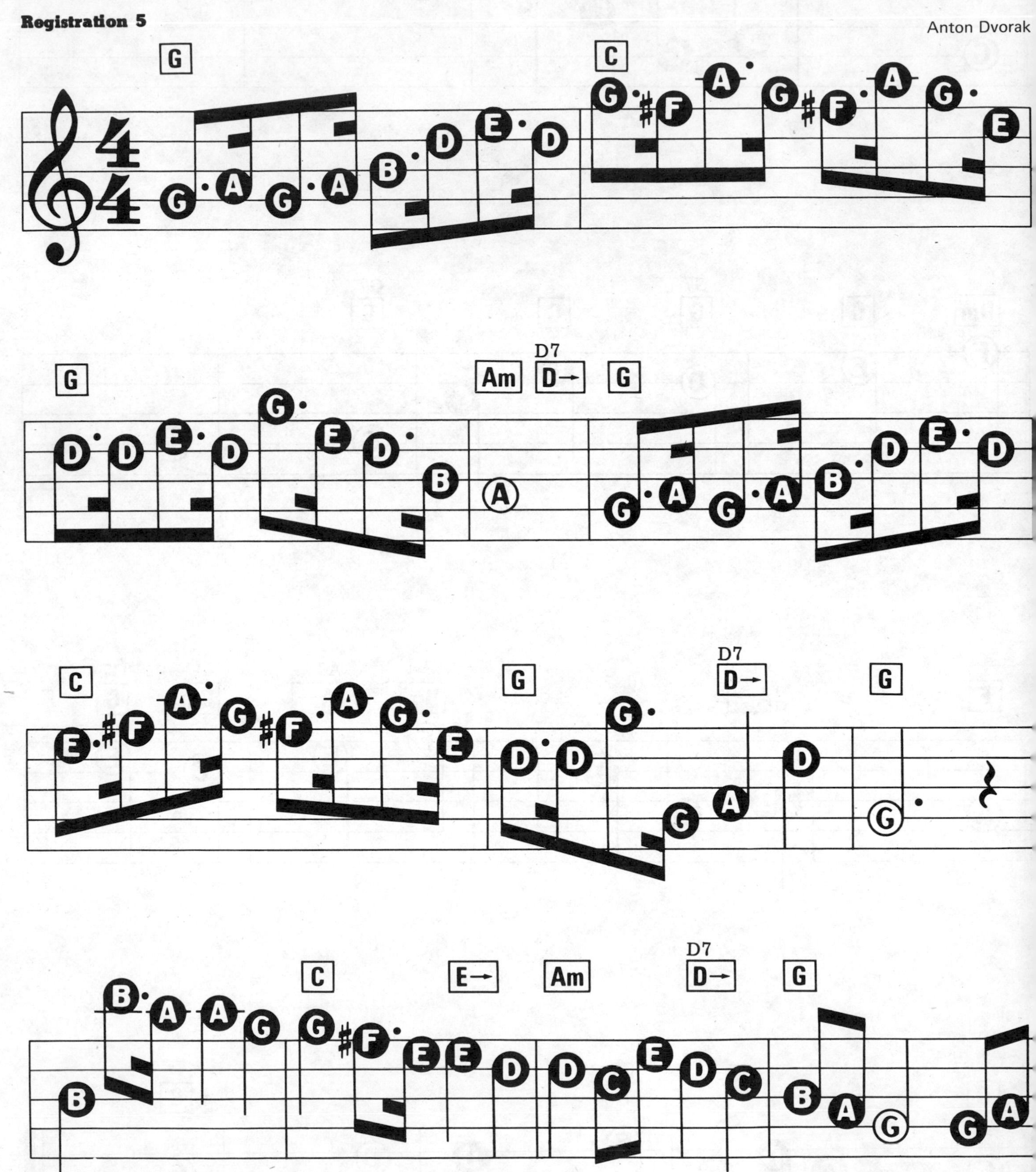

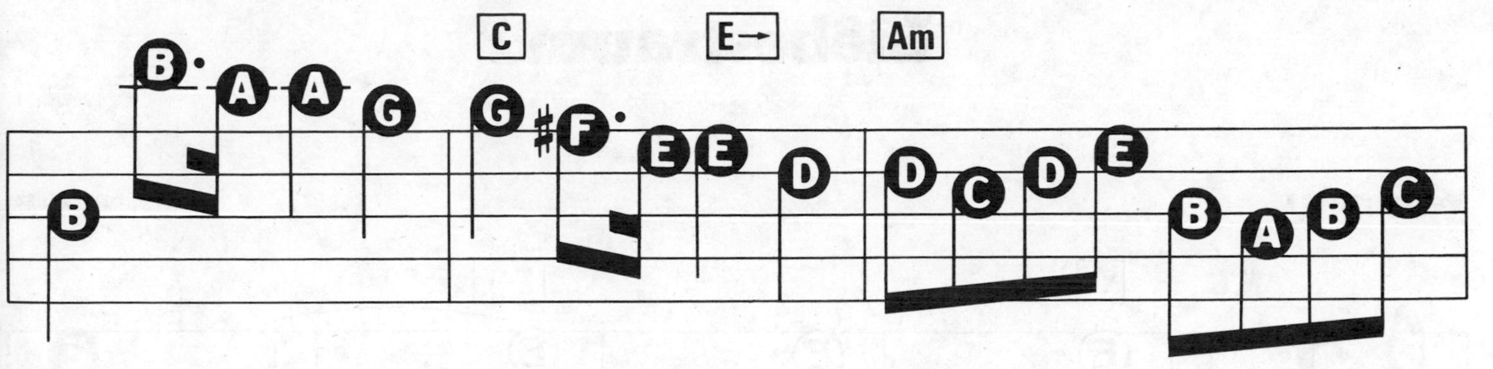
C
E→
Am

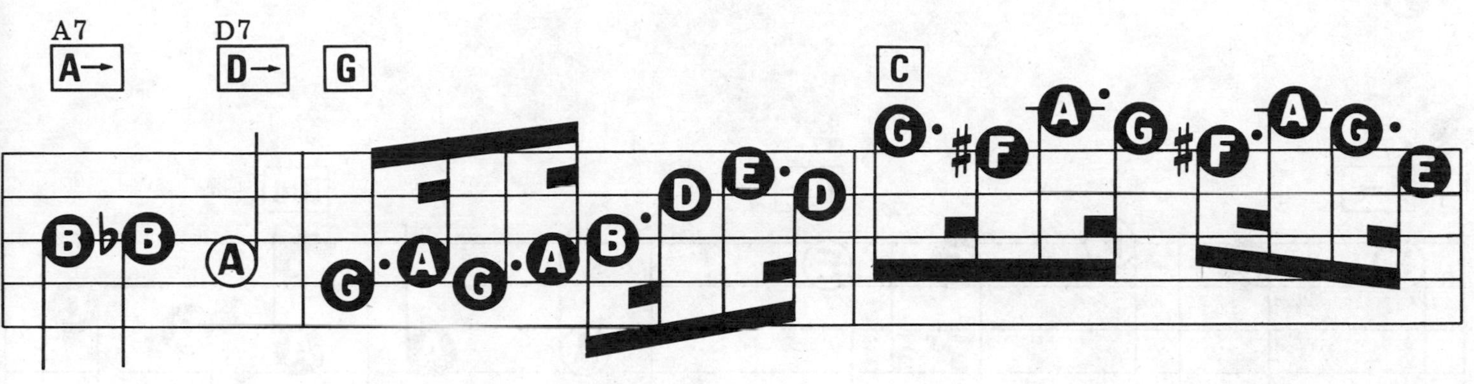
A7
A→
D7
D→
G
C

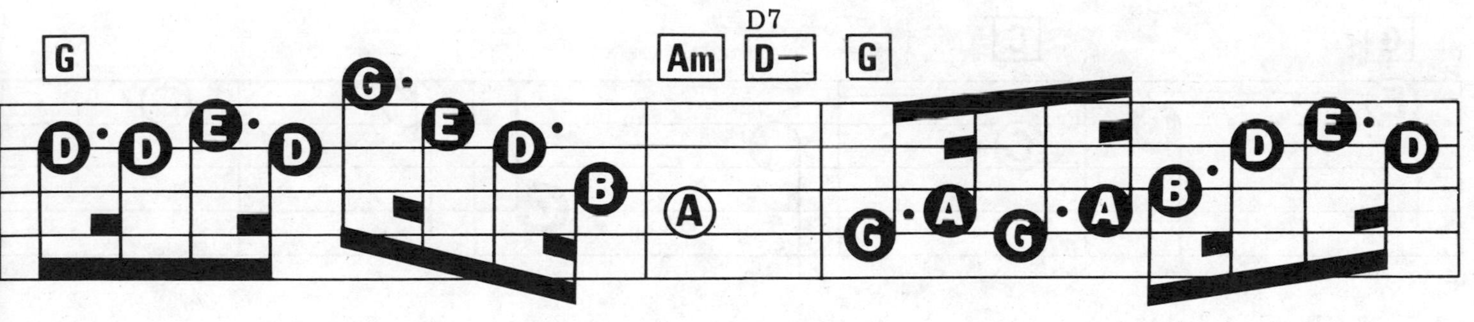
G
Am
D7
D→
G

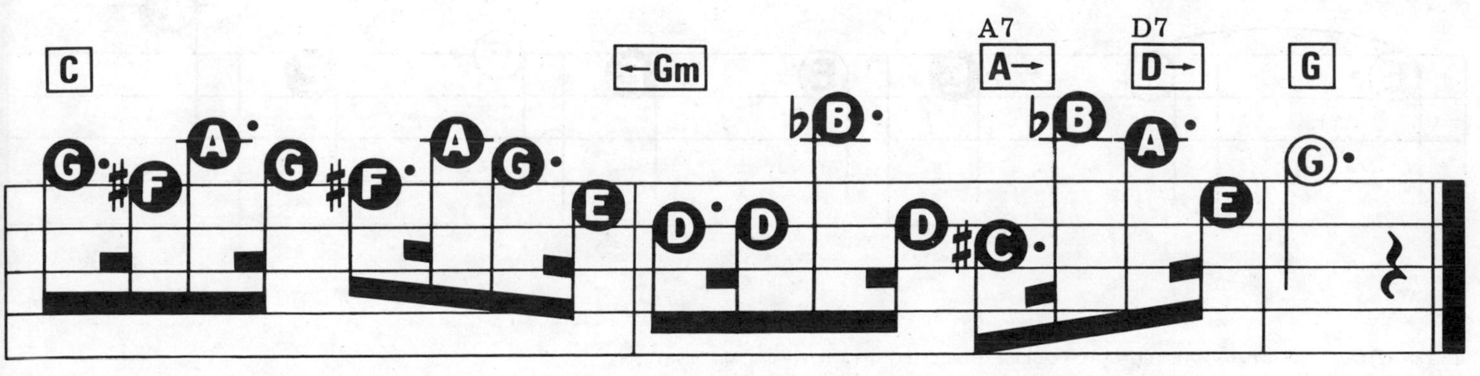
C
←Gm
A7
A→
D7
D→
G

Liebestraum

Registration 1

Franz Liszt

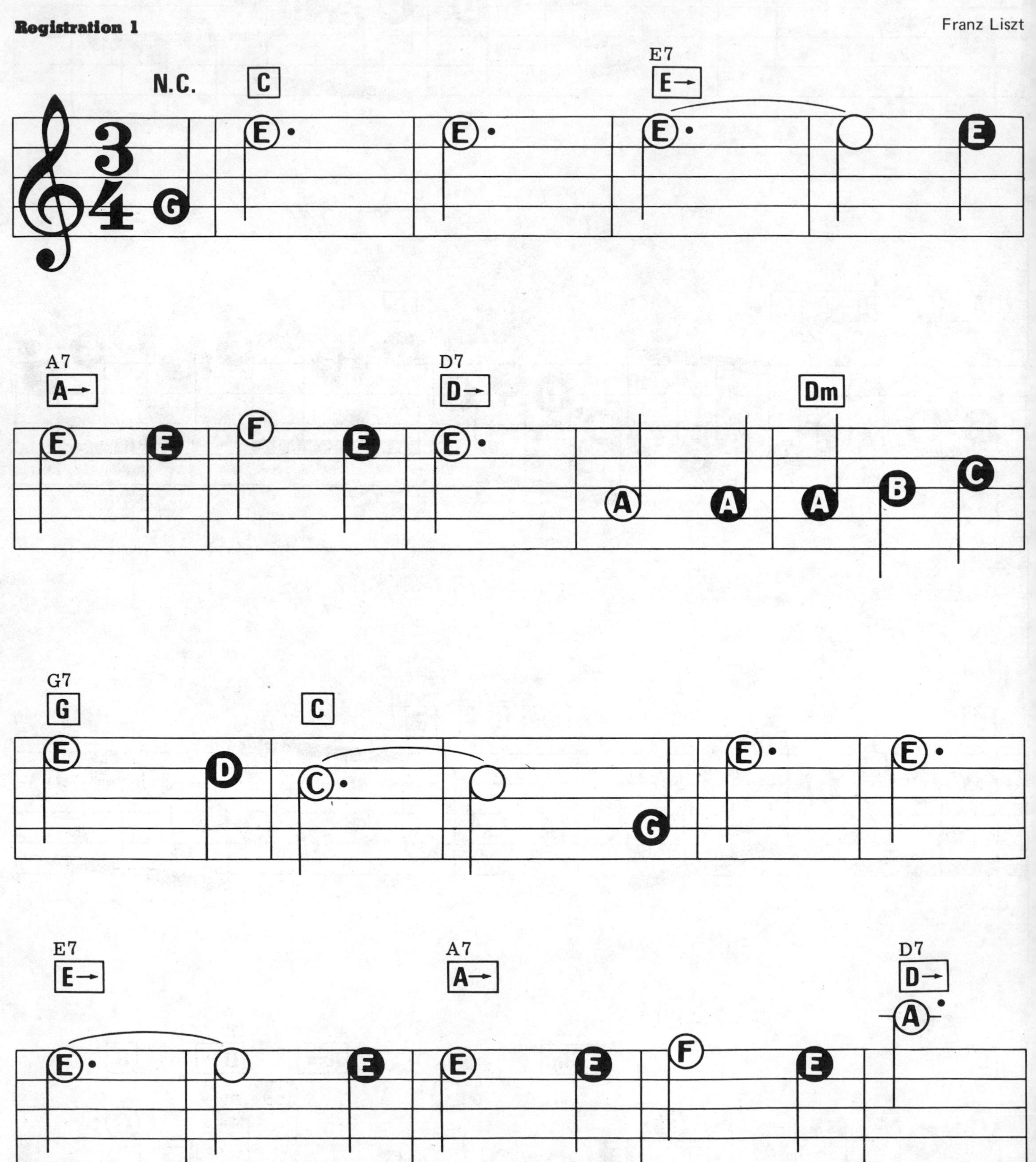

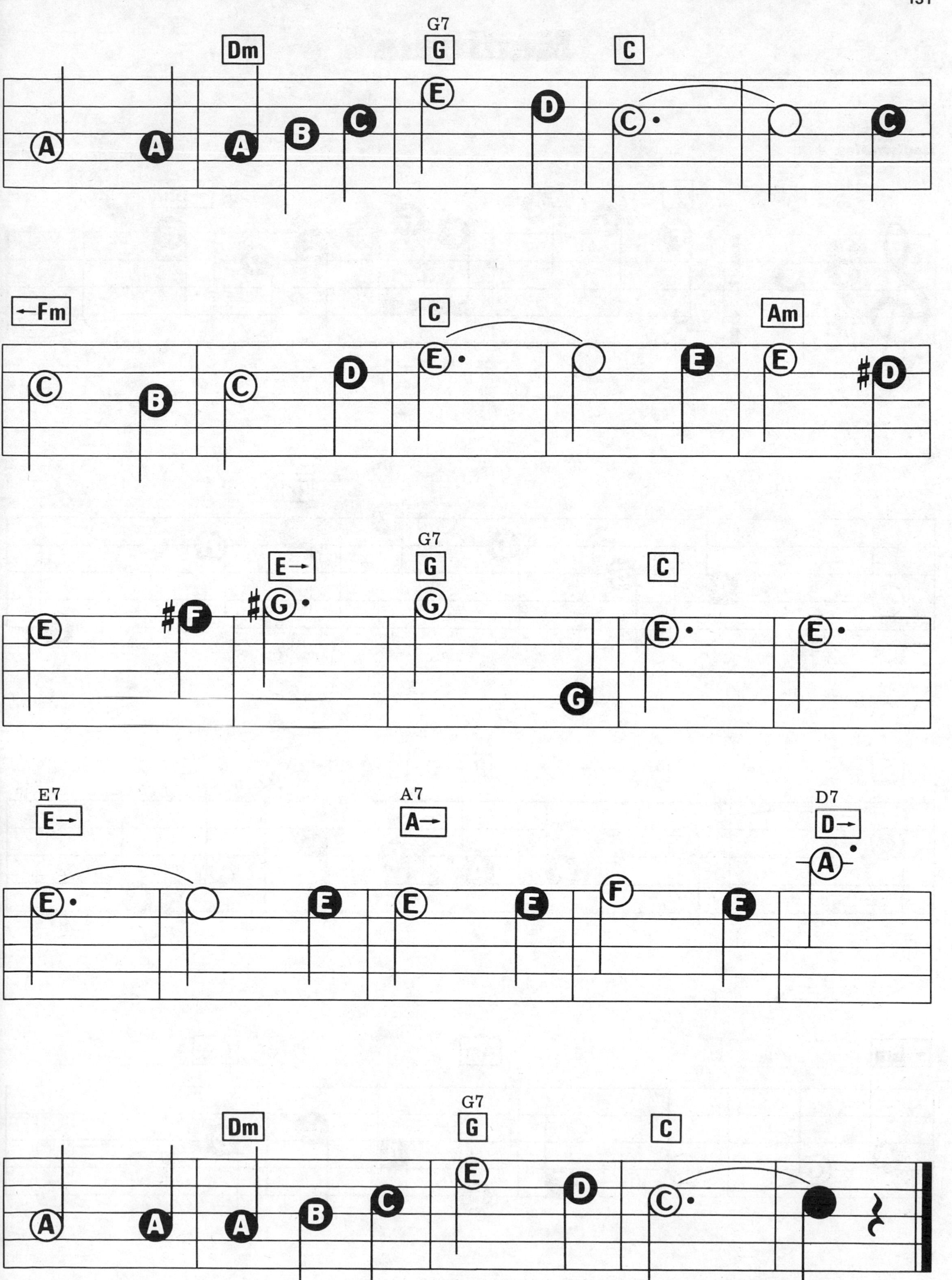
Dm G7 G C
A A A B C E D C C
←Fm C Am
C B C D E E E ♯D
E→ G7 G C
E ♯F ♯G G G E E
E7 E→ A7 A→ D7 D→
E E E E F E A
Dm G7 G C
A A A B C E D C

Mattinata

Registration 4

Ruggiero Leoncavallo

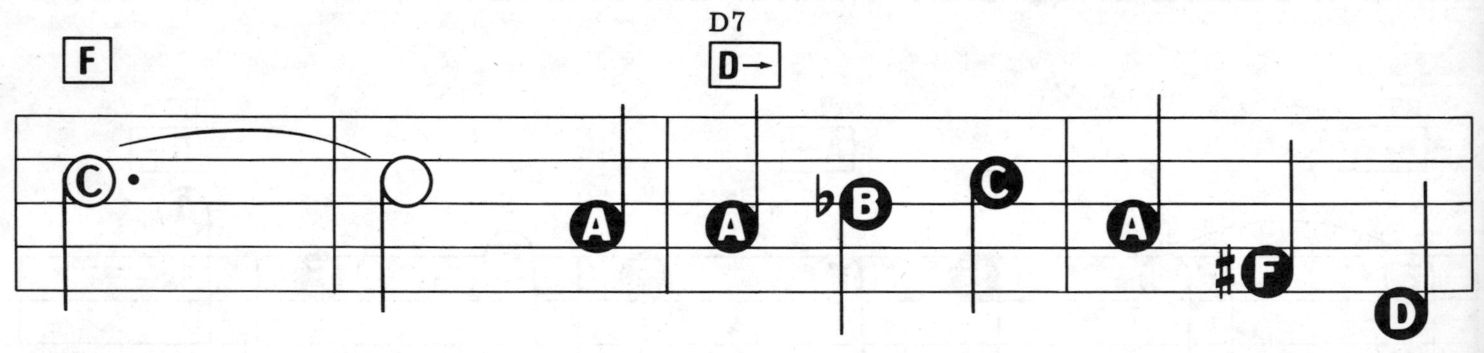

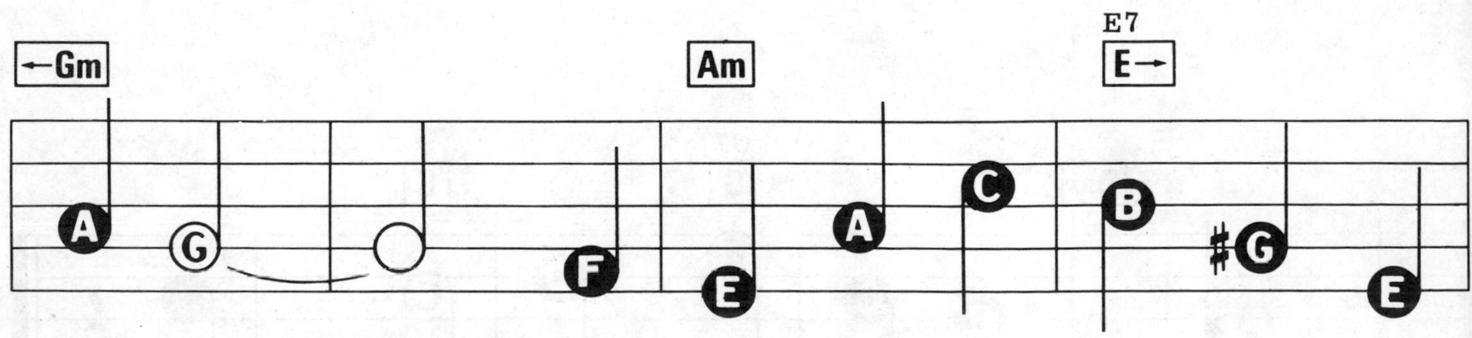

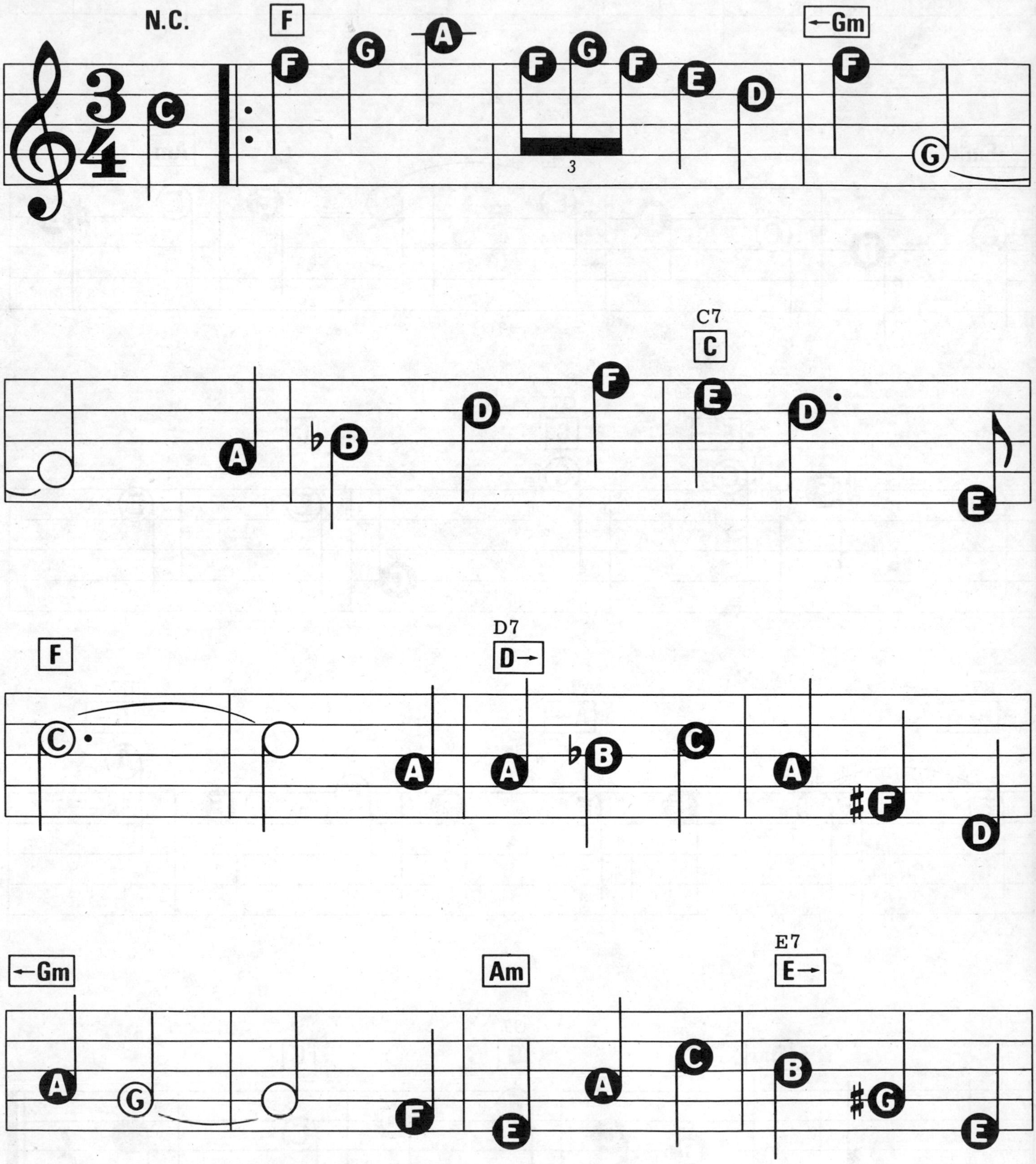

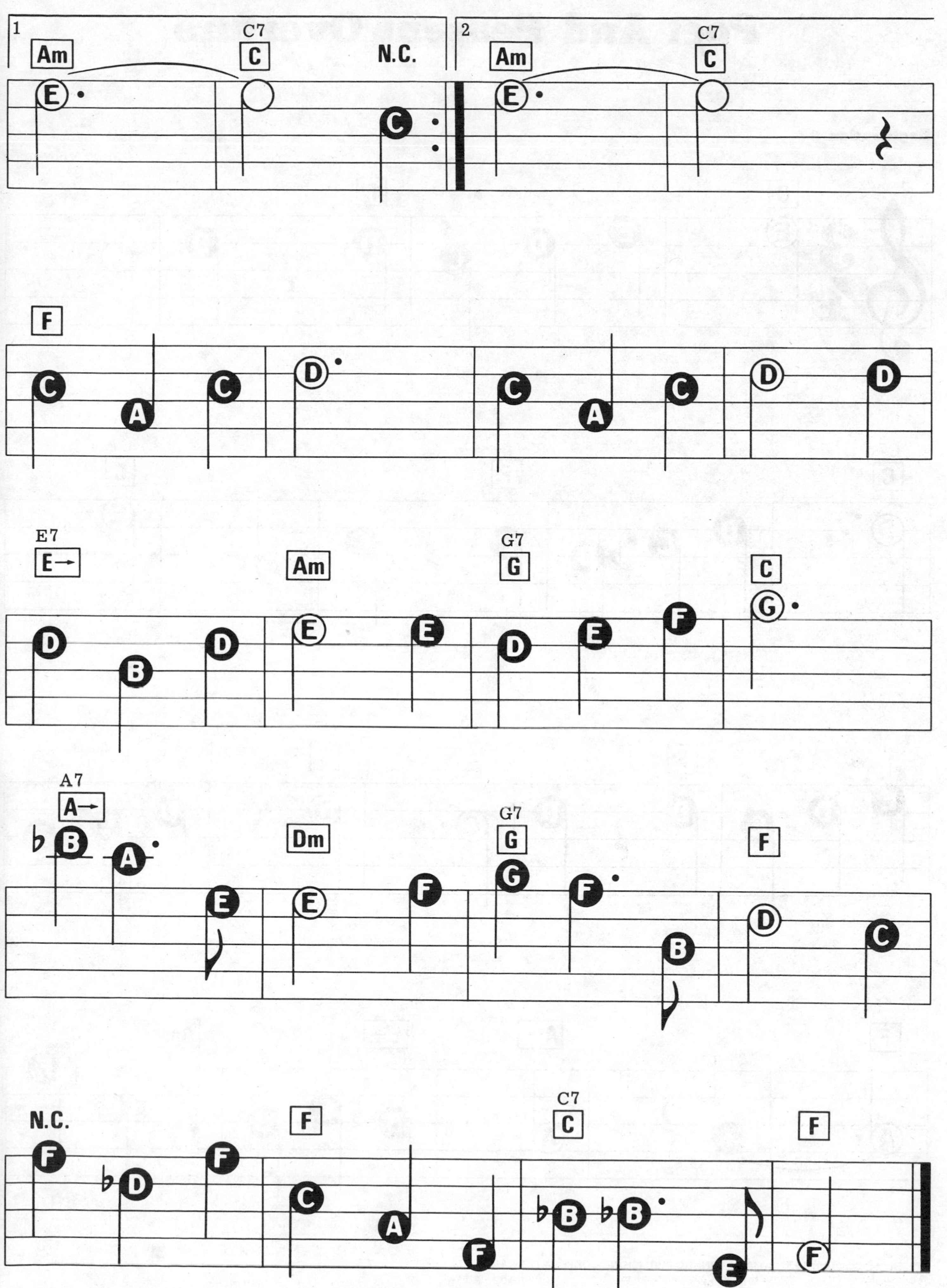
1
Am
C7
C
N.C.
2
Am
C7
C
F
E7
E→
Am
G7
G
C
A7
A→
Dm
G7
G
F
N.C.
F
C7
C
F

Poet And Peasant Overture

Registration 9

Franz Von Suppe

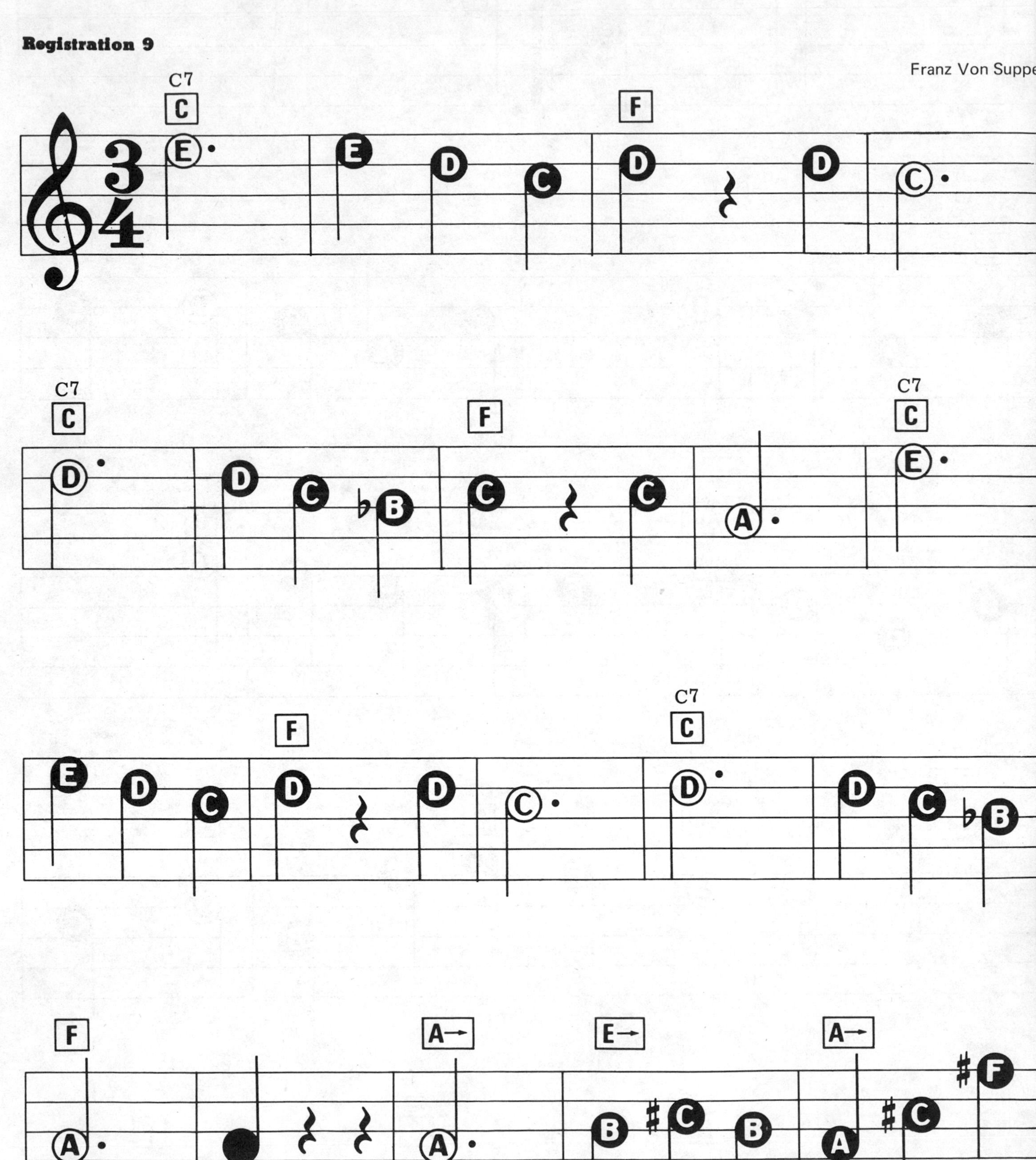

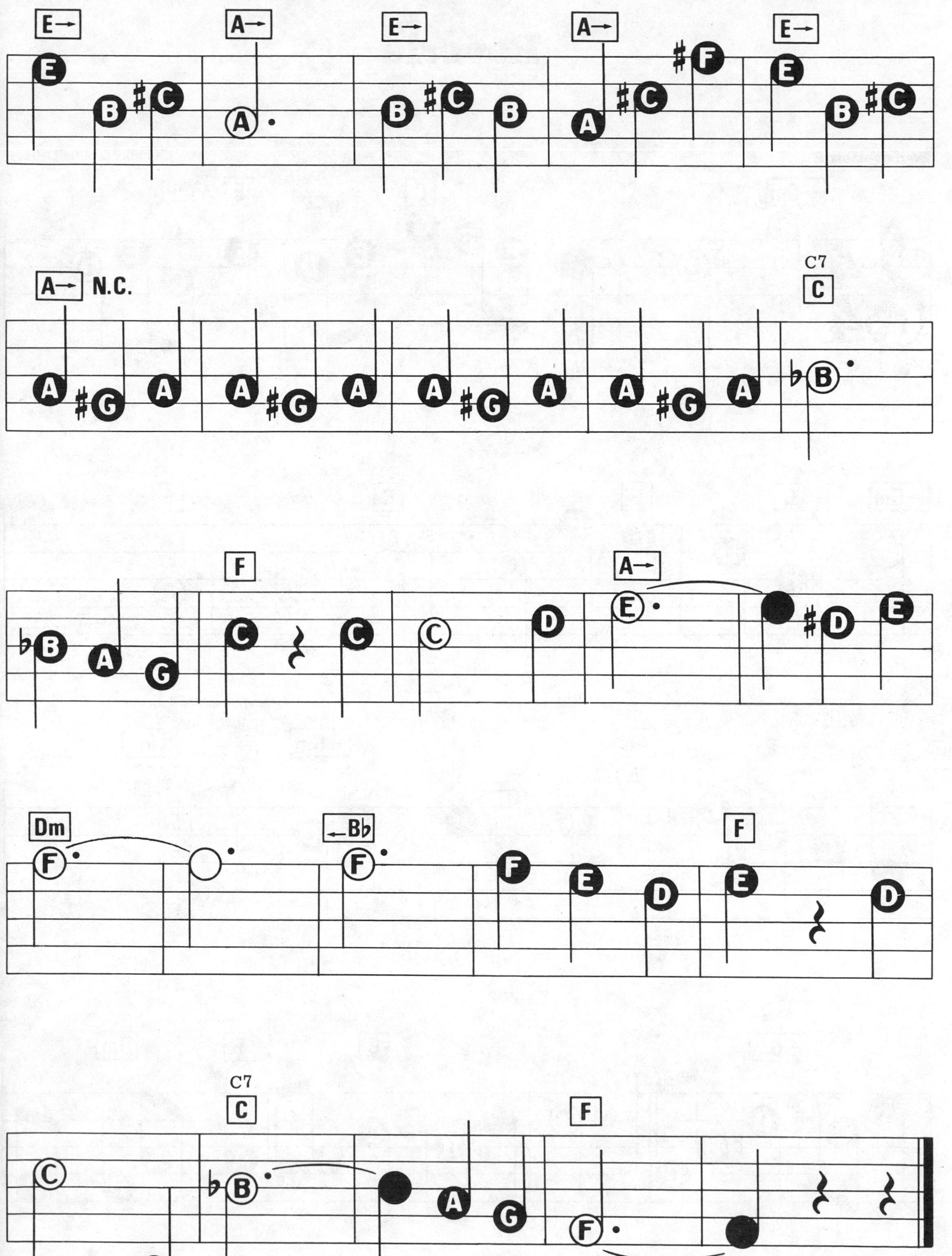
E→
A→
E→
A→
E→
E B ♯C A B ♯C B A ♯C ♯F E B ♯C
A→ N.C.
C7
C
A ♯G A A ♯G A A ♯G A A ♯G A ♭B
F
A→
♭B A G C C C D E ♯D E
Dm
←B♭
F
F F F E D E D
C7
C
F
C C ♭B A G F

Reverie

Registration 8

Achille Claude Debussy

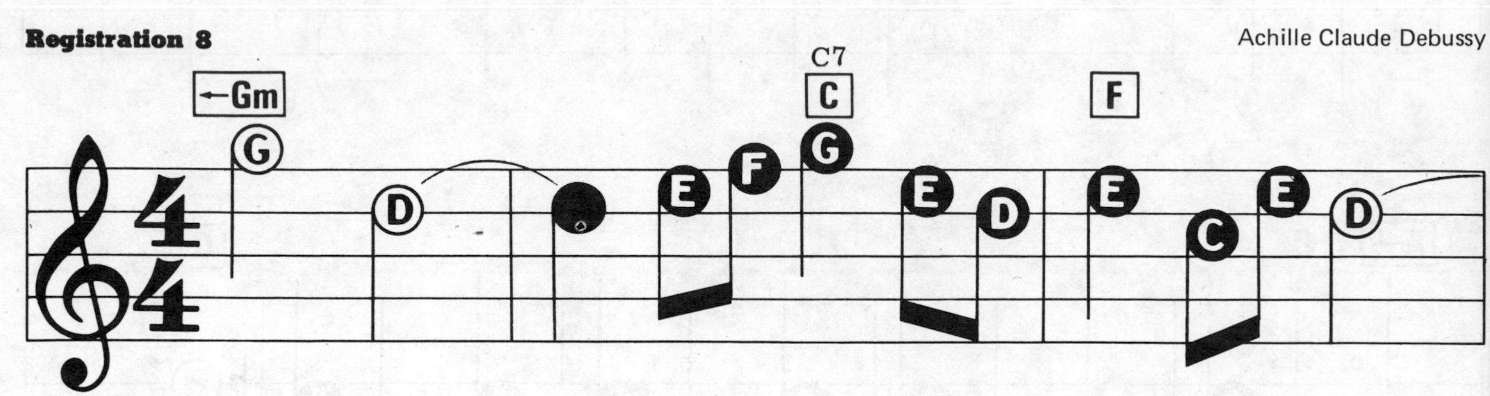

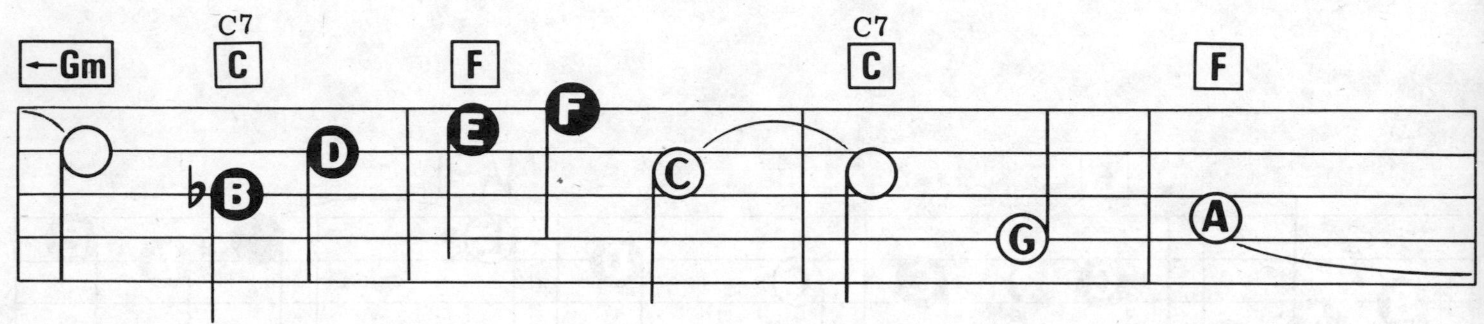

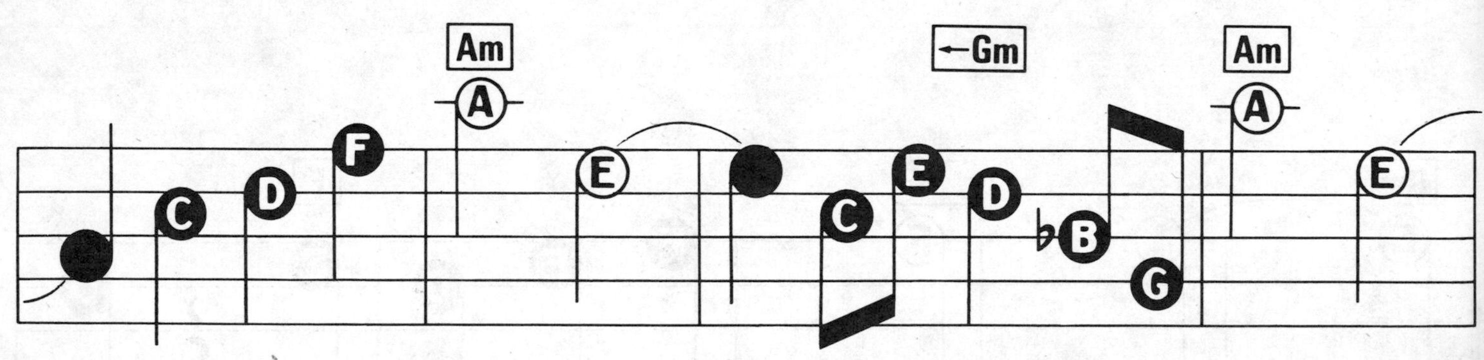

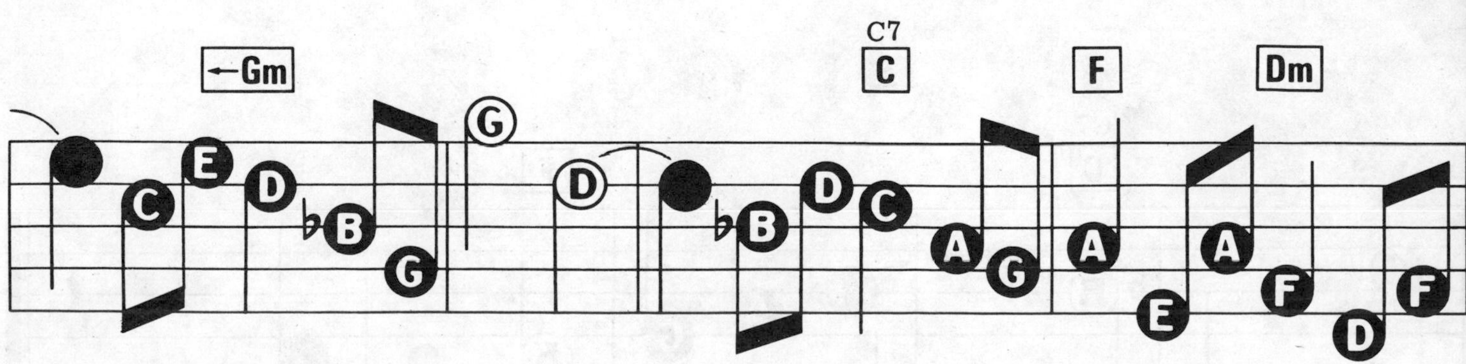

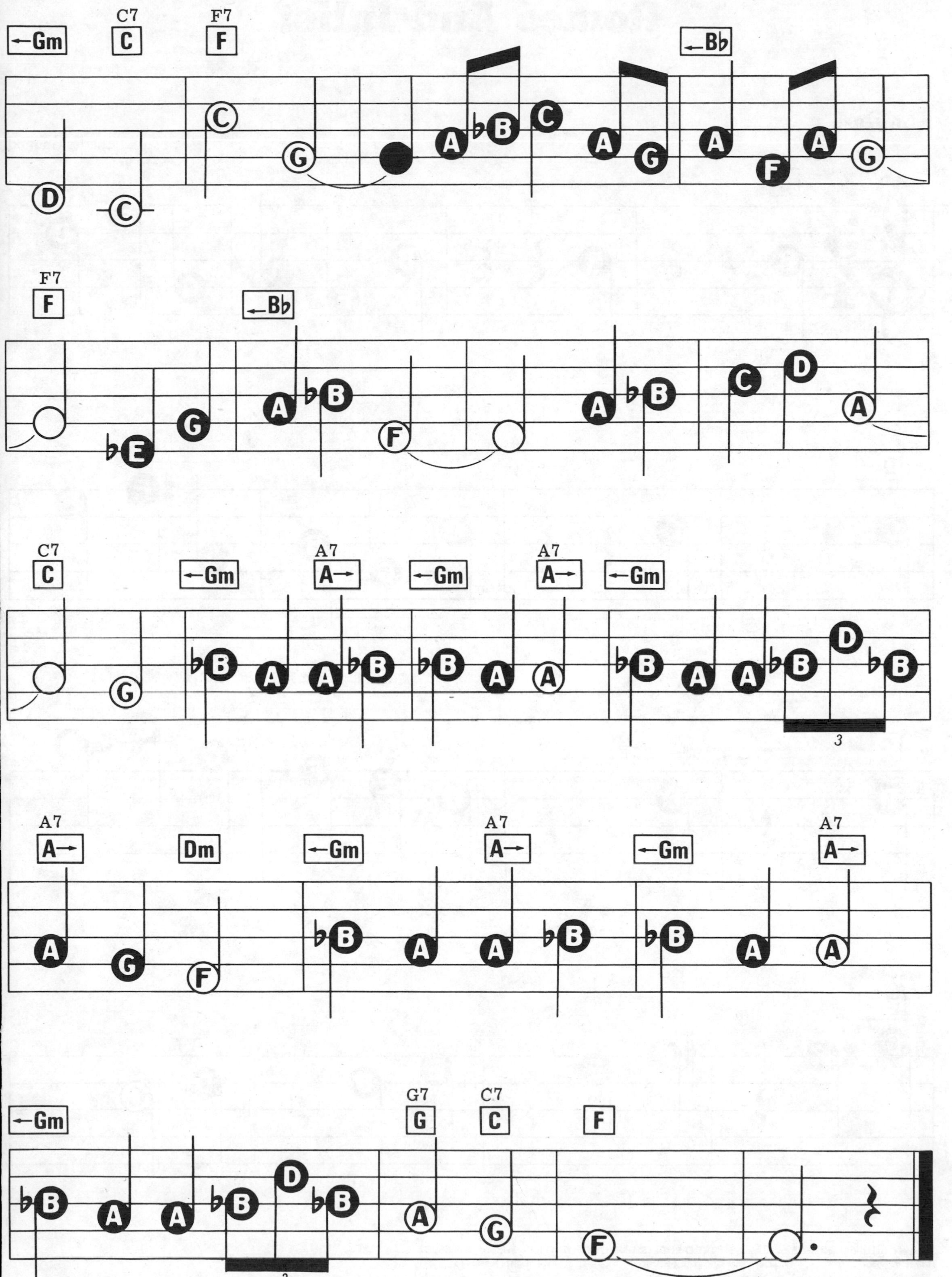
Gm C7 C F7 F Bb
F7 F Bb
C7 C Gm A7 A Gm A7 A Gm
A7 A Dm Gm A7 A Gm A7 A
Gm G7 G C7 C F

Romeo And Juliet

Registration 3

Charles Gounod

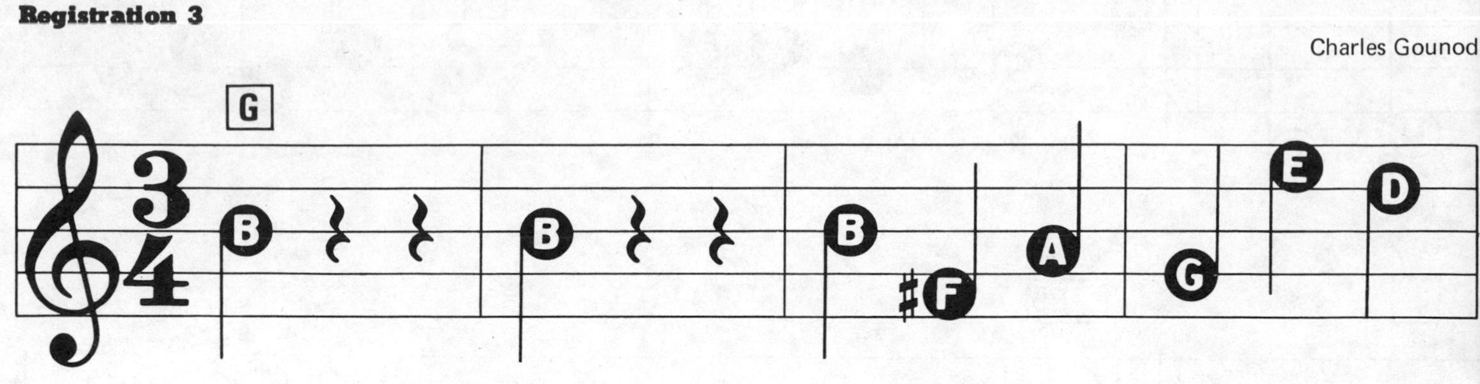

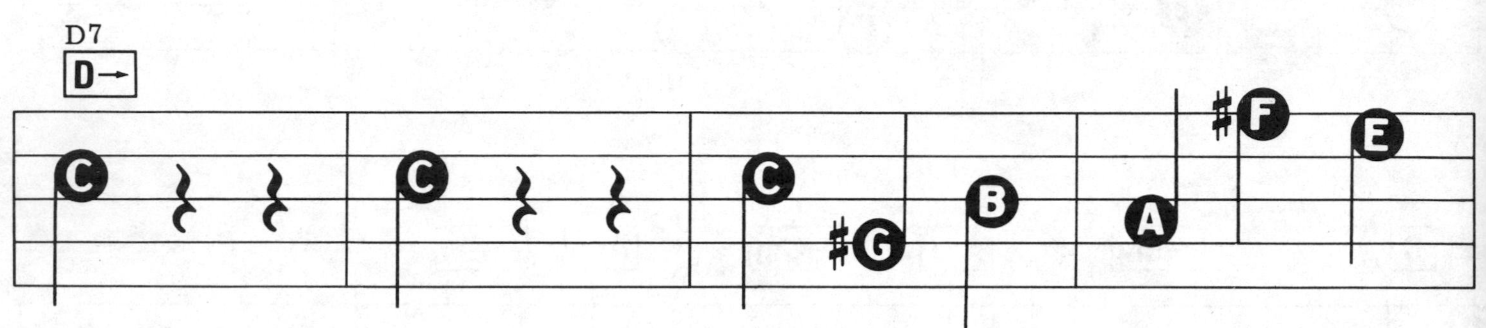

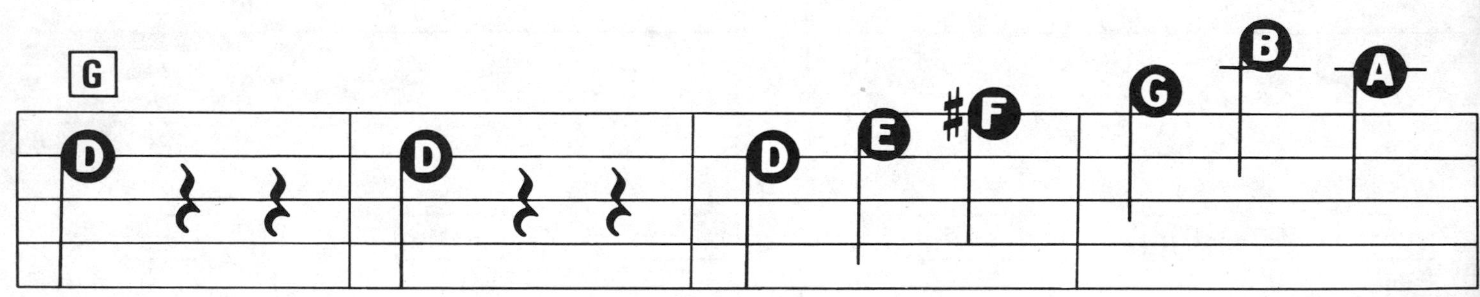

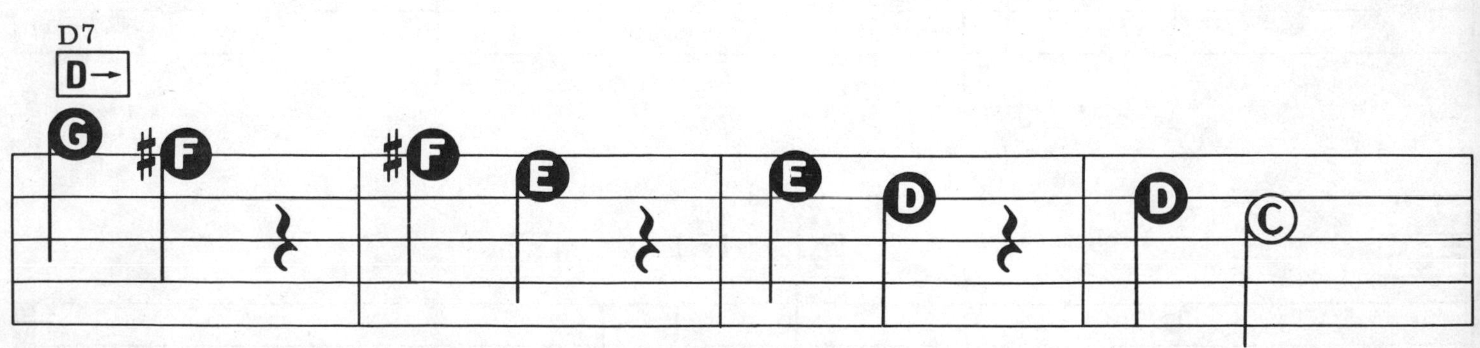

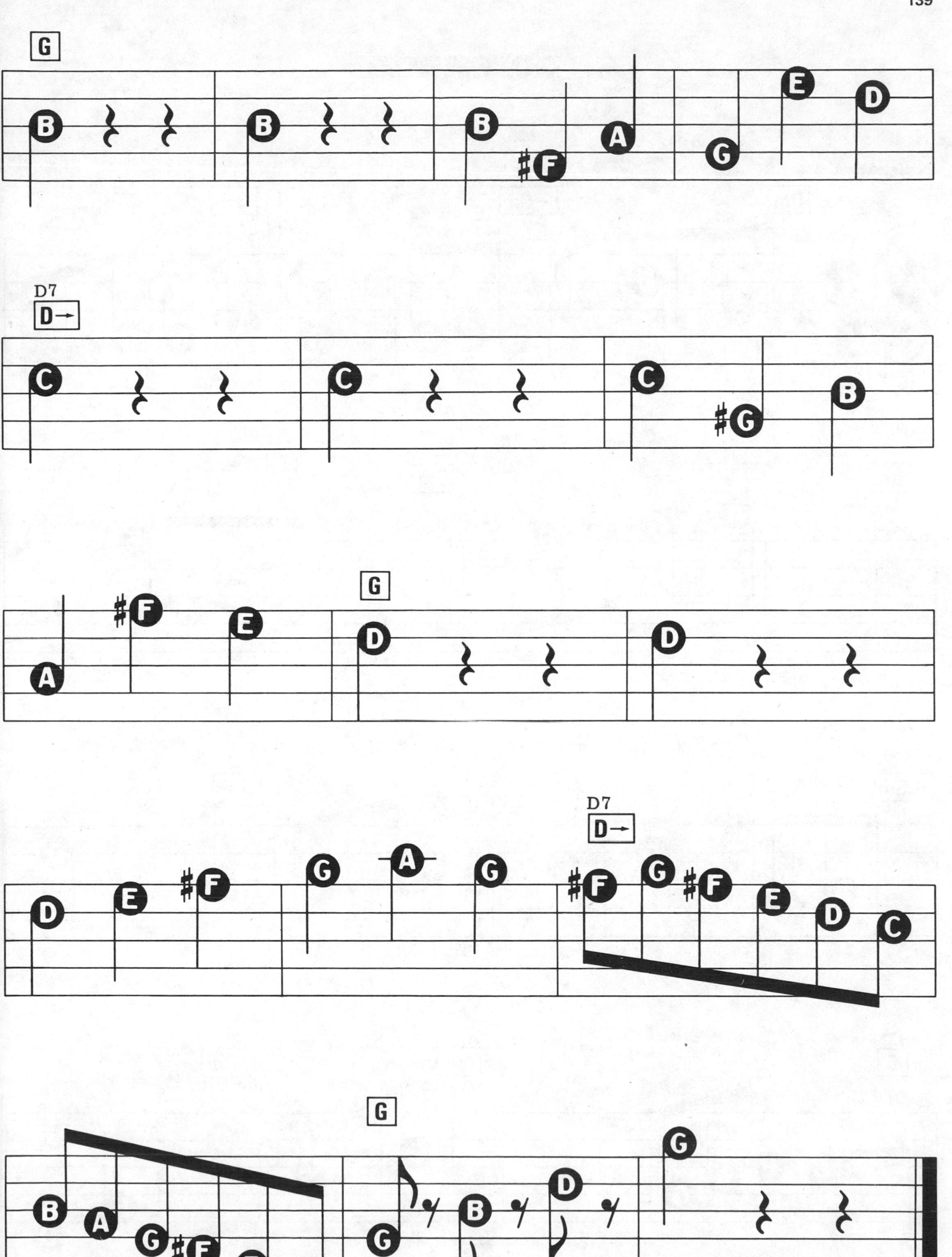
G
B B B ♯F A G E D
D7
D→
C C C ♯G B
A ♯F E
G
D D
D E ♯F G A G
D7
D→
♯F G ♯F E D C
B A G ♯F E D
G
G B D G

Serenade

Franz Schubert

Registration 4

Dm
←Gm
A7
A→
Dm
A7
A→
Dm
←Gm
C7
C
F
C7
C
F
A7
A→
Dm

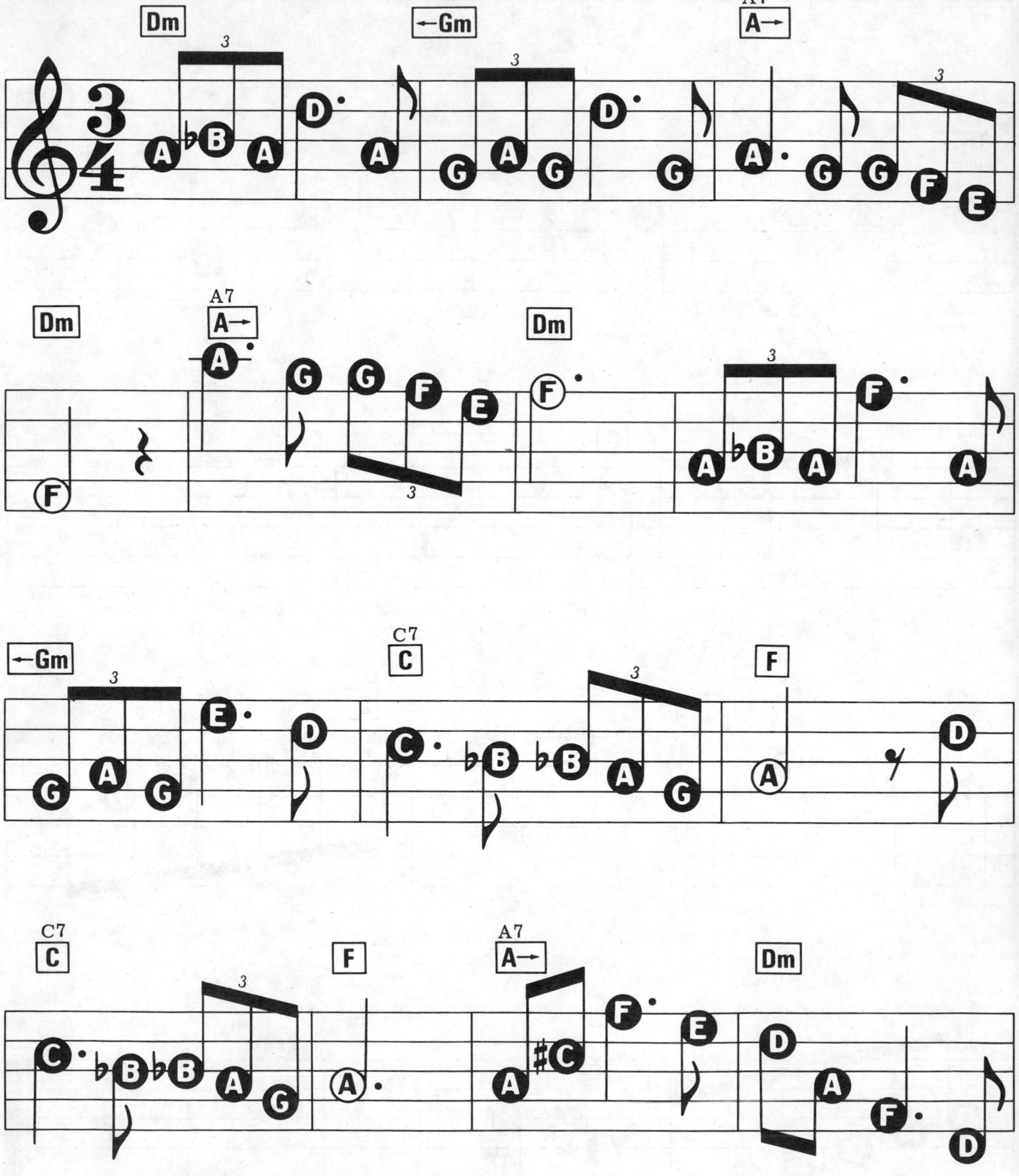

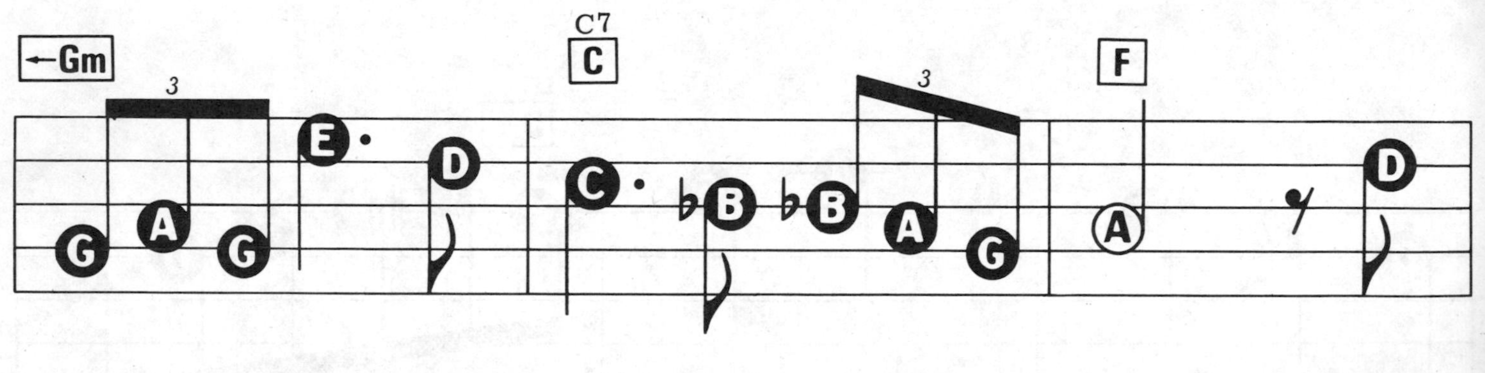

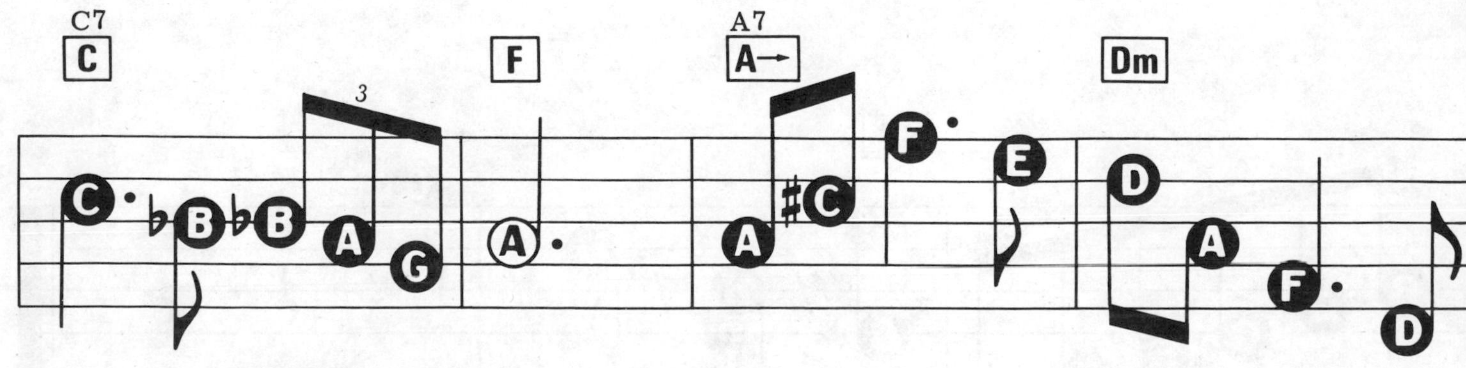

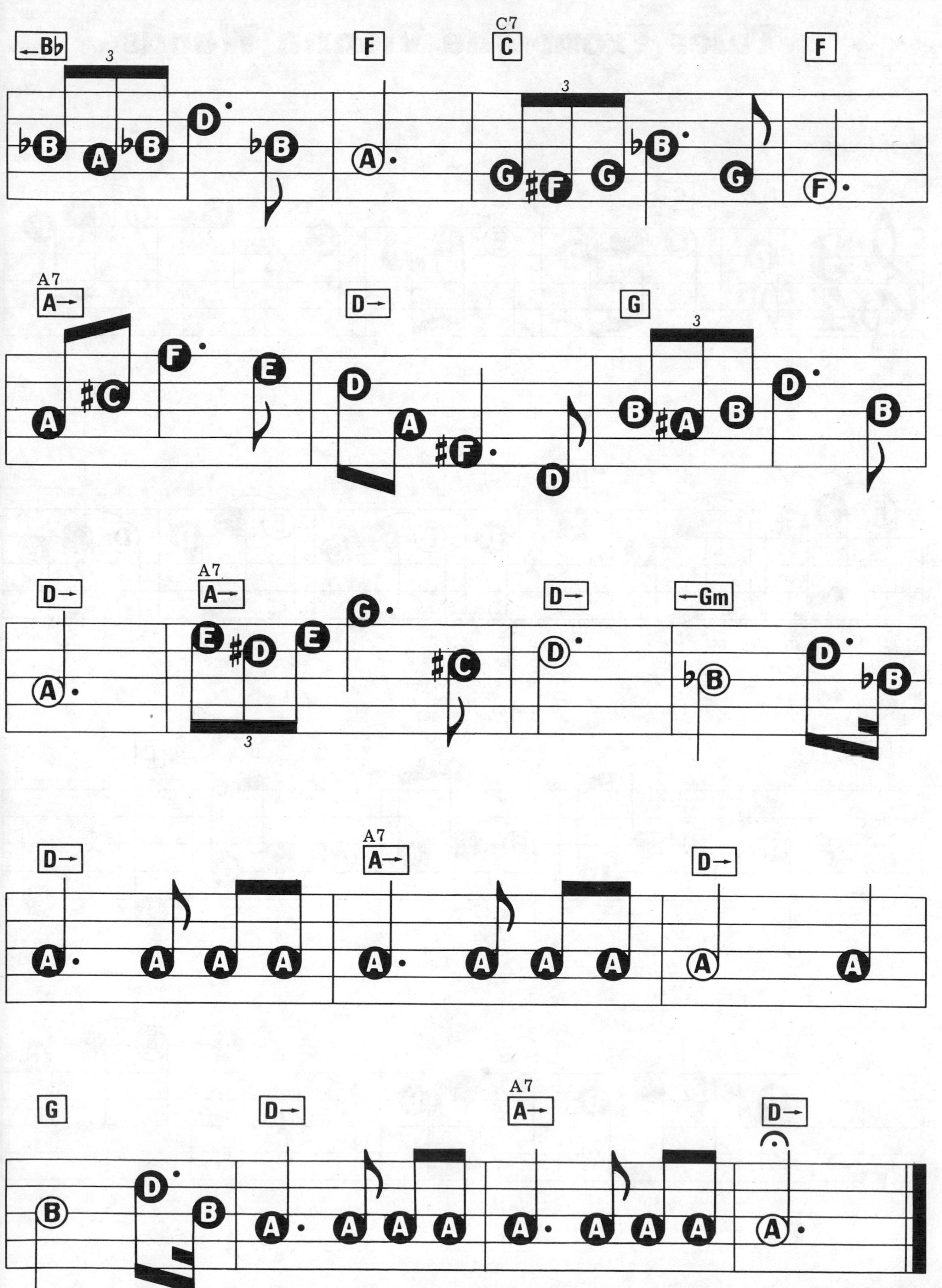
Bb F C7 C F
A7 A D G
D A7 A D Gm
D A7 A D
G D A7 A D

Tales From The Vienna Woods

Registration 4

Johann Strauss

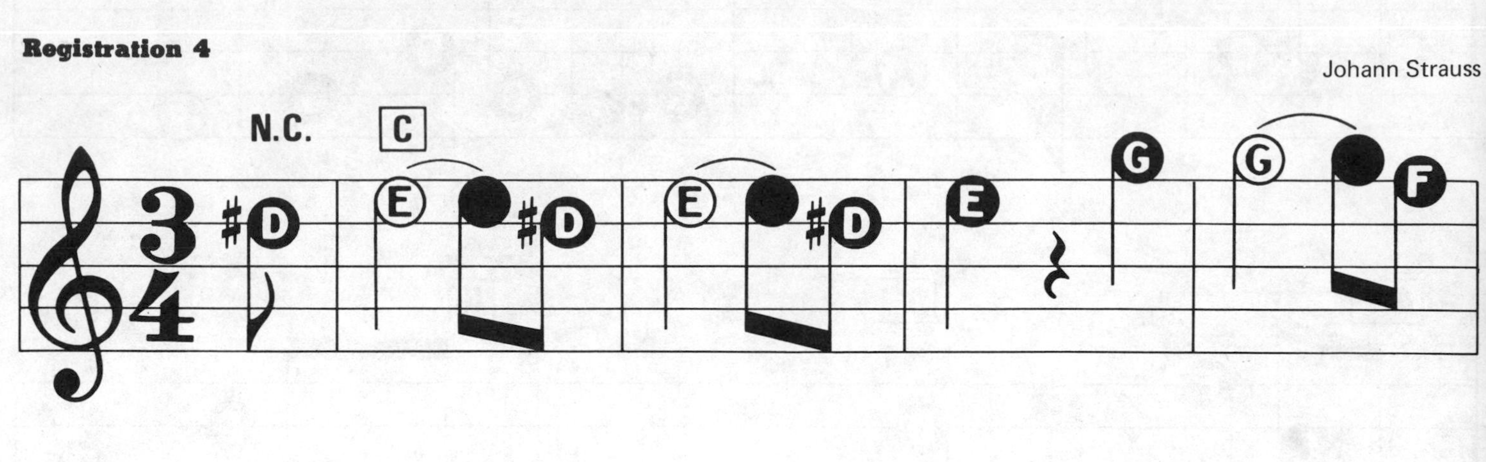

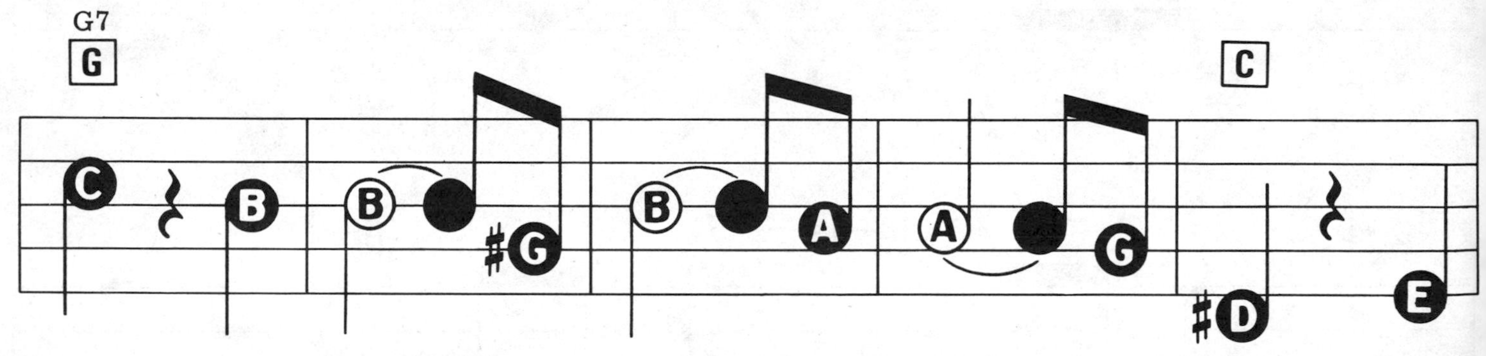

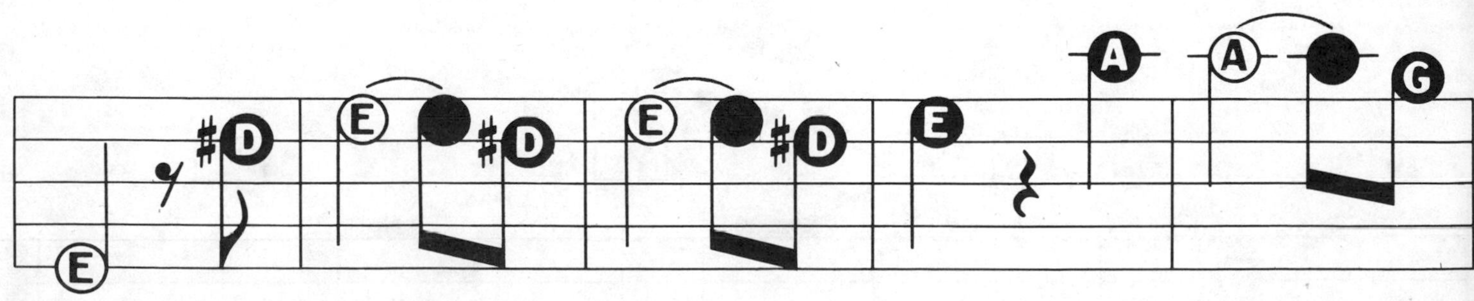

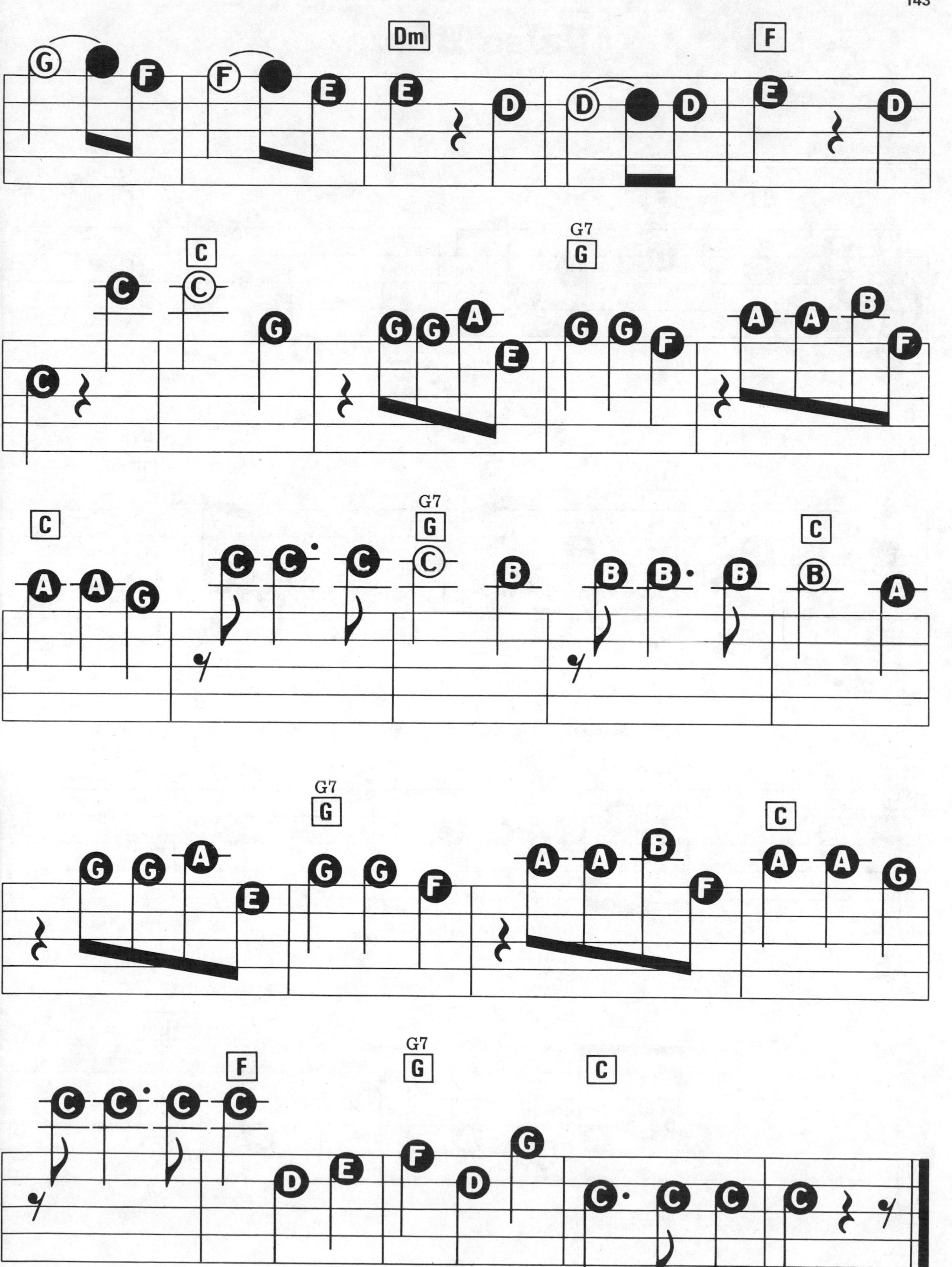
Dm
F
G F F E E D D D E D
C
G7
G
C C G G G A E G G F A A B F
C
G7
G
C
A A G C C C C B B B B B A
G7
G
C
G G A E G G F A A B F A A G
F
G7
G
C
C C C C D E F D G C C C C

Valse Bleue

Registration 3

Alfred Margis

C7
C
N.C.
F
D
C
A
F
D
D
F
A
C7
C
C
C
F
D
C
A
F
D
D
F
A
C7
C
C
F
C
D
C
B
C
3
F
E
←B♭
E
D
C
←Gm
♭B
C
D
F
A
C7
C
G
F
F

Vienna Life

Registration 5

Johann Strauss

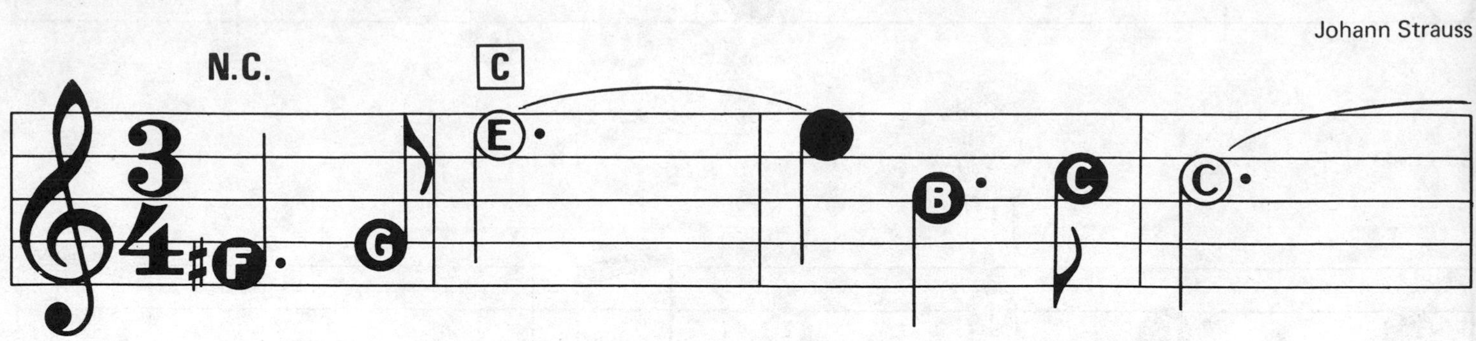

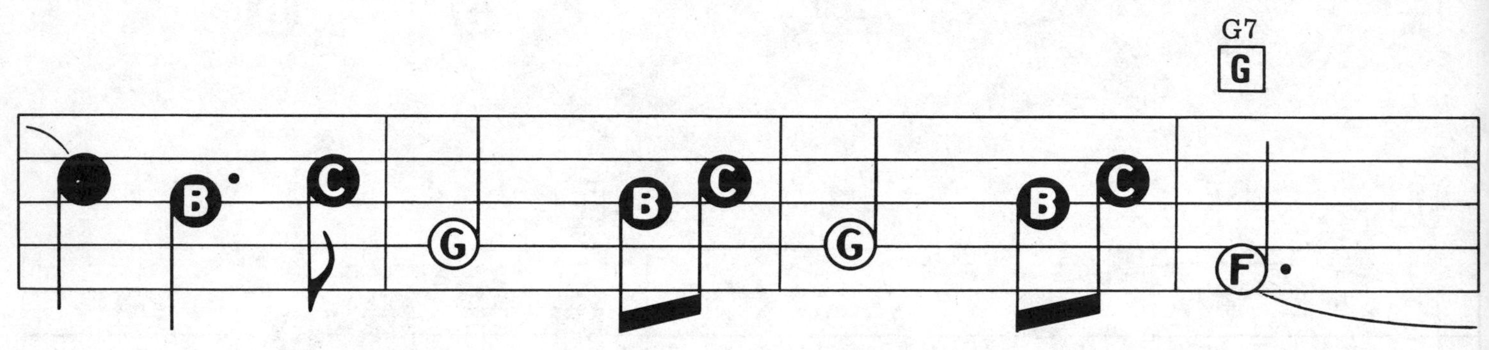

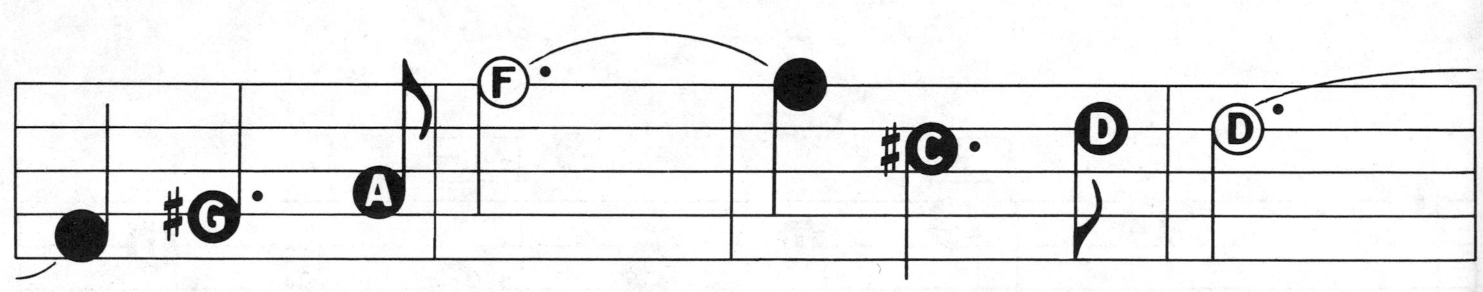

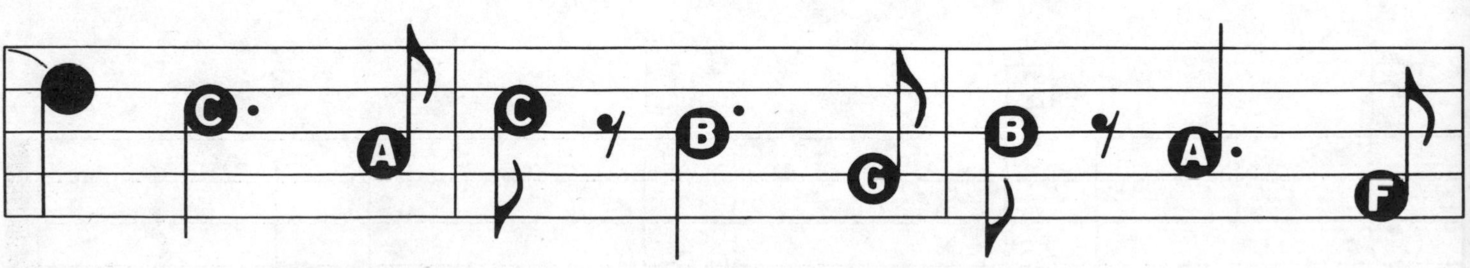

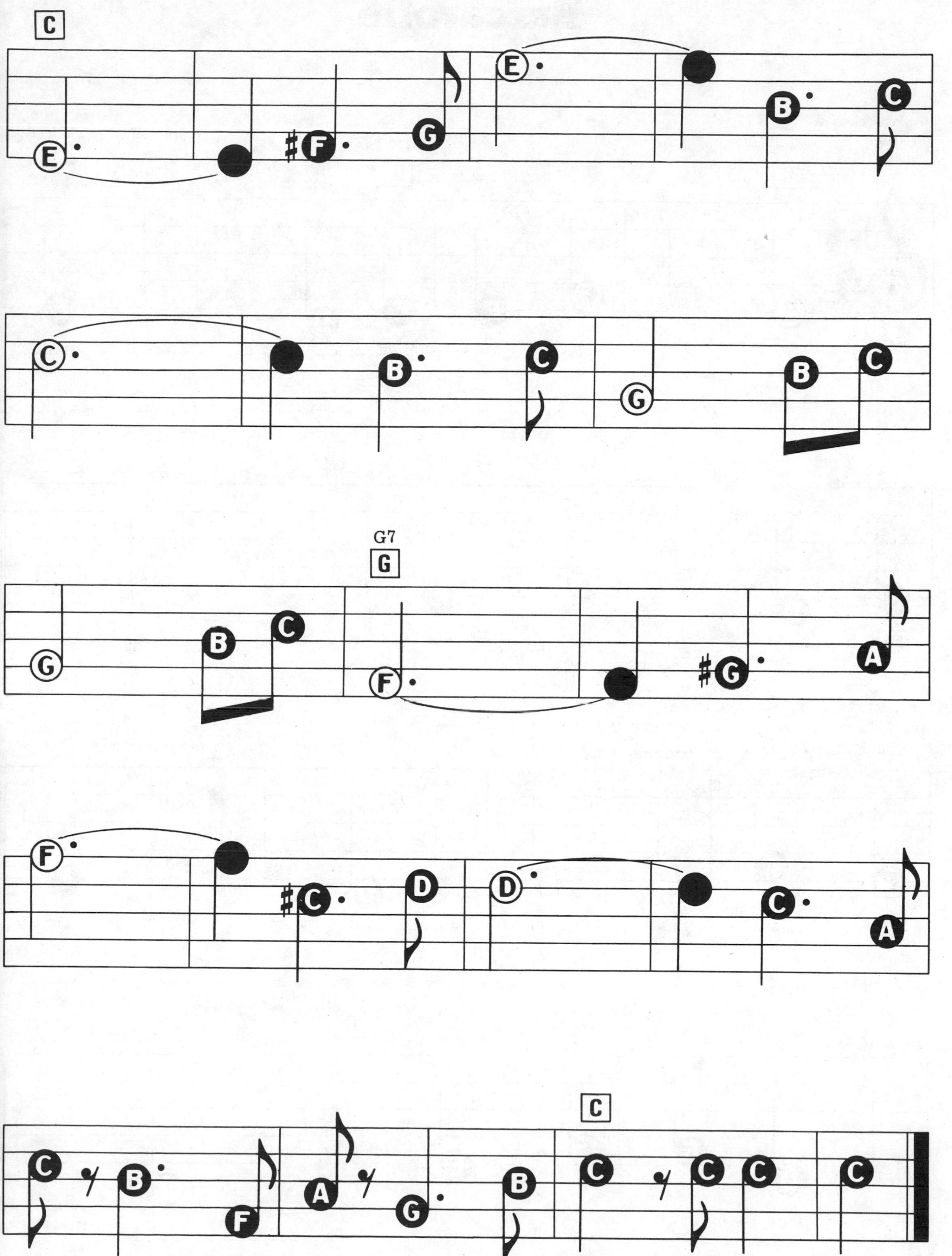
C
G7
G
C

Barcarolle

Registration 4

Offenbach

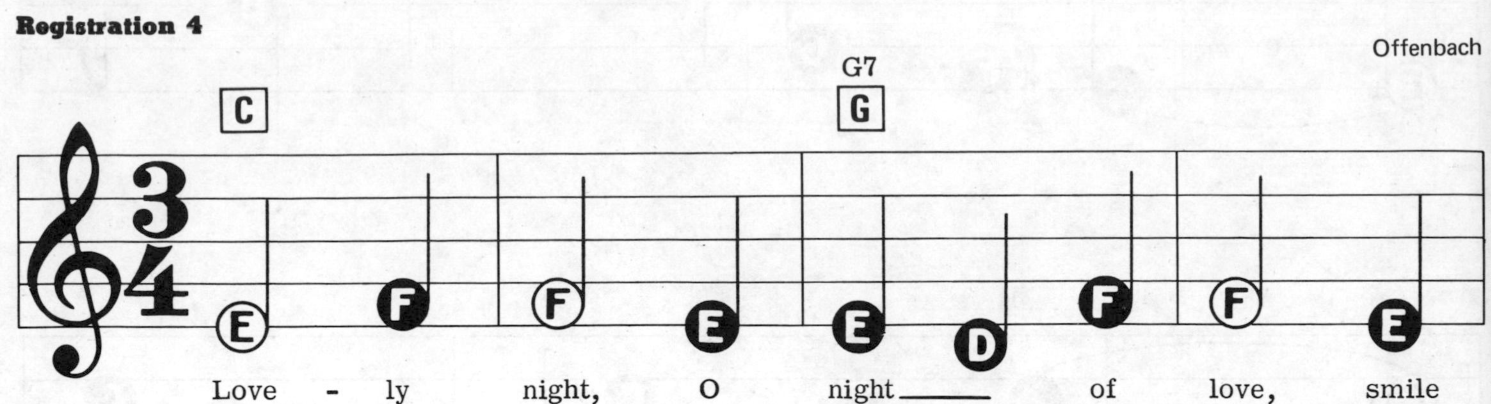

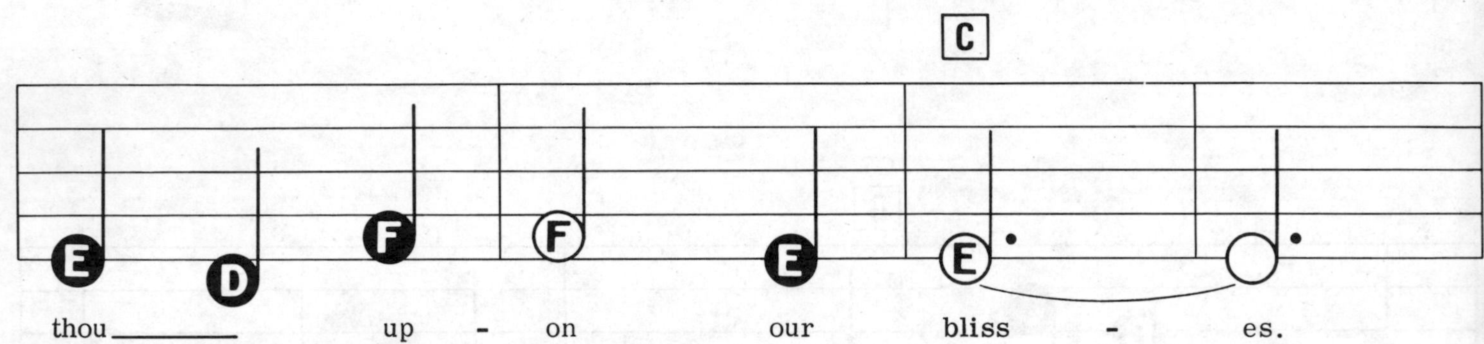

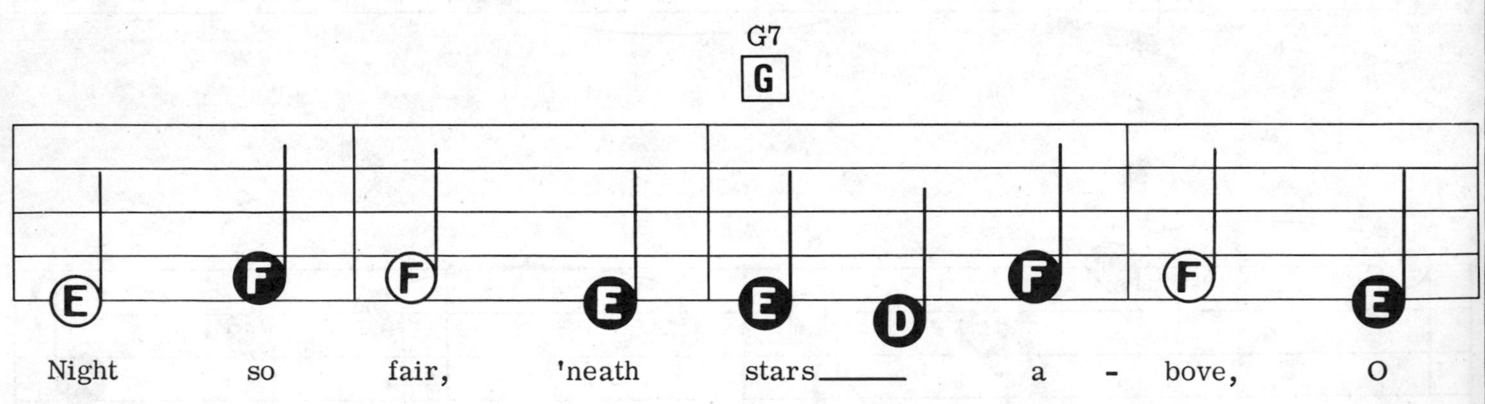

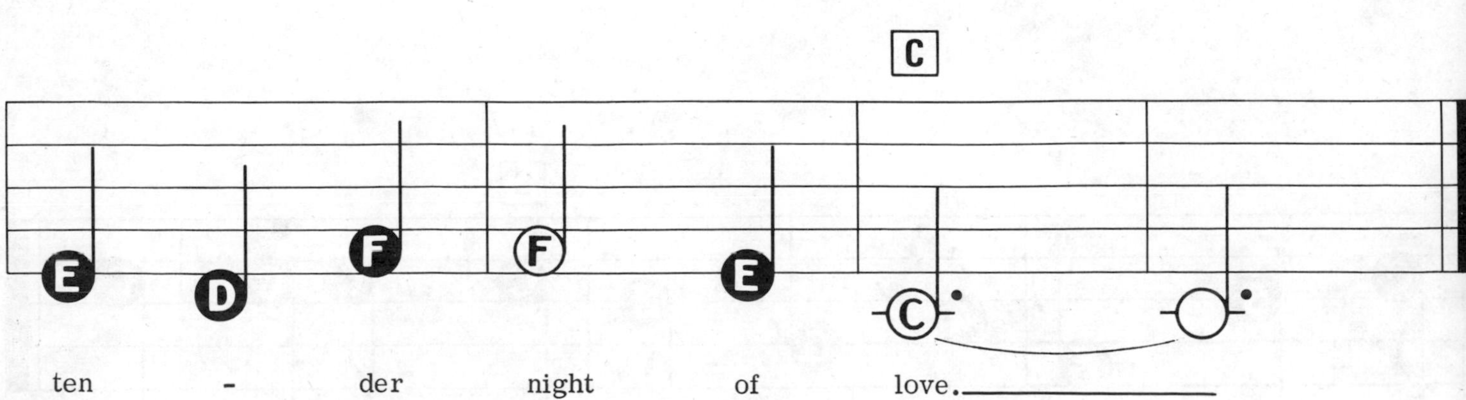

Dance Of The Hours

Registration 5

A. Ponchielli

Fur Elise

Registration 8

Ludvig von Beethoven

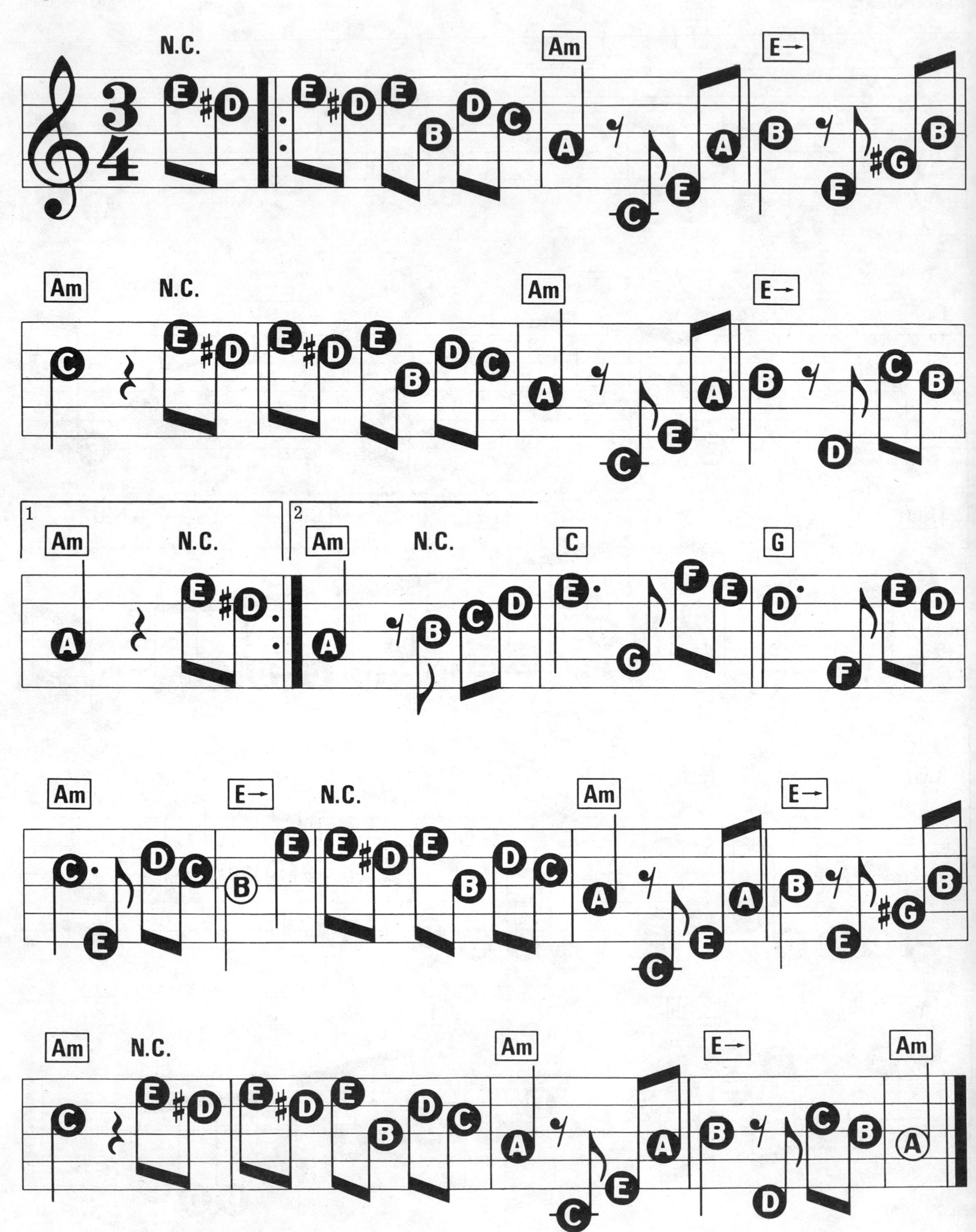

Il Bacio

Registration 5

Luigi Arditi

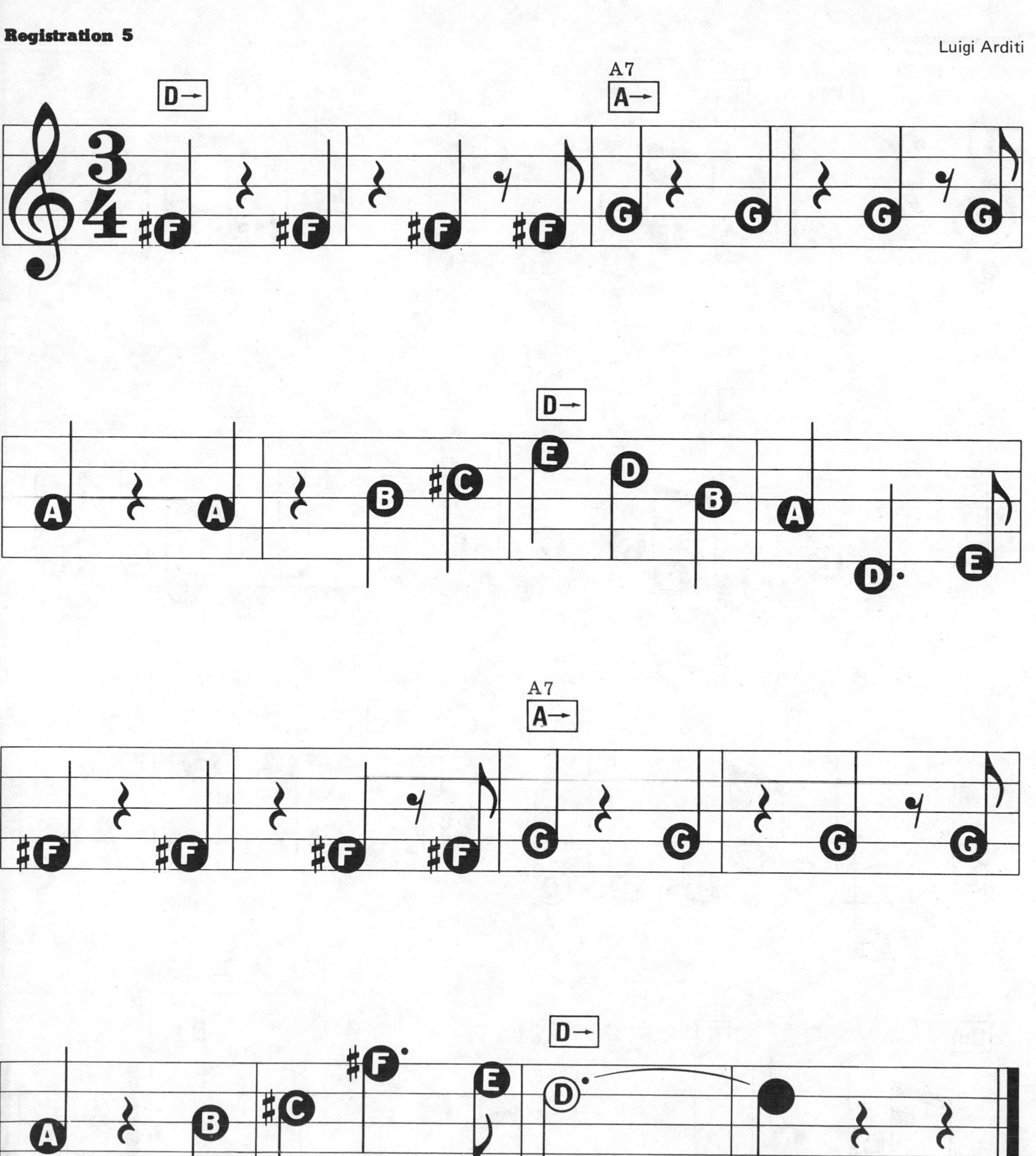

Prelude

Registration 8

Chopin

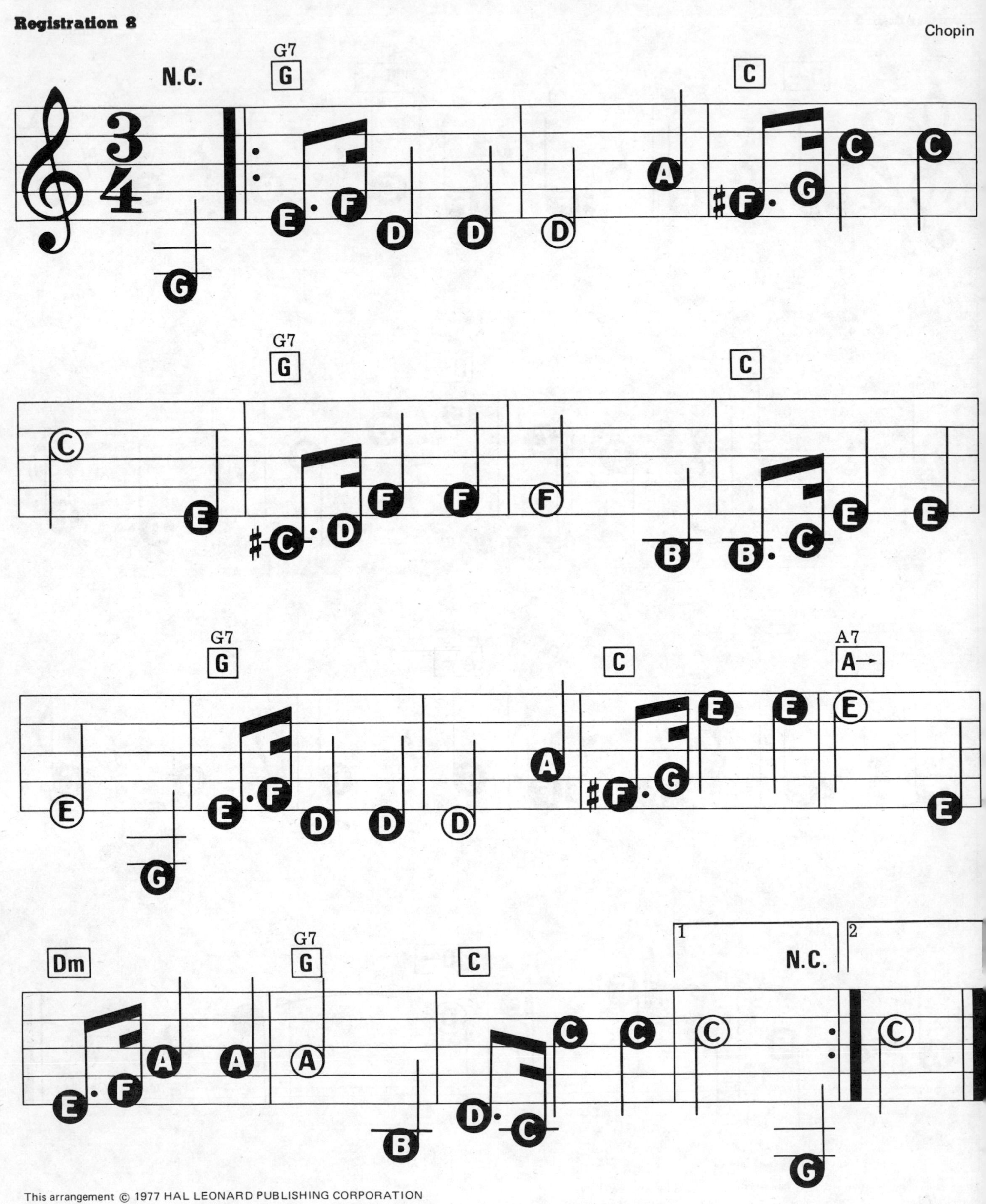

Theme From Polovetzian Dance

Registration 9

Alexander Borodin

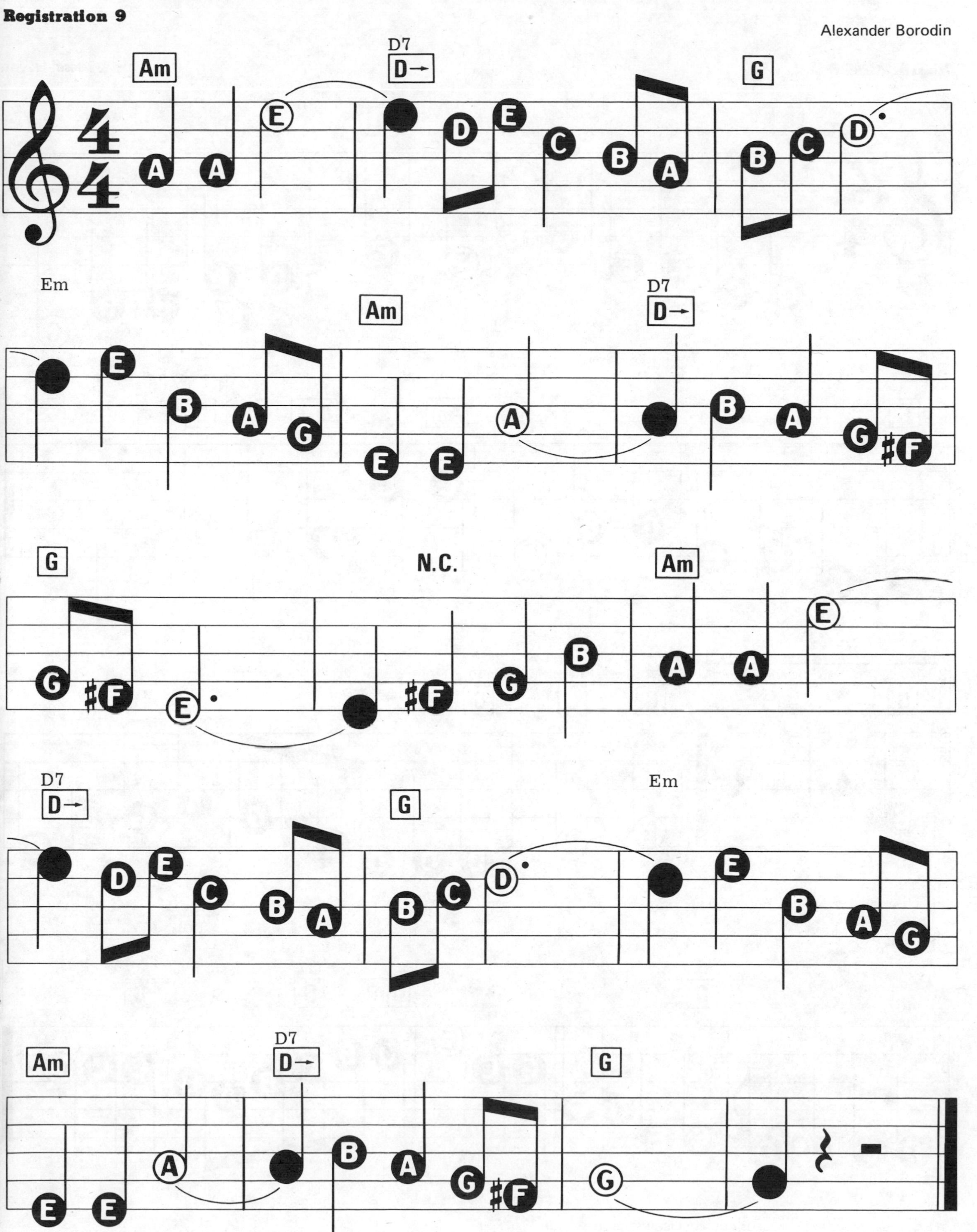

Theme From The Surprise Symphony

Registration 5

Jasef Haydn

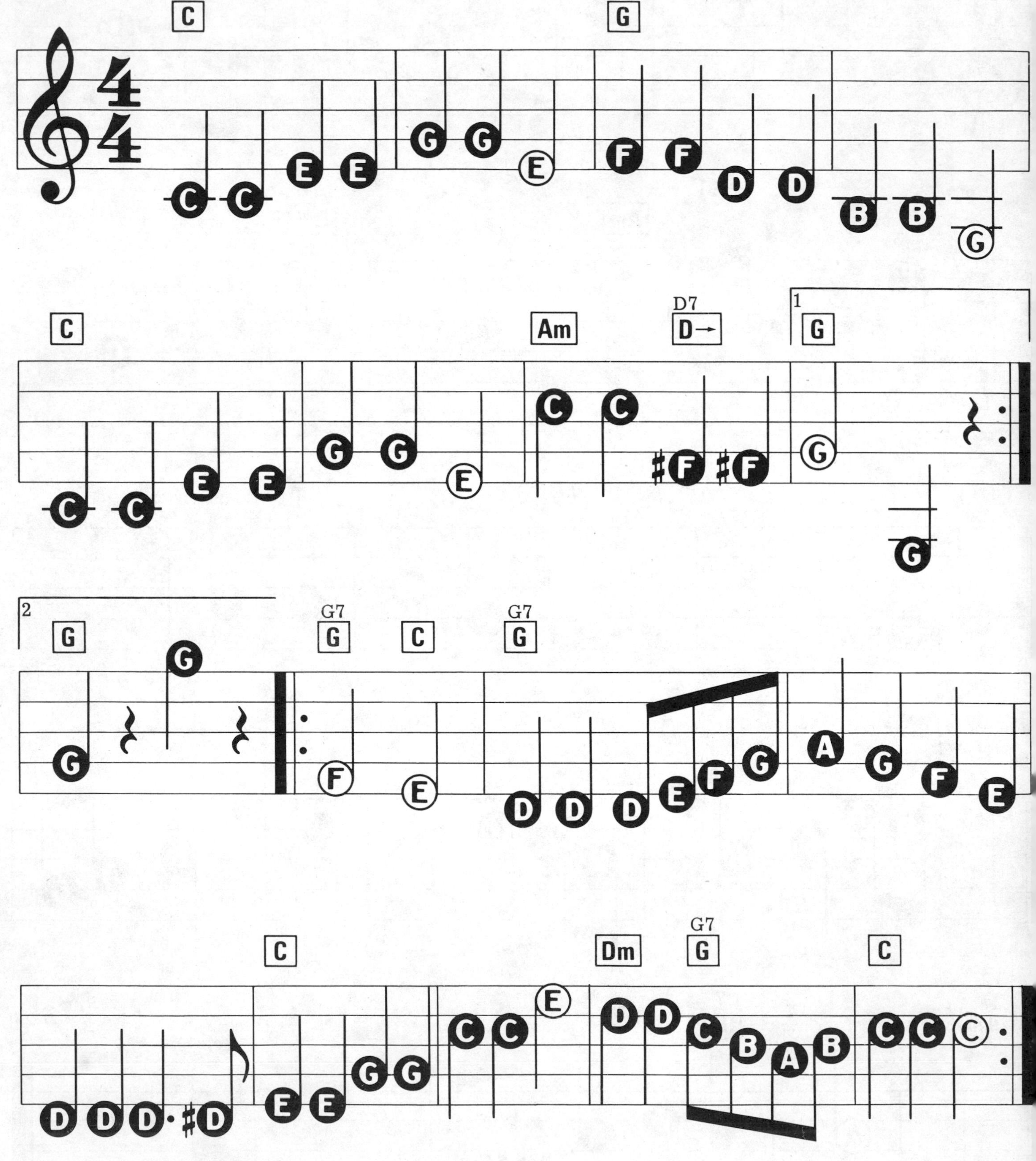

Unfinished Symphony

Registration 3

Franz Schubert

All Through The Night

Registration 6

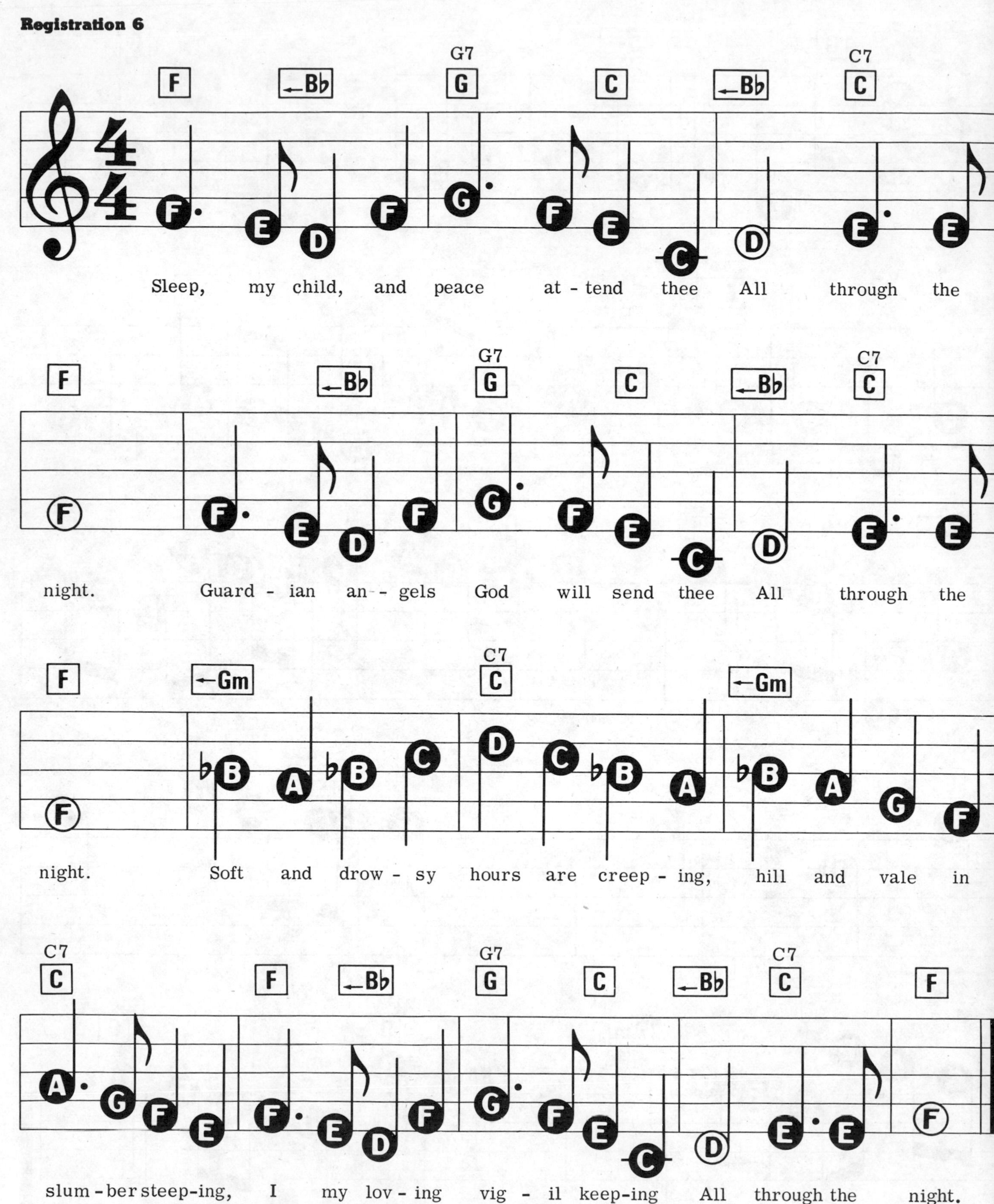

Beautiful Savior

(King Of Creation)

Registration 6

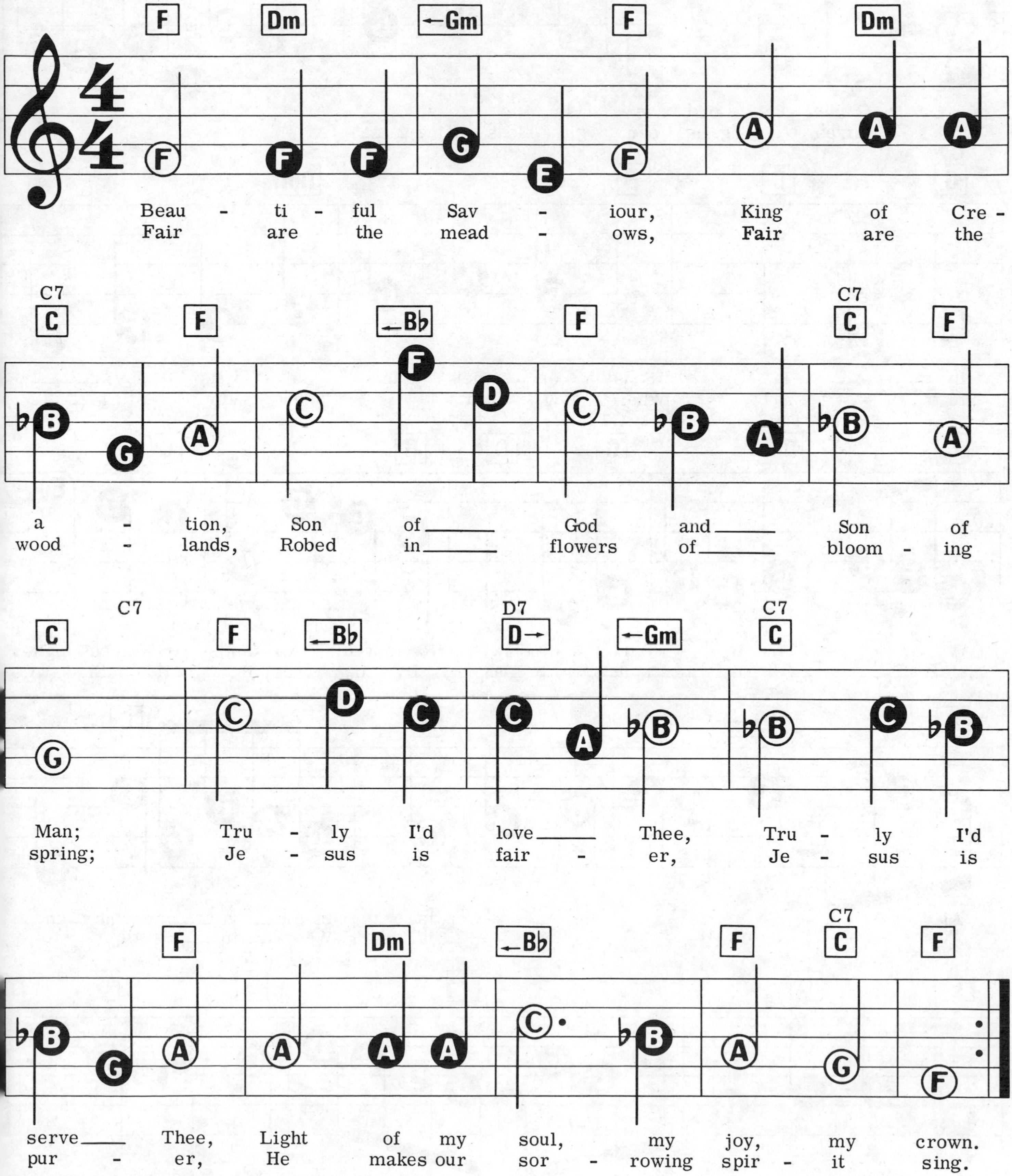

F Dm ←Gm F Dm

Beau - ti - ful Sav - iour, King of Cre -
Fair are the mead - ows, Fair are the

C7 C F ←B♭ F C7 C F

a - tion, Son of ___ God and ___ Son of
wood - lands, Robed in ___ flowers of ___ bloom - ing

C C7 F ←B♭ D7 D→ ←Gm C7 C

Man; Tru - ly I'd love ___ Thee, Tru - ly I'd
spring; Je - sus is fair - er, Je - sus is

F Dm ←B♭ F C7 C F

serve ___ Thee, Light of my soul, my joy, my crown.
pur - er, He makes our sor - rowing spir - it sing.

Christ The Lord Is Risen Today

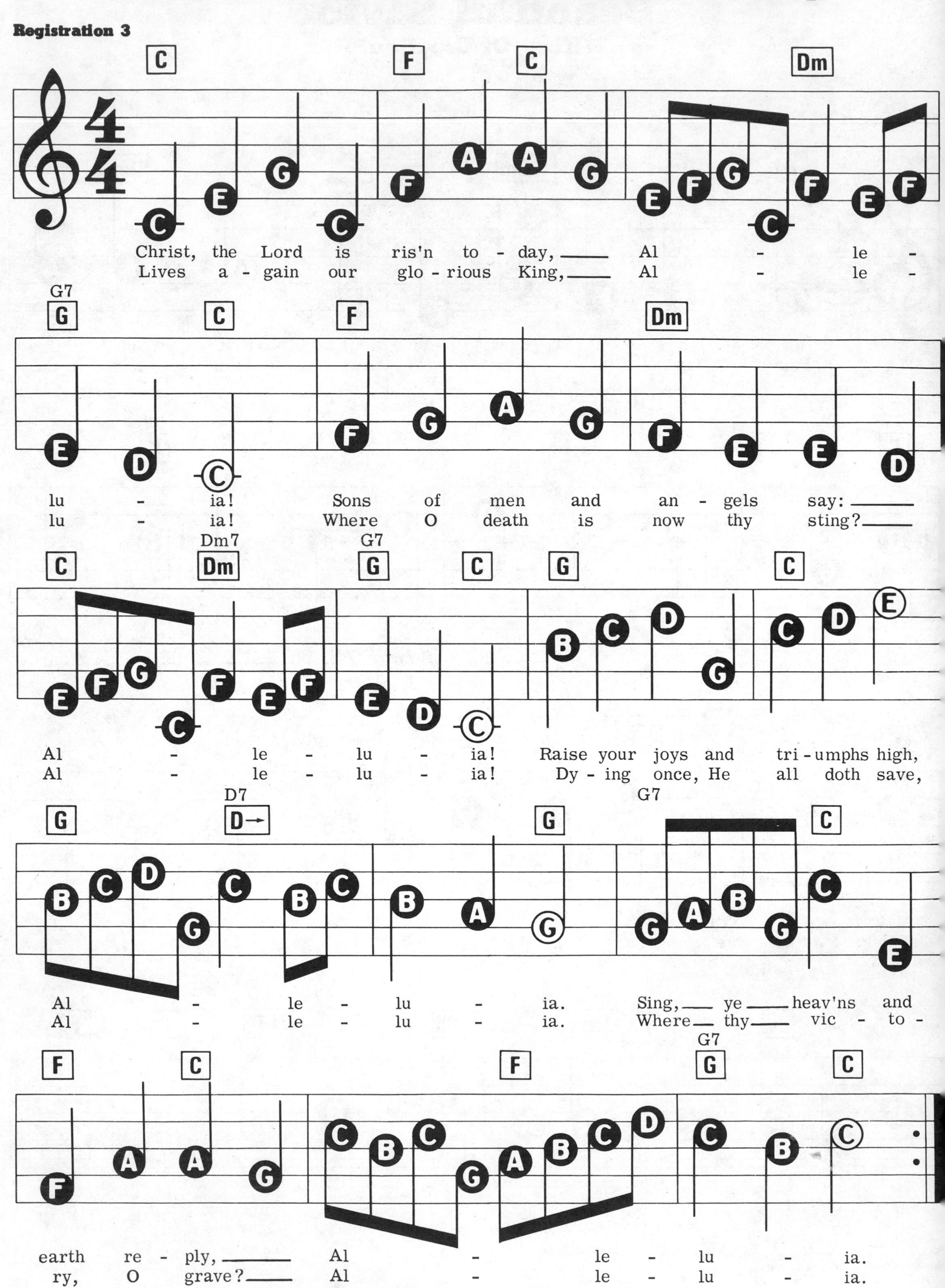

Come, Thou Almighty King

Registration 6

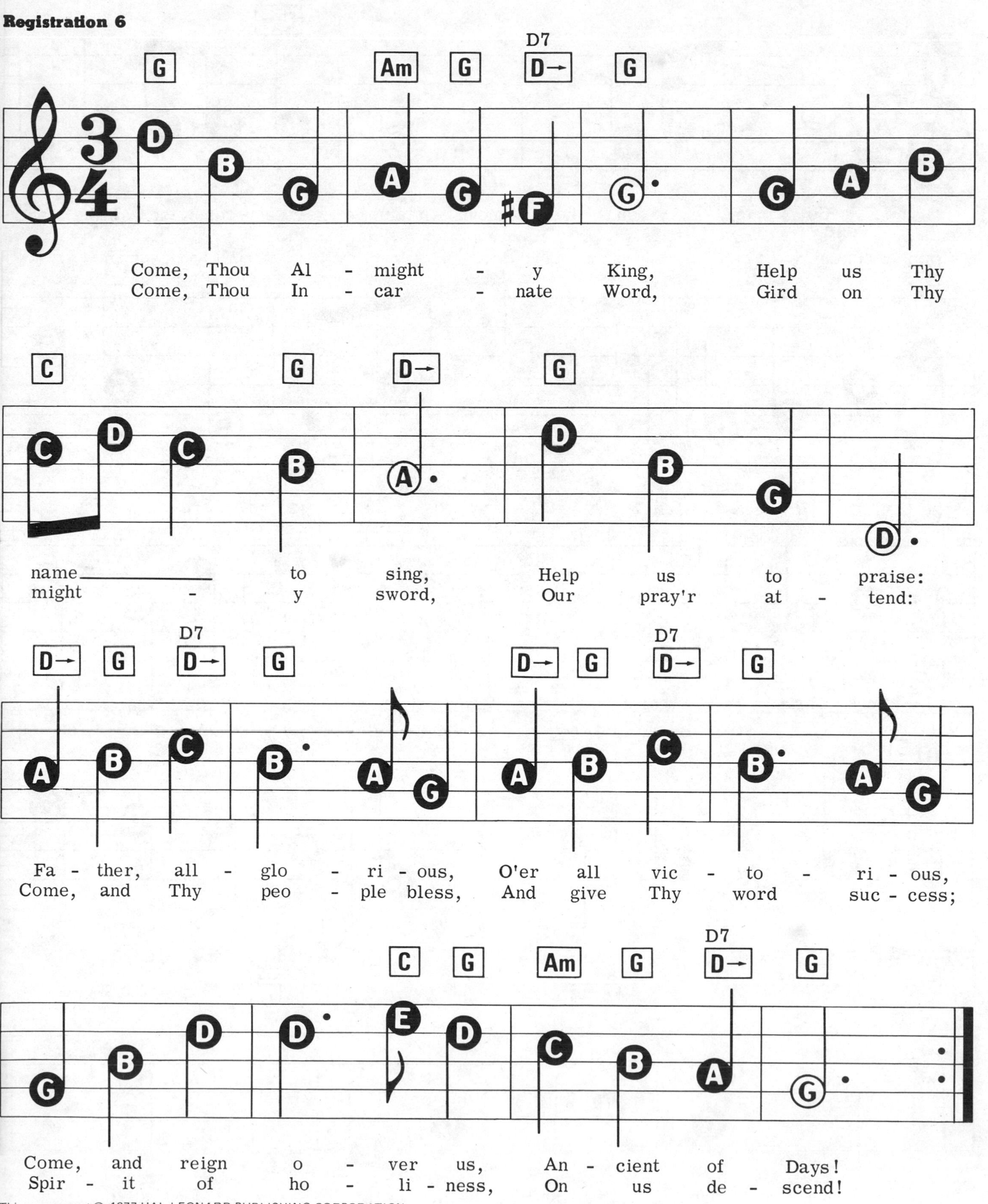

Go Tell It On The Mountain

Registration 4

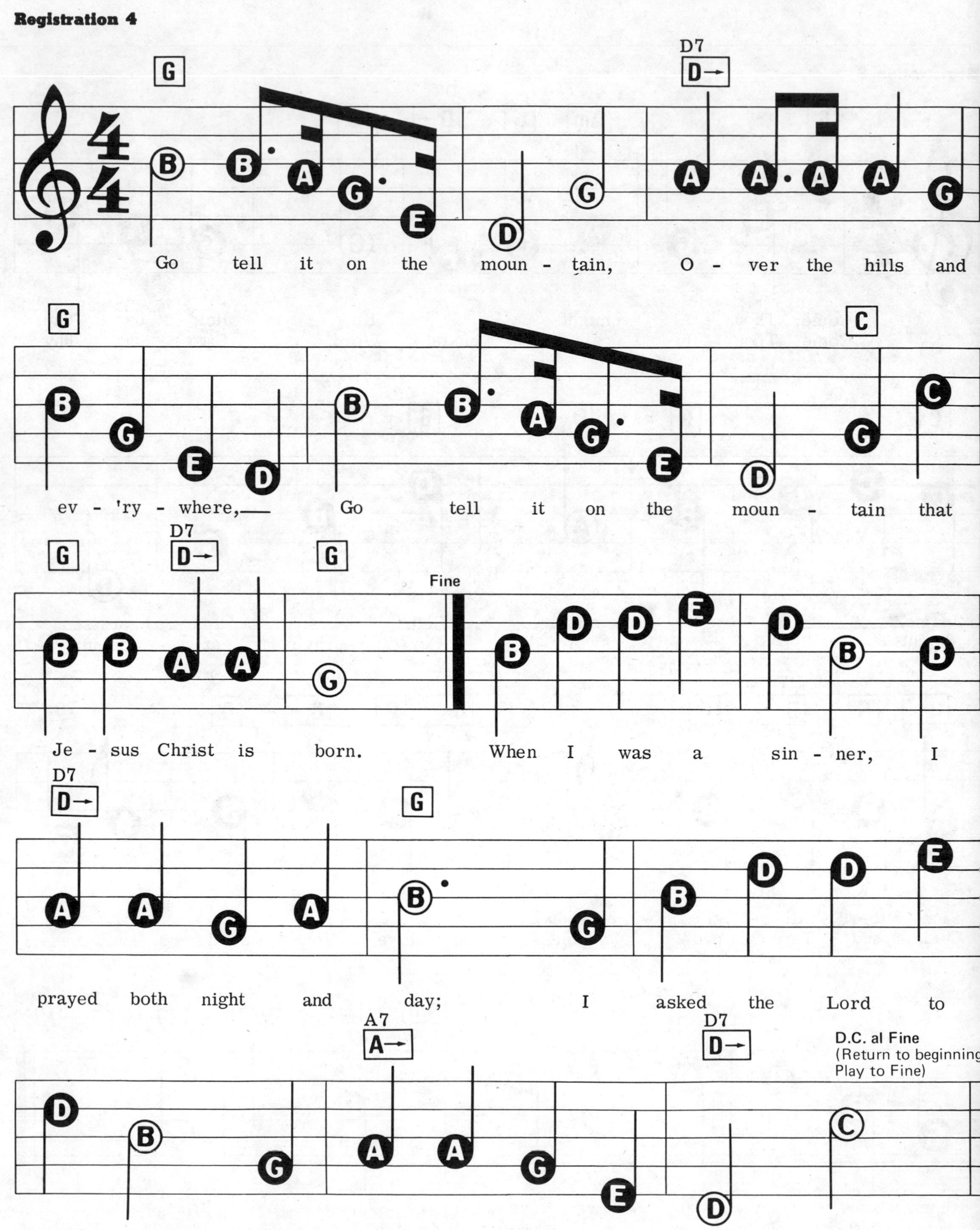

Holy, Holy, Holy

Registration 3

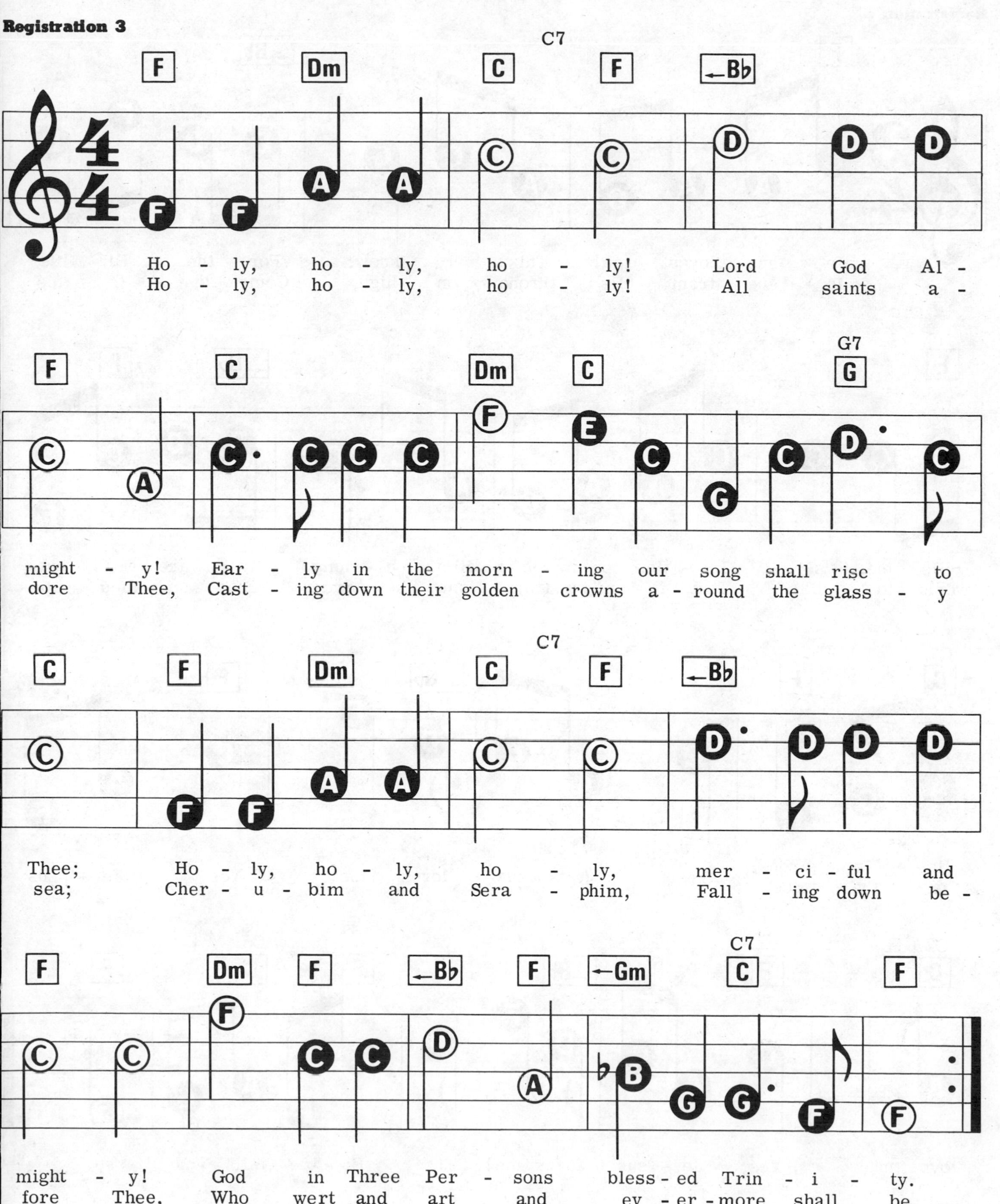

Jesus Loves Me

Registration 6

Just A Closer Walk With Thee

Registration 6

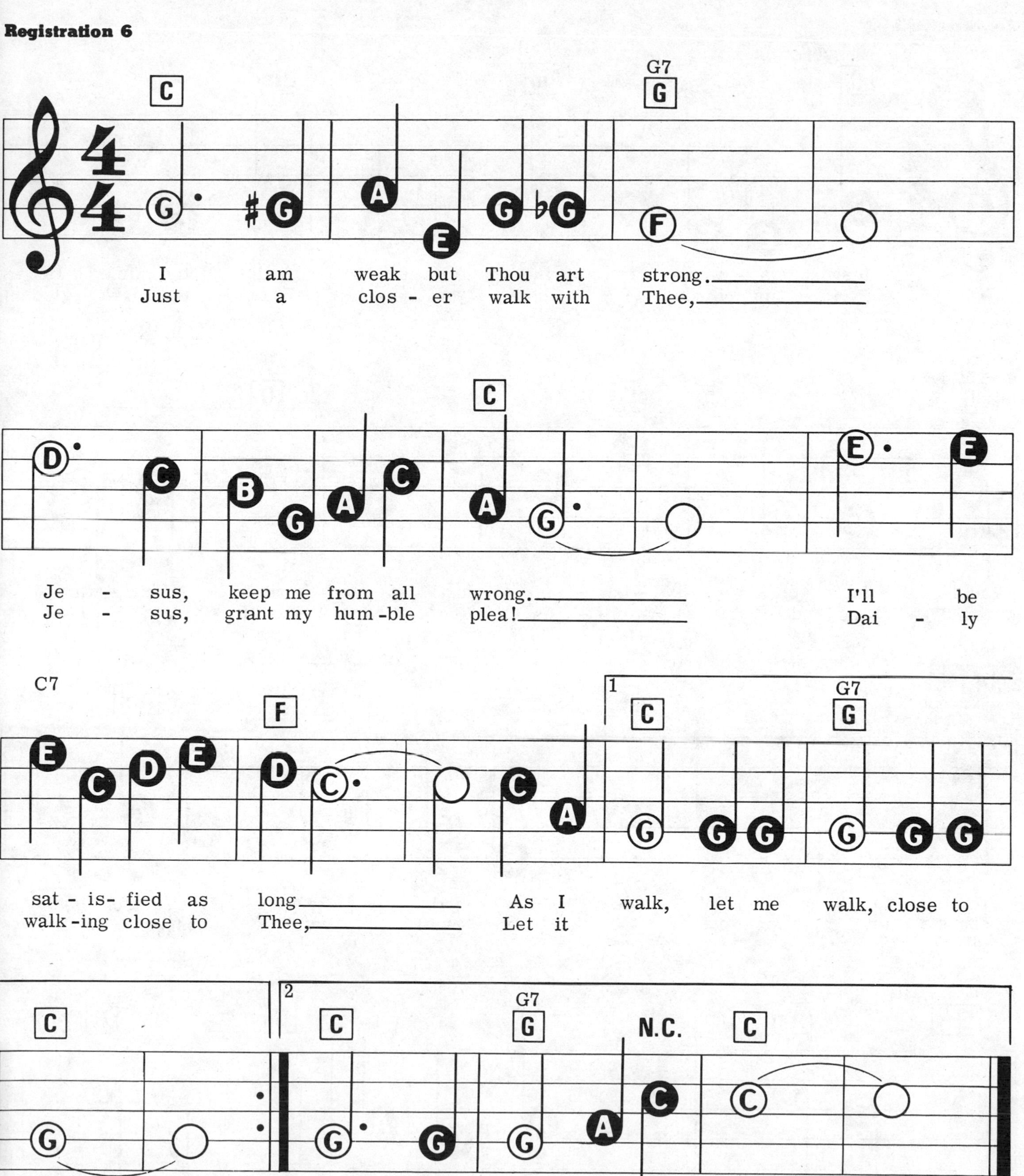

Just A-Wearyin' For You

Registration 1

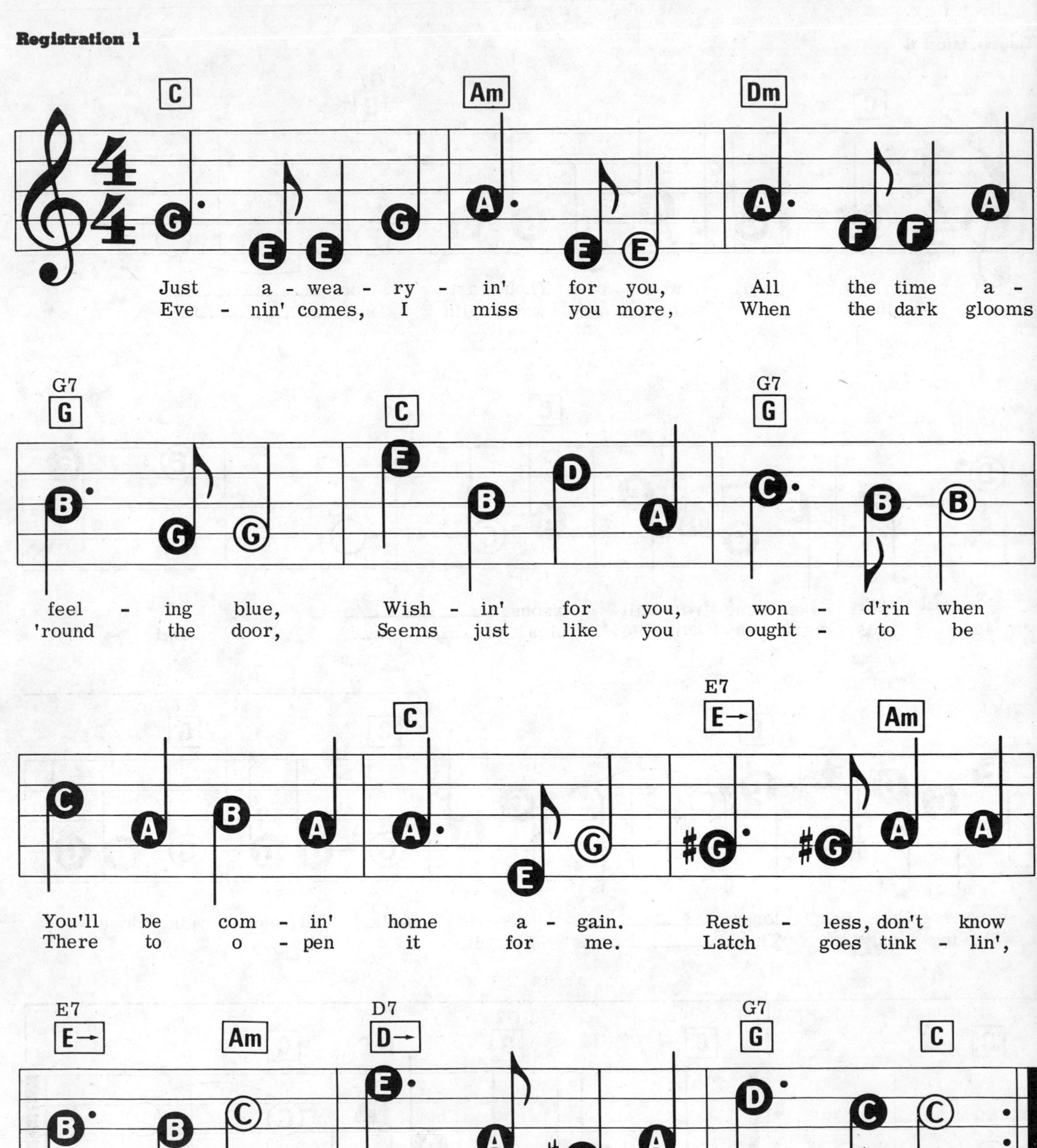

O Lord, I Am Not Worthy

Abide With Me

Registration 3

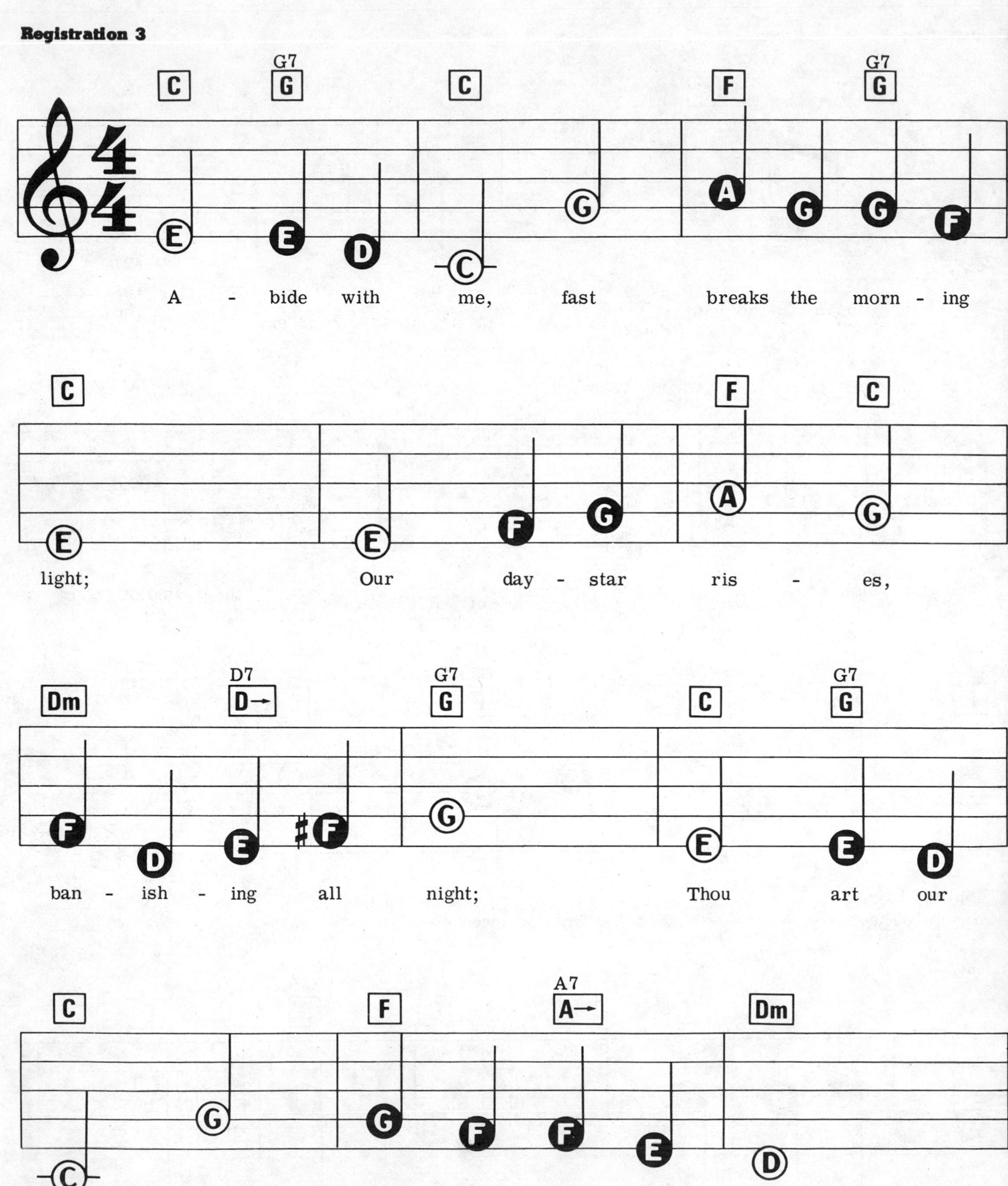

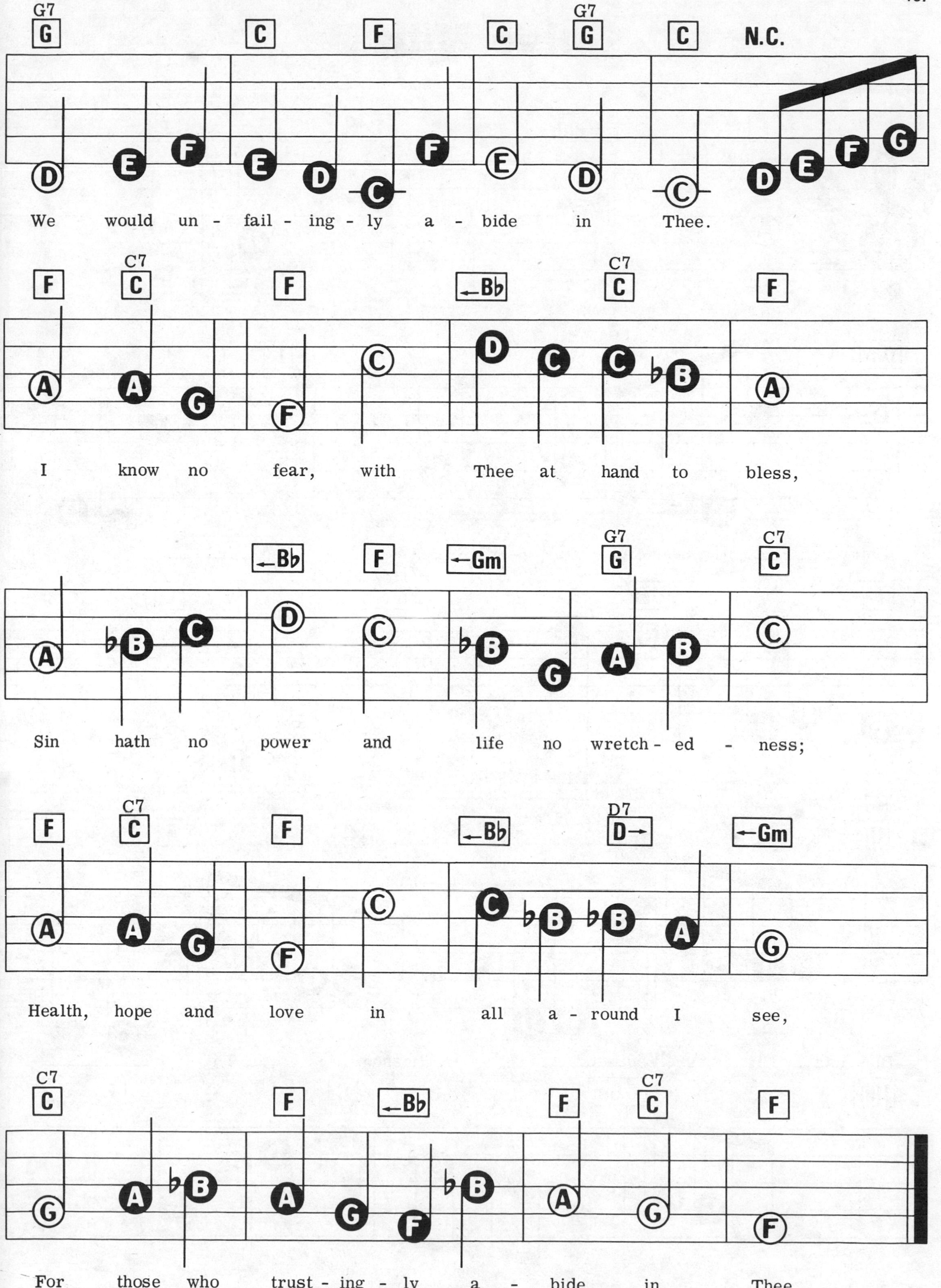
G7 G C F C G7 G C N.C.
D E F E D C F E D C D E F G
We would un - fail - ing - ly a - bide in Thee.
F C7 C F ←B♭ C7 C F
A A G F C D C C ♭B A
I know no fear, with Thee at hand to bless,
←B♭ F ←Gm G7 G C7 C
A ♭B C D C ♭B G A B C
Sin hath no power and life no wretch - ed - ness;
F C7 C F ←B♭ D7 D→ ←Gm
A A G F C C ♭B ♭B A G
Health, hope and love in all a - round I see,
C7 C F ←B♭ F C7 C F
G A ♭B A G F ♭B A G F
For those who trust - ing - ly a - bide in Thee.

Ave Maria

Registration 6

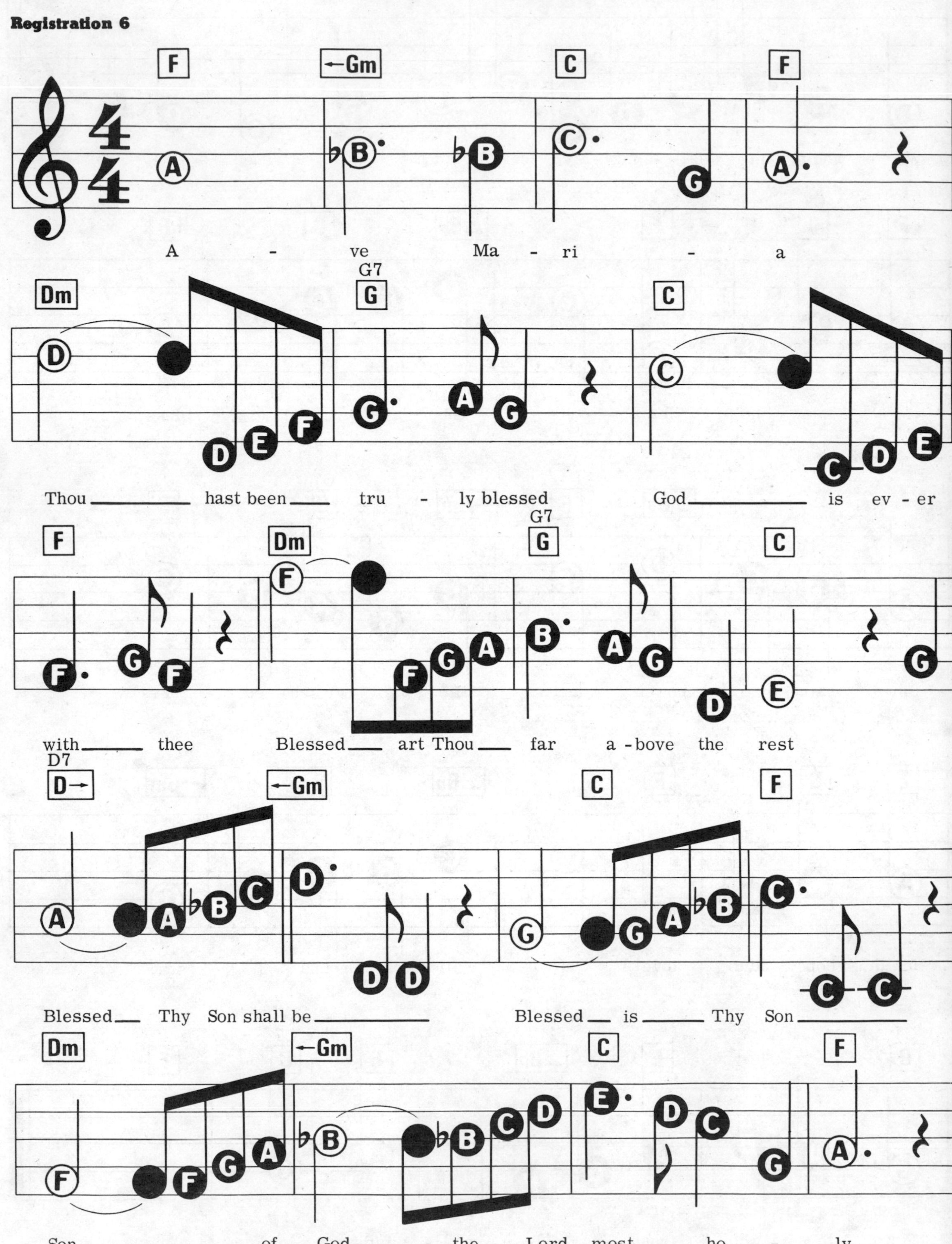

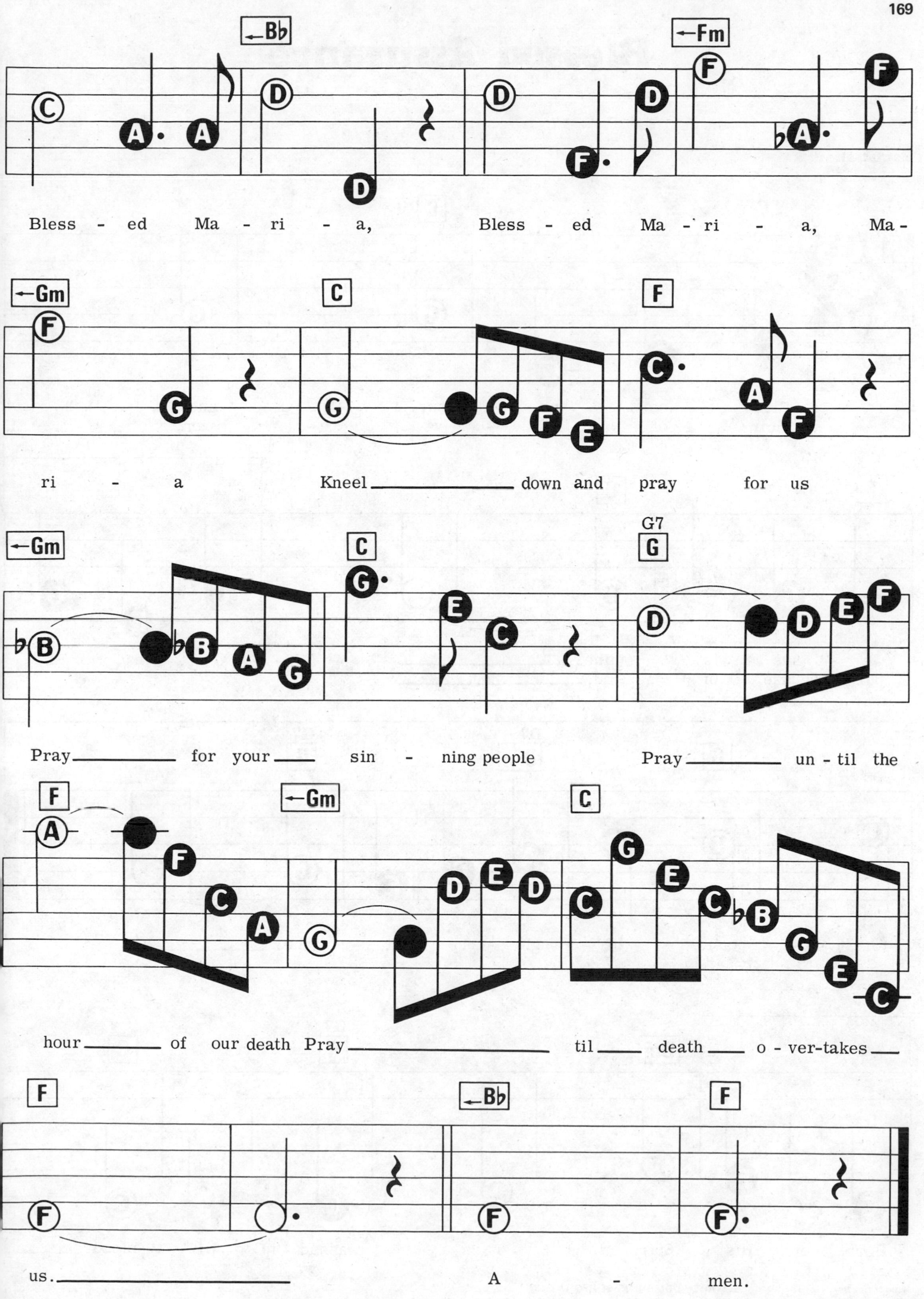
Bb
Fm
Bless - ed Ma - ri - a, Bless - ed Ma - ri - a, Ma -
Gm
C
F
ri - a Kneel down and pray for us
Gm
C
G7
G
Pray for your sin - ning people Pray un - til the
F
Gm
C
hour of our death Pray til death o - ver-takes
F
Bb
F
us. A - men.

Blessed Assurance

Registration 6

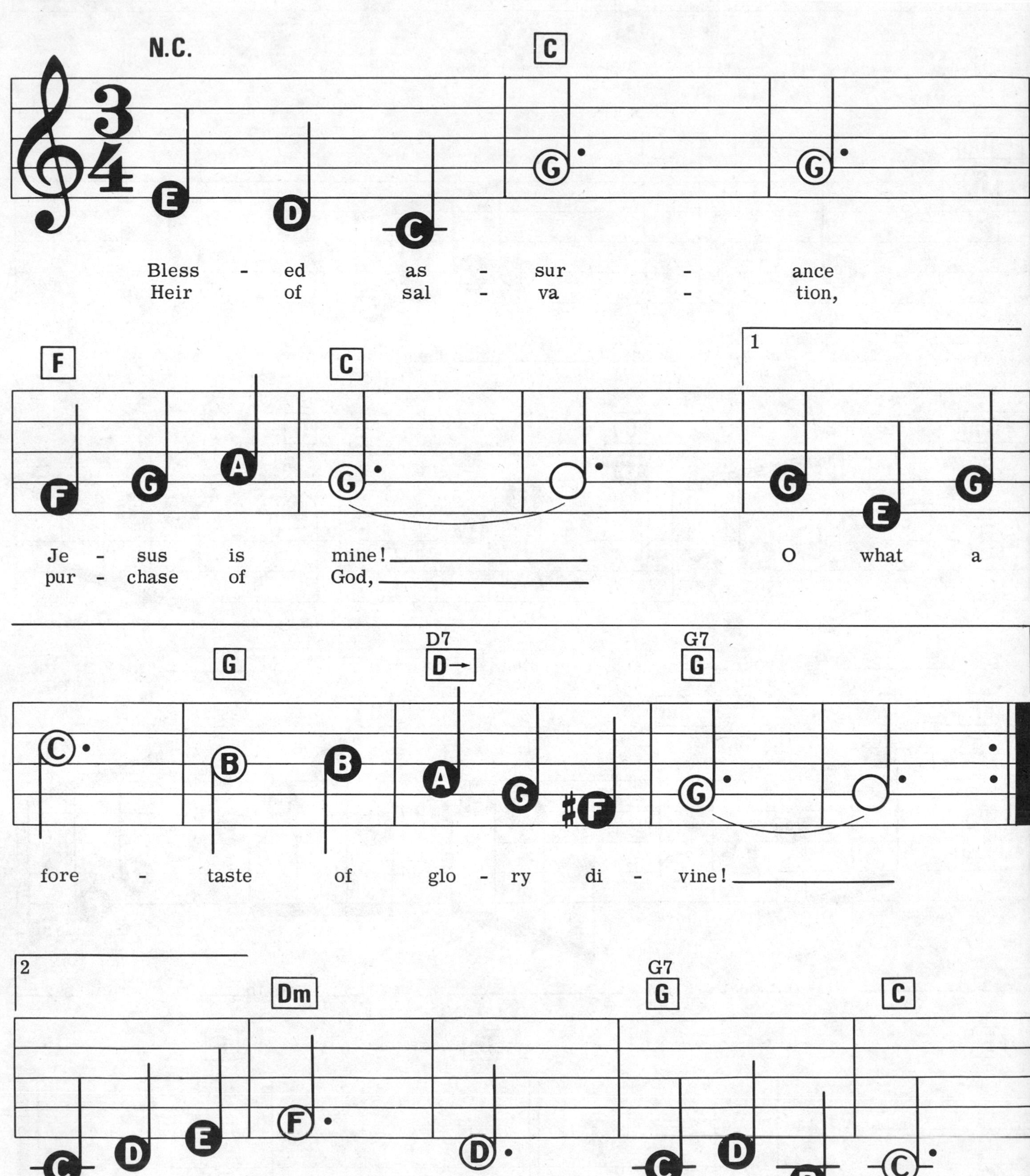

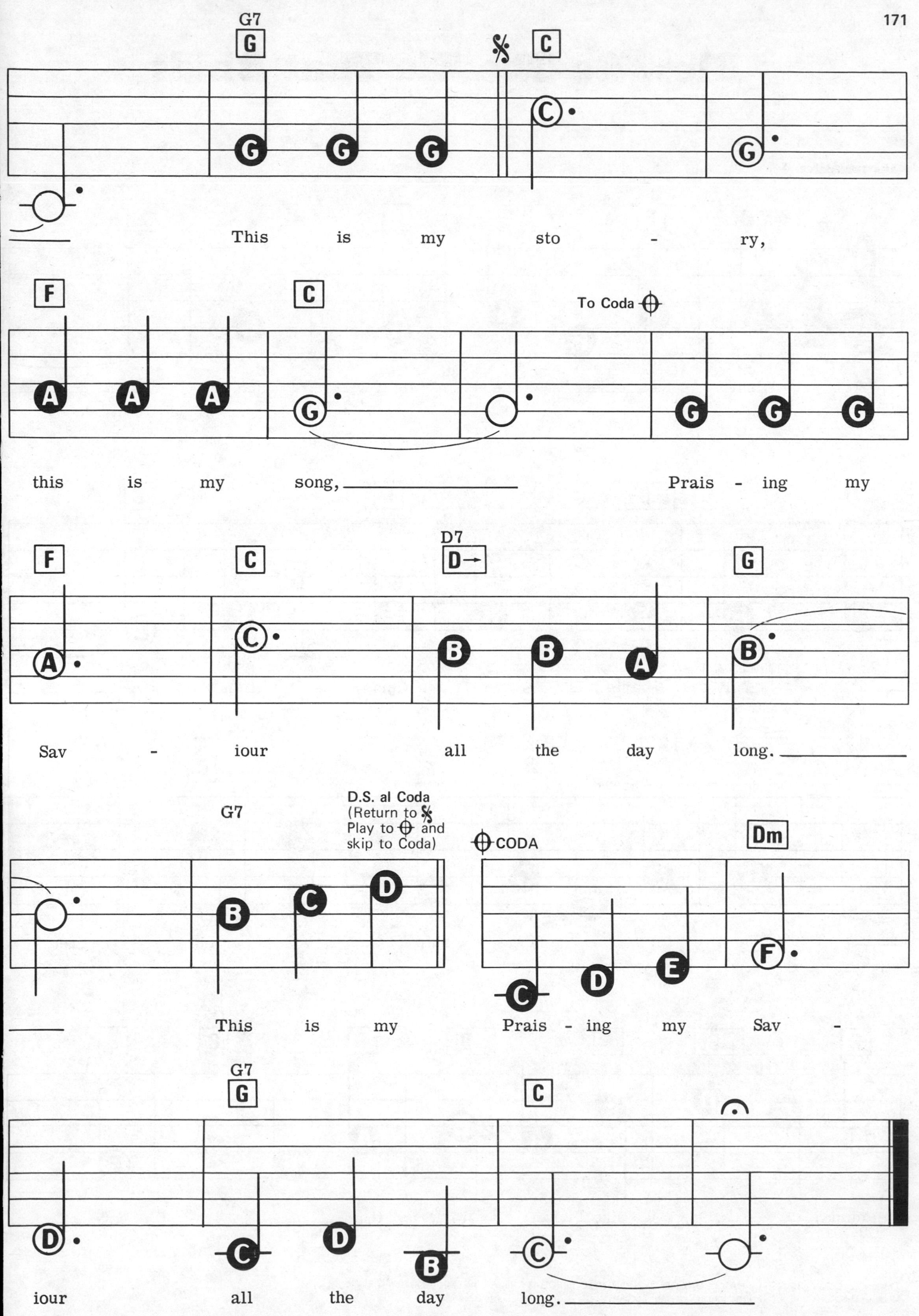
G7
G
C
This is my sto - ry,
F
C
To Coda
this is my song,
Prais - ing my
F
C
D7
D
G
Sav - iour all the day long.
G7
D.S. al Coda
(Return to
Play to and
skip to Coda)
CODA
Dm
This is my Prais - ing my Sav -
G7
G
C
iour all the day long.

Blest Be The Tie That Binds

Registration 4

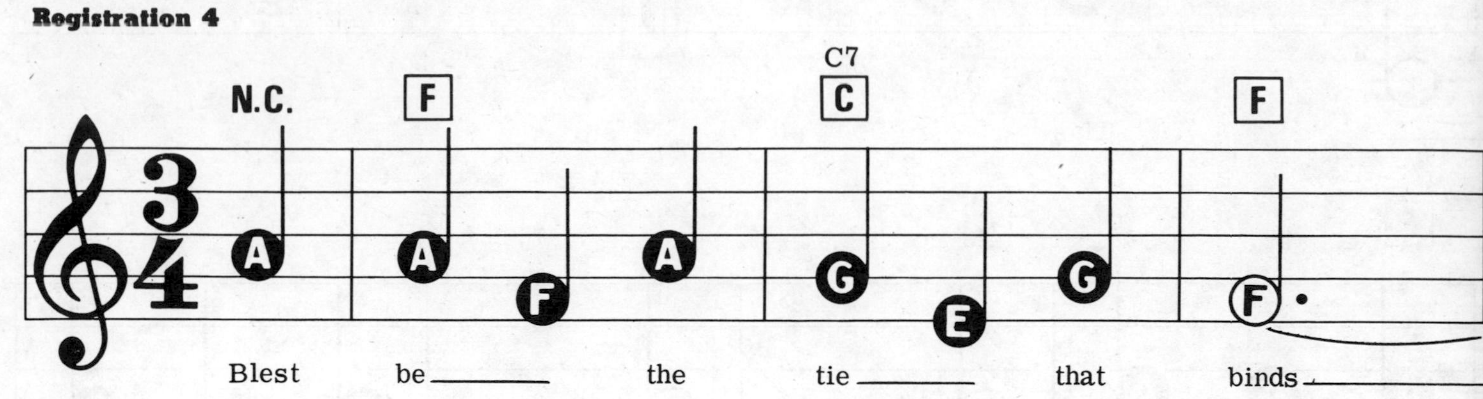

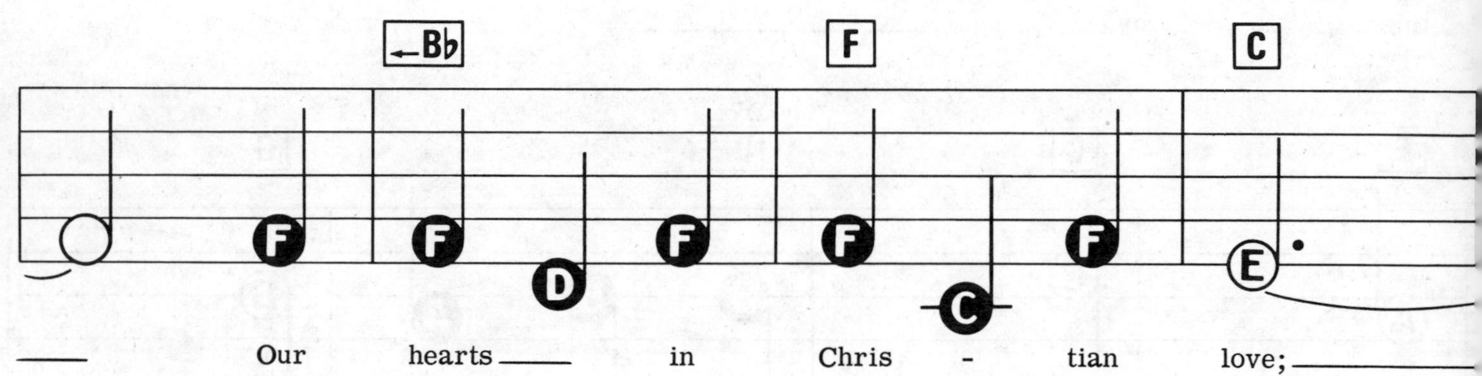

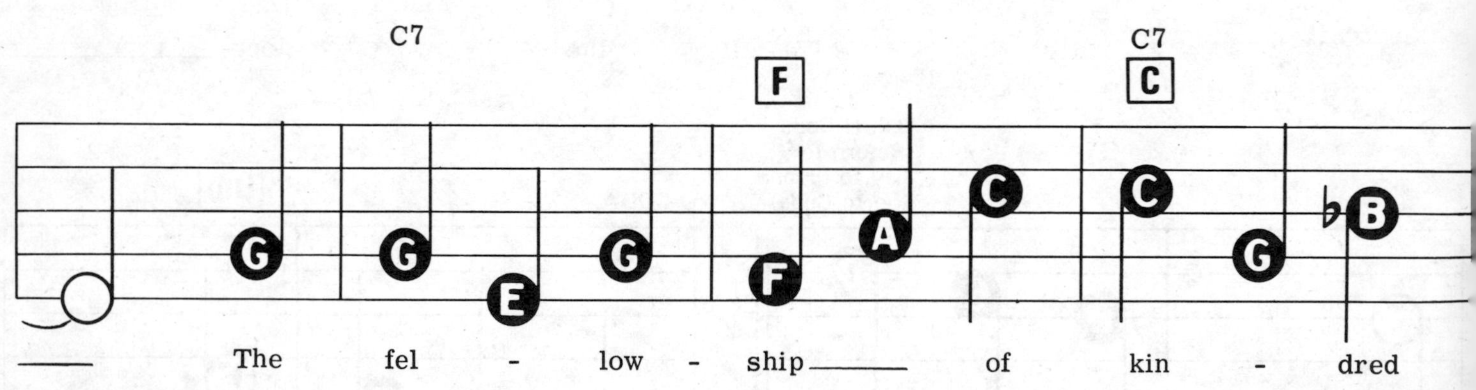

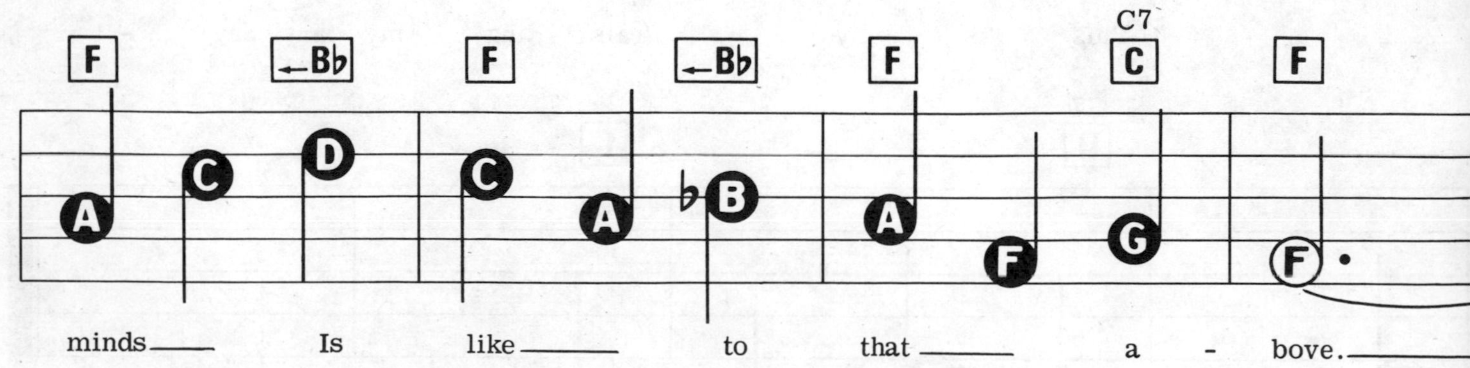

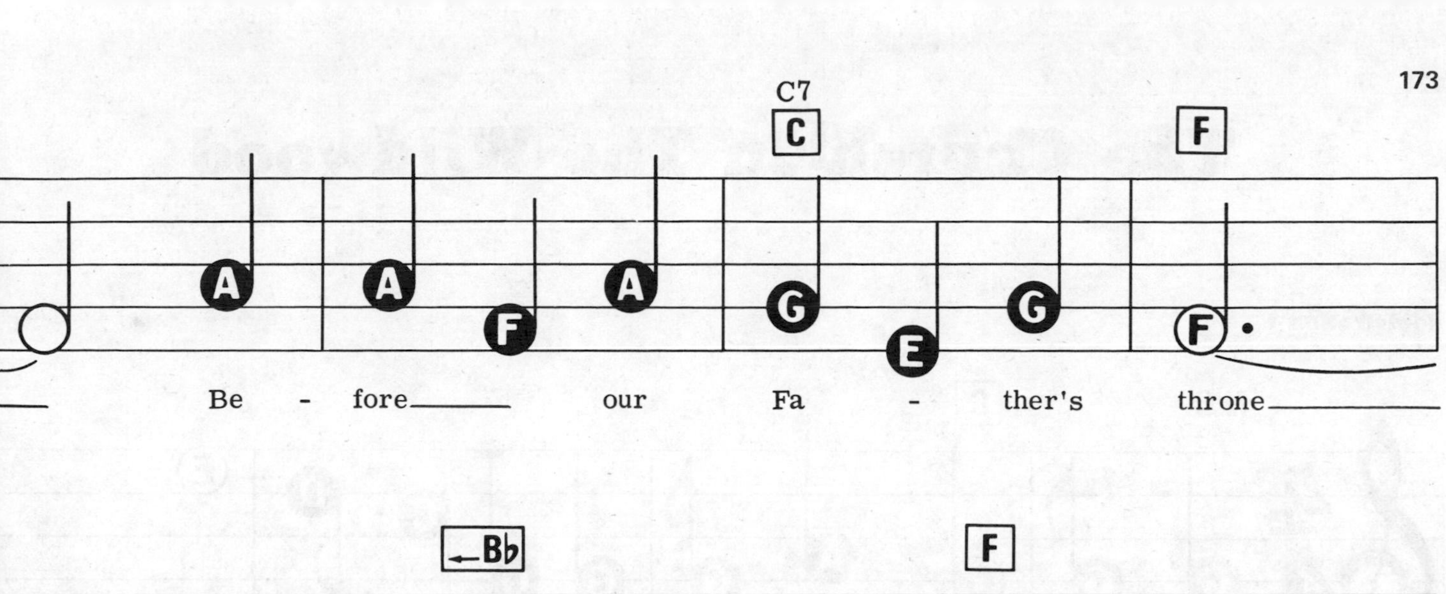
C7
C
F
A
A
F
A
G
E
G
F
Be - fore our Fa - ther's throne

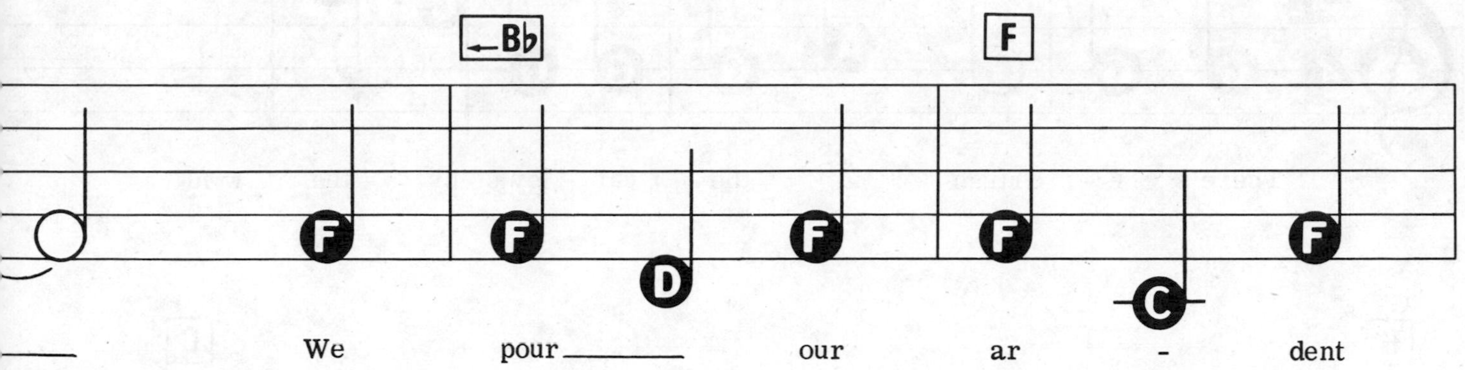
←B♭
F
F
F
D
F
F
C
F
We pour our ar - dent

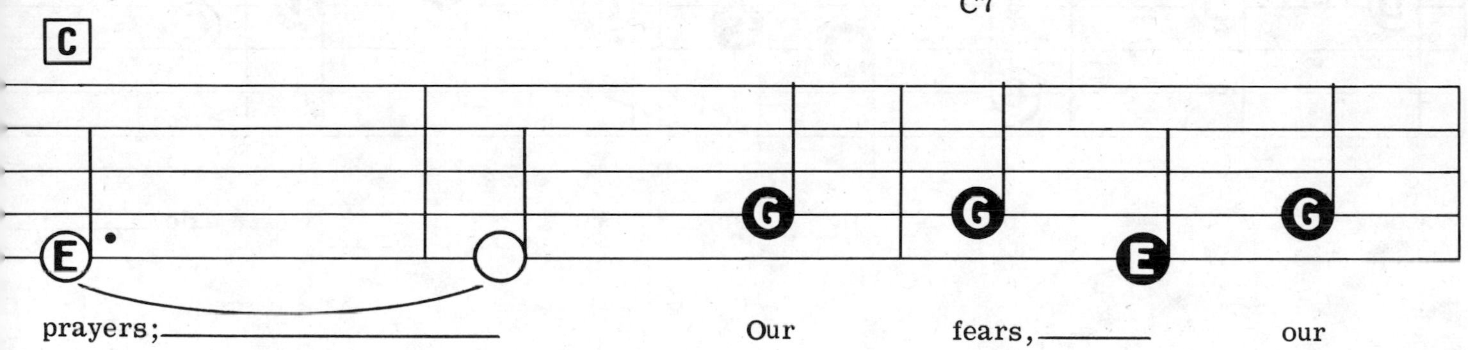
C
C7
E
G
G
E
G
prayers; Our fears, our

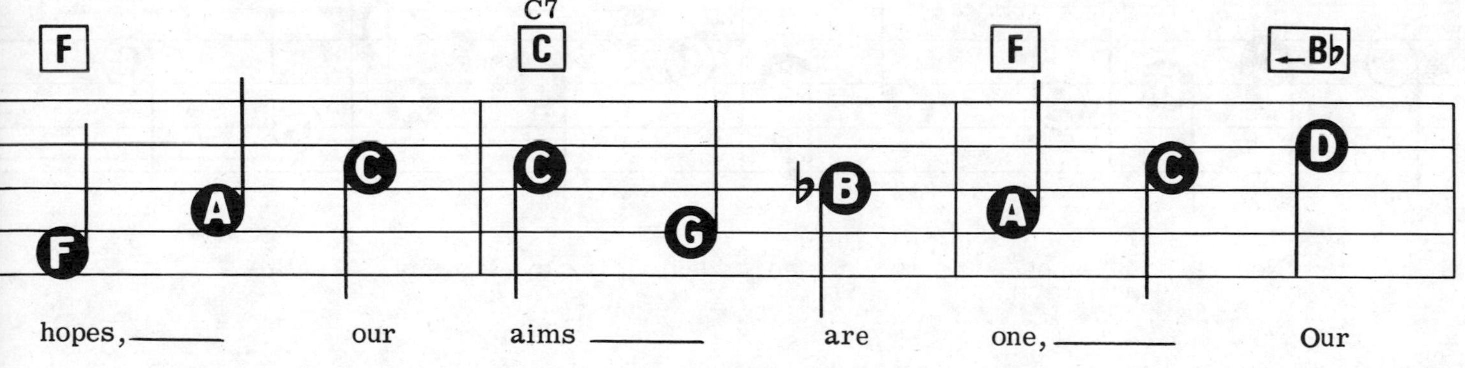
F
C7
C
F
←B♭
F
A
C
C
G
♭B
A
C
D
hopes, our aims are one, Our

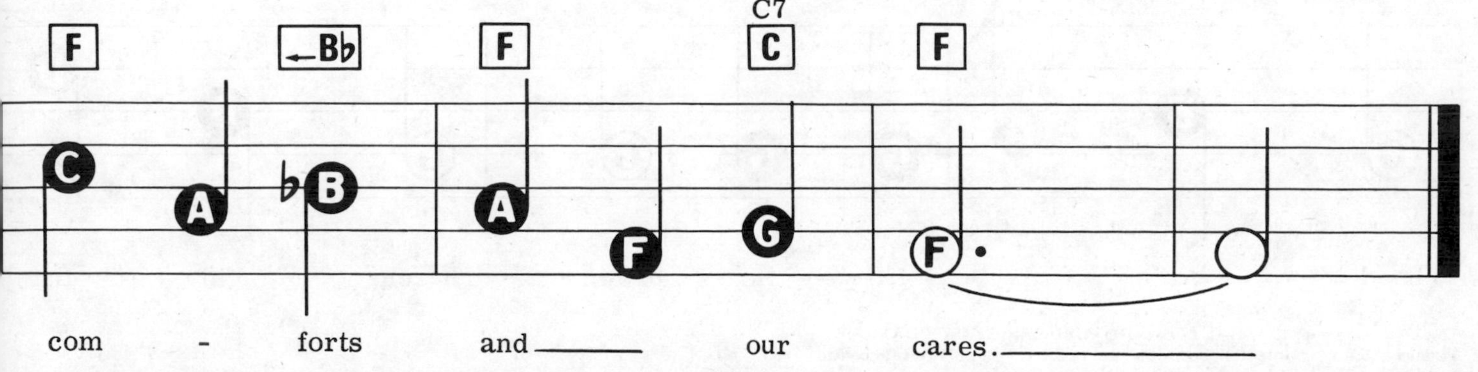
F
←B♭
F
C7
C
F
C
A
♭B
A
F
G
F
com - forts and our cares.

The Church In The Wildwood

Registration 6

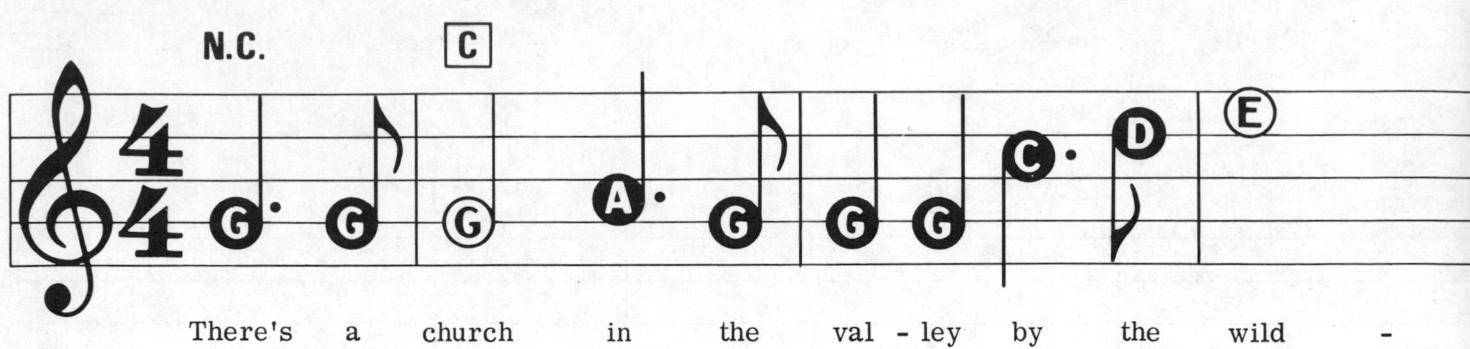

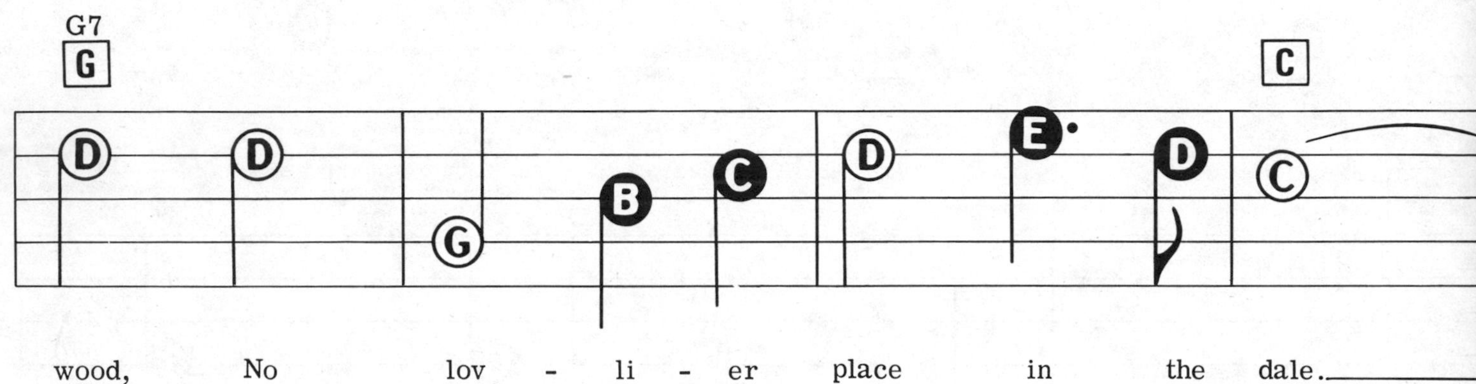

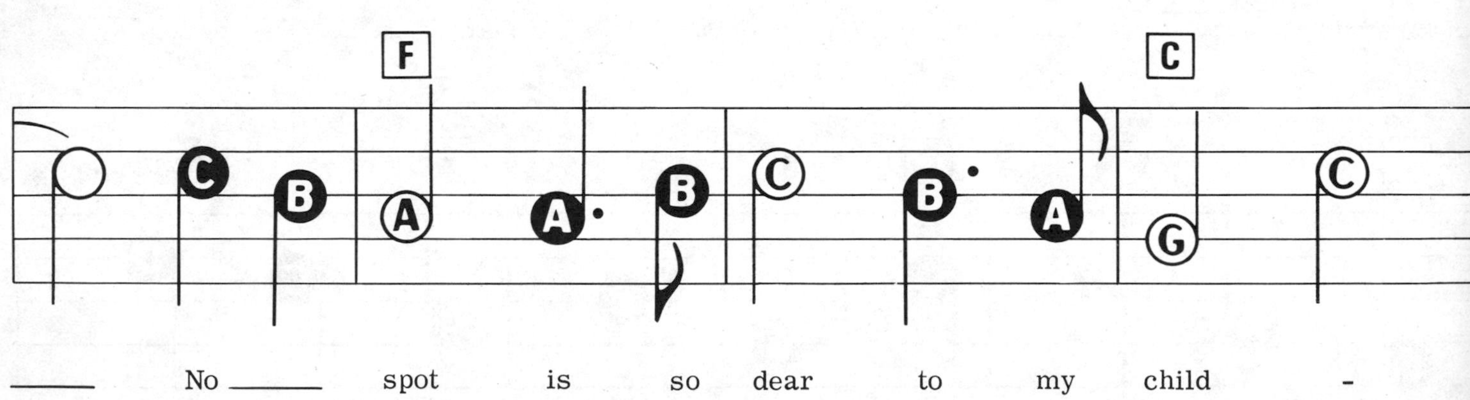

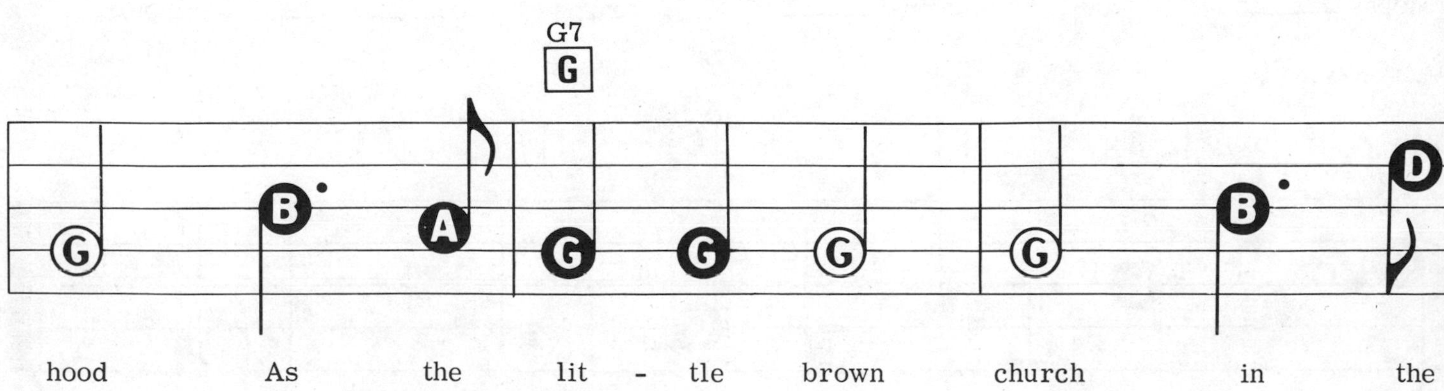

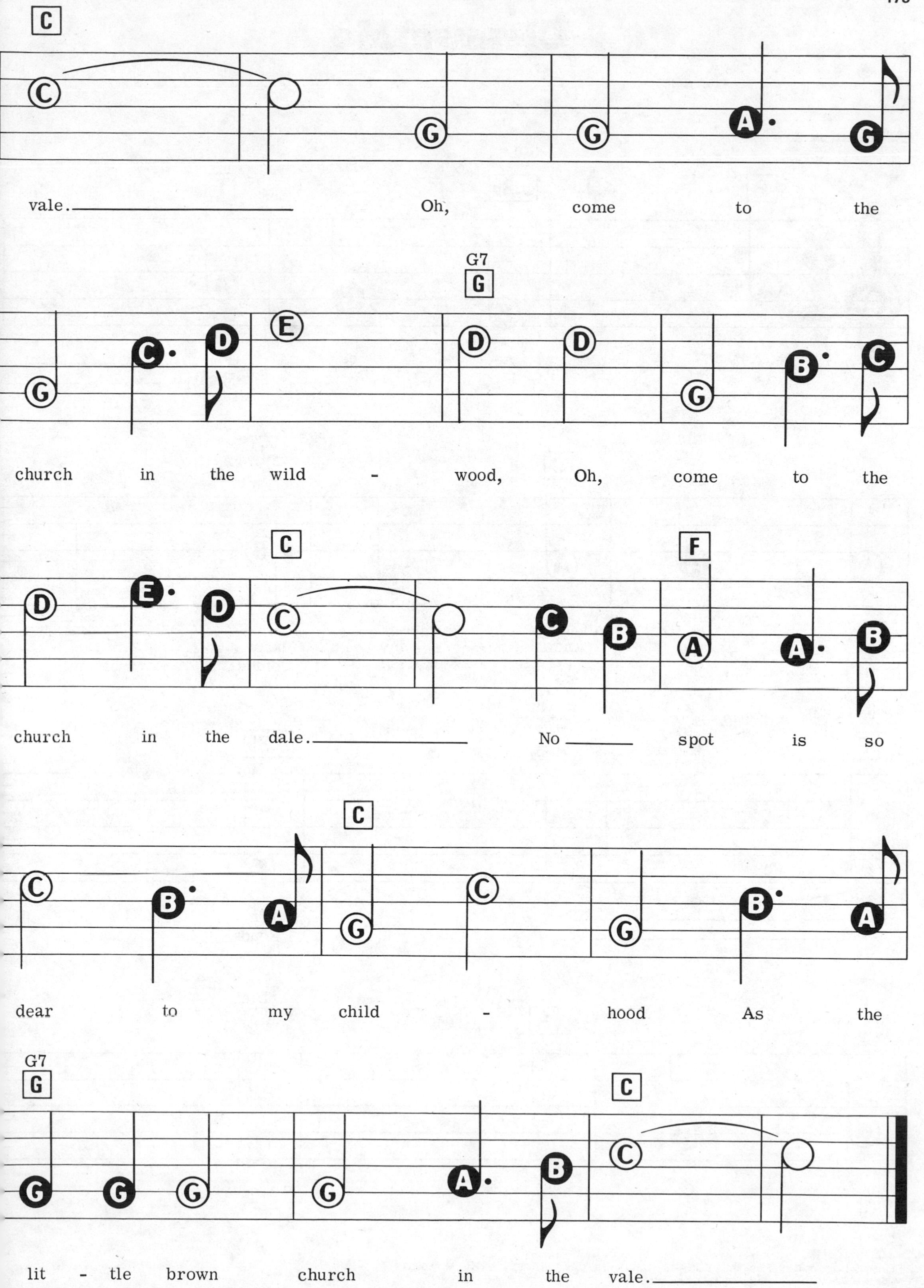
C
vale.
Oh, come to the
G7
G
church in the wild - wood, Oh, come to the
C
F
church in the dale. No spot is so
C
dear to my child - hood As the
G7
G
C
lit - tle brown church in the vale.

Cleanse Me

Registration 2

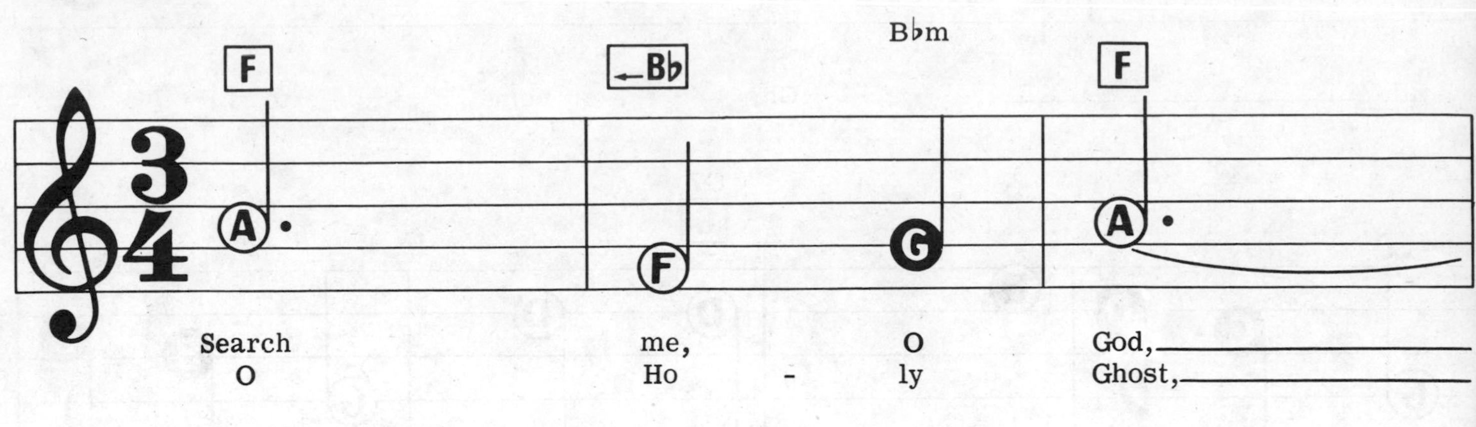

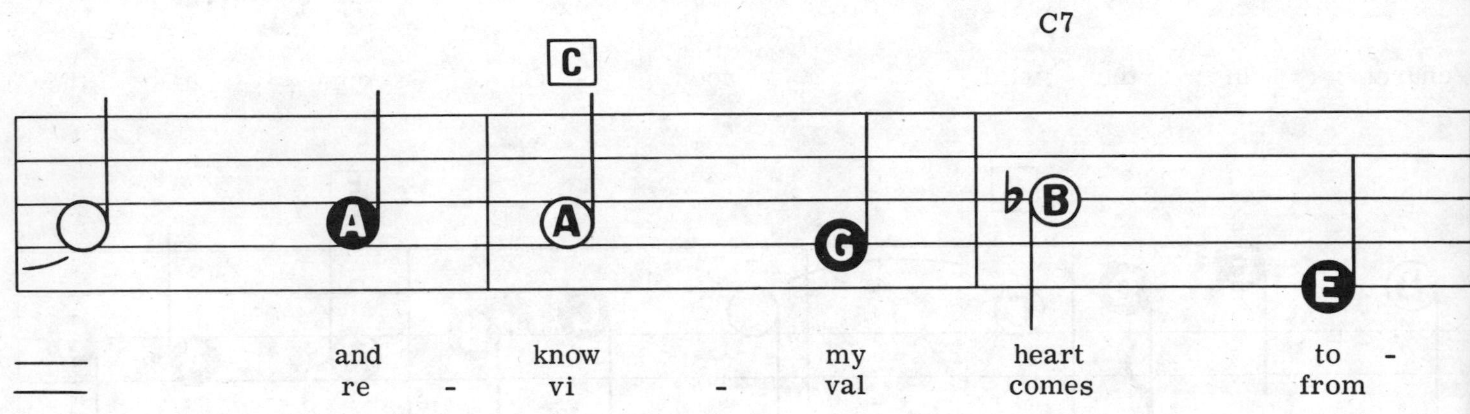

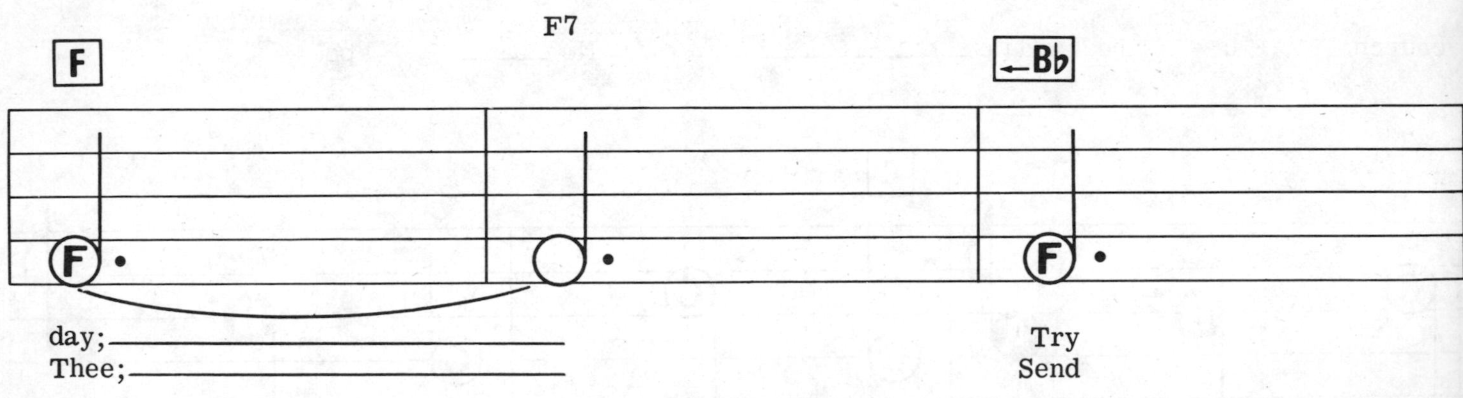

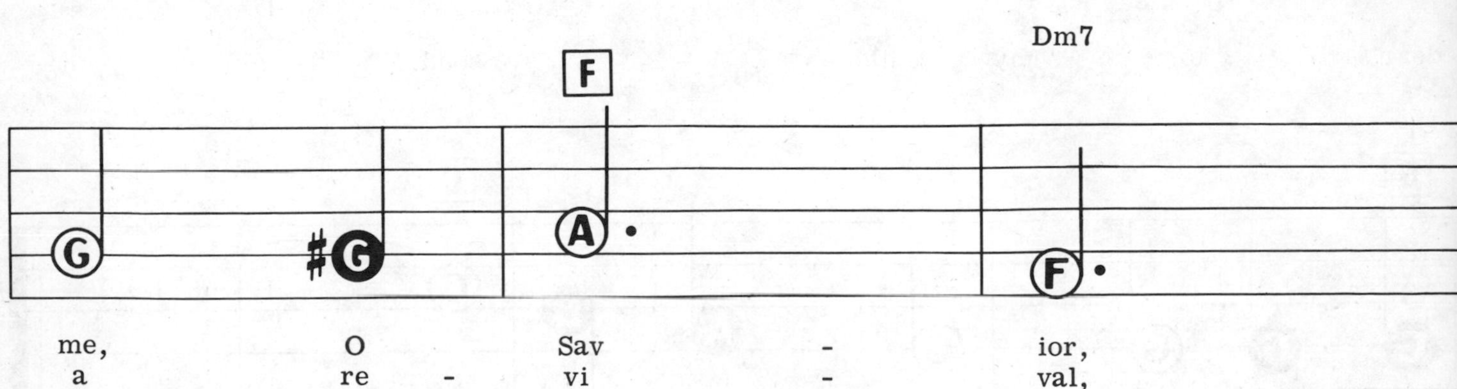

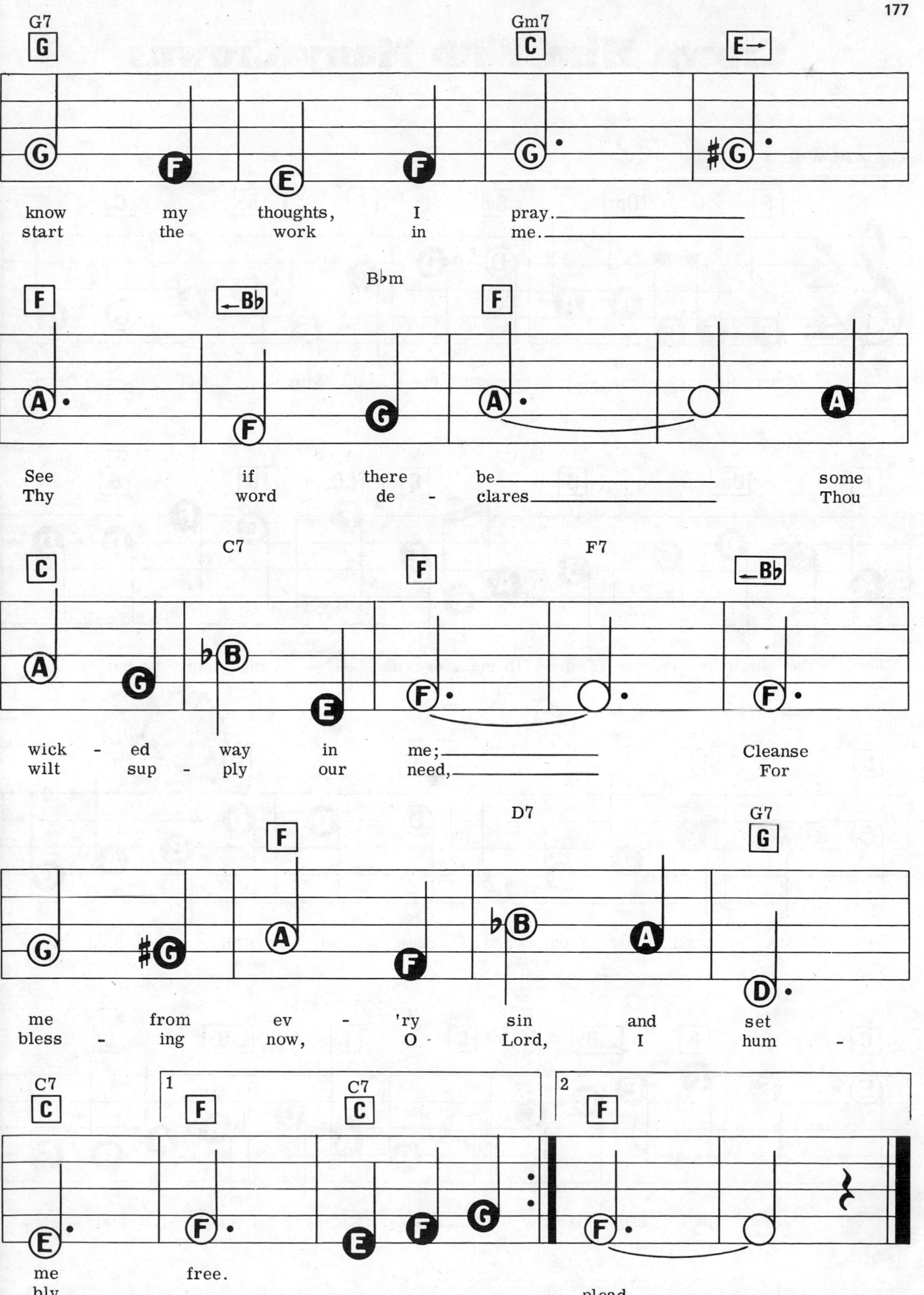
G7 Gm7
know my thoughts, I pray.
start the work in me.
B♭m
See if there be some
Thy word de - clares Thou
C7 F7
wick - ed way in me; Cleanse
wilt sup - ply our need, For
D7 G7
me from ev - 'ry sin and set
bless - ing now, O Lord, I hum -
C7 C7
me free.
bly plead.

Crown Him With Many Crowns

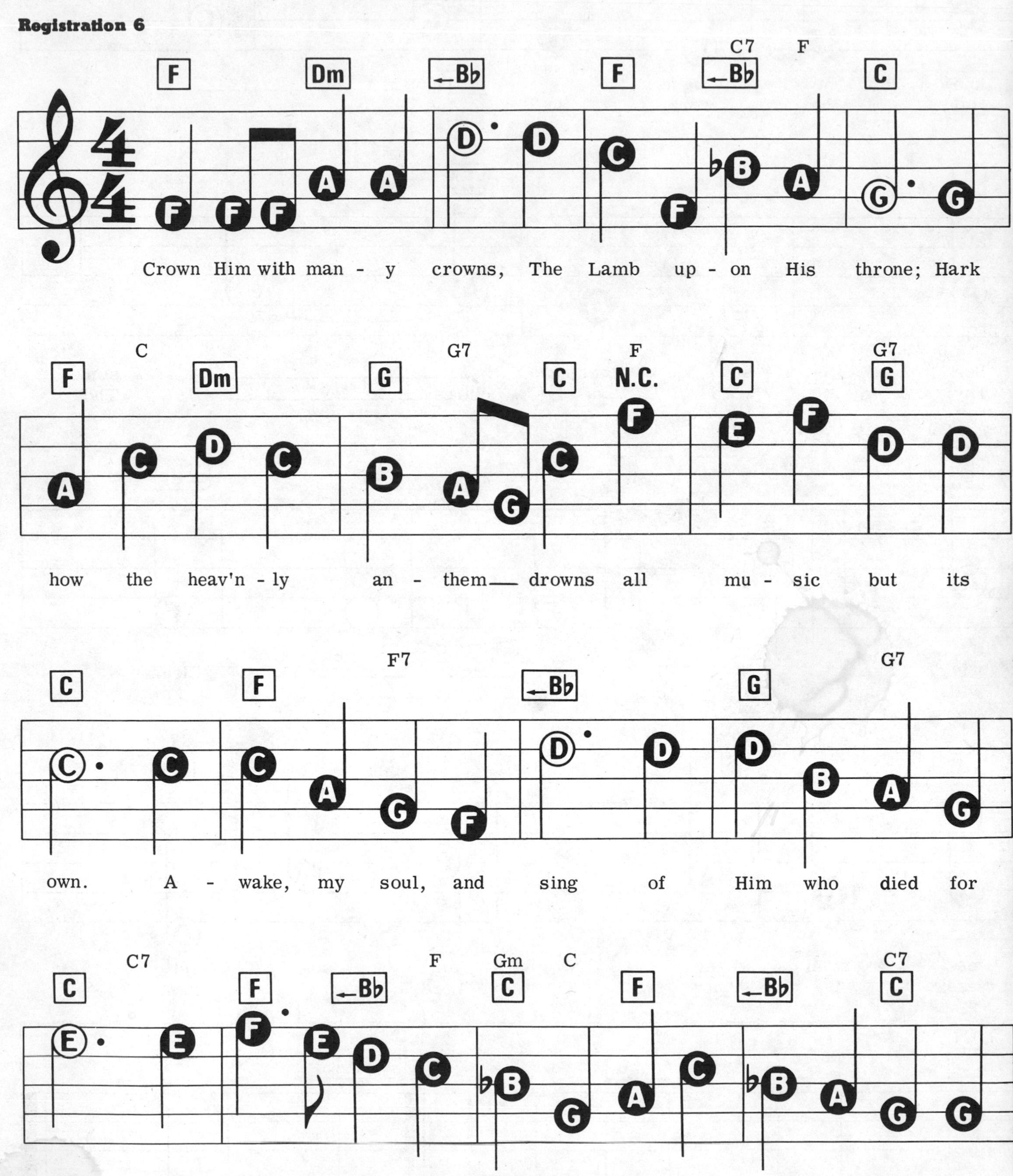

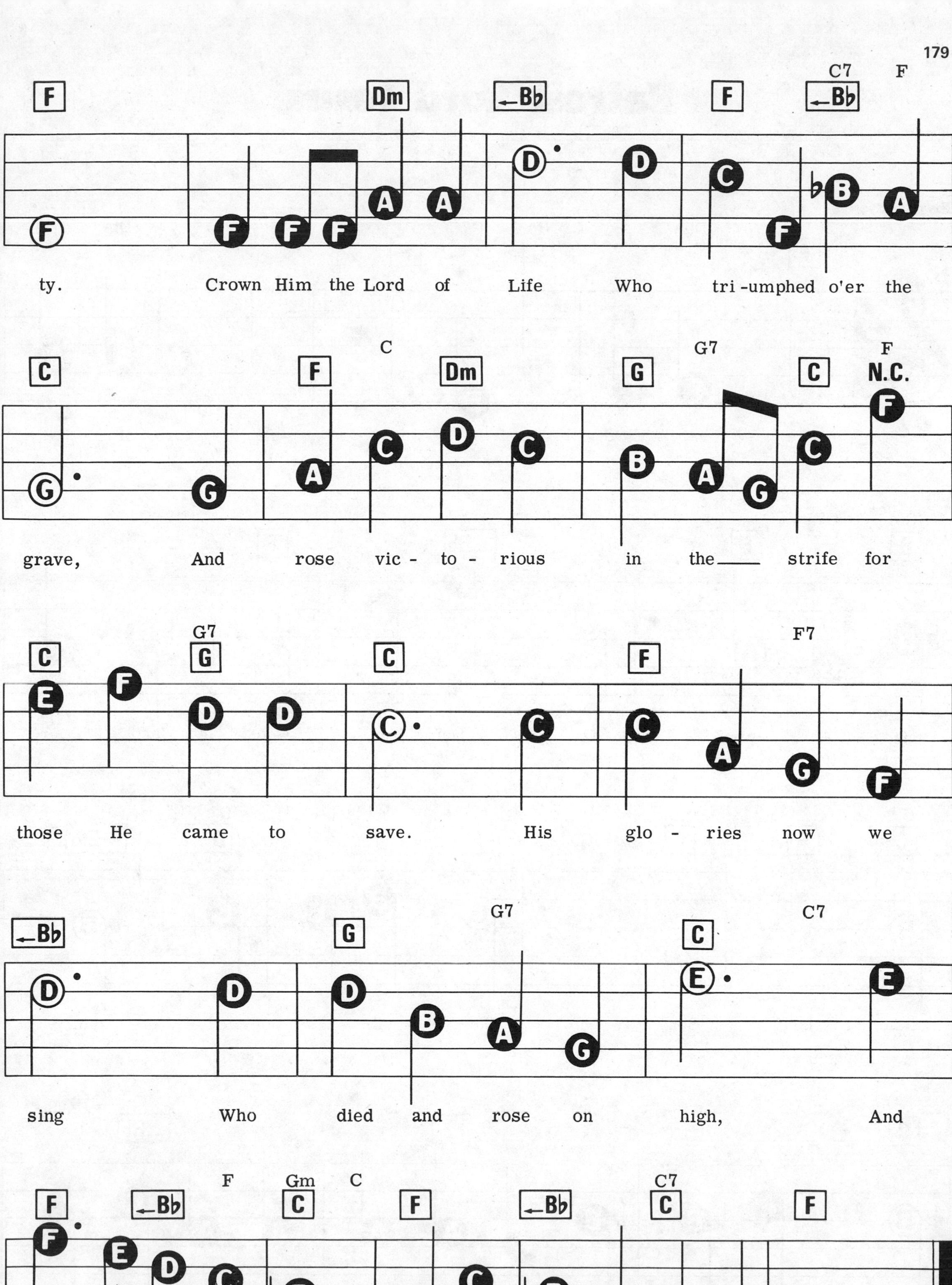

F Dm ←B♭ F C7 ←B♭ F
ty. Crown Him the Lord of Life Who tri-umphed o'er the
C F C Dm G G7 C F N.C.
grave, And rose vic - to - rious in the strife for
C G7 G C F F7
those He came to save. His glo - ries now we
←B♭ G G7 C C7
sing Who died and rose on high, And
F ←B♭ F Gm C C F ←B♭ C7 C F
died e - ter - nal life to bring and lives that death may die.

Fairest Lord Jesus

Registration 5

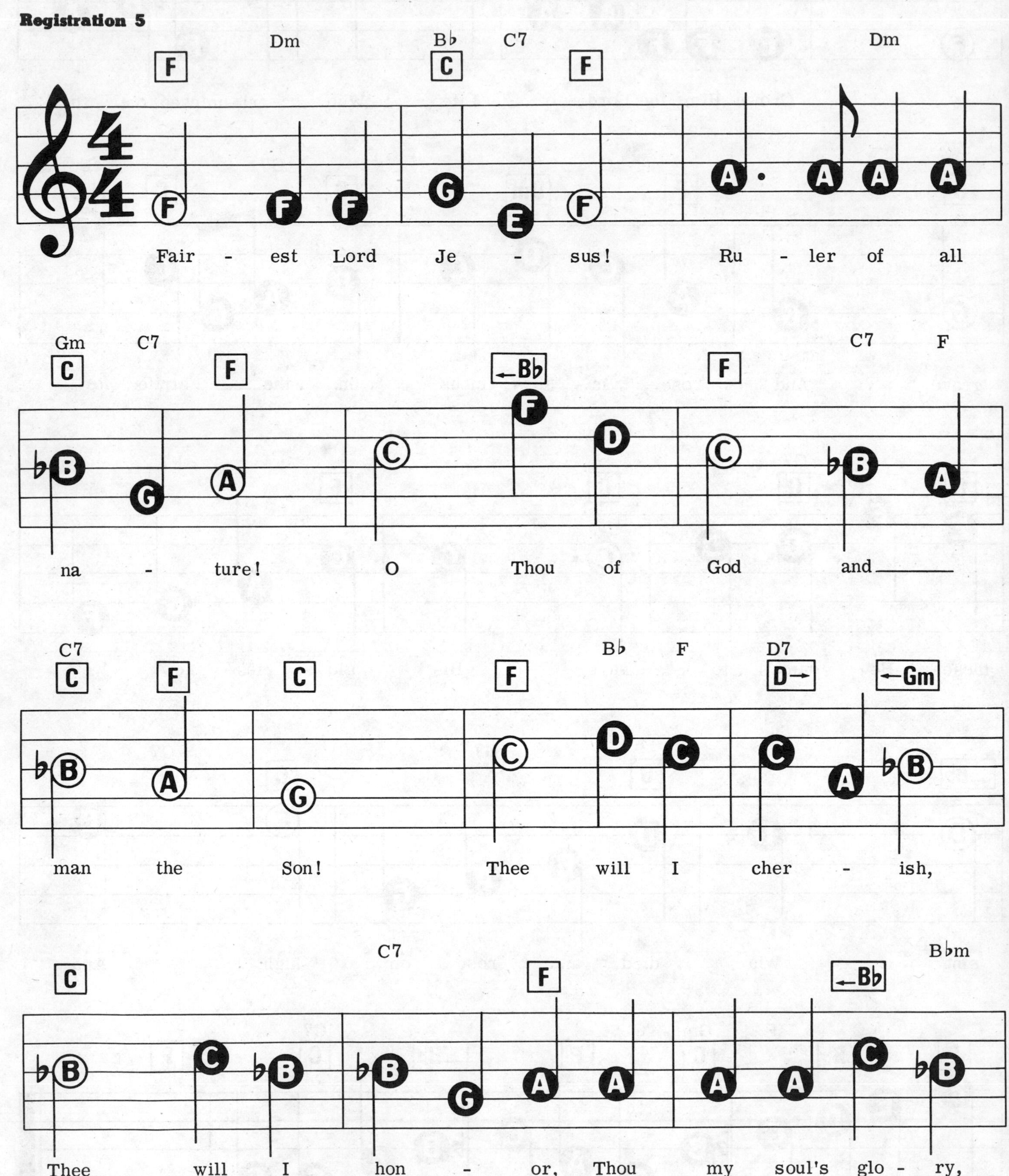

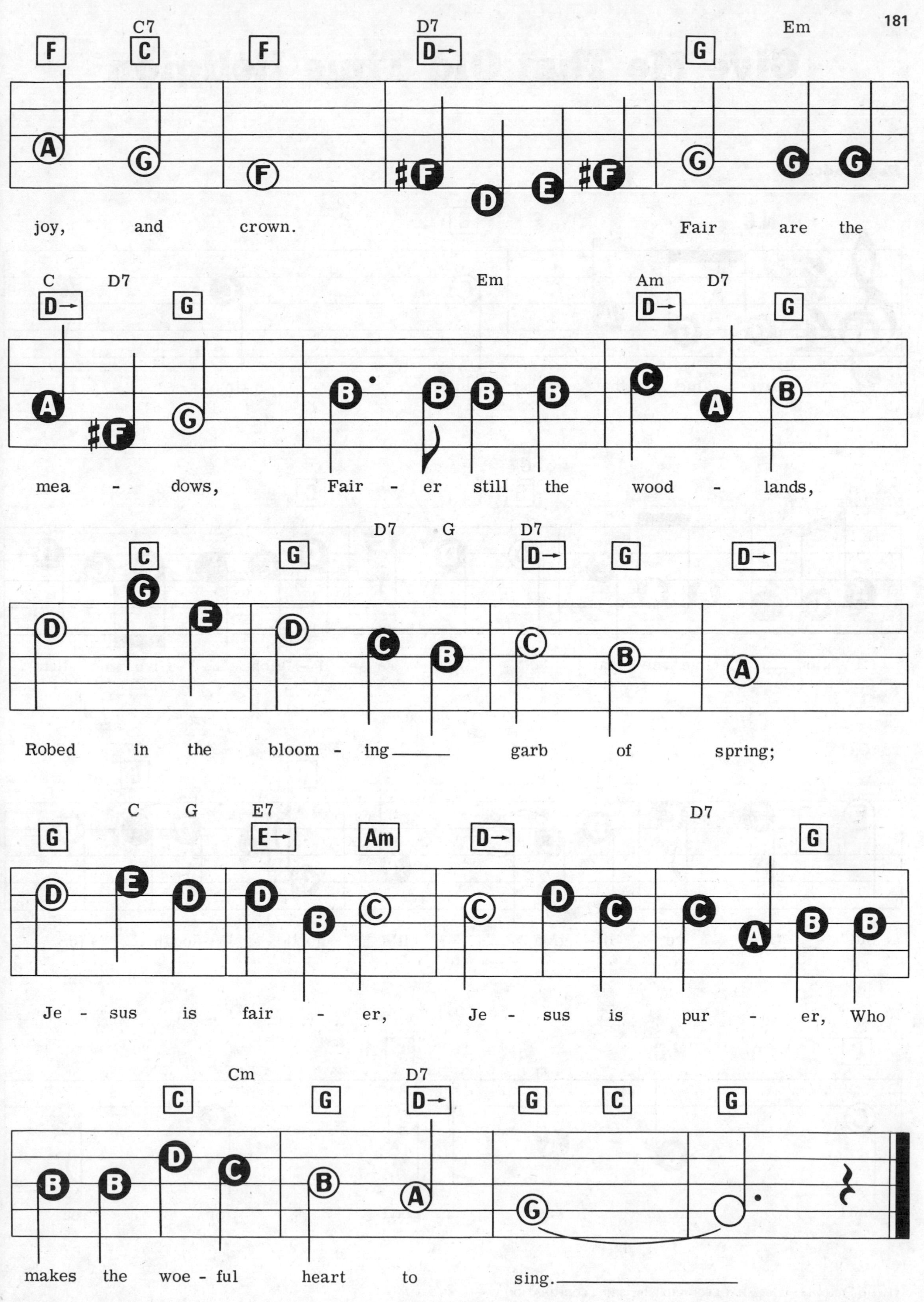
C7 D7 Em
F C F D→ G
joy, and crown. Fair are the
C D7 Em Am D7
D→ G D→ G
mea - dows, Fair - er still the wood - lands,
D7 G D7
C G D→ G D→
Robed in the bloom - ing garb of spring;
C G E7 D7
G E→ Am D→ G
Je - sus is fair - er, Je - sus is pur - er, Who
Cm D7
C G D→ G C G
makes the woe - ful heart to sing.

Give Me That Old Time Religion

Registration 5

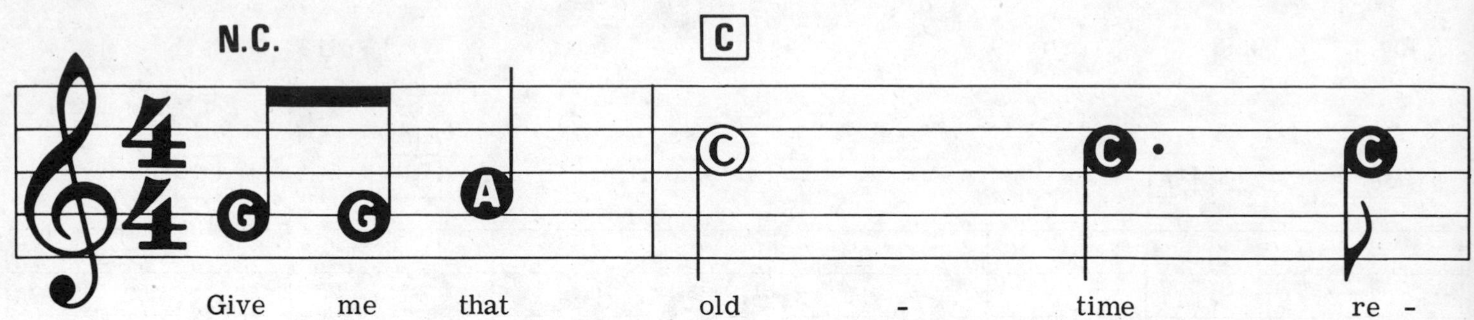

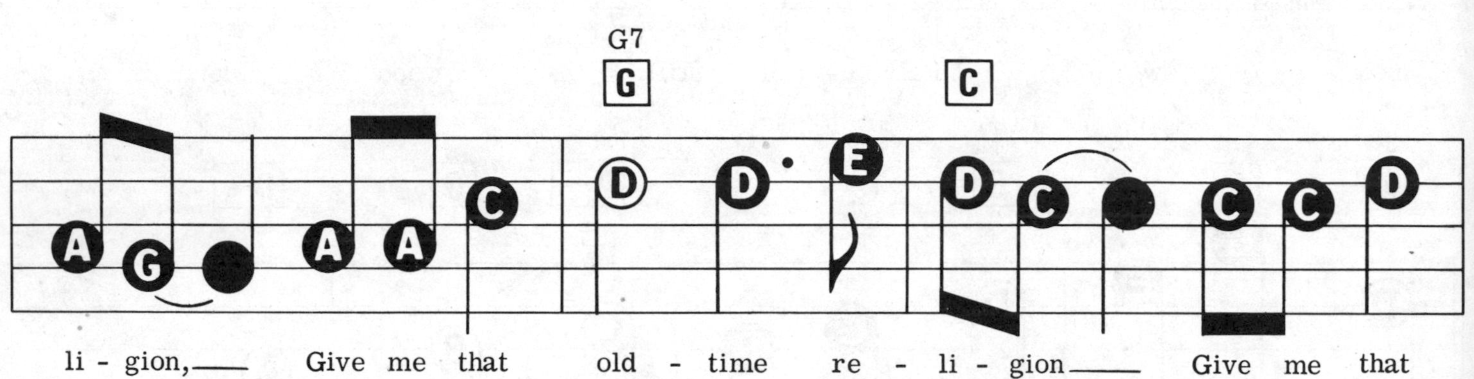

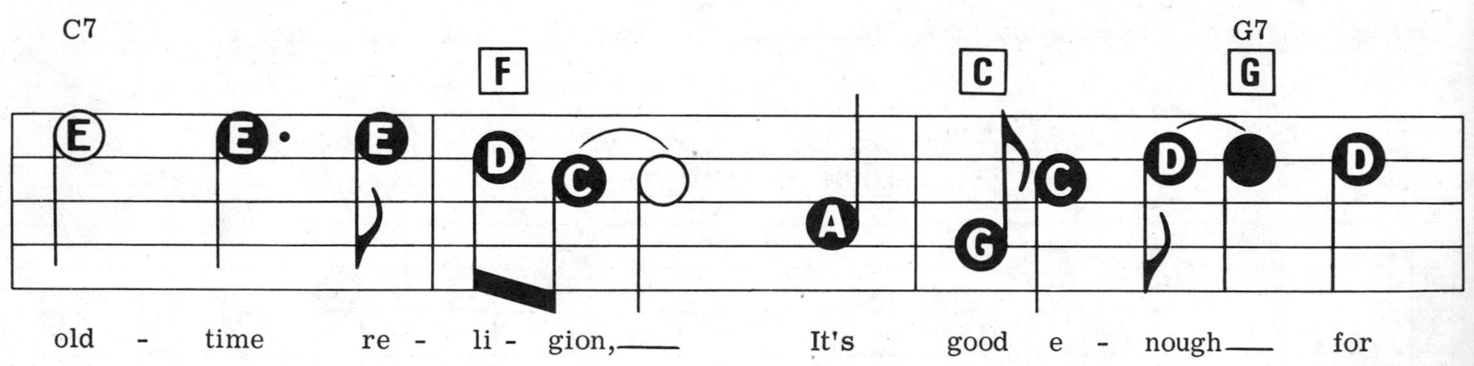

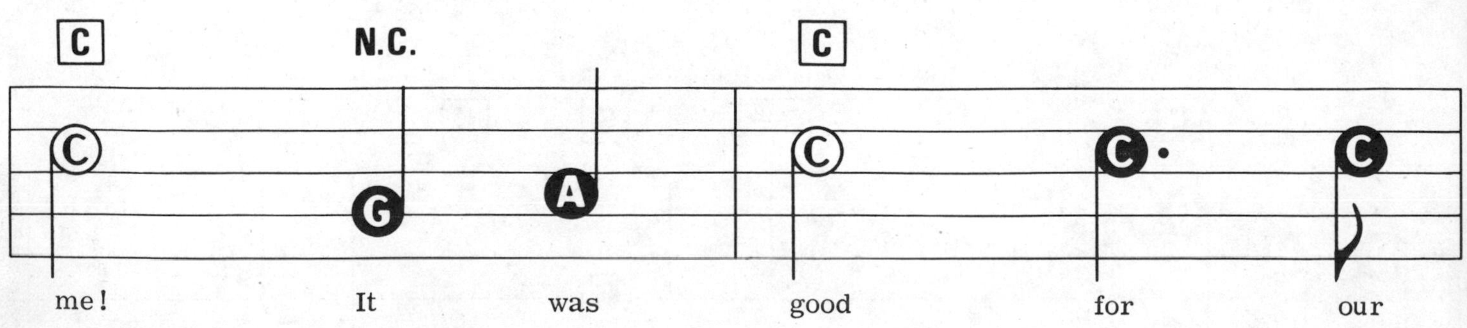

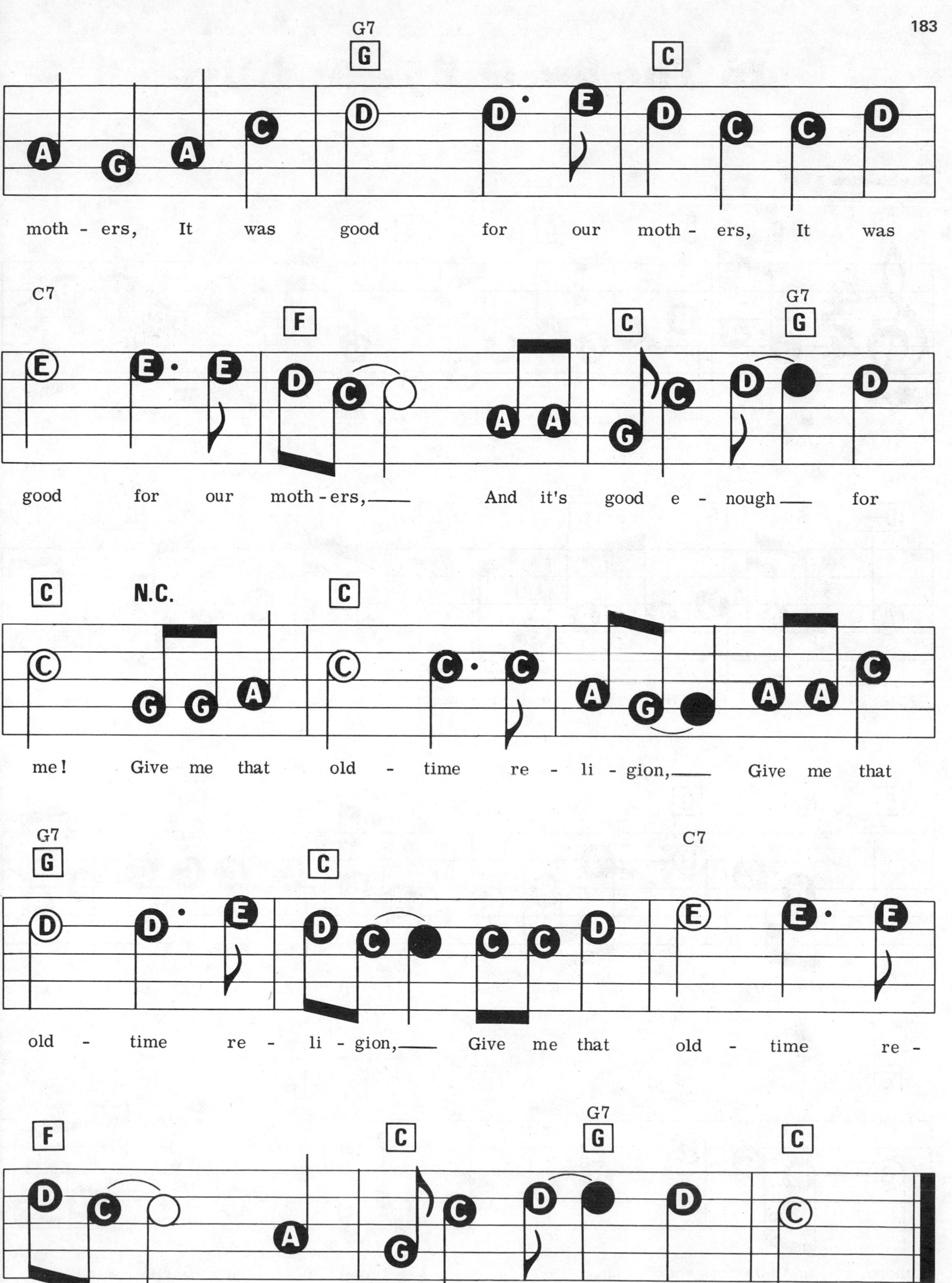
G7 G C
moth - ers, It was good for our moth - ers, It was
C7 F C G7 G
good for our moth - ers, And it's good e - nough for
C N.C. C
me! Give me that old - time re - li - gion, Give me that
G7 G C C7
old - time re - li - gion, Give me that old - time re -
F C G7 G C
li - gion, It's good e - nough for me!

In The Sweet Bye And Bye

Registration 1

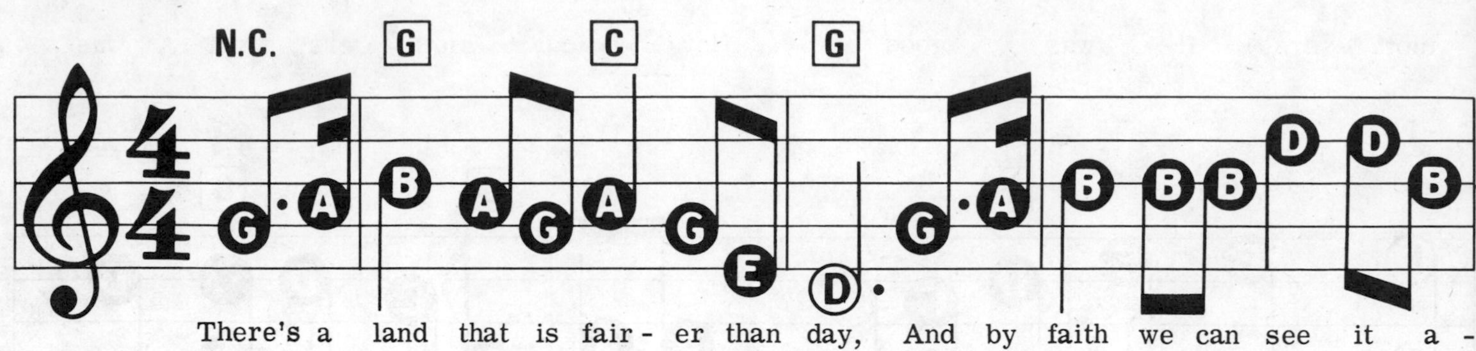

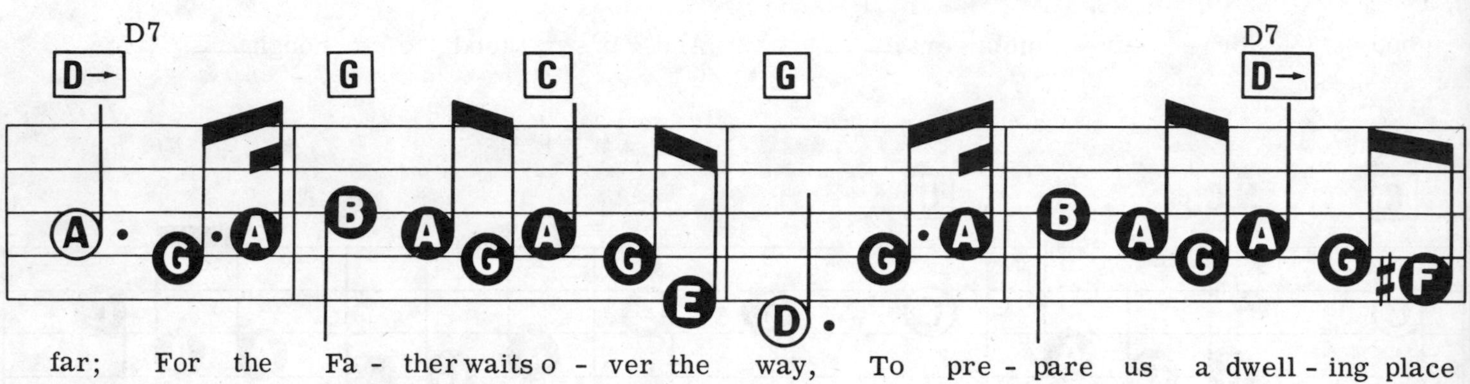

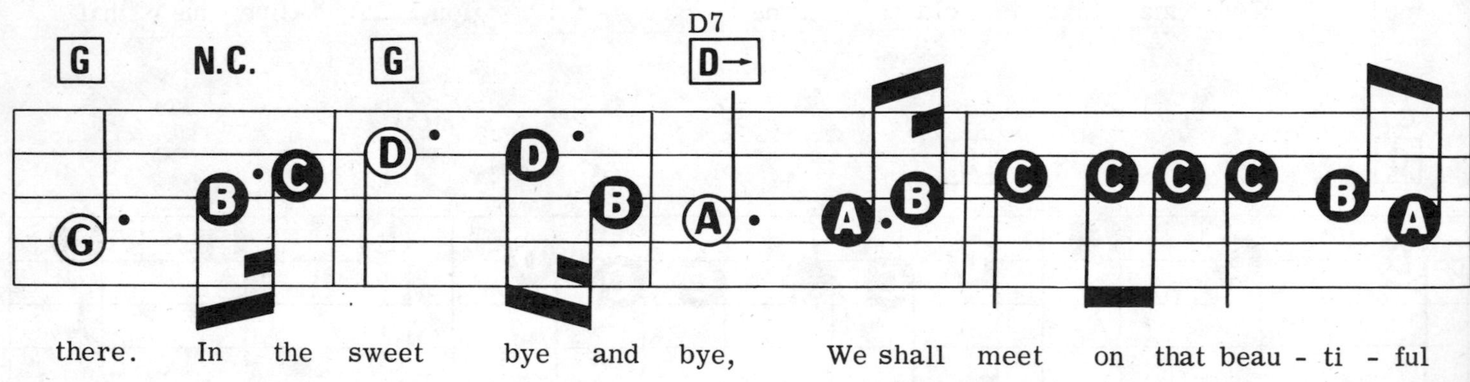

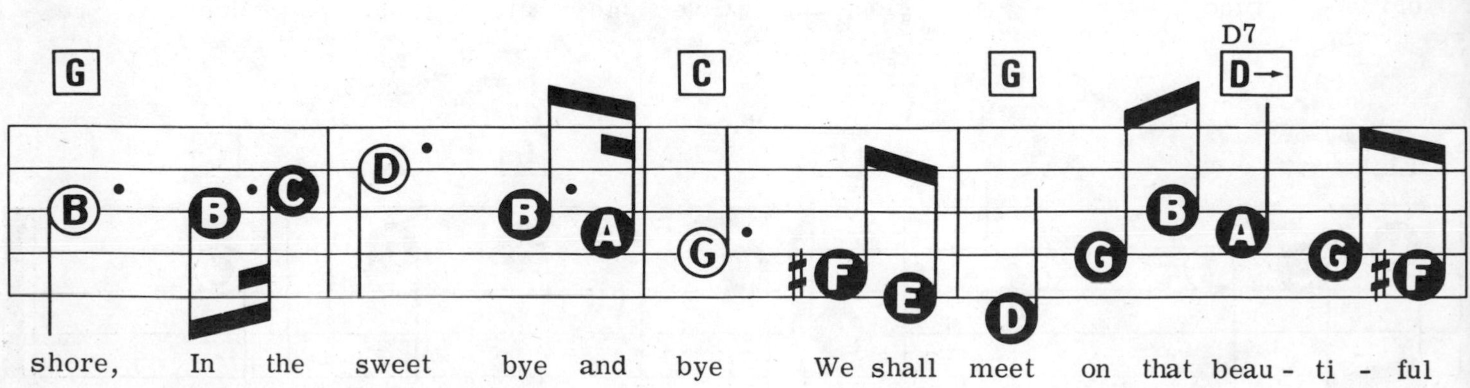

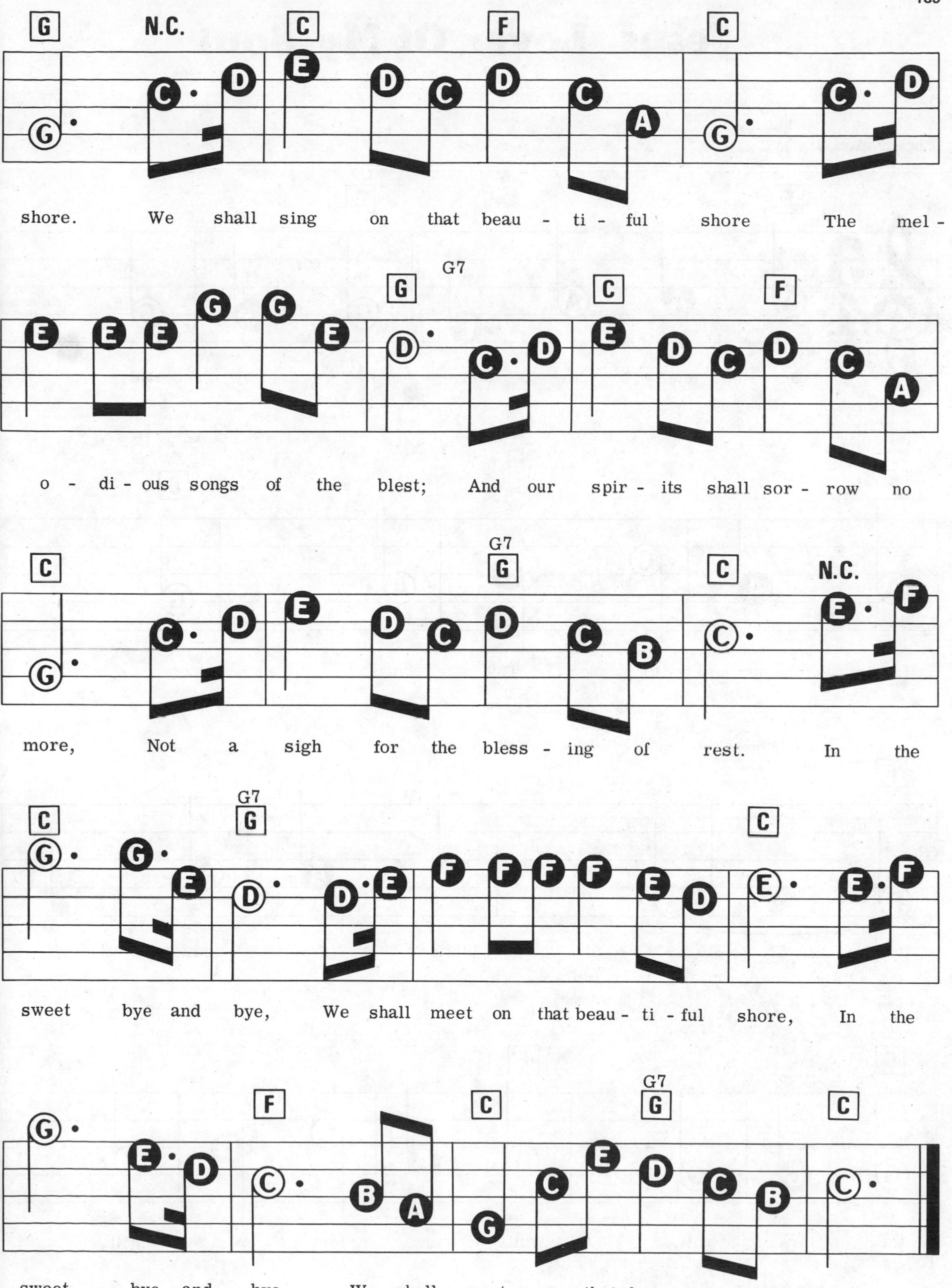
G
N.C.
C
F
C
G
C
D
E
D
C
D
C
A
G
C
D
shore. We shall sing on that beau - ti - ful shore The mel -
G7
G
C
F
E
E
E
G
G
E
D
C
D
E
D
C
D
C
A
o - di - ous songs of the blest; And our spir - its shall sor - row no
C
G7
G
C
N.C.
G
C
D
E
D
C
D
C
B
C
E
F
more, Not a sigh for the bless - ing of rest. In the
C
G7
G
C
G
G
E
D
D
E
F
F
F
F
E
D
E
E
F
sweet bye and bye, We shall meet on that beau - ti - ful shore, In the
F
C
G7
G
C
G
E
D
C
B
A
G
C
E
D
C
B
C
sweet bye and bye, We shall meet on that beau - ti - ful shore.

Jesus, Lover Of My Soul

Registration 3

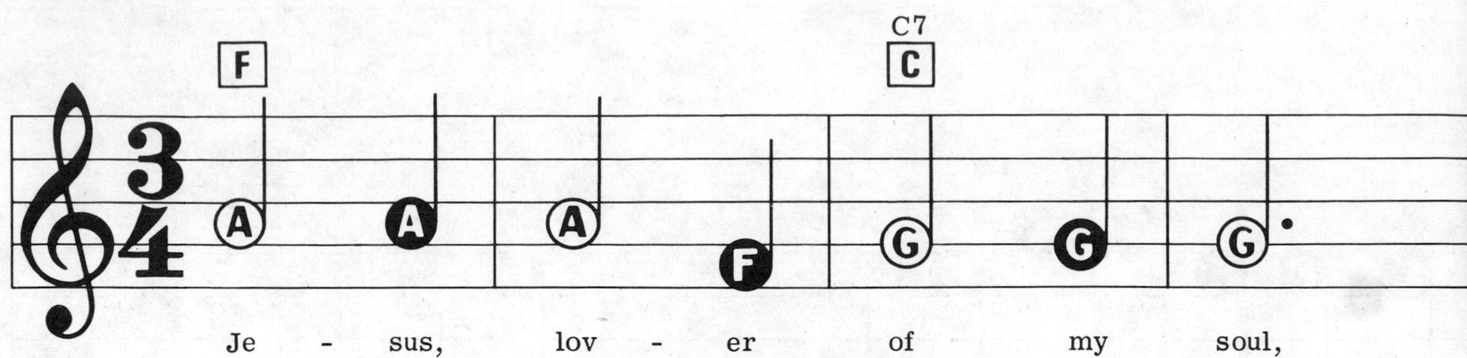

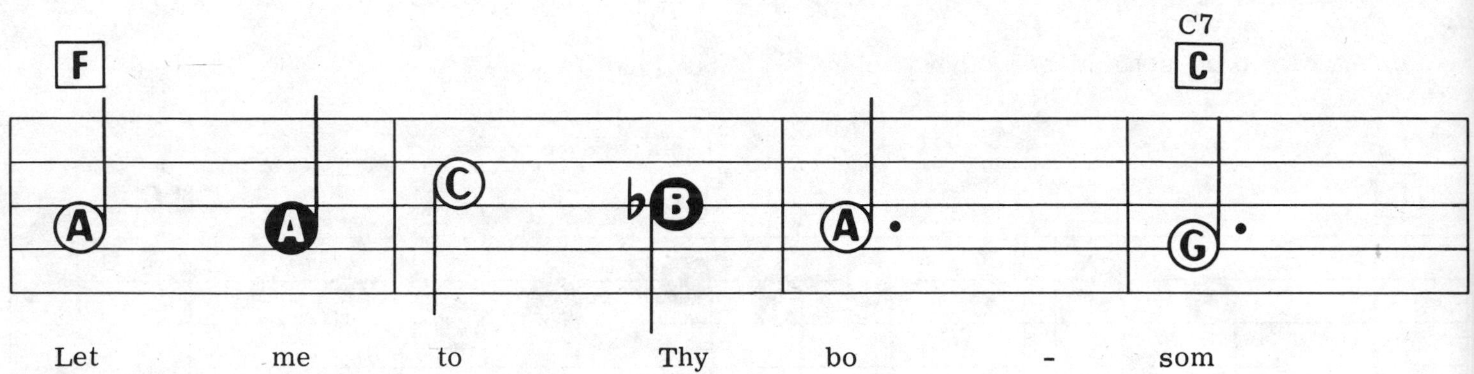

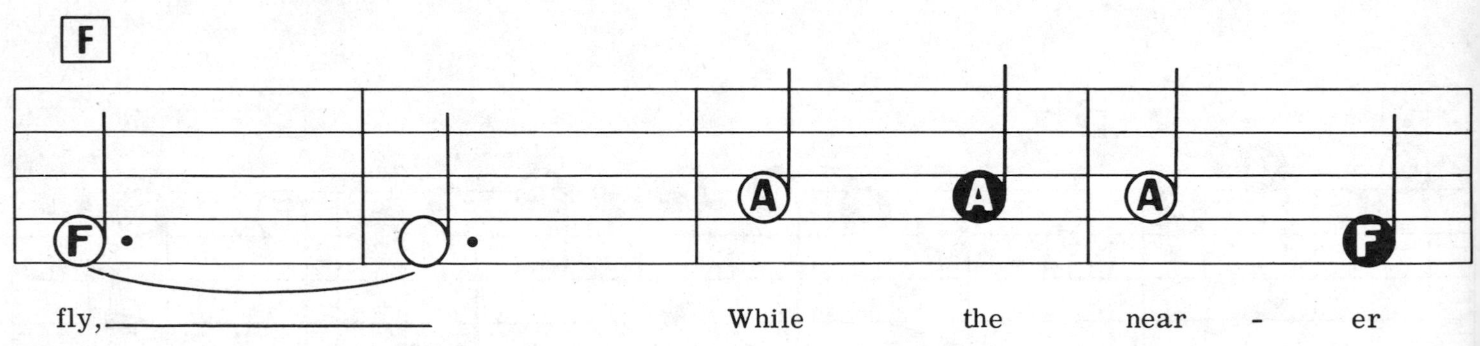

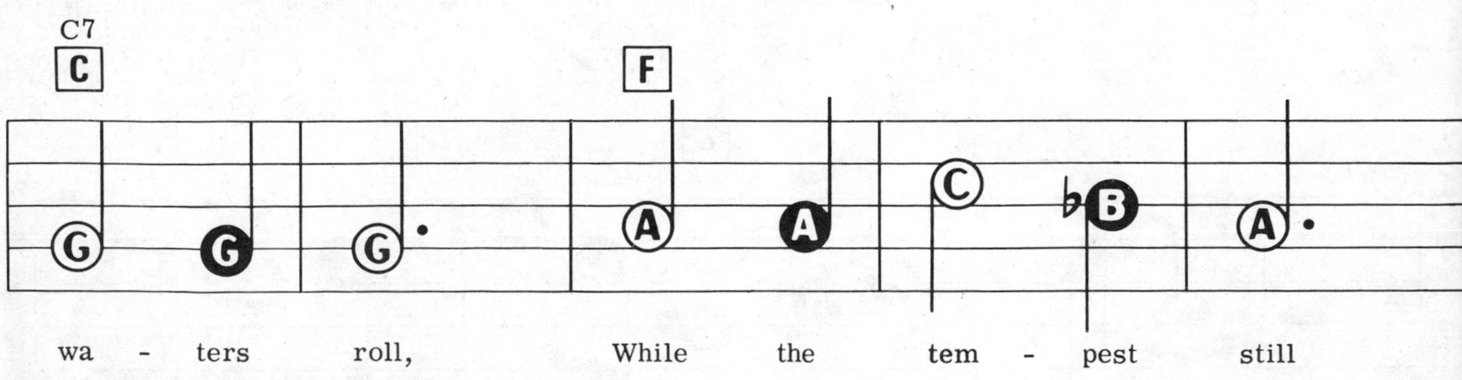

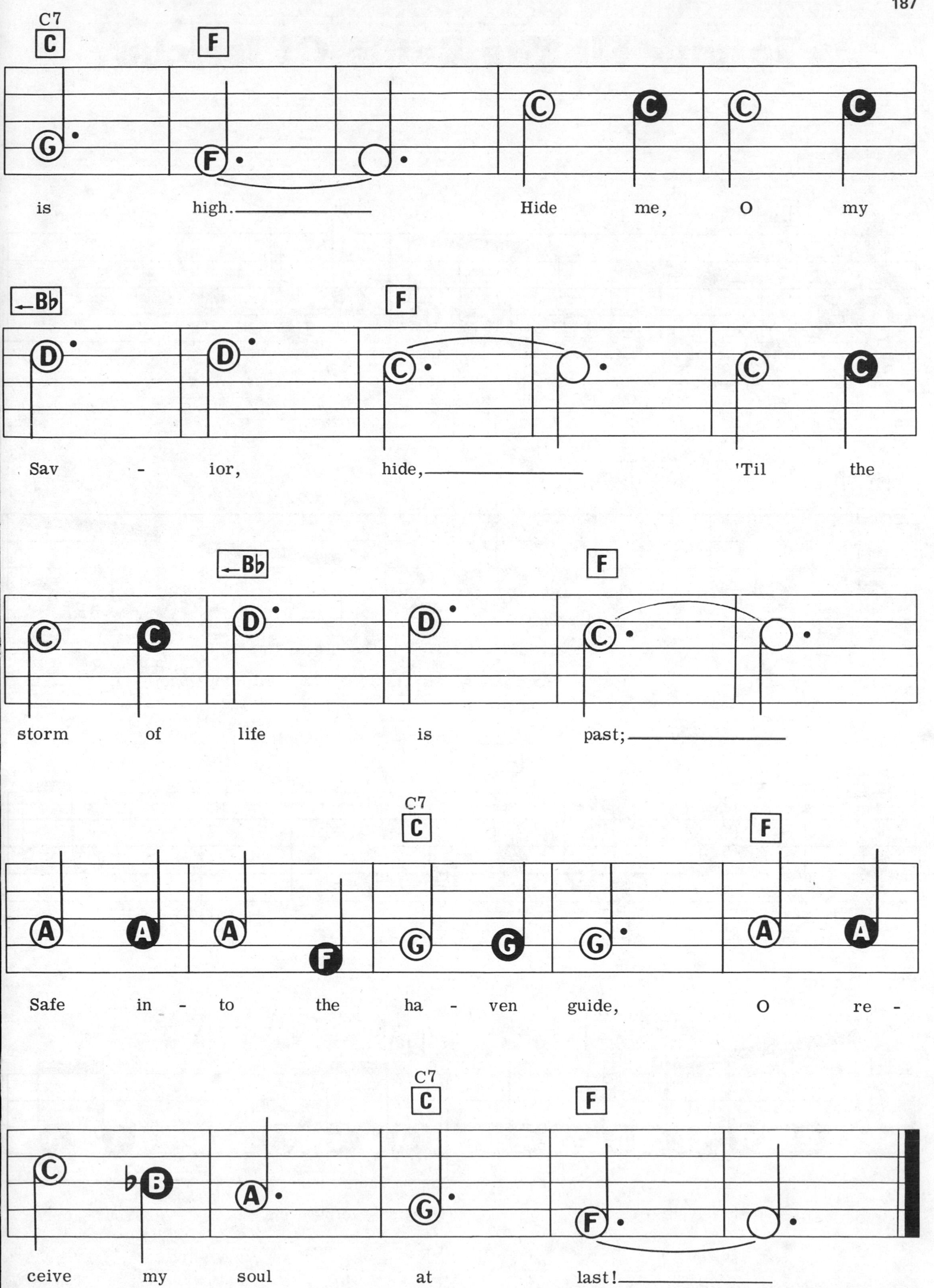
C7 C F
is high.
Hide me, O my
Bb F
Sav - ior, hide, 'Til the
Bb F
storm of life is past;
C7 C F
Safe in - to the ha - ven guide, O re -
C7 C F
ceive my soul at last!

Joshua Fit The Battle Of Jericho

Registration 6

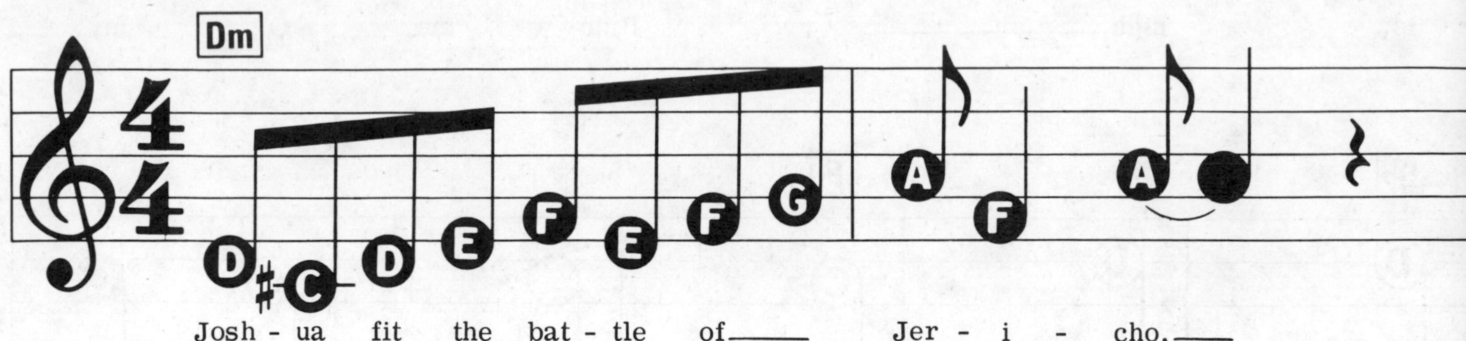

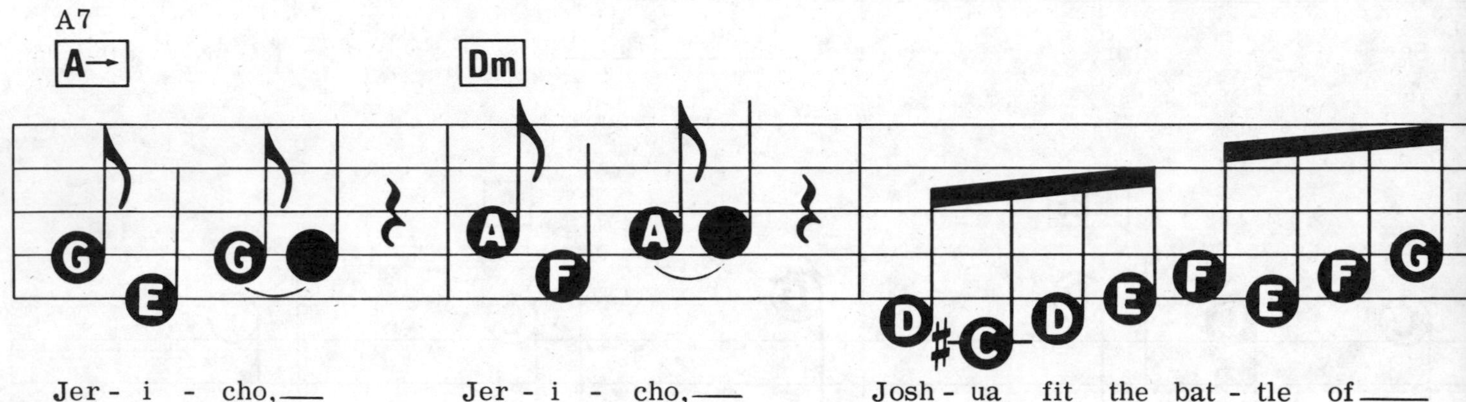

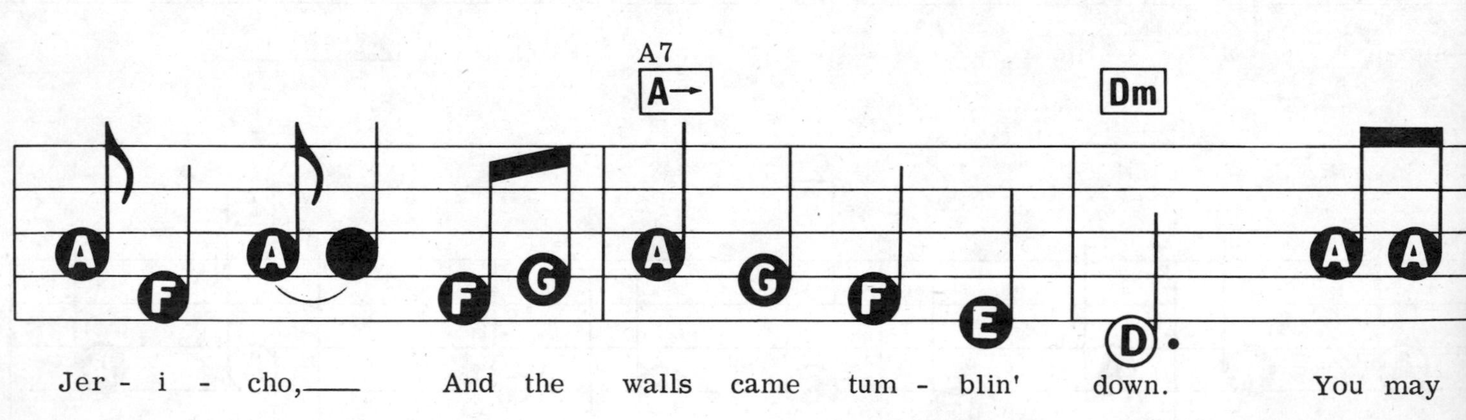

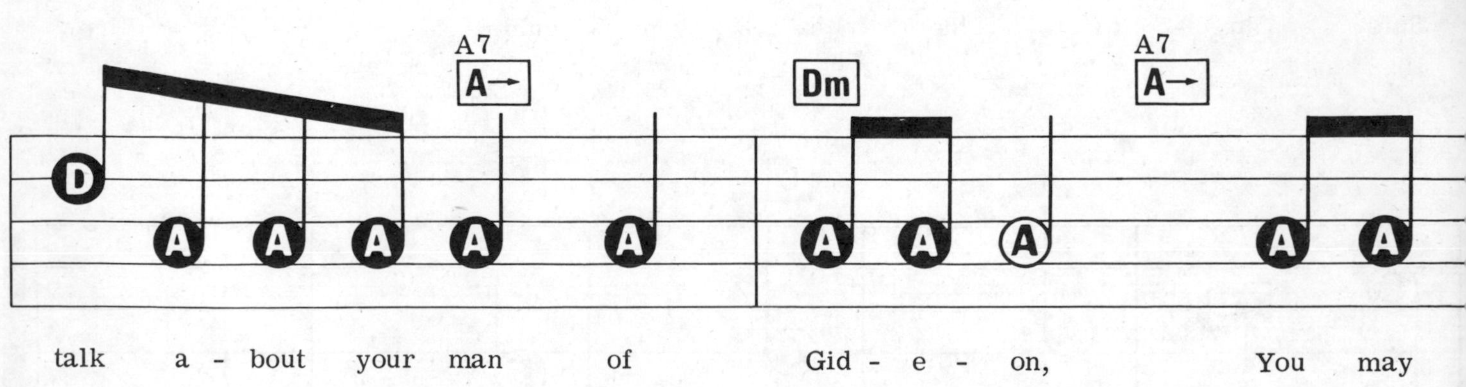

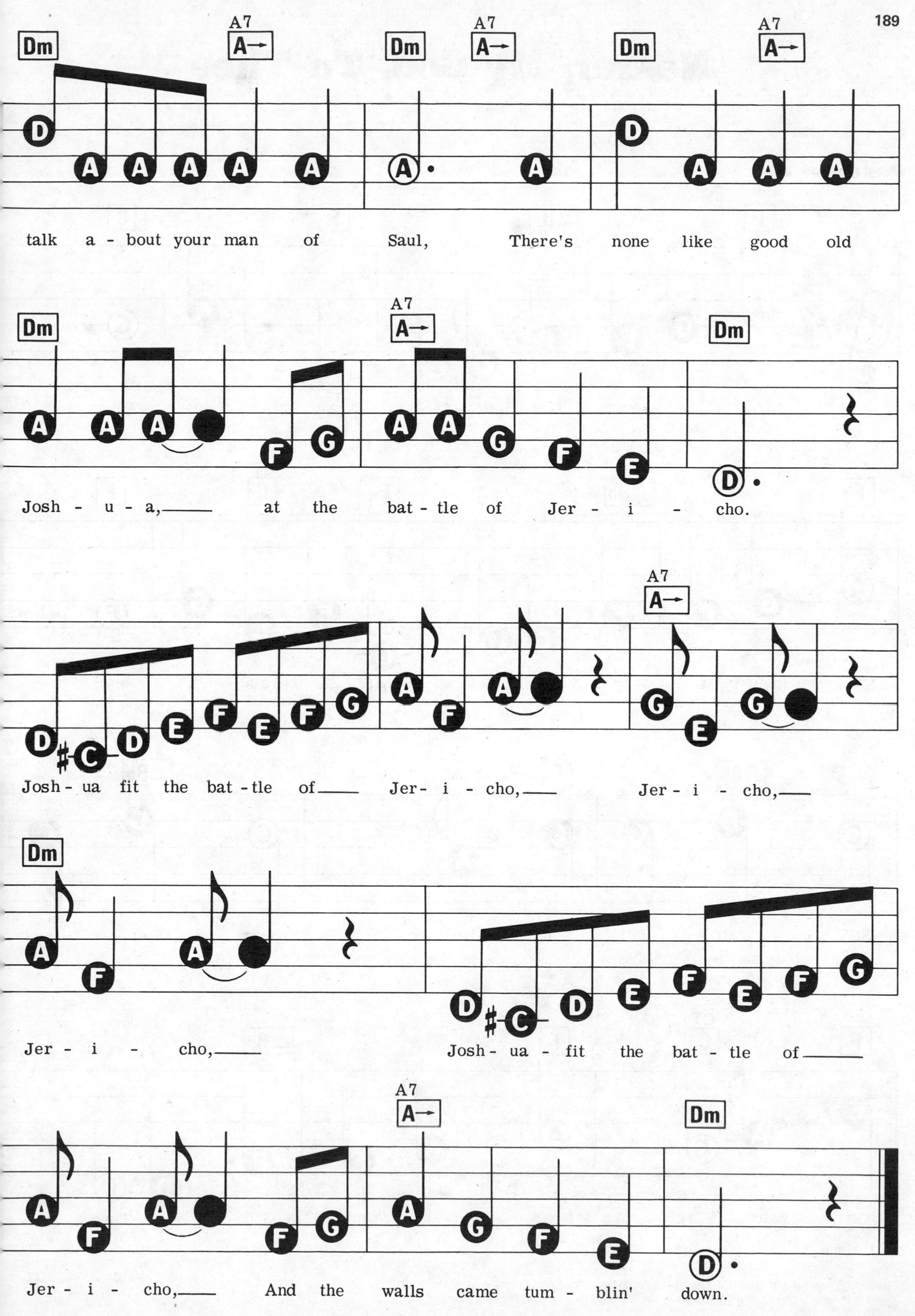
Dm A7 Dm A7 Dm A7
talk a - bout your man of Saul, There's none like good old
Dm A7 Dm
Josh - u - a, at the bat - tle of Jer - i - cho.
A7
Josh - ua fit the bat - tle of Jer - i - cho, Jer - i - cho,
Dm
Jer - i - cho, Josh - ua - fit the bat - tle of
A7 Dm
Jer - i - cho, And the walls came tum - blin' down.

Nearer, My God, To Thee

Registration 2

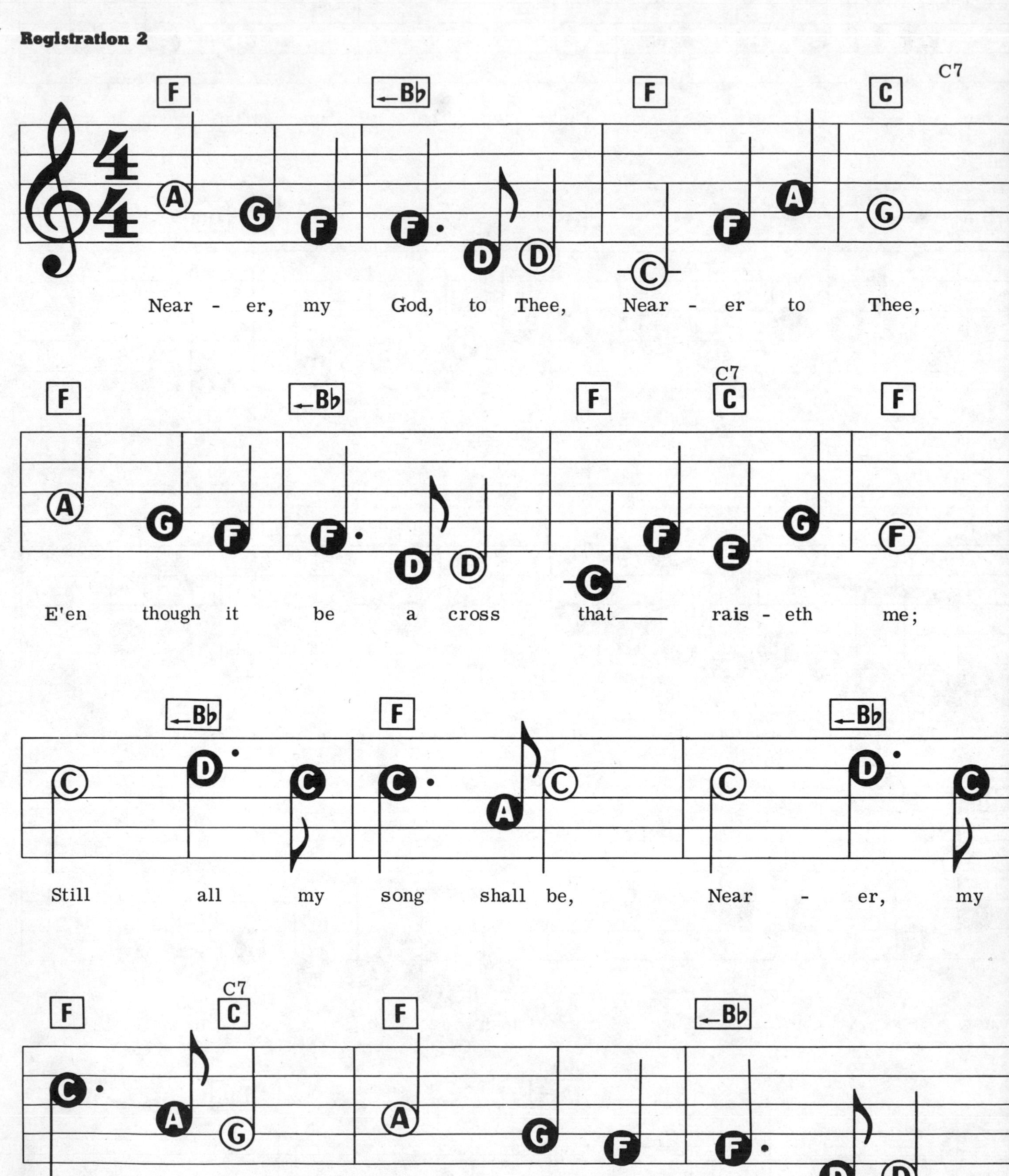

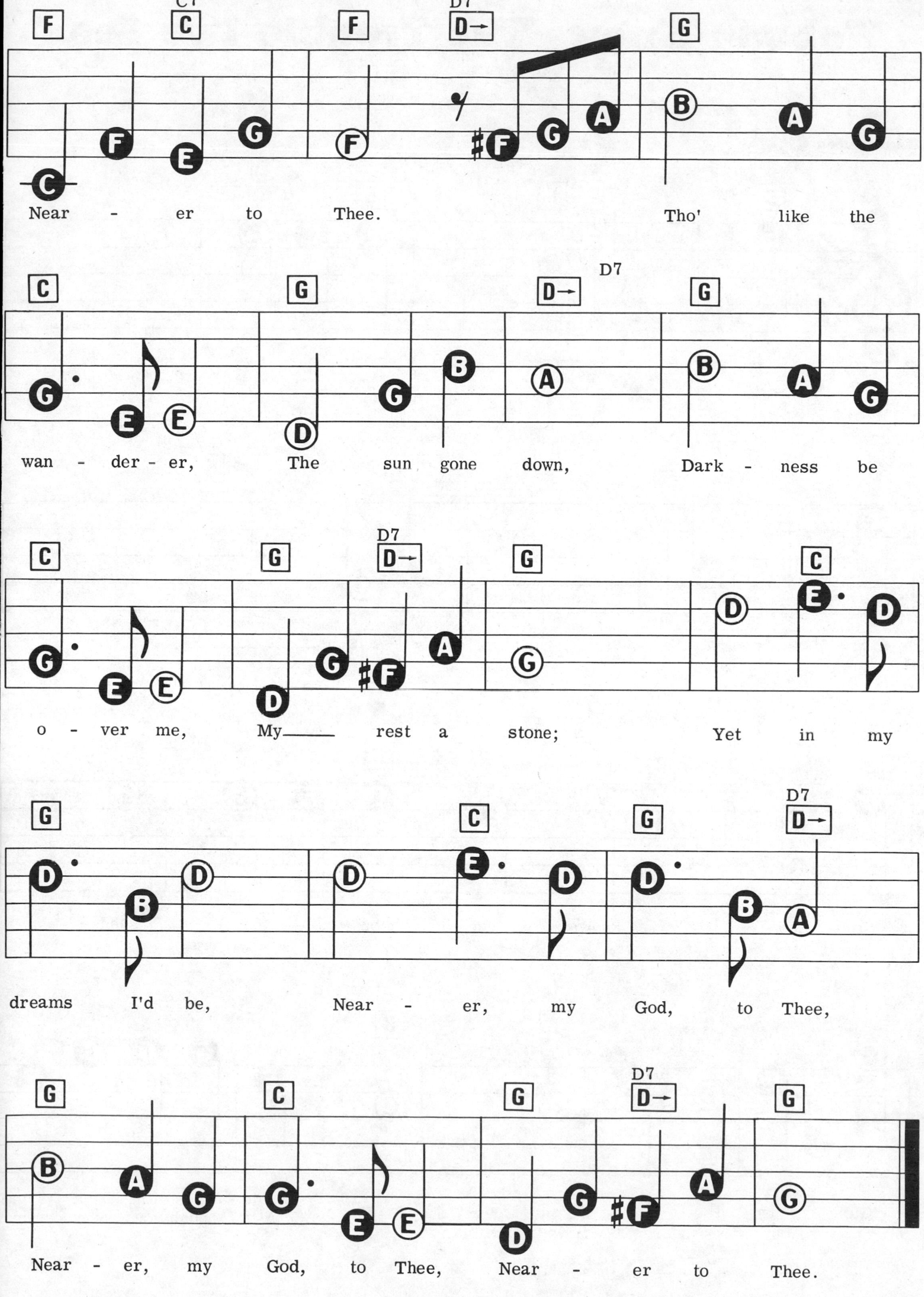

F C7 C F D7 D→ G

Near - er to Thee. Tho' like the

C G D→ D7 G

wan - der - er, The sun gone down, Dark - ness be

C G D7 D→ G C

o - ver me, My___ rest a stone; Yet in my

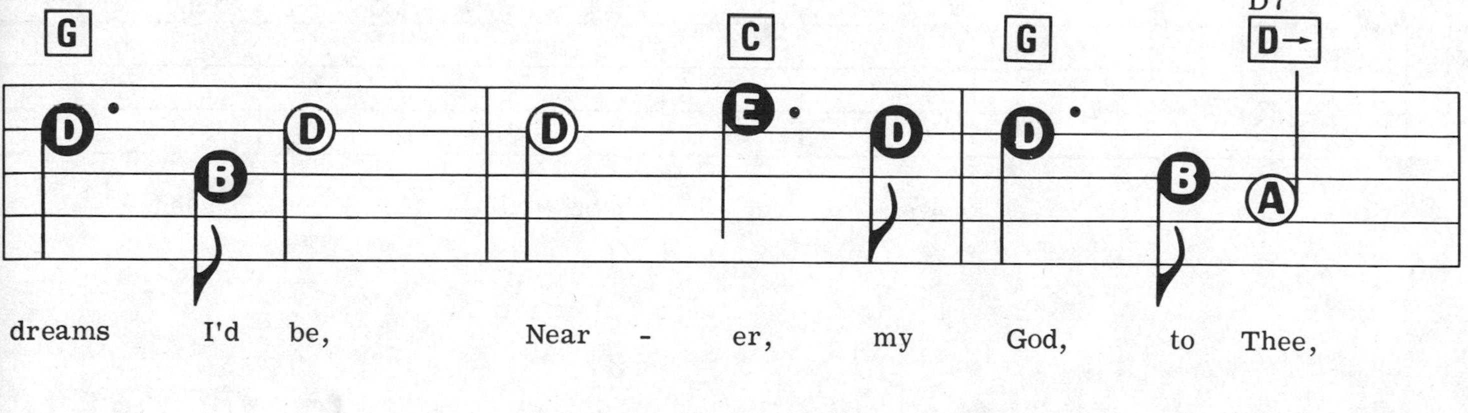

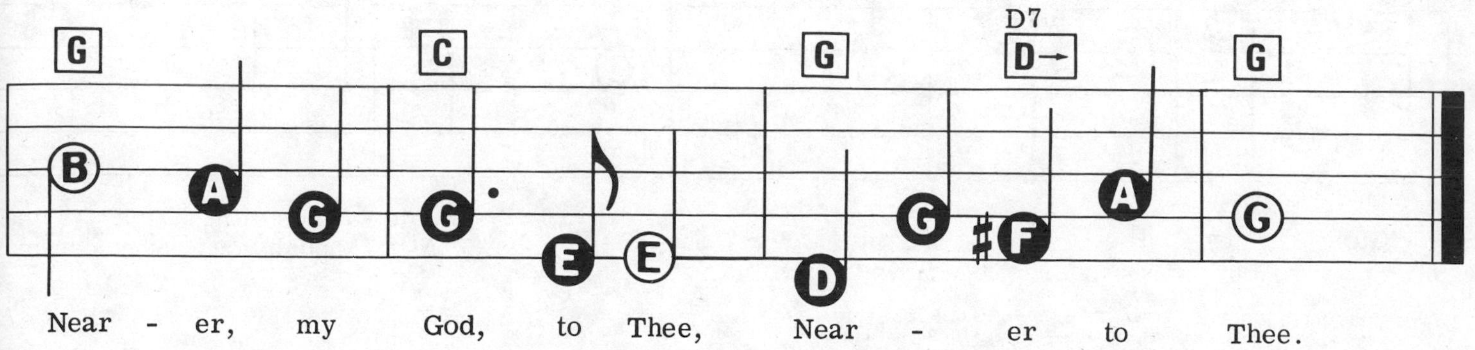

Nobody Knows The Trouble I've Seen

Registration 6

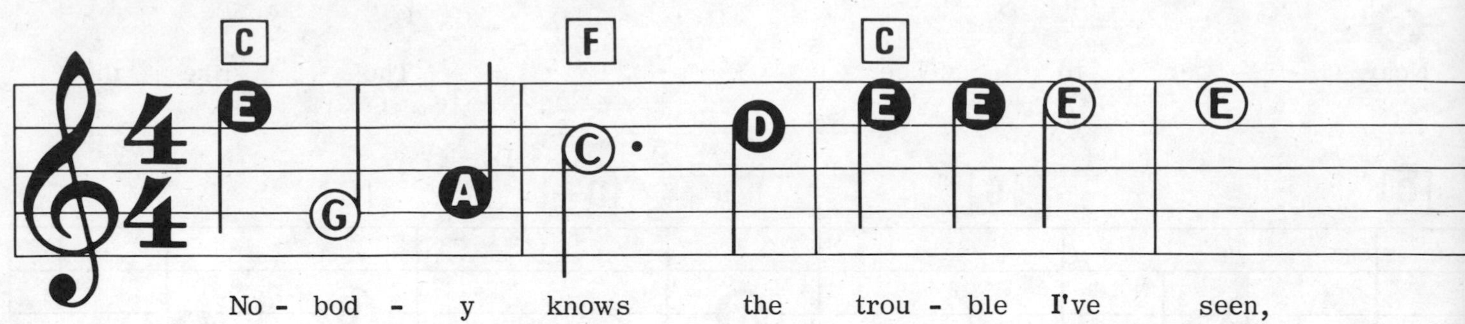

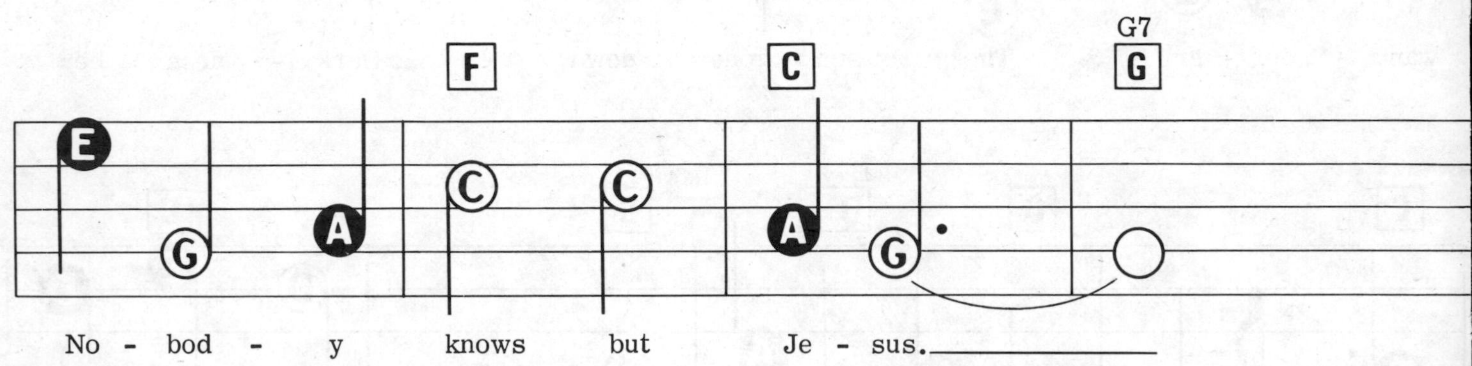

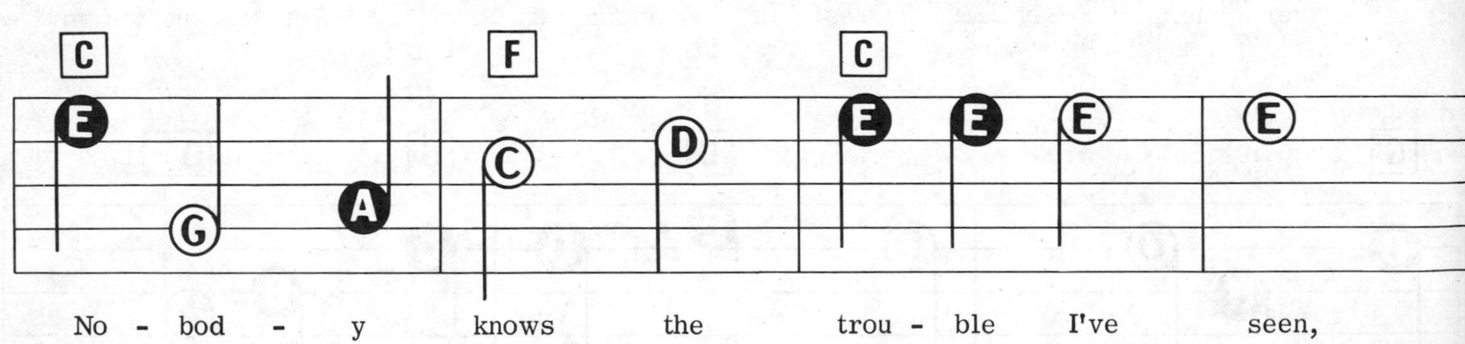

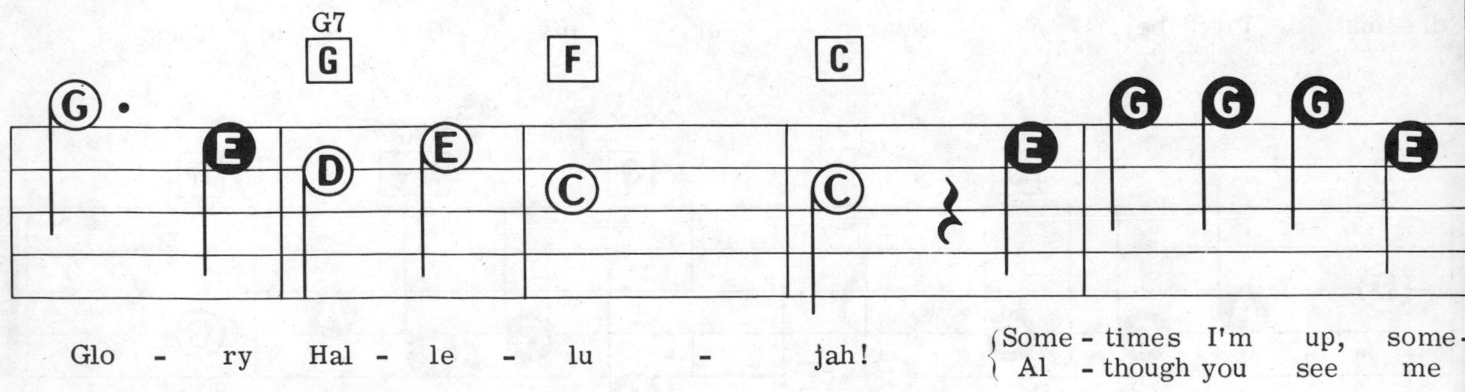

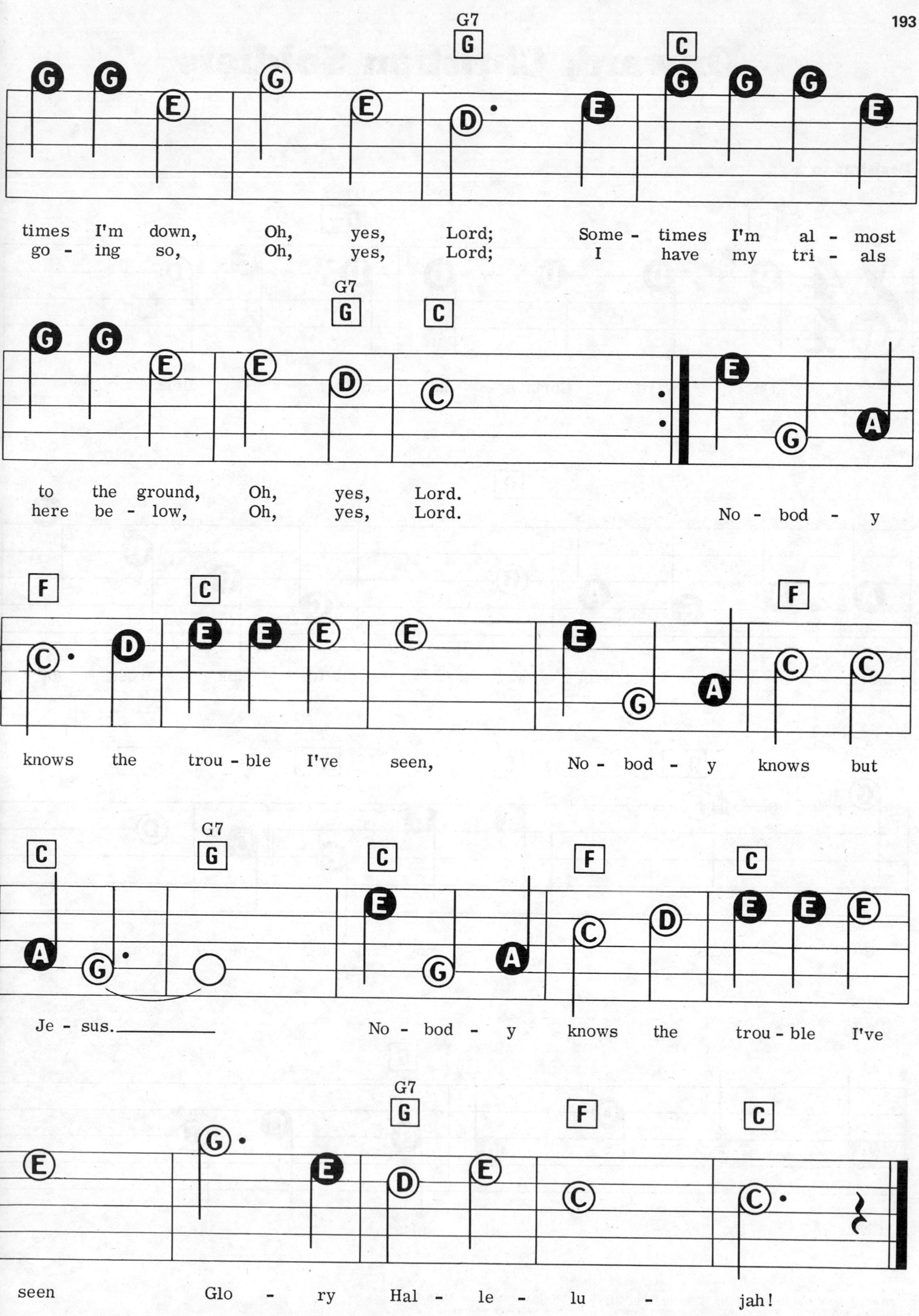
G7
G
C
G G E G E D E G G G E
times I'm down, Oh, yes, Lord; Some - times I'm al - most
go - ing so, Oh, yes, Lord; I have my tri - als
G7
G
C
G G E E D C E G A
to the ground, Oh, yes, Lord.
here be - low, Oh, yes, Lord. No - bod - y
F
C
F
C D E E E E E G A C C
knows the trou - ble I've seen, No - bod - y knows but
C
G7
G
C
F
C
A G E G A C D E E E
Je - sus.
No - bod - y knows the trou - ble I've
G7
G
F
C
E G E D E C C
seen Glo - ry Hal - le - lu - jah!

Onward, Christian Soldiers

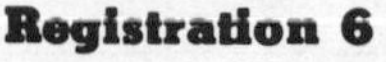

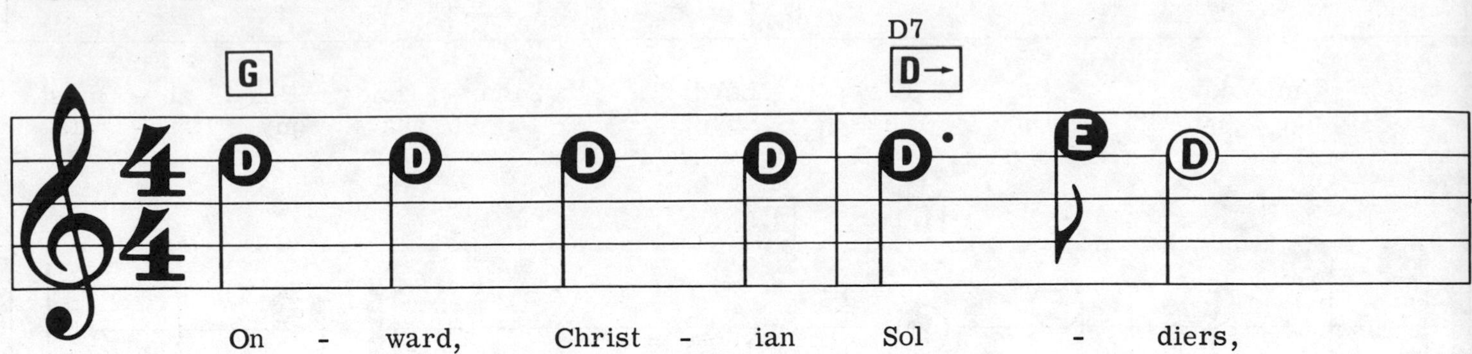

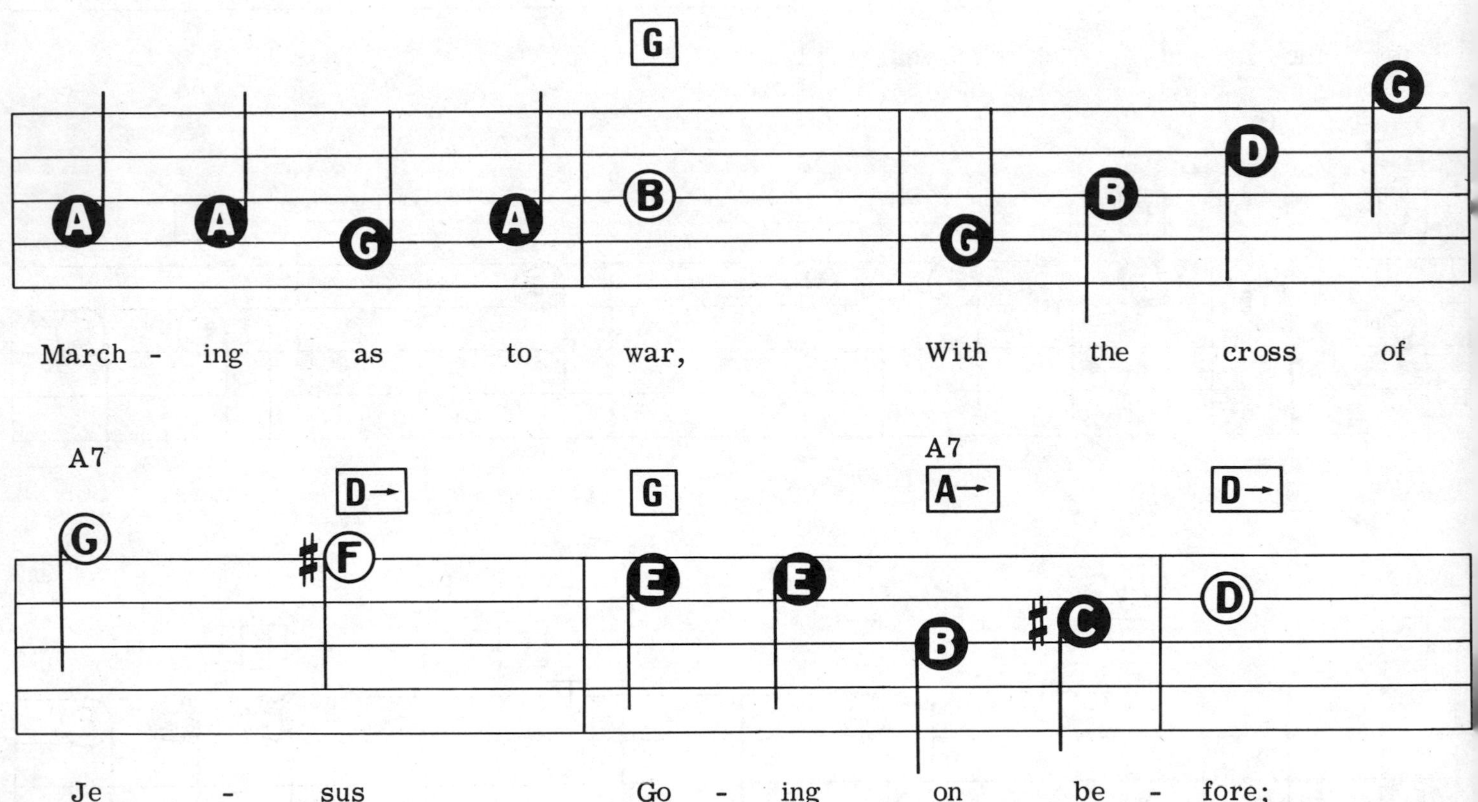

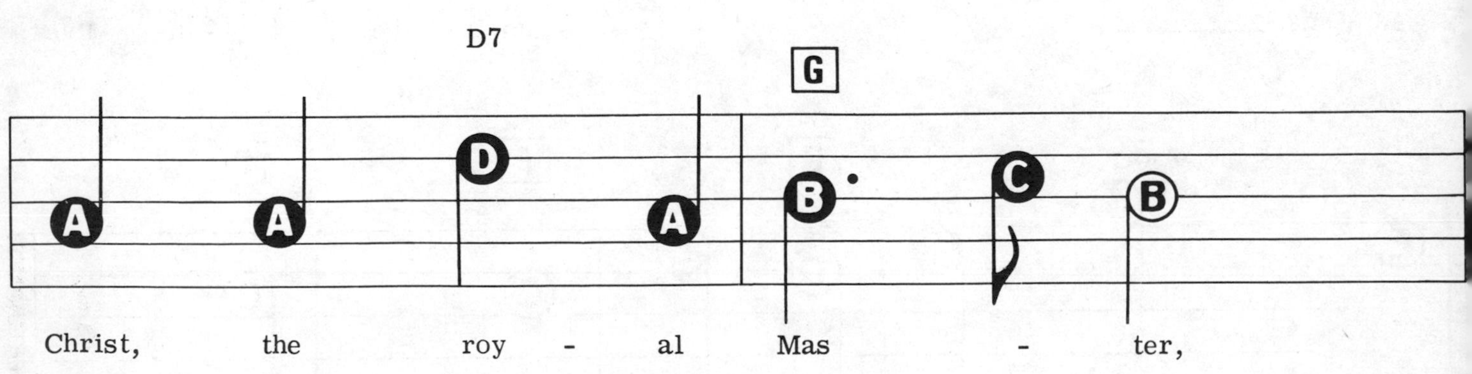

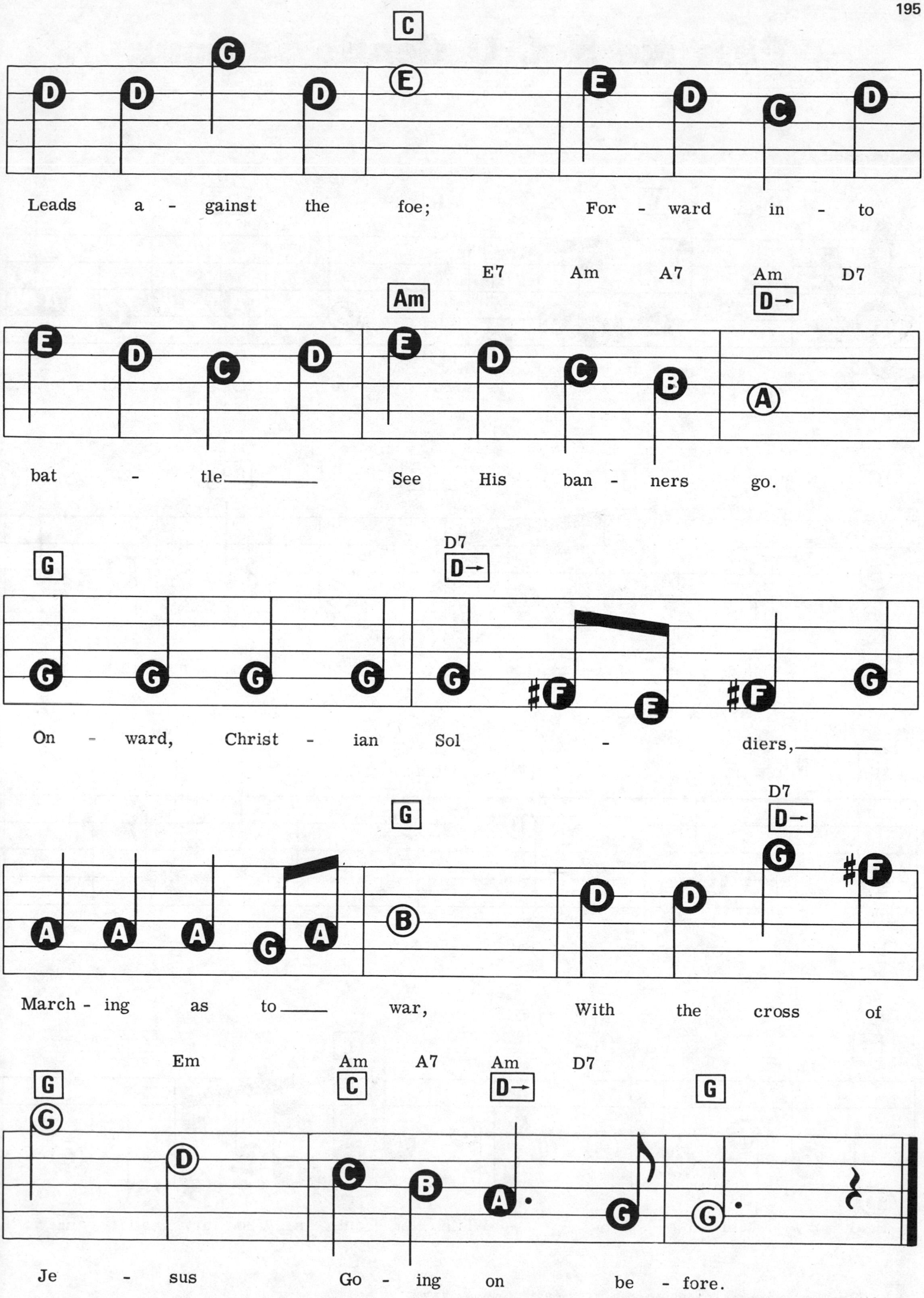

C

D D G D E E D C D

Leads a - gainst the foe; For - ward in - to

E7 Am A7 Am D7

Am D→

E D C D E D C B A

bat - tle______ See His ban - ners go.

G D7 D→

G G G G G ♯F E ♯F G

On - ward, Christ - ian Sol - diers,______

G D7 D→

A A A G A B D D G ♯F

March - ing as to____ war, With the cross of

Em Am A7 Am D7

G C D→ G

G D C B A G G

Je - sus Go - ing on be - fore.

Pass Me Not, O Gentle Saviour

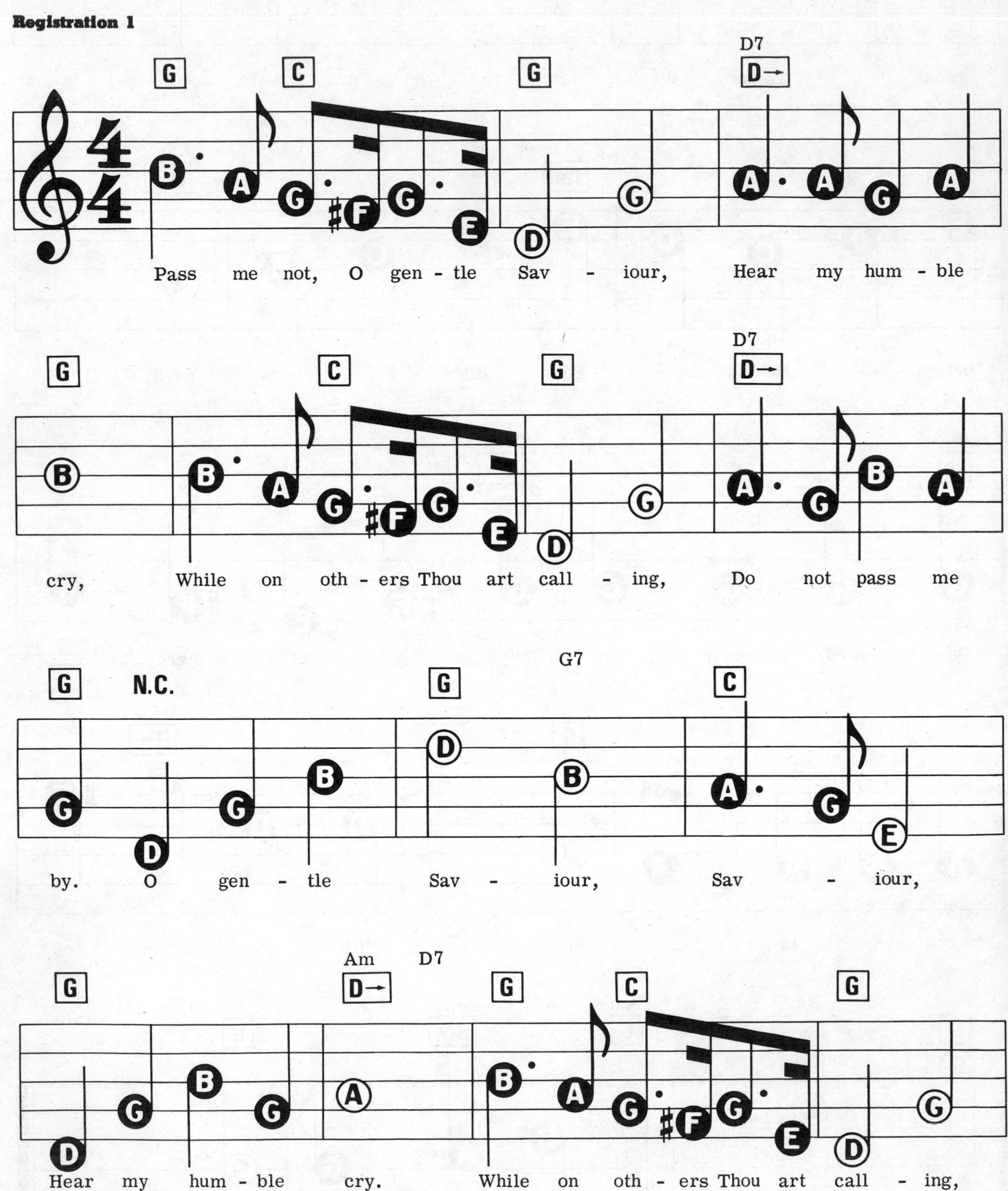

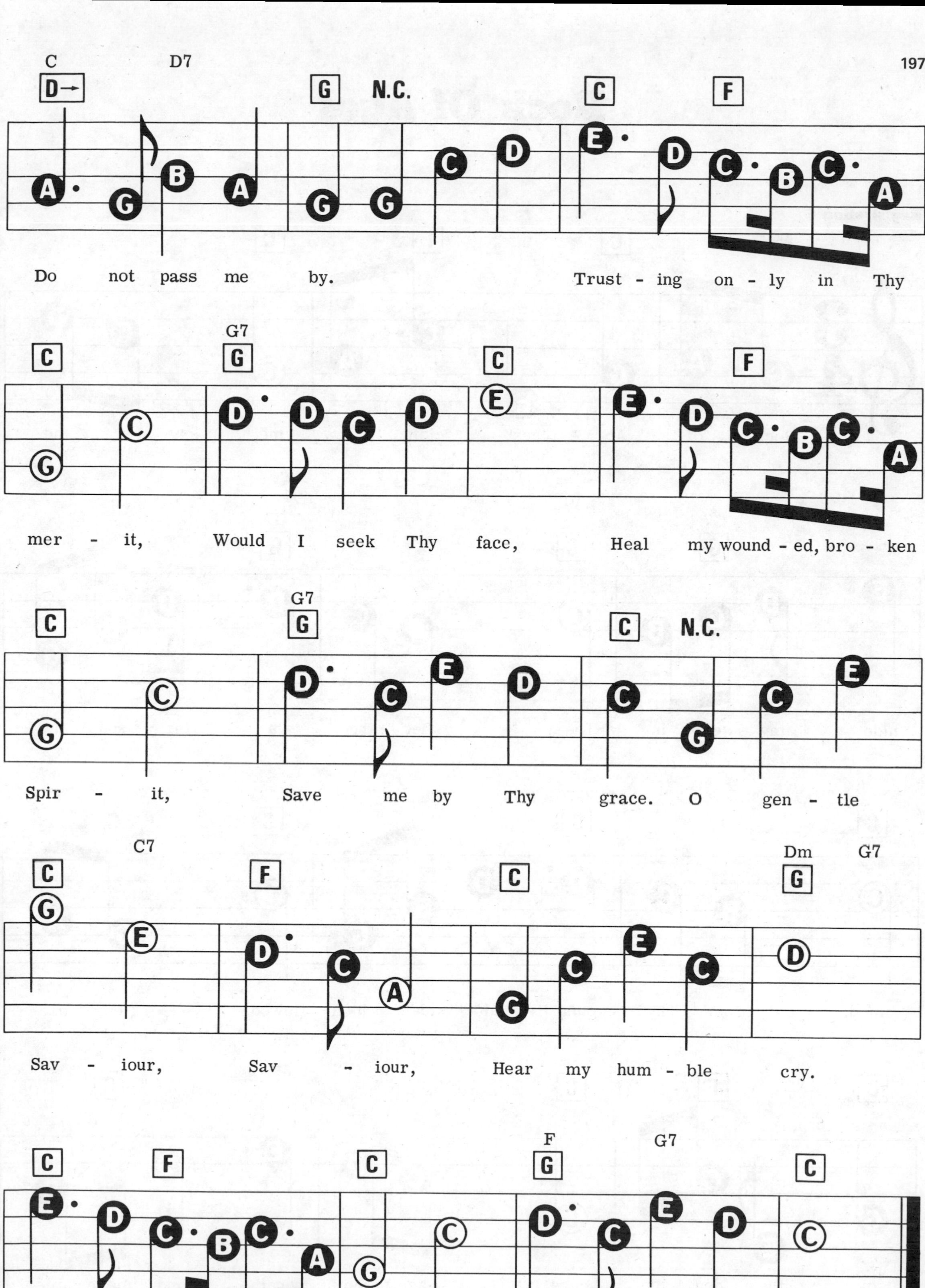
C D7 G N.C. C F
Do not pass me by. Trust - ing on - ly in Thy
C G7 C F
mer - it, Would I seek Thy face, Heal my wound - ed, bro - ken
C G7 C N.C.
Spir - it, Save me by Thy grace. O gen - tle
C C7 F C Dm G7
Sav - iour, Sav - iour, Hear my hum - ble cry.
C F C F G7 C
While on oth - ers Thou art call - ing, Do not pass me by.

Rock Of Ages

Registration 6

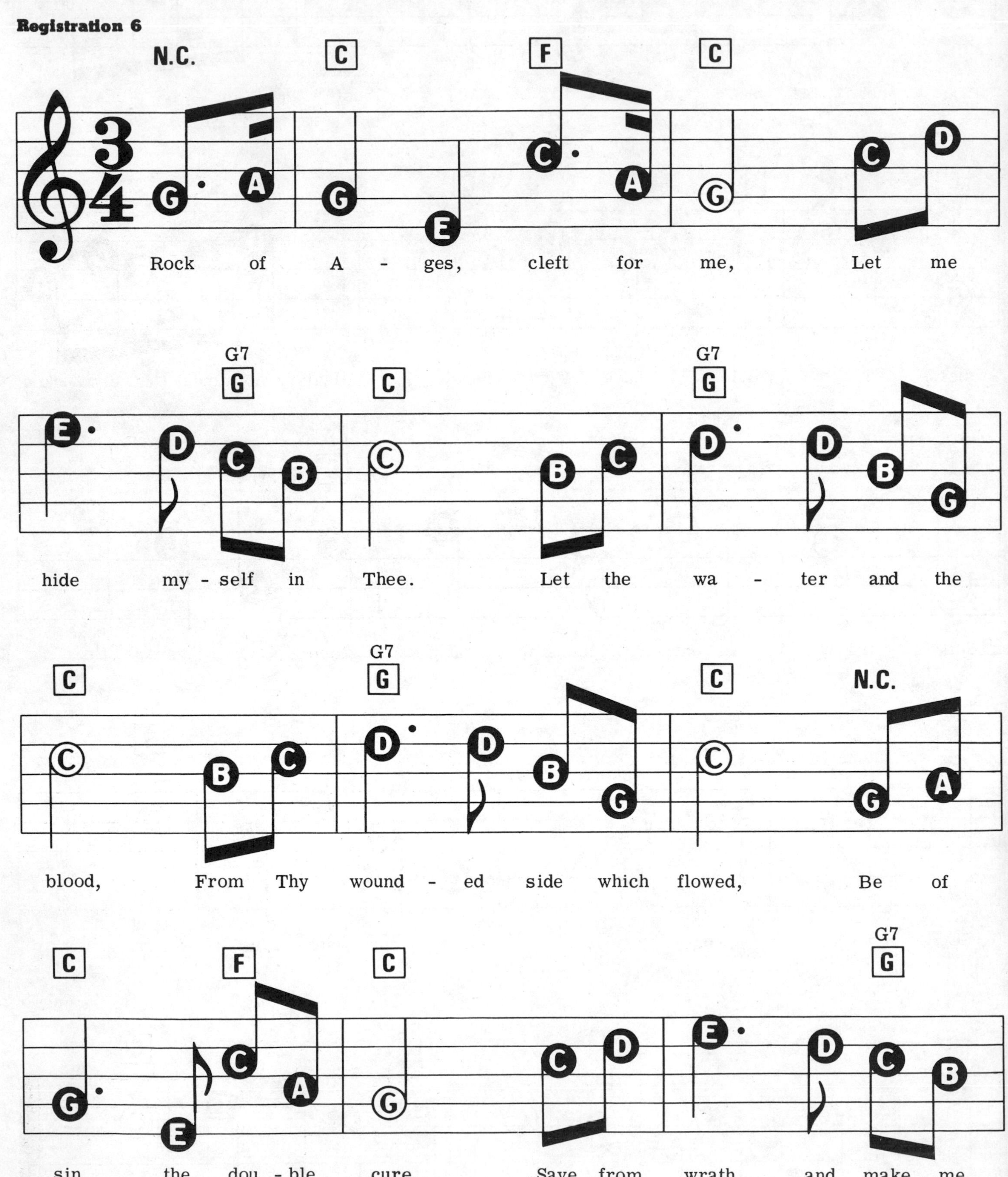

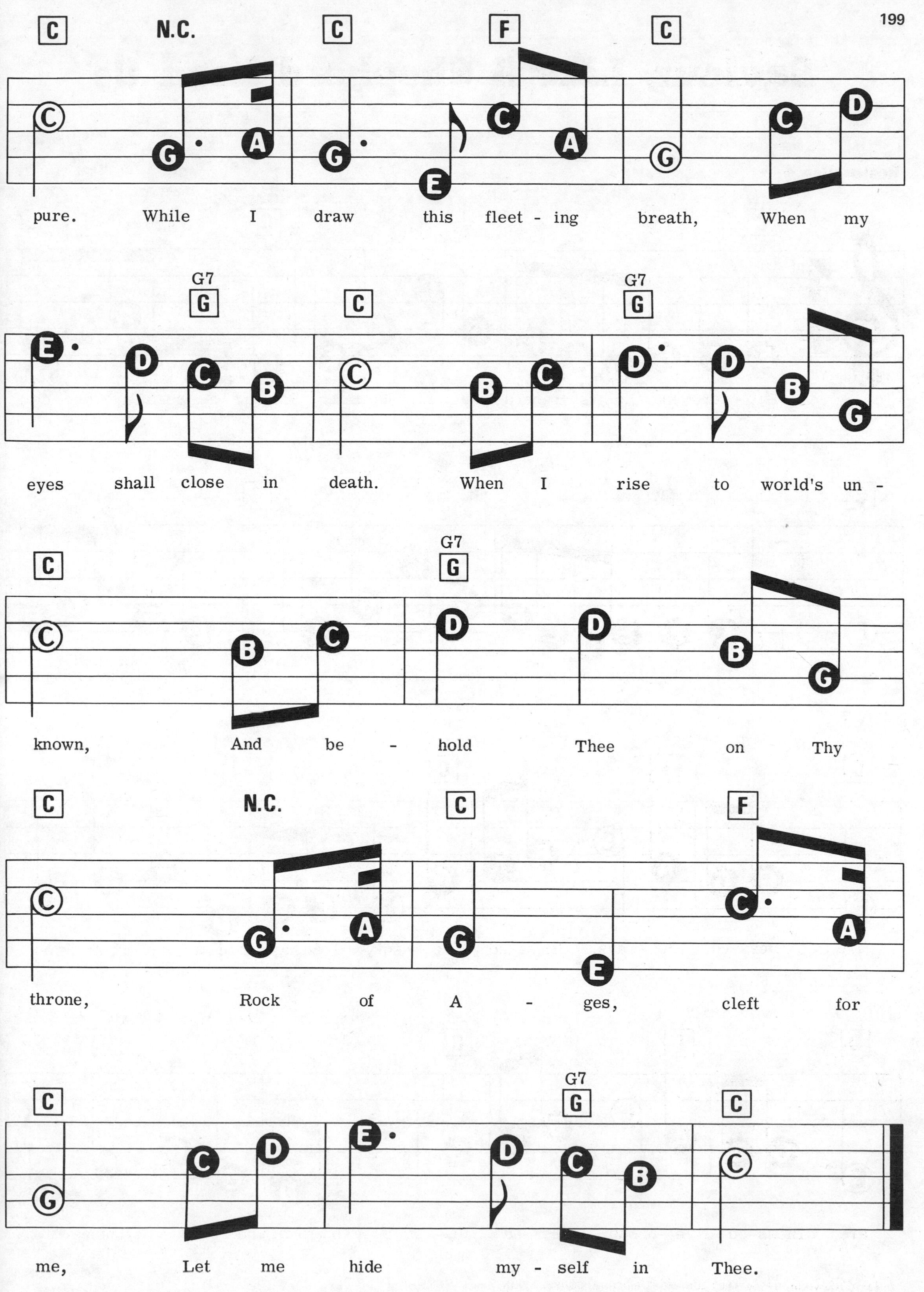
C
N.C.
C
F
C
pure. While I draw this fleet - ing breath, When my
G7
G
C
G7
G
eyes shall close in death. When I rise to world's un -
C
G7
G
known, And be - hold Thee on Thy
C
N.C.
C
F
throne, Rock of A - ges, cleft for
C
G7
G
C
me, Let me hide my - self in Thee.

Saviour, Like A Shepherd Lead Us

Registration 4

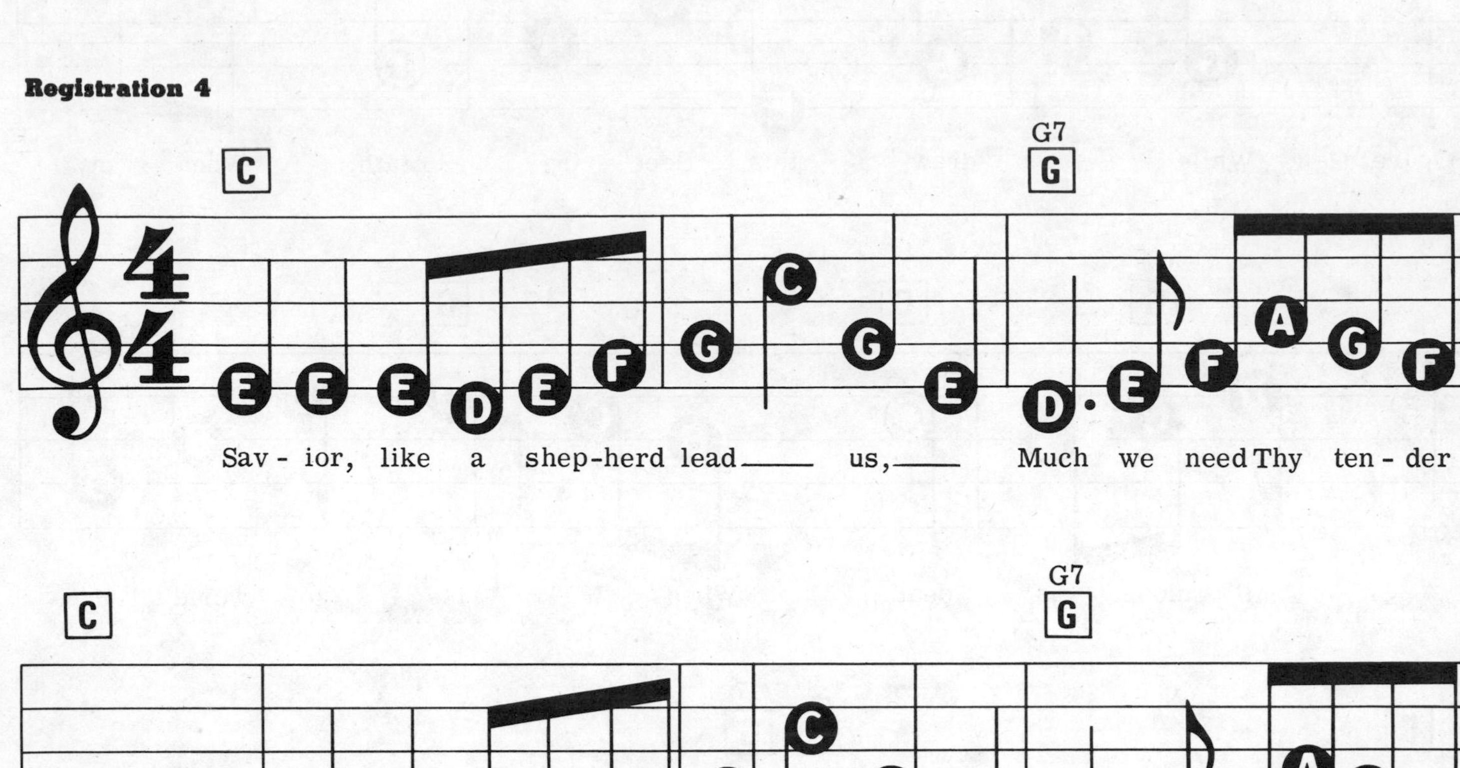

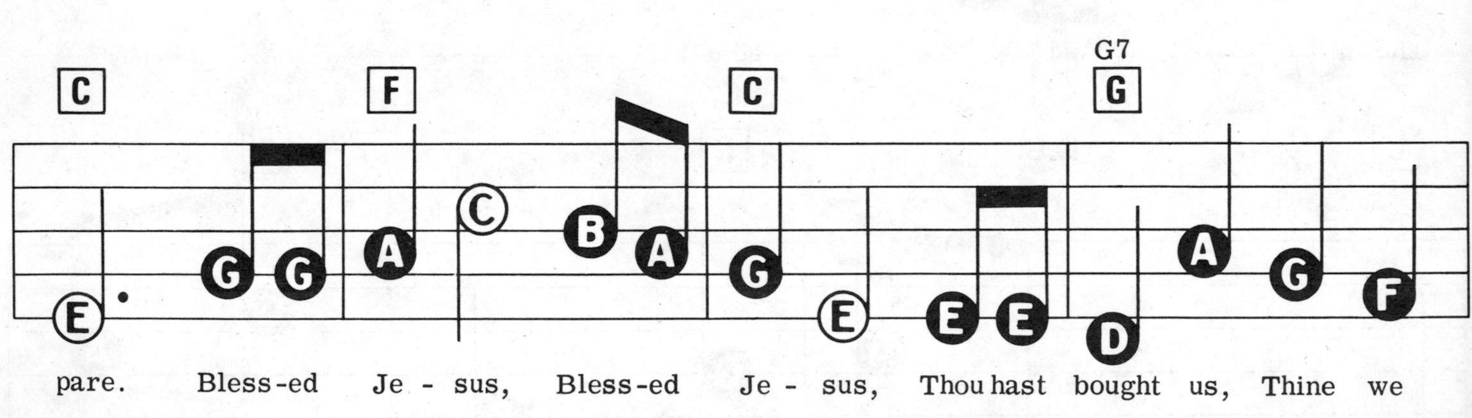

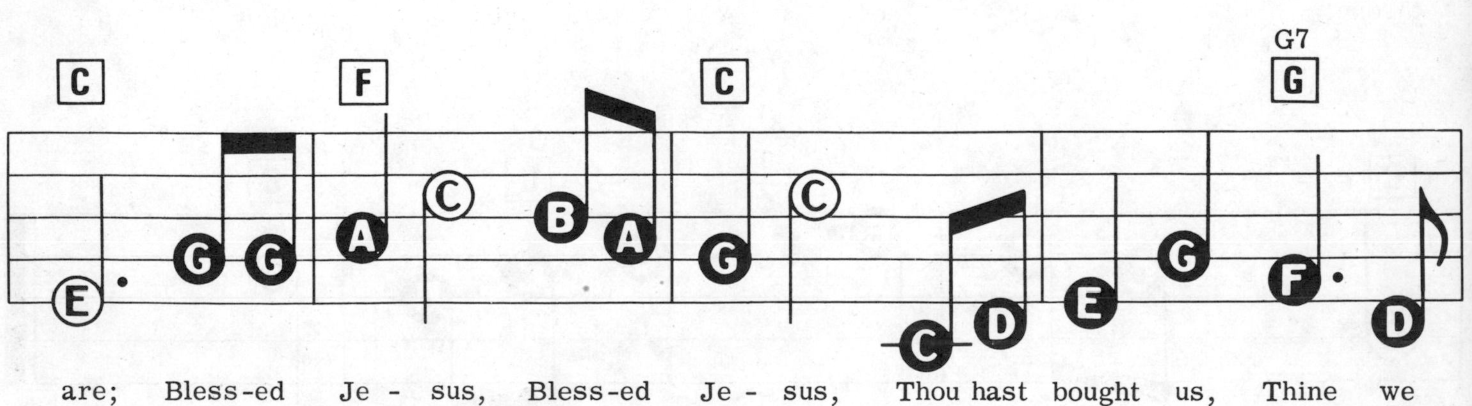

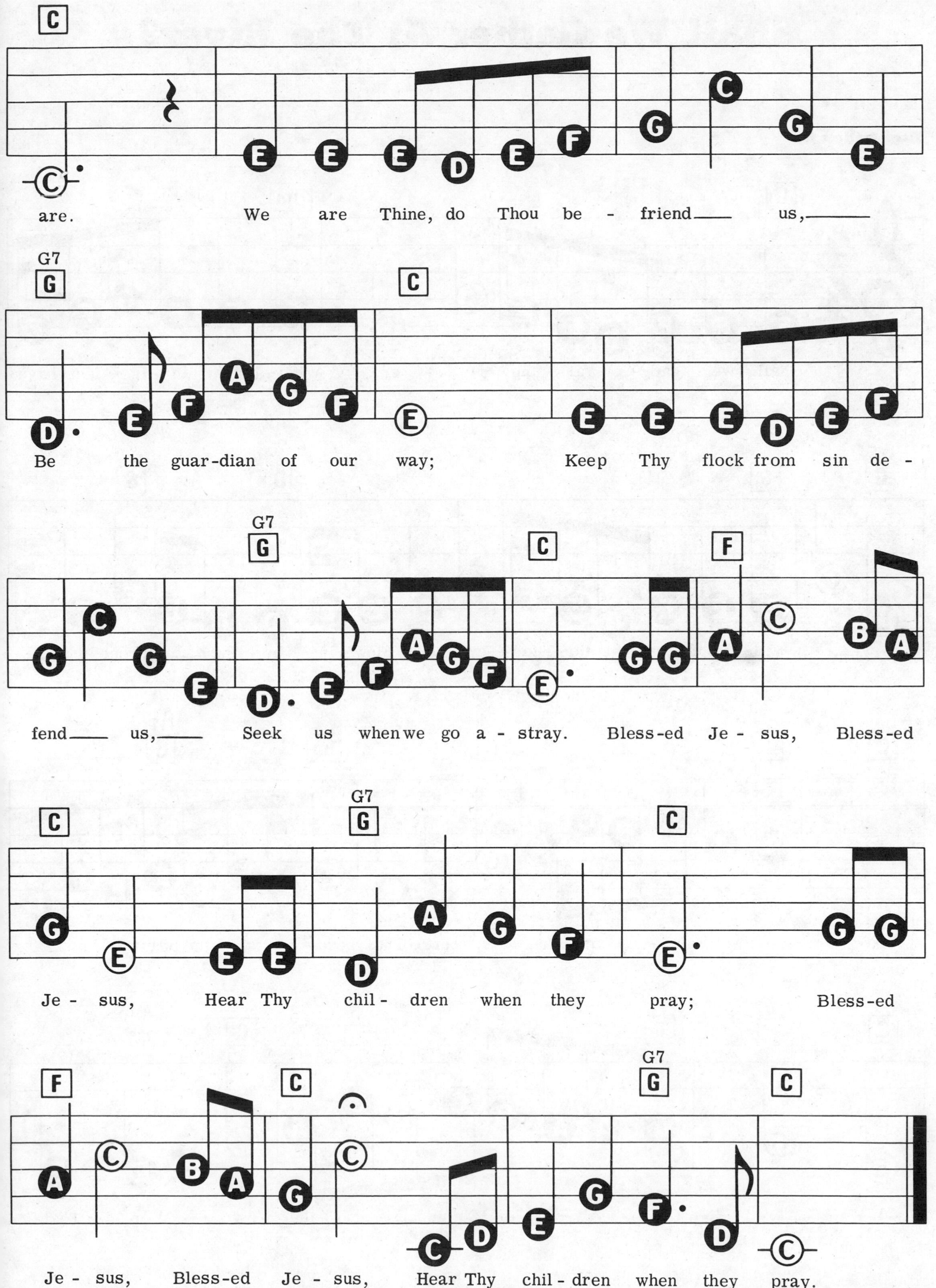
C
are. We are Thine, do Thou be - friend us,
G7 G C
Be the guar-dian of our way; Keep Thy flock from sin de -
G7 G C F
fend us, Seek us when we go a - stray. Bless-ed Je - sus, Bless-ed
C G7 G C
Je - sus, Hear Thy chil - dren when they pray; Bless-ed
F C G7 G C
Je - sus, Bless-ed Je - sus, Hear Thy chil - dren when they pray.

Shall We Gather At The River?

Registration 6

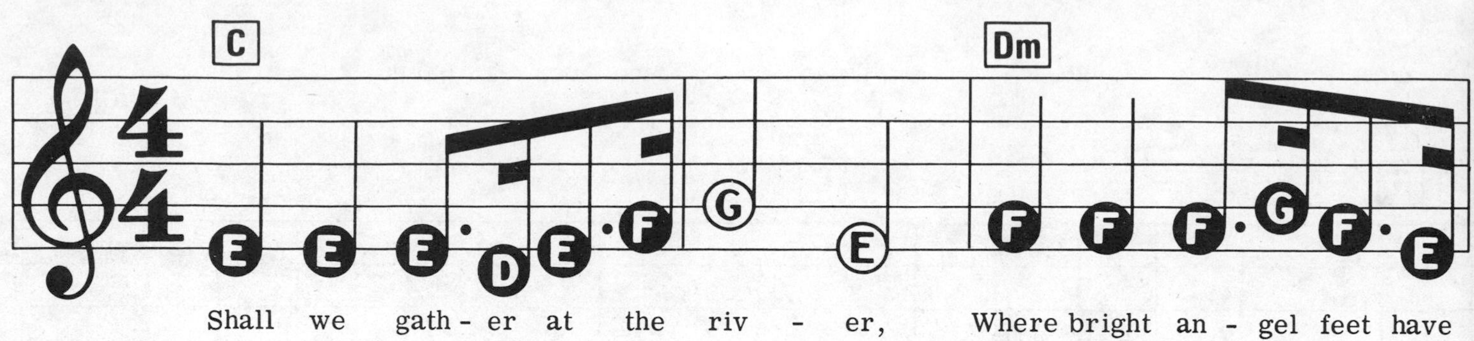

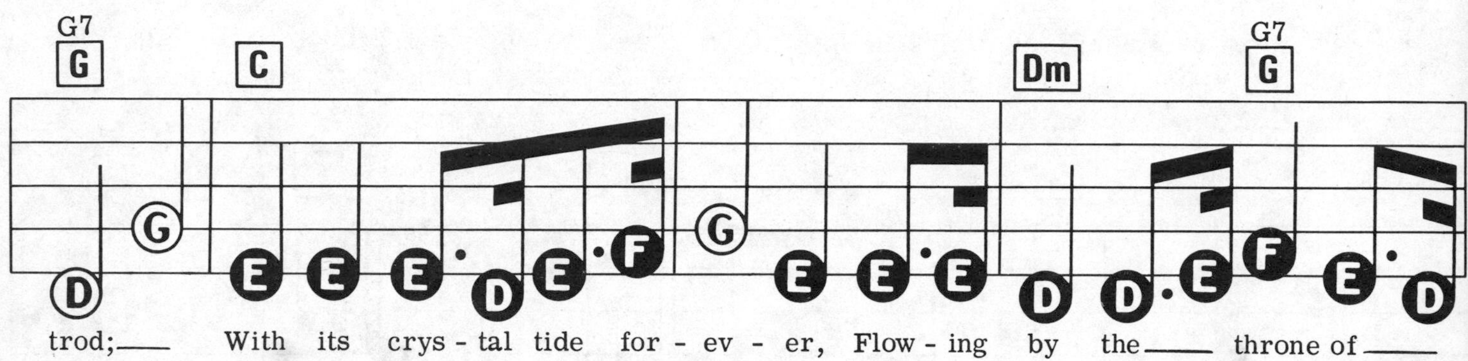

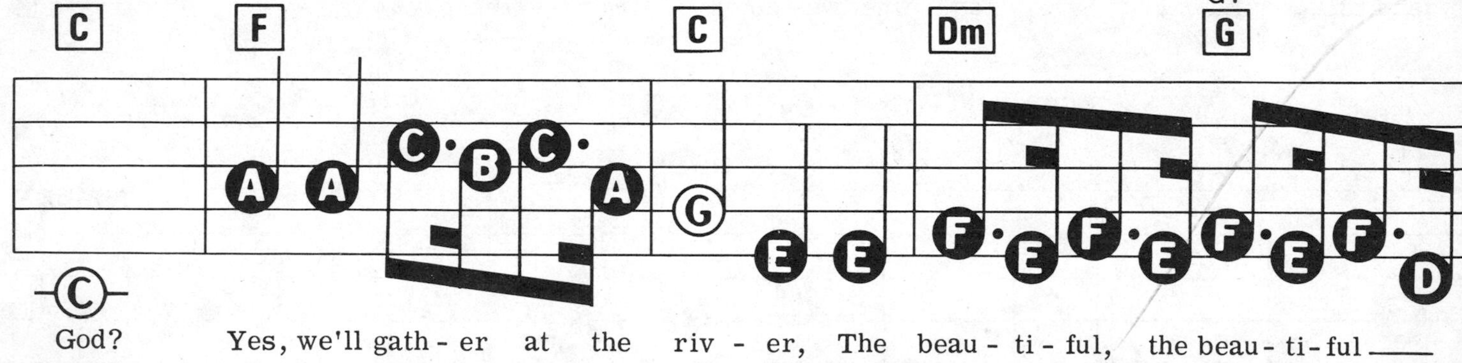

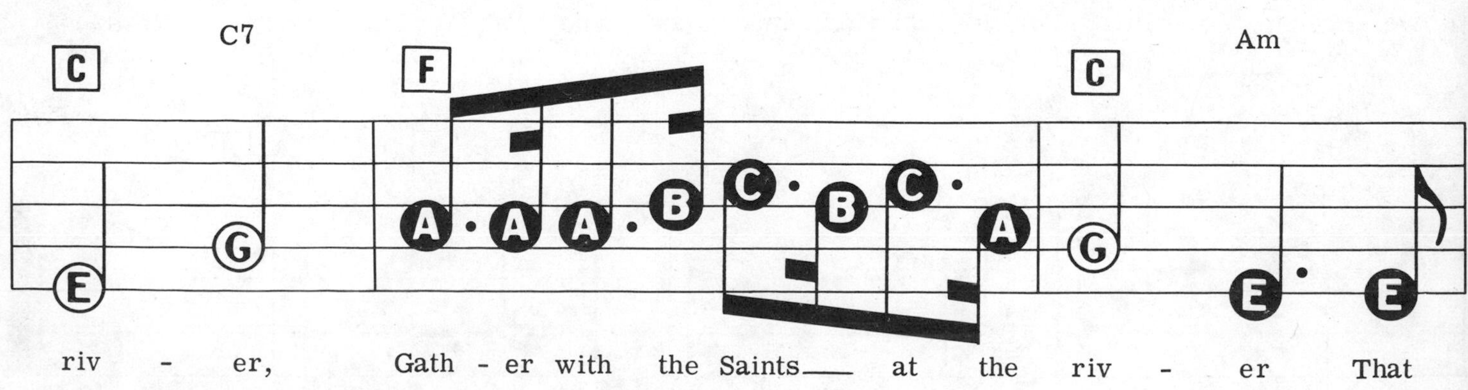

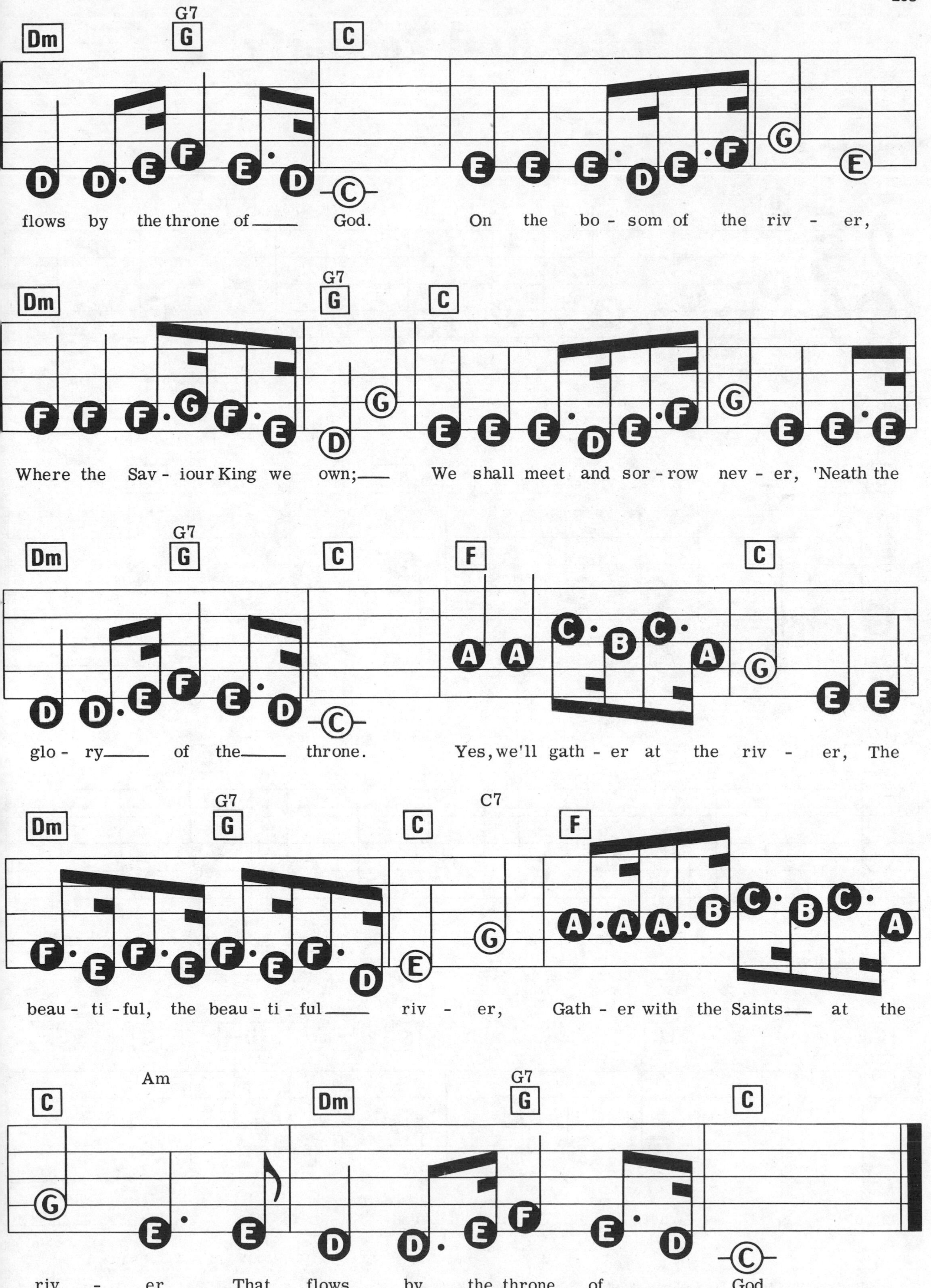
Dm
G7
G
C
D D E F E D C
flows by the throne of God.
E E E D E F G E
On the bo - som of the riv - er,
Dm
G7
G
C
F F F G F E D G
Where the Sav - iour King we own;
E E E D E F G E E E
We shall meet and sor - row nev - er, 'Neath the
Dm
G7
G
C
F
C
D D E F E D C
glo - ry of the throne.
A A C B C A G E E
Yes, we'll gath - er at the riv - er, The
Dm
G7
G
C
C7
F
F E F E F E F D E G
beau - ti - ful, the beau - ti - ful riv - er,
A A A B C B C A
Gath - er with the Saints at the
C
Am
Dm
G7
G
C
G E E D D E F E D C
riv - er That flows by the throne of God.

Softly And Tenderly

Registration 2

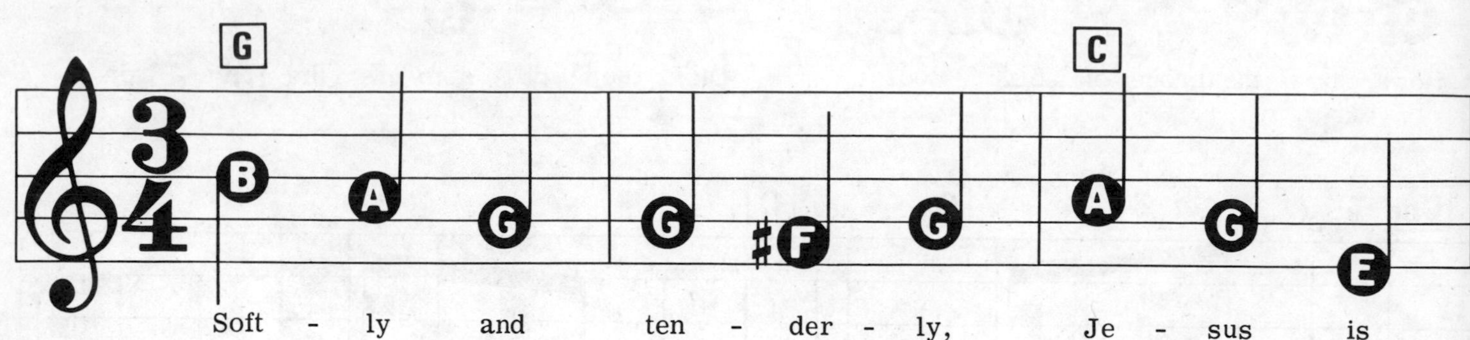

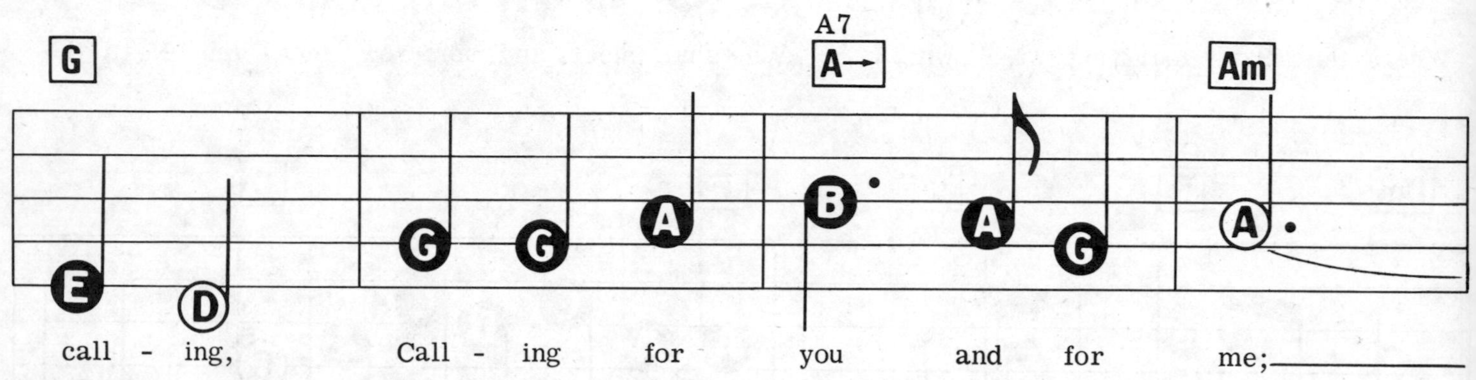

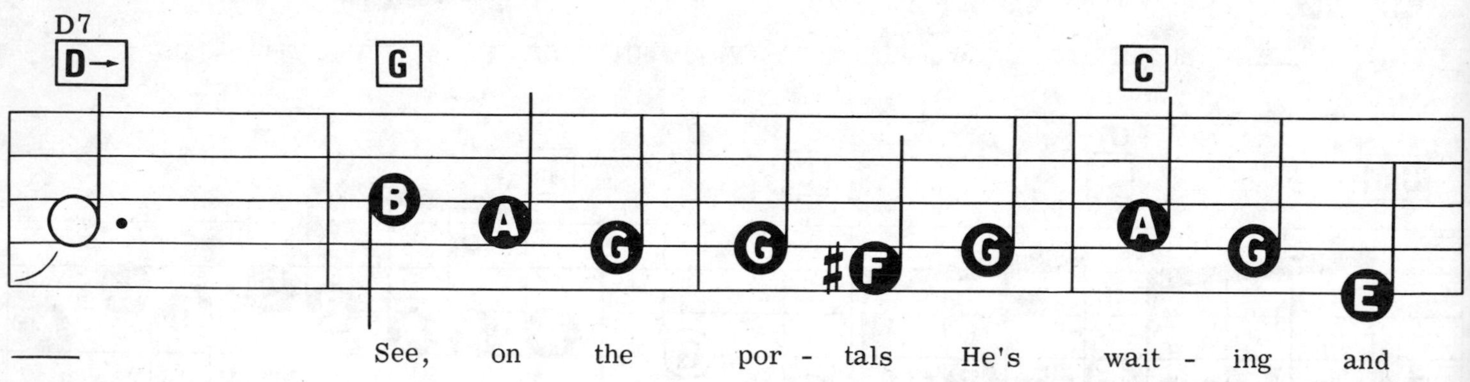

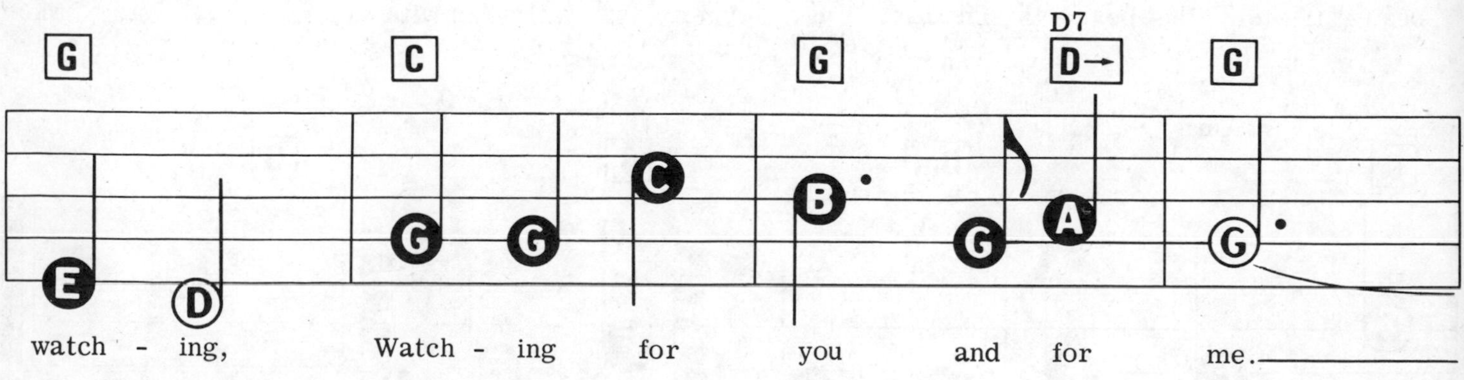

D7
D→
G
D7
D→
Come home, Come home,
G
D→
A7
A→
D→
A7
A→
Ye who are wea - ry, come home.
D7
D→
G
Ear - nest - ly, ten - der - ly,
C
G
C
Je - sus is call - ing, Call - ing, Oh,
G
D7
D→
G
sin - ner, come home.

Swing Low, Sweet Chariot

Registration 5

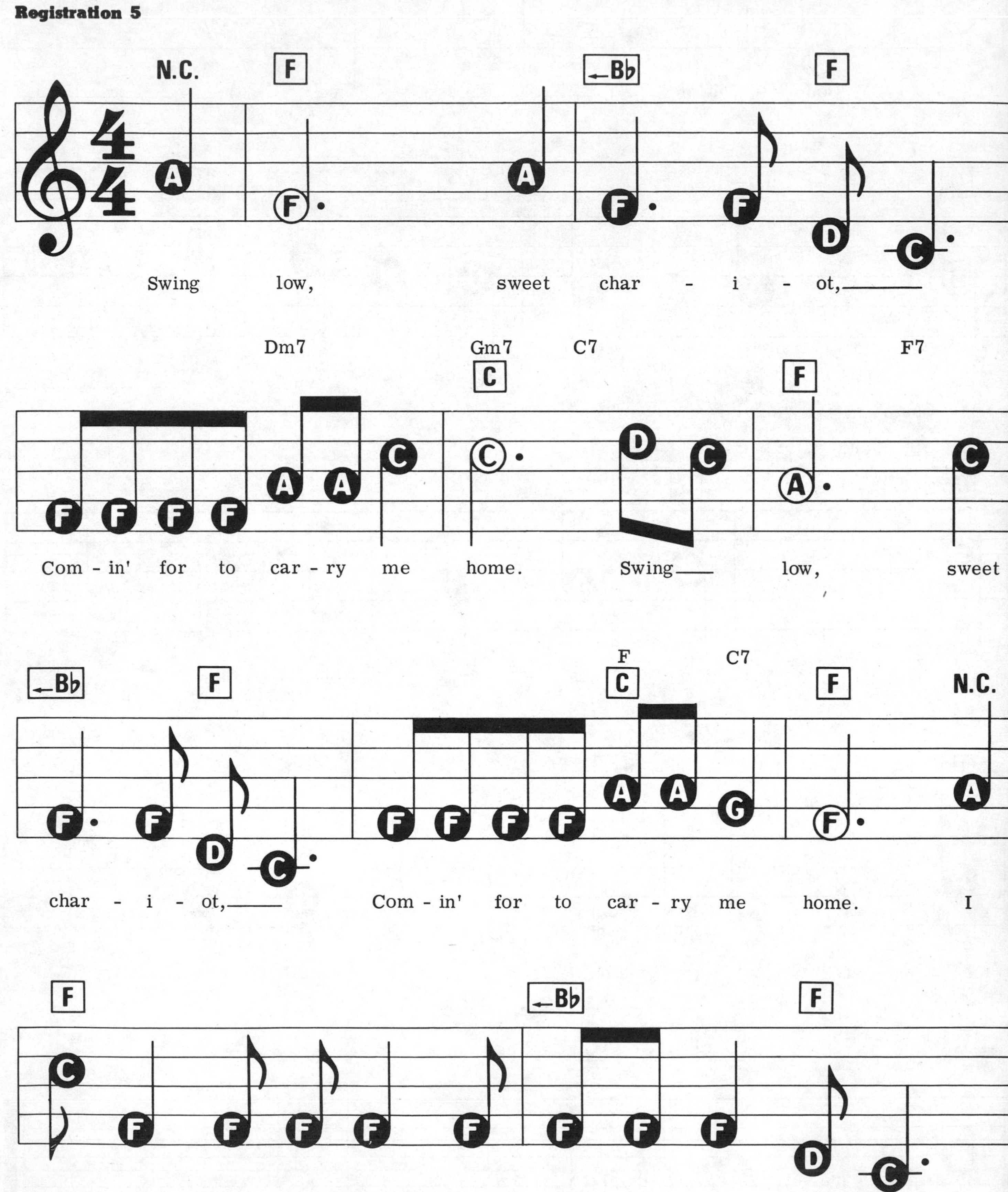

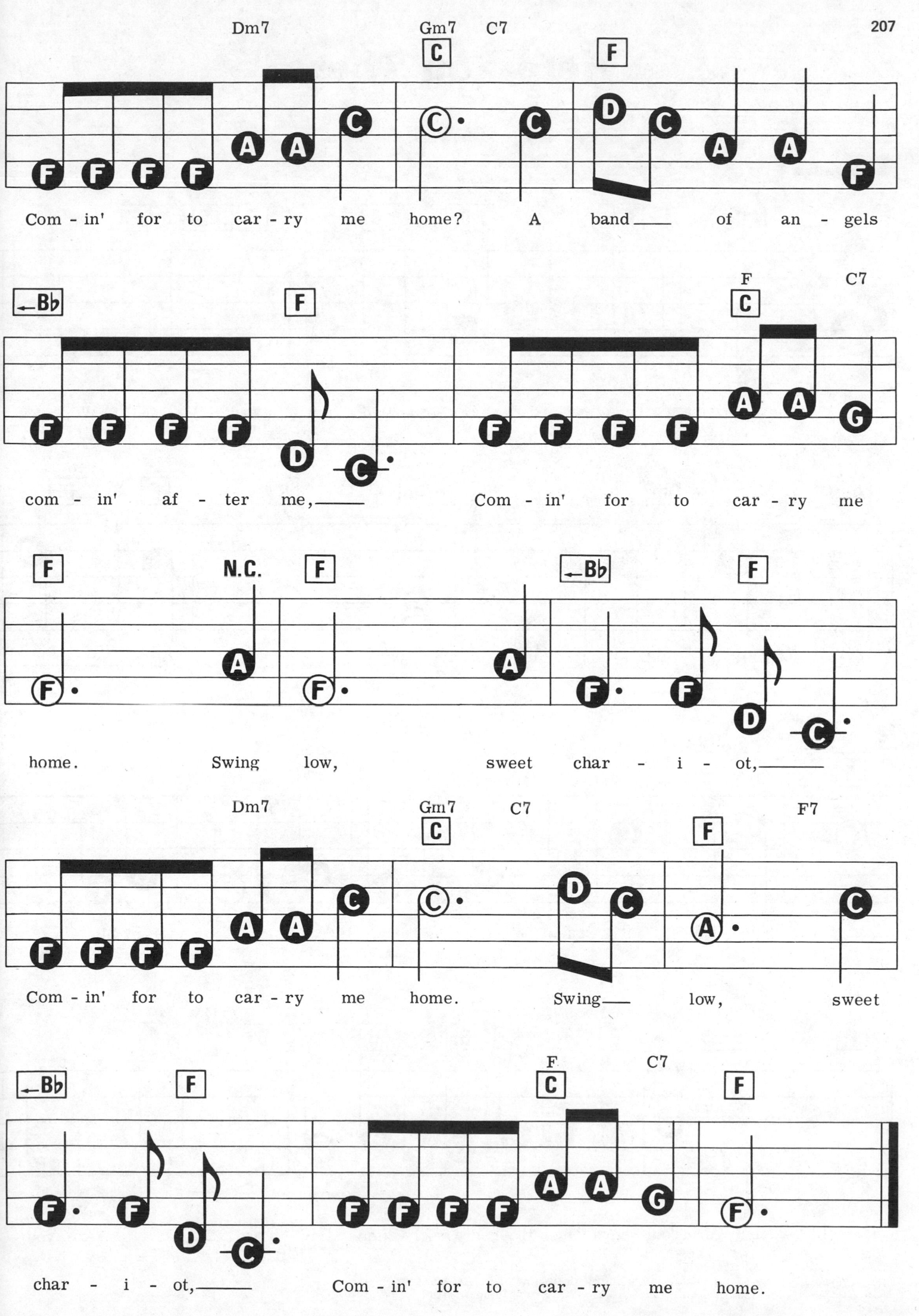
Dm7
Gm7 C7
C
F
Com - in' for to car - ry me home? A band of an - gels
Bb
F
F C7
C
com - in' af - ter me, Com - in' for to car - ry me
F
N.C.
F
Bb
F
home. Swing low, sweet char - i - ot,
Dm7
Gm7 C7
C
F
F7
Com - in' for to car - ry me home. Swing low, sweet
Bb
F
F C7
C
F
char - i - ot, Com - in' for to car - ry me home.

Were You There?

Registration 6

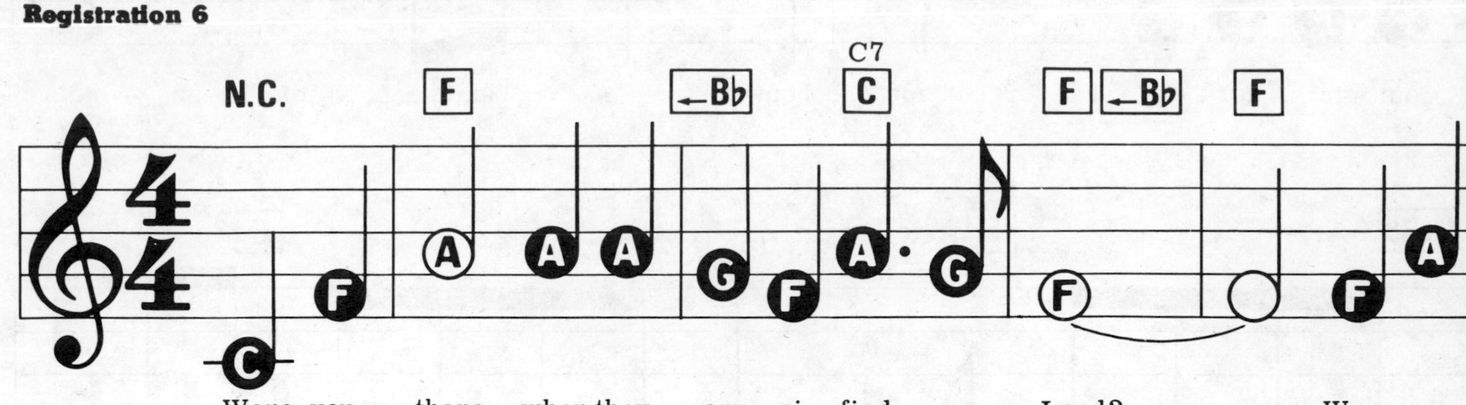

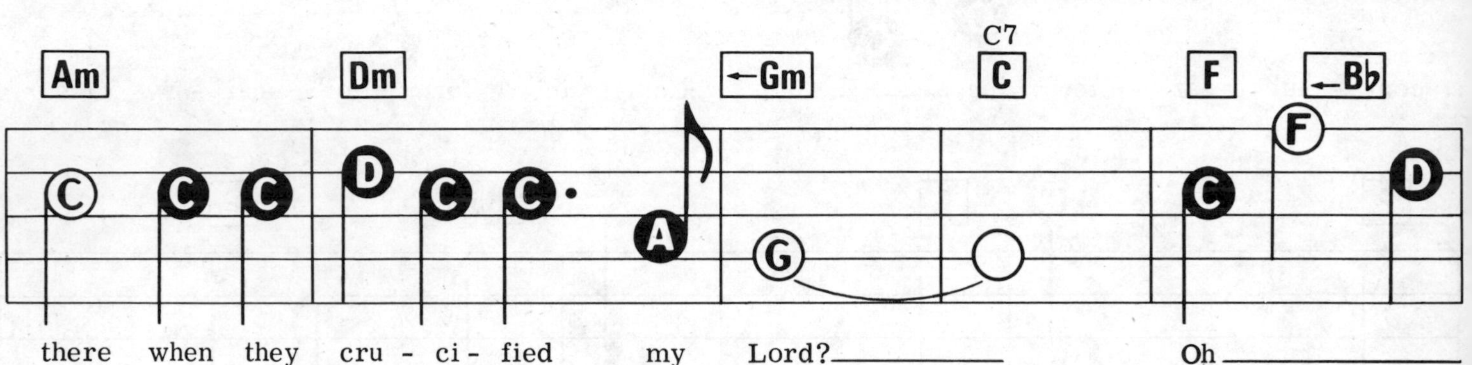

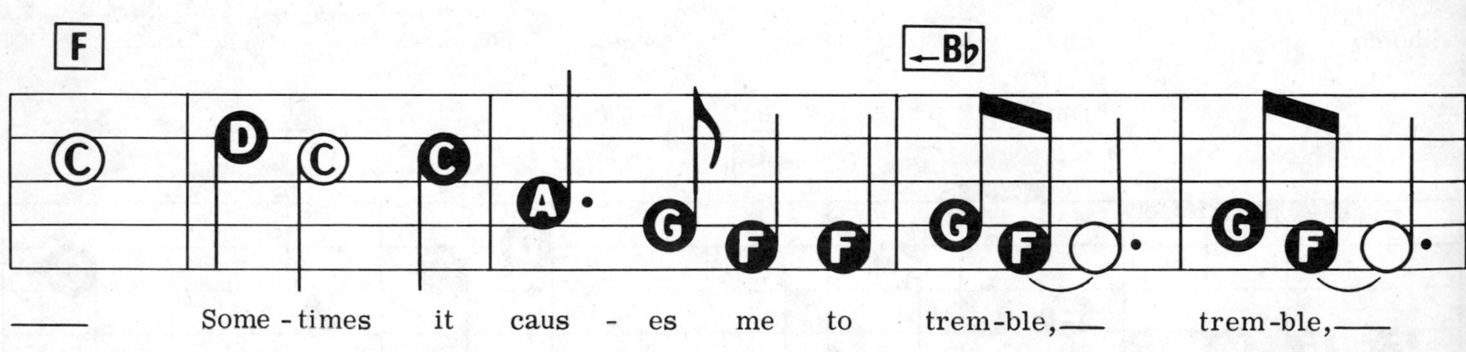

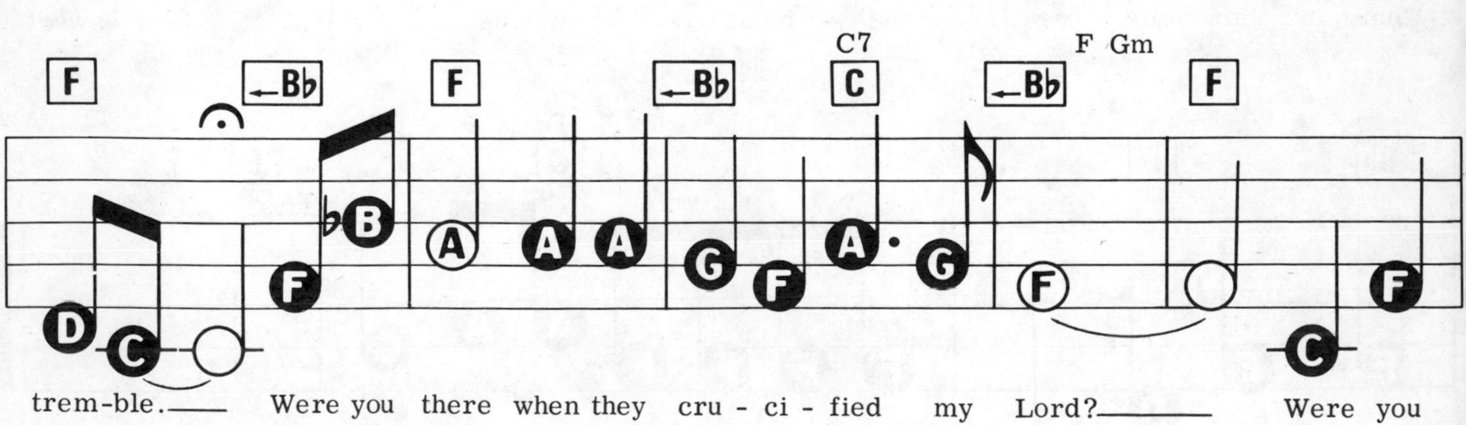

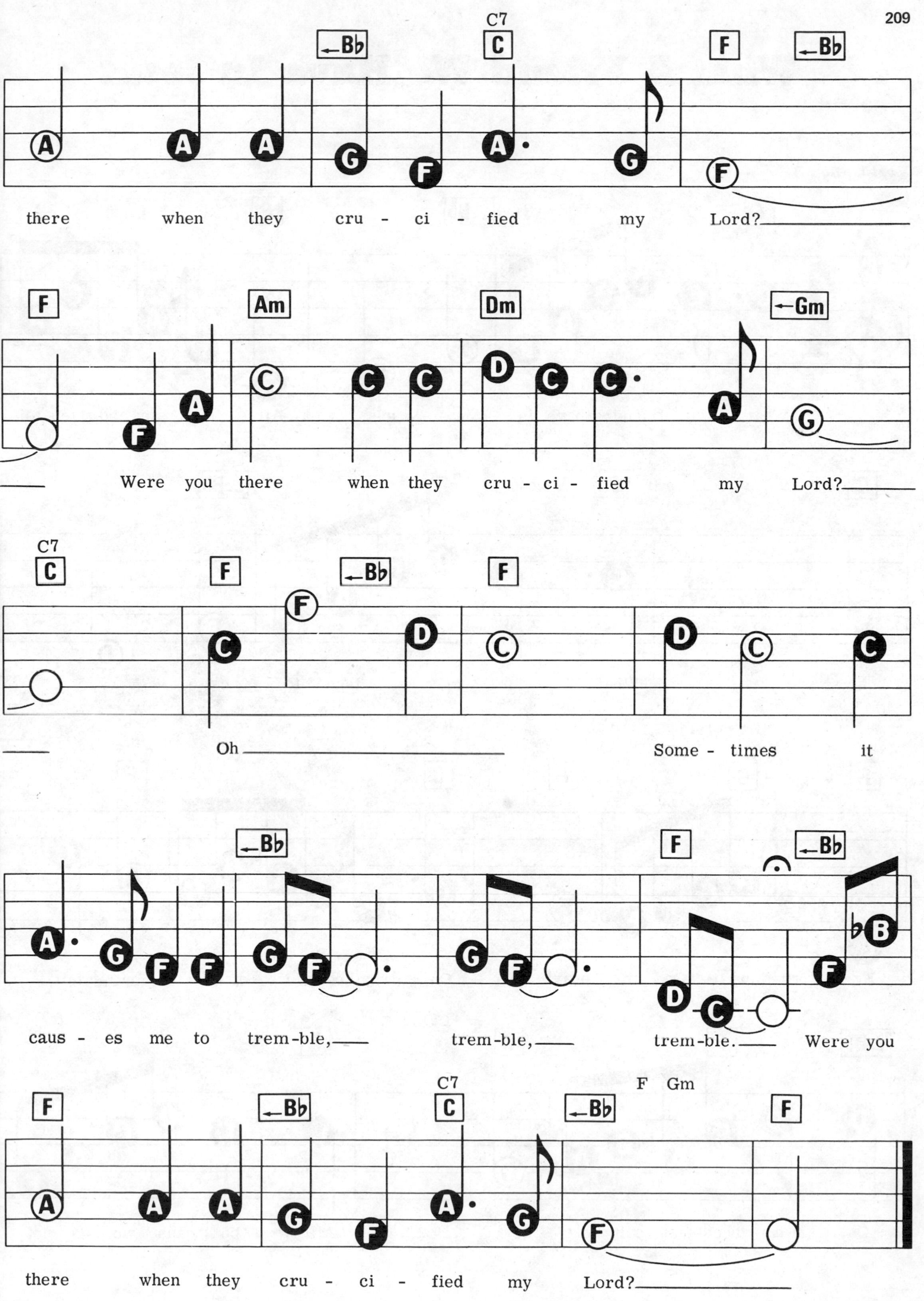
C7
Bb C F Bb
there when they cru - ci - fied my Lord?
F Am Dm Gm
Were you there when they cru - ci - fied my Lord?
C7
C F Bb F
Oh
Some - times it
Bb F Bb
caus - es me to trem-ble,
trem-ble,
trem-ble.
Were you
C7
F Gm
F Bb C Bb F
there when they cru - ci - fied my Lord?

What A Friend We Have In Jesus

Registration 3

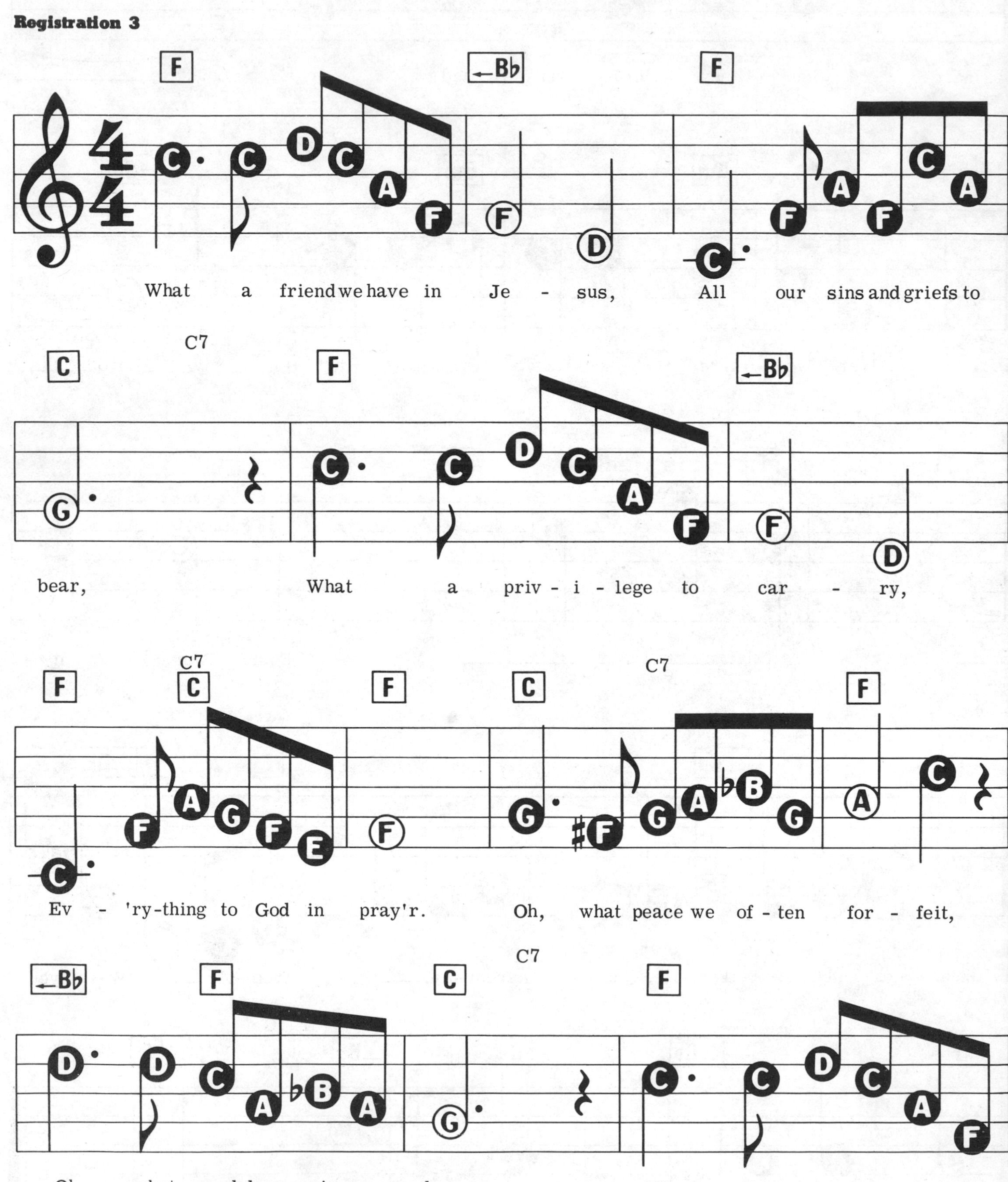

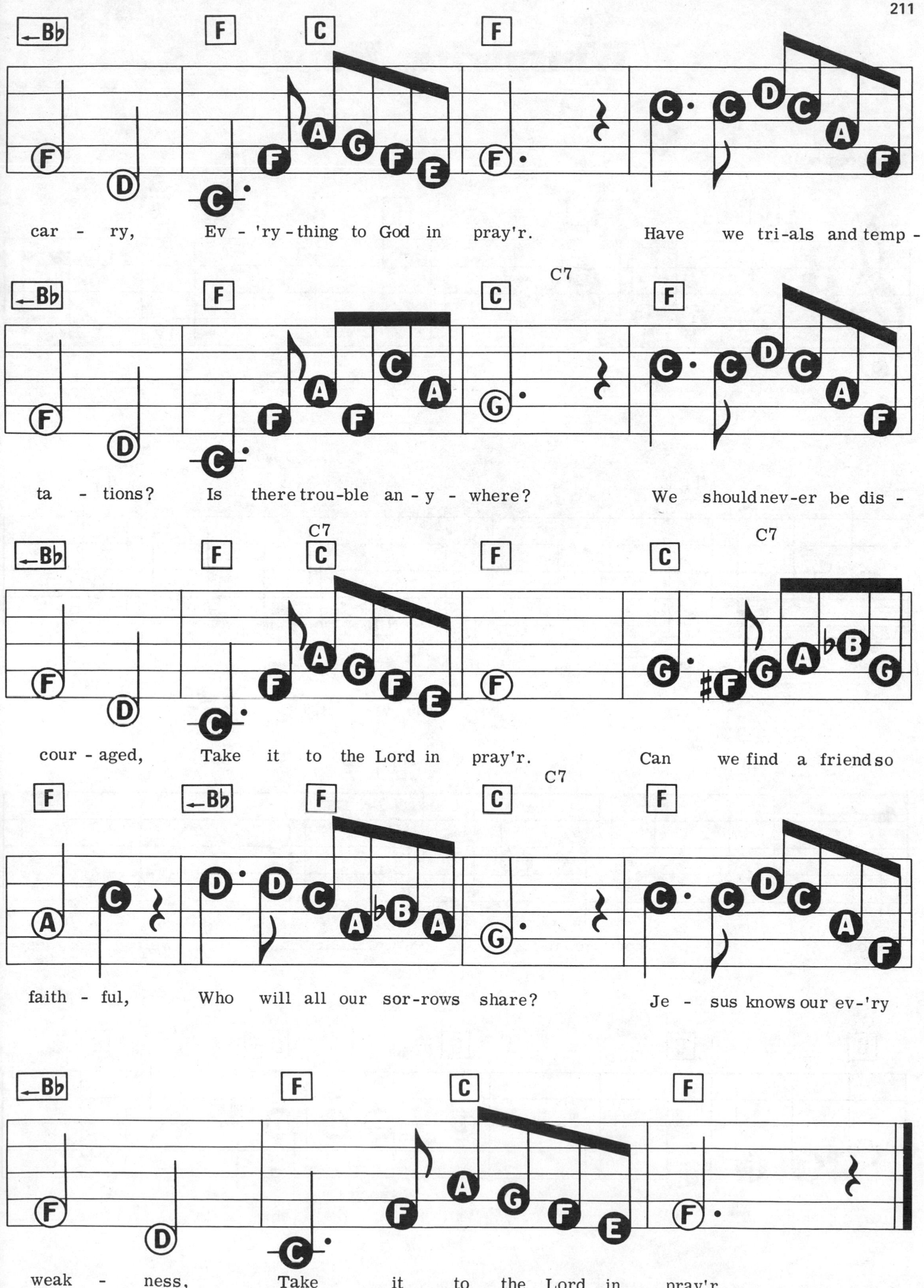
Bb F C F
car - ry, Ev - 'ry - thing to God in pray'r. Have we tri-als and temp -
Bb F C7 C F
ta - tions? Is there trou-ble an - y - where? We should nev-er be dis -
Bb F C7 C F C7 C
cour - aged, Take it to the Lord in pray'r. Can we find a friend so
F Bb F C7 C F
faith - ful, Who will all our sor-rows share? Je - sus knows our ev-'ry
Bb F C F
weak - ness, Take it to the Lord in pray'r.

Whispering Hope

Registration 10

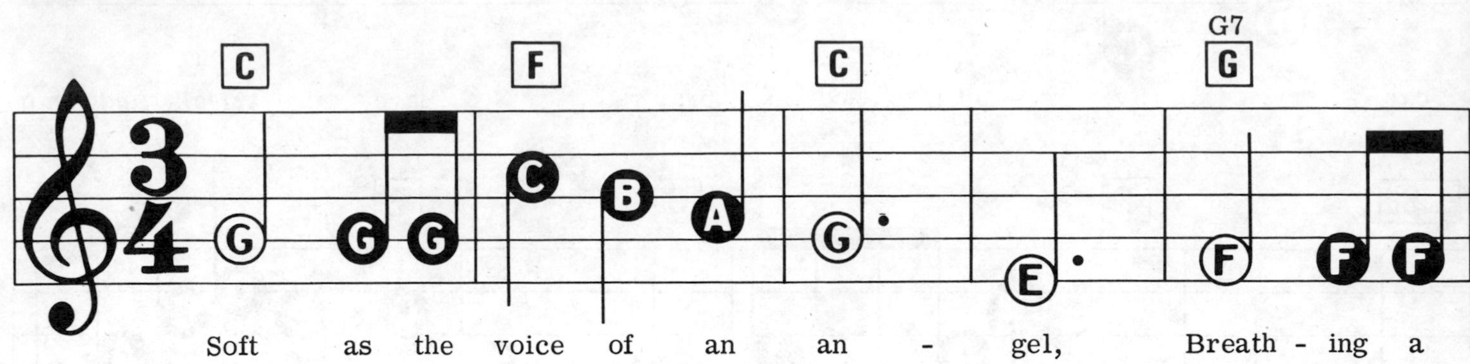

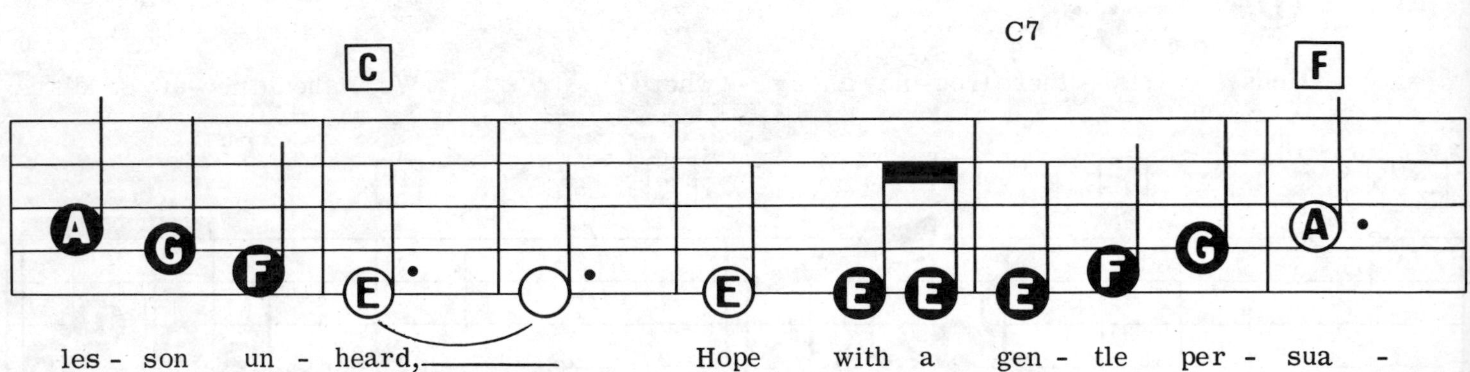

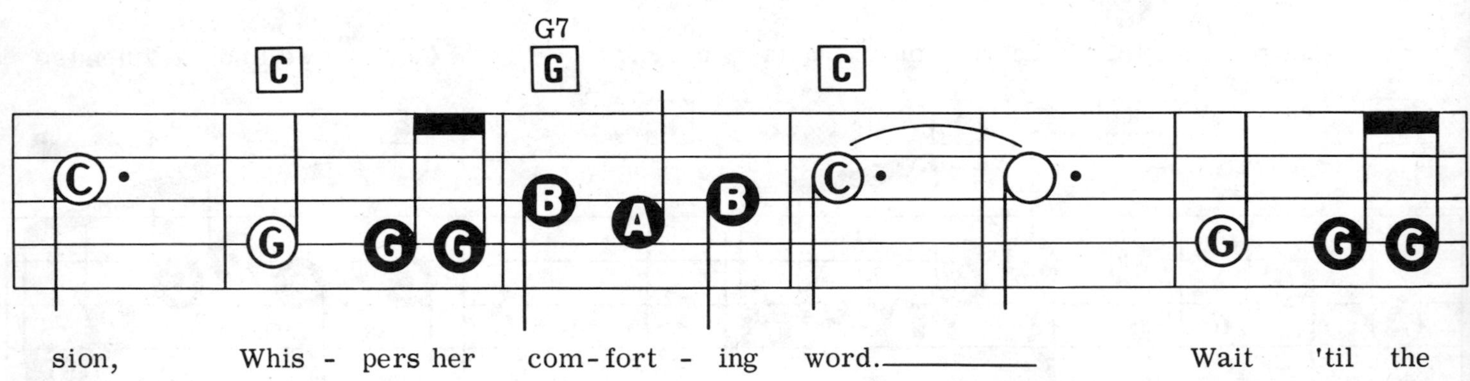

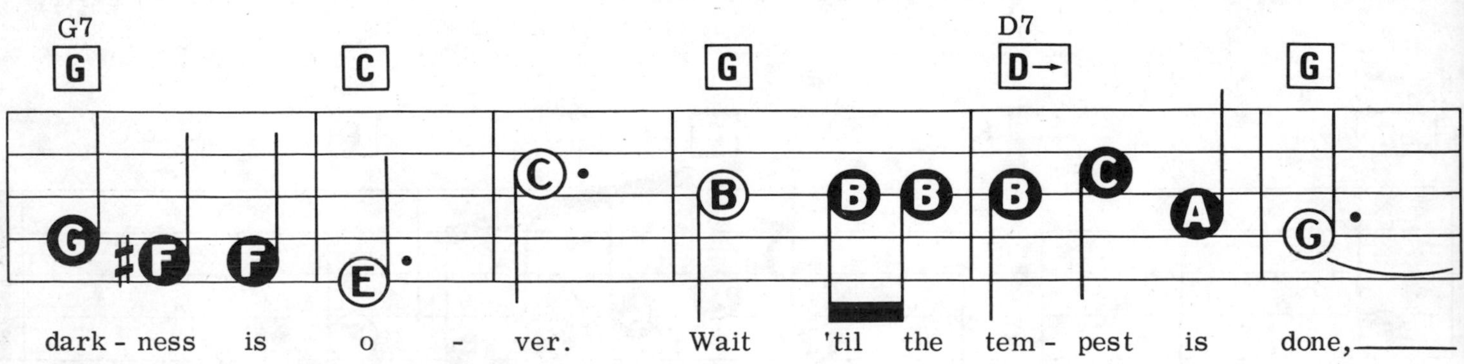

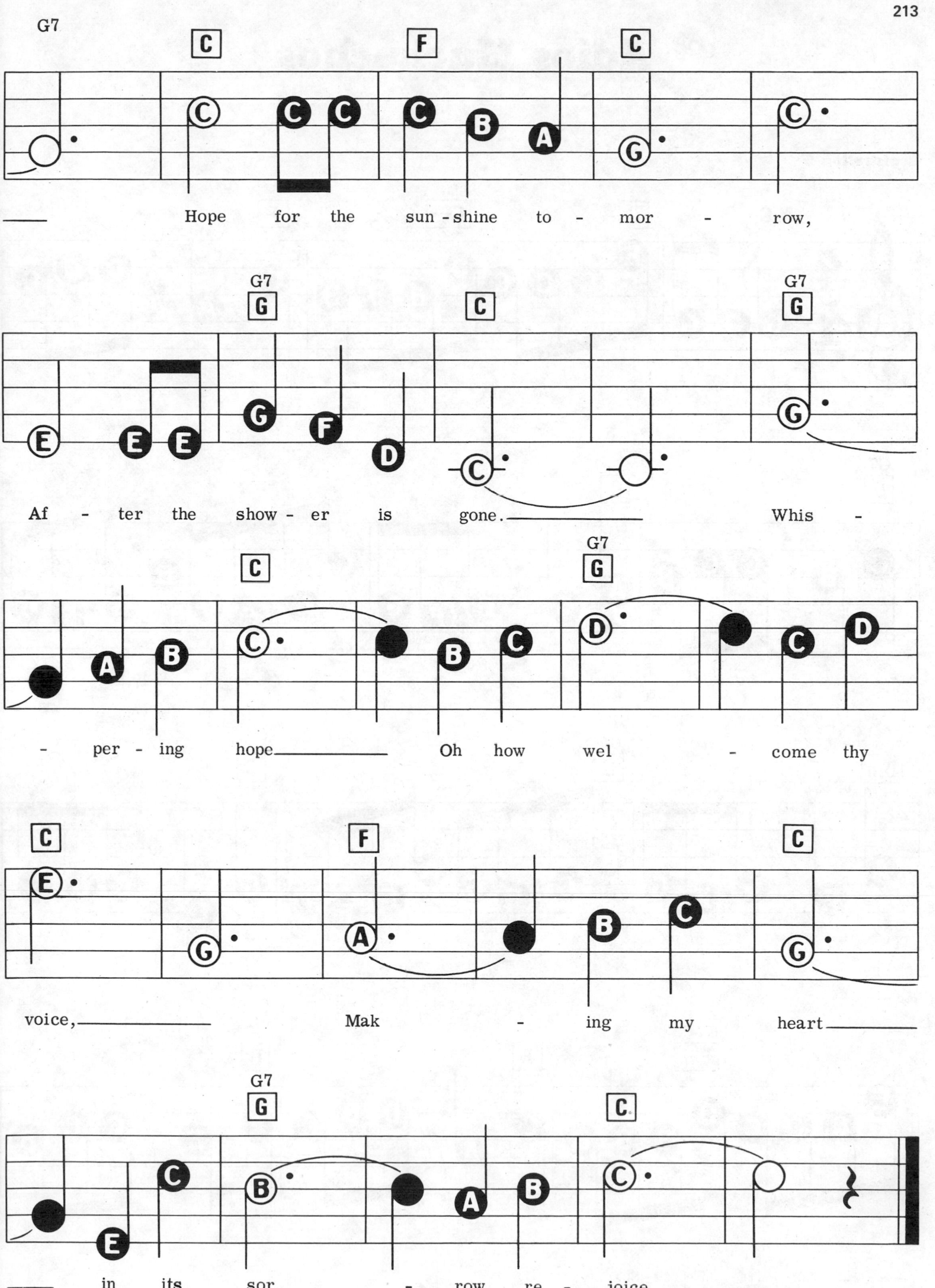
G7
C
F
C
Hope for the sun - shine to - mor - row,
G7
G
C
G7
G
Af - ter the show - er is gone.
Whis -
C
G7
G
- per - ing hope
Oh how wel - come thy
C
F
C
voice,
Mak - ing my heart
G7
G
C
in its sor - row re - joice.

Adios Muchachos

Registration 5

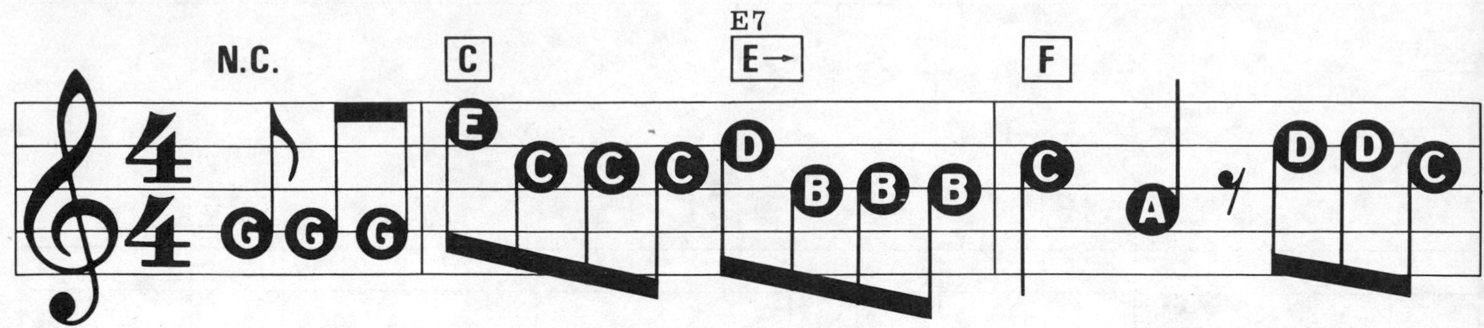

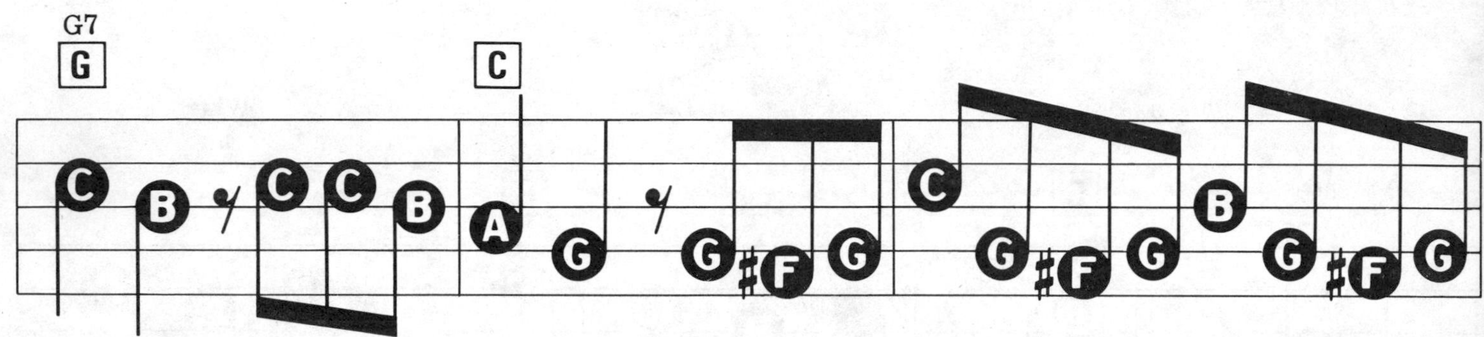

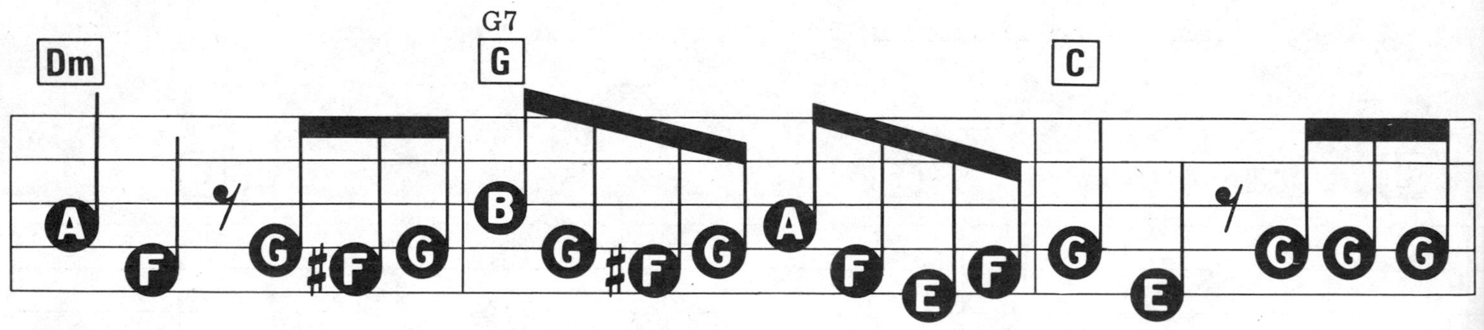

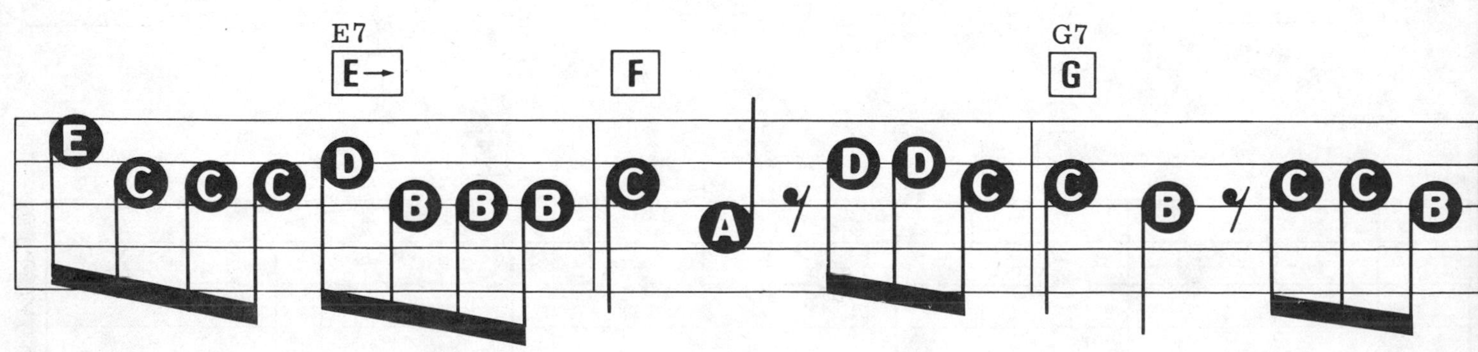

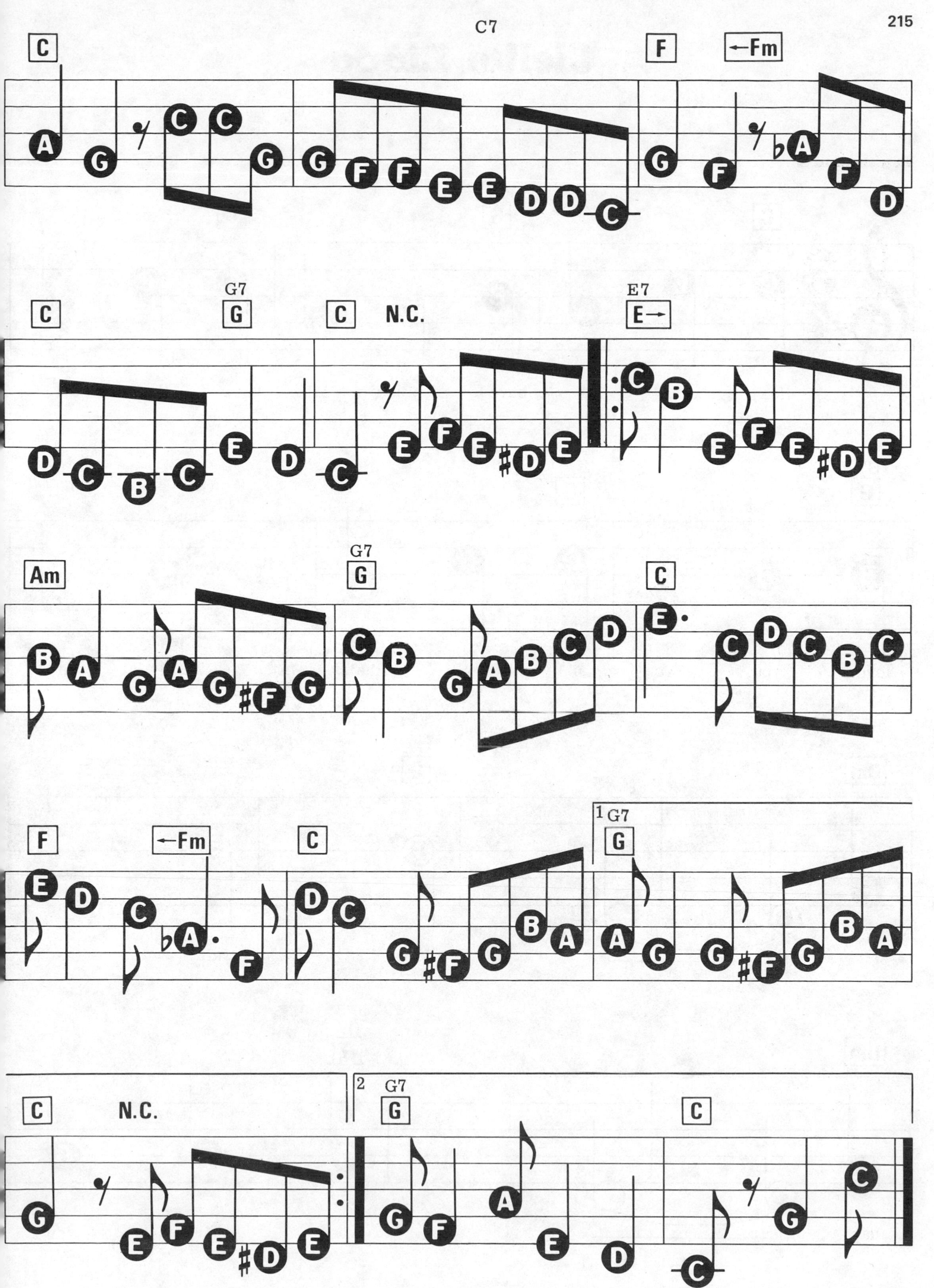
C C7 F ←Fm
C G7 G C N.C. E7 E→
Am G7 G C
F ←Fm C 1 G7 G
C N.C. 2 G7 G C

Cielito Lindo

Registration 4

Mexican

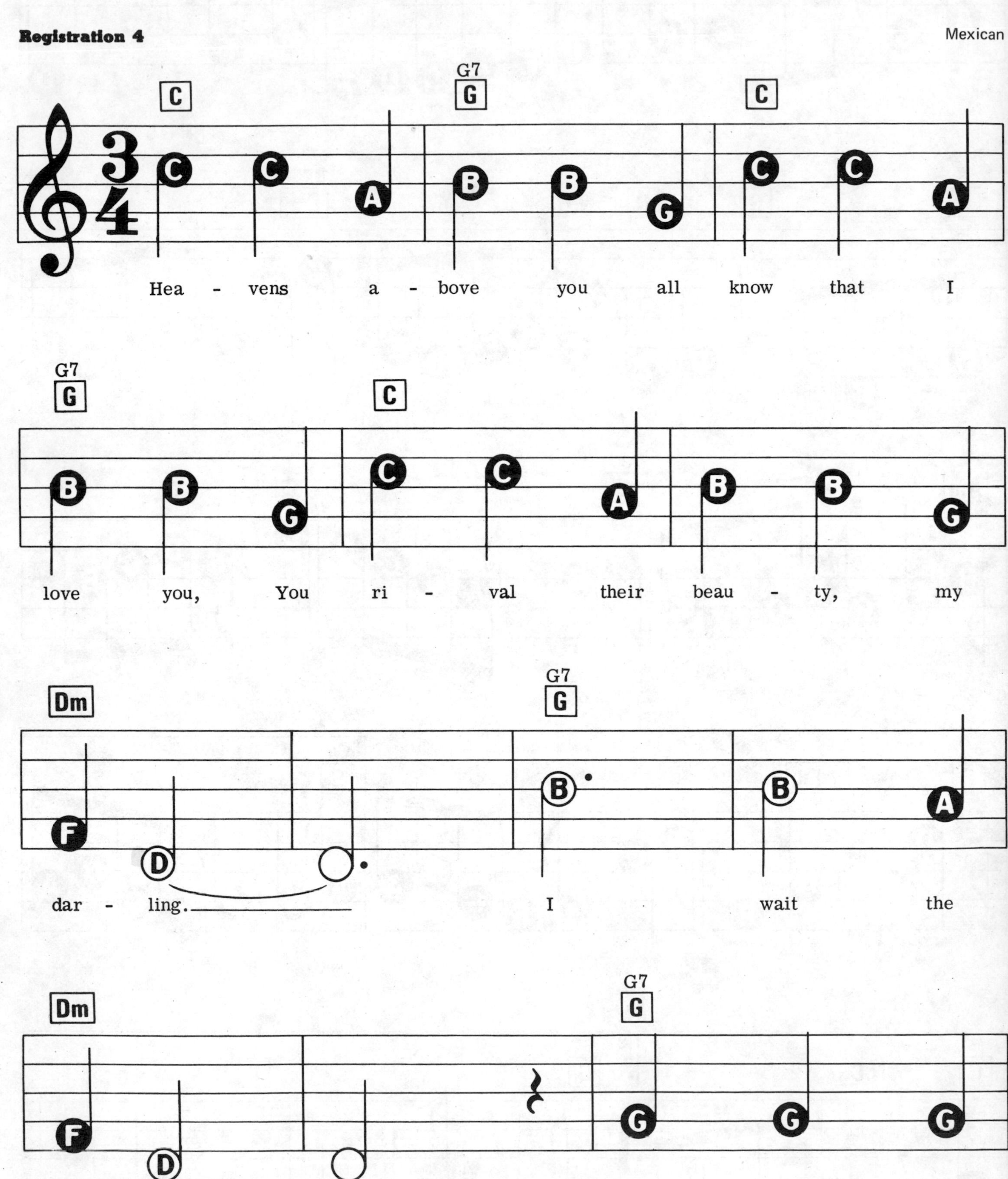

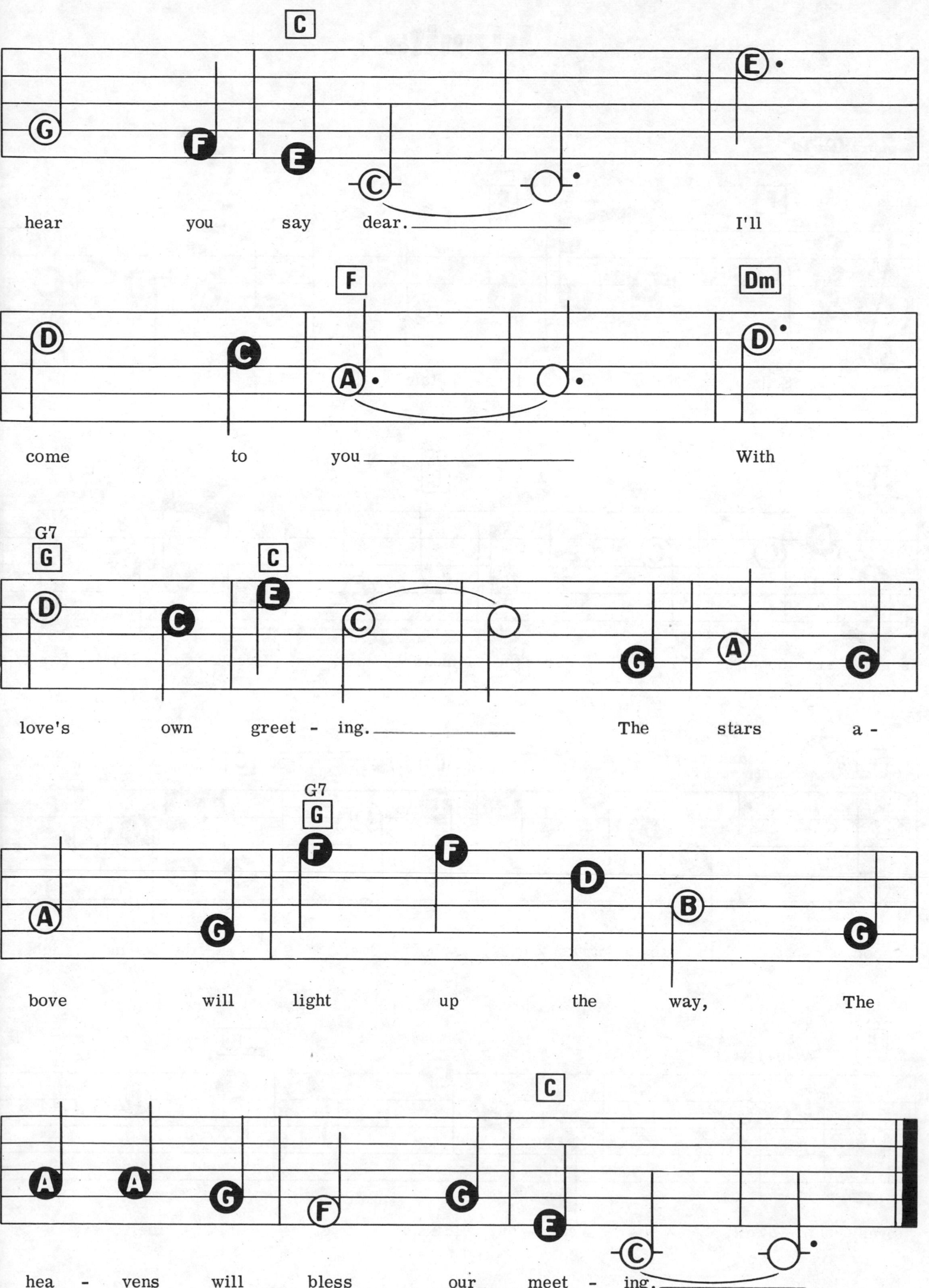
C
hear you say dear. I'll
F Dm
come to you With
G7 G C
love's own greet - ing. The stars a -
G7 G
bove will light up the way, The
C
hea - vens will bless our meet - ing.

Juanita

Registration 10 Spanish

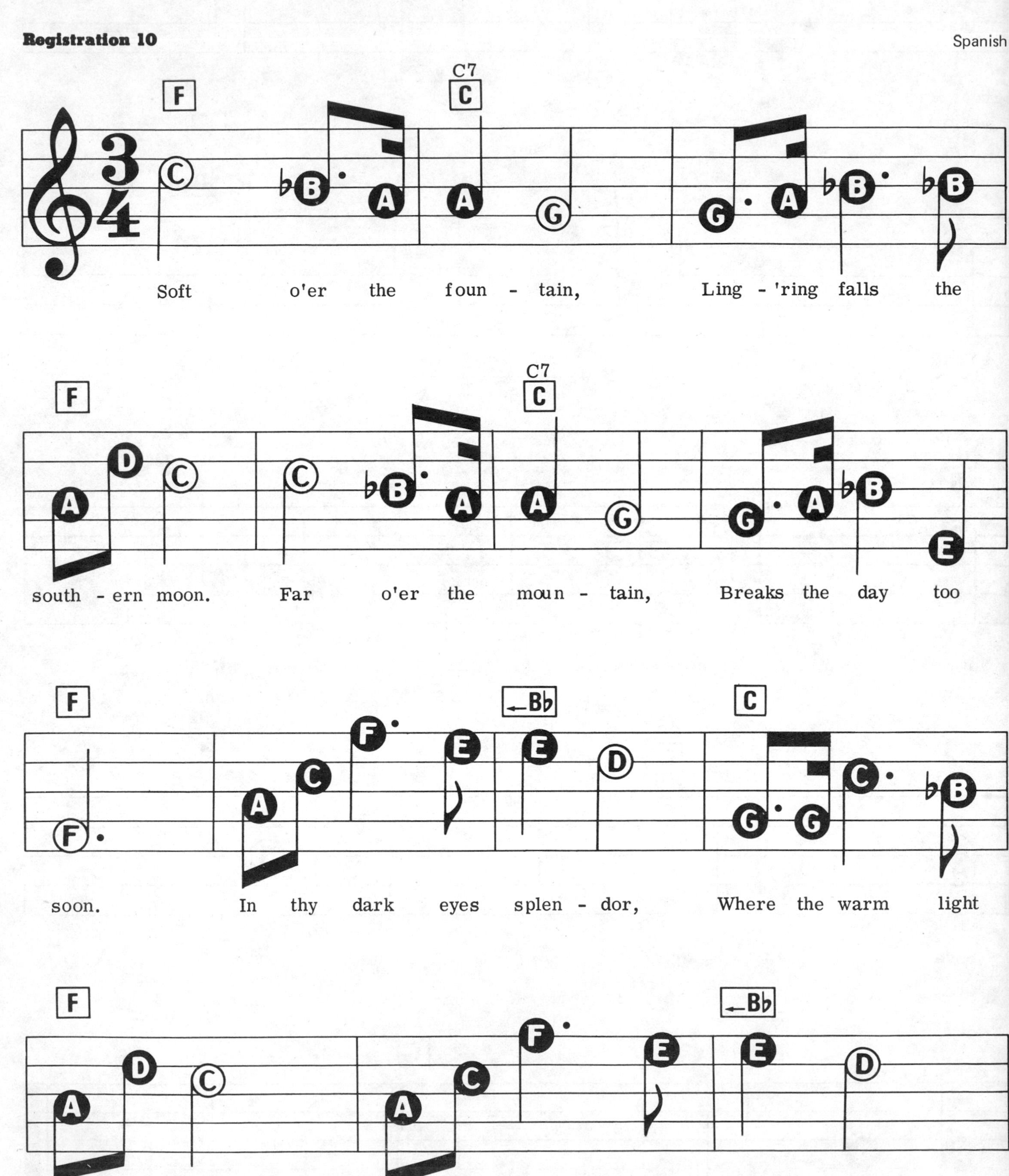

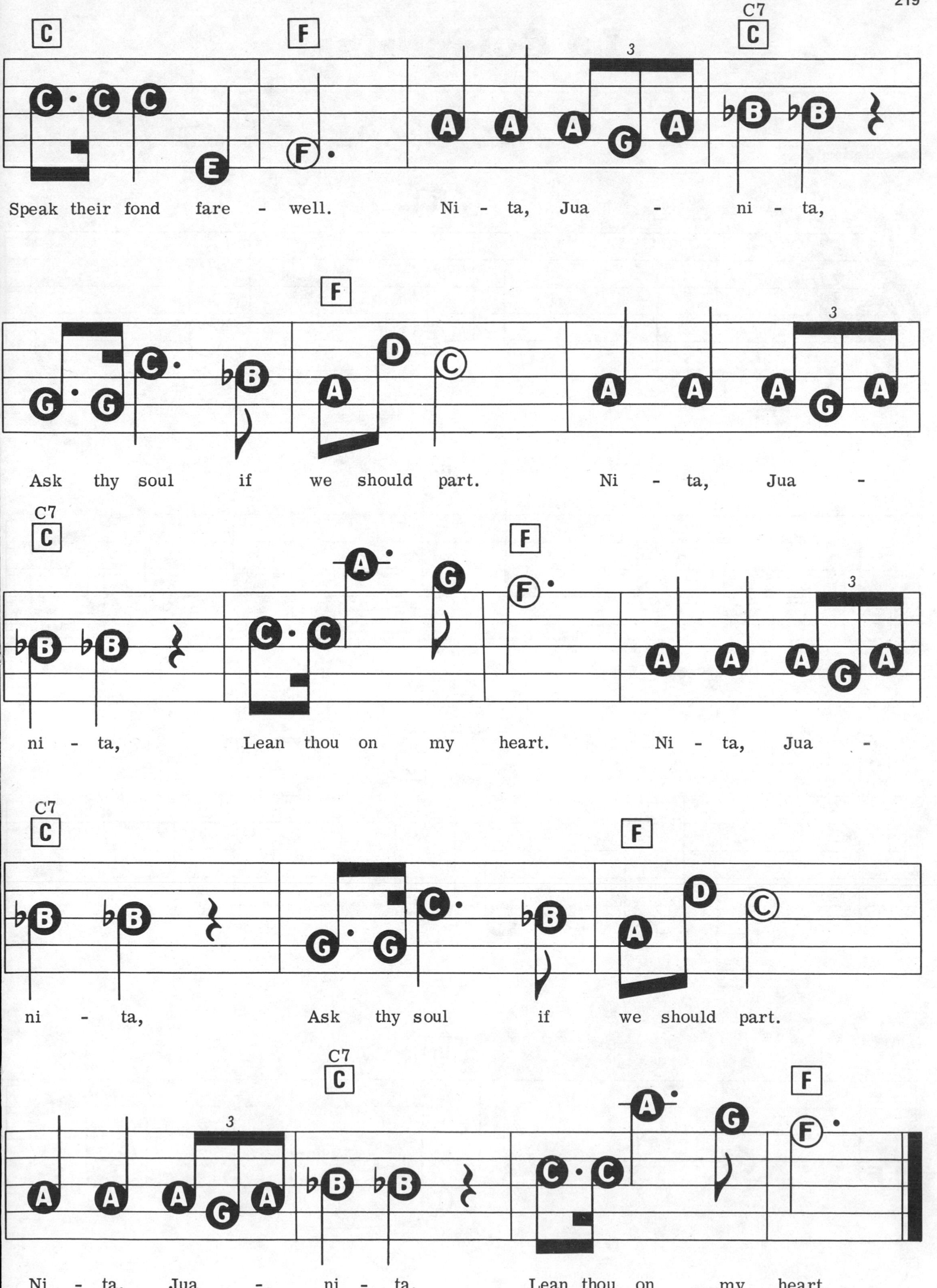
C F C7 C
Speak their fond fare - well. Ni - ta, Jua - ni - ta,
F
Ask thy soul if we should part. Ni - ta, Jua -
C7 C F
ni - ta, Lean thou on my heart. Ni - ta, Jua -
C7 C F
ni - ta, Ask thy soul if we should part.
C7 C F
Ni - ta, Jua - ni - ta, Lean thou on my heart.

La Golondrina

Registration 2

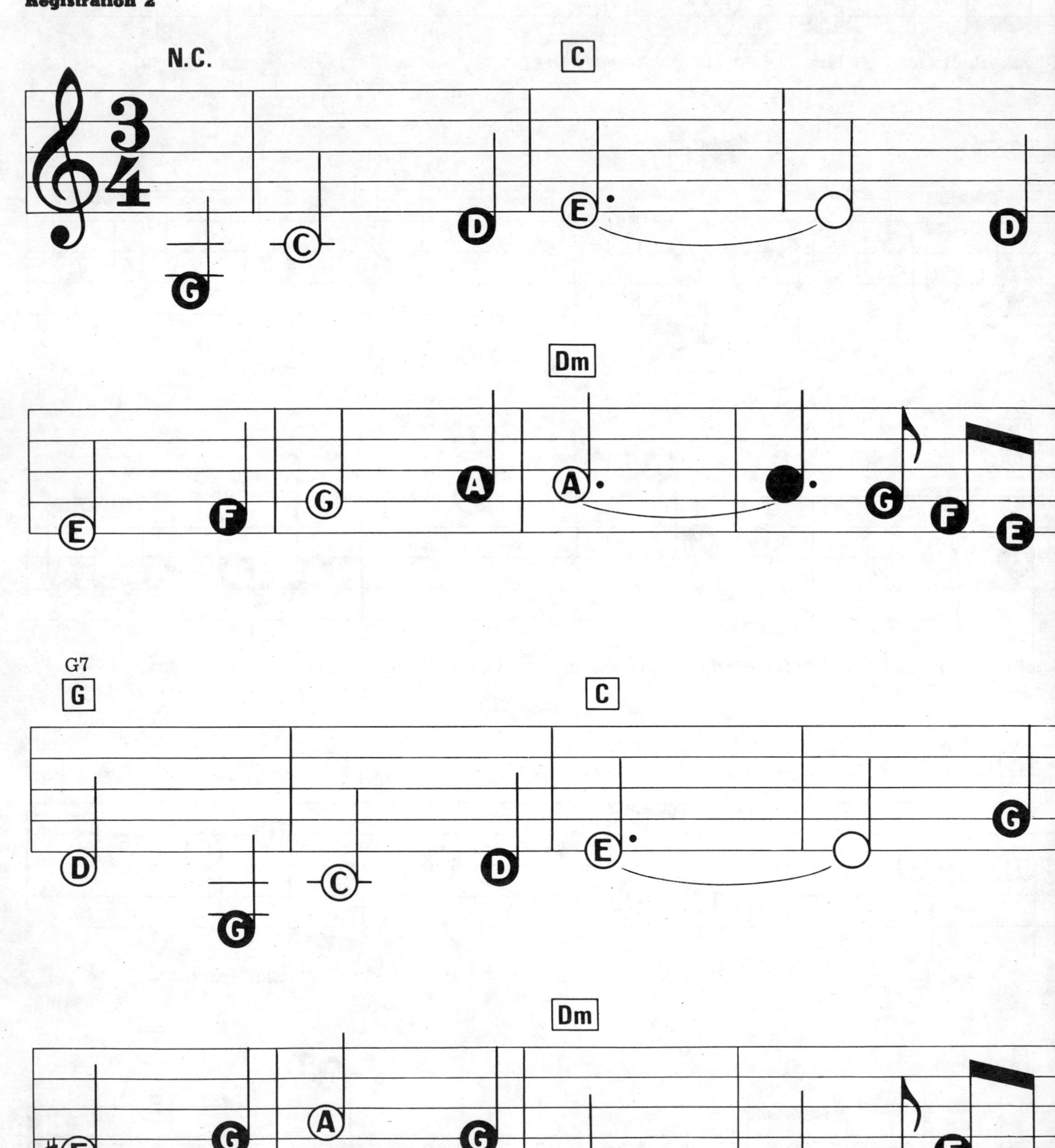

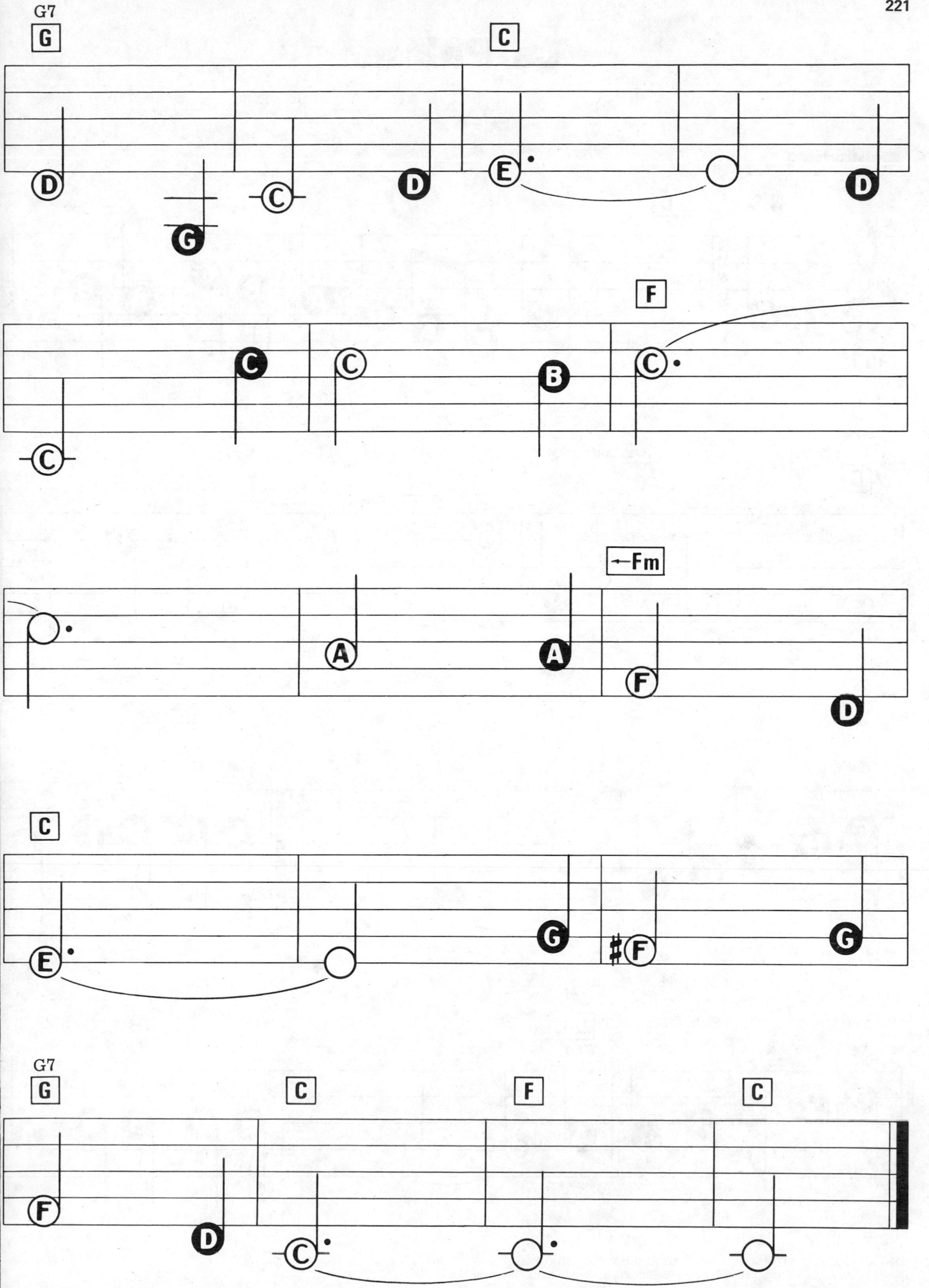
G7
G
C
D
G
C
D
E
D
C
C
C
B
F
C
A
A
←Fm
F
D
C
E
G
♯F
G
G7
G
C
F
C
F
D
C

La Paloma

Registration 3

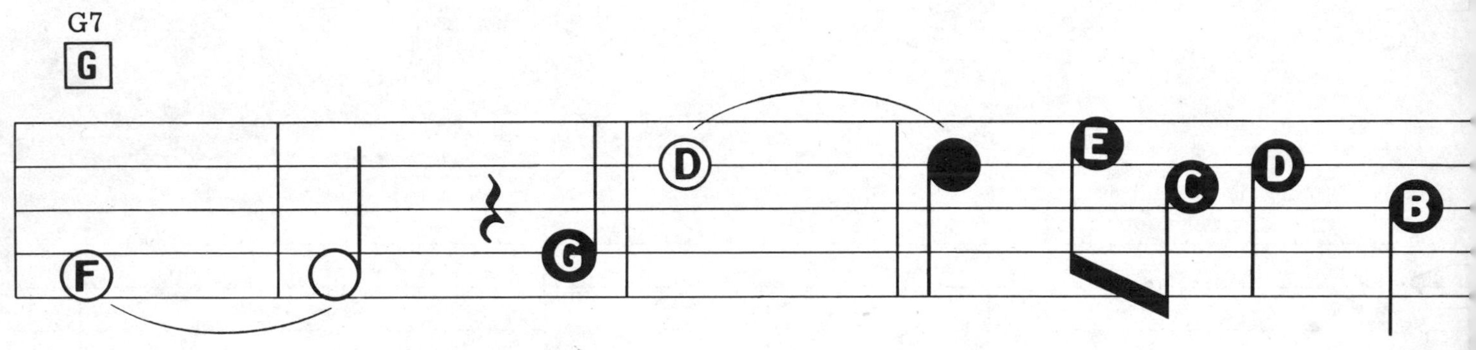

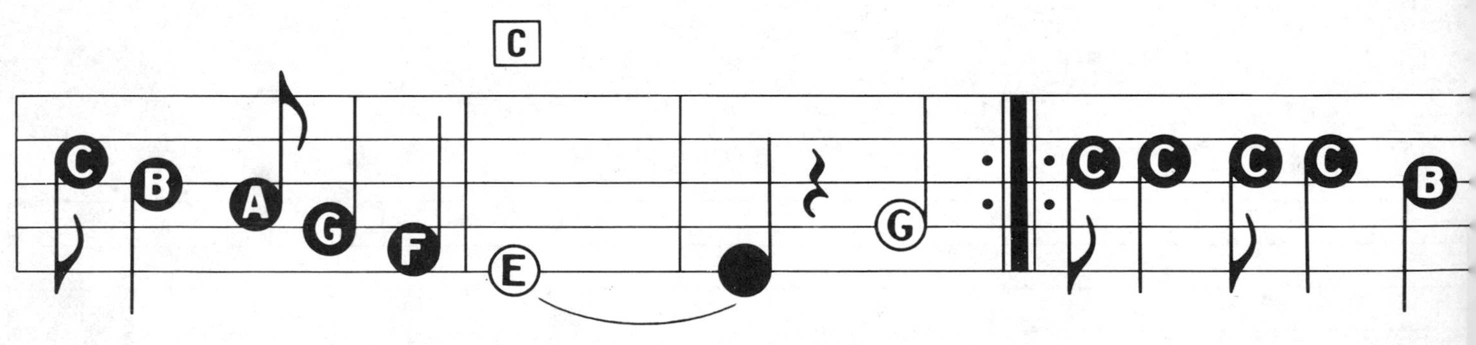

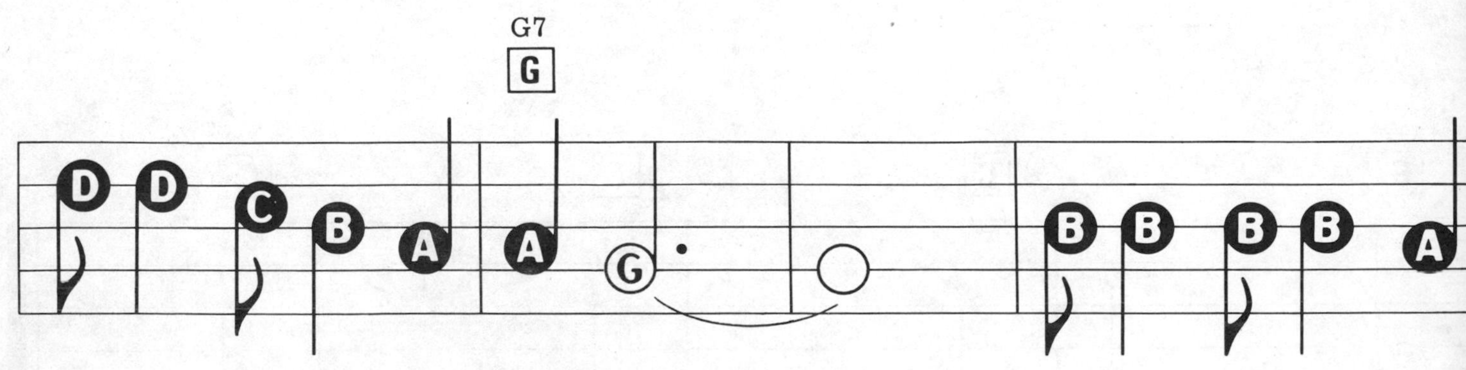

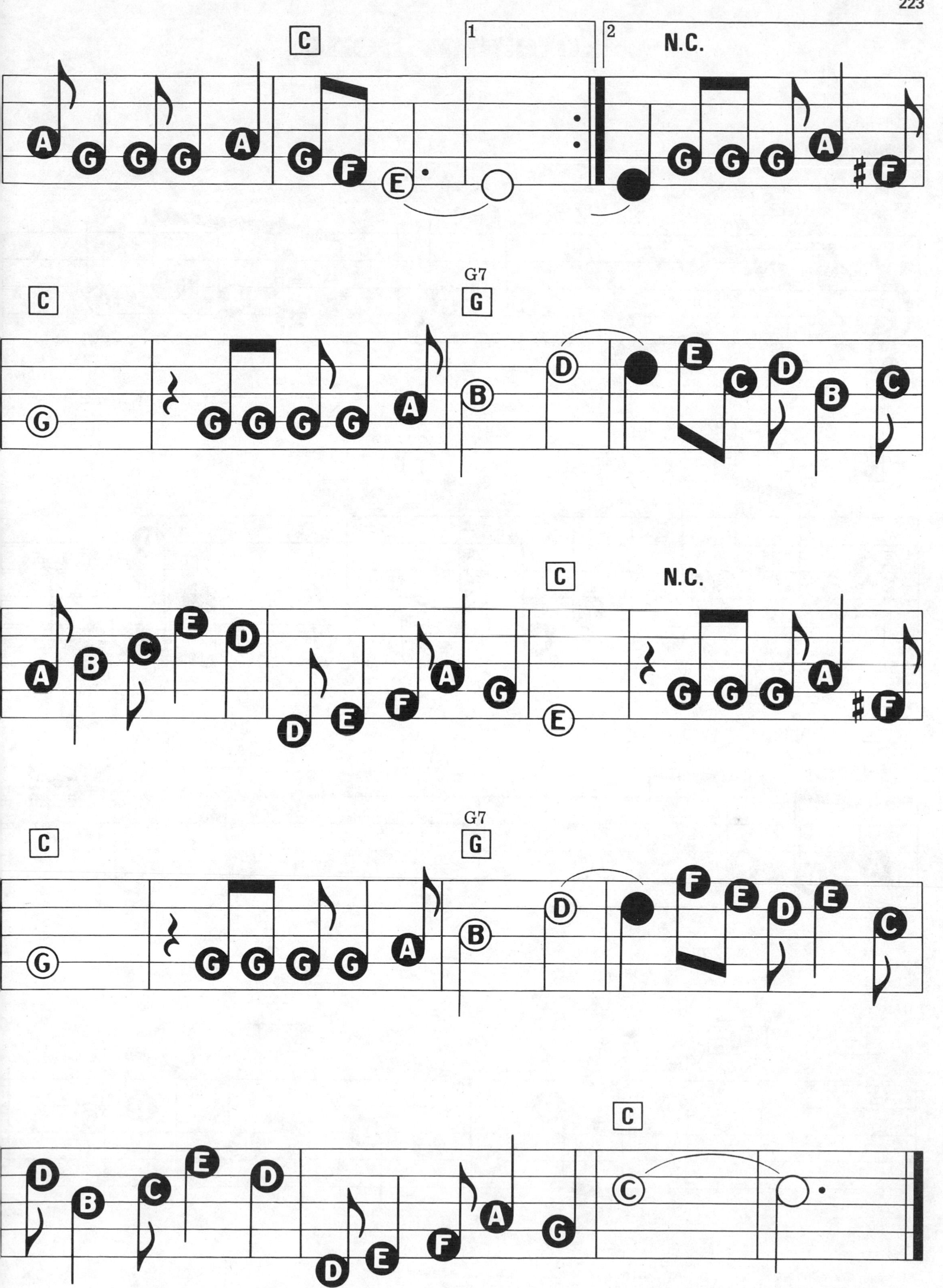
C
1
2
N.C.
C
G7
G
C
N.C.
C
G7
G
C

Toreador Song

Registration 1

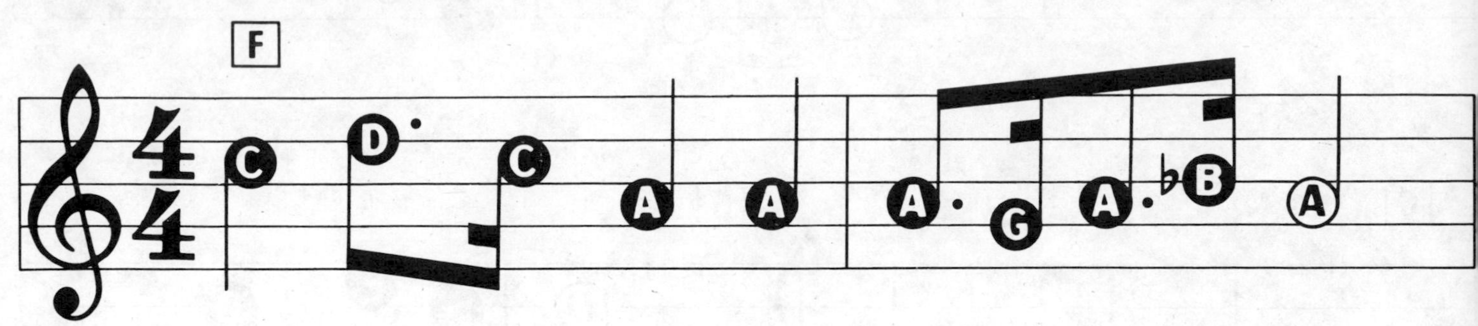

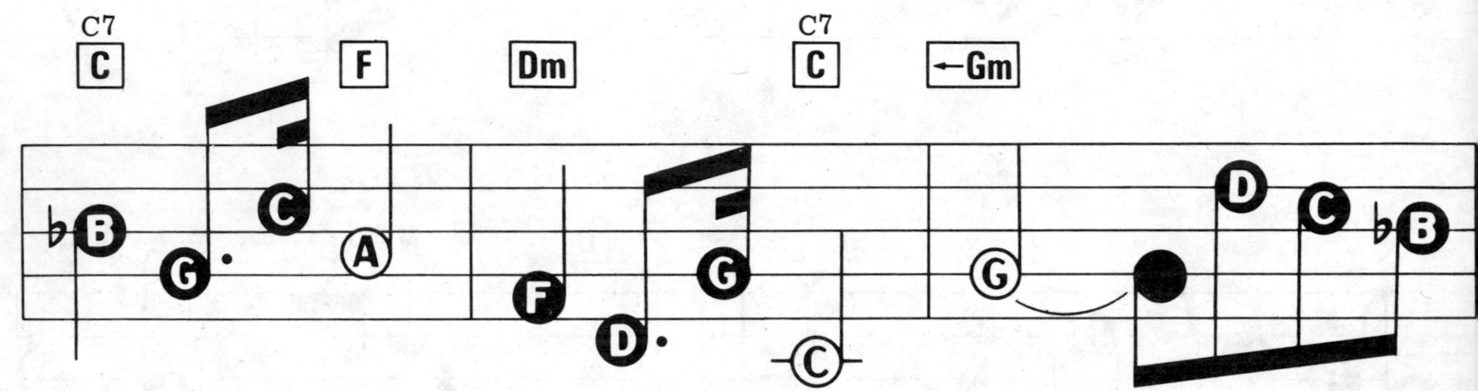

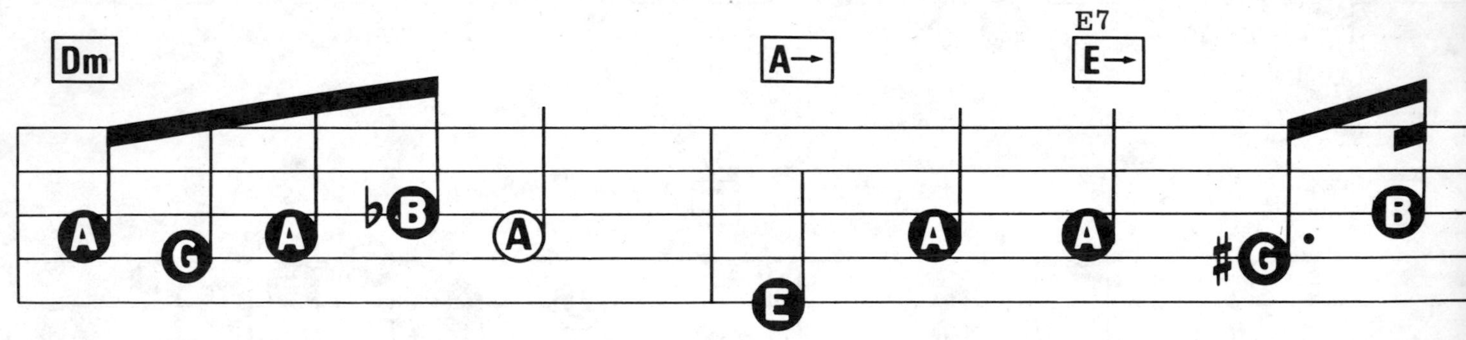

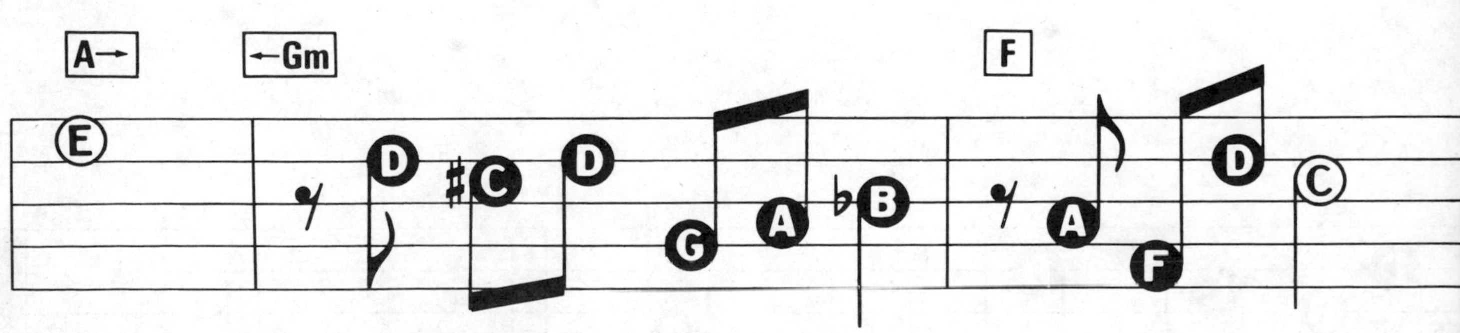

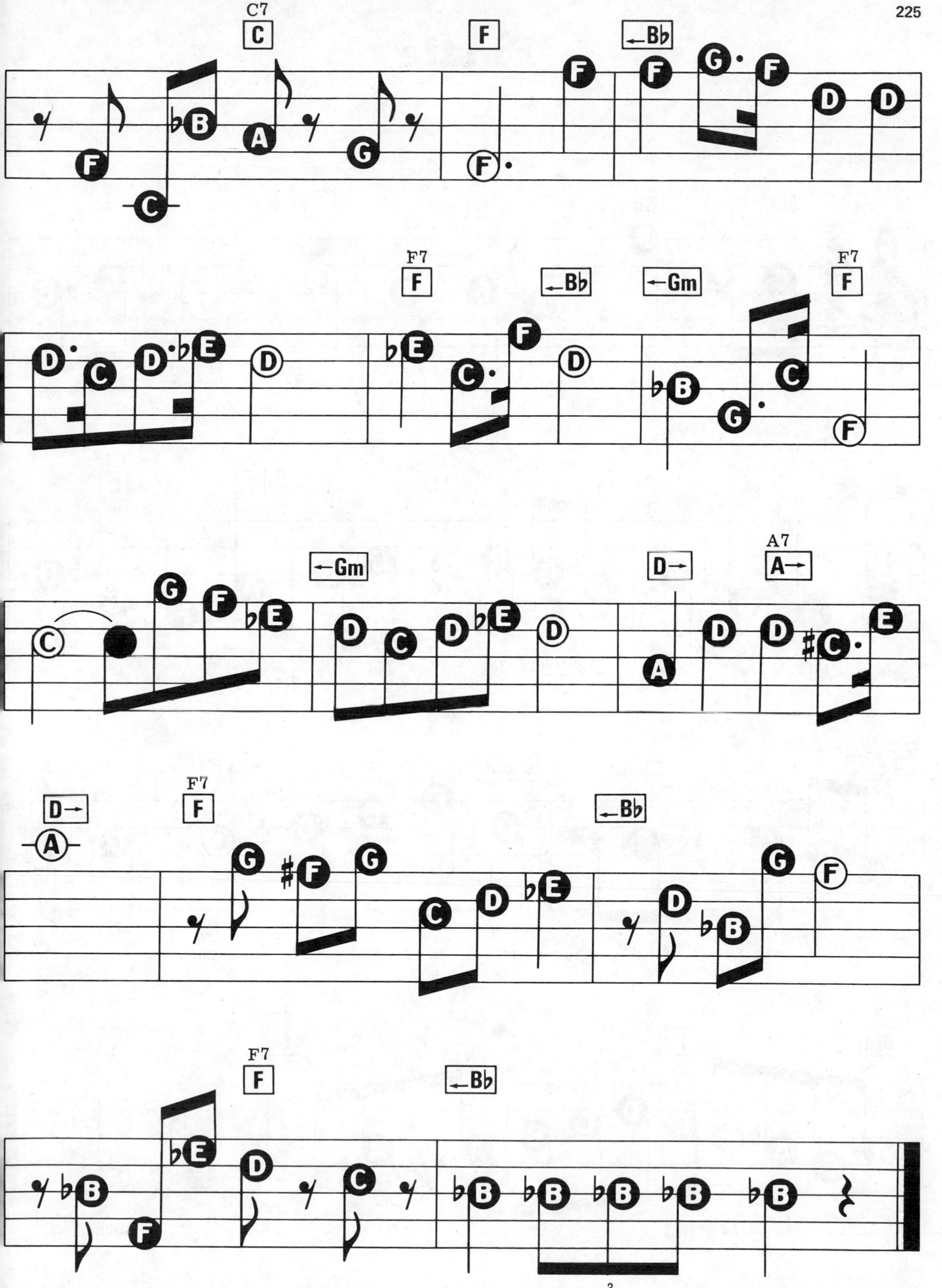
C7
C
F
←Bb
F7
F
←Bb
←Gm
F7
F
←Gm
D→
A7
A→
D→
F7
F
←Bb
F7
F
←Bb
3

Finale

Registration 3

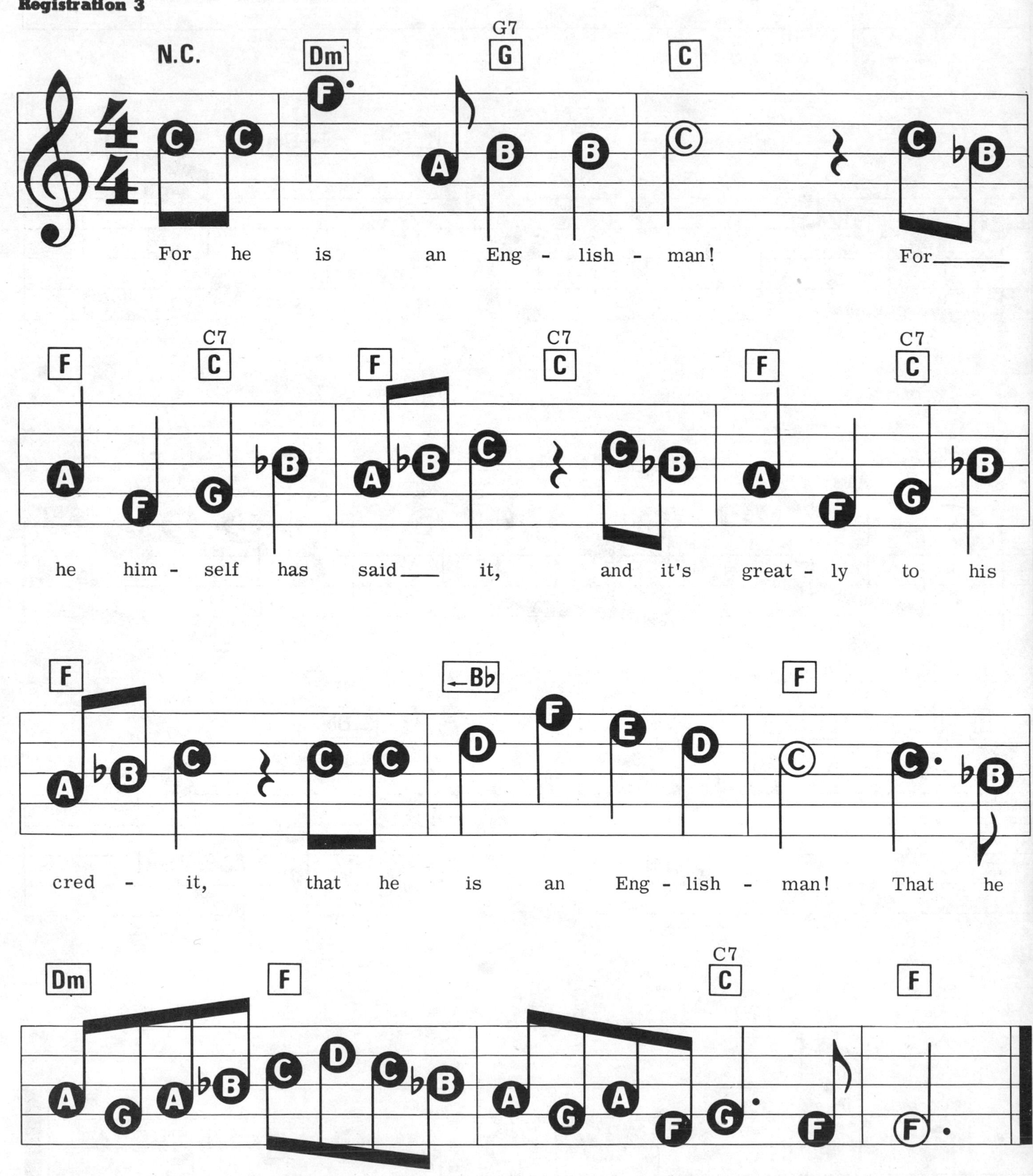

When I Was A Lad

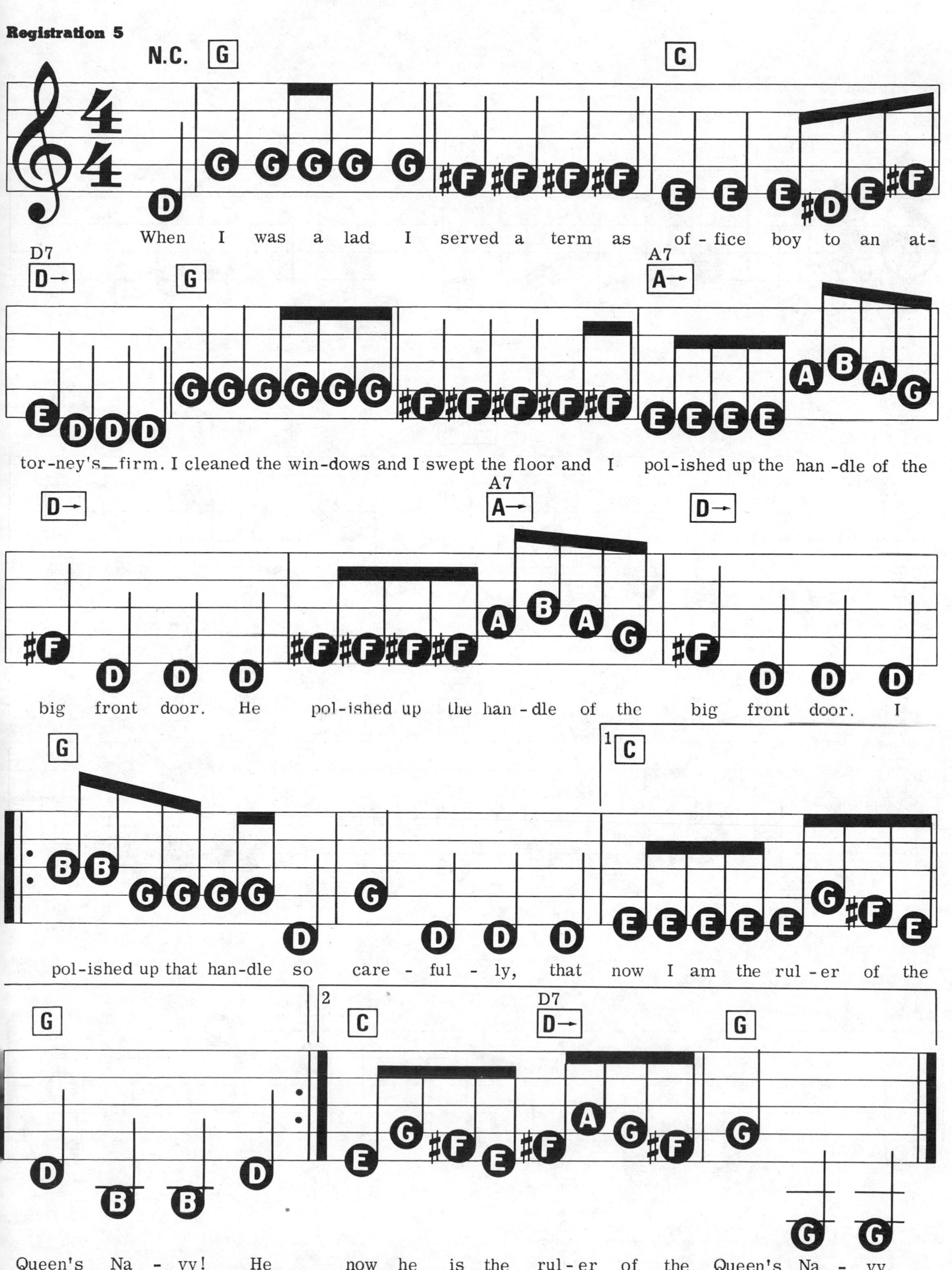

Hear The Waltz

Registration 10

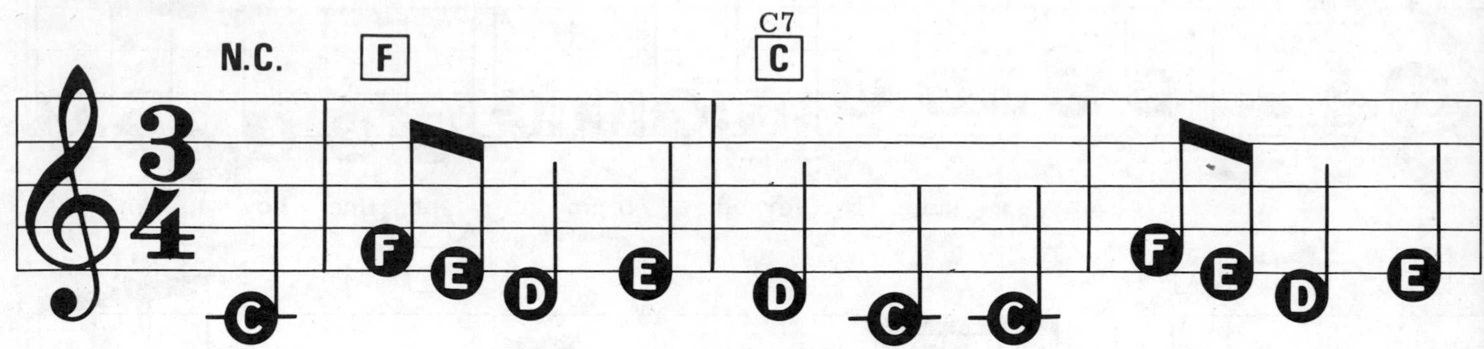

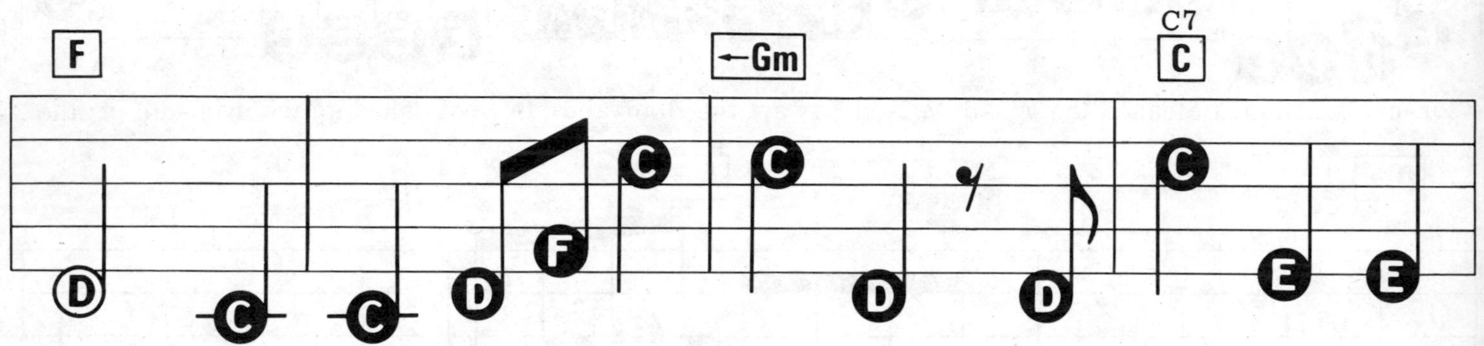

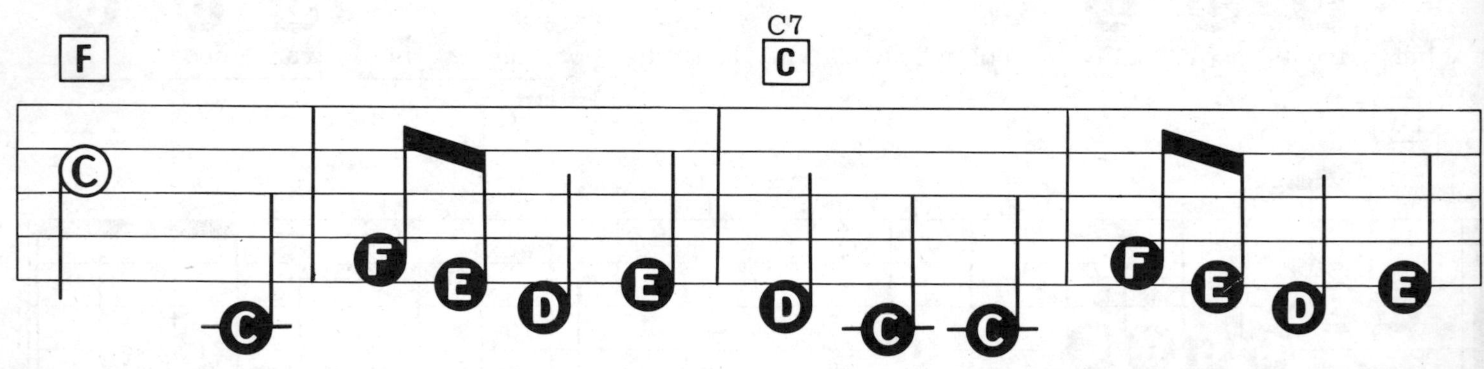

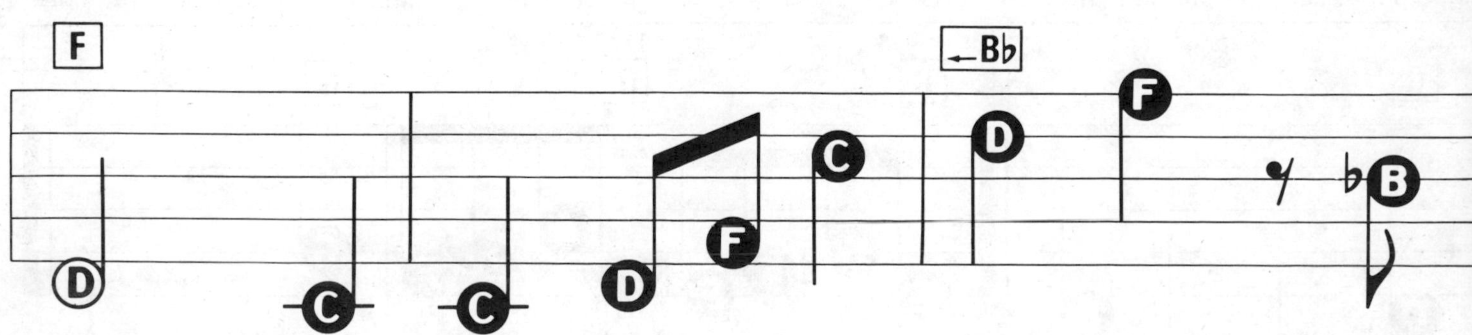

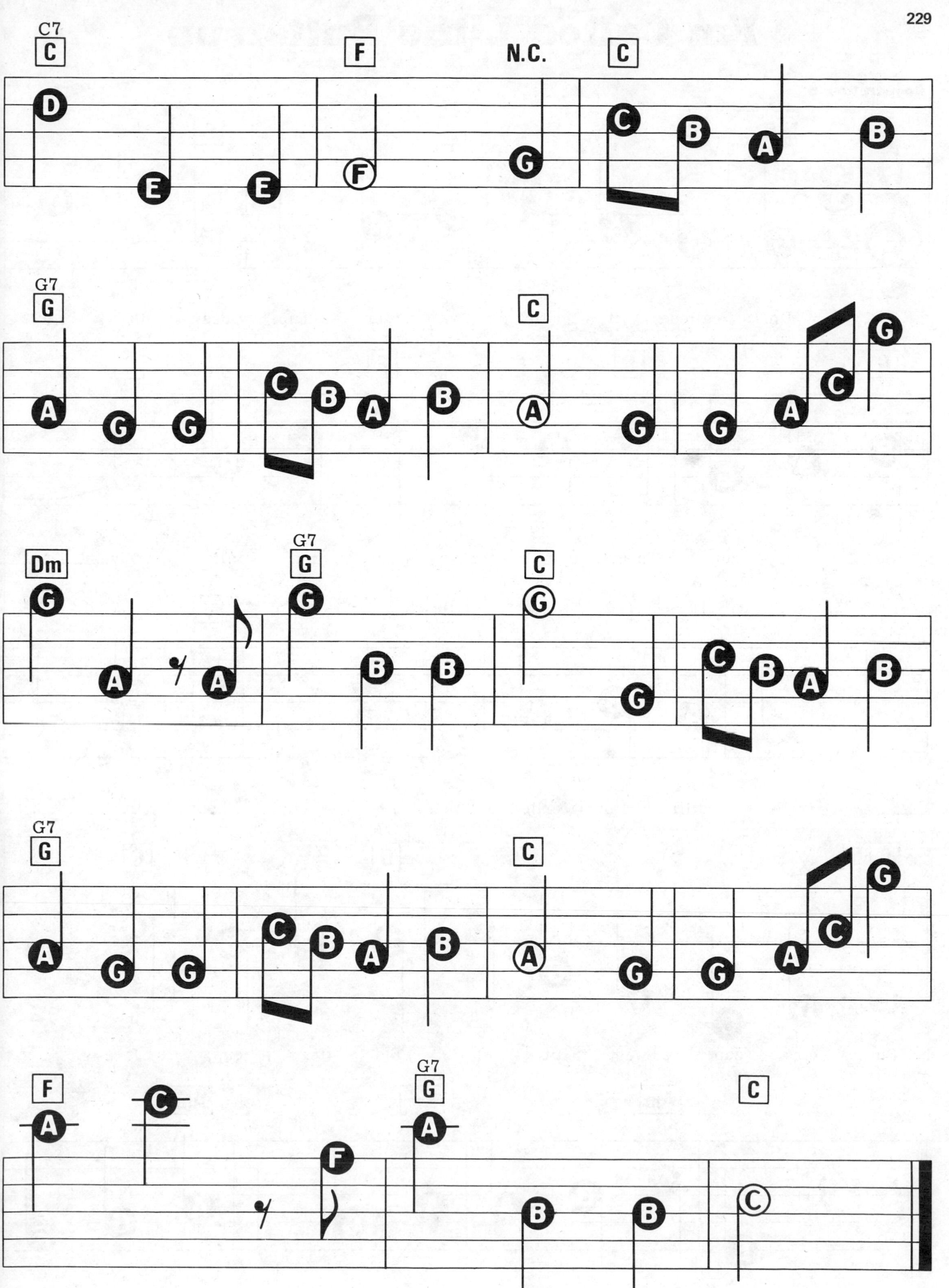
C7
C
F
N.C.
C
D
E
E
F
G
C
B
A
B
G7
G
C
A
G
G
C
B
A
B
A
G
G
A
C
G
Dm
G7
G
C
G
A
A
G
B
B
G
G
C
B
A
B
G7
G
C
A
G
G
C
B
A
B
A
G
G
A
C
G
F
G7
G
C
A
C
F
A
B
B
C

I'm Called Little Buttercup

Registration 5

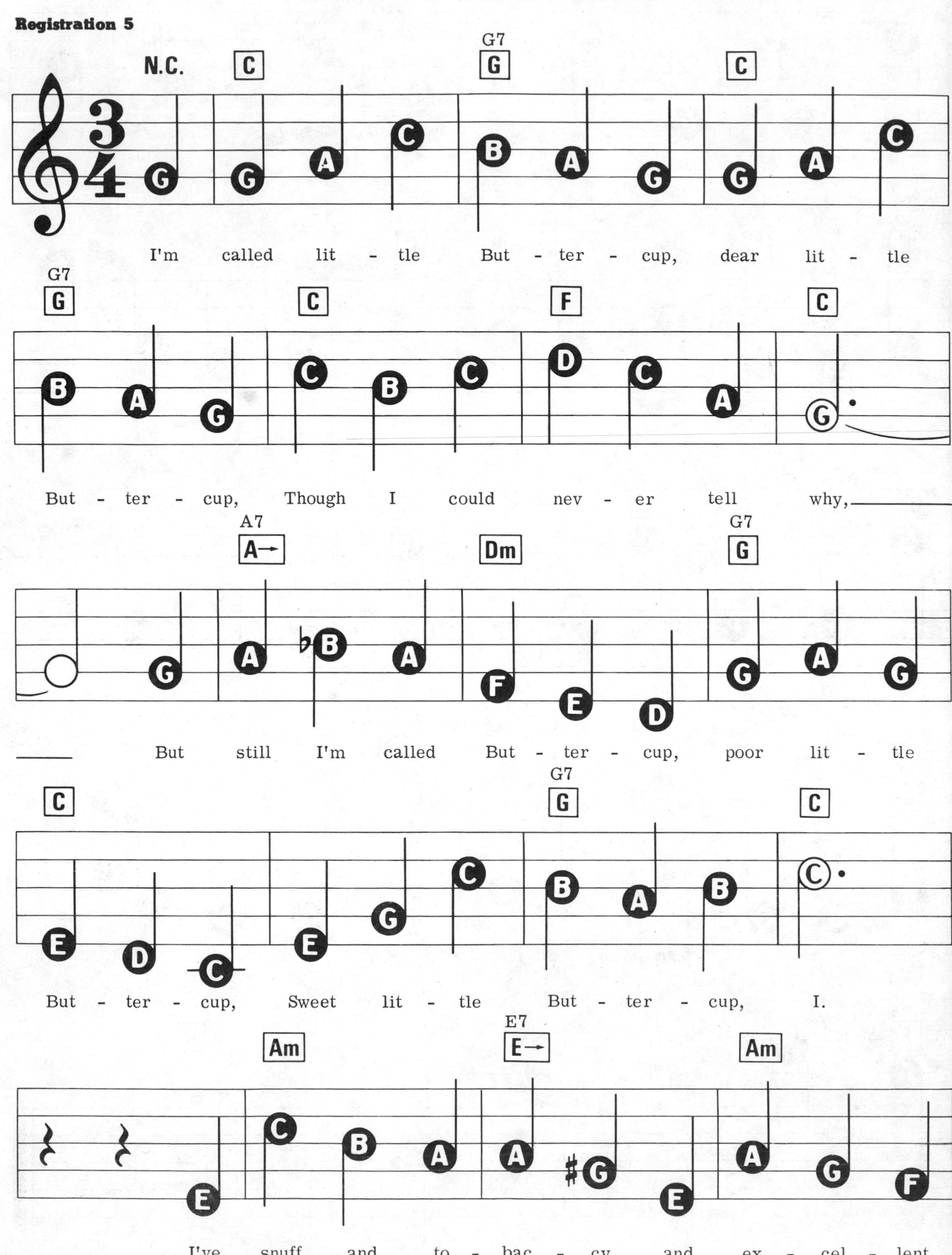

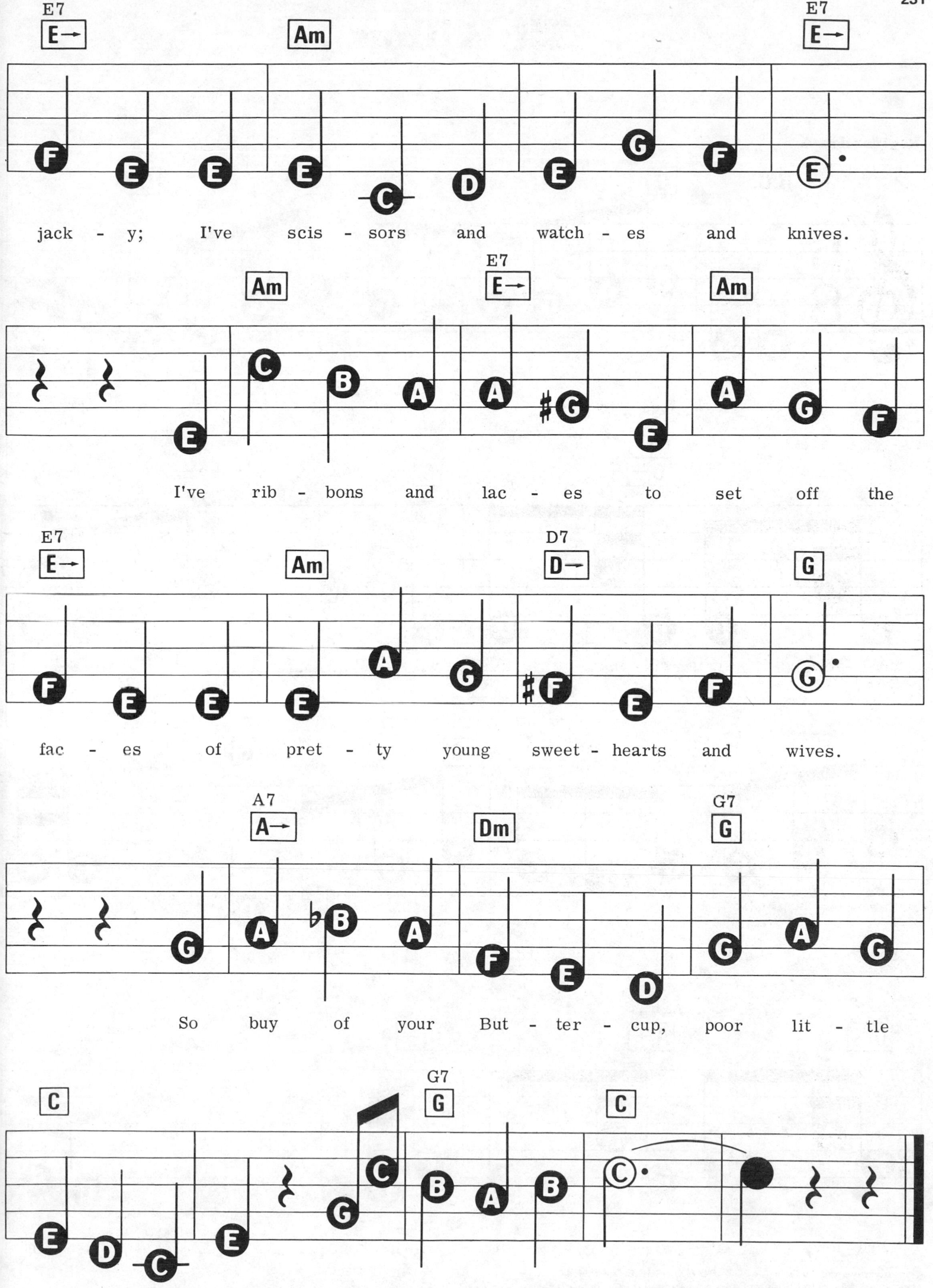
E7 E→ Am E7 E→
jack - y; I've scis - sors and watch - es and knives.
Am E7 E→ Am
I've rib - bons and lac - es to set off the
E7 E→ Am D7 D→ G
fac - es of pret - ty young sweet - hearts and wives.
A7 A→ Dm G7 G
So buy of your But - ter - cup, poor lit - tle
C G7 G C
But - ter - cup, come, of your But - ter - cup buy.

Tit Willow

Registration 4

N.C. G C G

D D B A G G ♯F G A G E D B C

On a tree by a riv - er a lit - tle tom - tit sang___

D7
D→ G

D G D D A D G D D D

"Wil - low, tit - wil - low, tit - wil - low!"___ And I

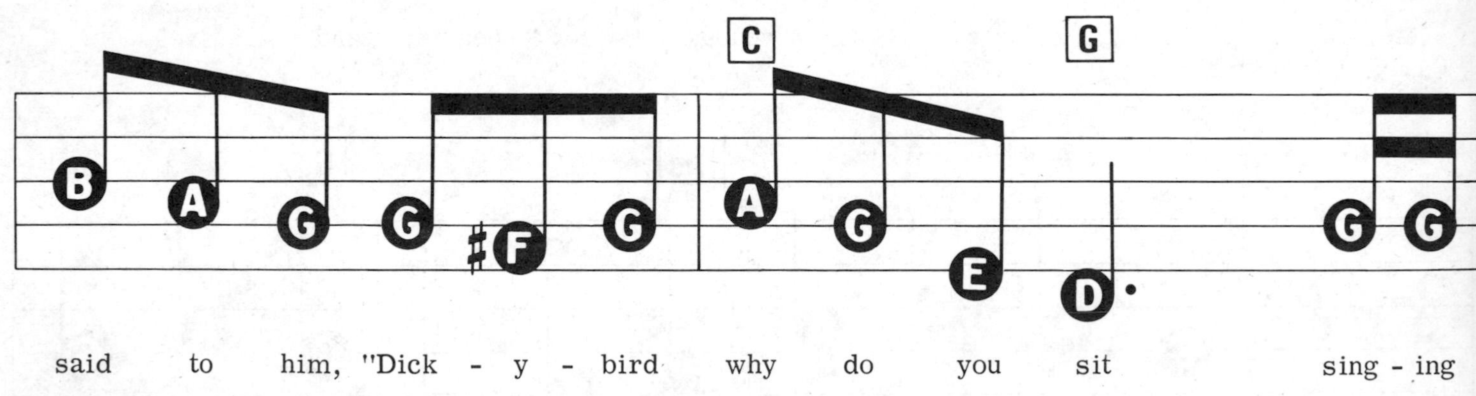

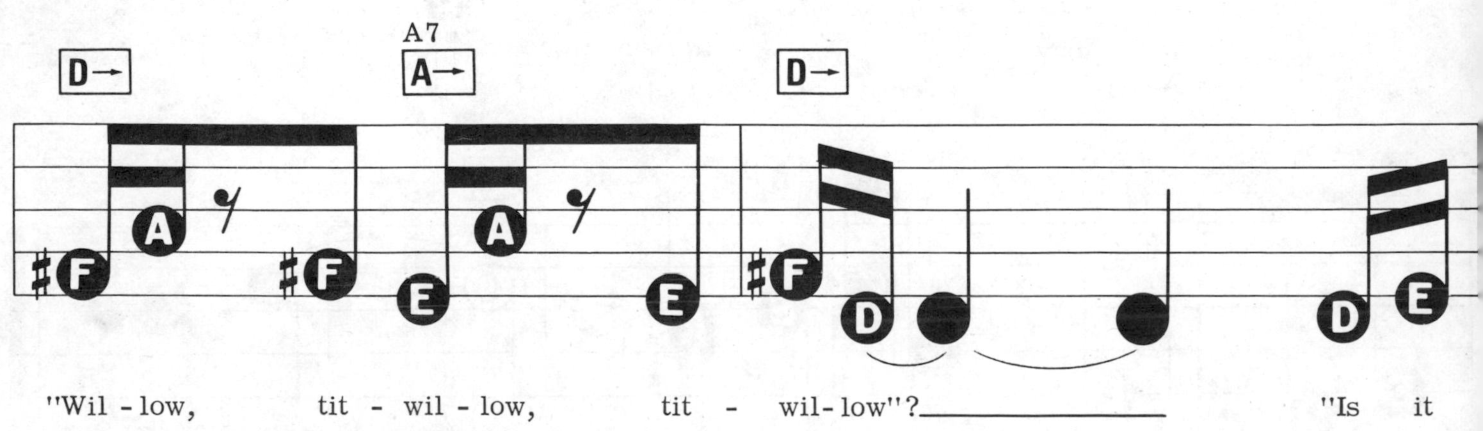

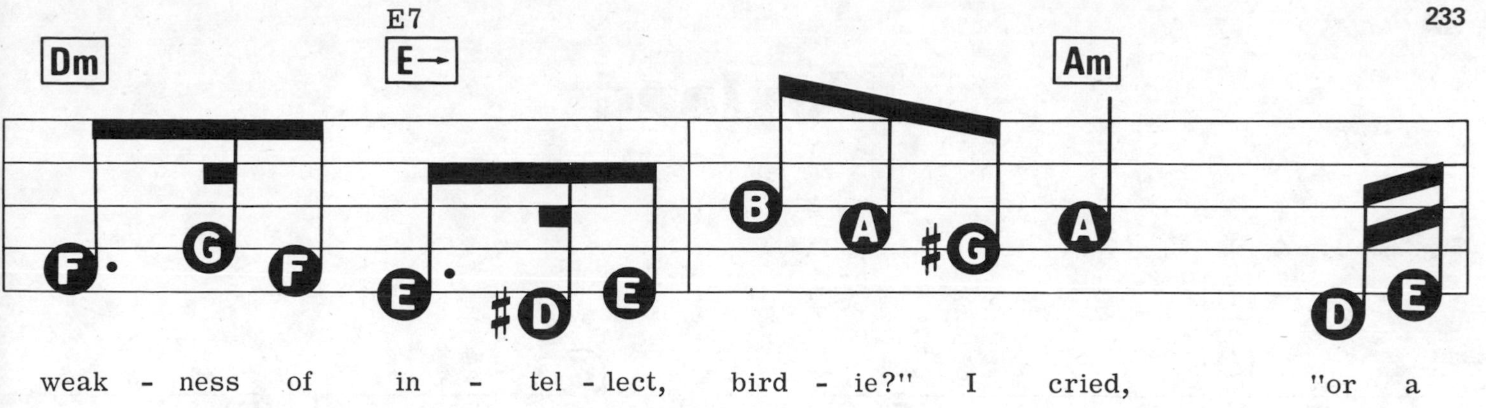
E7
Dm
E→
Am
F G F E D E B A G A D E
weak - ness of in - tel - lect, bird - ie?" I cried, "or a

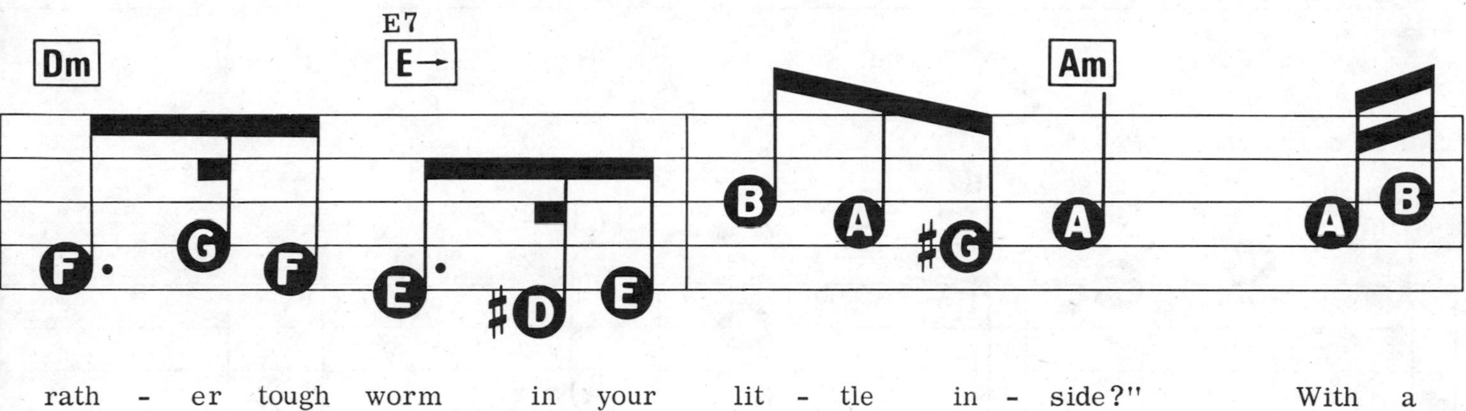
E7
Dm
E→
Am
F G F E D E B A G A A B
rath - er tough worm in your lit - tle in - side?" With a

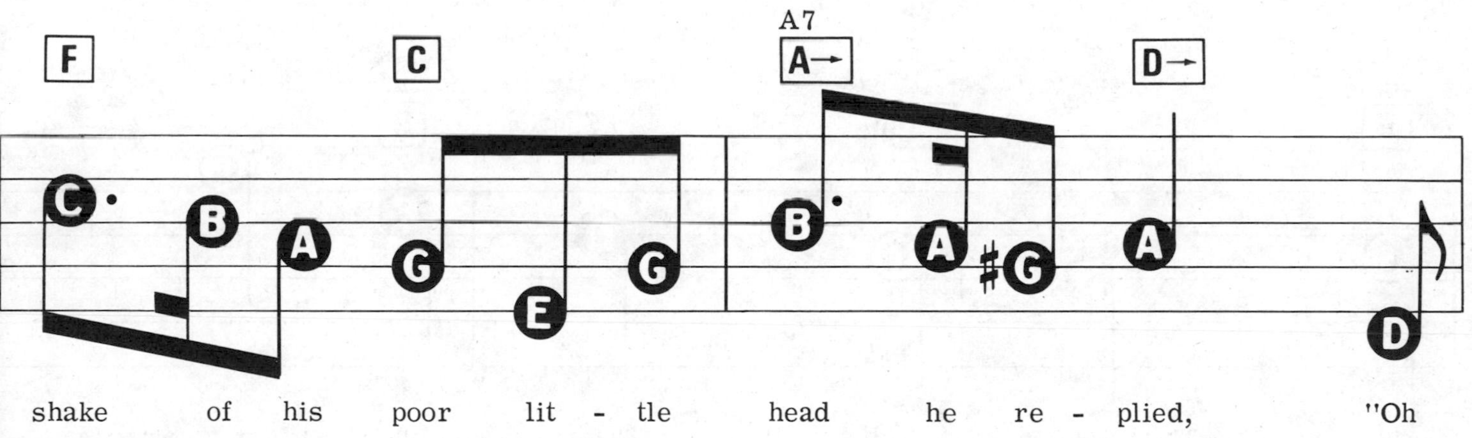
A7
F
C
A→
D→
C B A G E G B A G A D
shake of his poor lit - tle head he re - plied, "Oh

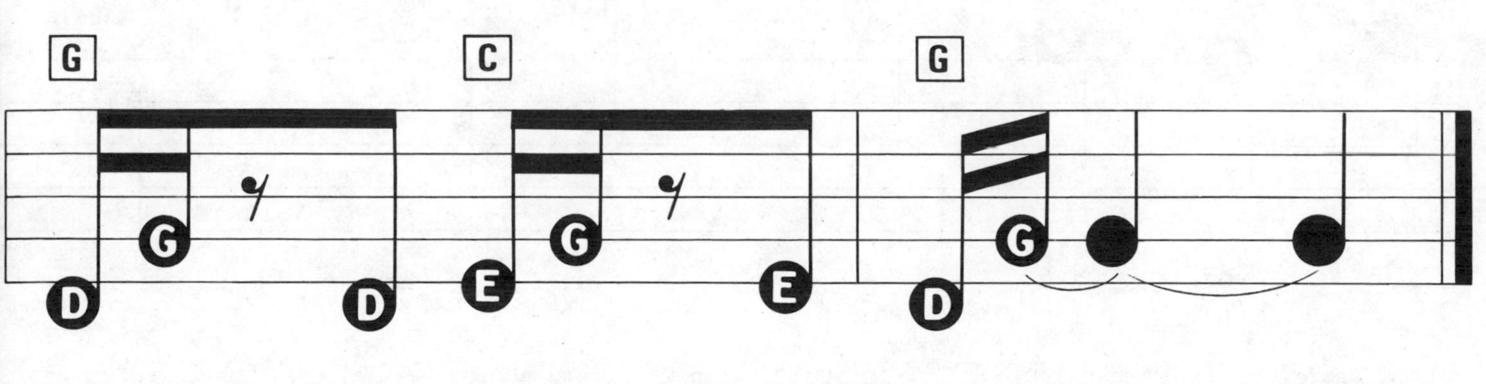
G
C
G
D G D E G E D G
wil - low, tit - wil - low, tit - wil - low!"

Toyland

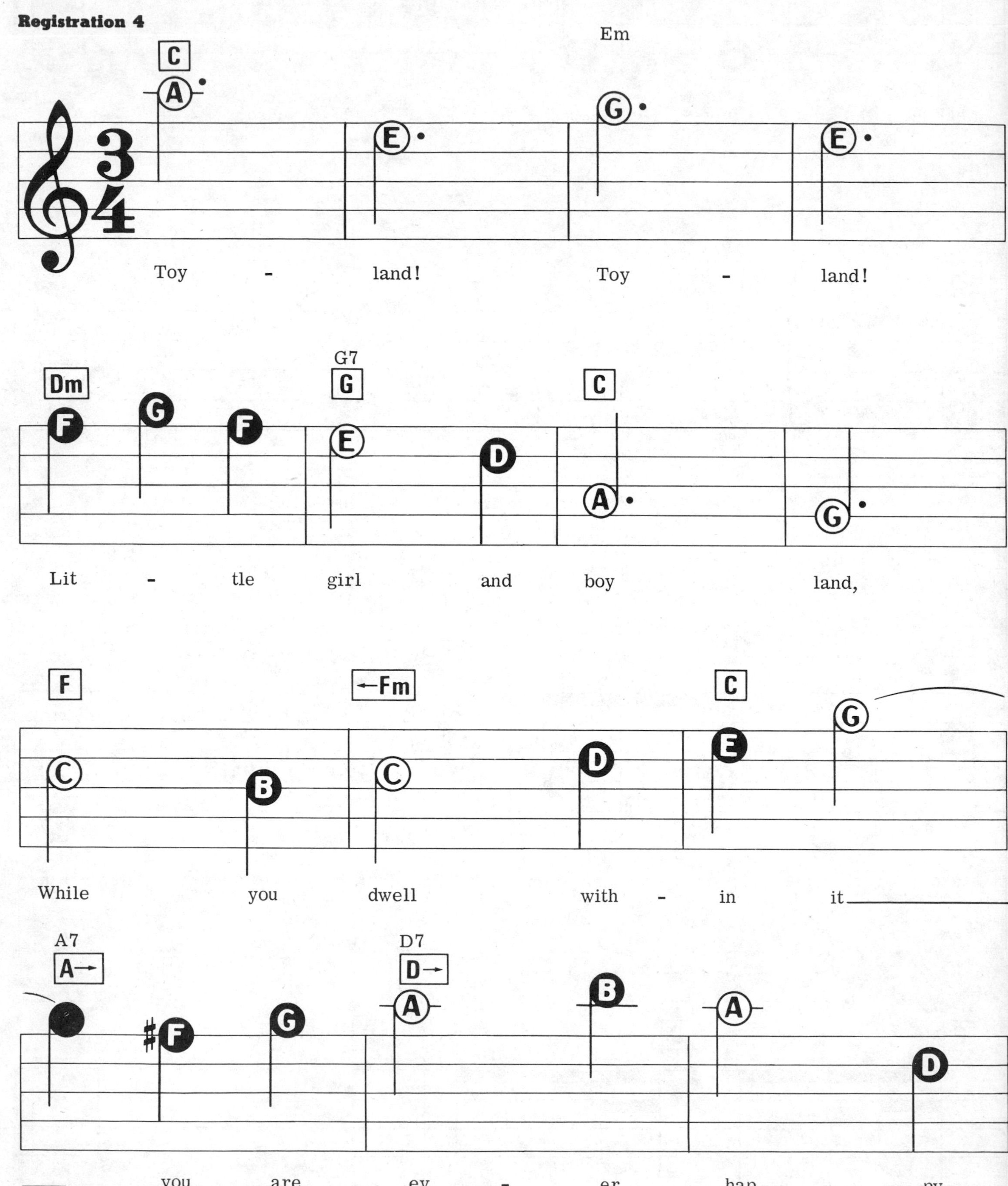
Registration 4
C
Em
Toy - land! Toy - land!
Dm
G7
G
C
Lit - tle girl and boy land,
F
←Fm
C
While you dwell with - in it
A7
A→
D7
D→
you are ev - er hap - py

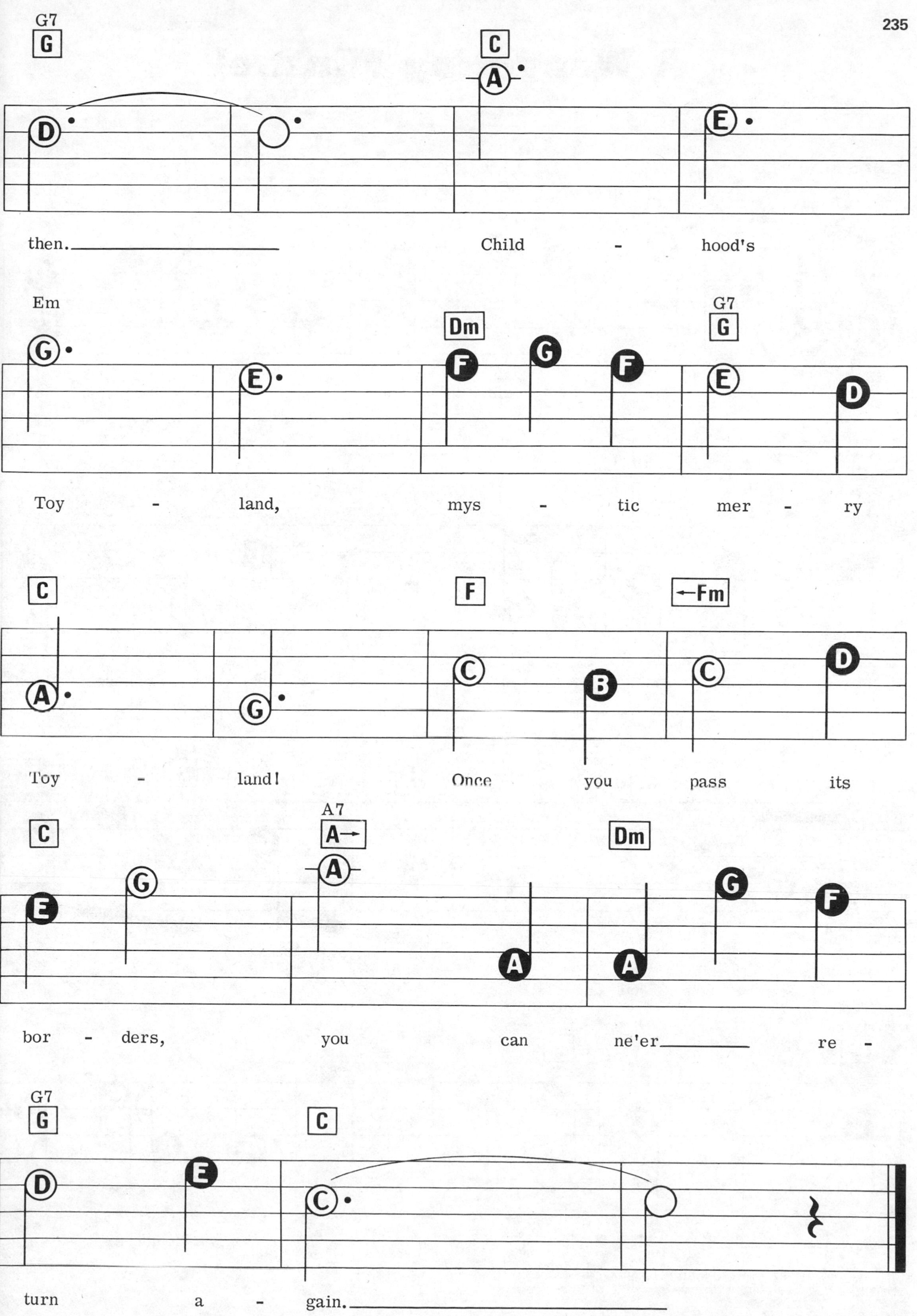
G7
G
C
D
A
E
then.
Child - hood's
Em
Dm
G7
G
G
E
F
G
F
E
D
Toy - land, mys - tic mer - ry
C
F
←Fm
A
G
C
B
C
D
Toy - land! Once you pass its
C
A7
A→
Dm
E
G
A
A
A
G
F
bor - ders, you can ne'er re -
G7
G
C
D
E
C
turn a - gain.

A Wandering Minstrel

Registration 5

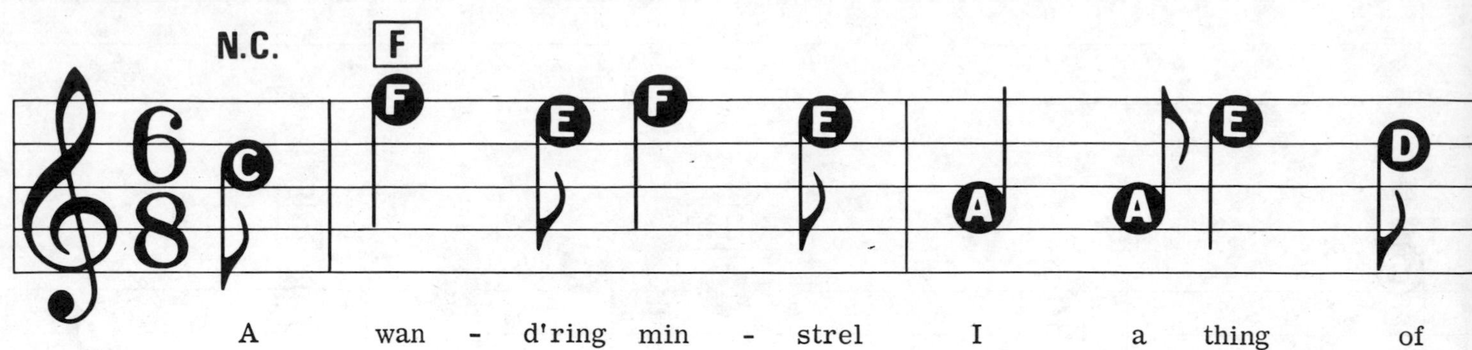

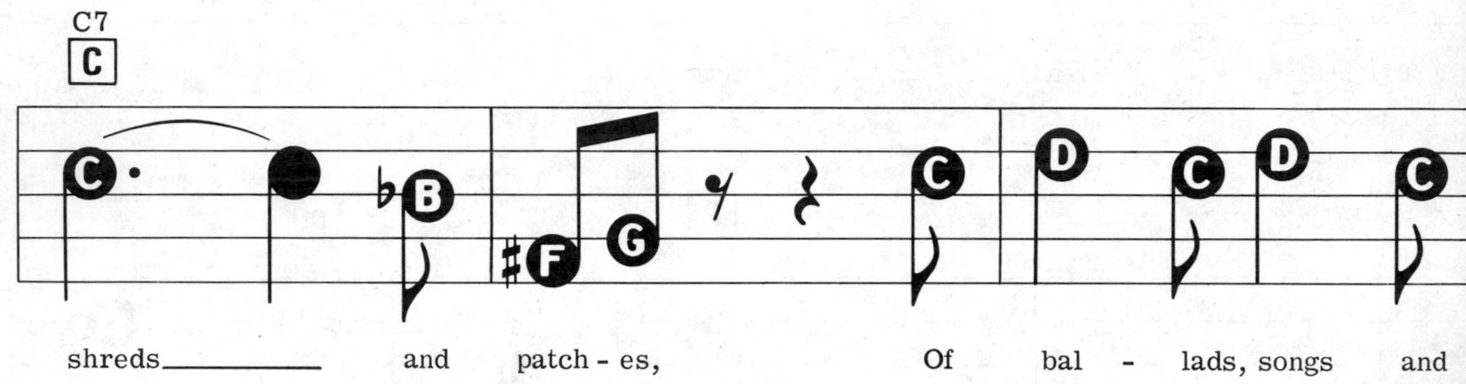

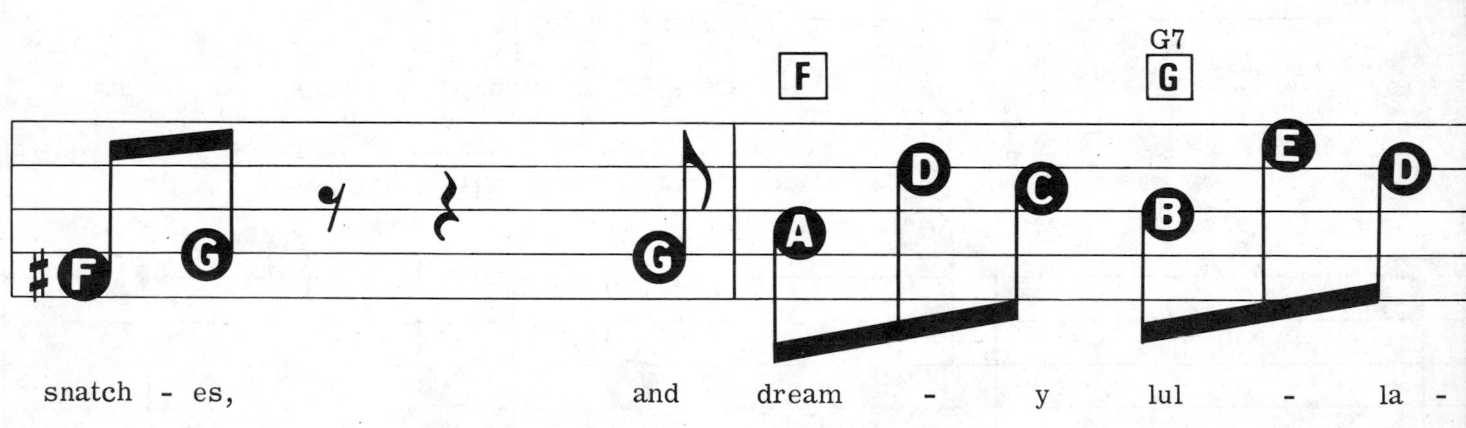

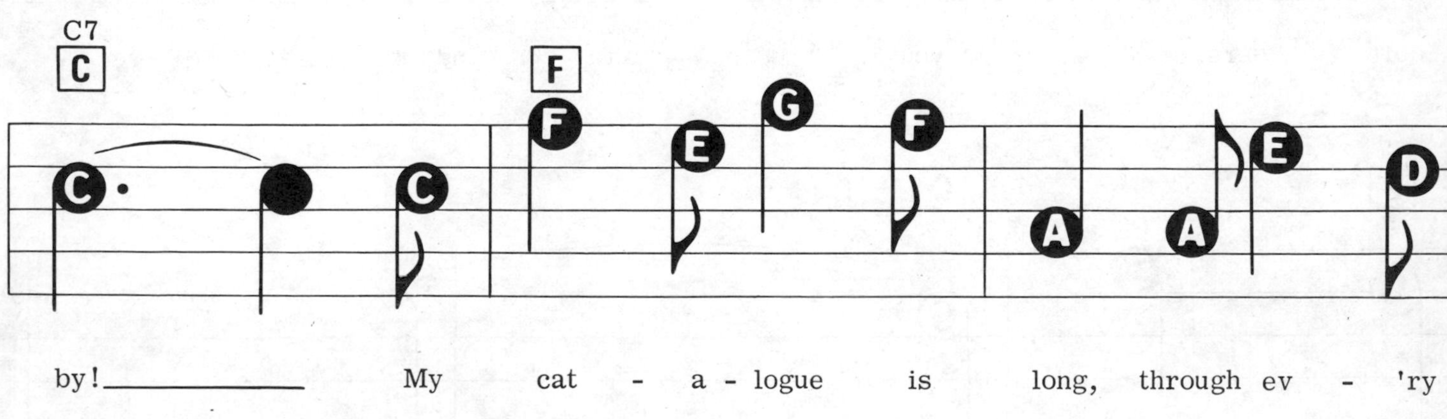

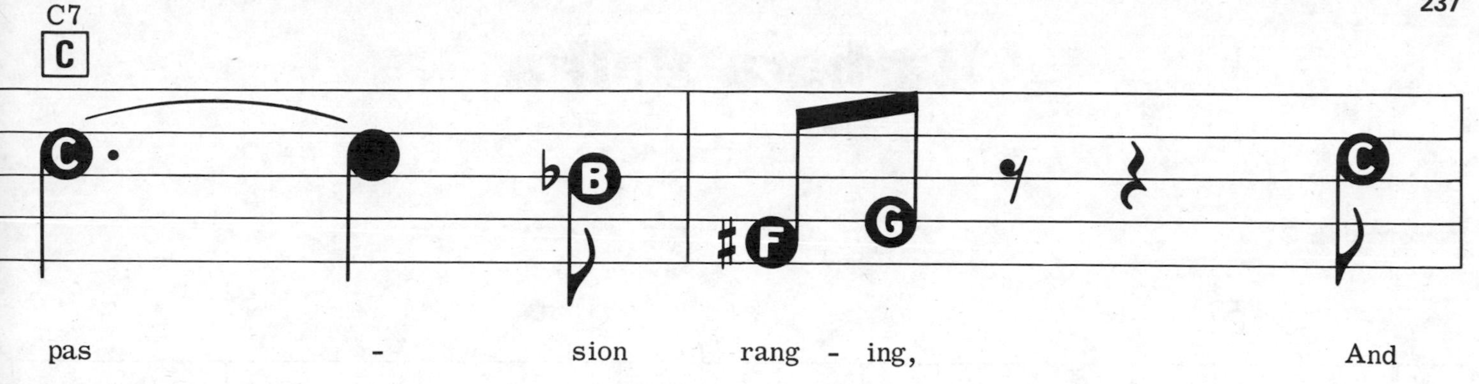
C7
C
pas - sion rang - ing, And

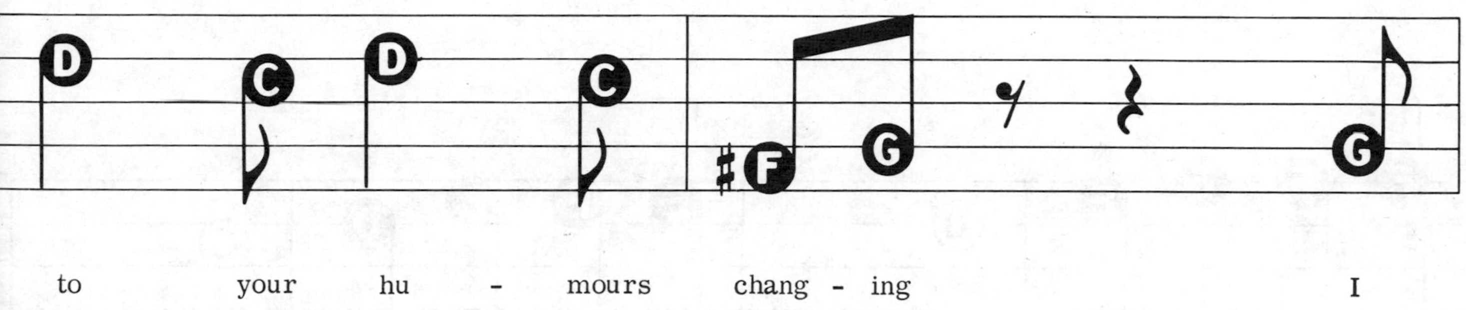
to your hu - mours chang - ing I

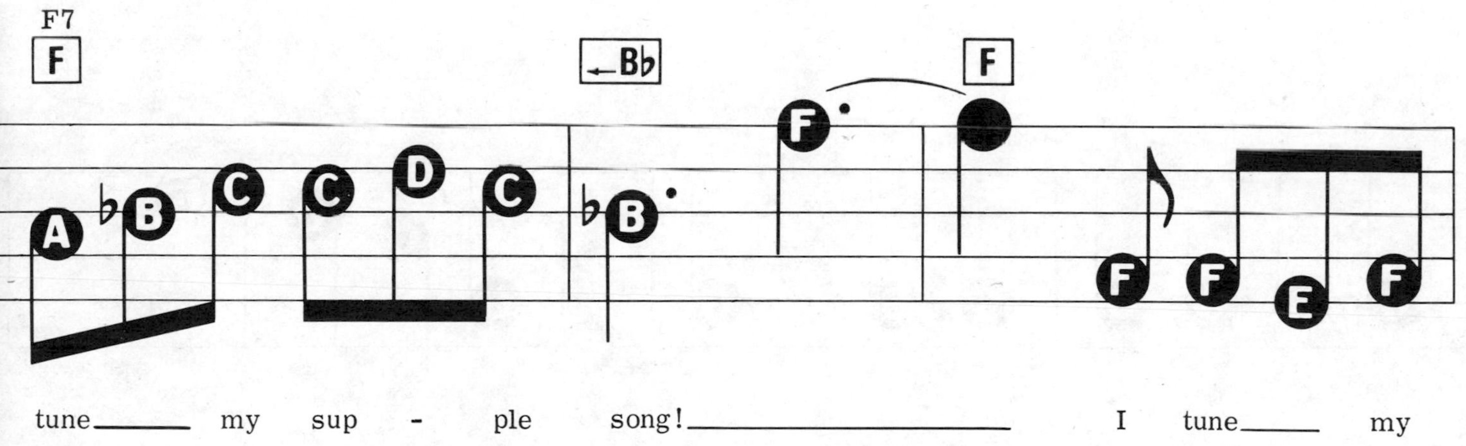
F7
F
←B♭
F
tune my sup - ple song! I tune my

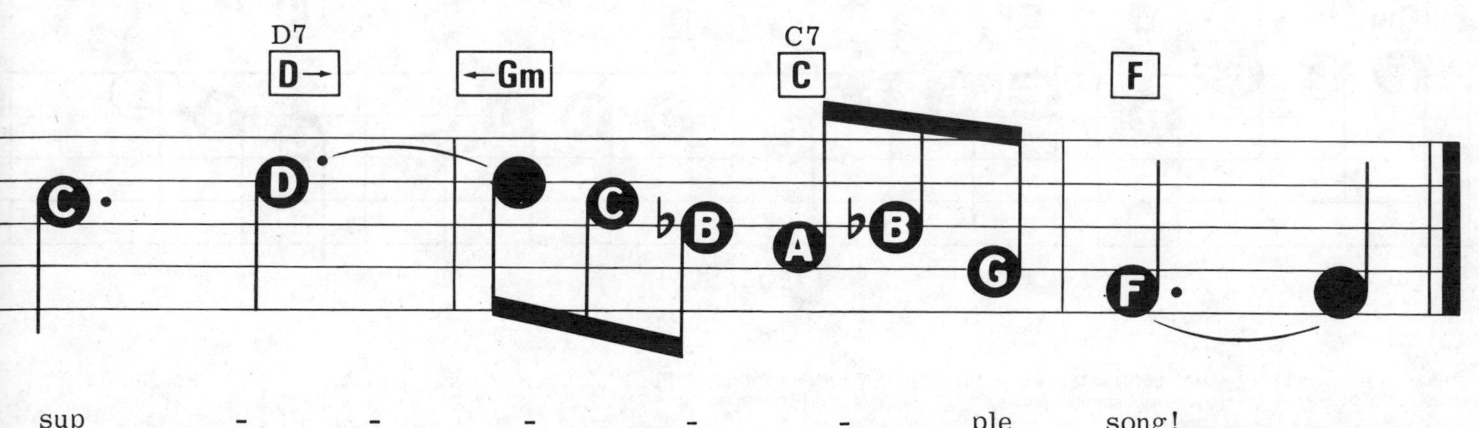
D7
D→
←Gm
C7
C
F
sup - - - - - ple song!

Barbara Polka

Registration 3

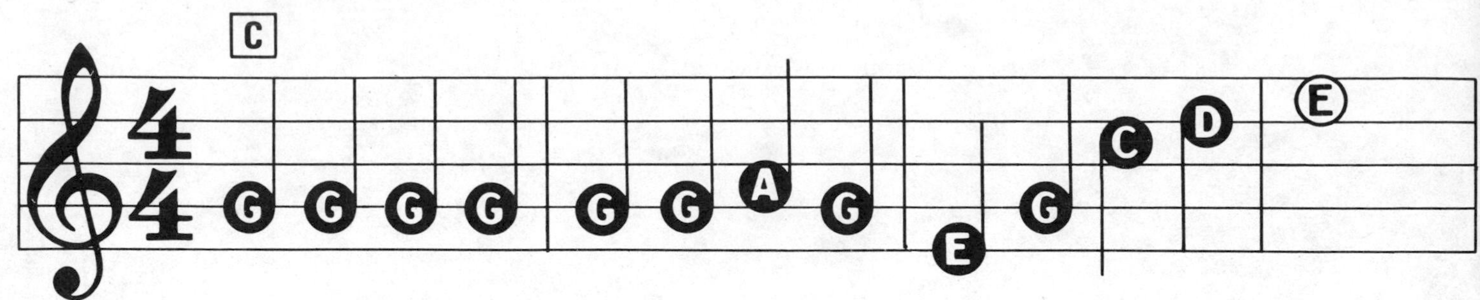

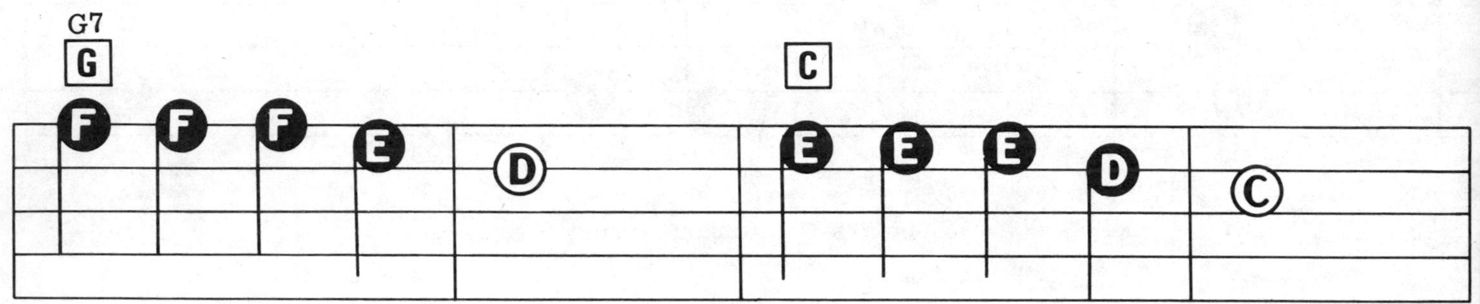

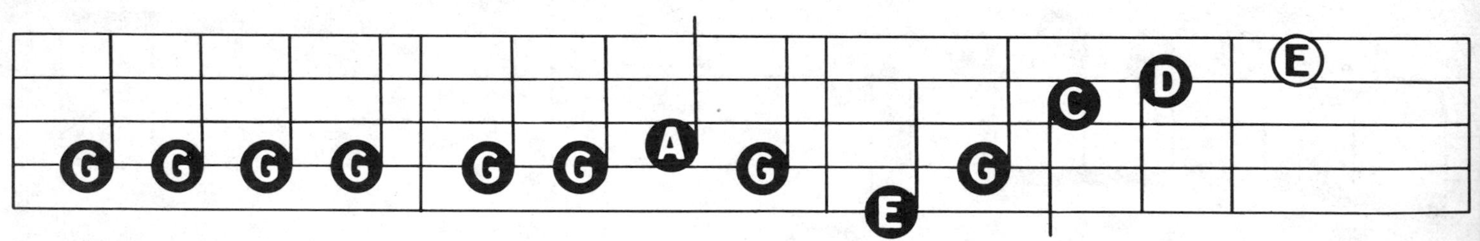

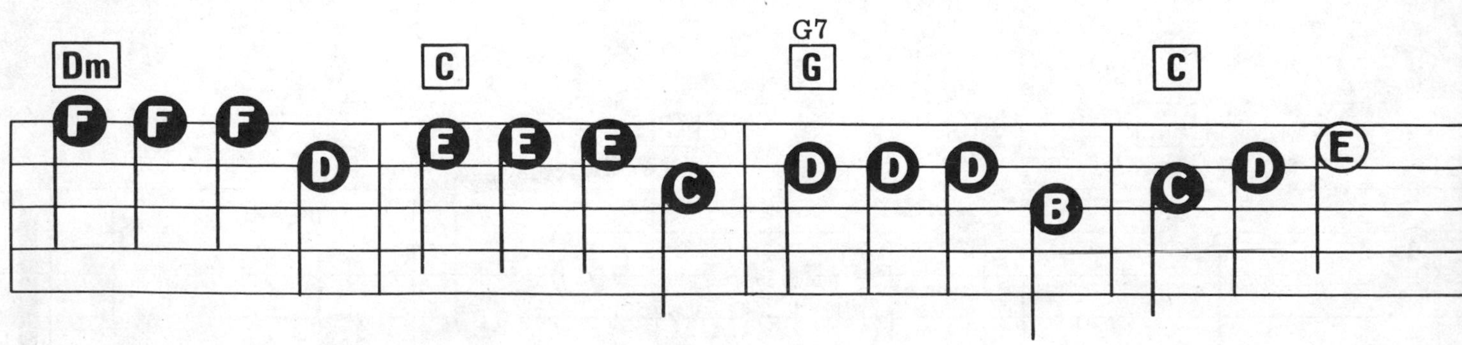

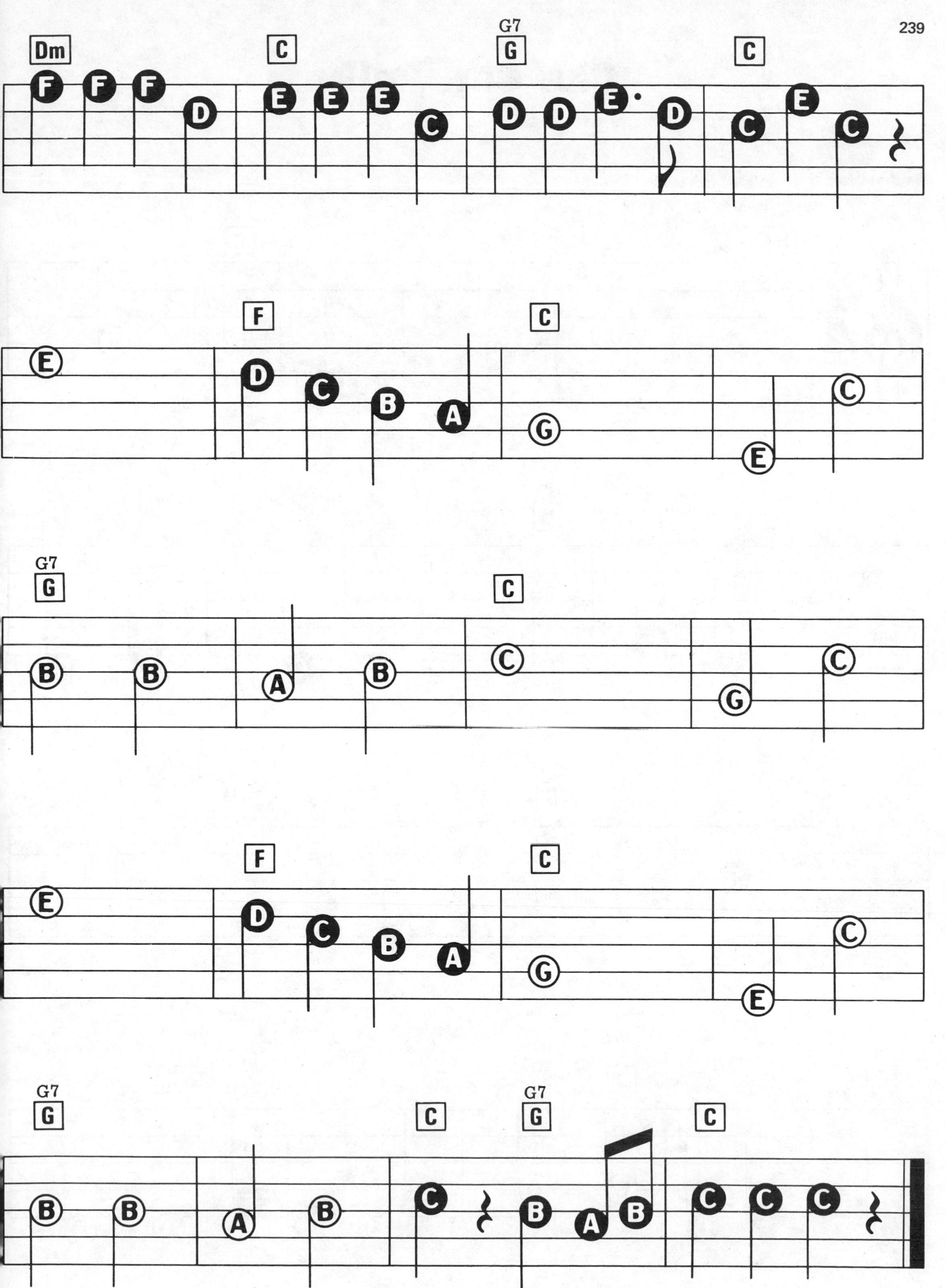
Dm C G7 G C
F F F D E E E C D D E D C E C
F C
E D C B A G E C
G7 G C
B B A B C G C
F C
E D C B A G E C
G7 G C G7 G C
B B A B C B A B C C C

Can Can Polka

Registration 5

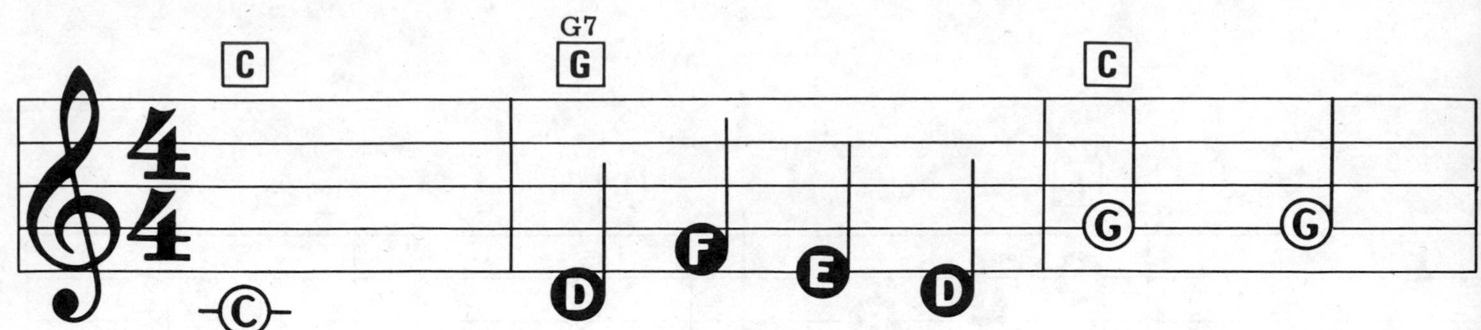

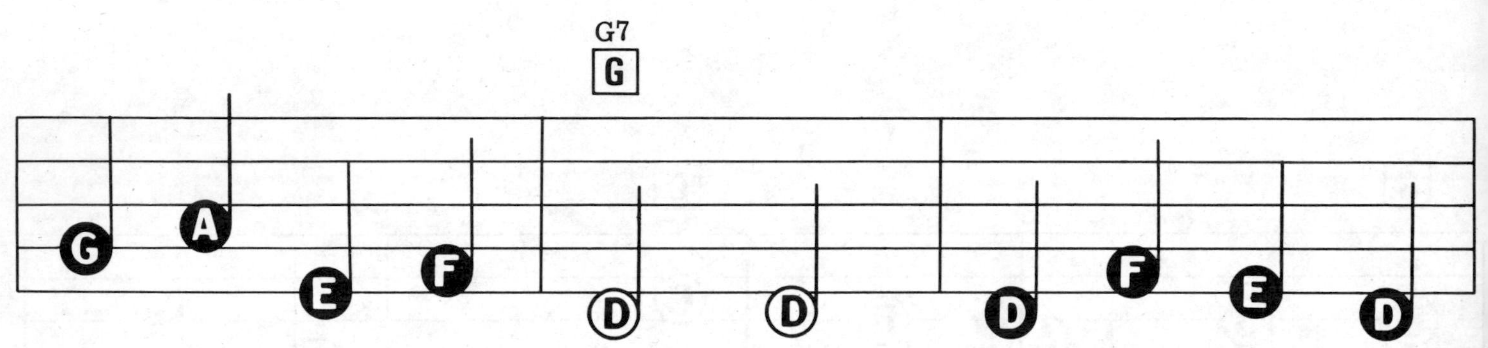

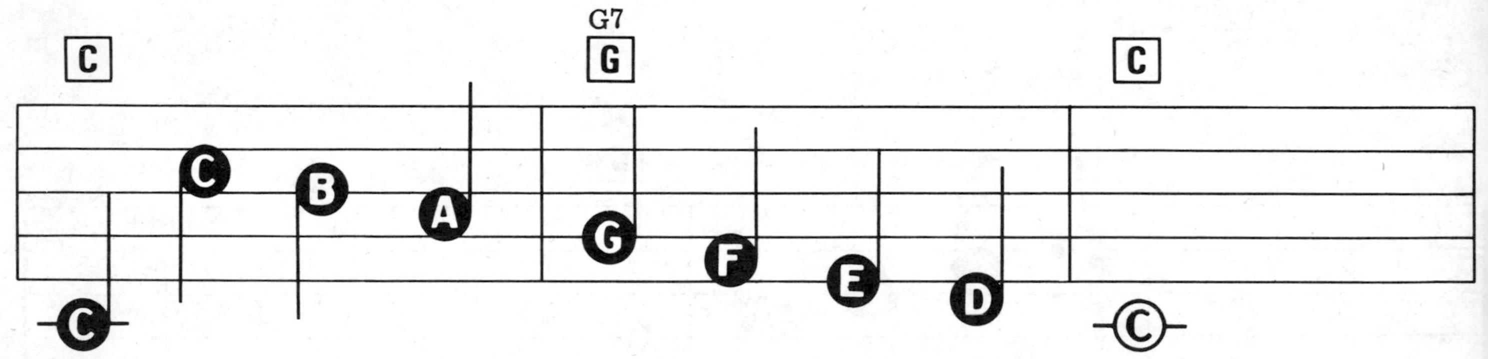

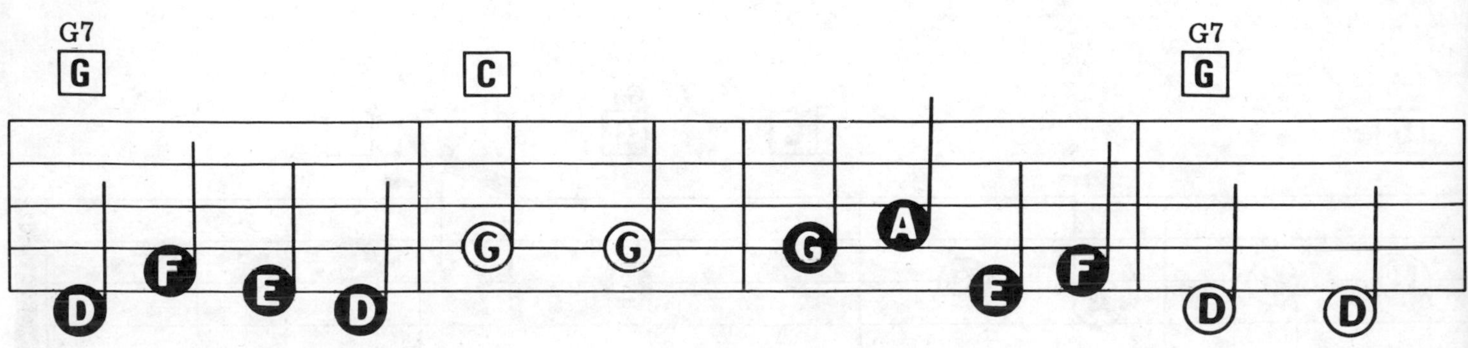

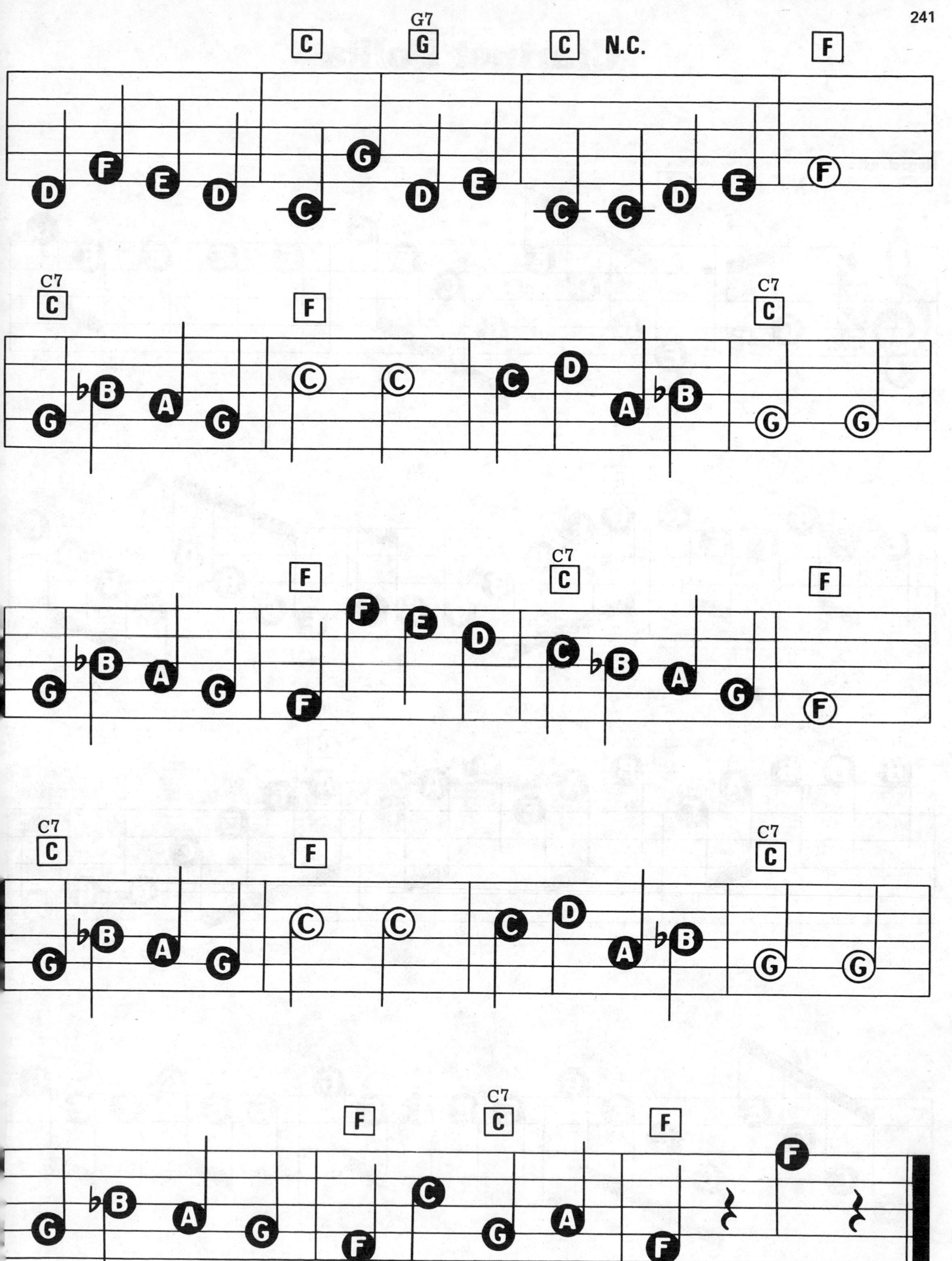
C
G7
G
C
N.C.
F
C7
C
F
C7
C
F
C7
C
F
C7
C
F
C7
C
F
C7
C
F

Clarinet Polka

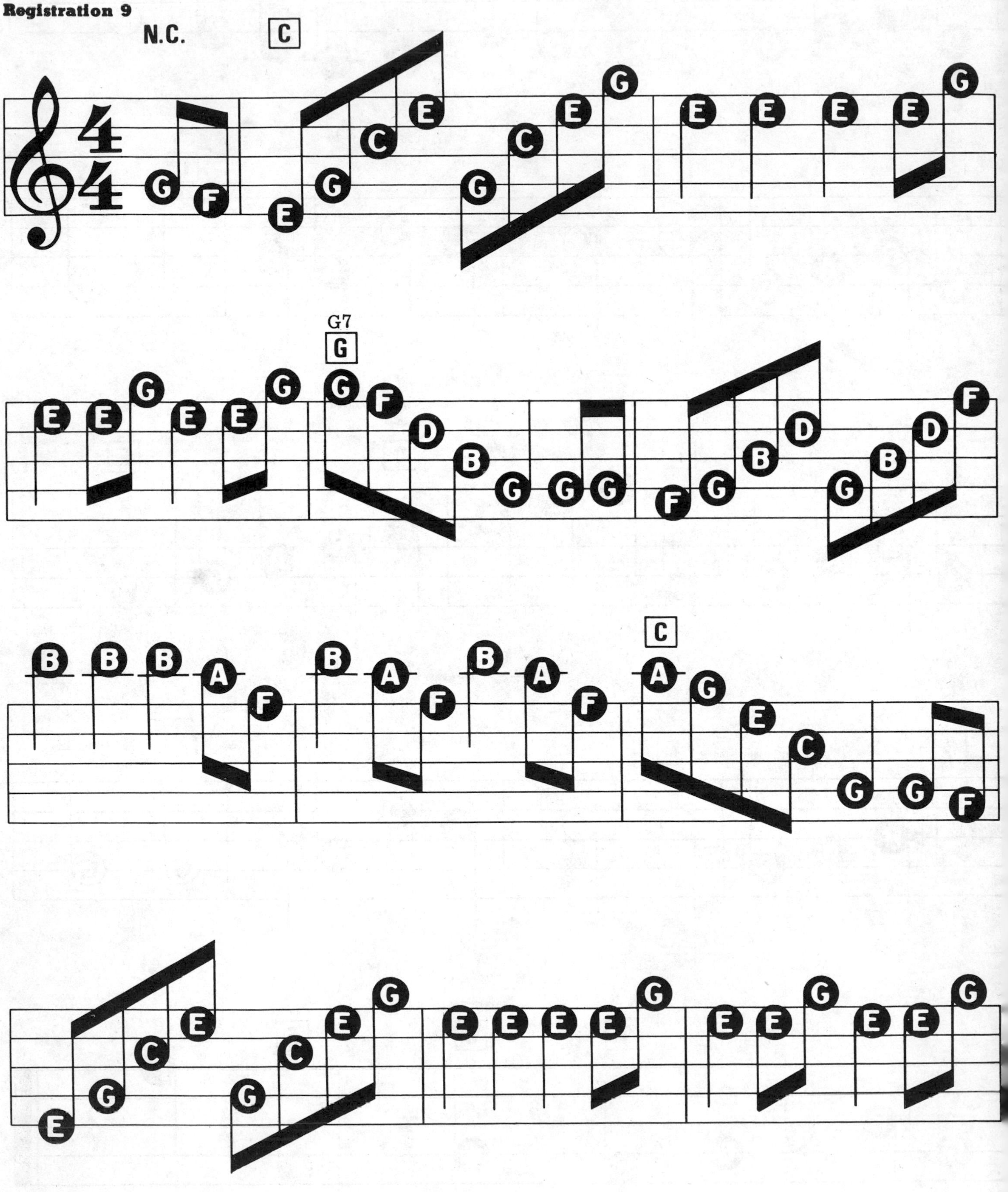

Registration 9

N.C. C

G7 G

C

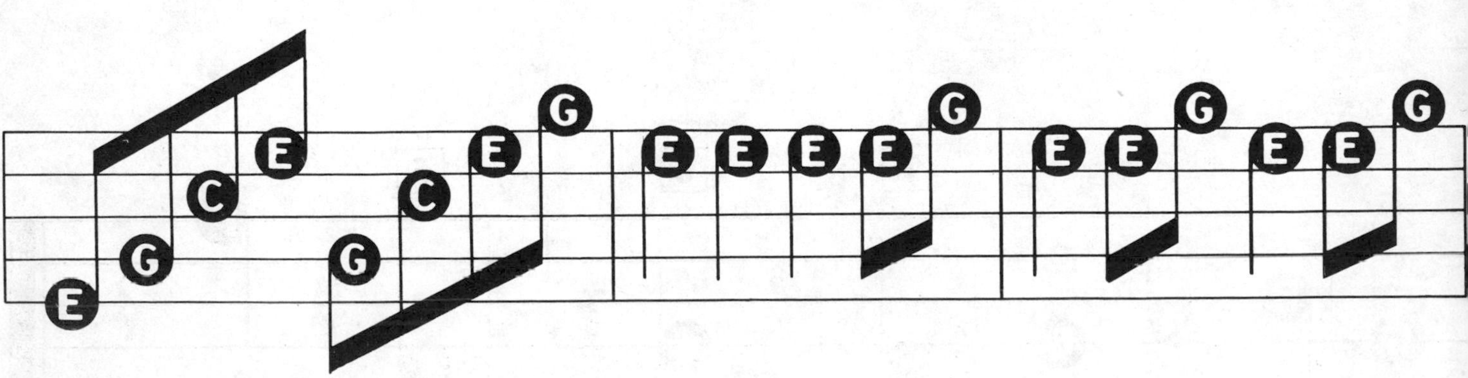

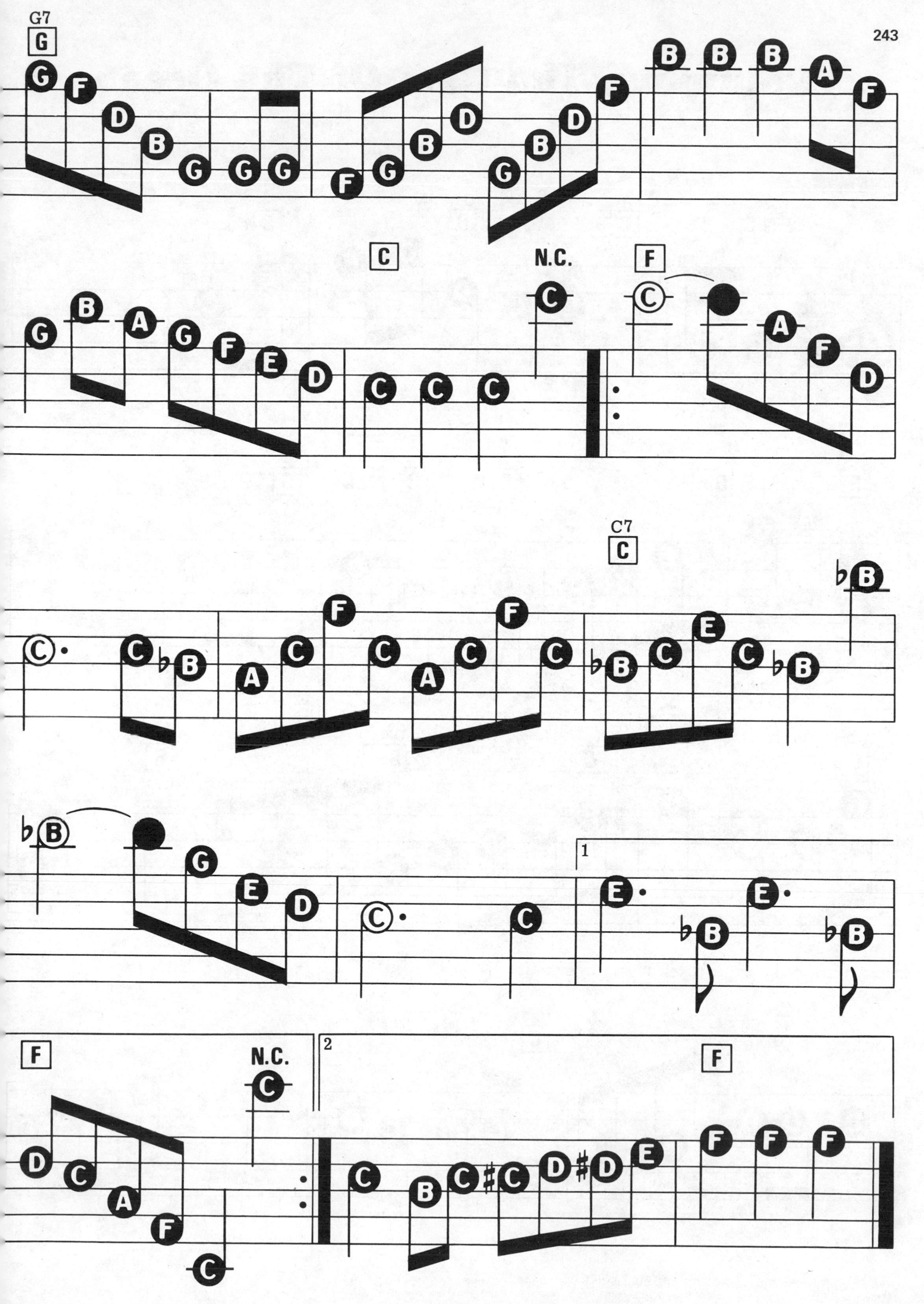
G7
G
C
N.C.
F
C7
C
1
F
N.C.
2
F

Columbia, The Gem Of The Ocean

Registration 4

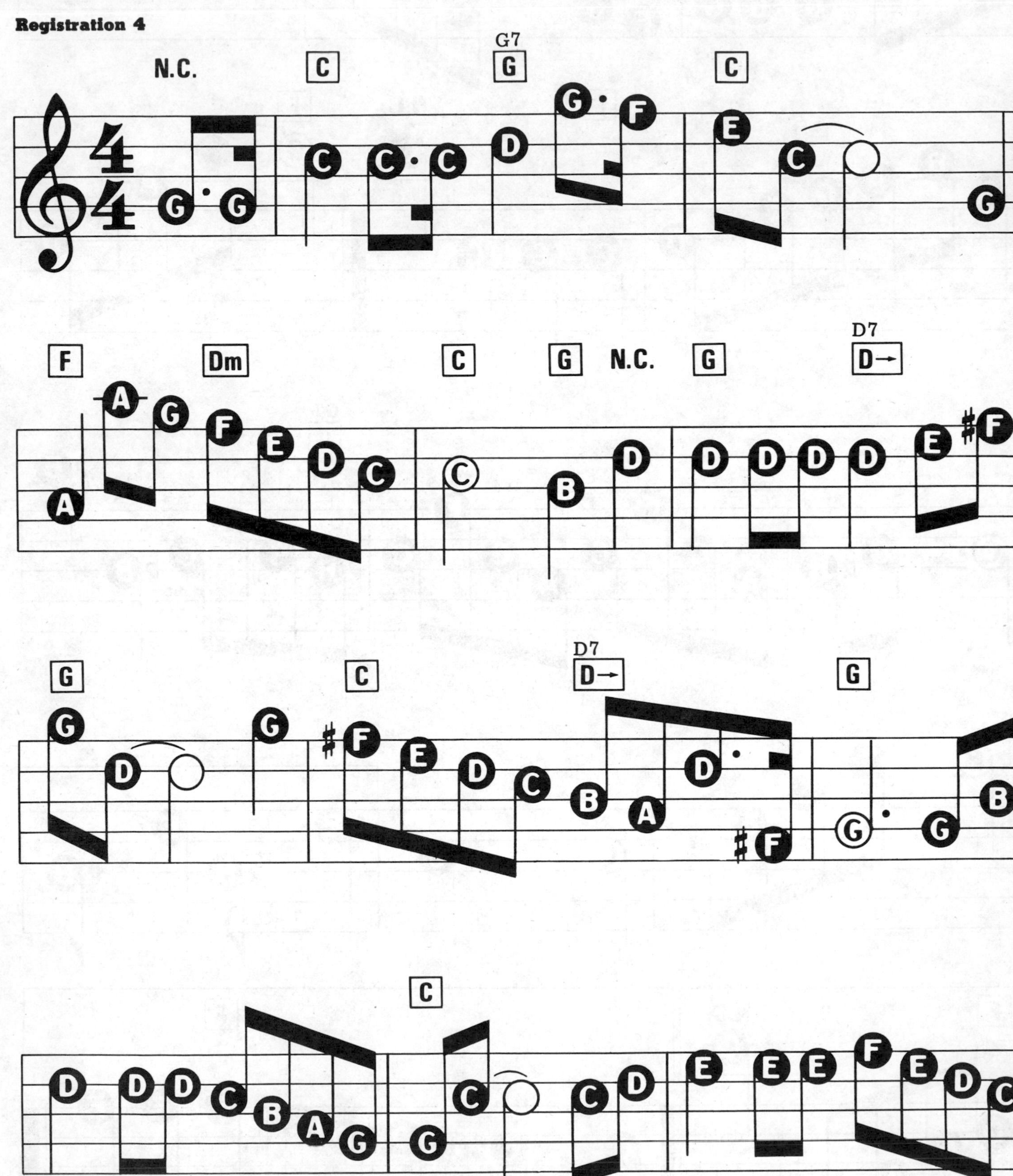

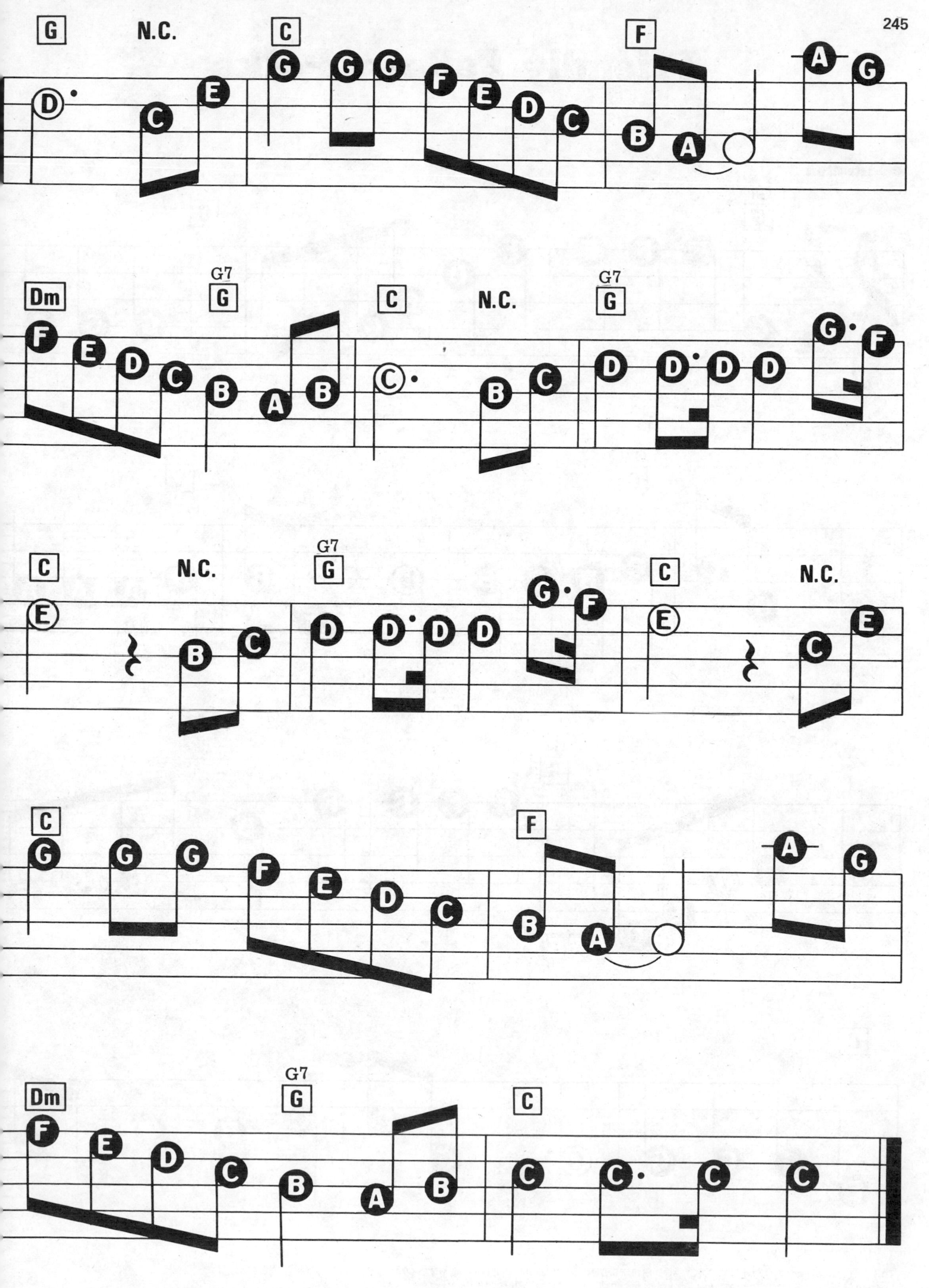
G N.C. C F
Dm G7 G C N.C. G7 G
C N.C. G7 G C N.C.
C F
Dm G7 G C

Friendly Fellows Polka

Registration 3

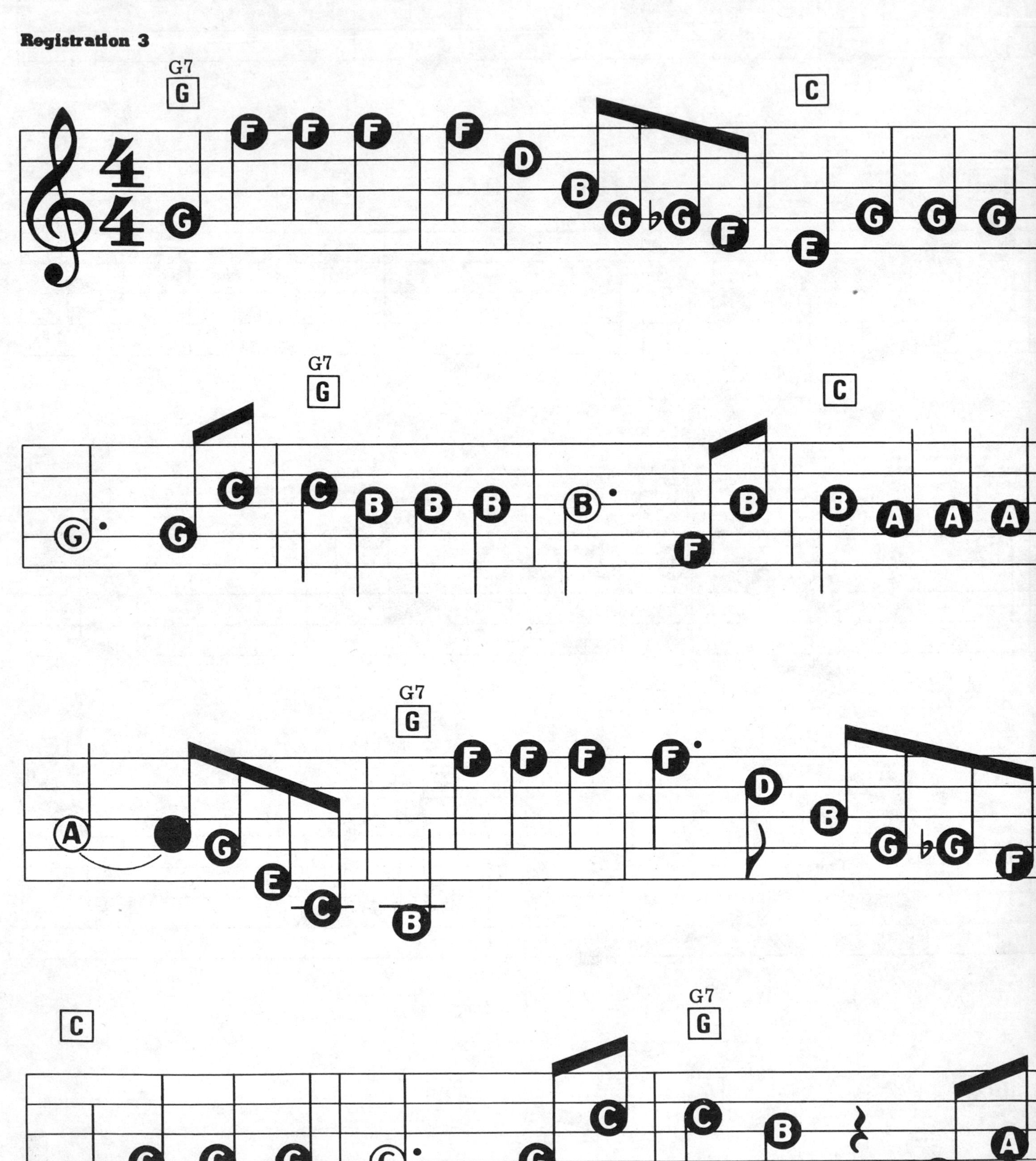

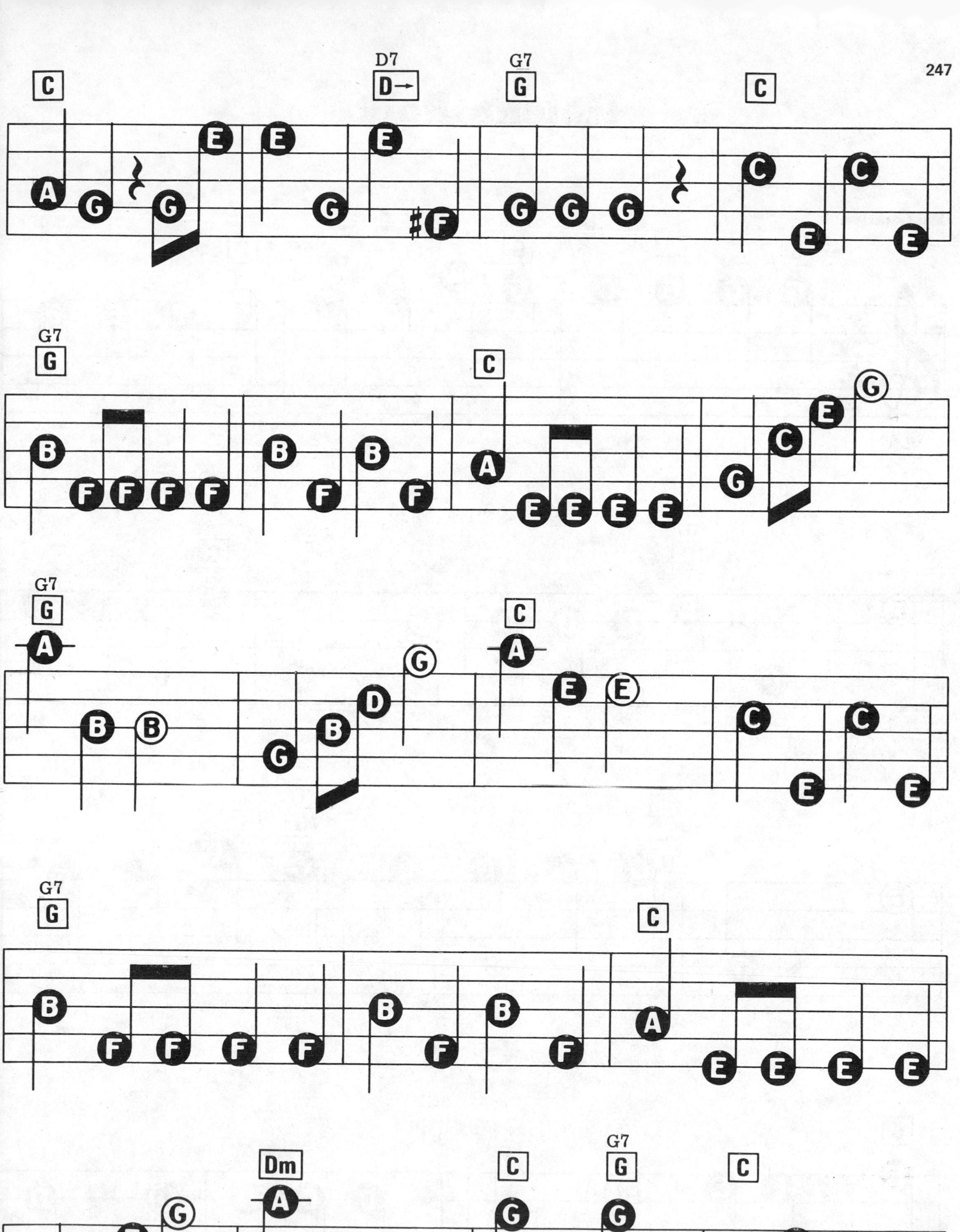
C D7 D G7 G C
G7 G C
G7 G C
G7 G C
Dm C G7 G C

Helena Polka

Registration 9

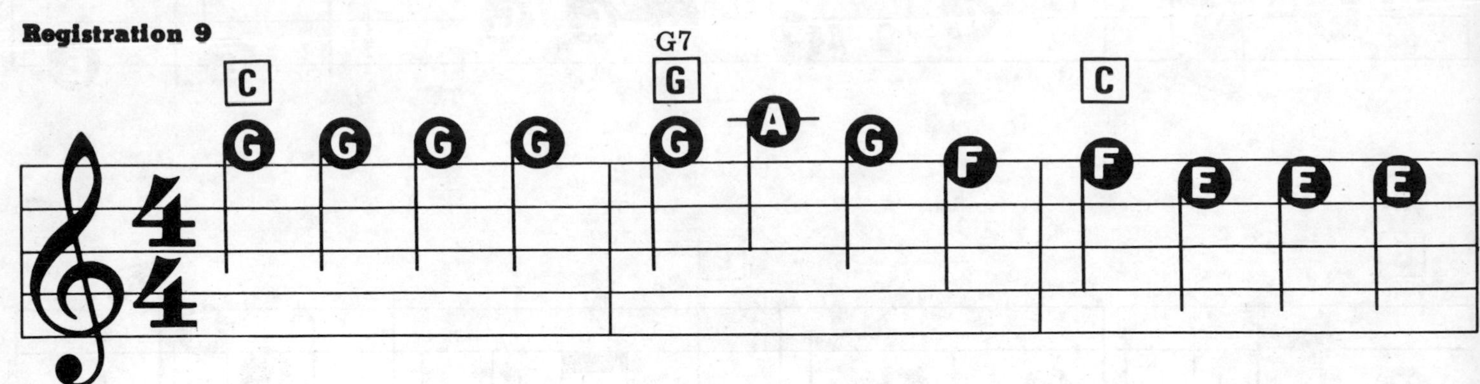

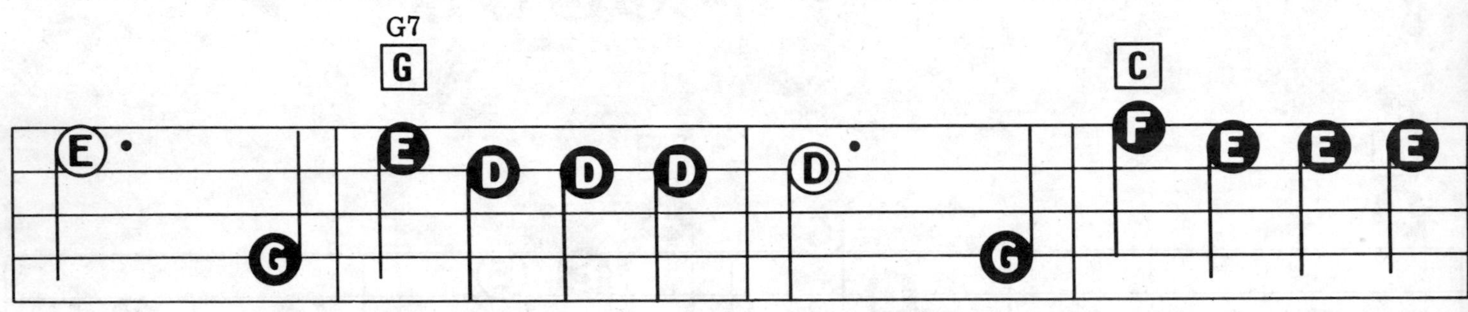

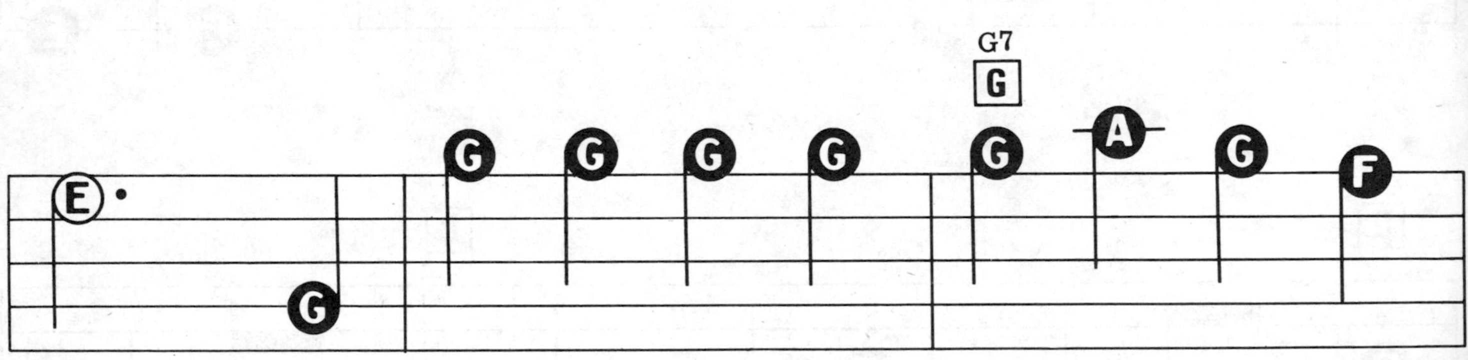

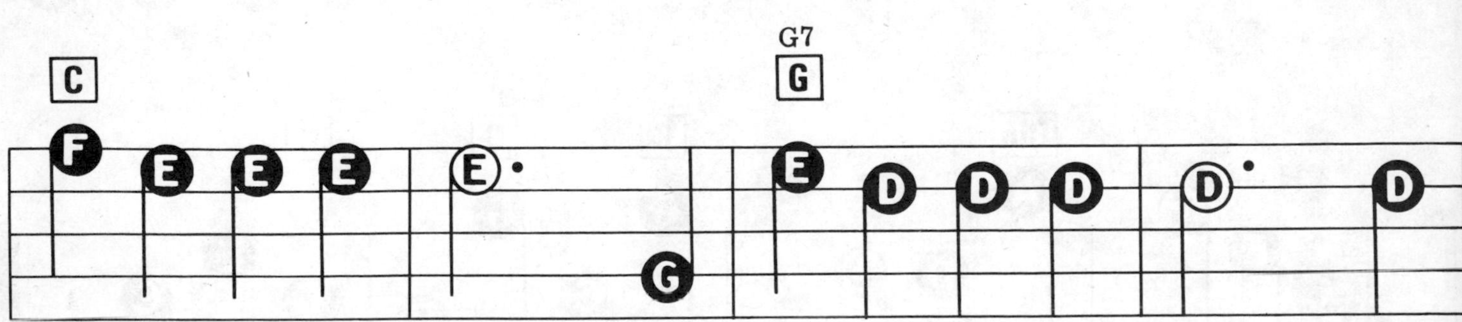

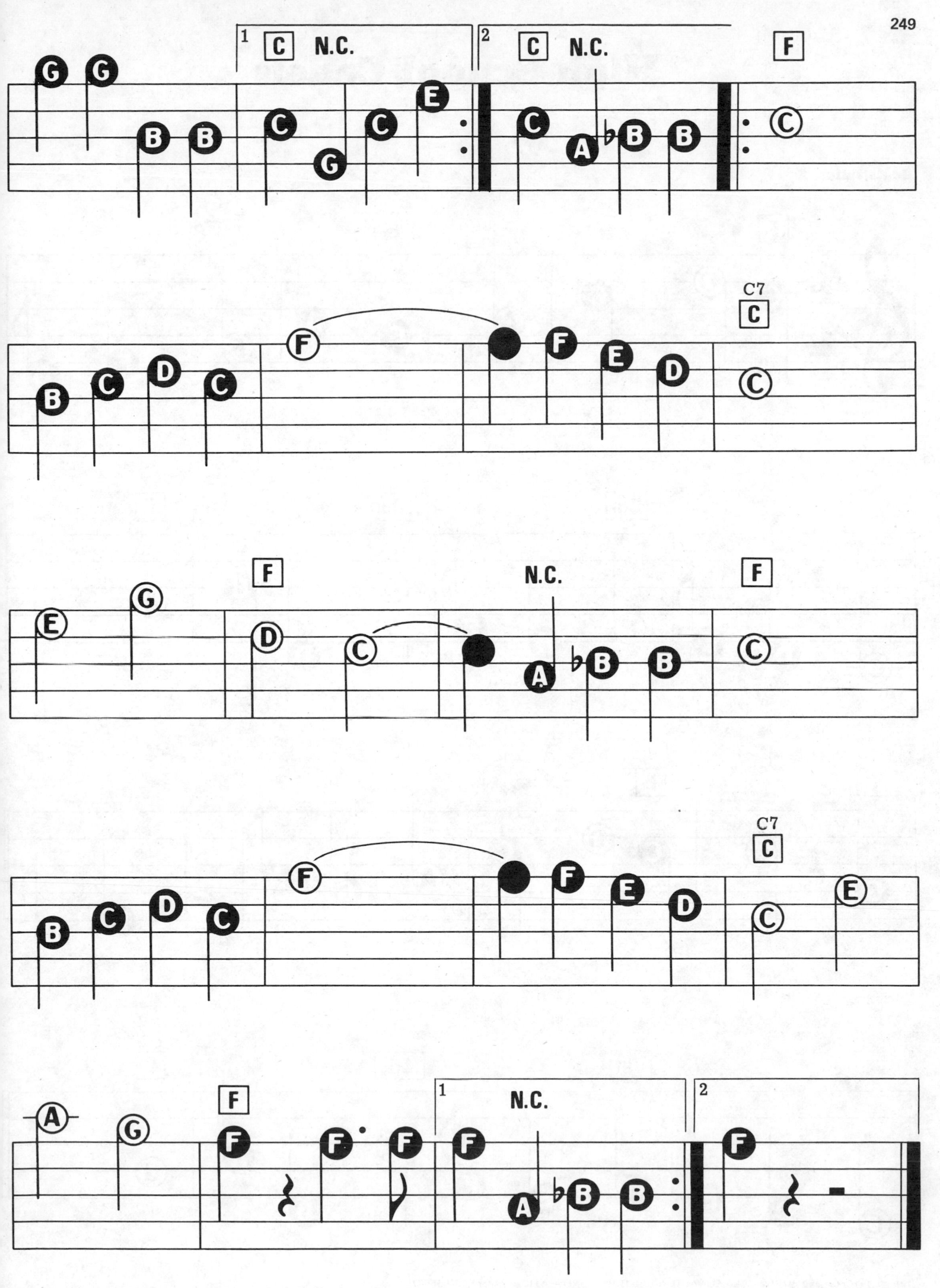
1
C
N.C.
2
C
N.C.
F
C7
C
F
N.C.
F
C7
C
F
1
N.C.
2

High School Cadets

Registration 2

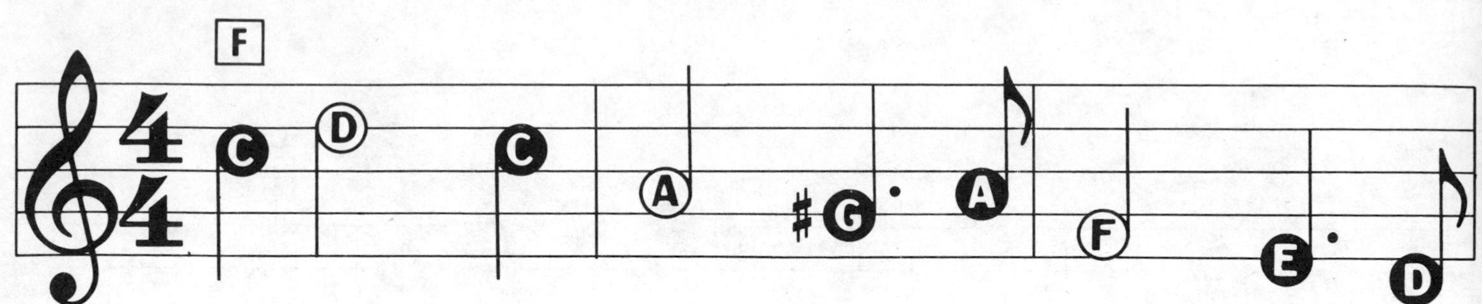

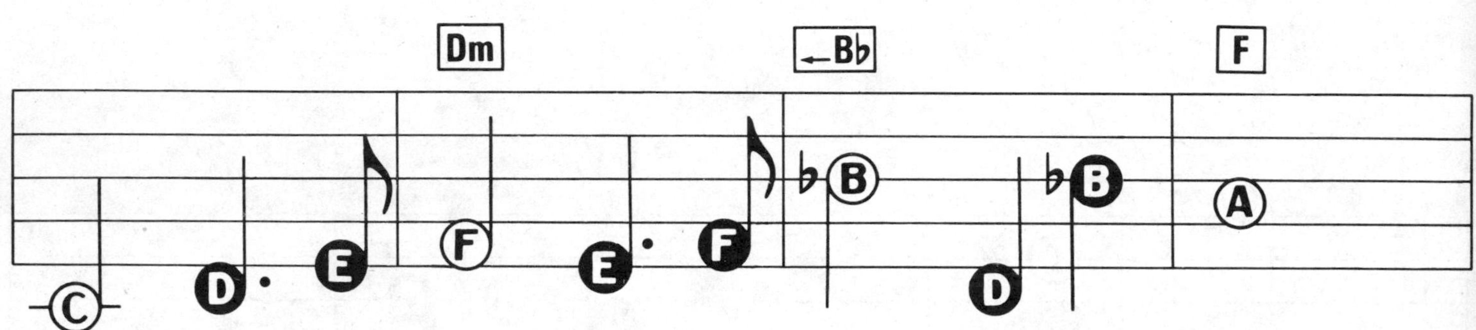

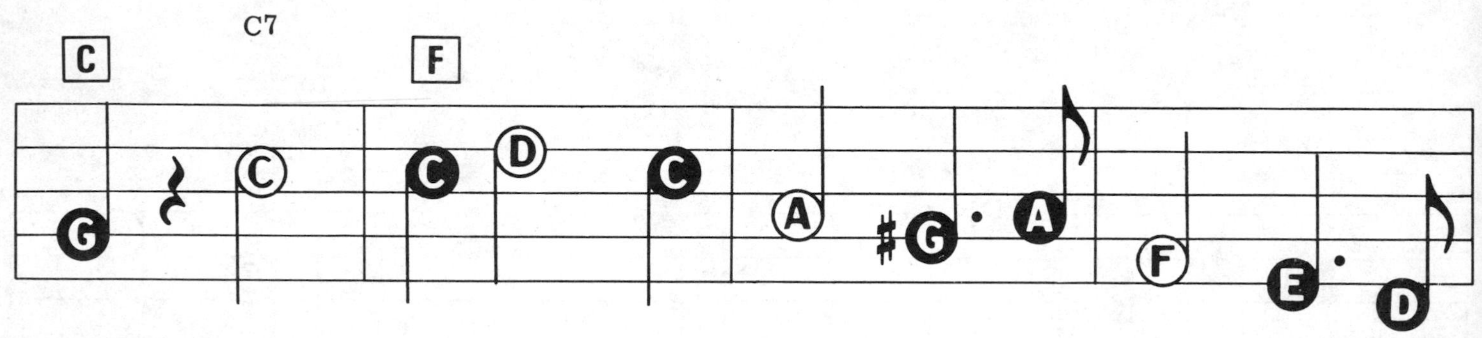

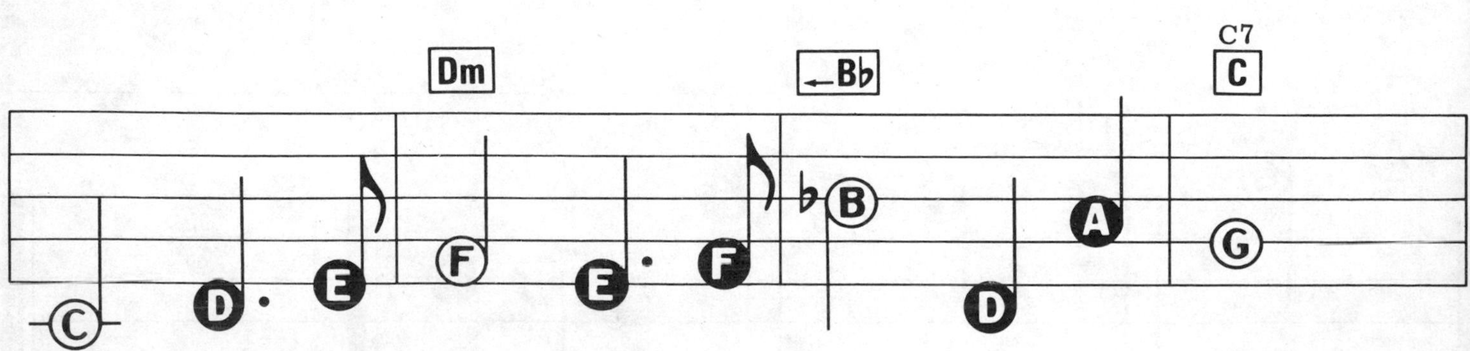

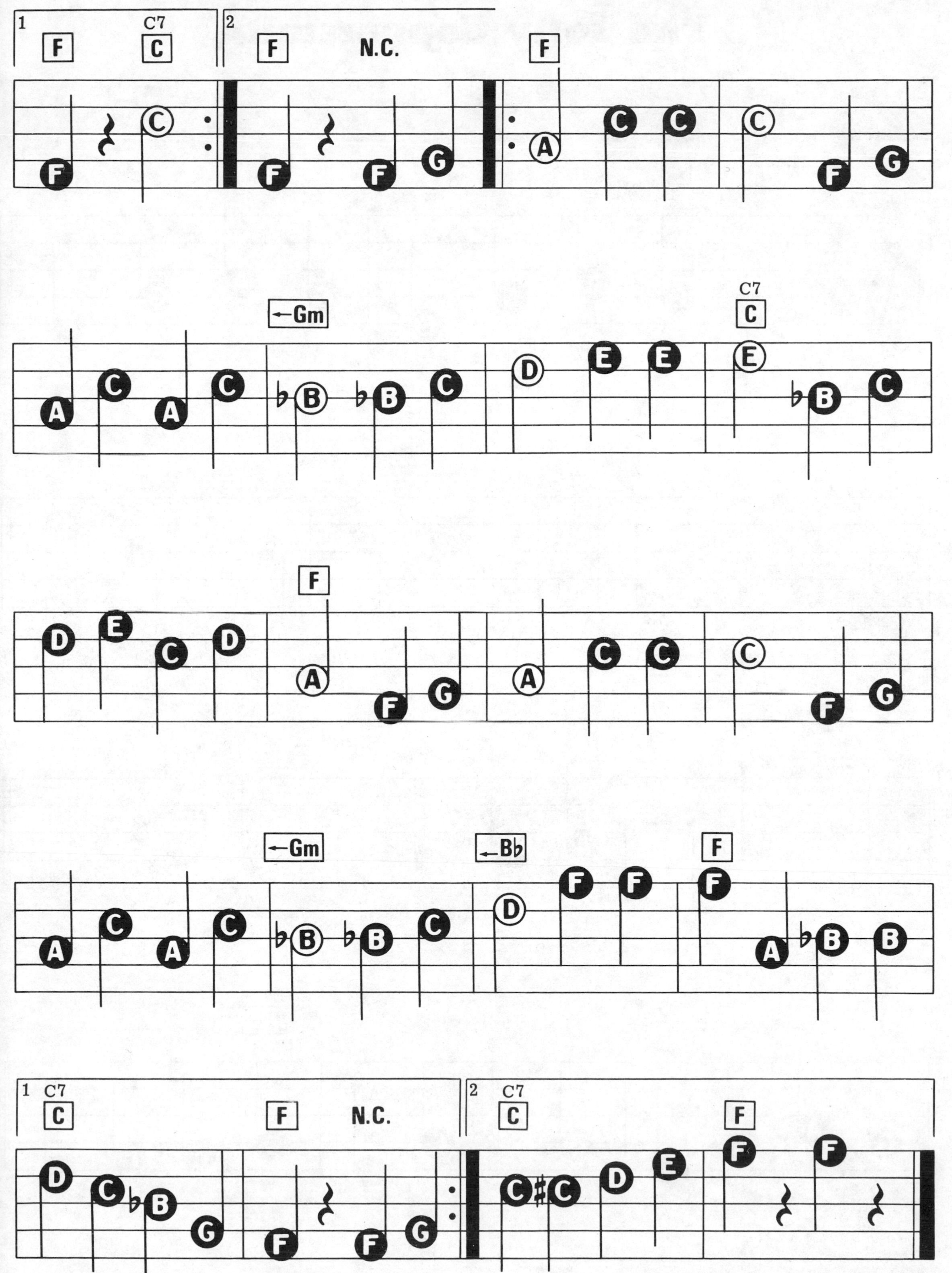
1
C7
F C
2
F N.C. F
C7
←Gm C
F
←Gm ←B♭ F
1 C7
C F N.C.
2 C7
C F

The Jolly Coppersmith

Registration 4

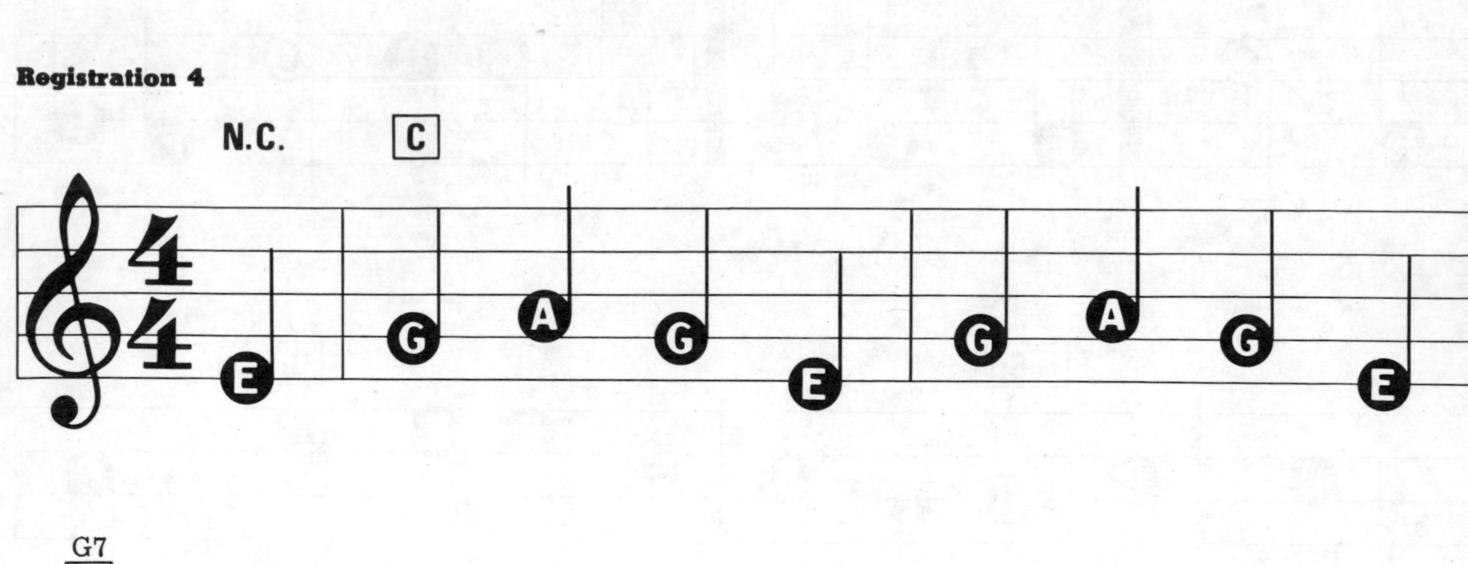

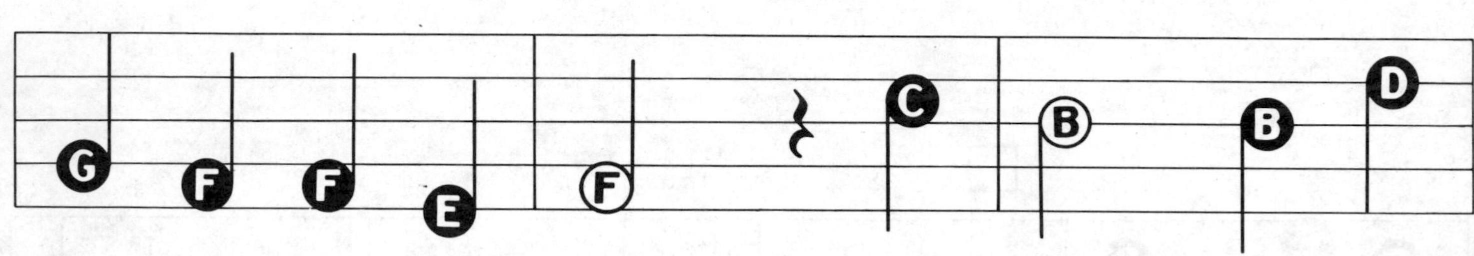

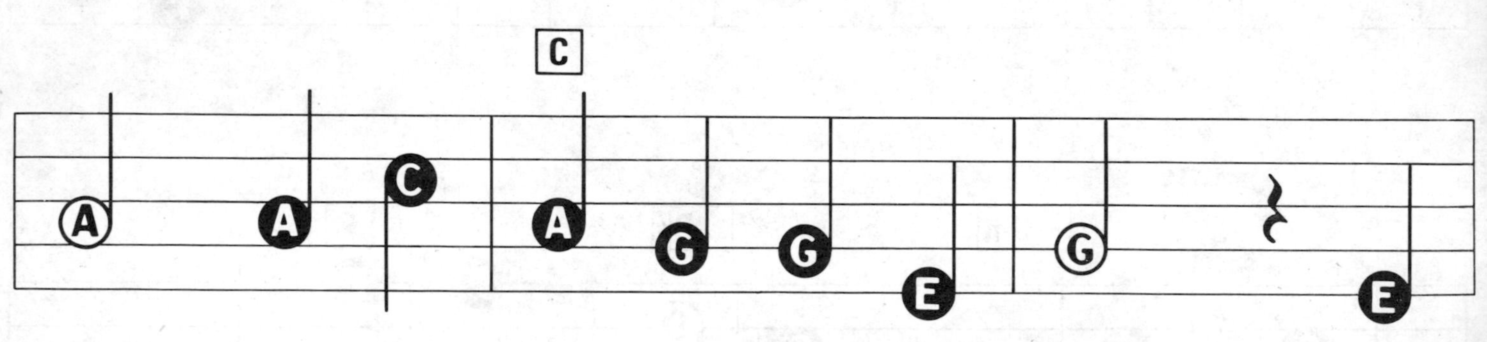

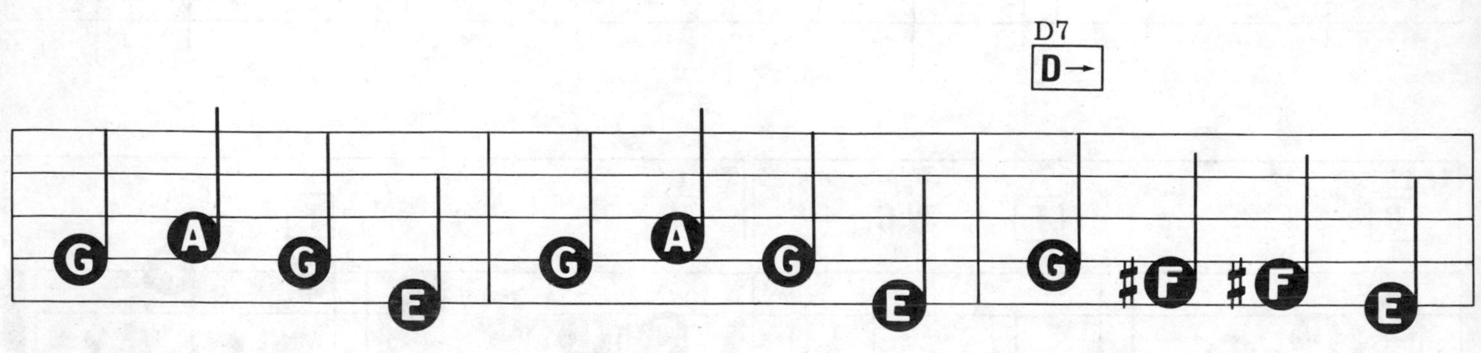

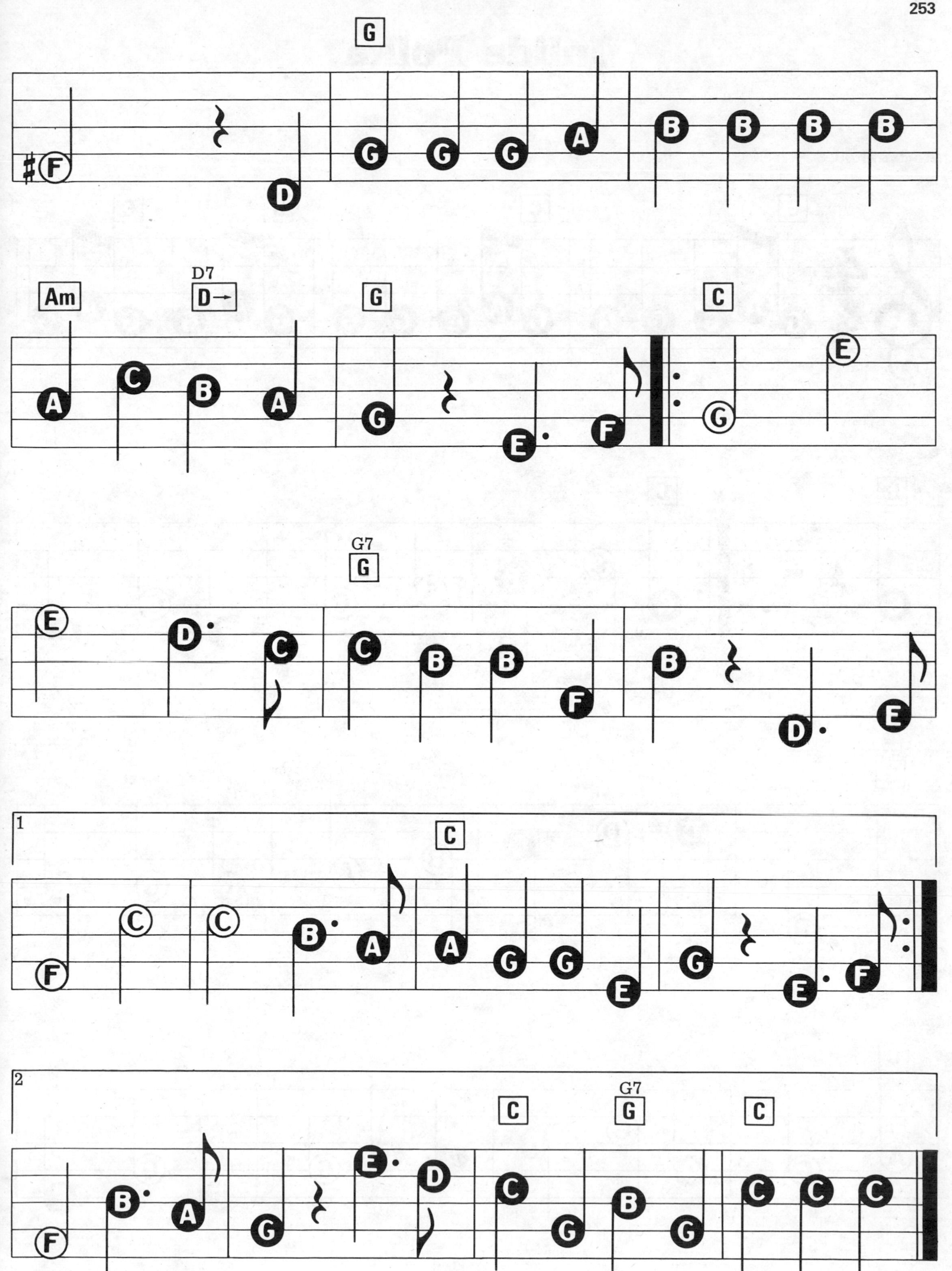
G
♯F D G G G A B B B B
Am
D7
D→
G
C
A C B A G E F G E
G7
G
E D C C B B F B D E
1
C
F C C B A A G G E G E F
2
C
G7
G
C
F B A G E D C G B G C C C

Julida Polka

Registration 4

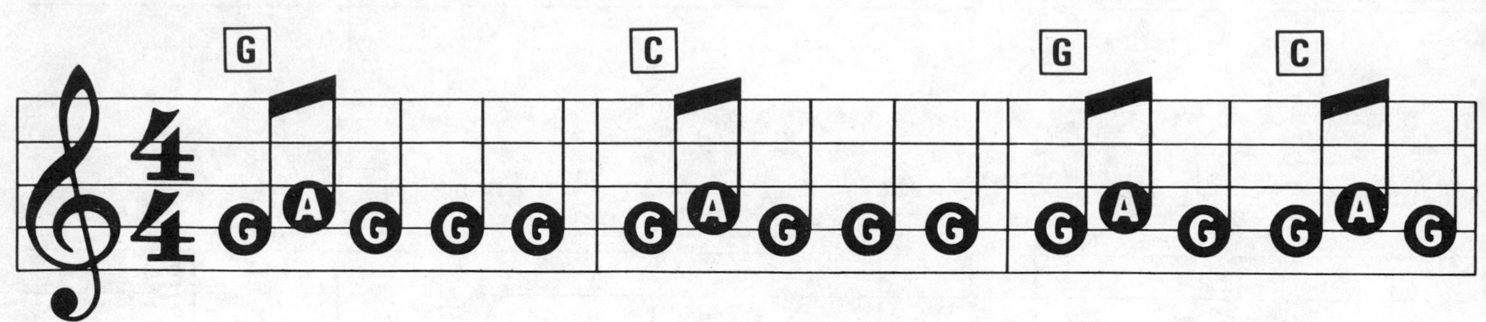

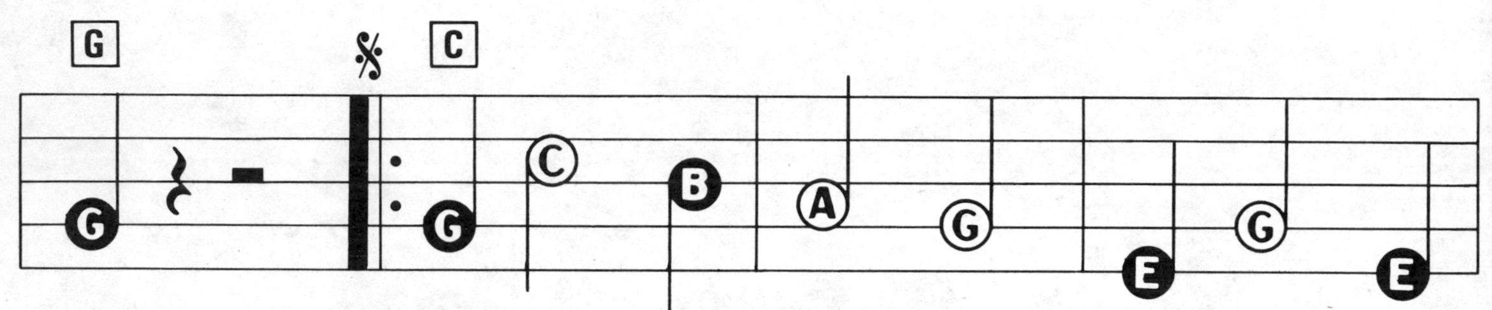

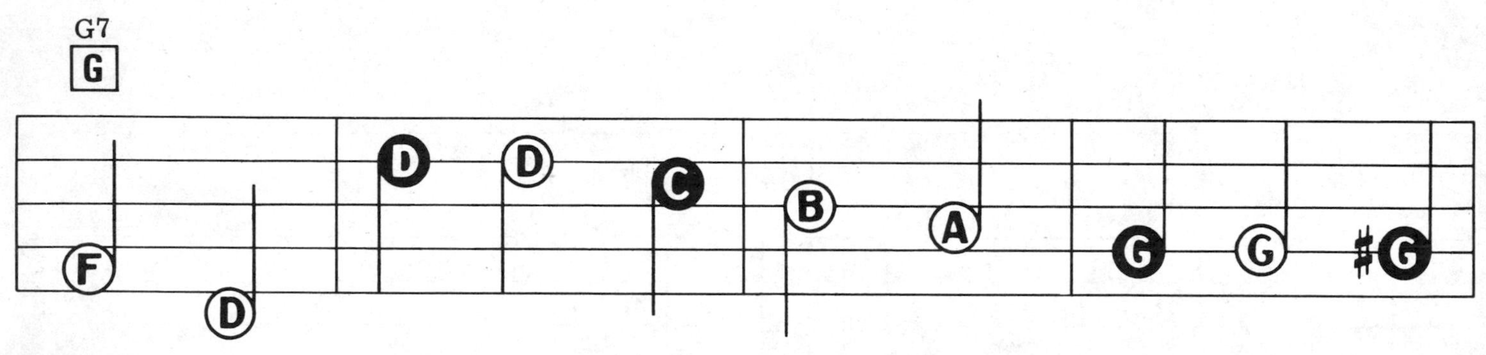

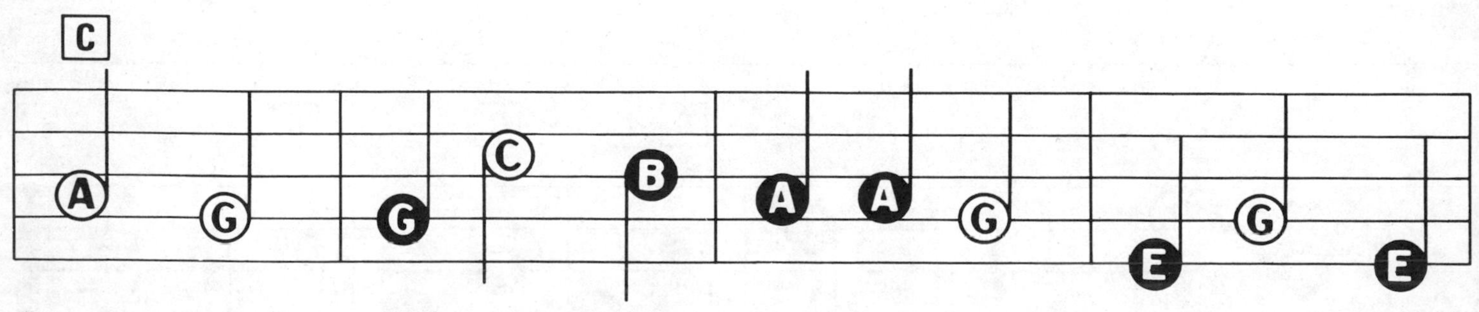

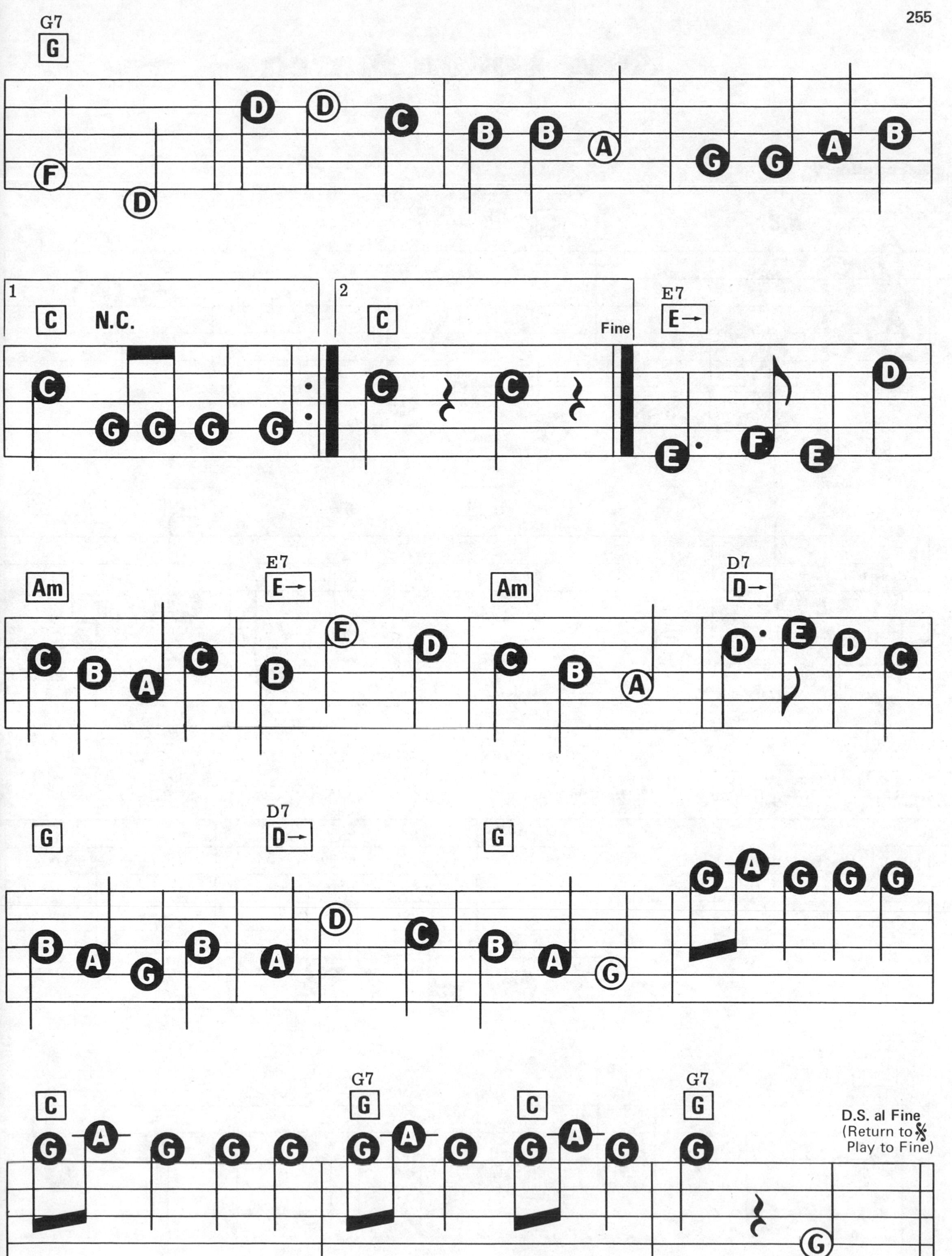
G7
G
F
D
D
D
C
B
B
A
G
G
A
B
1
C
N.C.
C
G
G
G
G
2
C
C
C
Fine
E7
E→
E
F
E
D
Am
C
B
A
C
E7
E→
B
E
D
Am
C
B
A
D7
D→
D
E
D
C
G
B
A
G
B
D7
D→
A
D
C
G
B
A
G
G
A
G
G
G
C
G
A
G
G
G
G7
G
G
A
G
C
G
A
G
G7
G
G
G
D.S. al Fine
(Return to 𝄋 Play to Fine)

King Cotton March

Registration 5

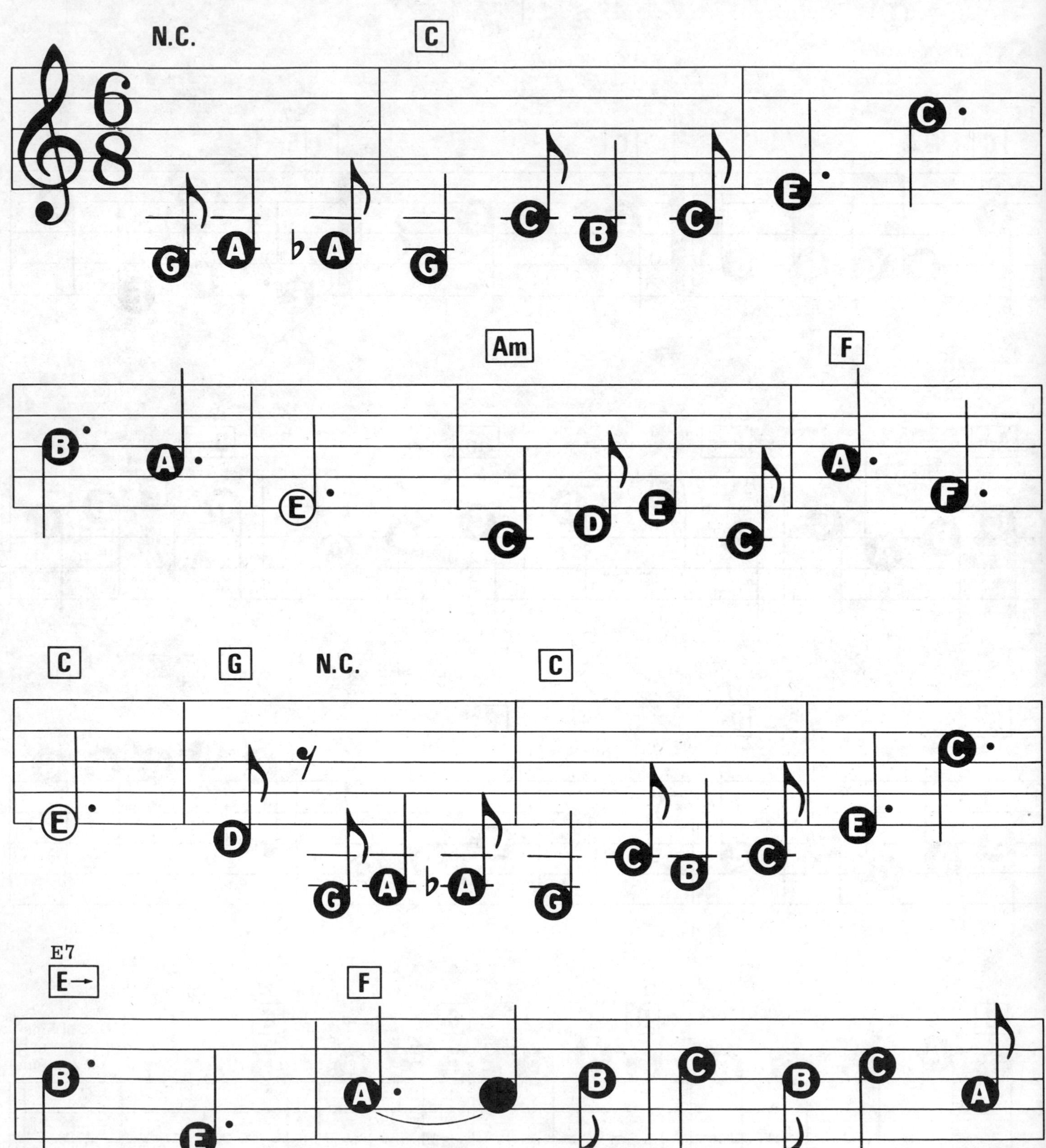

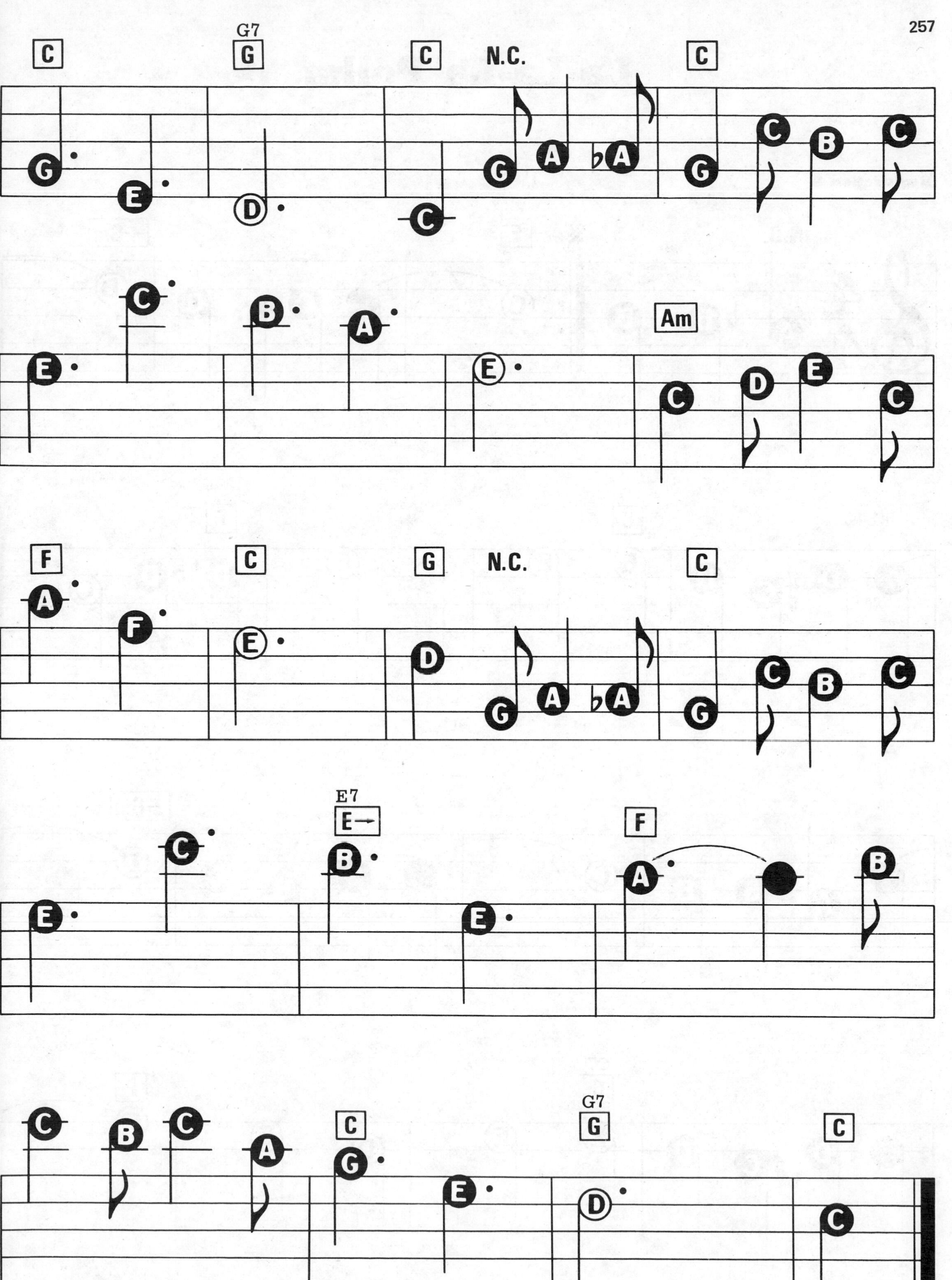
C G7 G C N.C. C
Am
F C G N.C. C
E7 E F
C G7 G C

La-La-La Polka

Registration 8

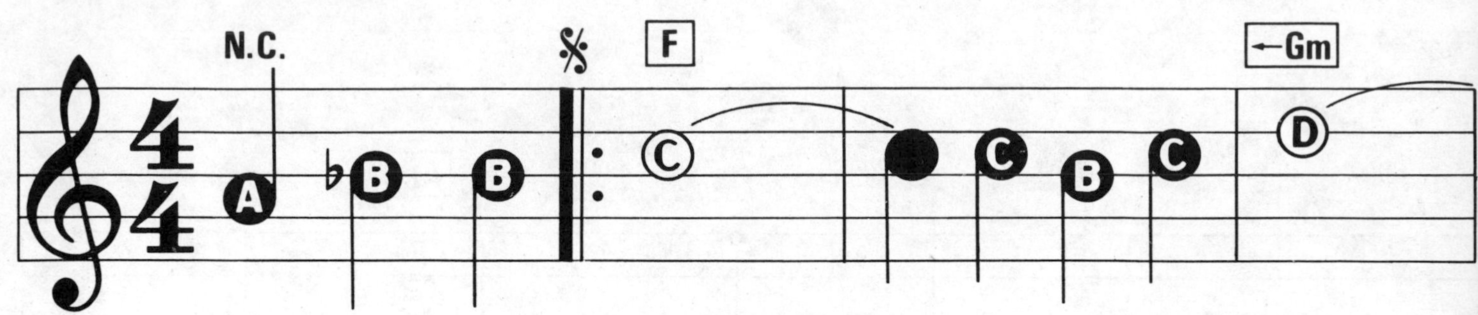

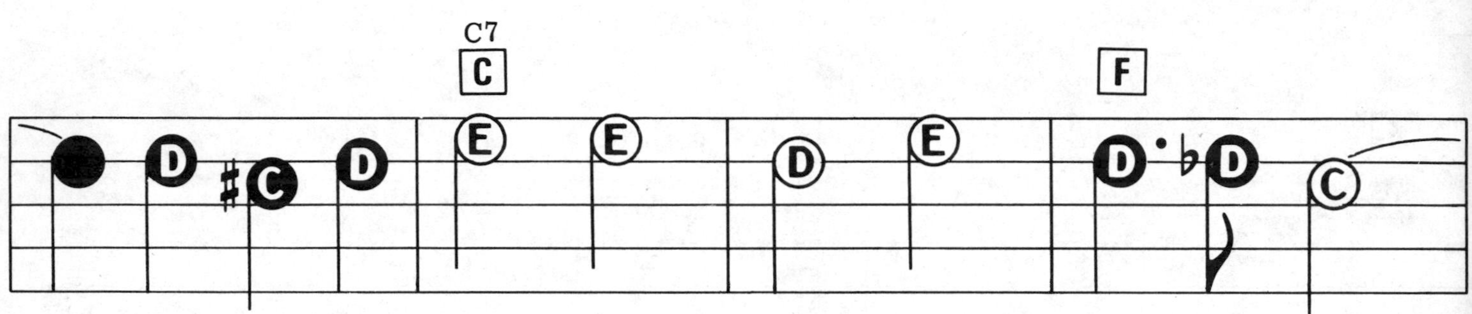

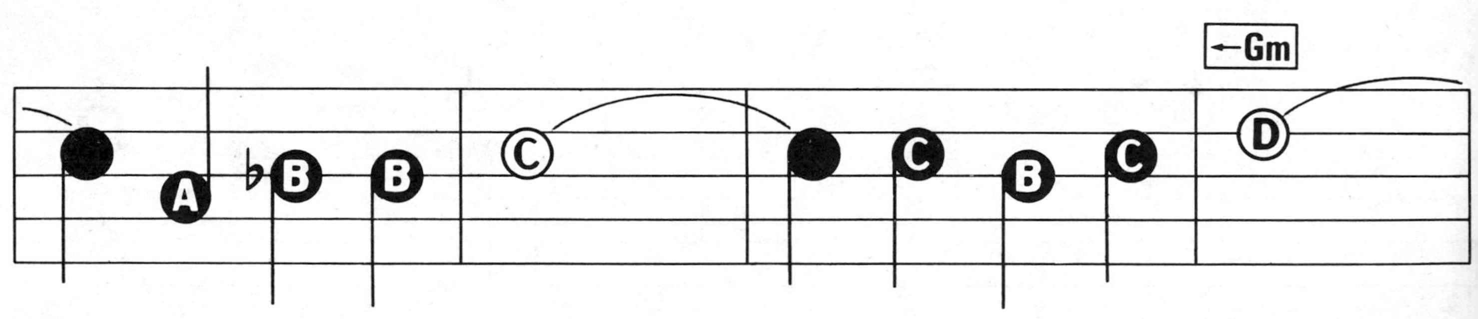

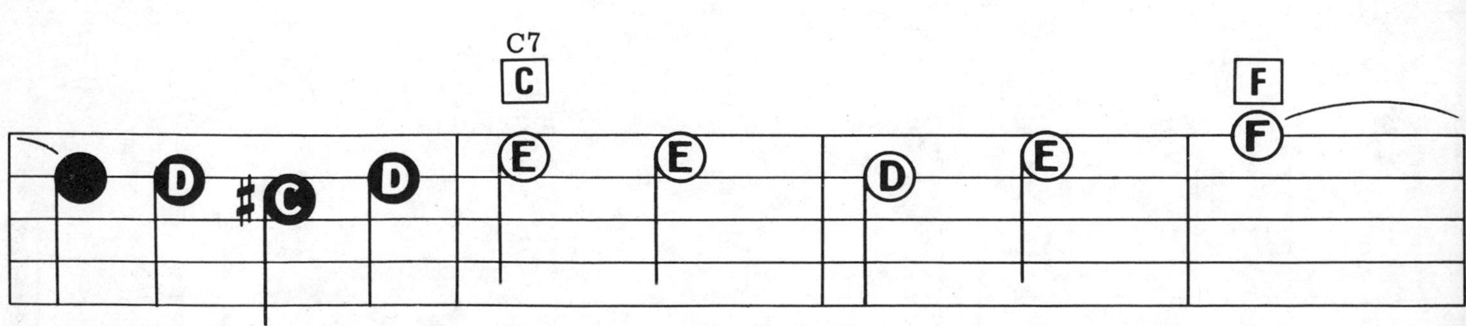

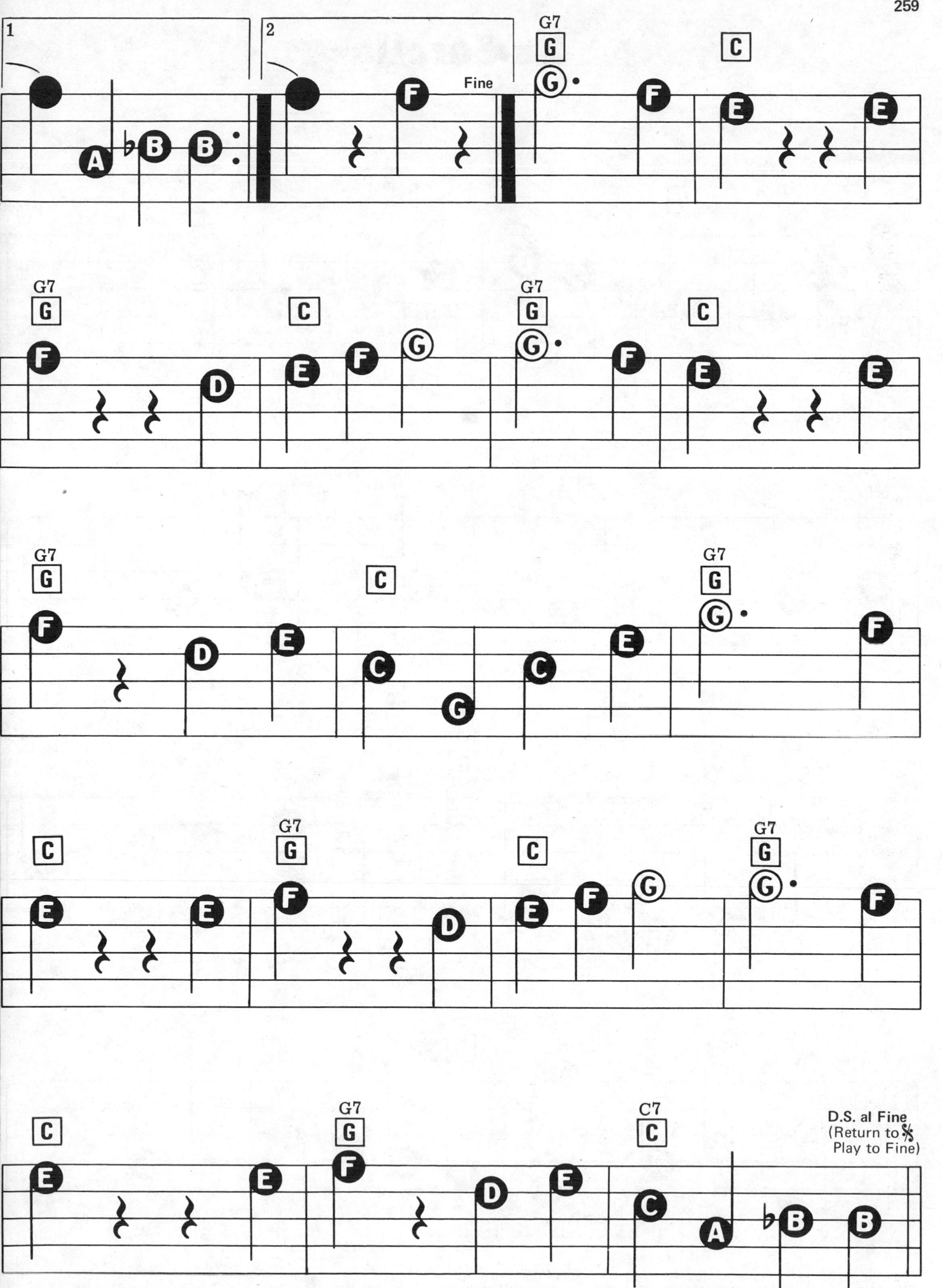
1
2
Fine
G7
C
D.S. al Fine
(Return to 𝄋
Play to Fine)
C7

La Sorella

Registration 1

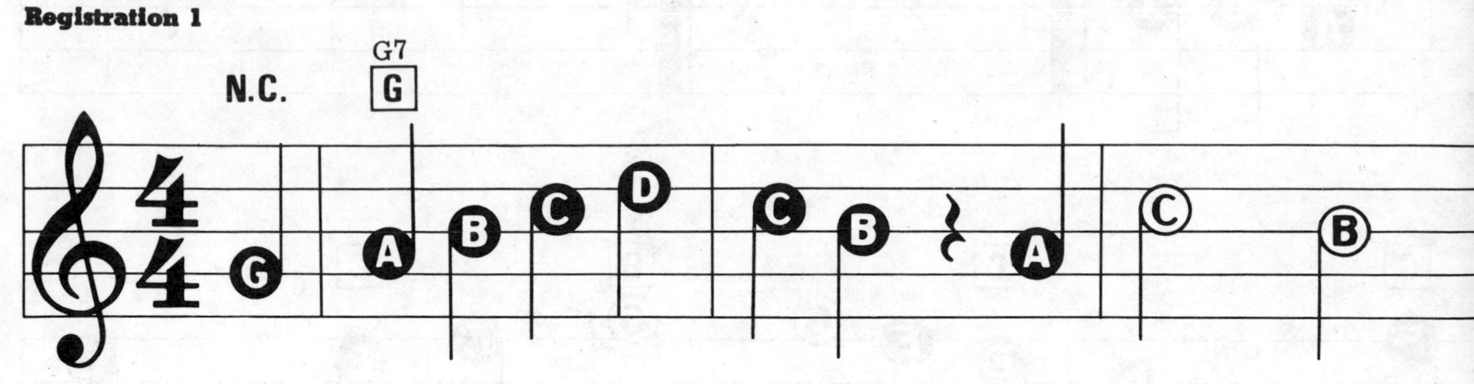

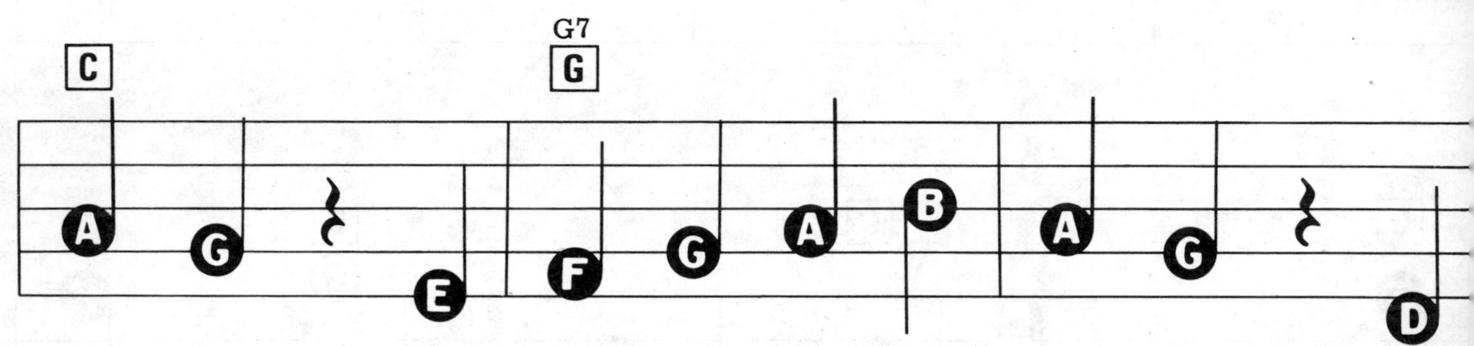

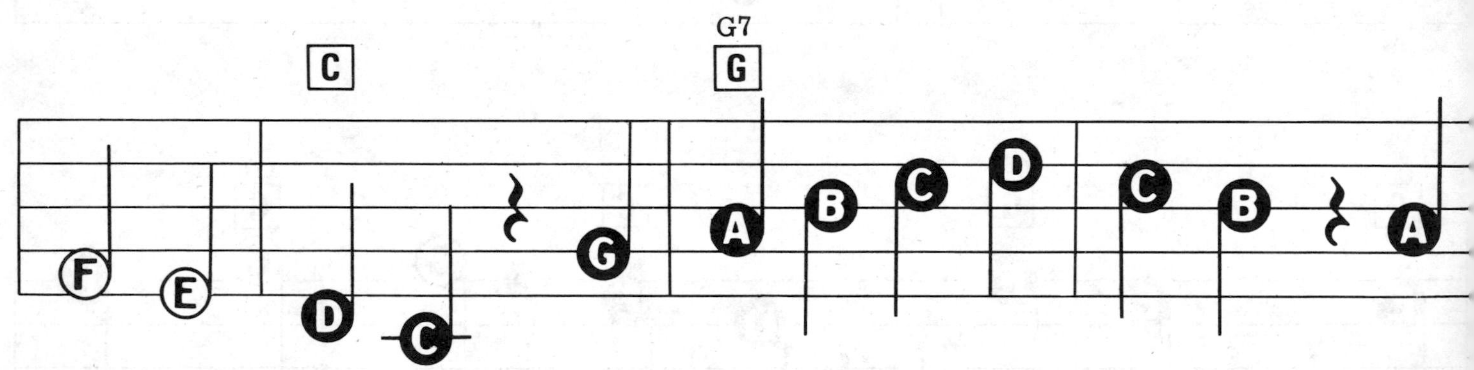

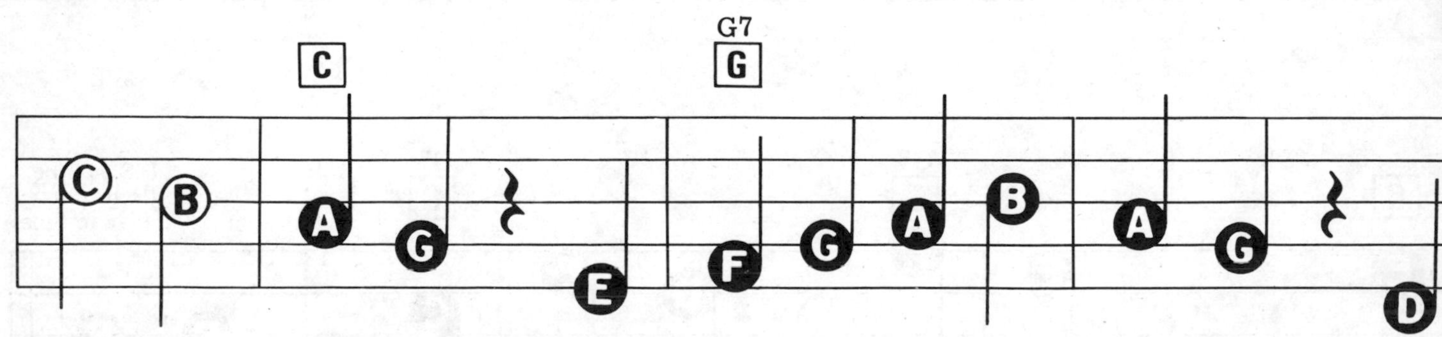

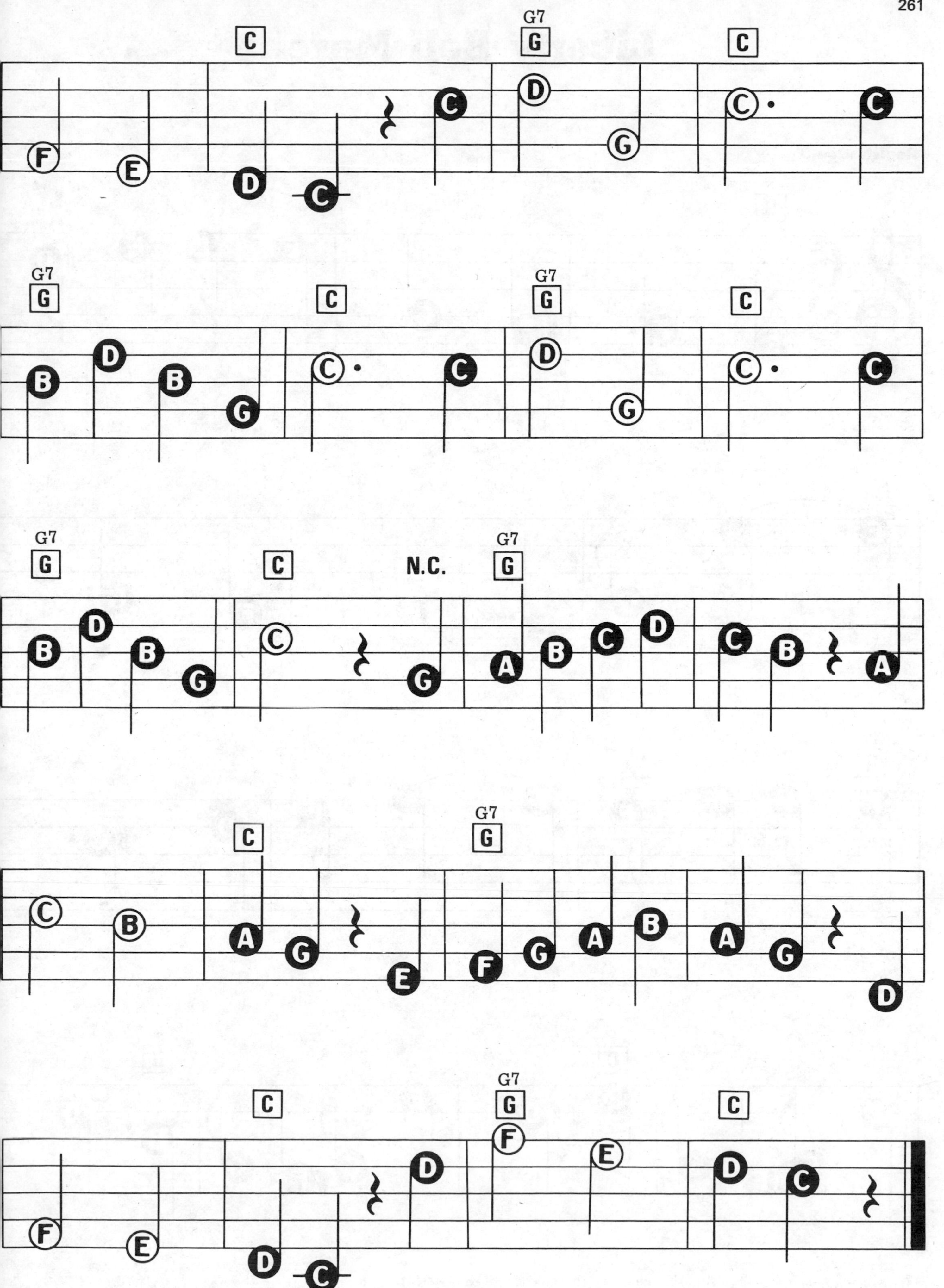
C
G7 G
C
G7 G
C
G7 G
C
G7 G
C
N.C.
G7 G
C
G7 G
C
G7 G
C

Liberty Bell March

Registration 3

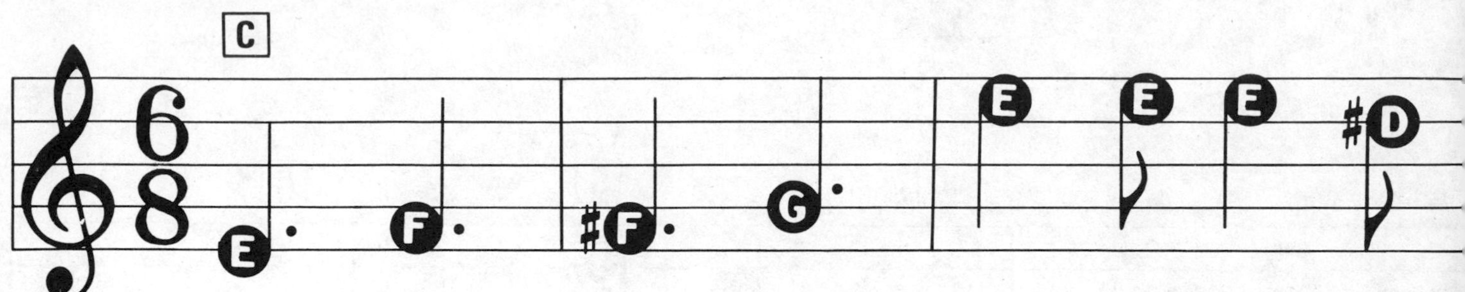

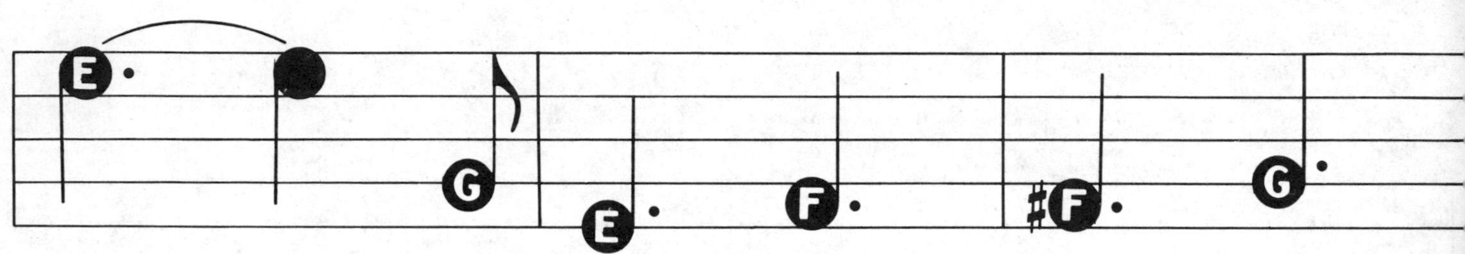

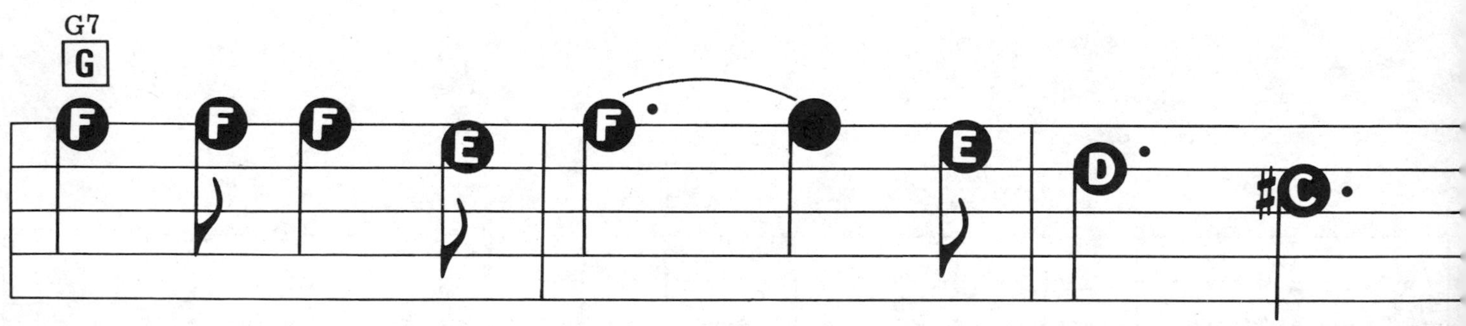

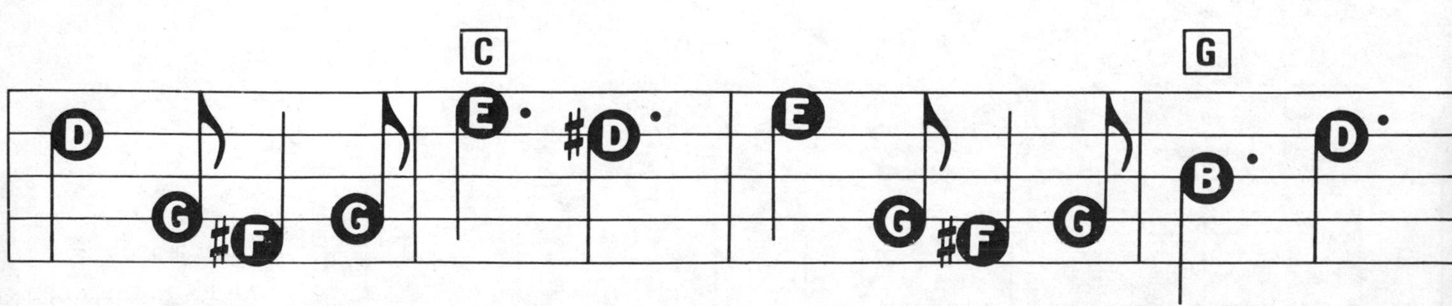

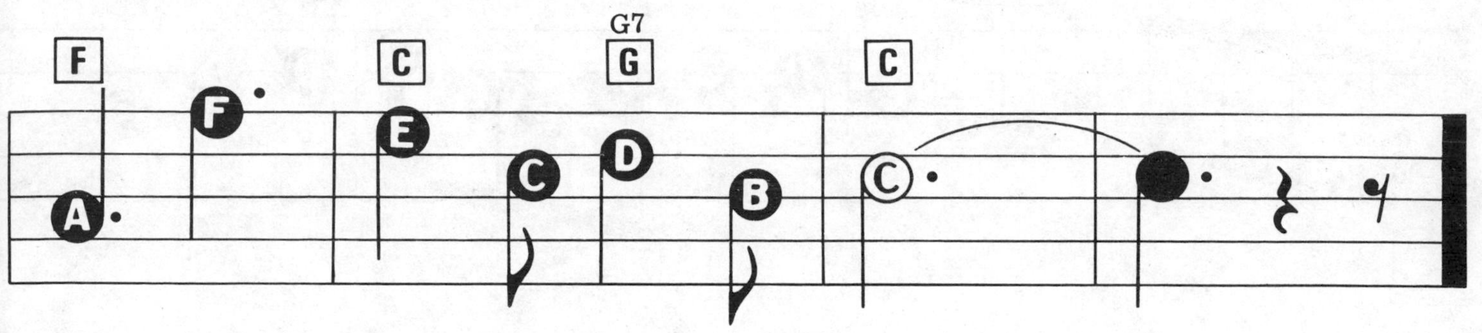
F
C
G7
G
C
A F E C D B C

Lucia Polka

Registration 4

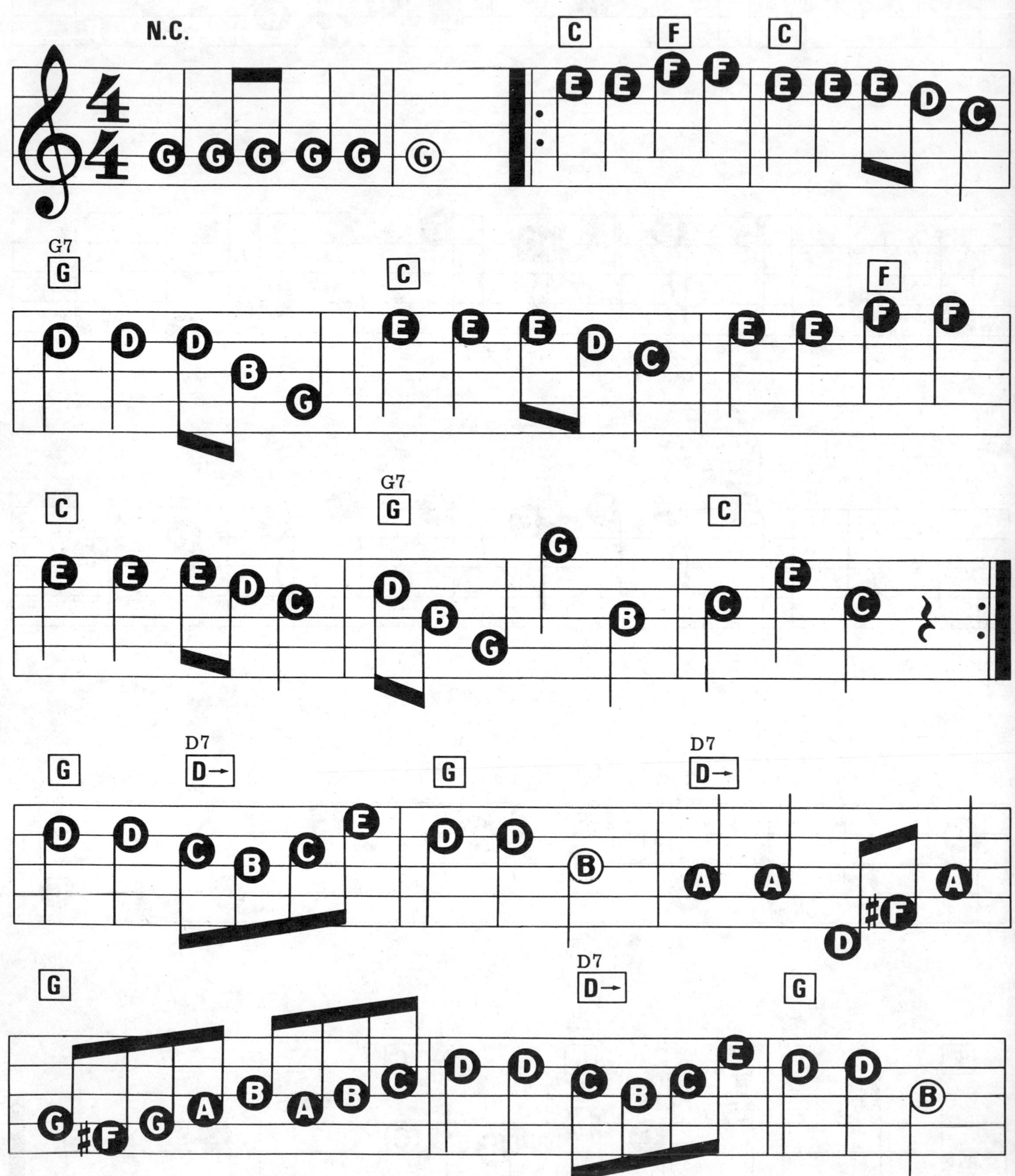

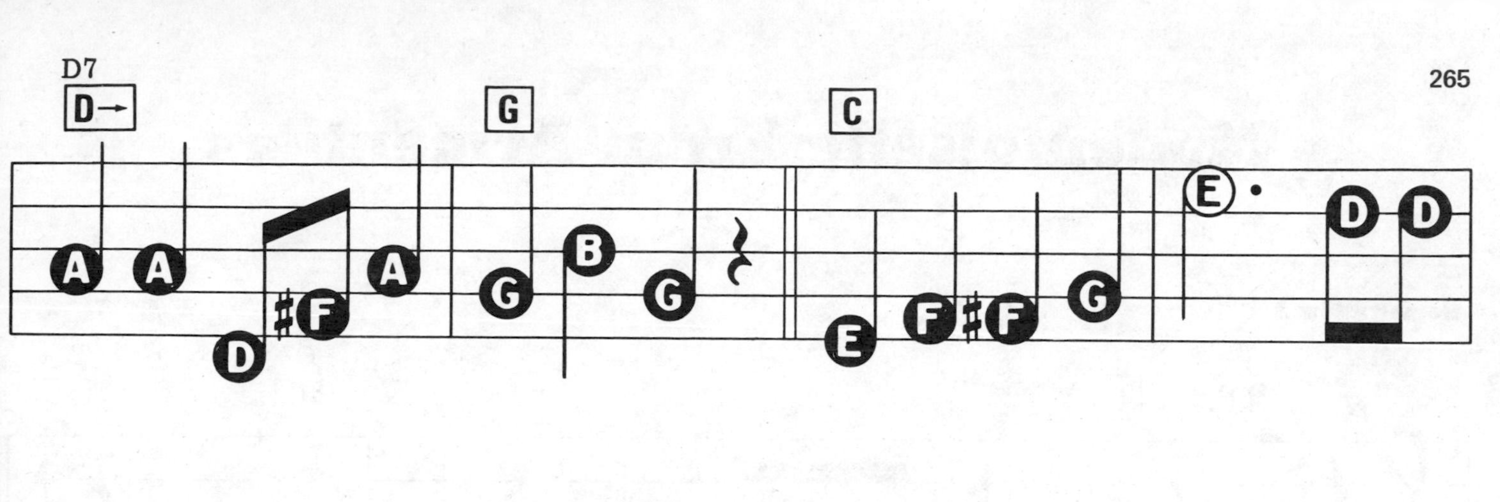
D7
D→
A A D ♯F A
G
G B G
C
E F ♯F G
E D D

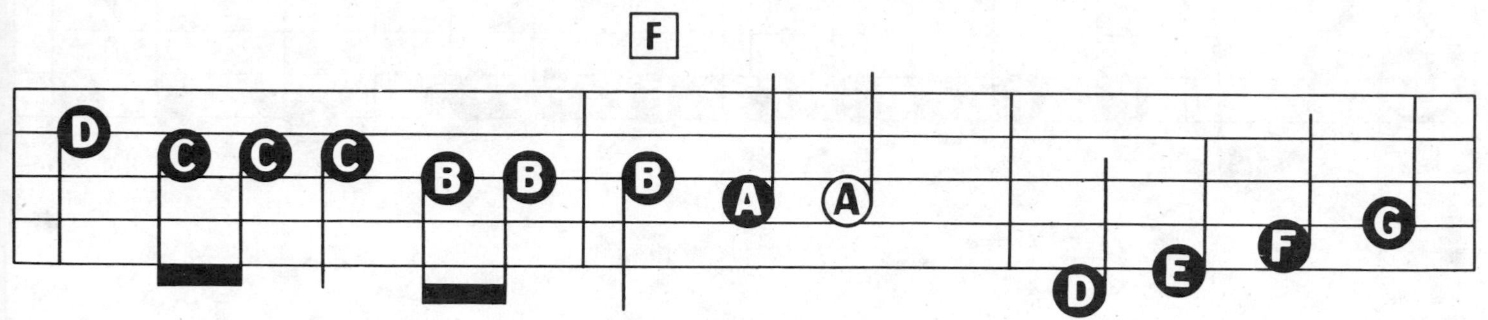
D C C C B B
F
B A A
D E F G

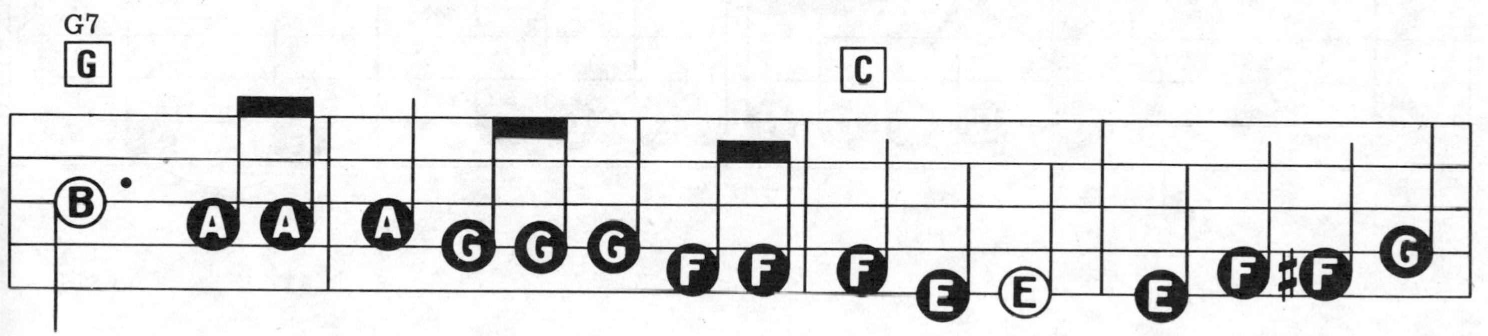
G7
G
B A A A G G G F F
C
F E E
E F ♯F G

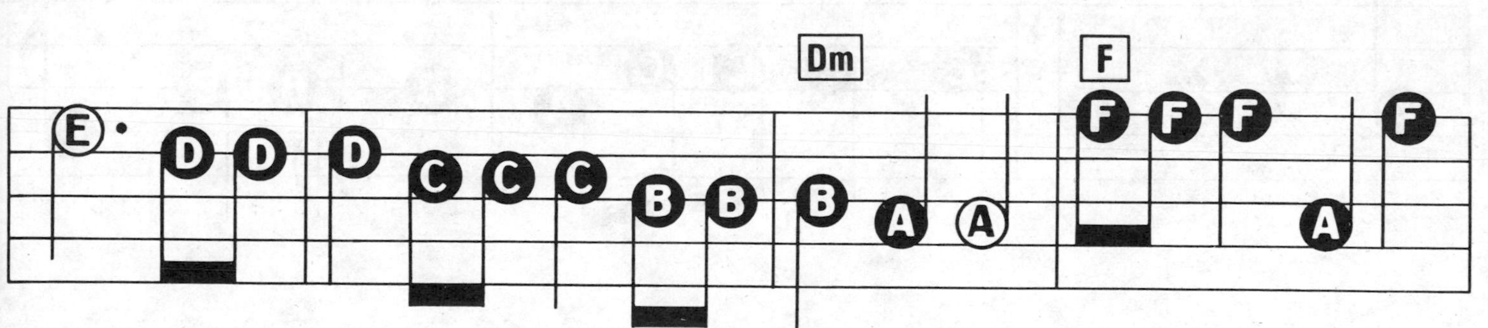
E D D D C C C B B
Dm
B A A
F
F F F A F

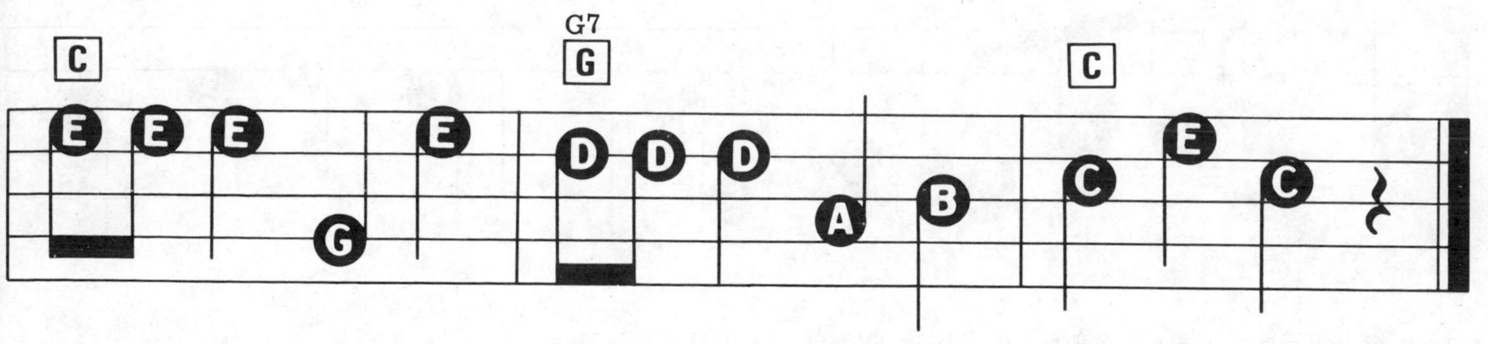
C
E E E G E
G7
G
D D D A B
C
C E C

Mademoiselle From Armentiers

Registration 2

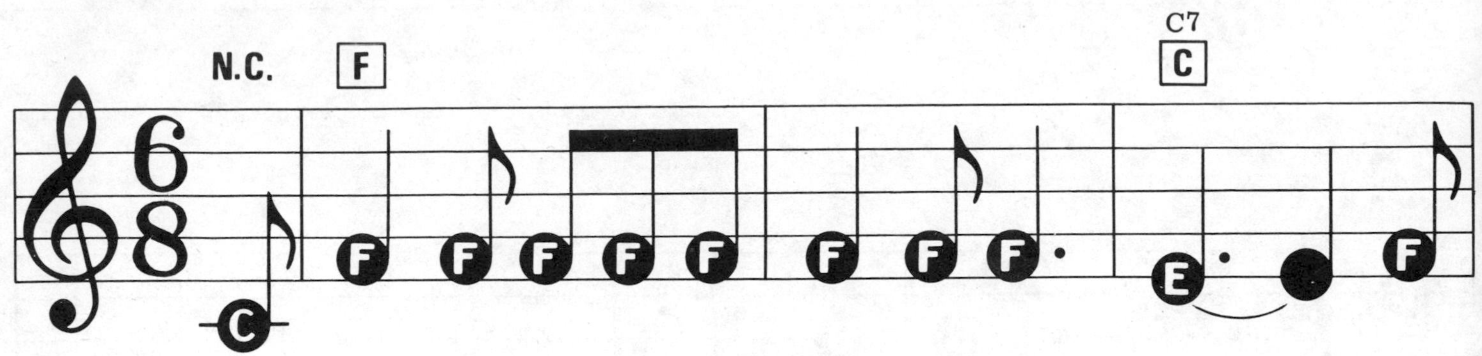

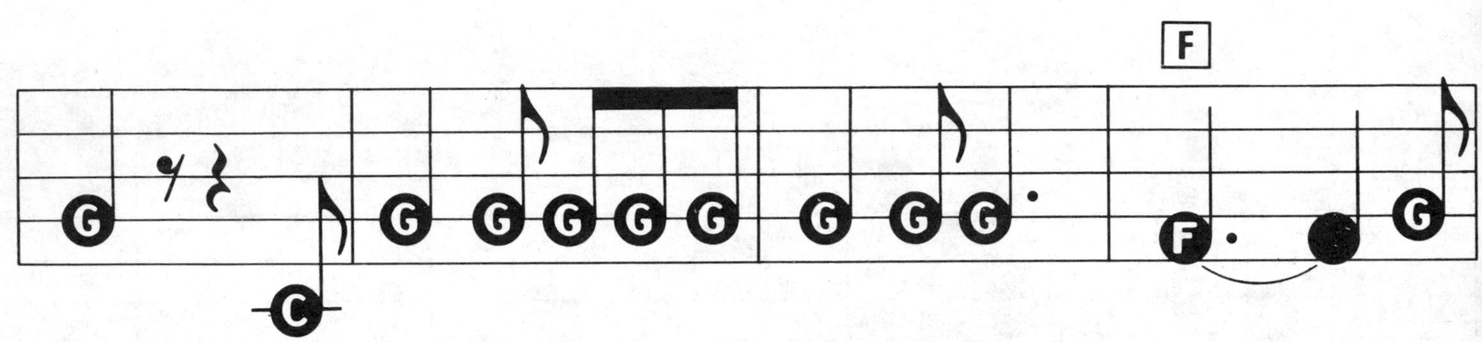

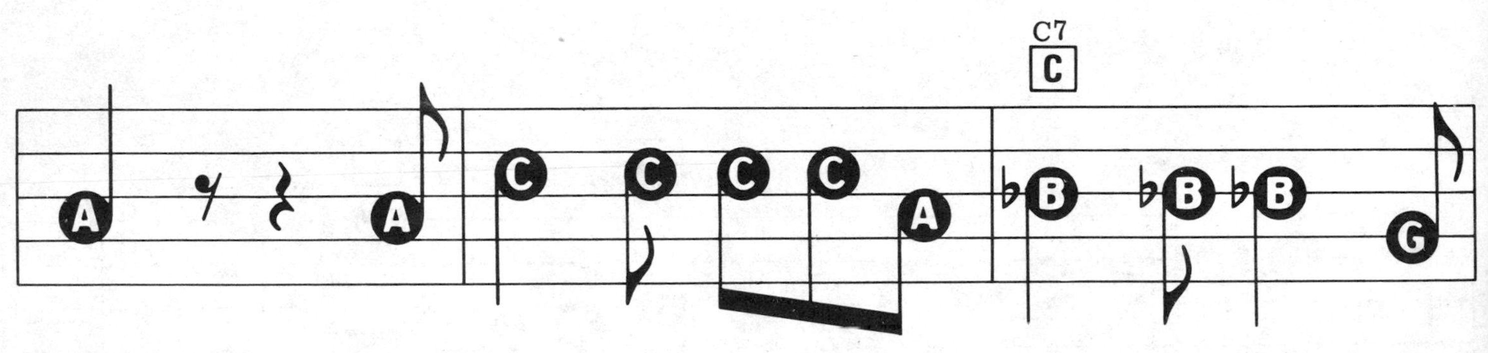

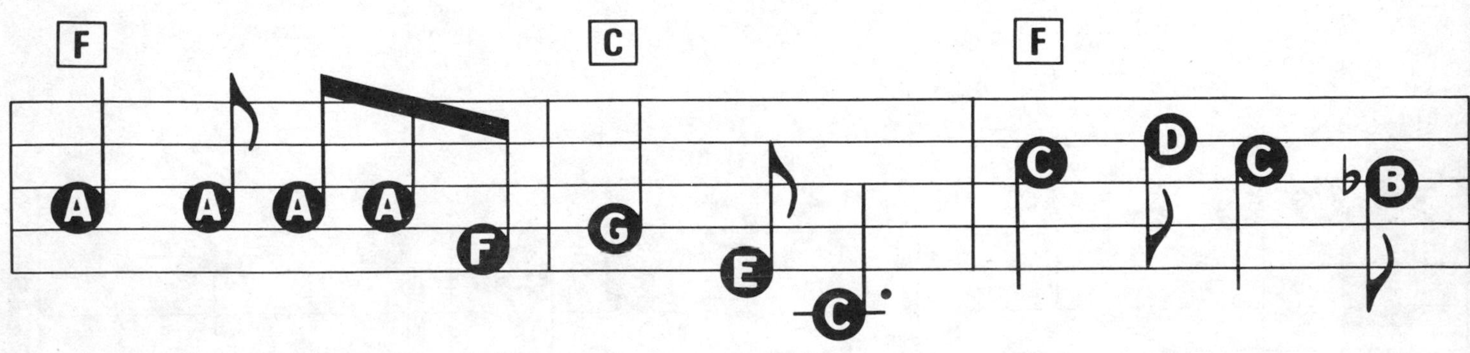

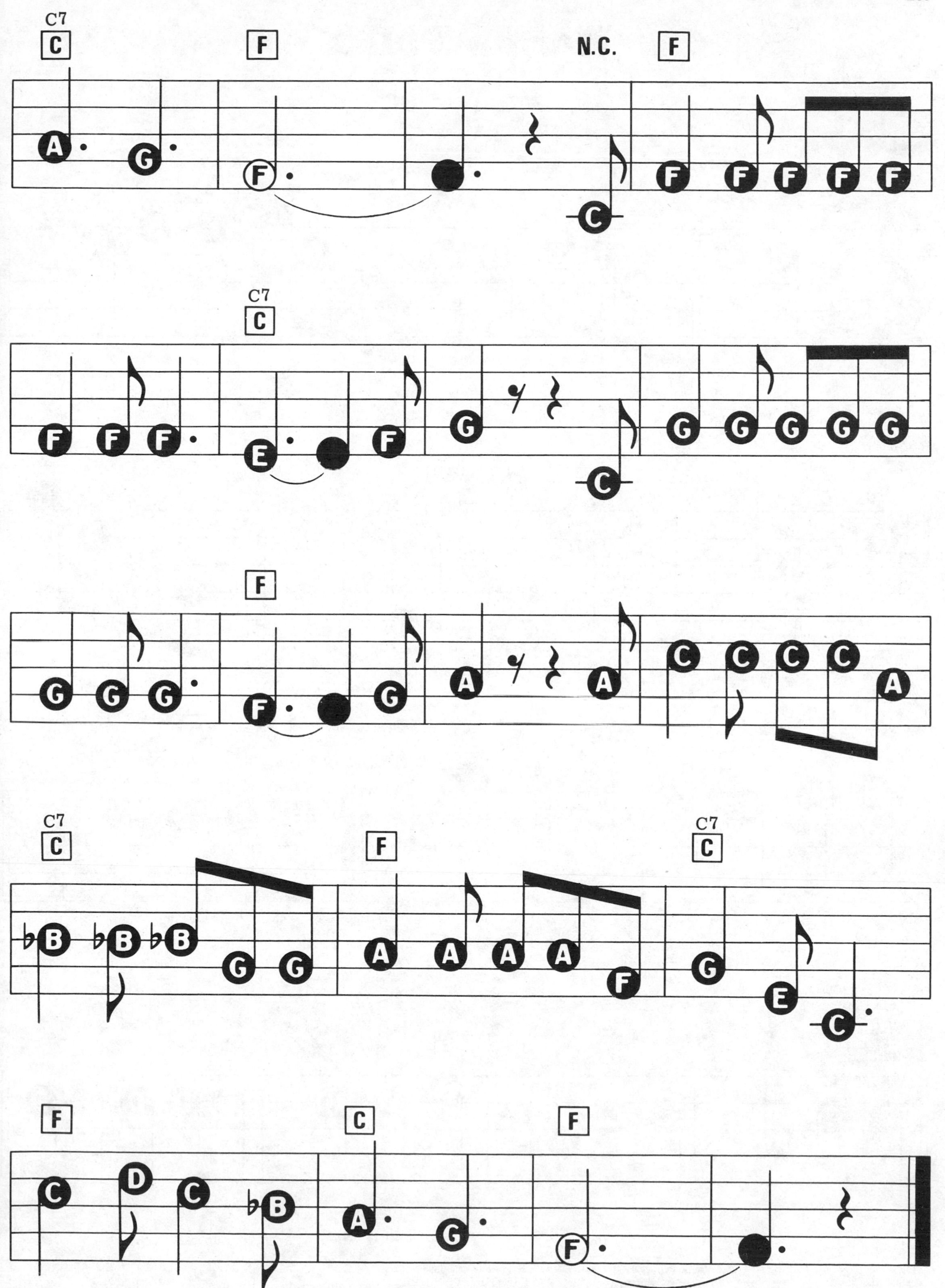
C7 C F N.C. F
C7 C
F
C7 C F C7 C
F C F

Martha Polka

Registration 4

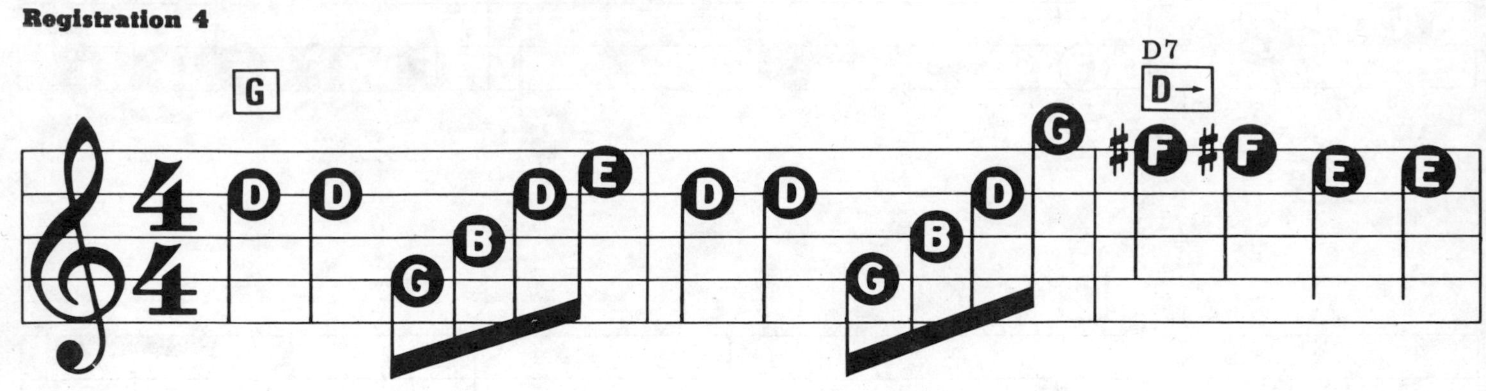

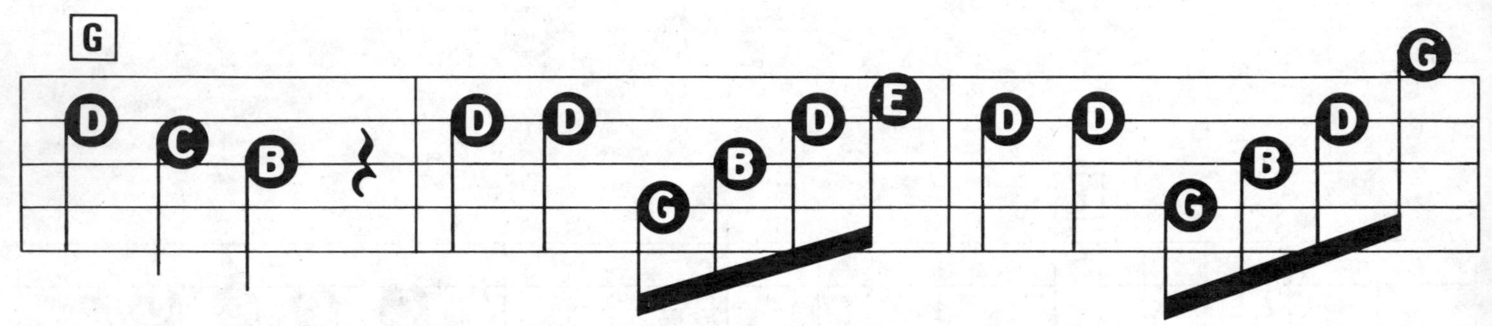

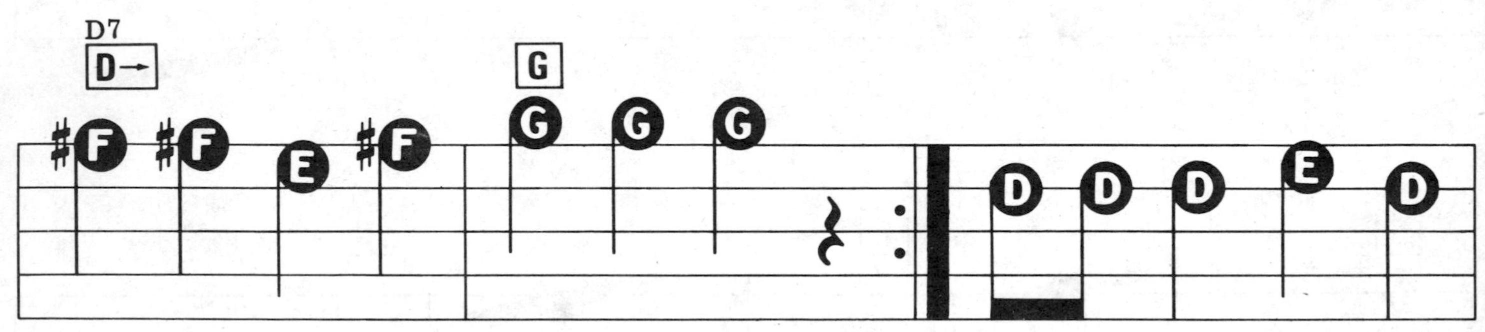

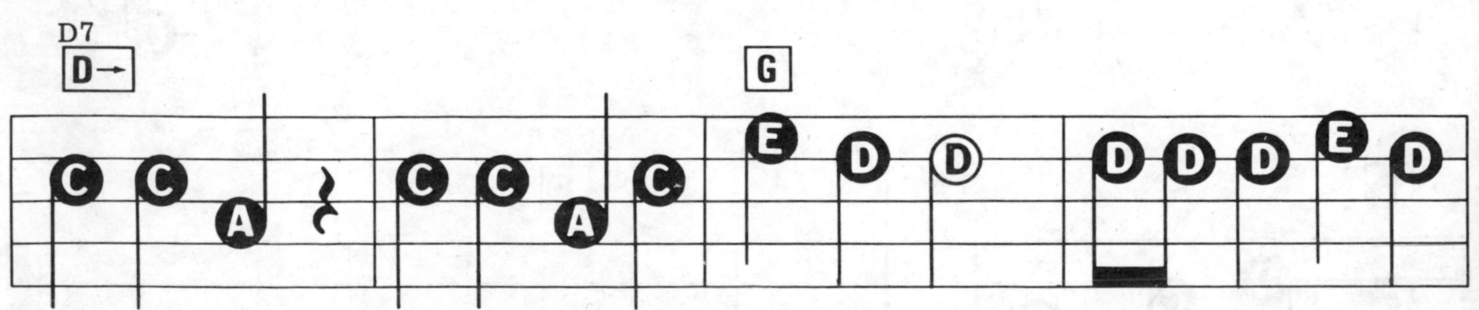

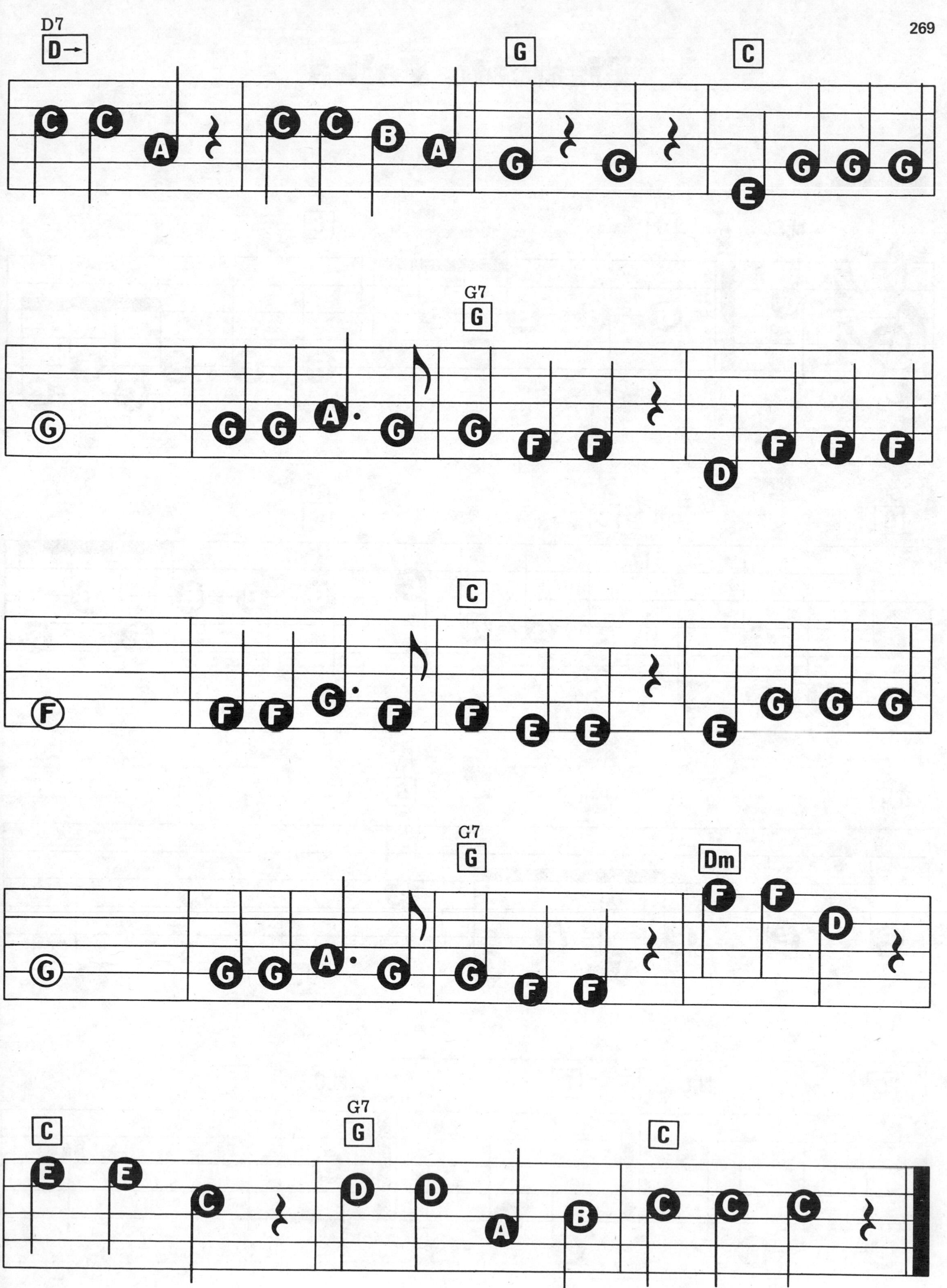
D7
D→
G
C
C C A C C B A G G E G G G
G7
G
G G G A G G F F D F F F
C
F F F G F F E E E G G G
G7
G
Dm
G G G A G G F F F F D
C
G7
G
C
E E C D D A B C C C

Pizzicato Polka

Registration 10

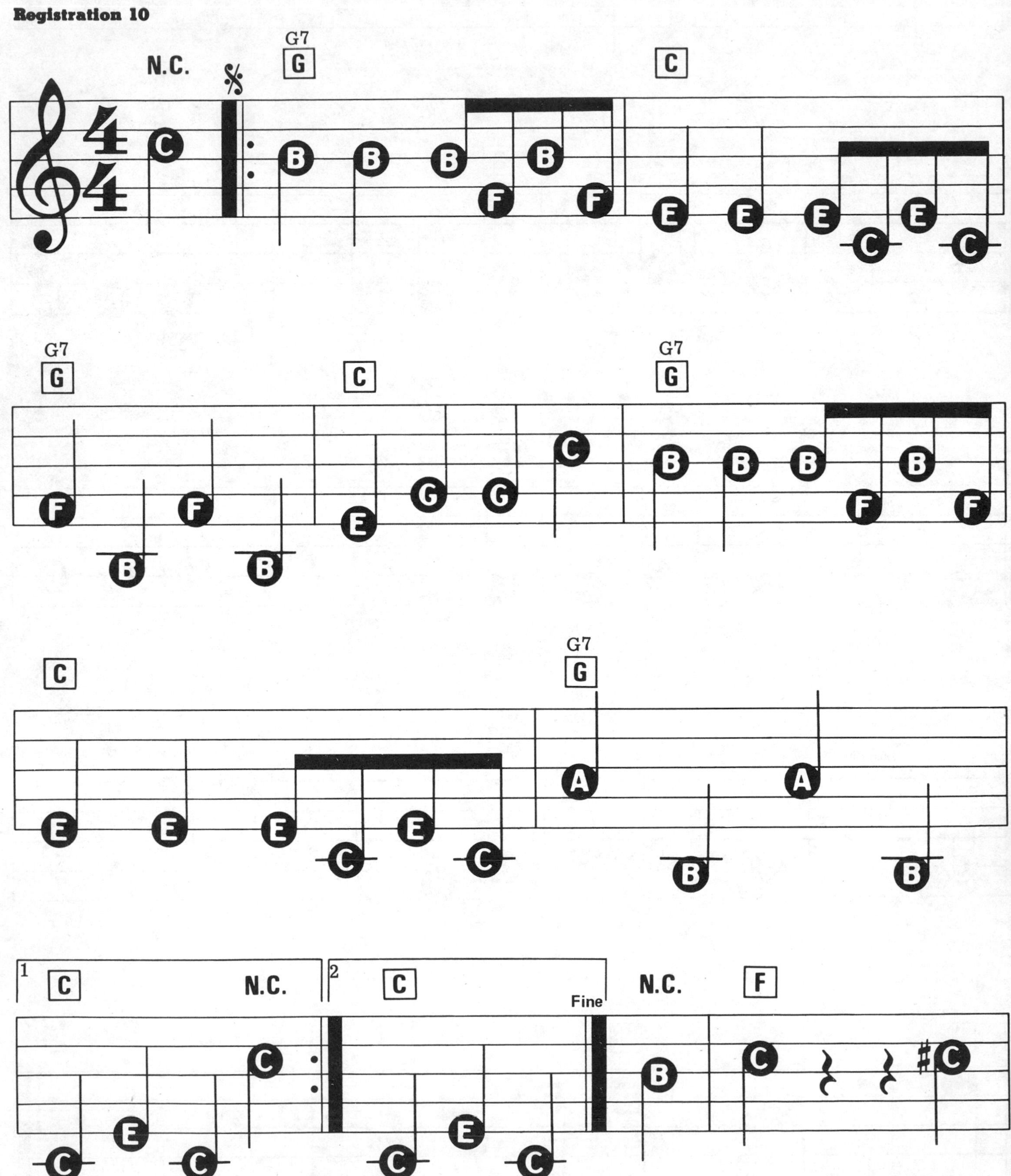

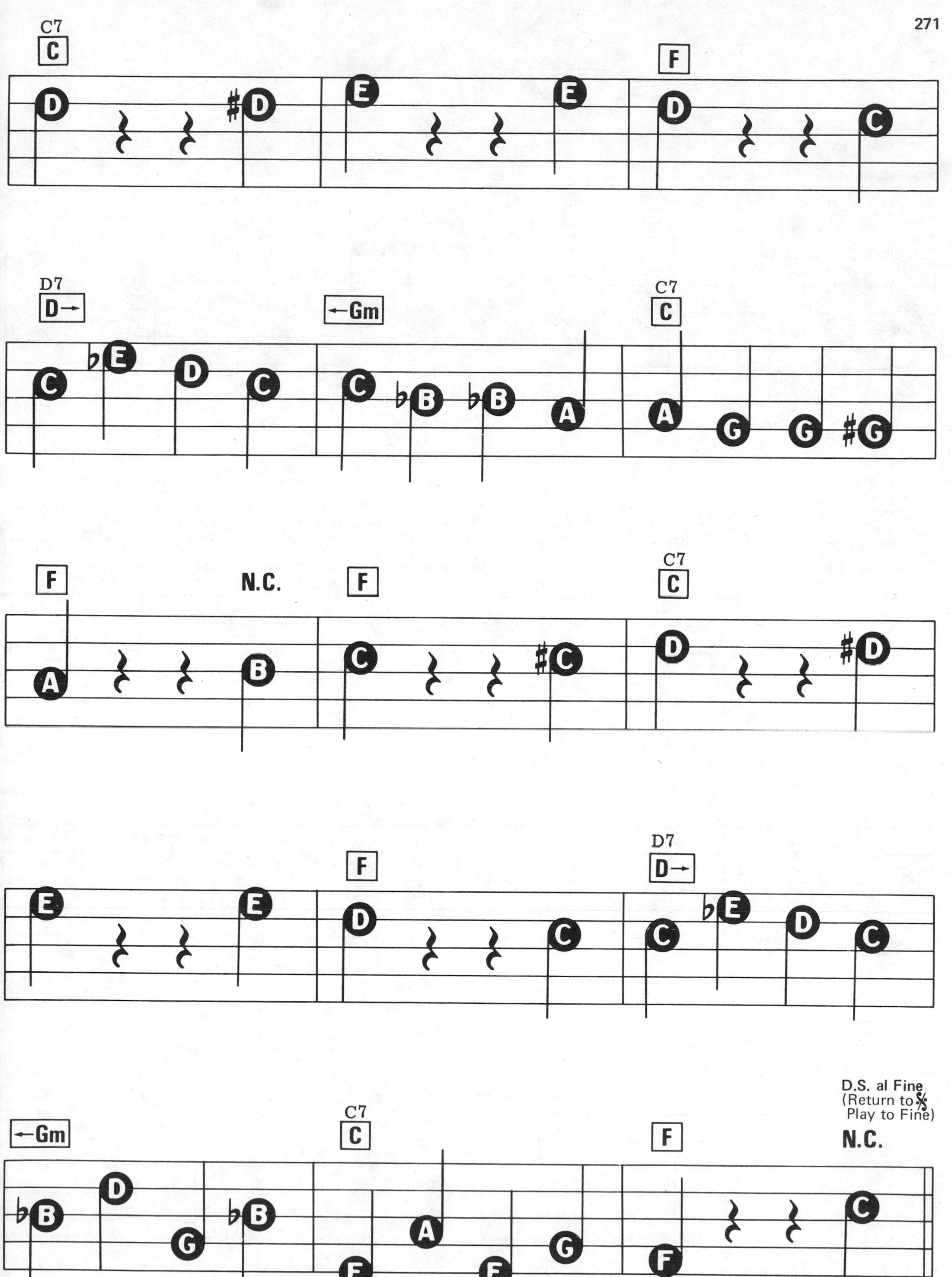
C7
C
F
D7
D→
←Gm
C7
C
F
N.C.
F
C7
C
F
D7
D→
←Gm
C7
C
F
D.S. al Fine
(Return to 𝄋
Play to Fine)
N.C.

Semper Fidelis

Registration 5

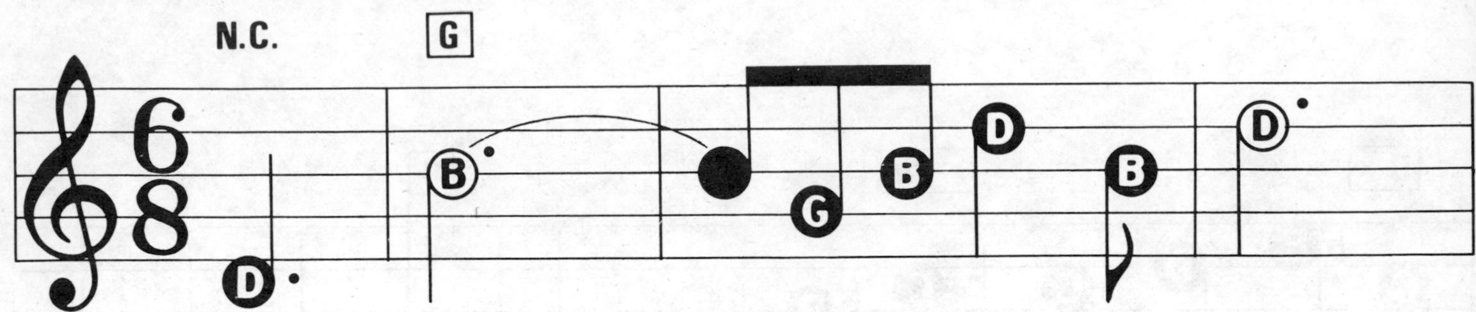

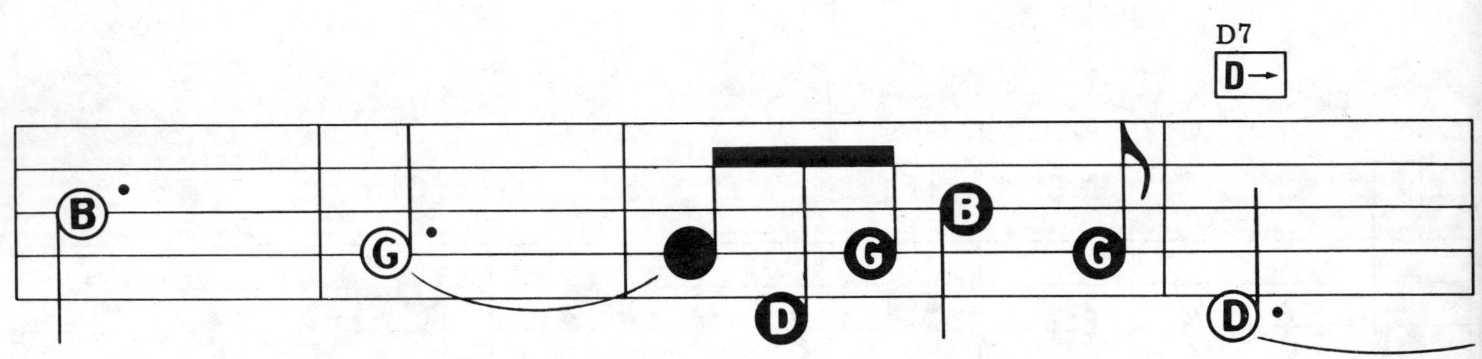

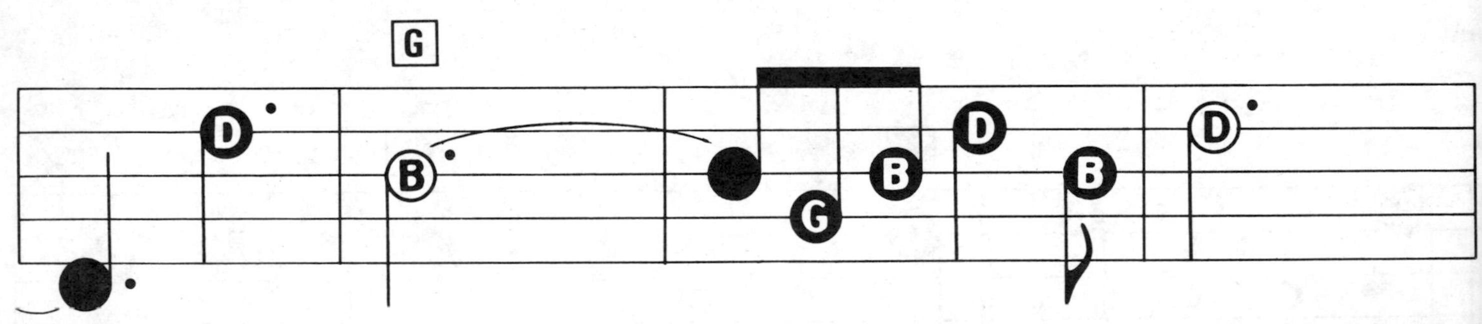

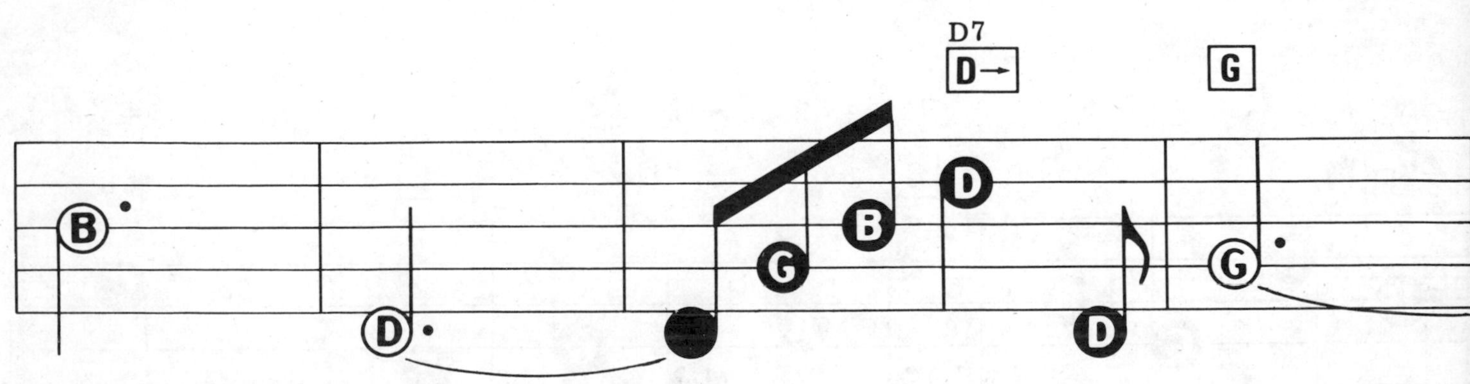

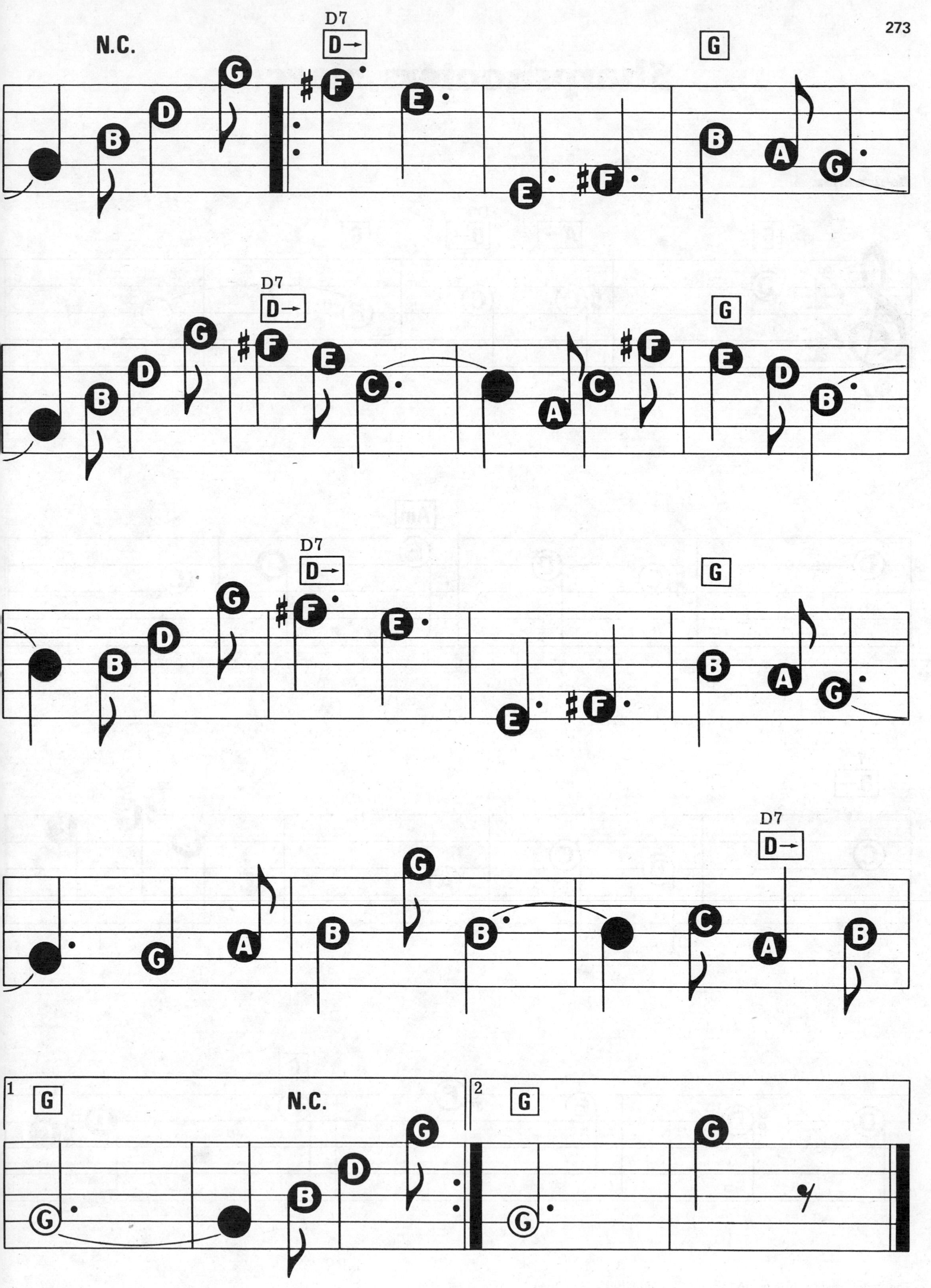
N.C.
D7
D→
G
D7
D→
G
D7
D→
G
D7
D→
1
G
N.C.
2
G

Sharpshooters March

Registration 4

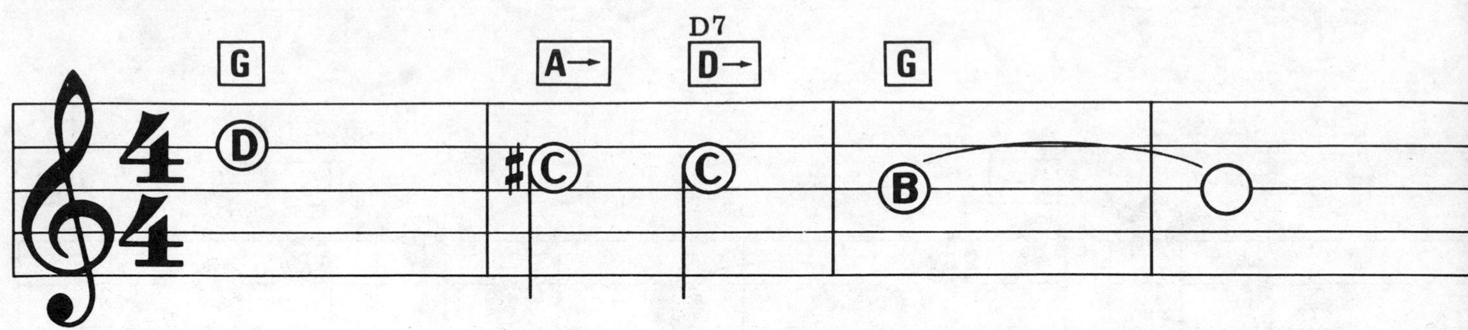

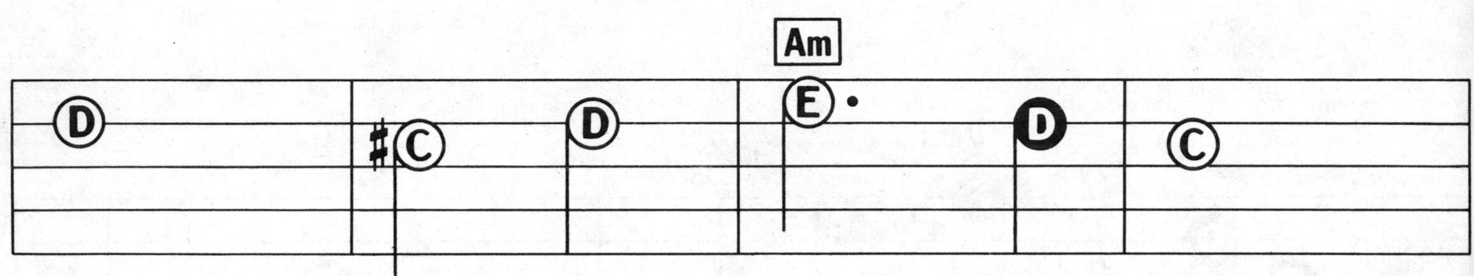

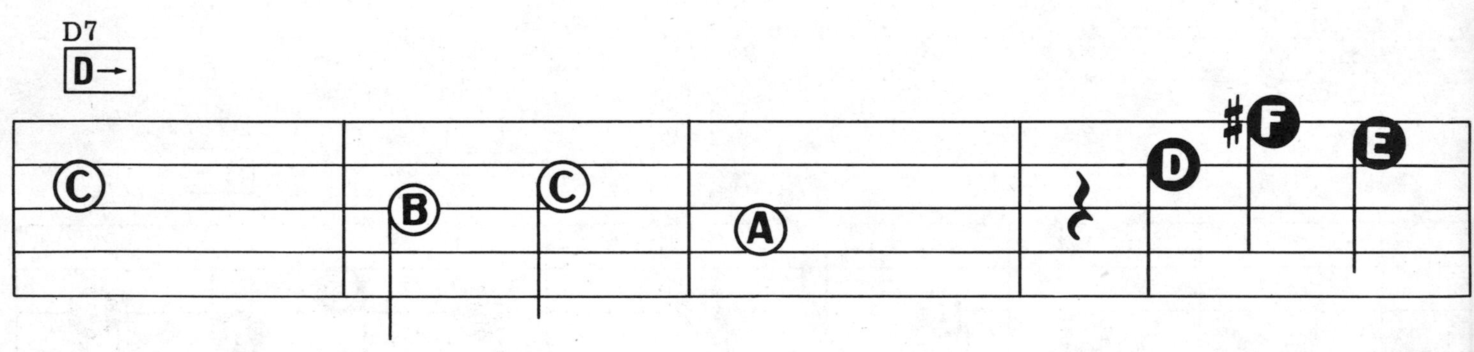

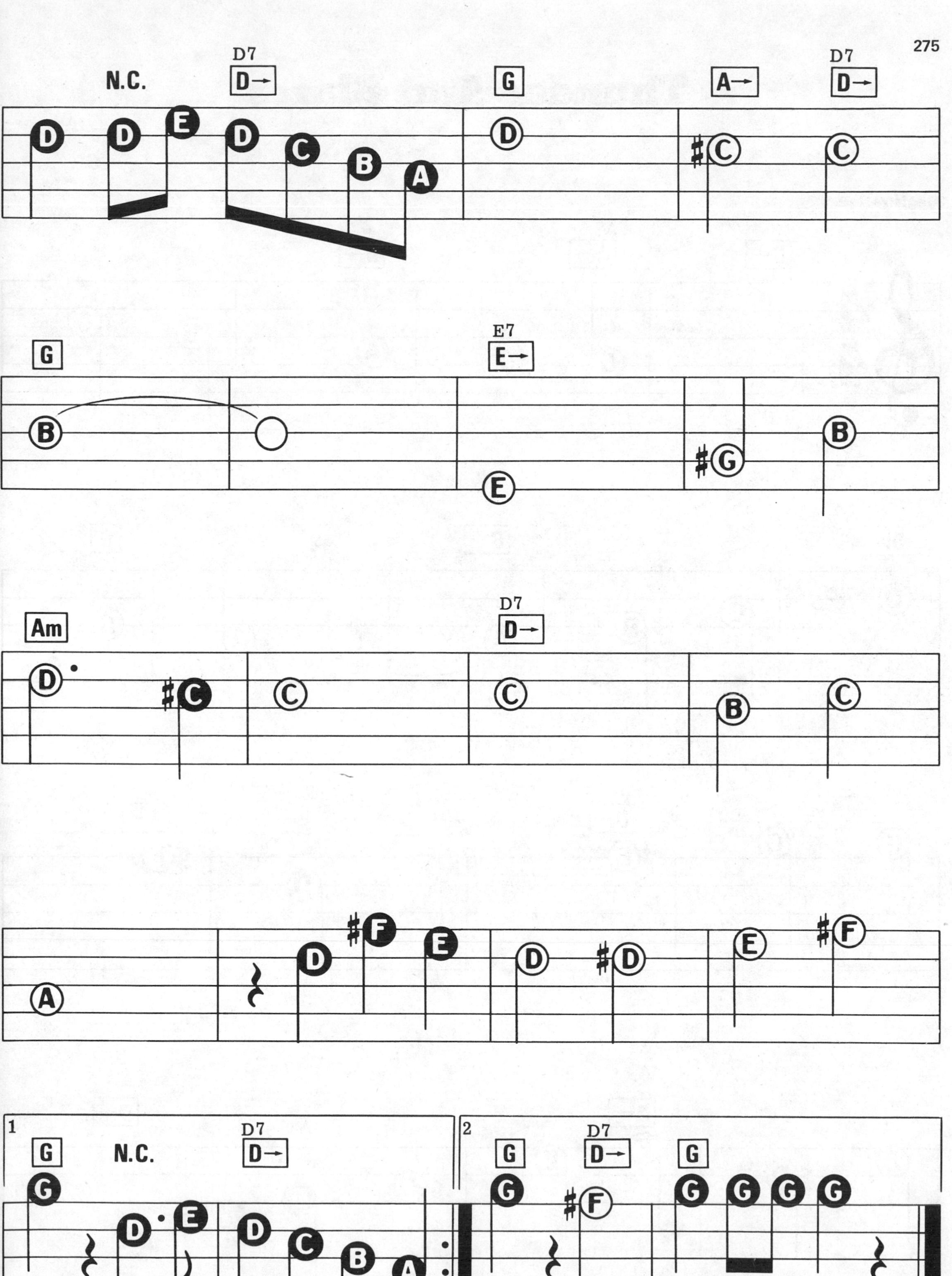
N.C. D7 D→ G A→ D7 D→
D D E D C B A D ♯C C
G E7 E→
B E ♯G B
Am D7 D→
D ♯C C C B C
A D ♯F E D ♯D E ♯F
1 G N.C. D7 D→
G D E D C B A
2 G D7 D→ G
G ♯F G G G G

Thunder And Blazes

Registration 5

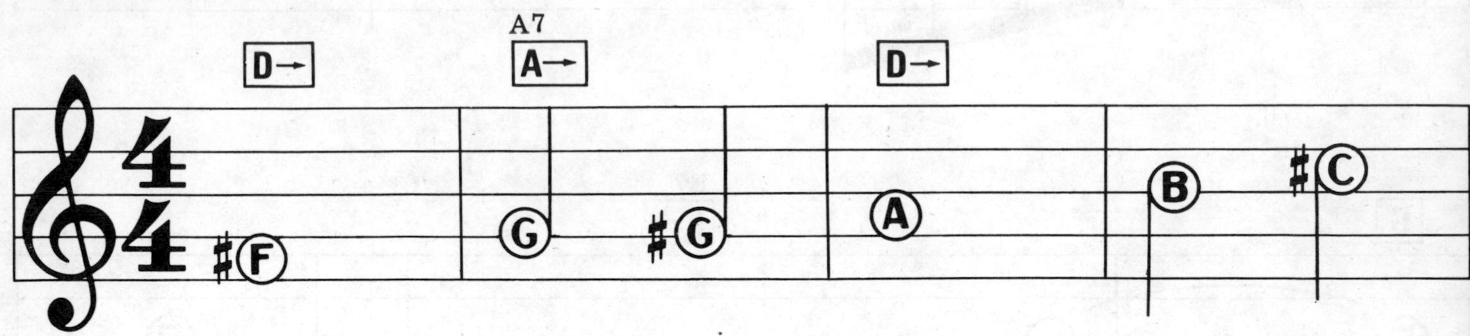

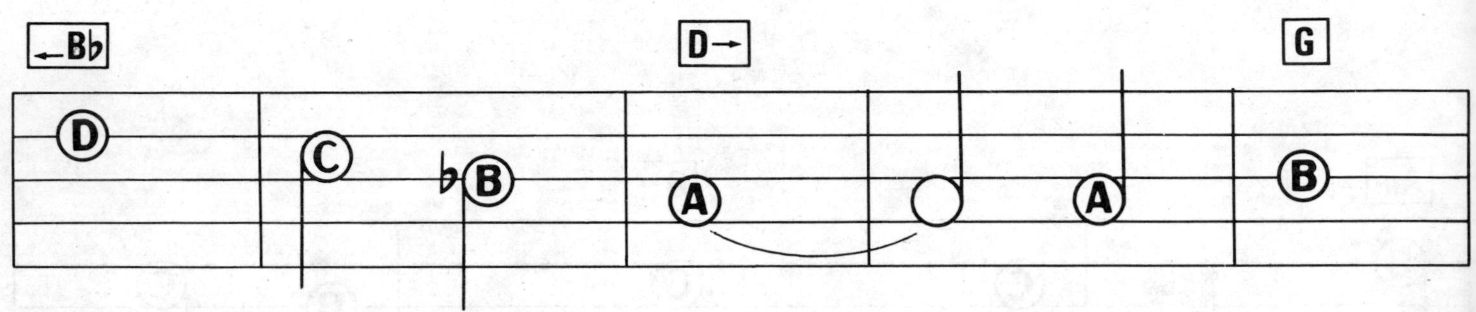

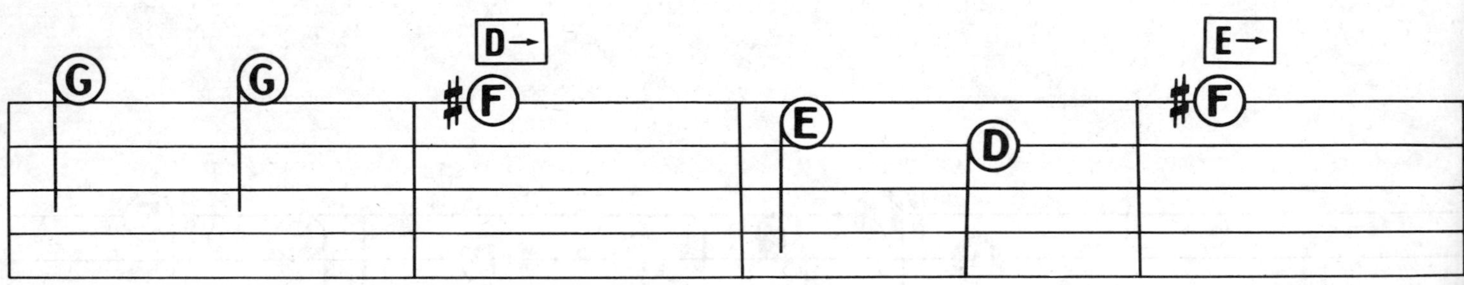

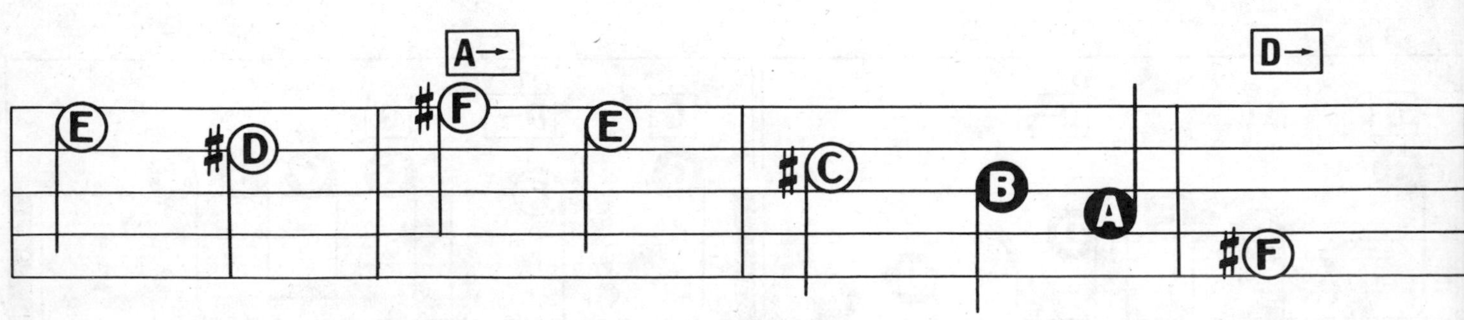

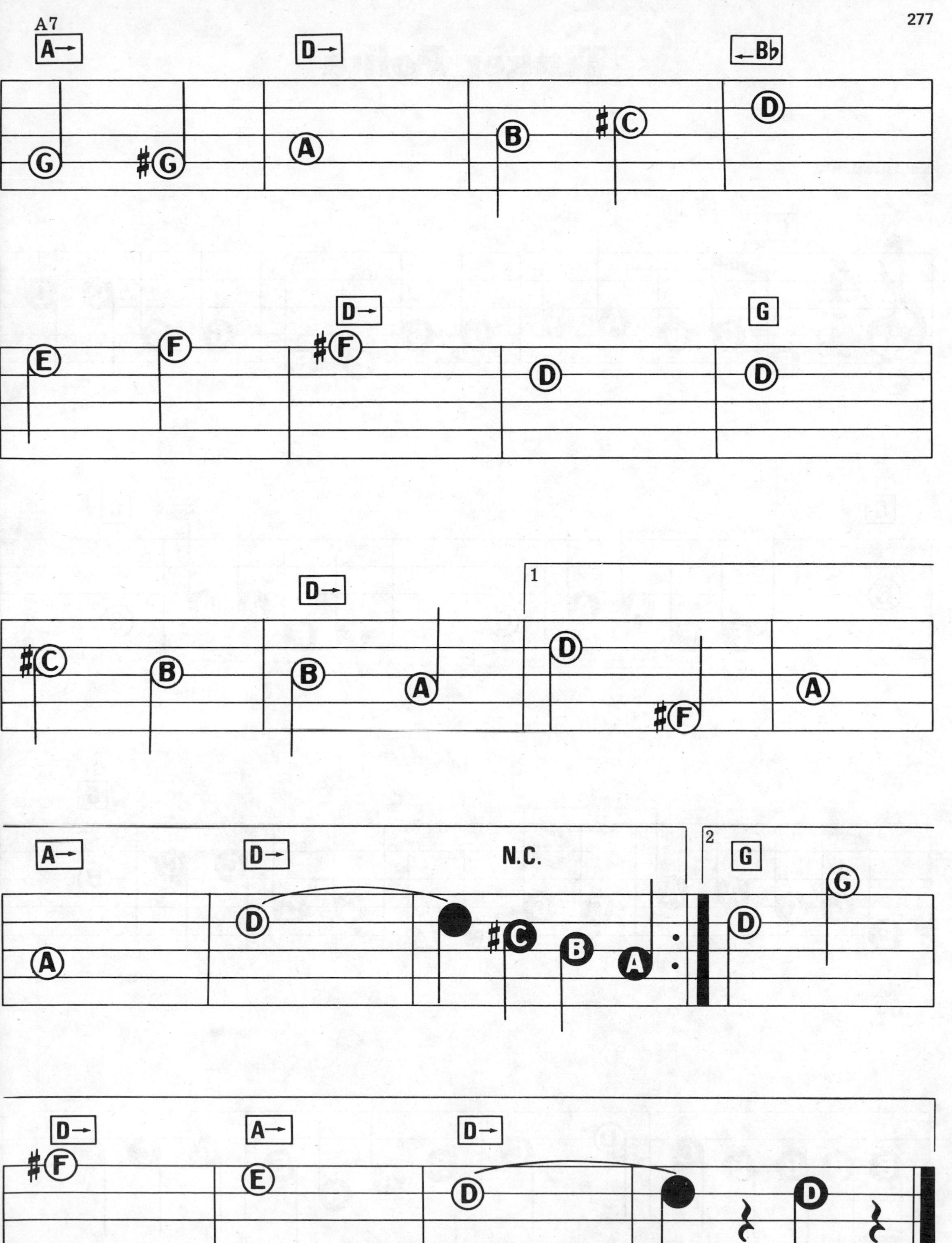
A7
A→
G
♯G
D→
A
B
♯C
←B♭
D
E
F
D→
♯F
D
G
D
♯C
B
D→
B
A
1
D
♯F
A
A→
A
D→
D
N.C.
♯C
B
A
2
G
D
G
D→
♯F
A→
E
D→
D
D

Tinker Polka

Registration 3

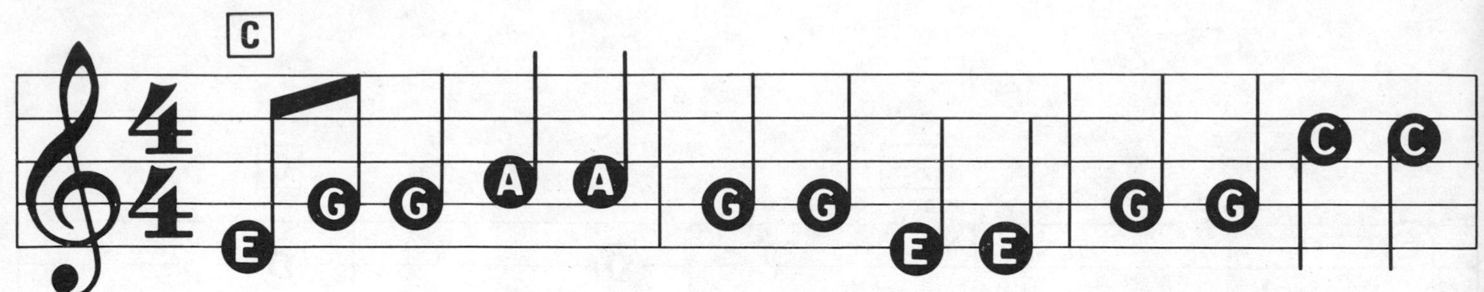

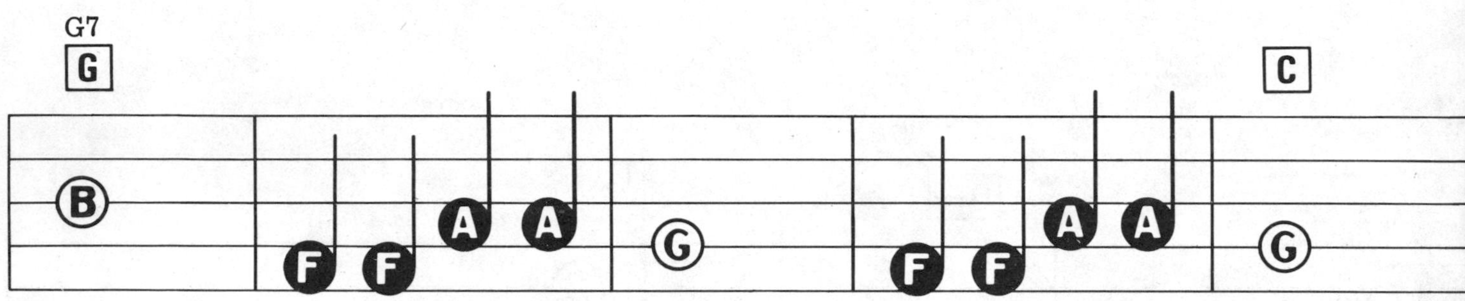

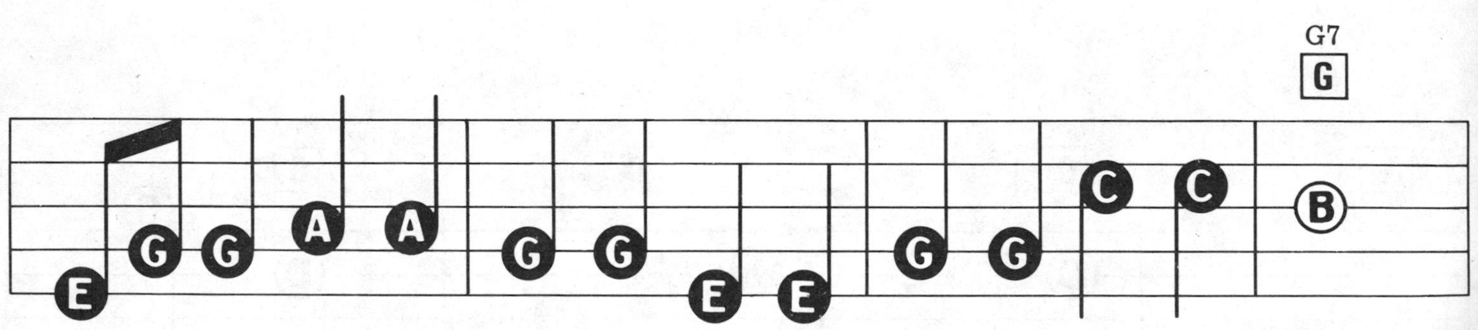

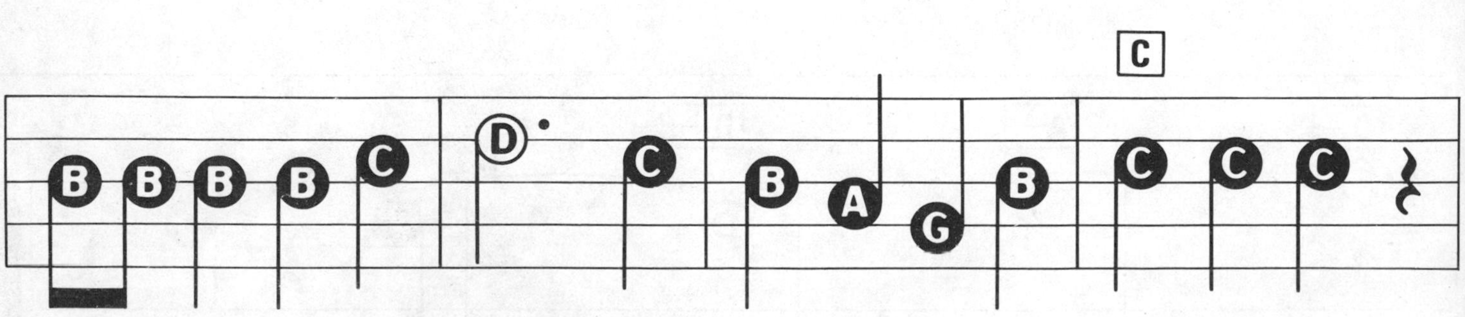

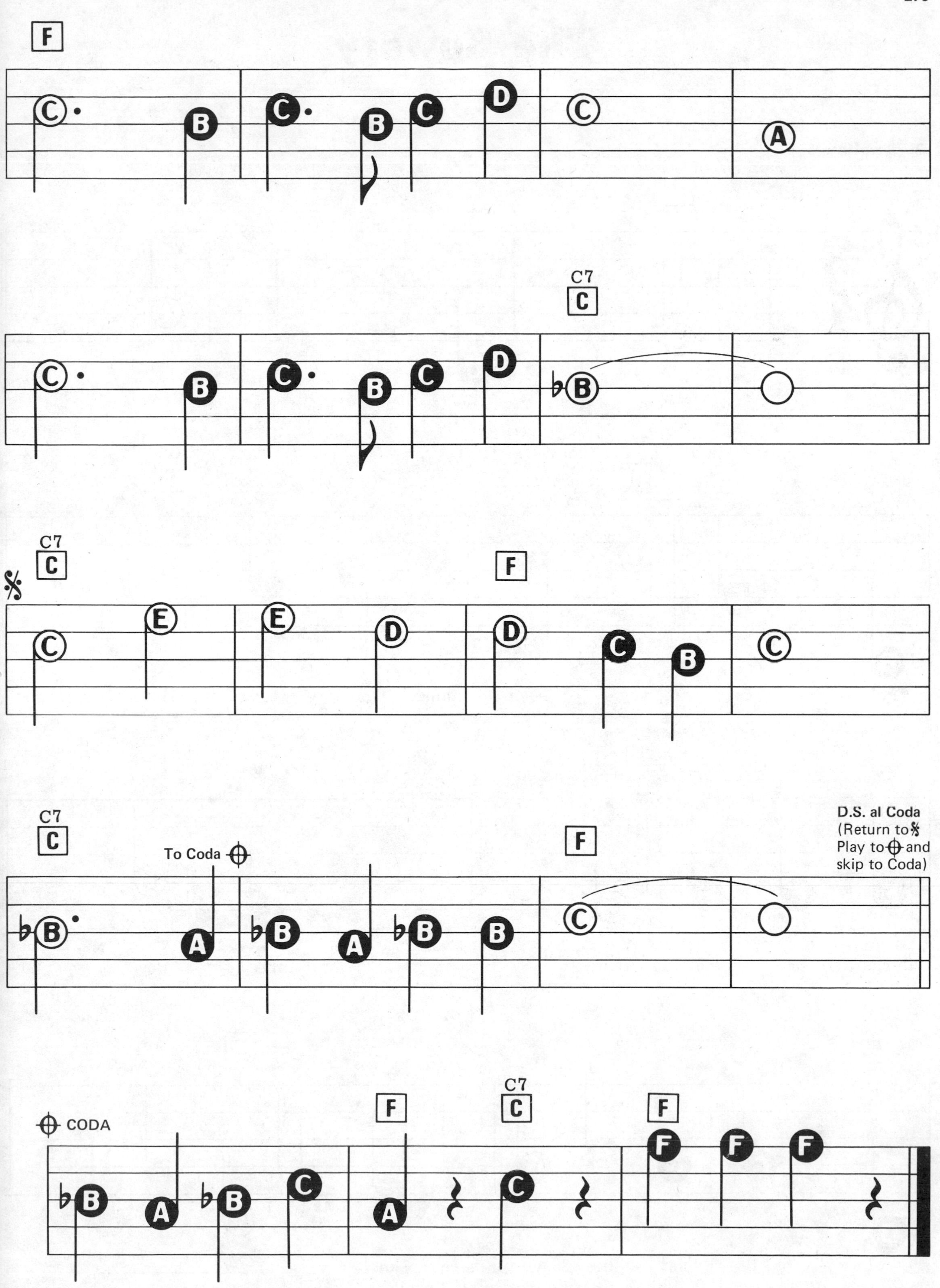
F
C
B
C
B
C
D
C
A
C
B
C
B
C
D
C7
C
♭B
C7
C
C
E
E
D
F
D
C
B
C
C7
C
♭B
To Coda
A
♭B
A
♭B
B
F
C
D.S. al Coda
(Return to 𝄋
Play to ⊕ and
skip to Coda)
⊕ CODA
♭B
A
♭B
C
F
A
C7
C
C
F
F
F
F

The Bowery

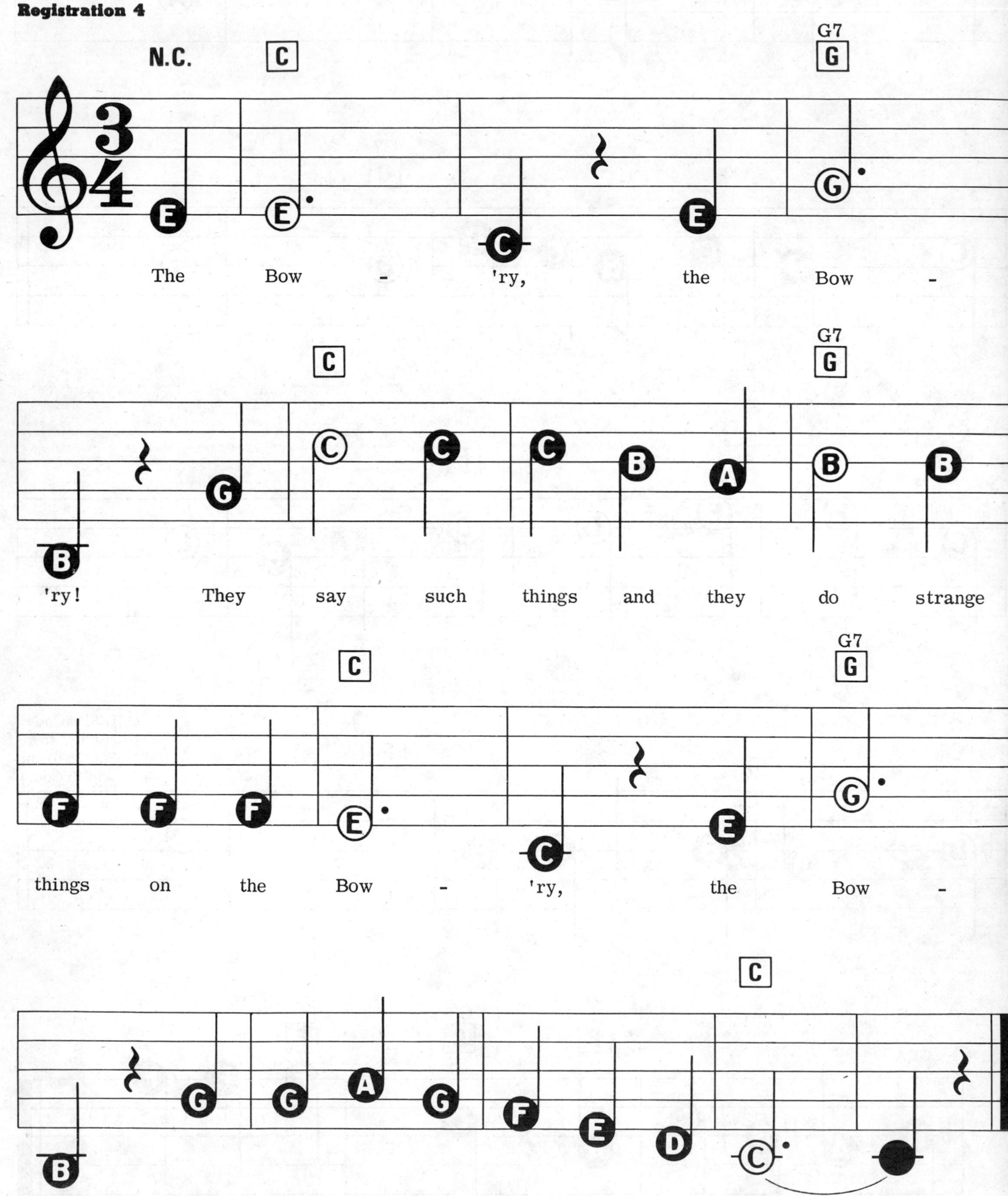
Registration 4
N.C.
C
G7
G
The Bow - 'ry, the Bow -
'ry! They say such things and they do strange
things on the Bow - 'ry, the Bow -
'ry! I'll nev - er go there an - y - more.

Dolores Waltz

Registration 2

Estudiantina

Registration 3

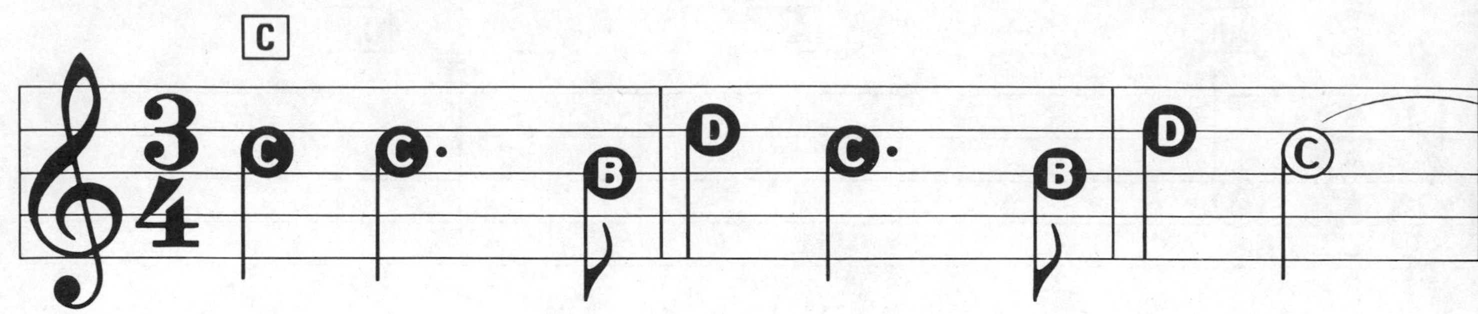

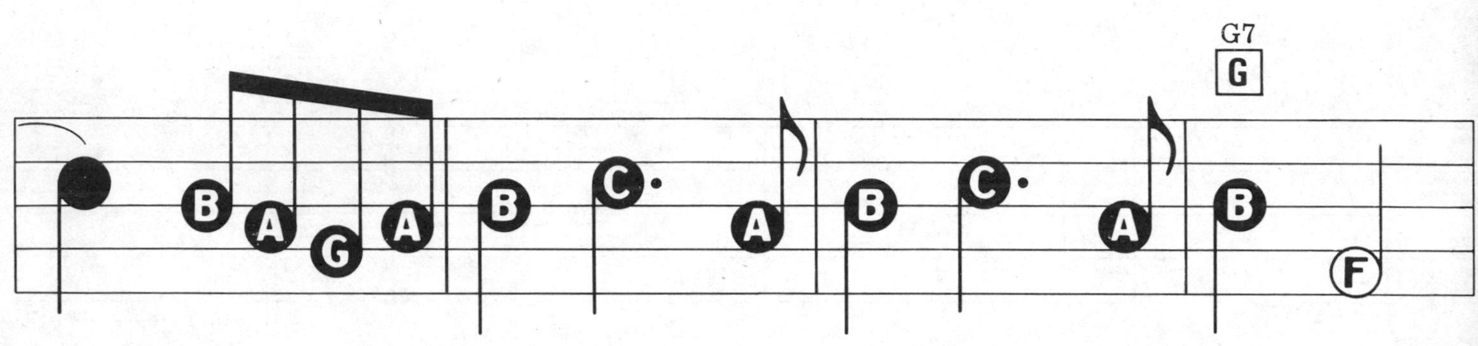

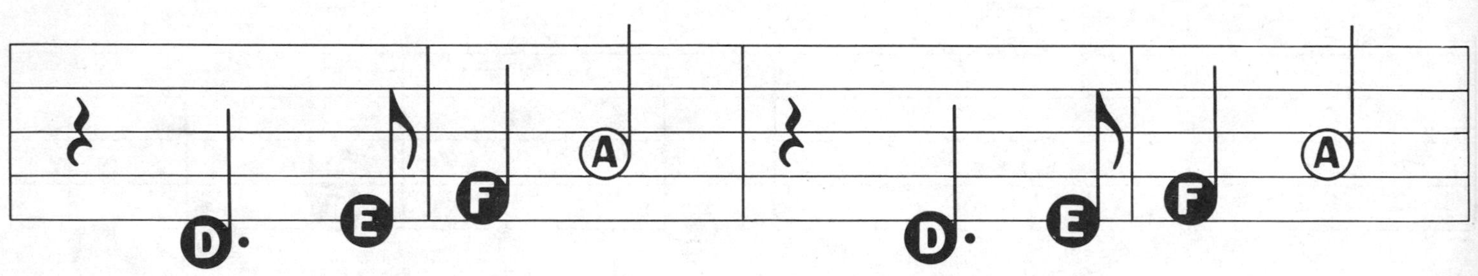

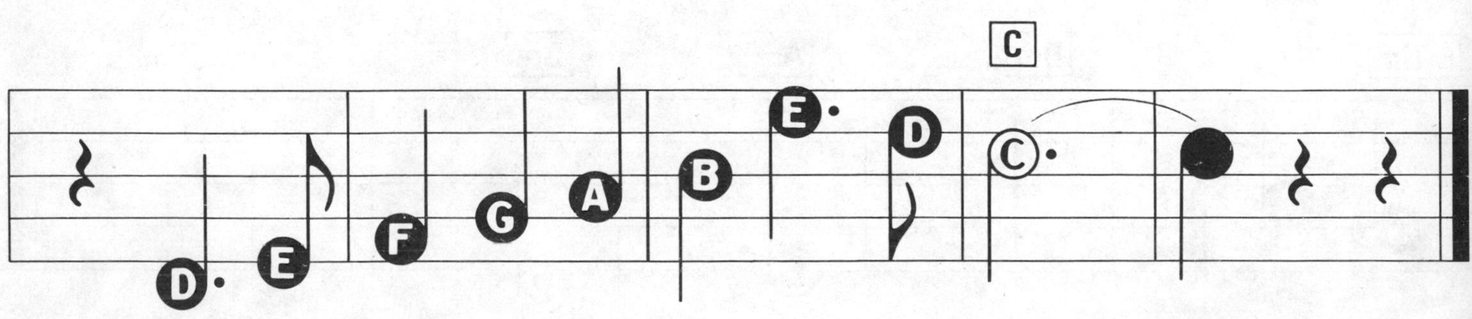

Marguerite Waltz

Registration 5

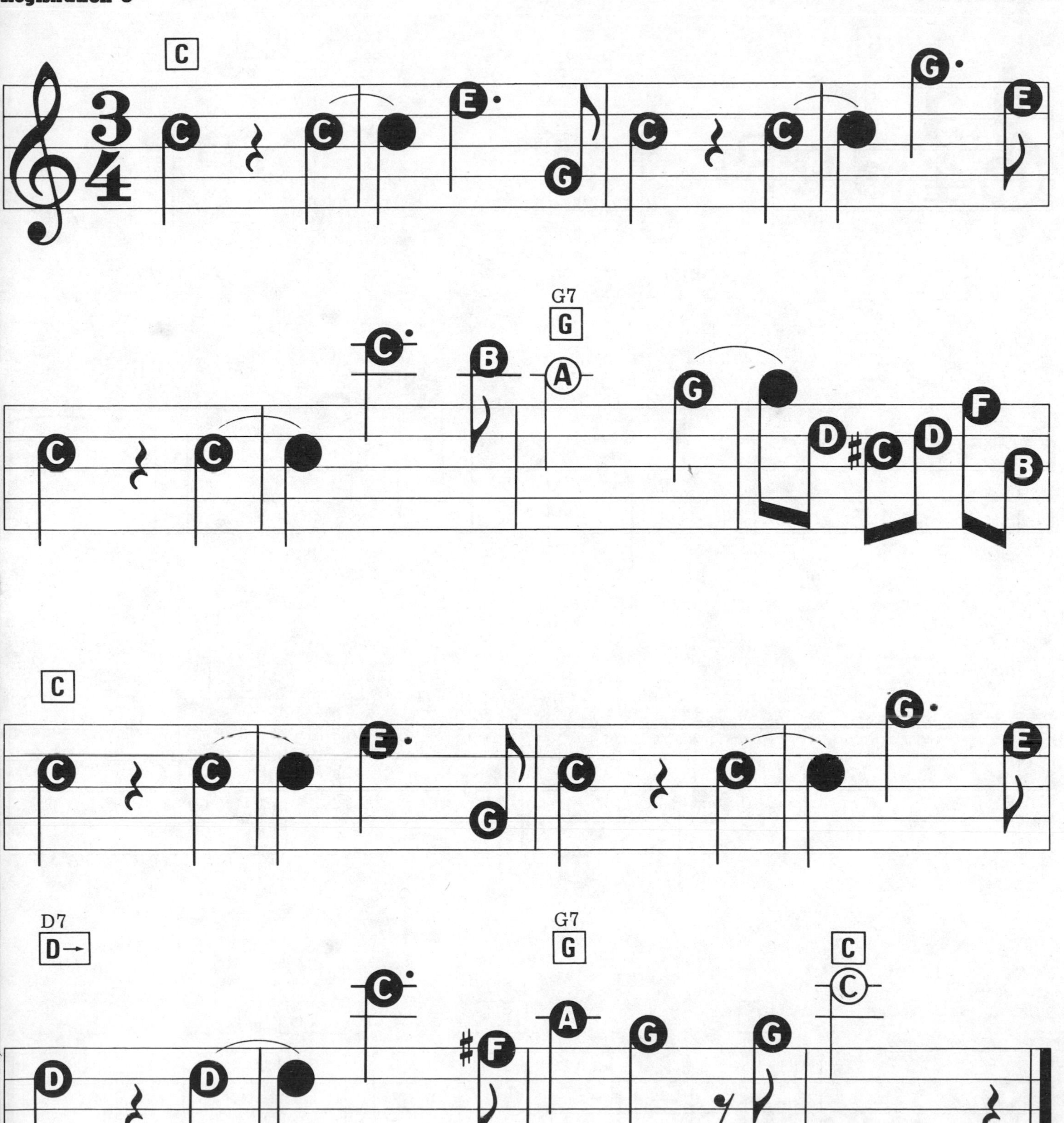

My Dear Marquis

Registration 4

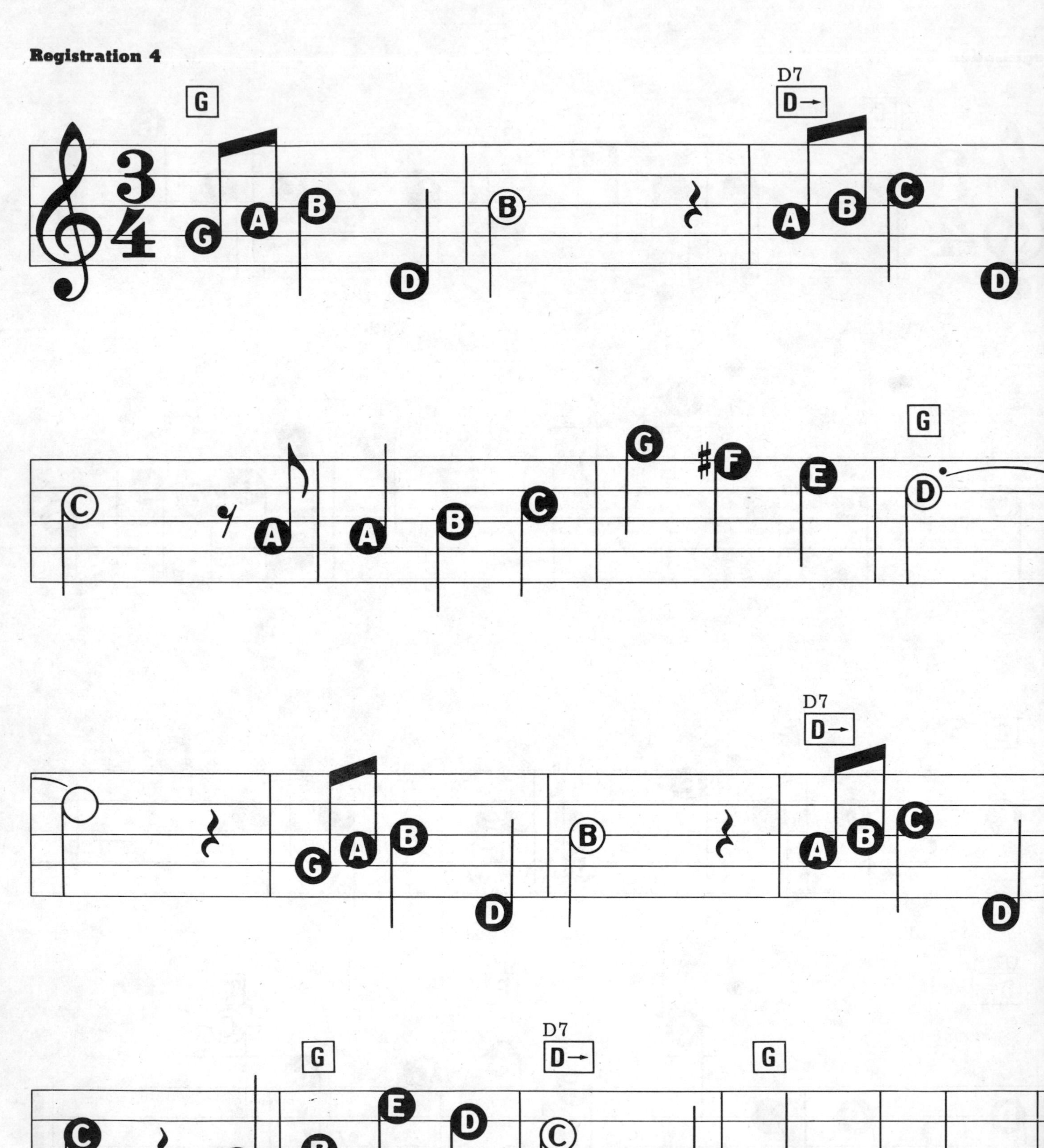

Treasure Waltz

Registration 4

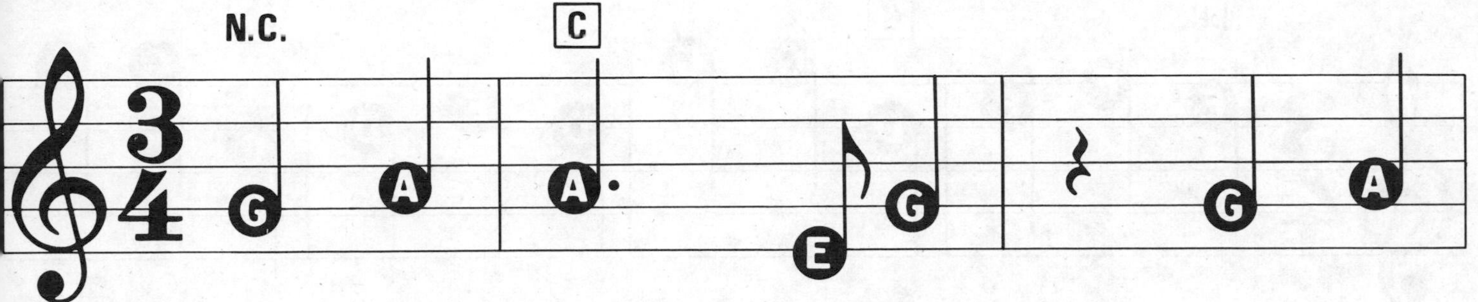

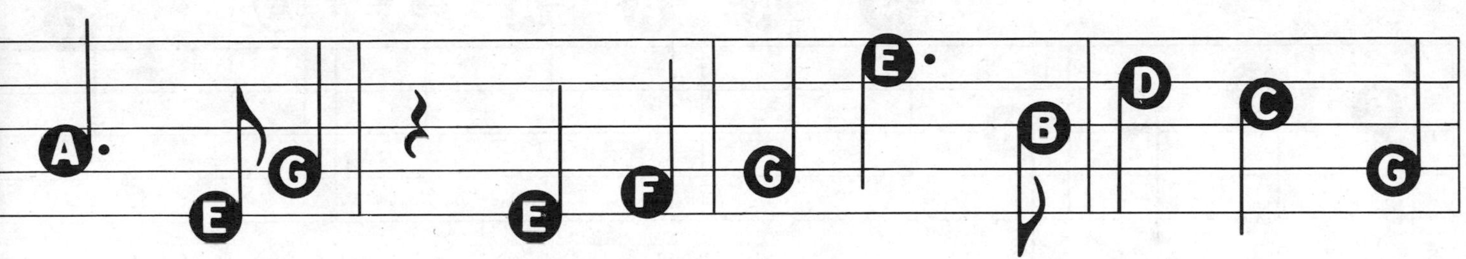

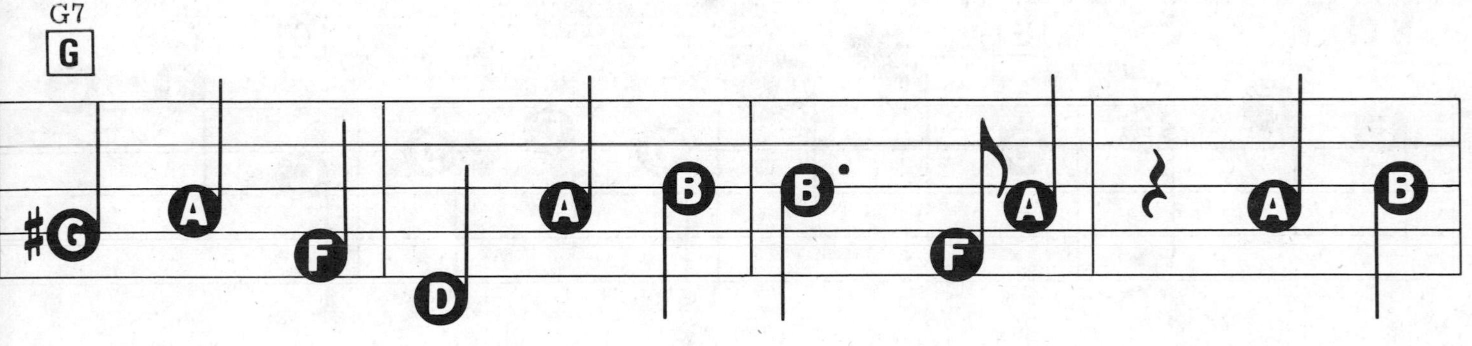

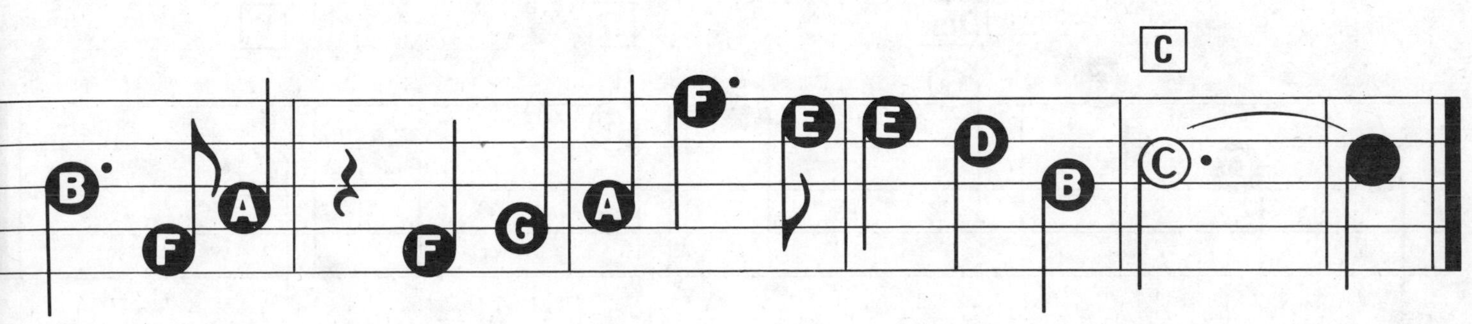

Wine, Women And Song

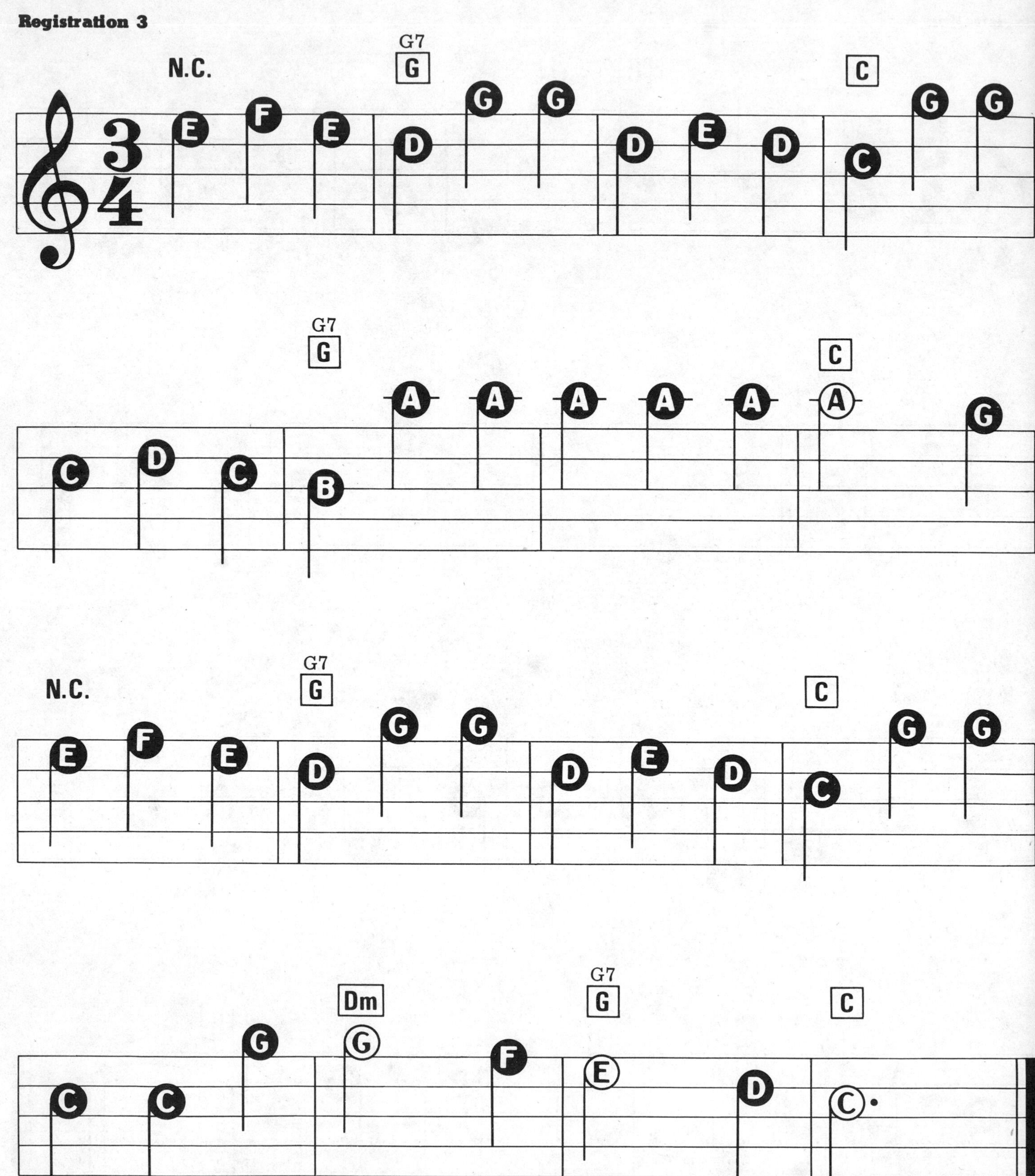

Waltz Of The Flowers

Registration 6

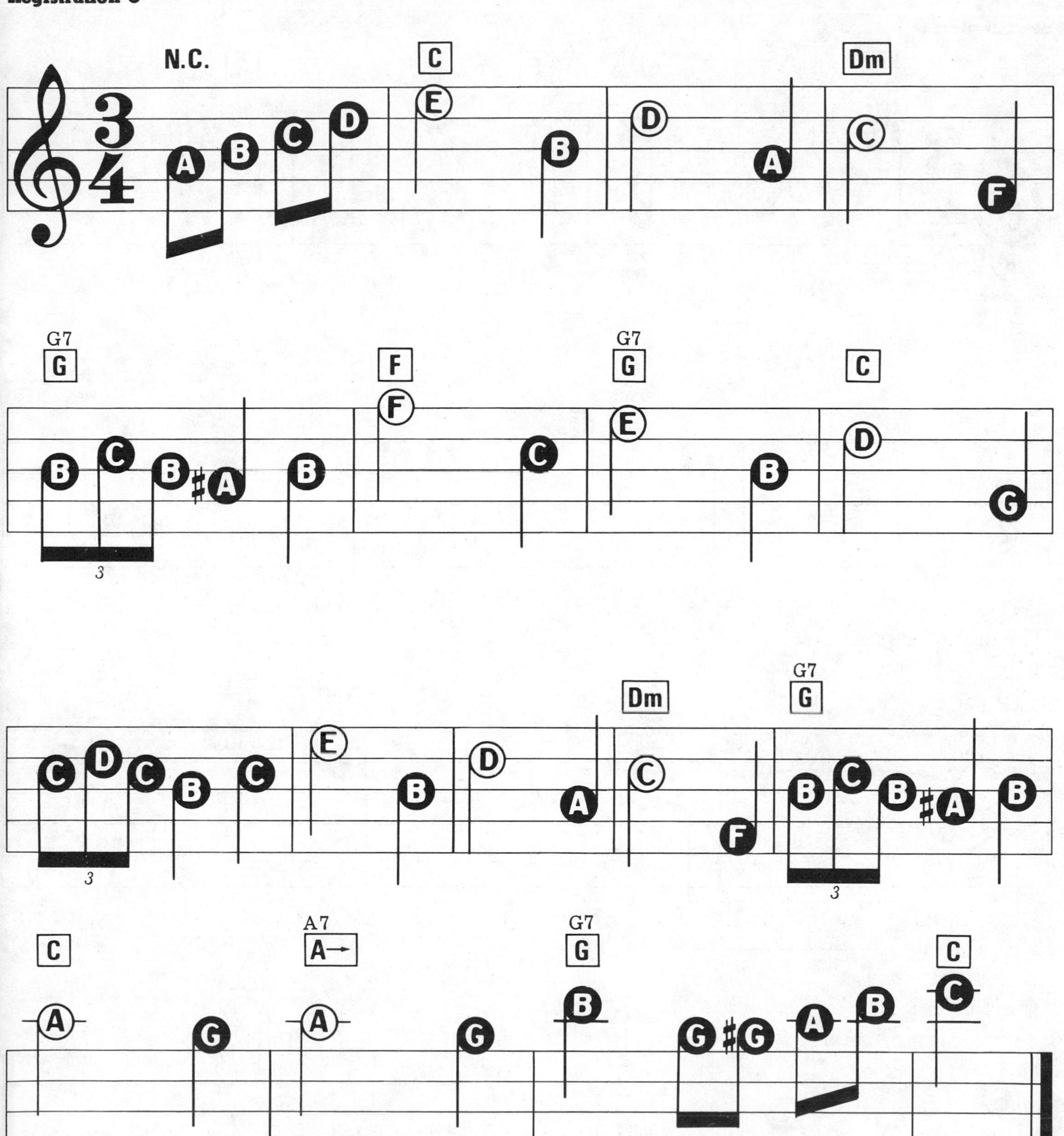

After The Ball

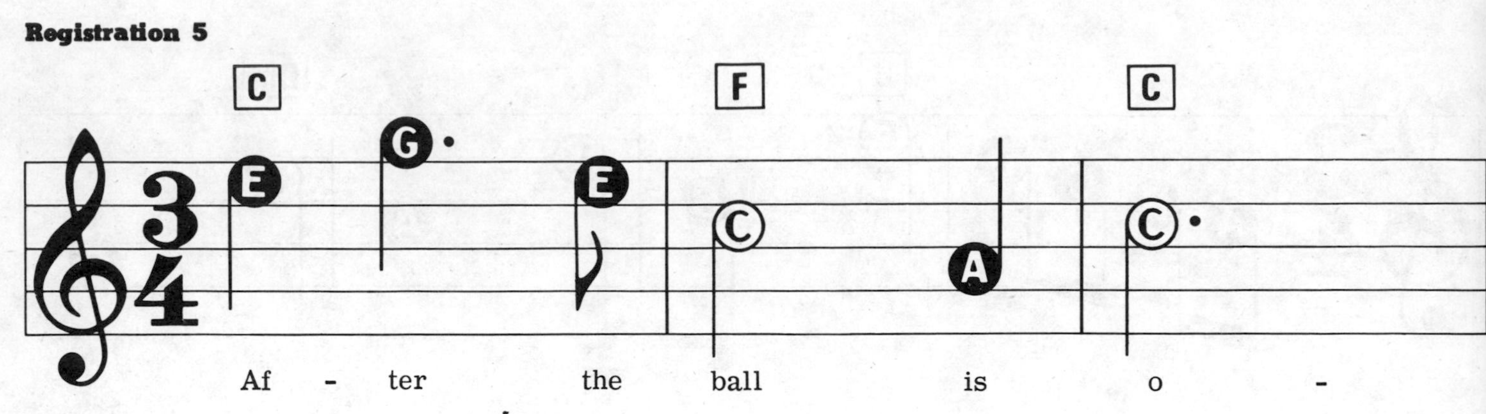

G
E
G
E
C
A
ver, Af - ter the break of

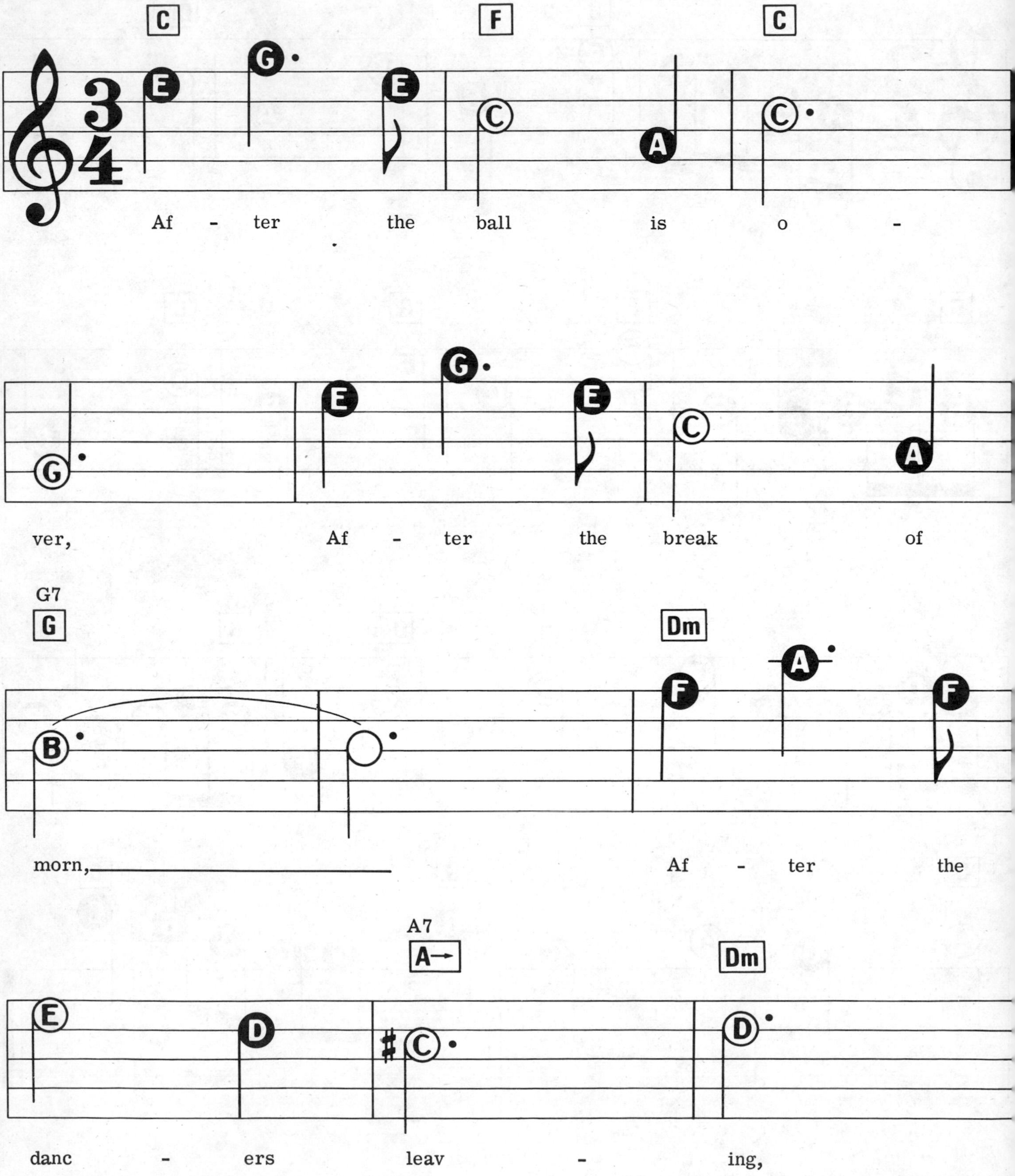

G7
G
Dm
B
F
A
F
morn, Af - ter the

A7
A→
Dm
E
D
♯C
D
danc - ers leav - ing,

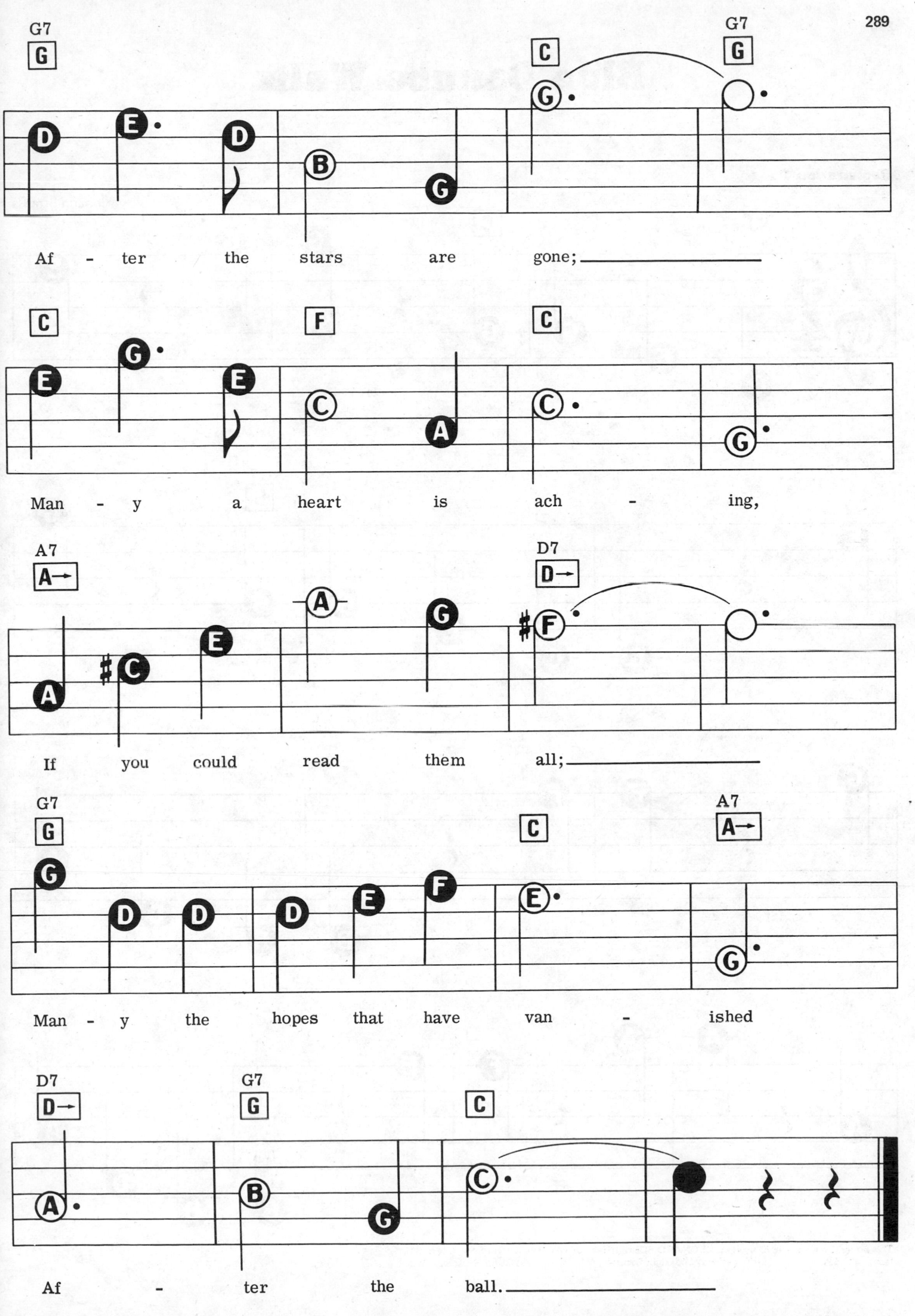

G7 G C G7 G
D E D B G G
Af - ter the stars are gone;
C F C
E G E C A C G
Man - y a heart is ach - ing,
A7 A→ D7 D→
A C E A G F
If you could read them all;
G7 G C A7 A→
G D D D E F E G
Man - y the hopes that have van - ished
D7 D→ G7 G C
A B G C
Af - ter the ball.

Blue Danube Waltz

Registration 2

Johann Strauss

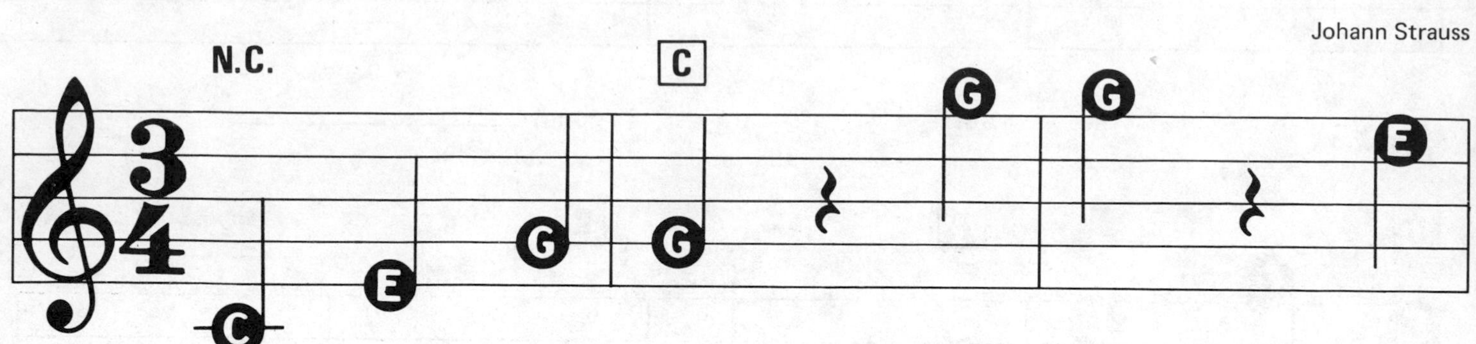

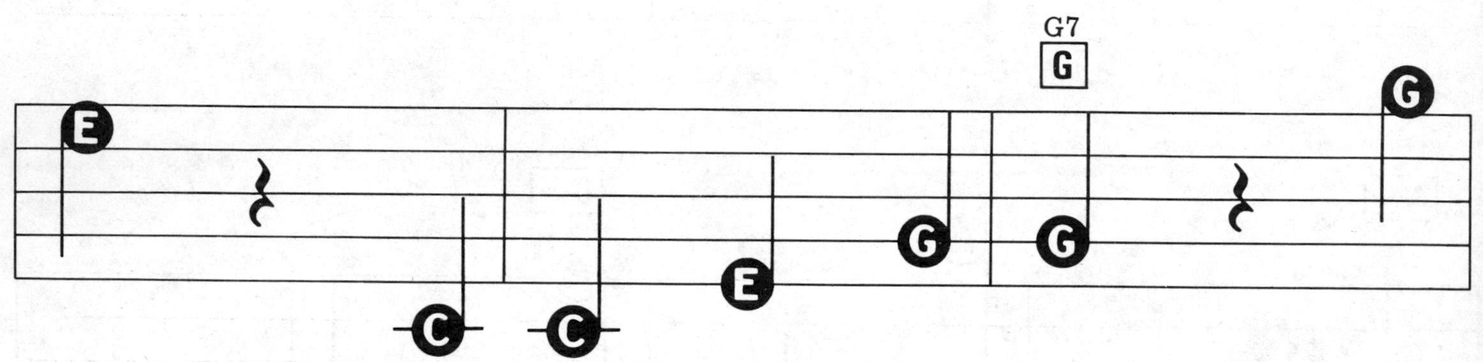

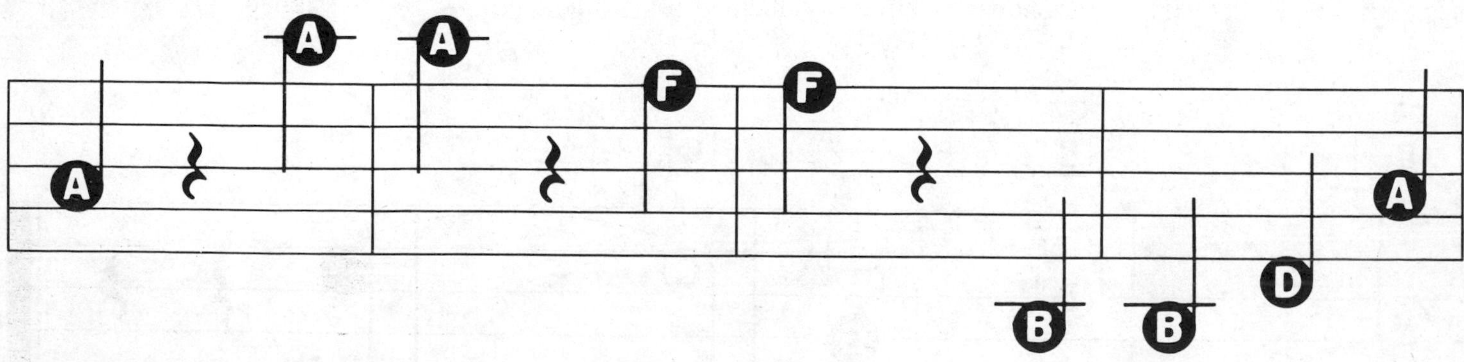

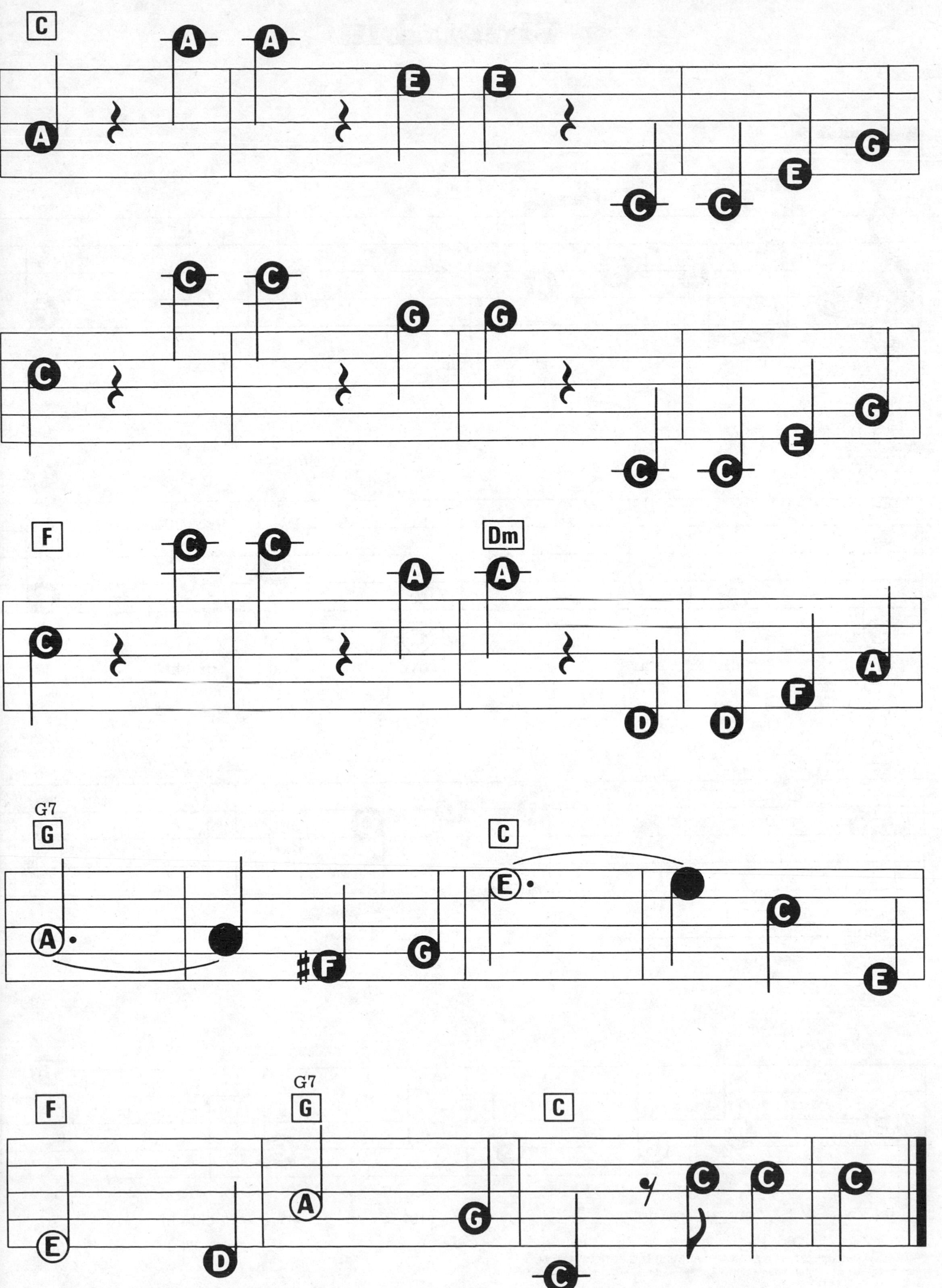
C
A A A E E C C E G
C C C G G C C E G
F Dm
C C C A A D D F A
G7 G C
A ♯F G E C E
F G7 G C
E D A G C C C C

Ciribiribin

Registration 9

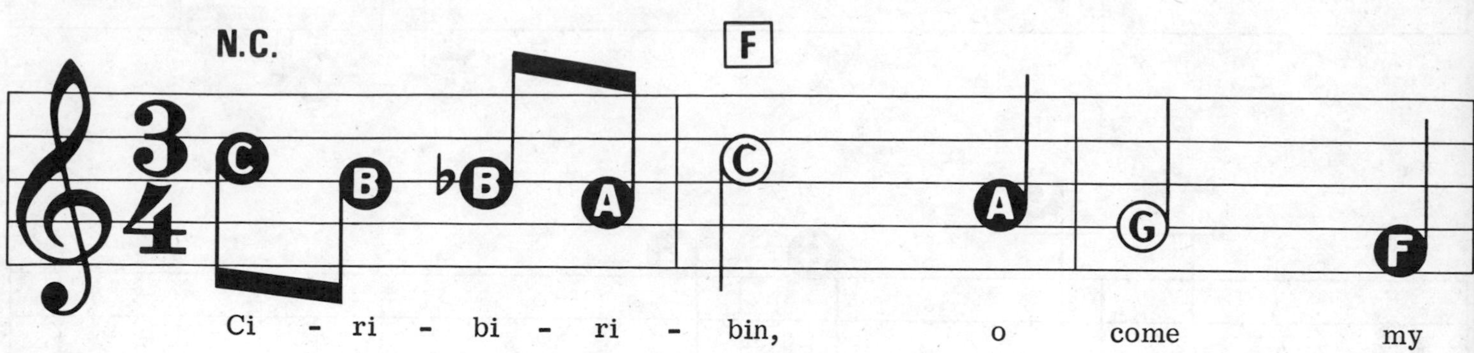

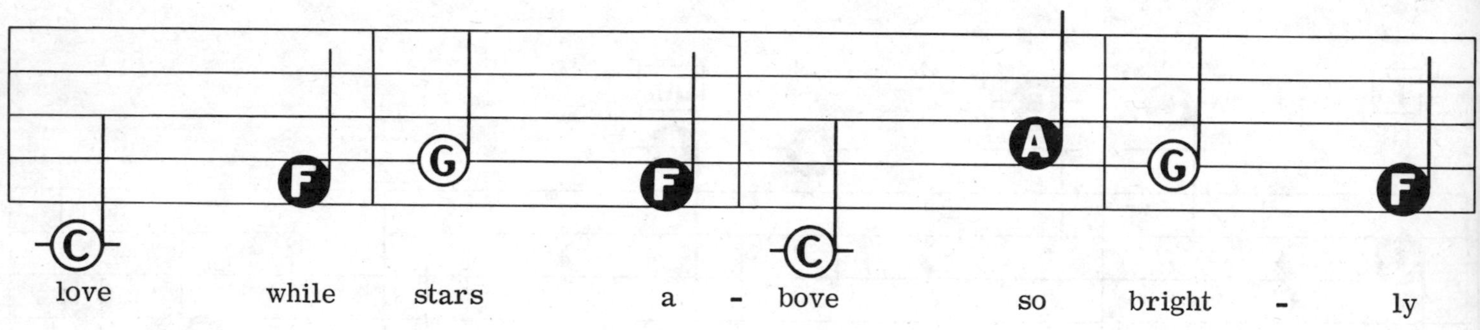

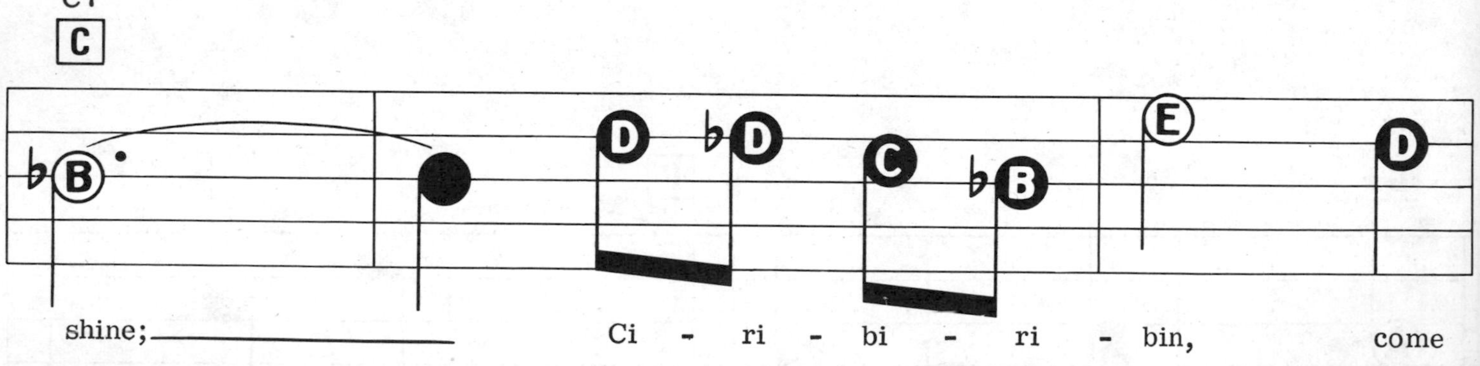

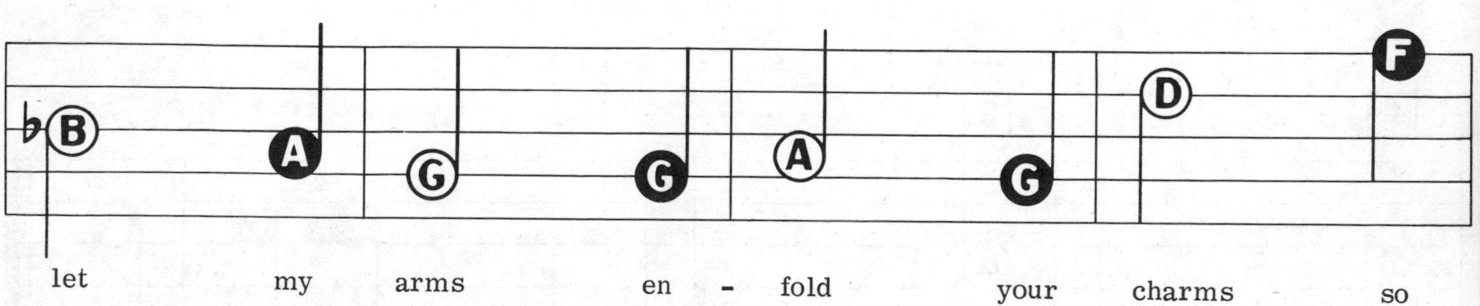

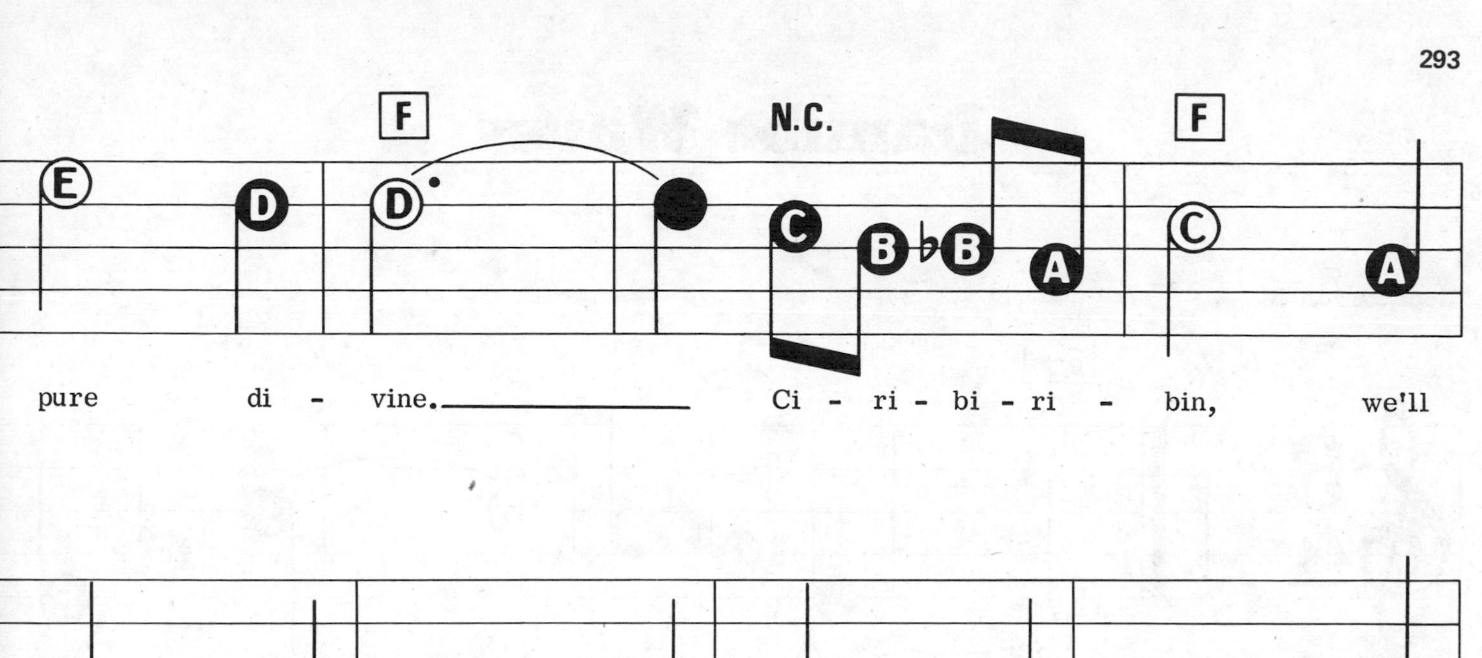
F
N.C.
F
E D D C B ♭B A C A
pure di - vine. Ci - ri - bi - ri - bin, we'll

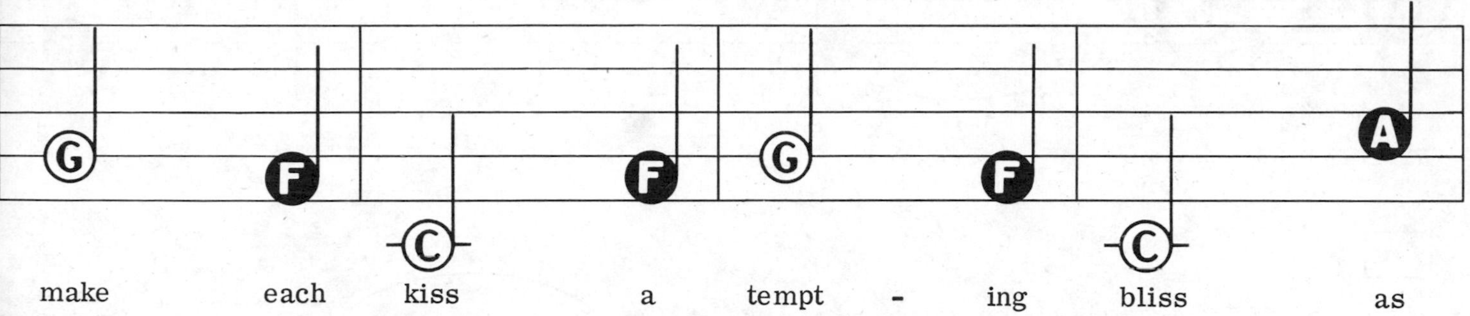
G F C F G F C A
make each kiss a tempt - ing bliss as

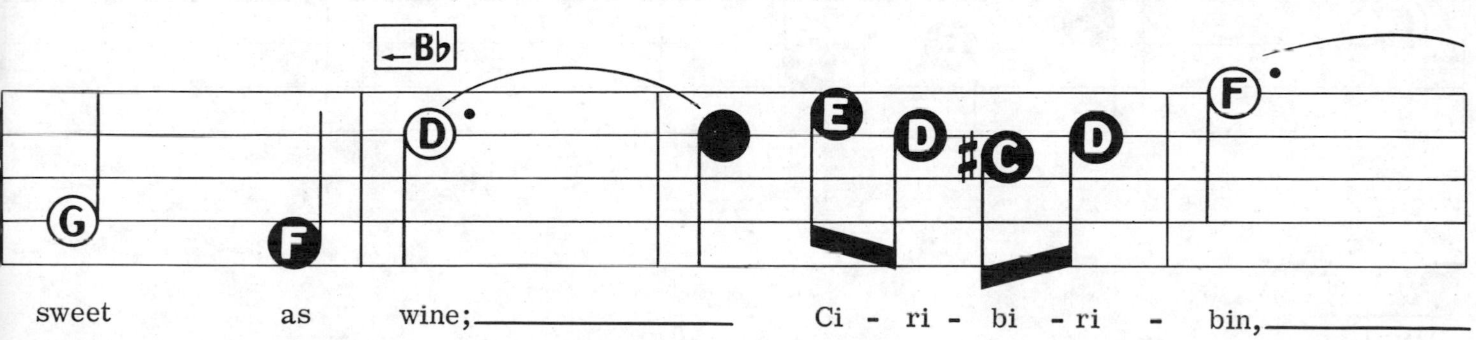
←B♭
G F D E D ♯C D F
sweet as wine; Ci - ri - bi - ri - bin,

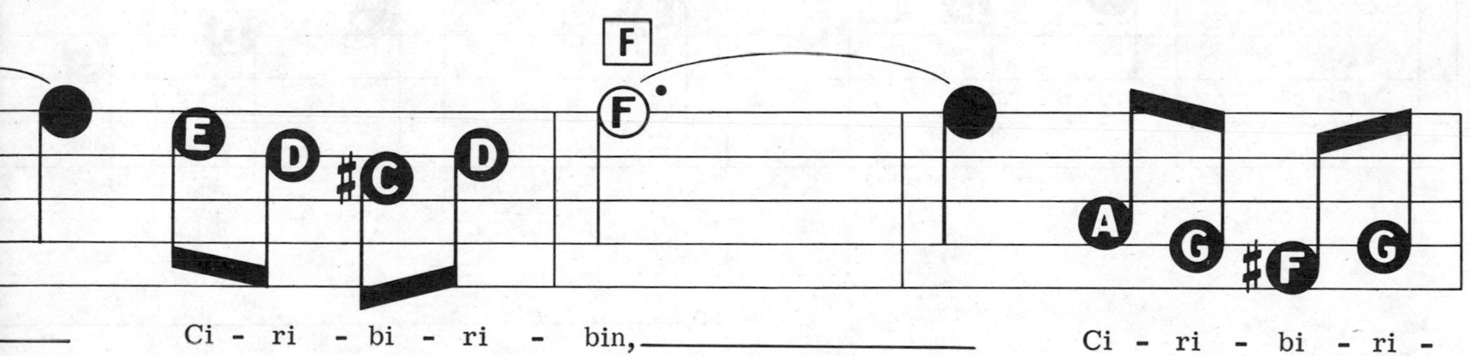
F
E D ♯C D F A G ♯F G
Ci - ri - bi - ri - bin, Ci - ri - bi - ri -

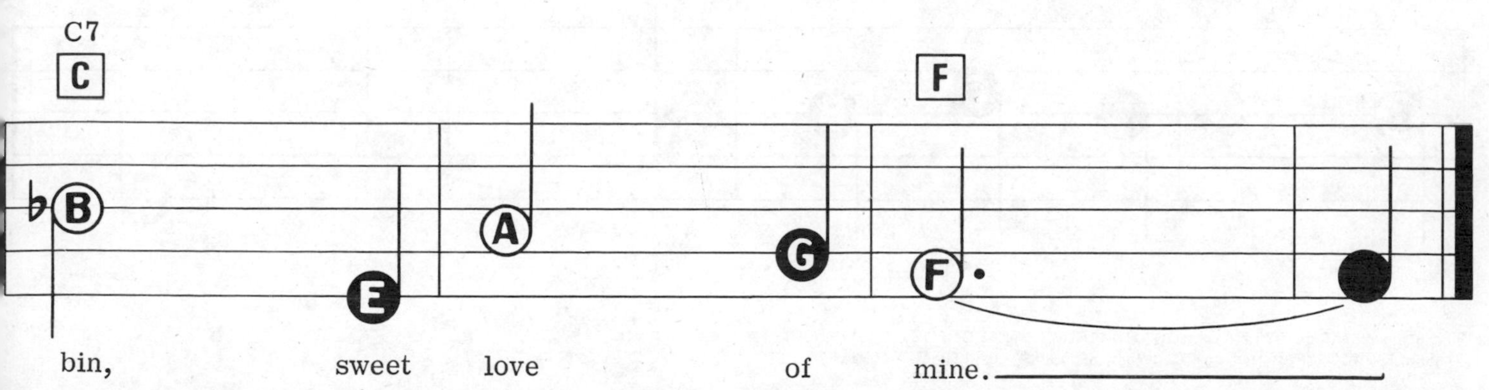
C7
C
F
♭B E A G F
bin, sweet love of mine.

Danube Waves

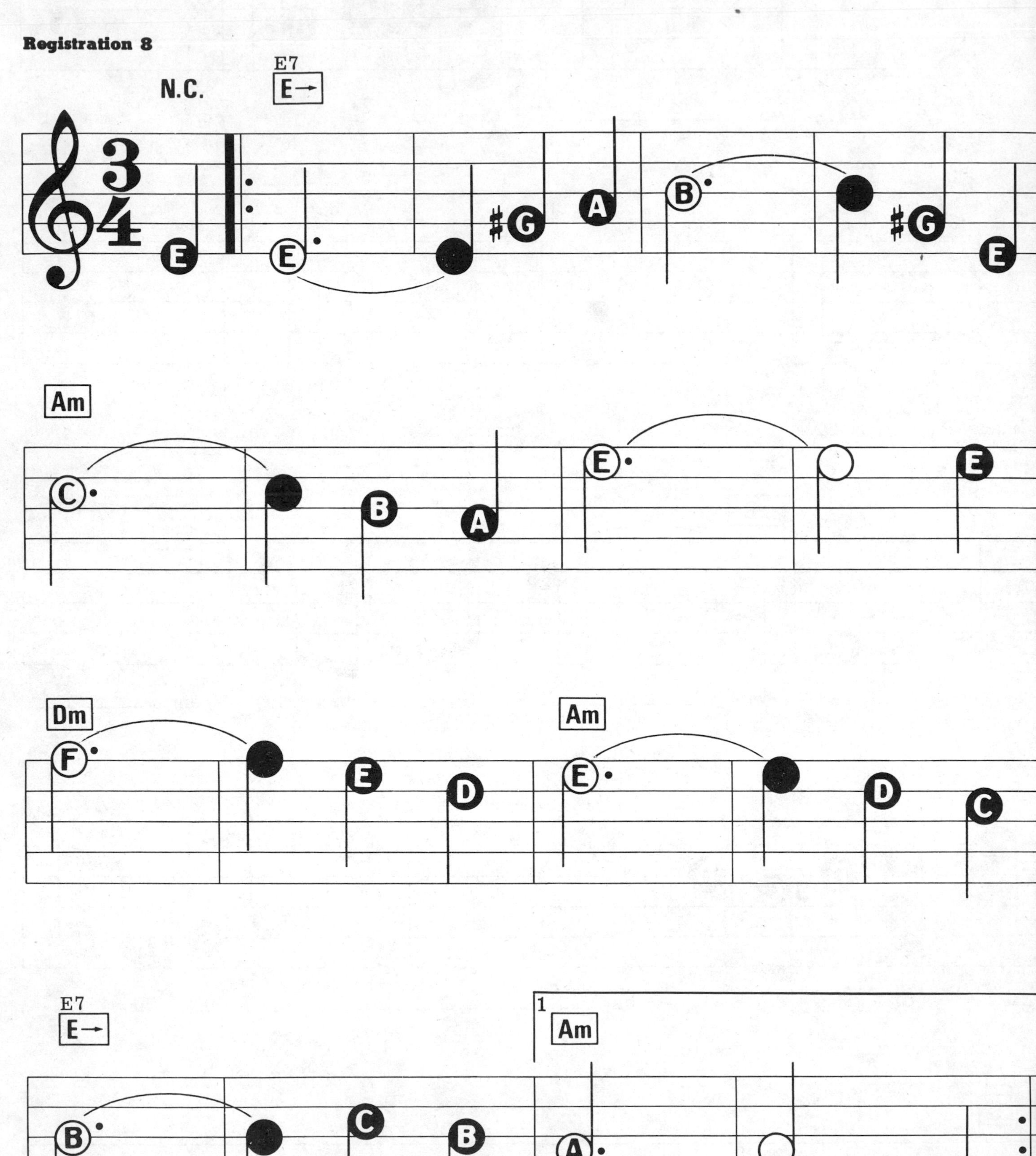

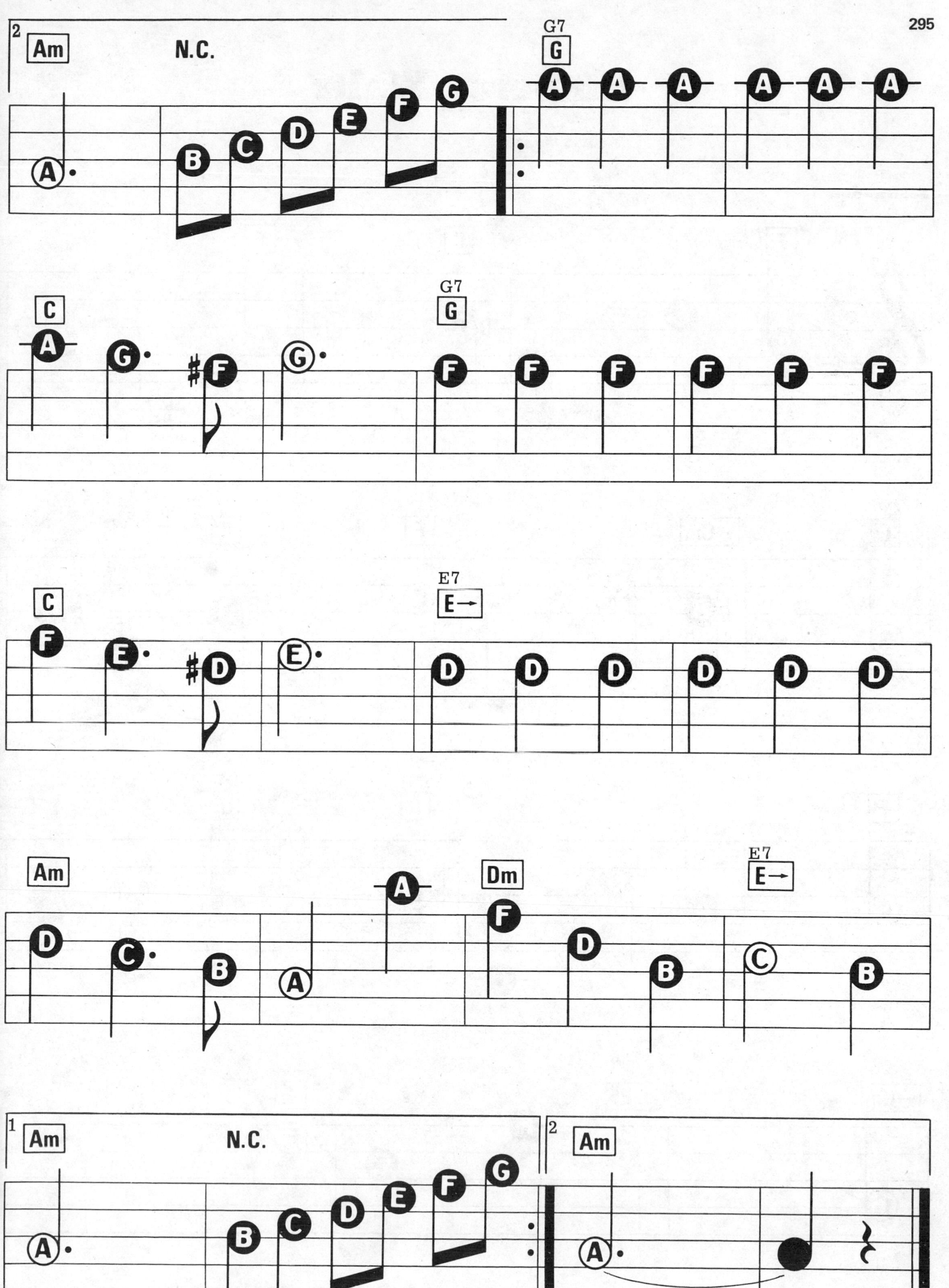
2
Am
N.C.
G7
G
C
G7
G
C
E7
E→
Am
Dm
E7
E→
1
Am
N.C.
2
Am

Emperor Waltz

Registration 3

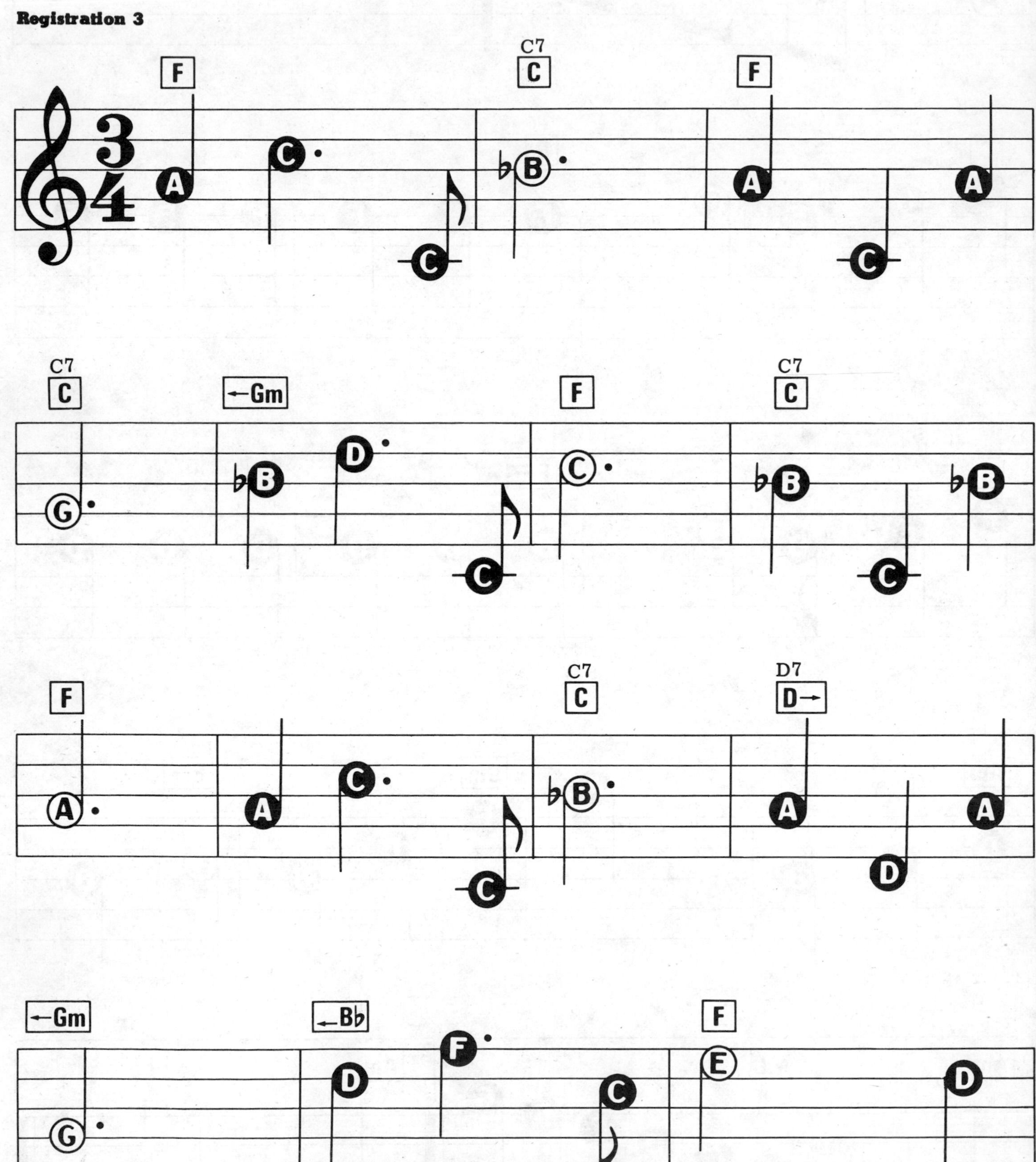

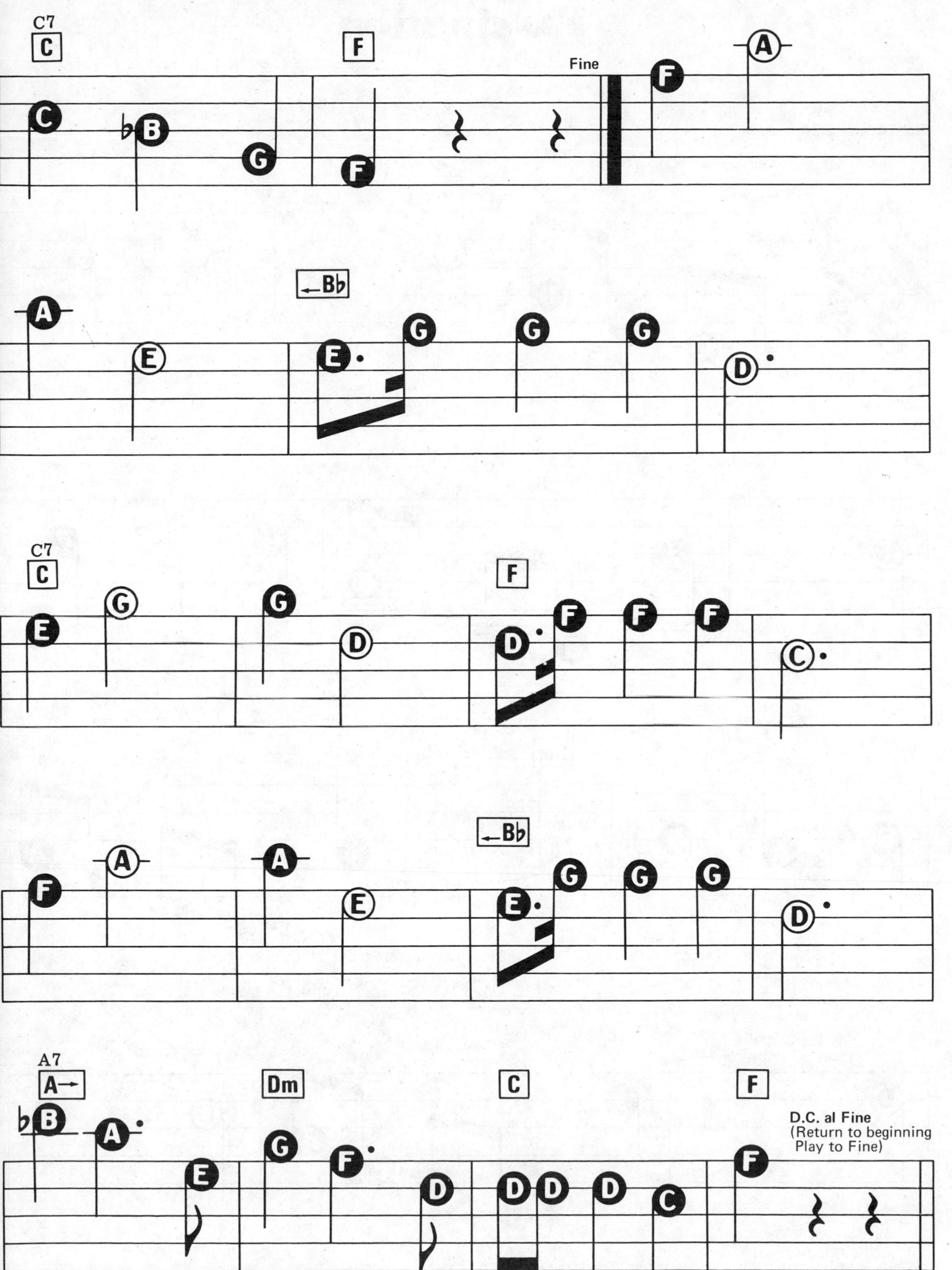
C7
C
F
Fine
←B♭
C7
C
F
←B♭
A7
A→
Dm
C
F
D.C. al Fine
(Return to beginning
Play to Fine)

Fascination

Registration 10

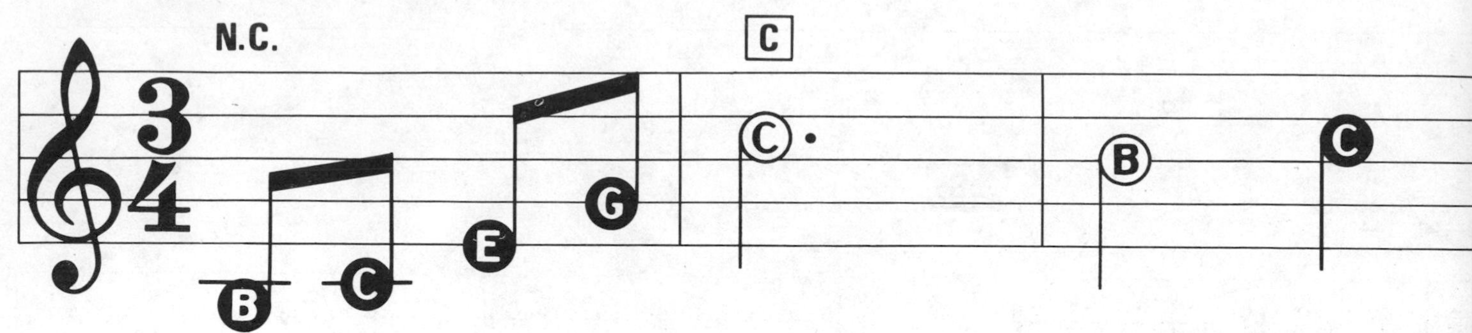

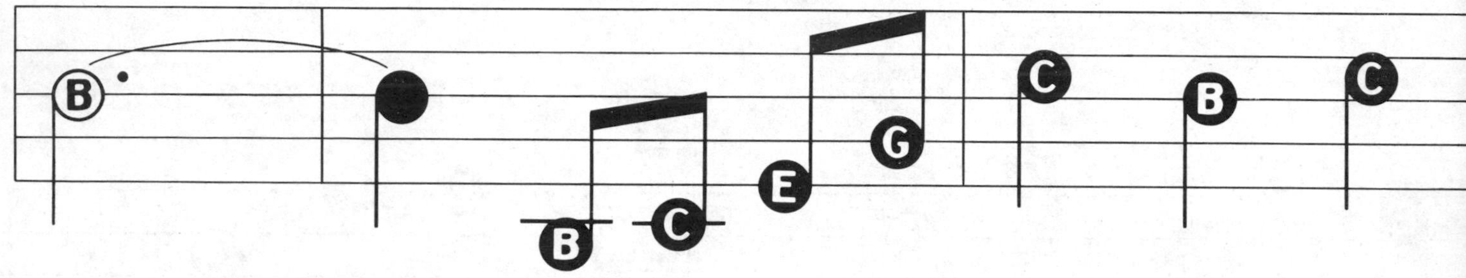

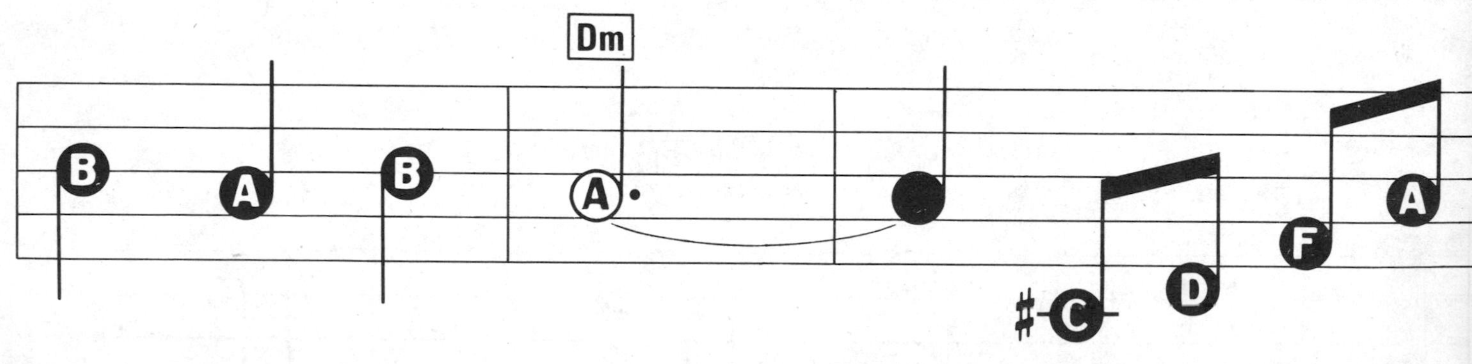

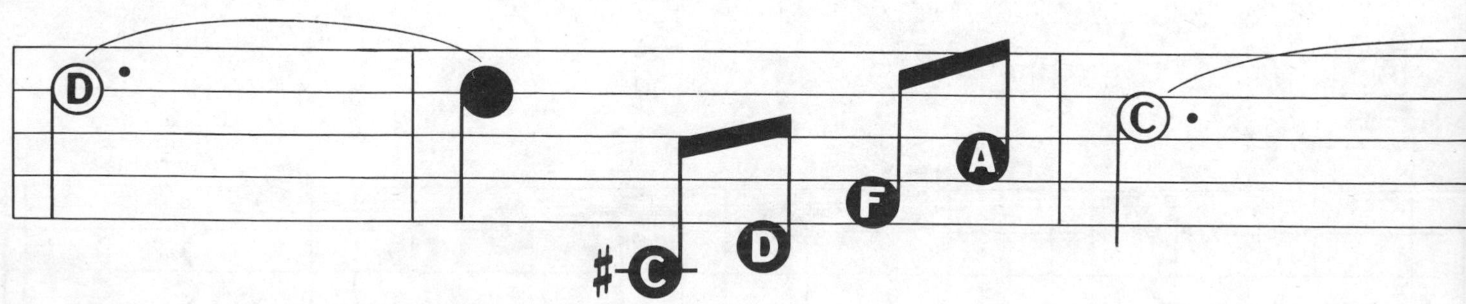

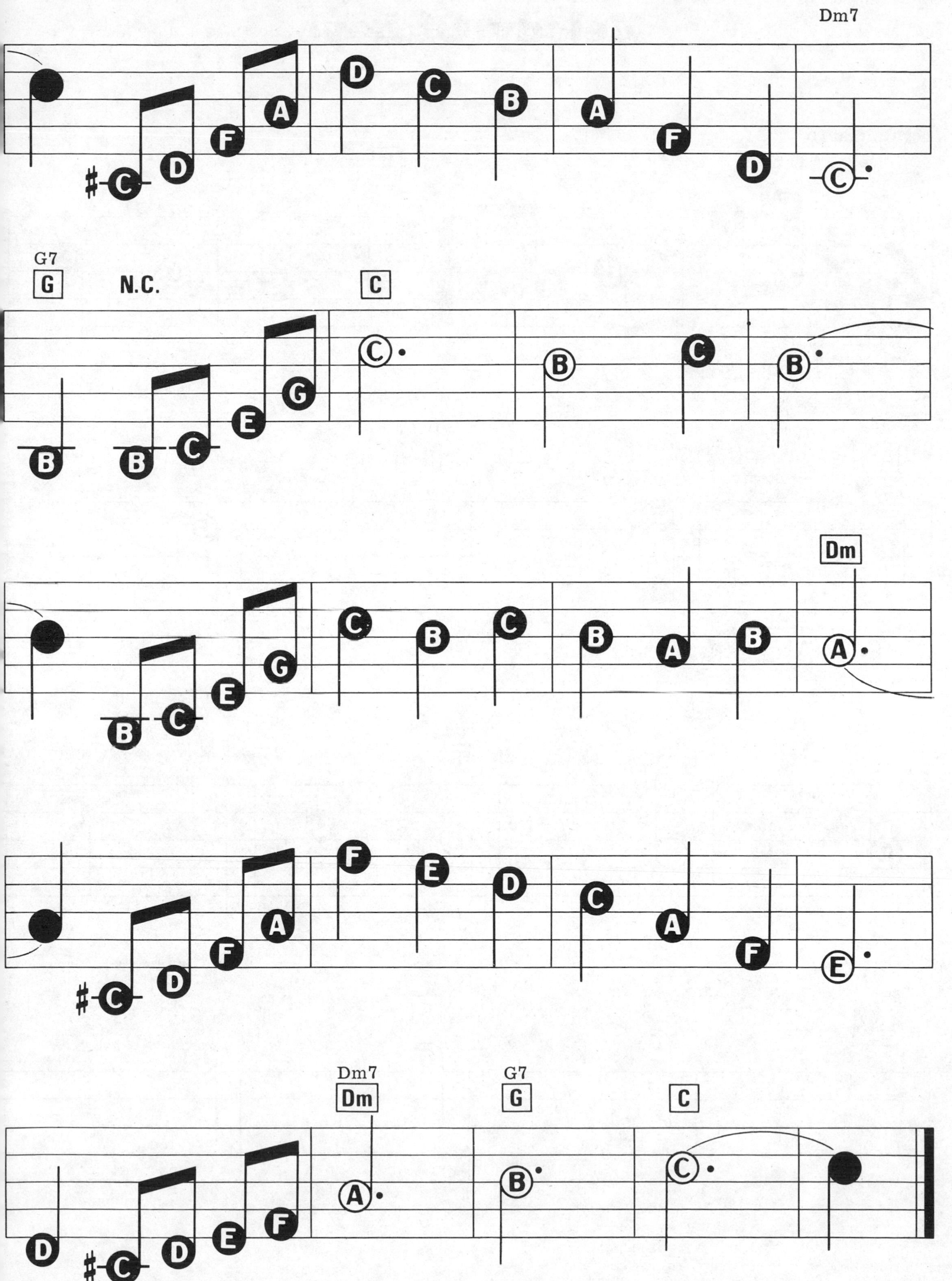
Dm7
G7
G
N.C.
C
Dm
Dm7
Dm
G7
G
C

Melody Of Love

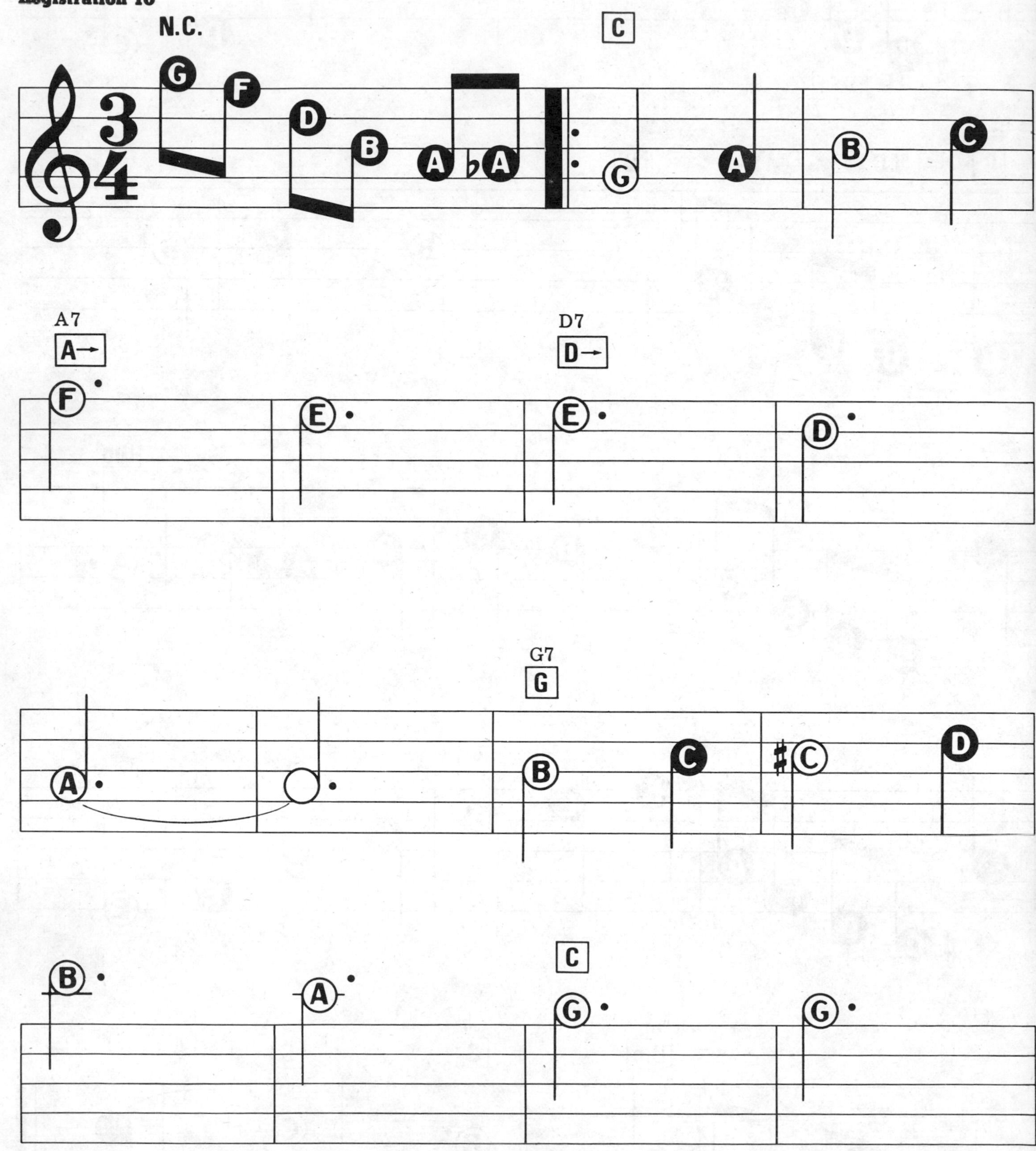

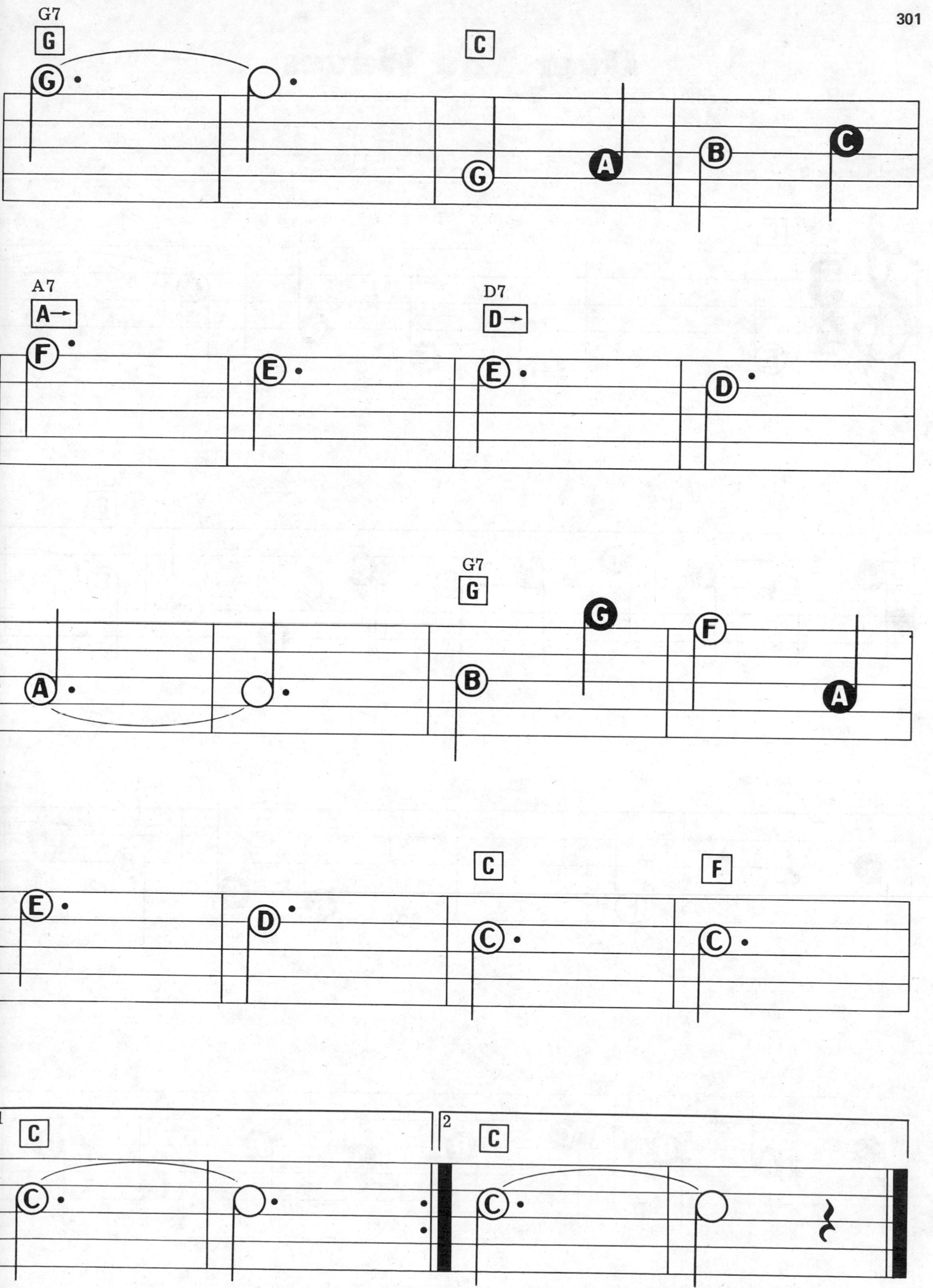
G7
G
G
C
G
A
B
C
A7
A→
F
E
D7
D→
E
D
G7
G
A
B
G
F
A
C
F
E
D
C
C
1
C
C
2
C
C

Over The Waves

Registration 3

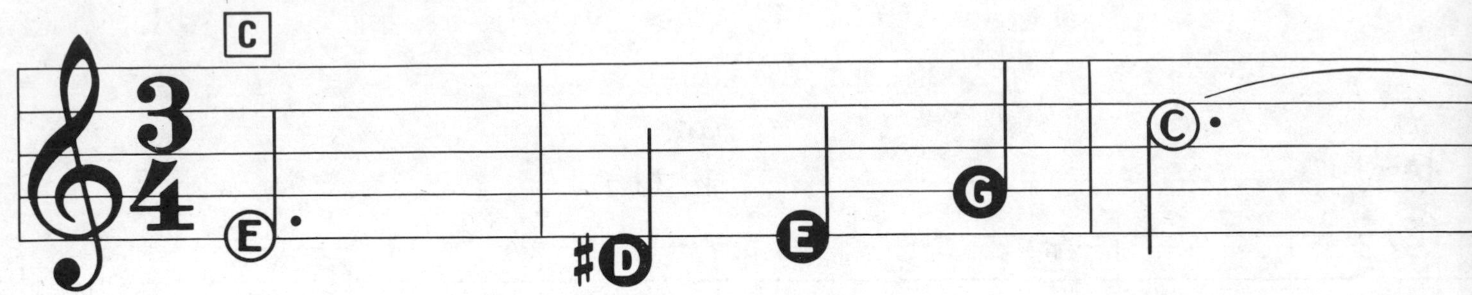

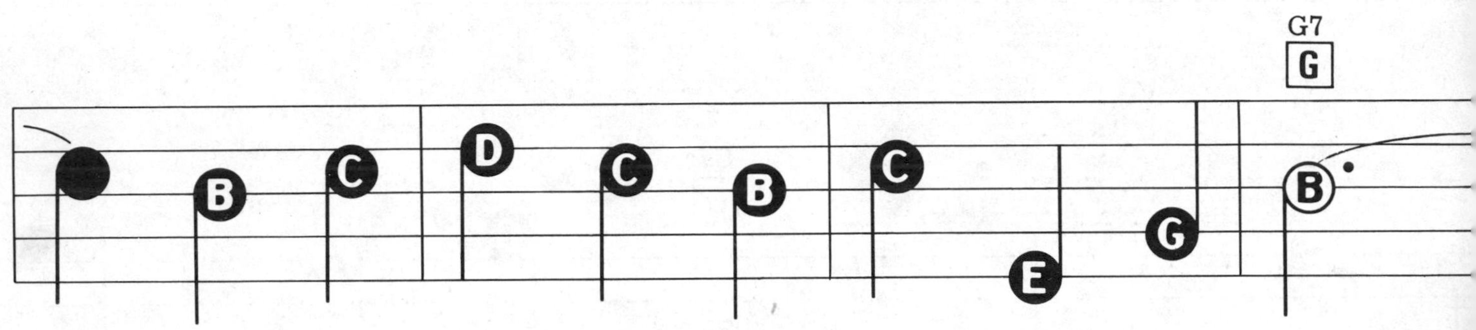

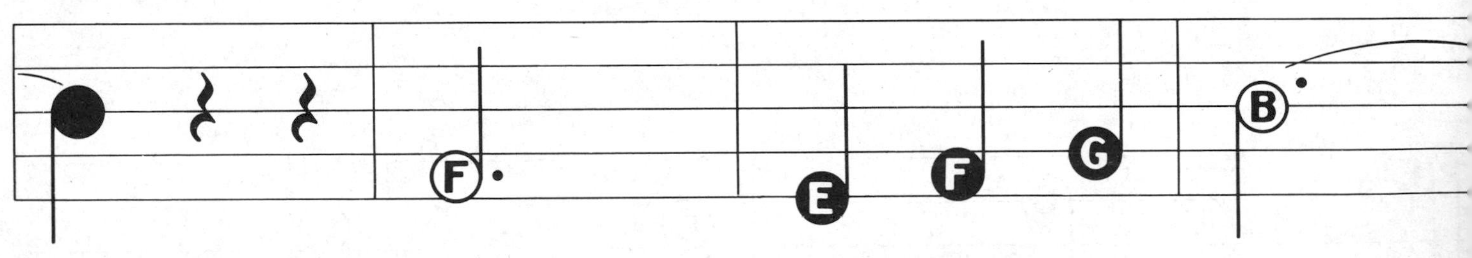

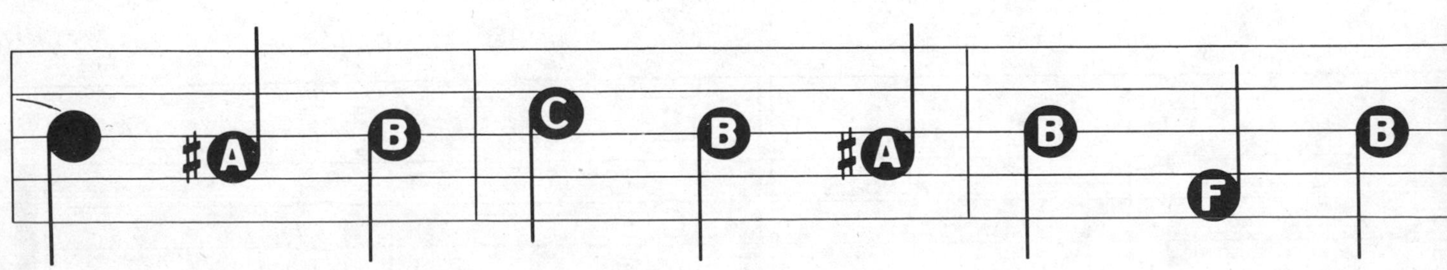

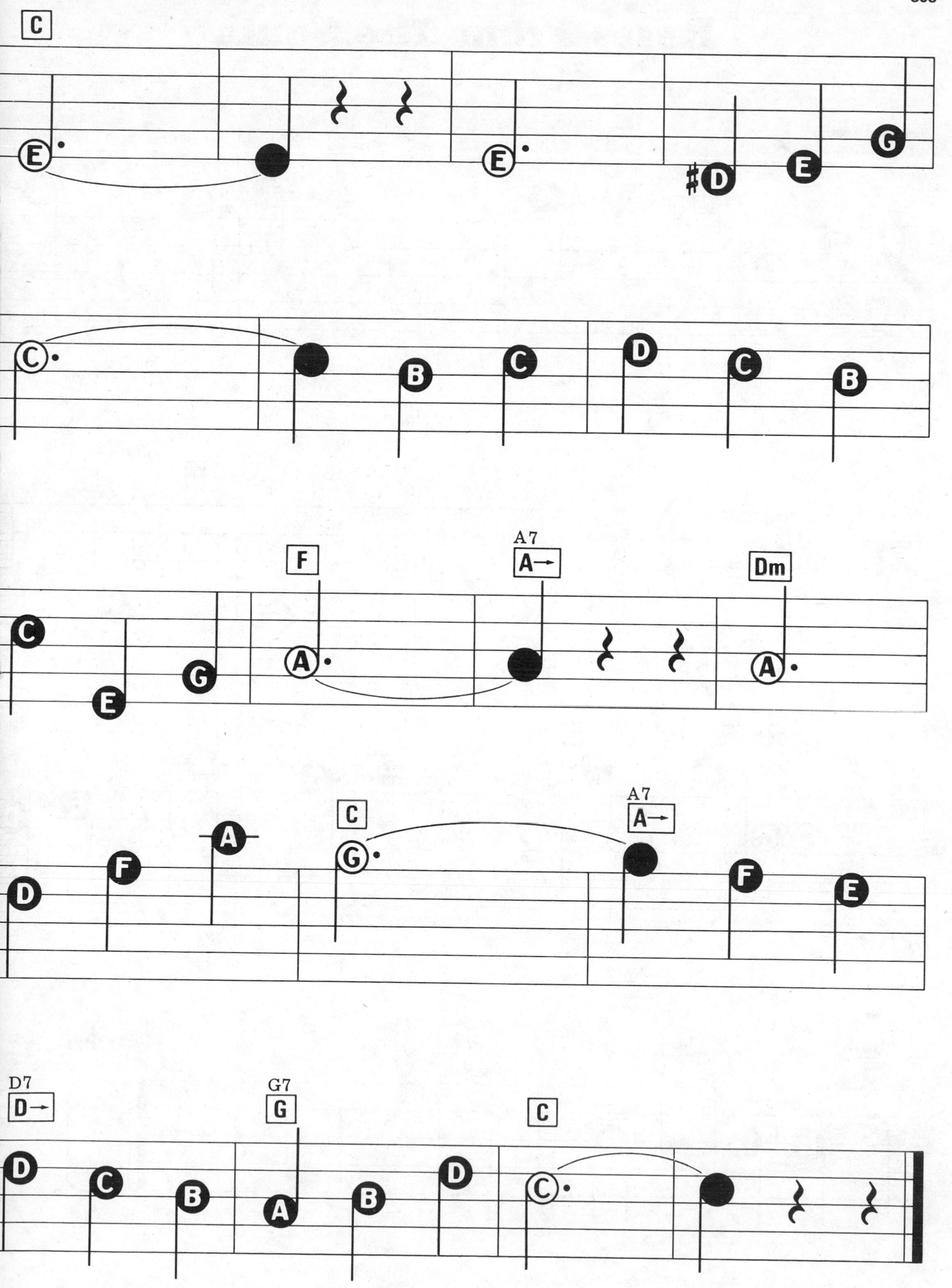
C
E E E ♯D E G
C B C D C B
C E G
F
A
A7
A→
Dm
A
D F A
C
G
A7
A→
F E
D7
D→
D C B
G7
G
A B D
C
C

Roses From The South

Registration 5

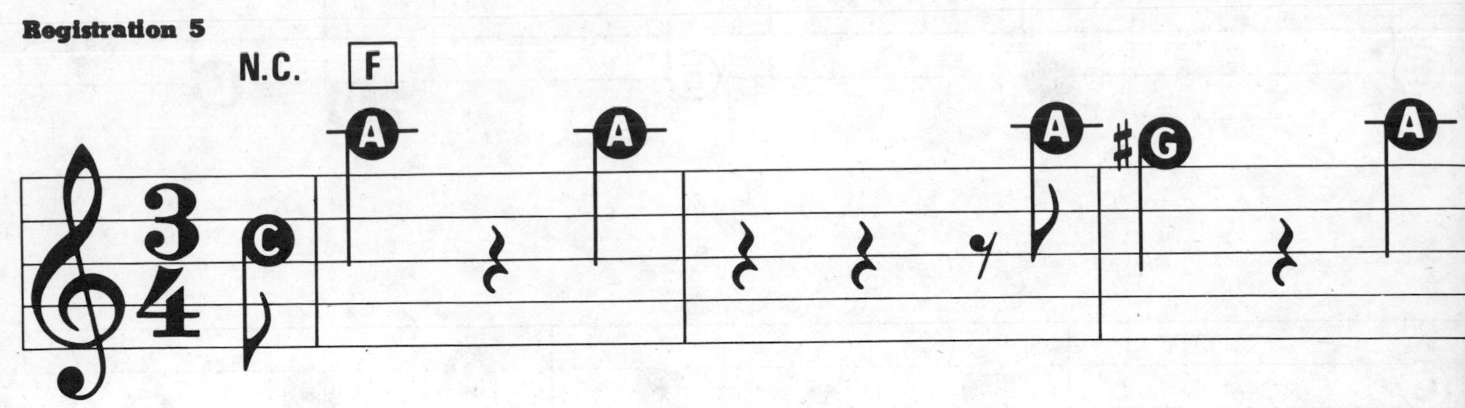

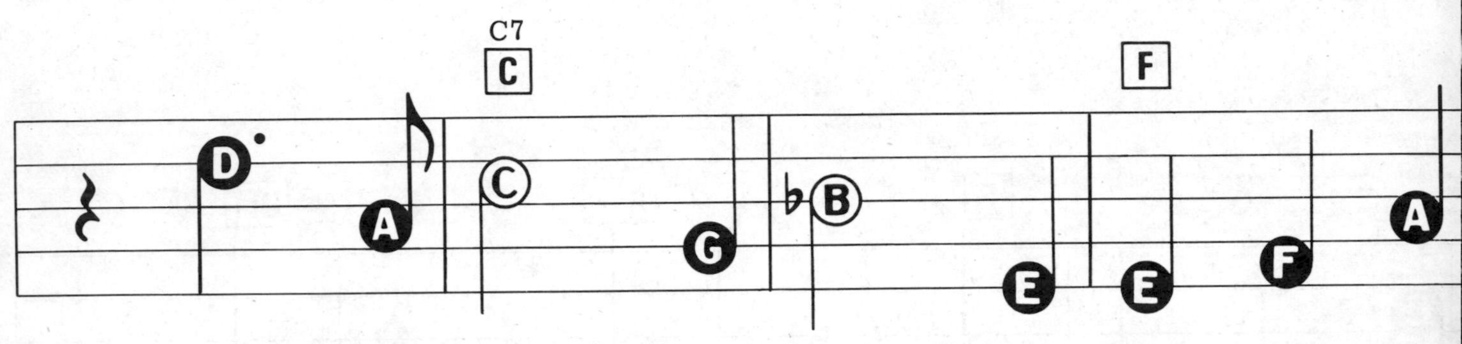

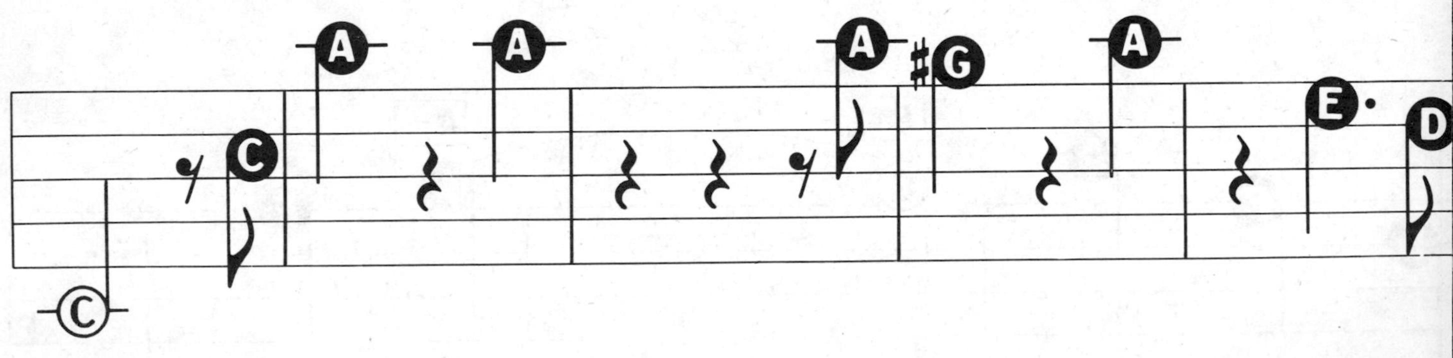

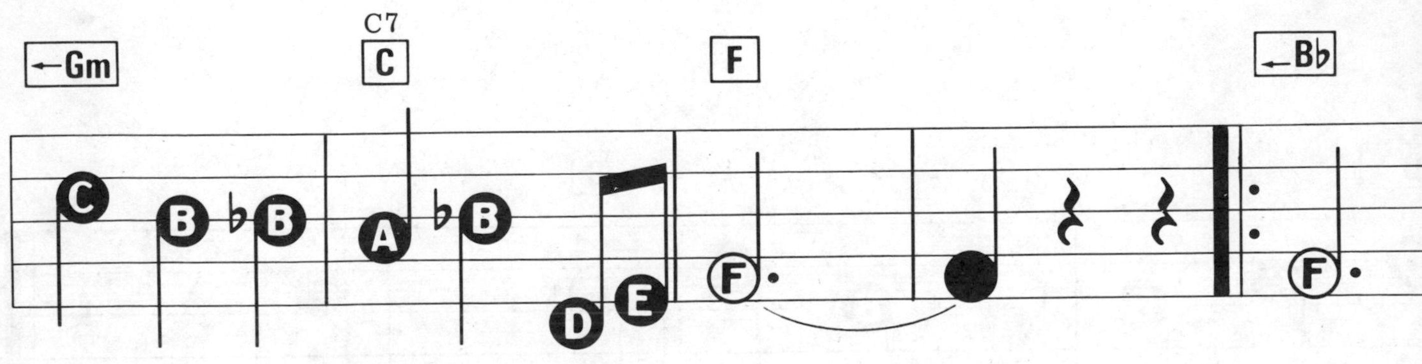

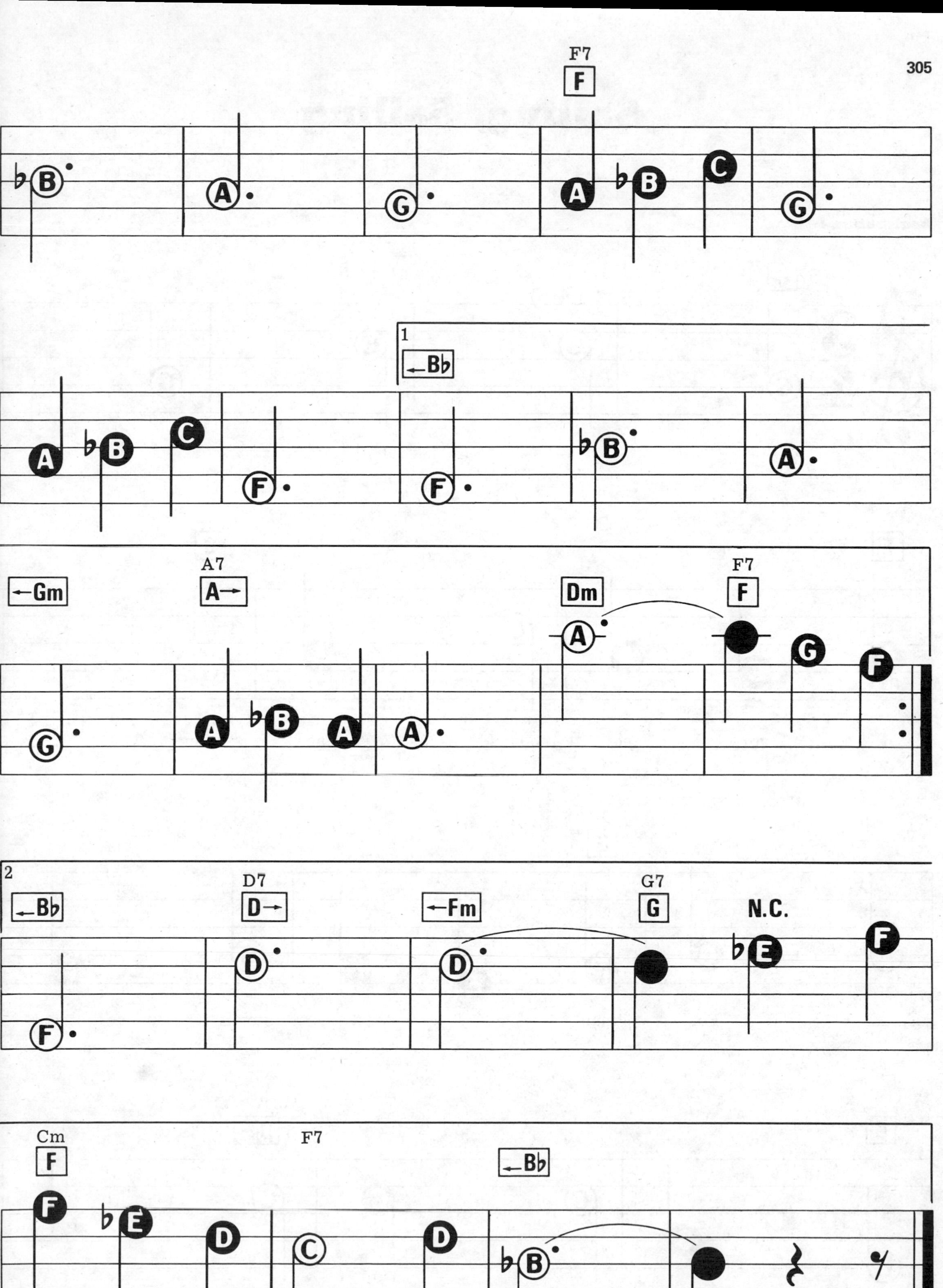
F7
F
1
Bb
Gm
A7
A
Dm
F7
F
2
Bb
D7
D
Fm
G7
G
N.C.
Cm
F
F7
Bb

Sailing, Sailing

Registration 5

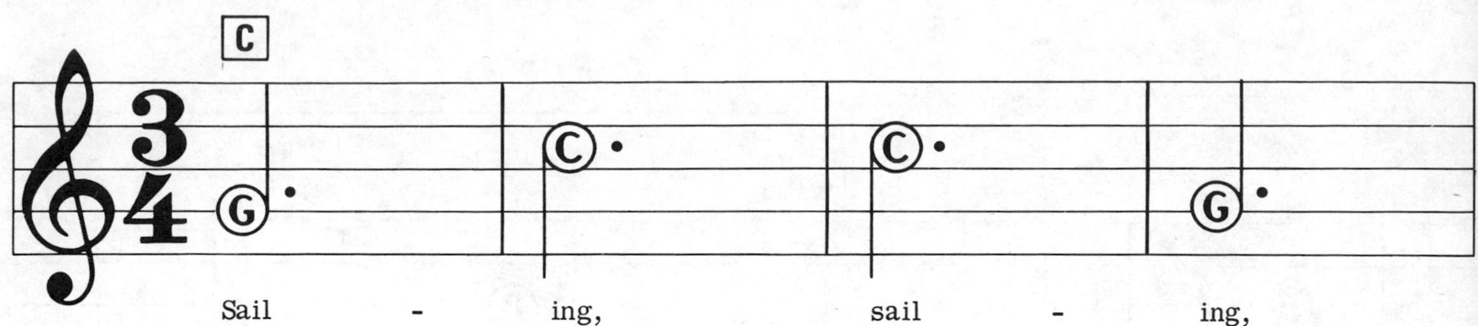

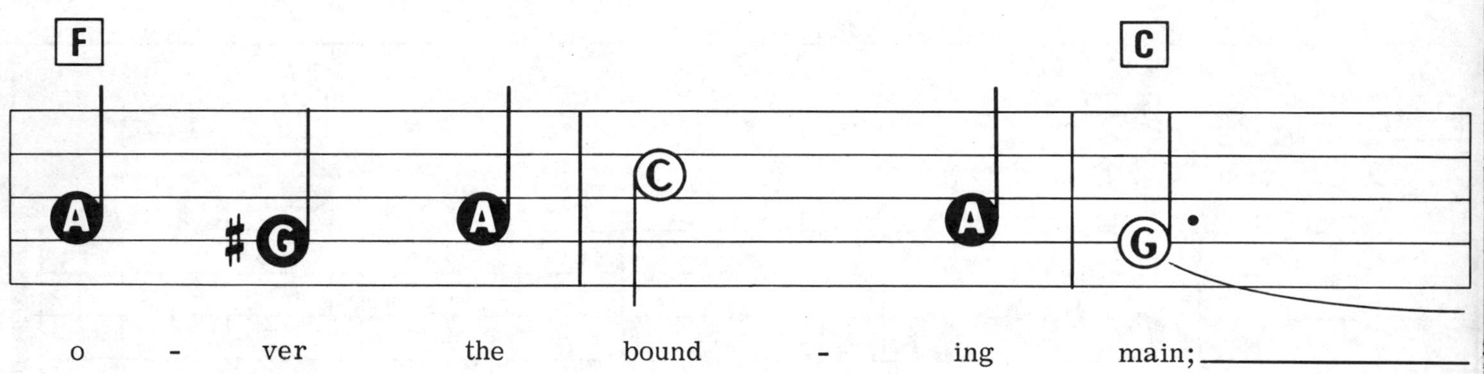

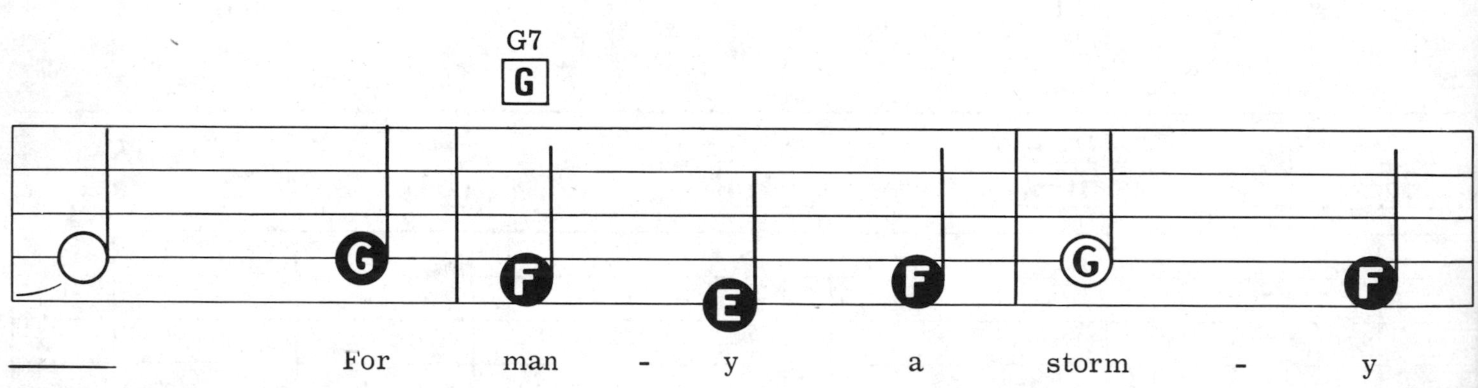

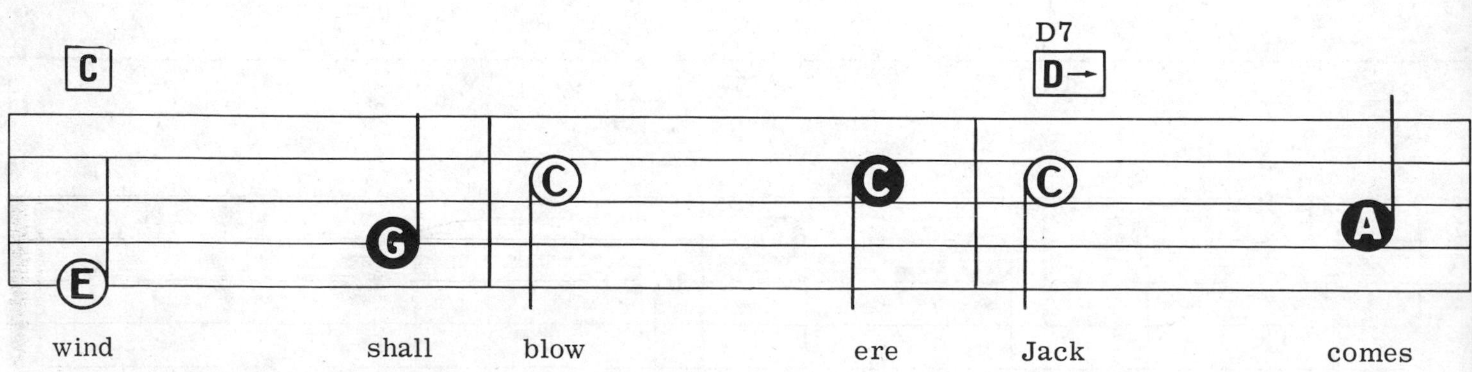

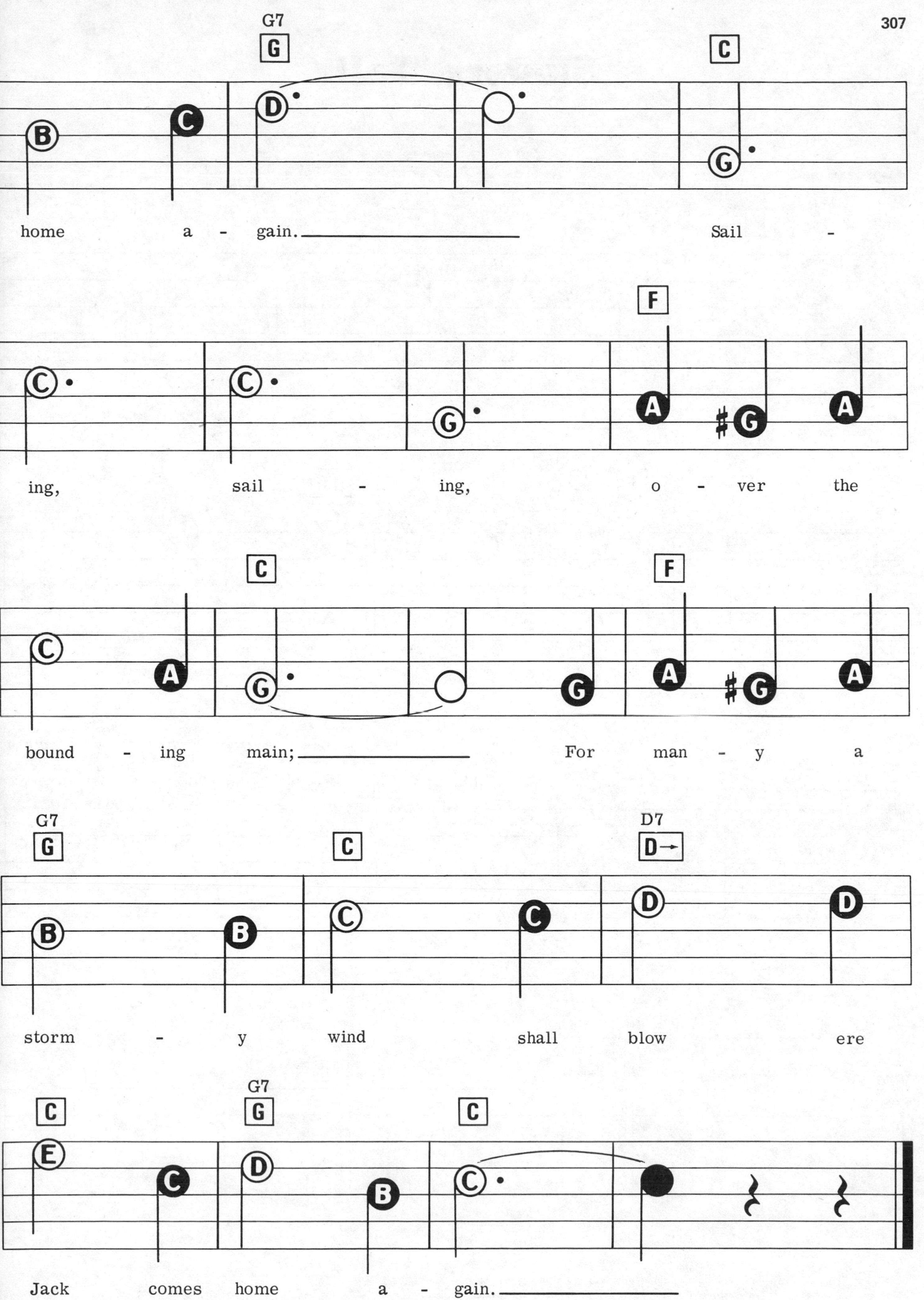
G7 G C
home a - gain. Sail -
F
ing, sail - ing, o - ver the
C F
bound - ing main; For man - y a
G7 G C D7 D
storm - y wind shall blow ere
C G7 G C
Jack comes home a - gain.

Skaters Waltz

Registration 5

Emil Waldteufel

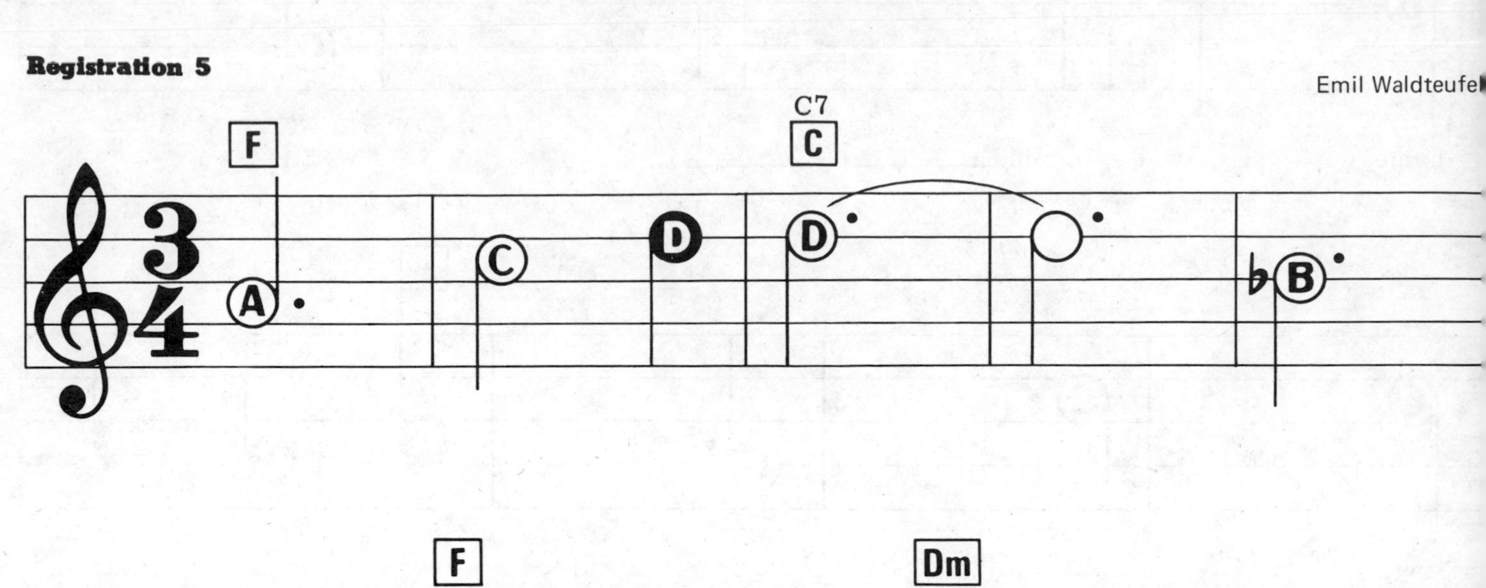

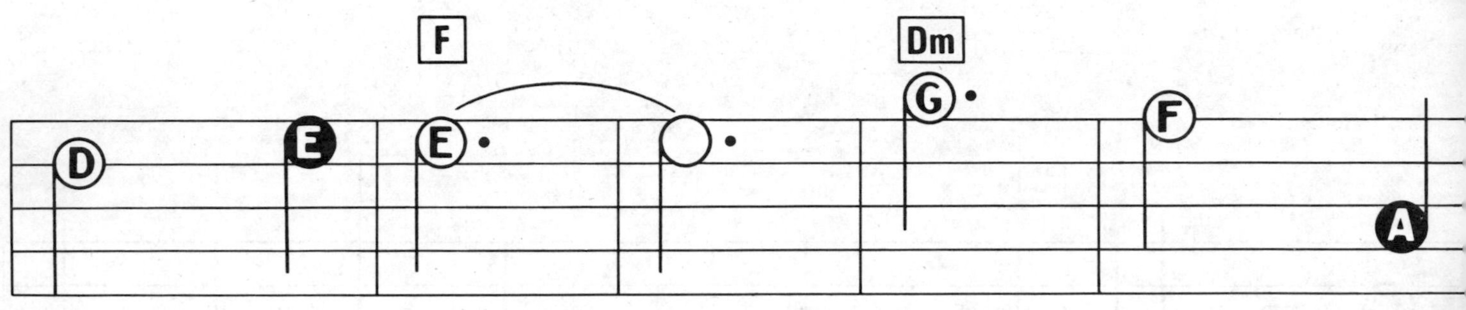

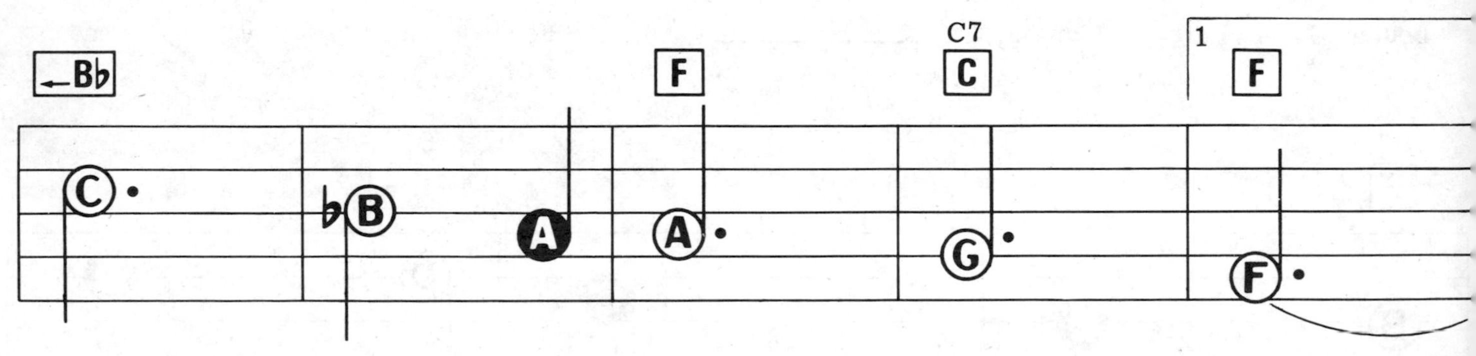

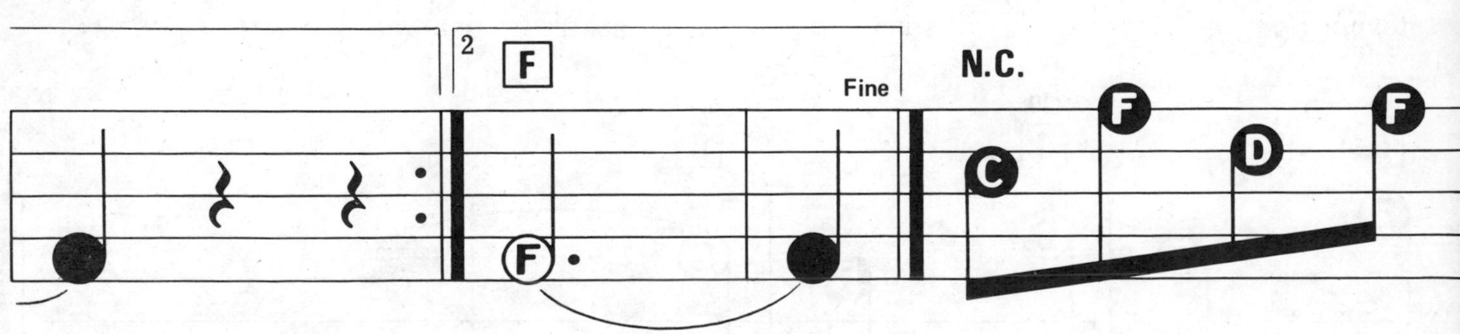

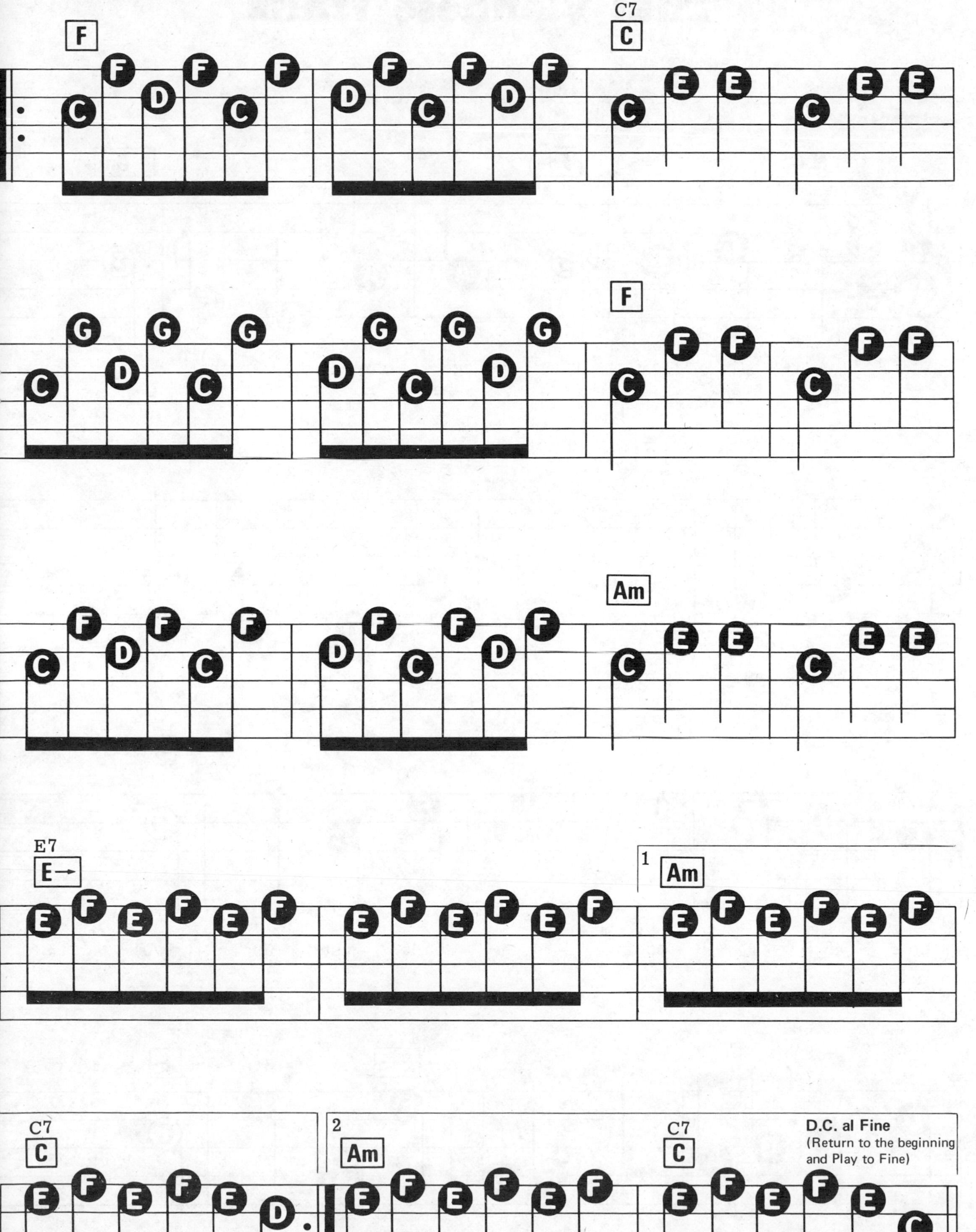
F
C7
C
F
Am
E7
E→
1
Am
C7
C
2
Am
C7
C
D.C. al Fine
(Return to the beginning
and Play to Fine)

That Viennese Waltz

Registration 3

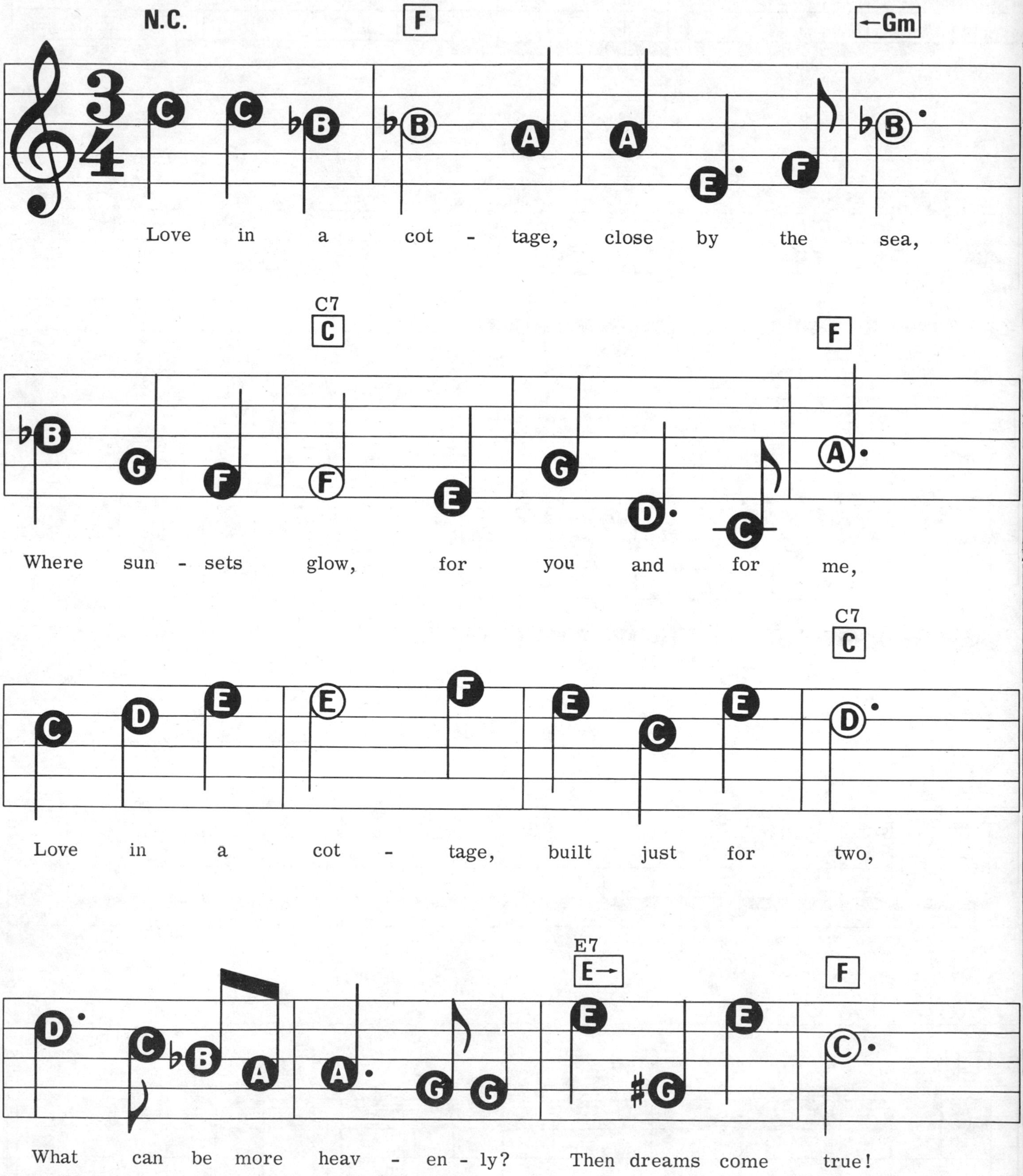

N.C.
F
←Gm
Love in a cot - tage, close by the sea,
C7
C
F
Where sun - sets glow, for you and for me,
C7
C
Love in a cot - tage, built just for two,
E7
E→
F
What can be more heav - en - ly? Then dreams come true!

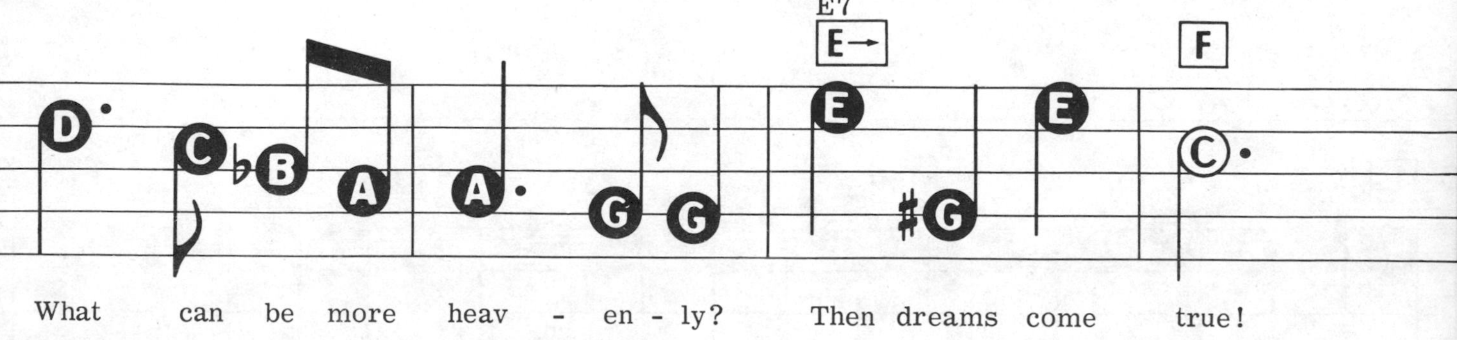

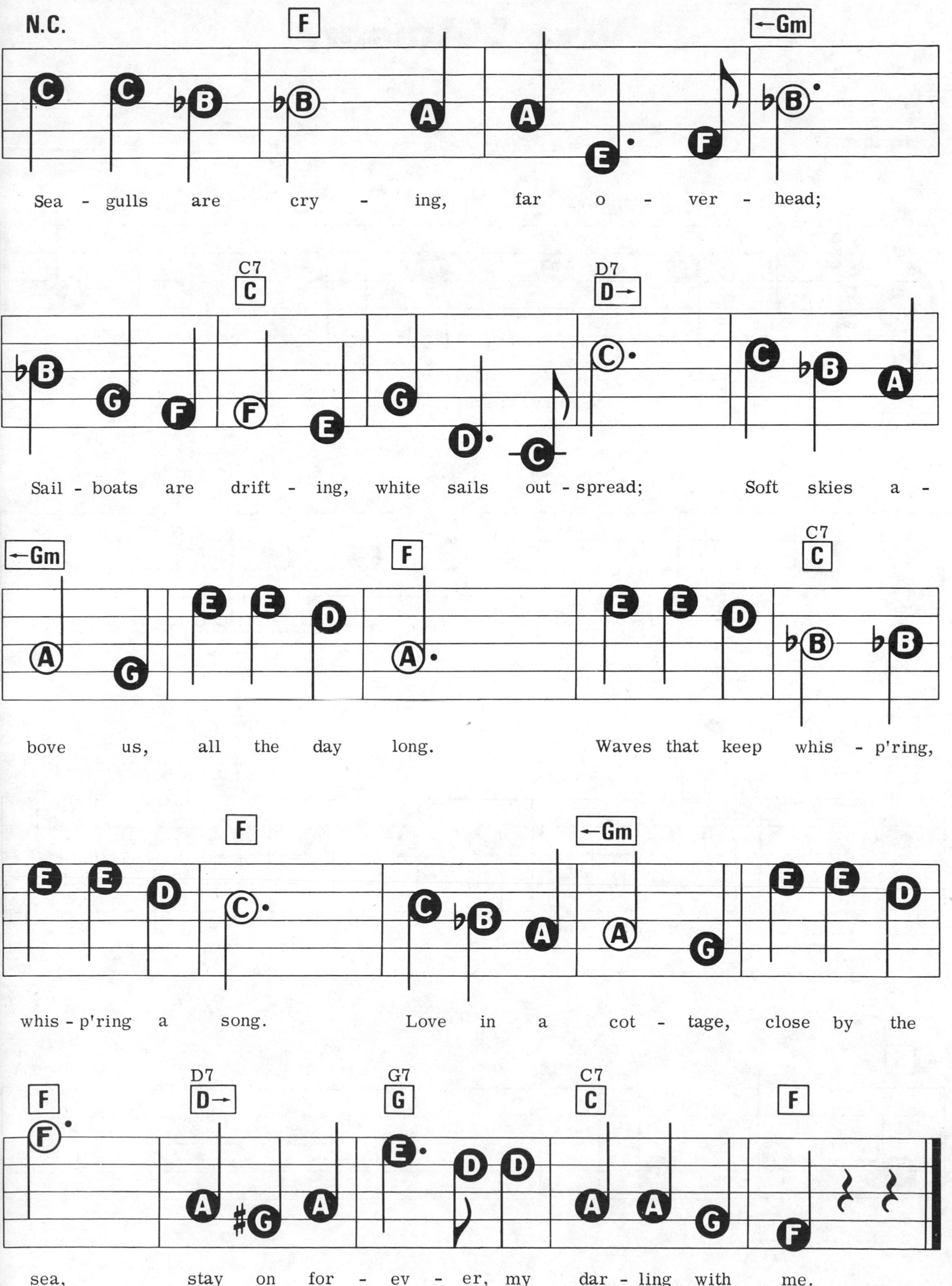
N.C.
F
←Gm
Sea - gulls are cry - ing, far o - ver - head;
C7
C
D7
D→
Sail - boats are drift - ing, white sails out - spread; Soft skies a -
←Gm
F
C7
C
bove us, all the day long. Waves that keep whis - p'ring,
F
←Gm
whis - p'ring a song. Love in a cot - tage, close by the
F
D7
D→
G7
G
C7
C
F
sea, stay on for - ev - er, my dar - ling with me.

Viva L'Amour

Registration 3

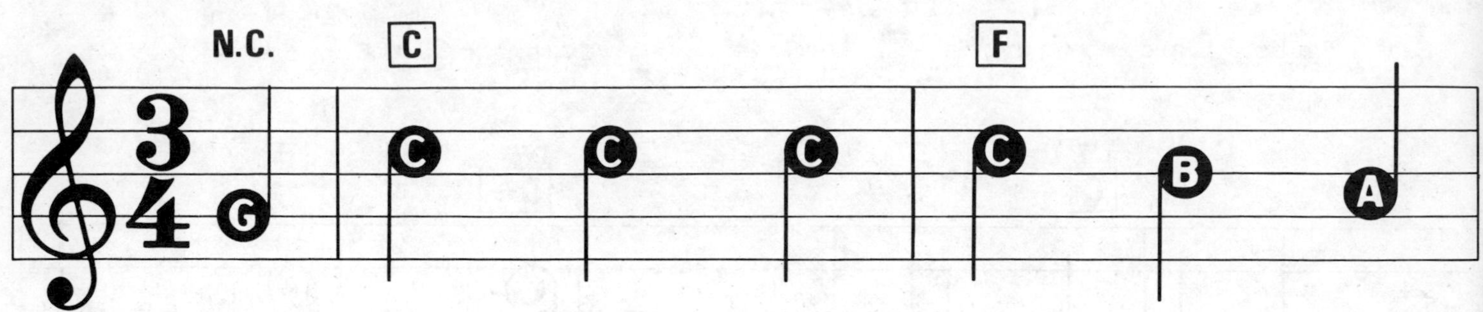

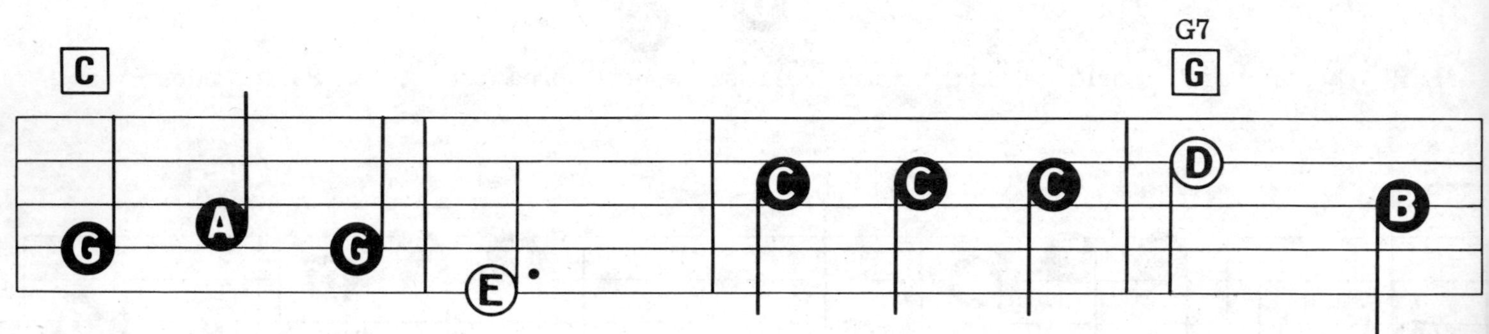

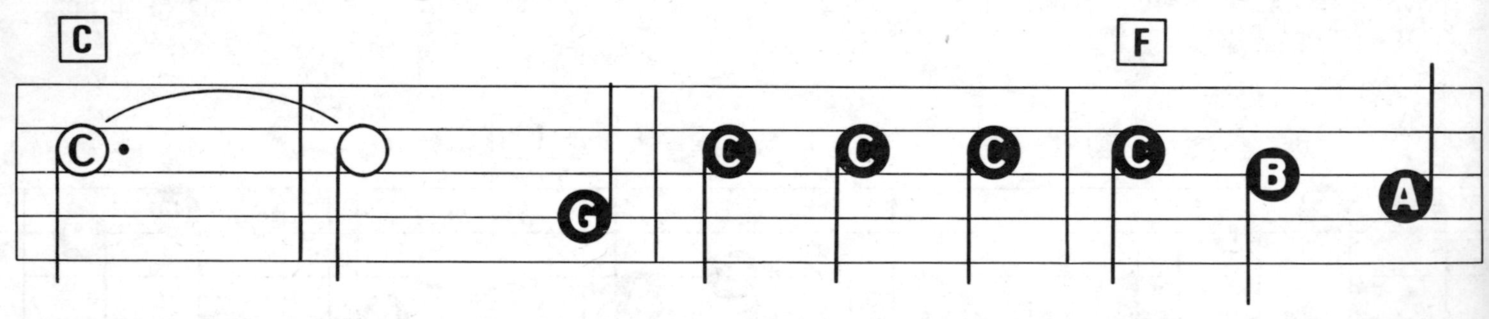

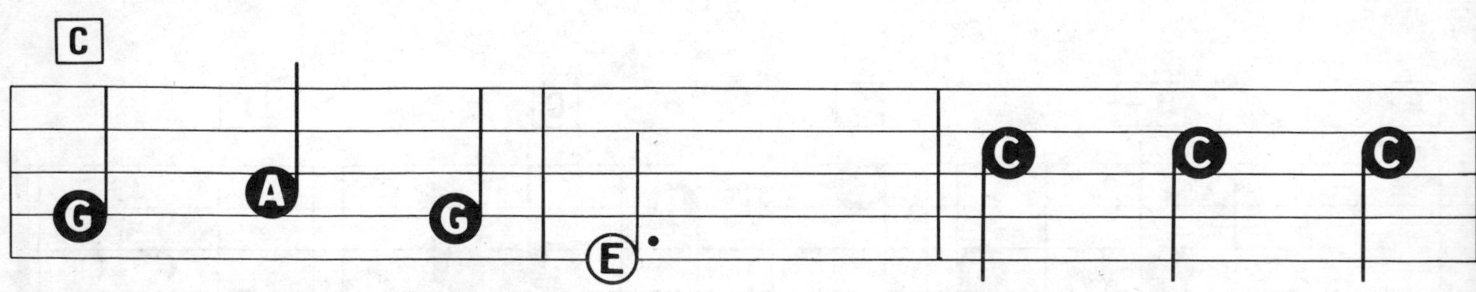

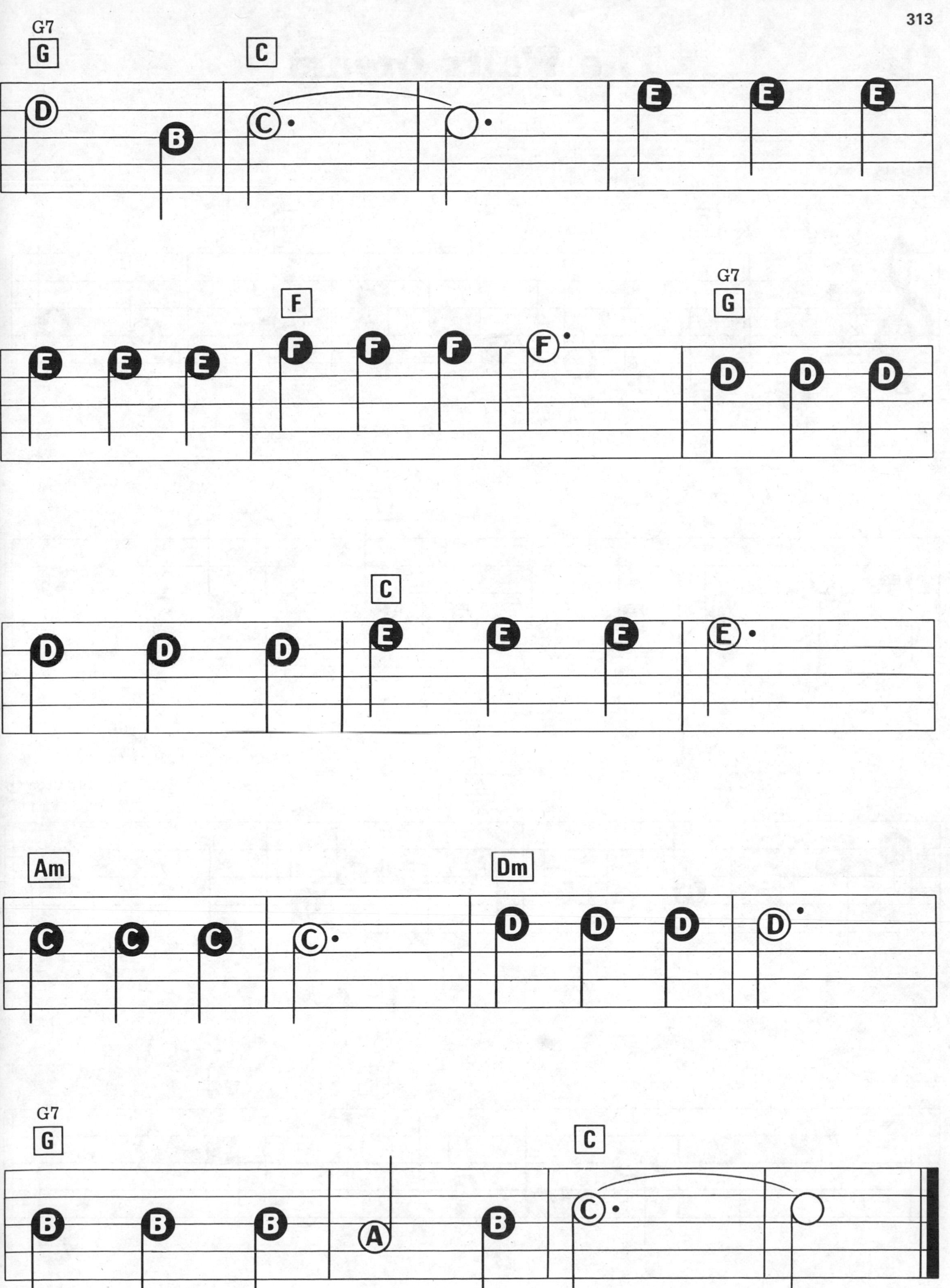
G7 G
D B
C
C
E E E
E E E
F
F F F F
G7 G
D D D
D D D
C
E E E E
Am
C C C C
Dm
D D D D
G7 G
B B B A B
C
C

The Waltz Dream

Registration 9

Oscar Strauss

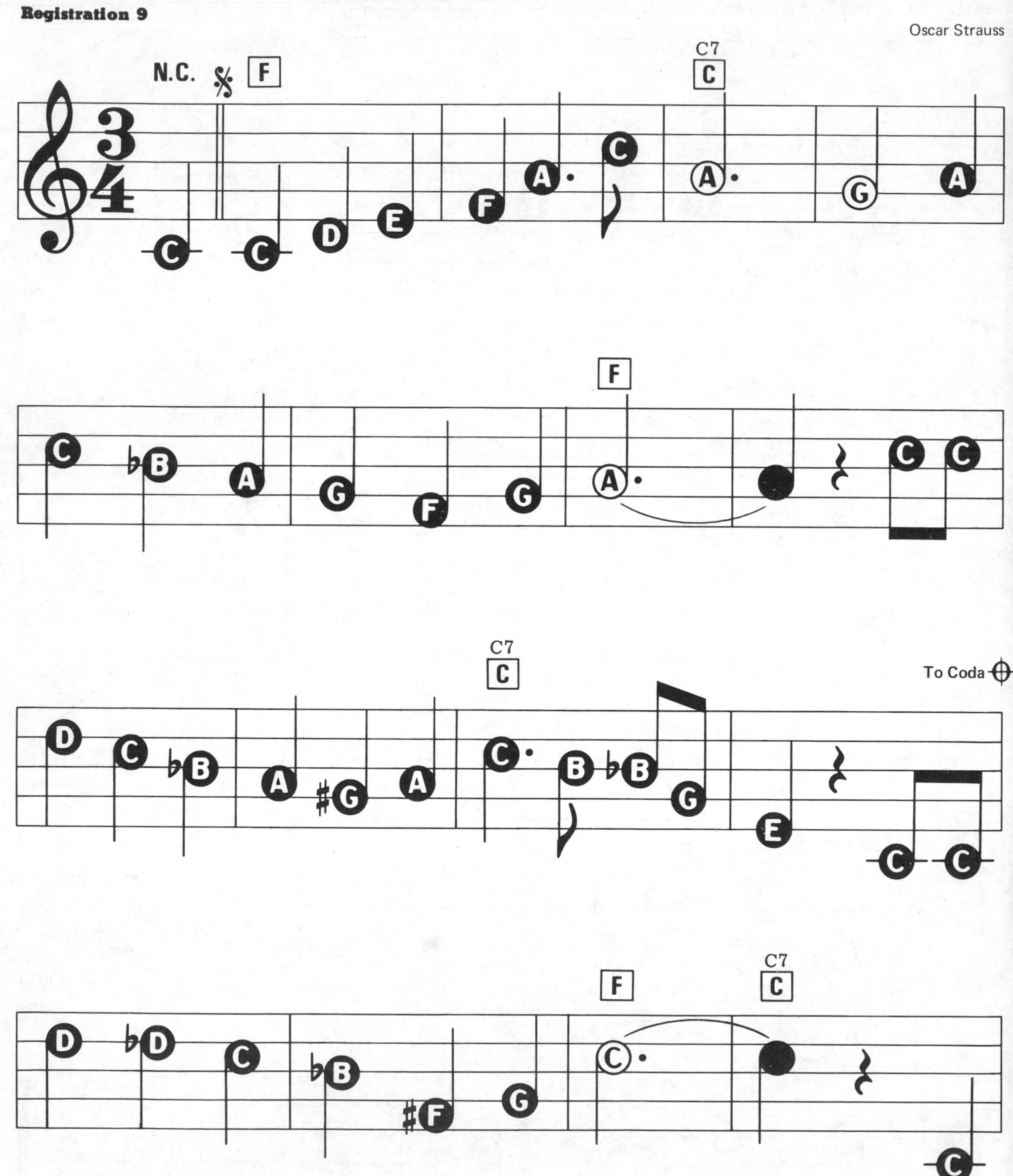

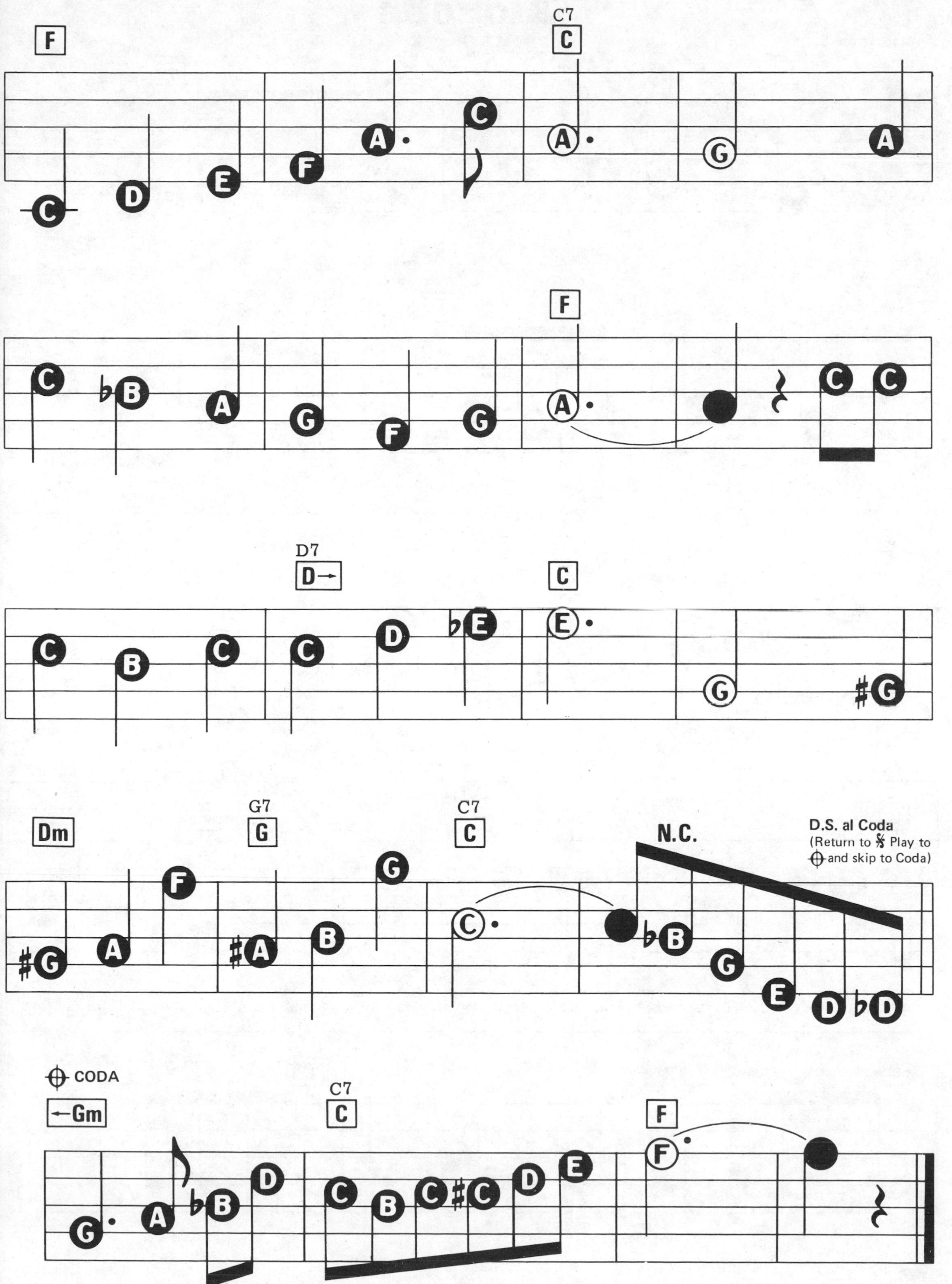
F
C7
C
F
D7
D→
C
Dm
G7
G
C7
C
N.C.
D.S. al Coda
(Return to 𝄋 Play to
𝄌 and skip to Coda)
𝄌 CODA
←Gm
C7
C
F

Alouette

Registration 3

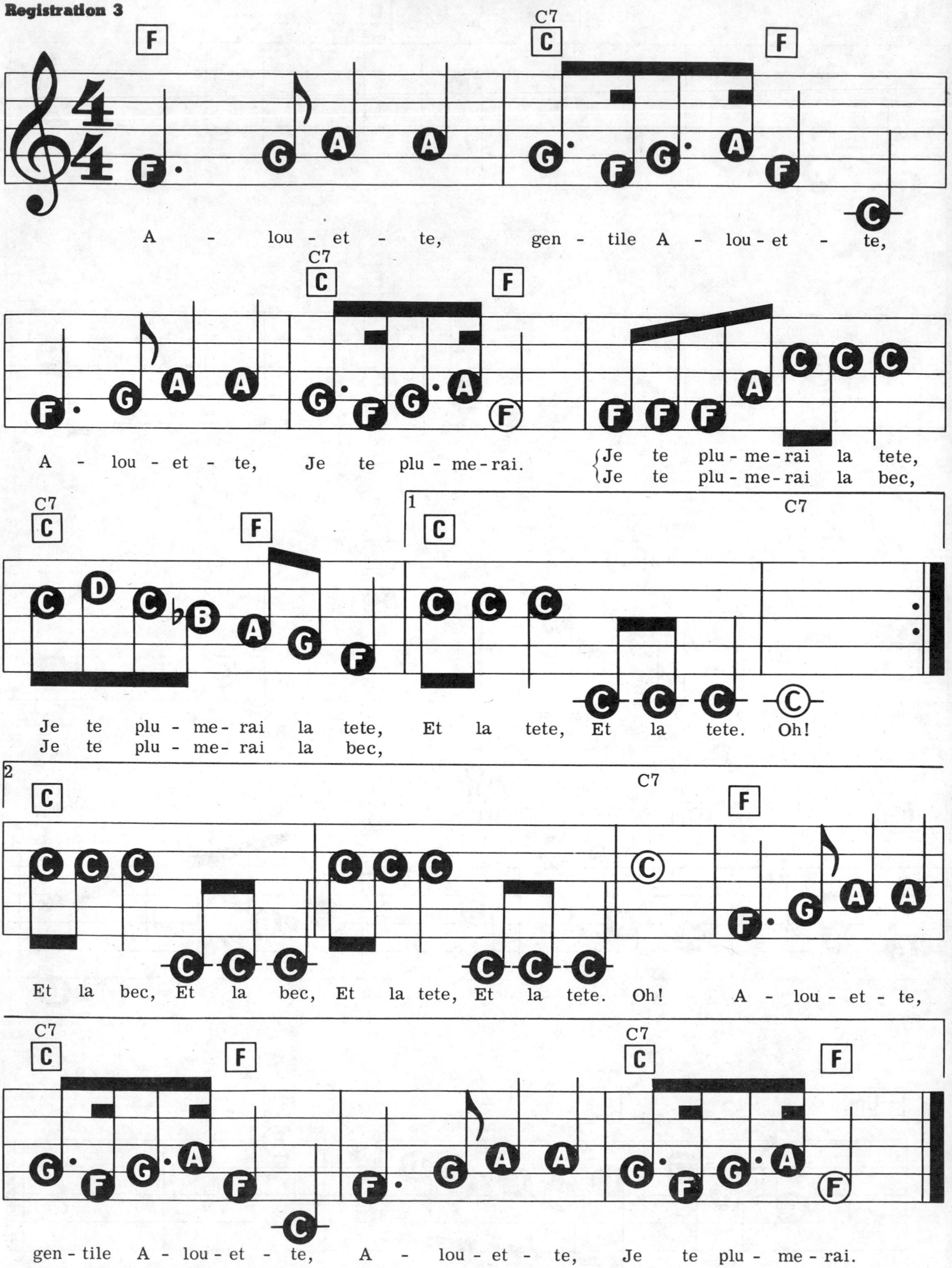

F C7 F

A - lou - et - te, gen - tile A - lou - et - te,

C7 F

A - lou - et - te, Je te plu - me - rai. {Je te plu - me - rai la tete,
Je te plu - me - rai la bec,

C7 F 1 C7

Je te plu - me - rai la tete, Et la tete, Et la tete. Oh!
Je te plu - me - rai la bec,

2 C7 F

Et la bec, Et la bec, Et la tete, Et la tete. Oh! A - lou - et - te,

C7 F C7 F

gen - tile A - lou - et - te, A - lou - et - te, Je te plu - me - rai.

Goodnight Ladies

Registration 3

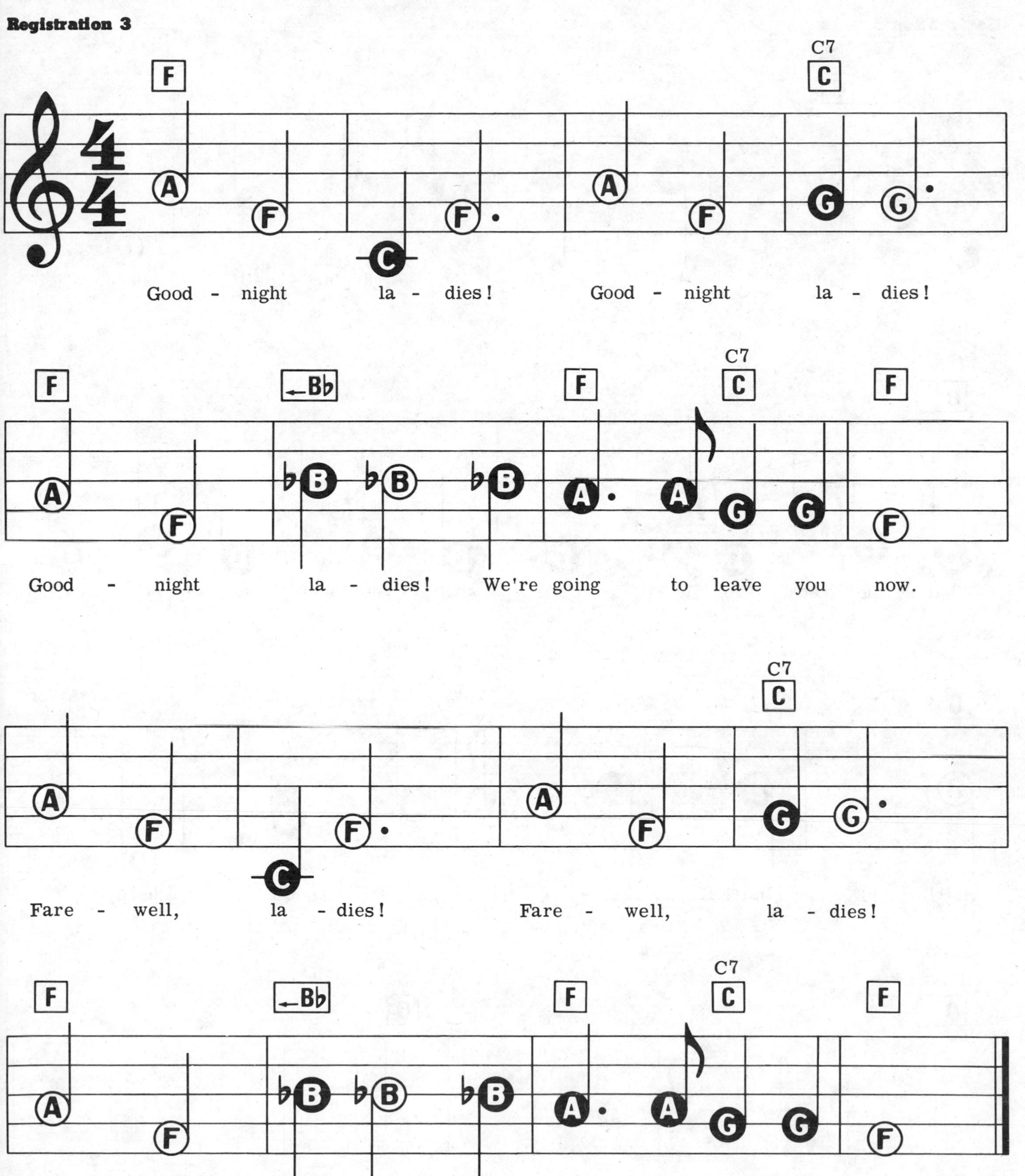

Hail, Hail The Gang's All Here

Registration 5

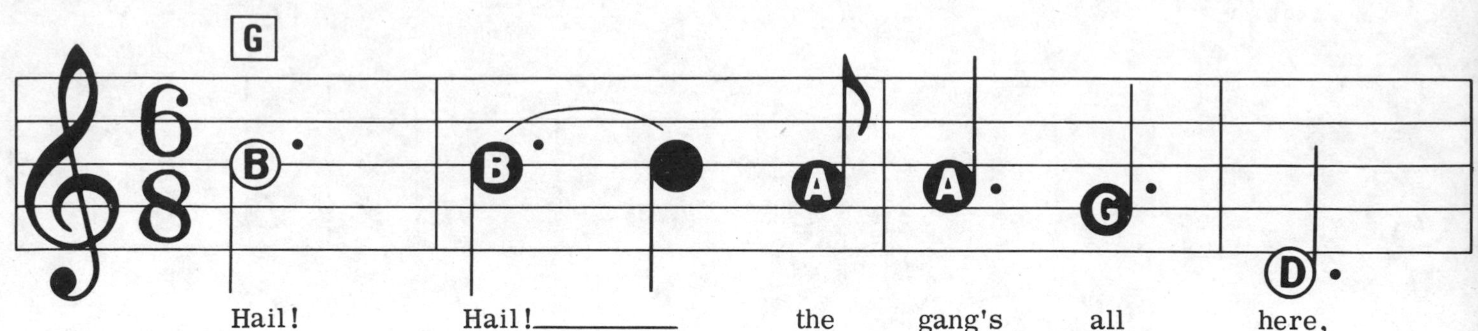

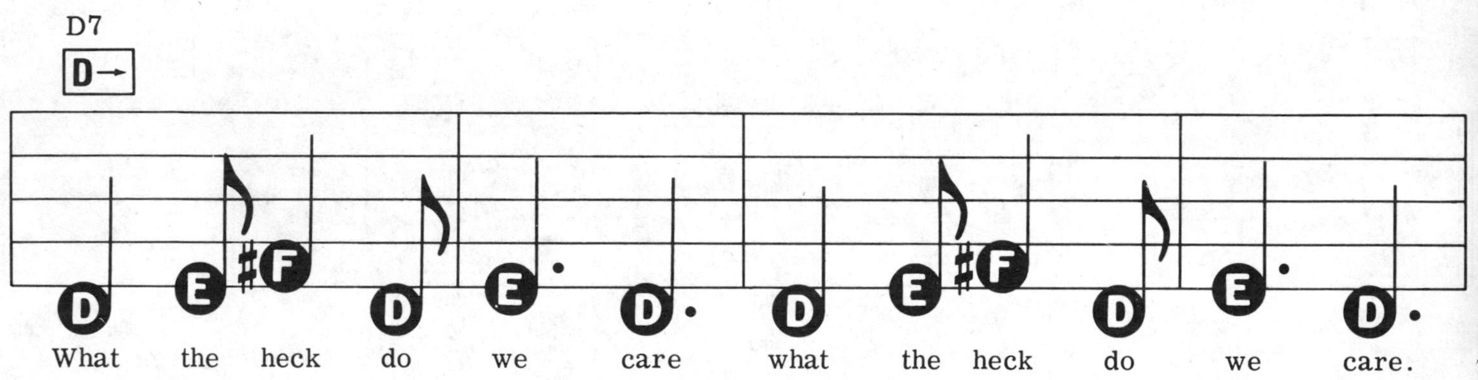

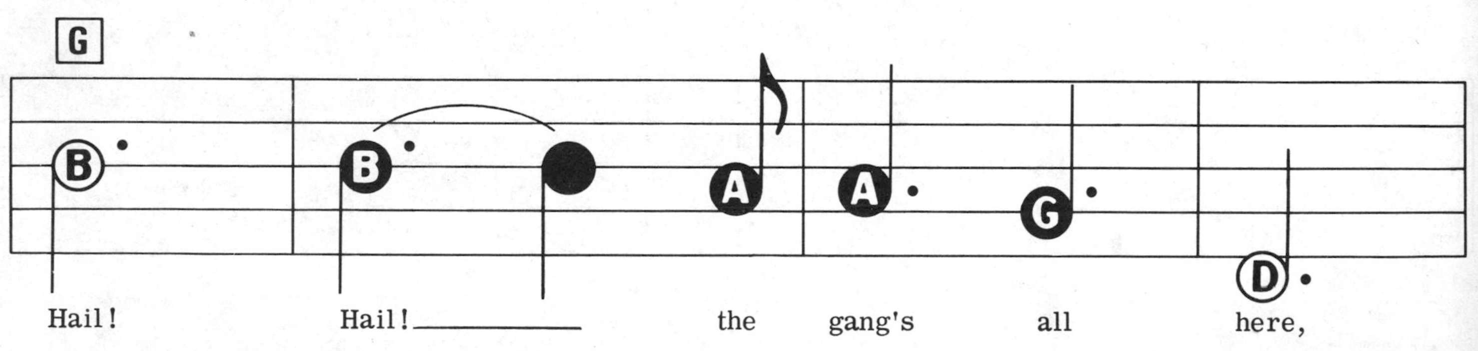

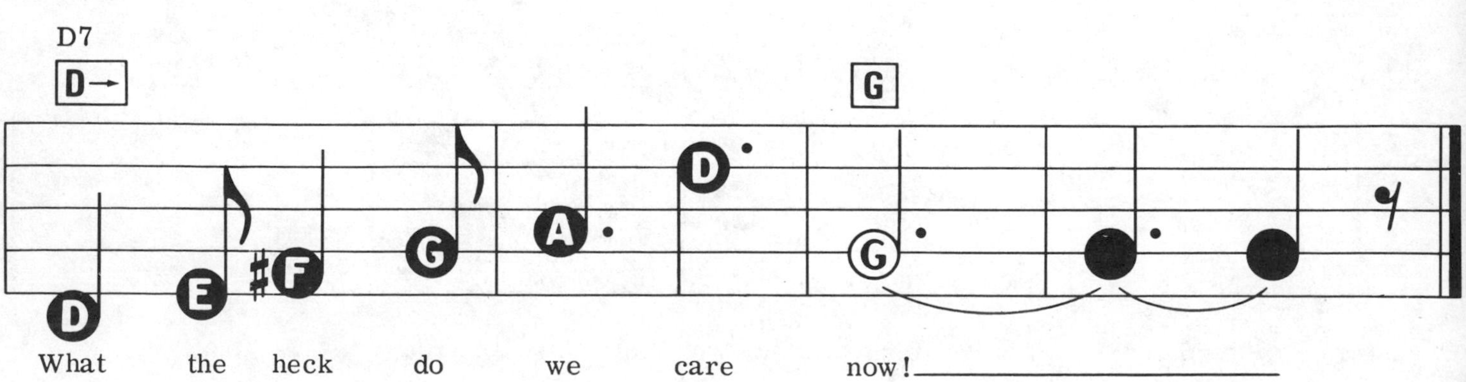

A Hot Time In The Old Town Tonight

Registration 7

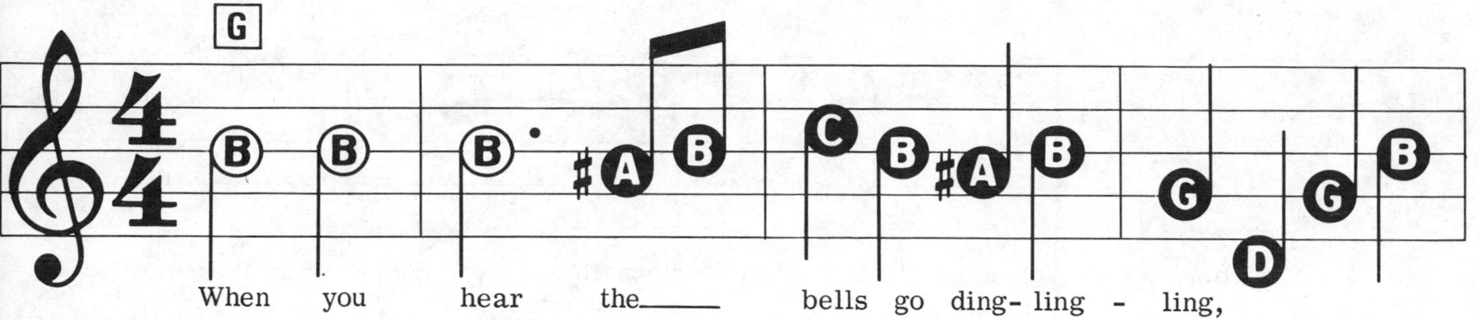

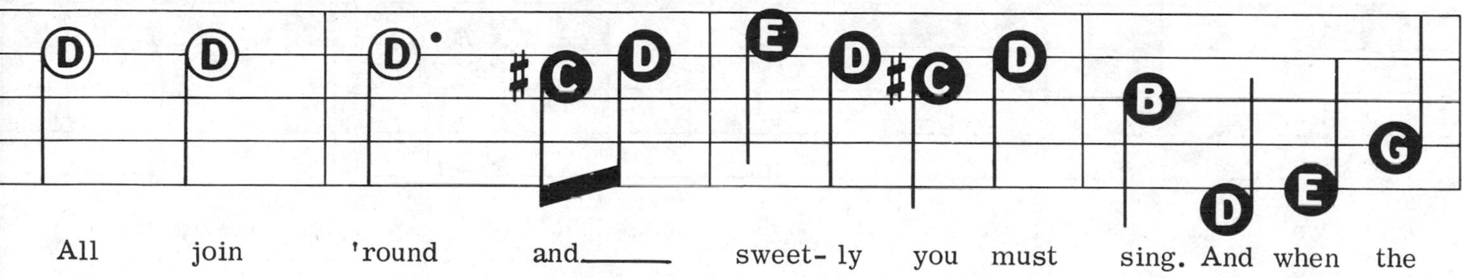

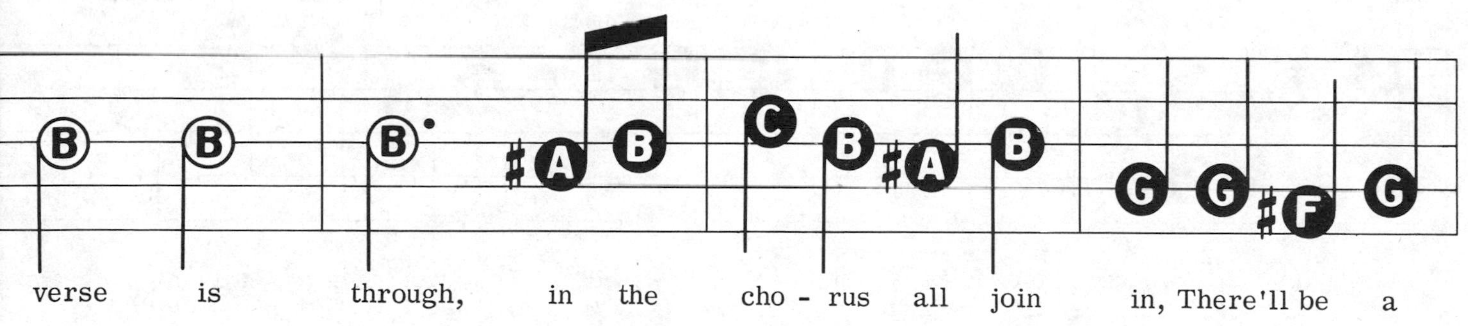

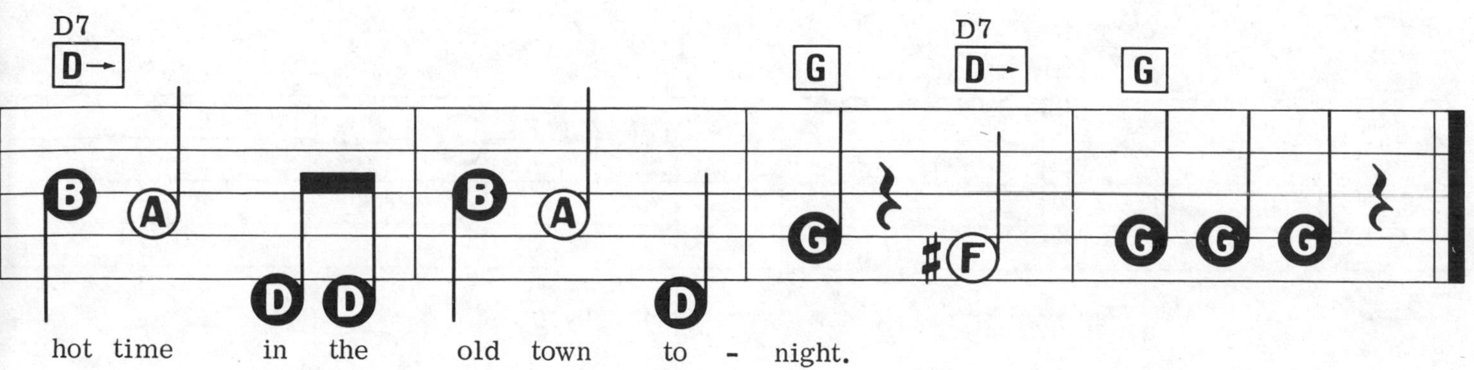

In The Evenin' By The Moonlight

Registration 2

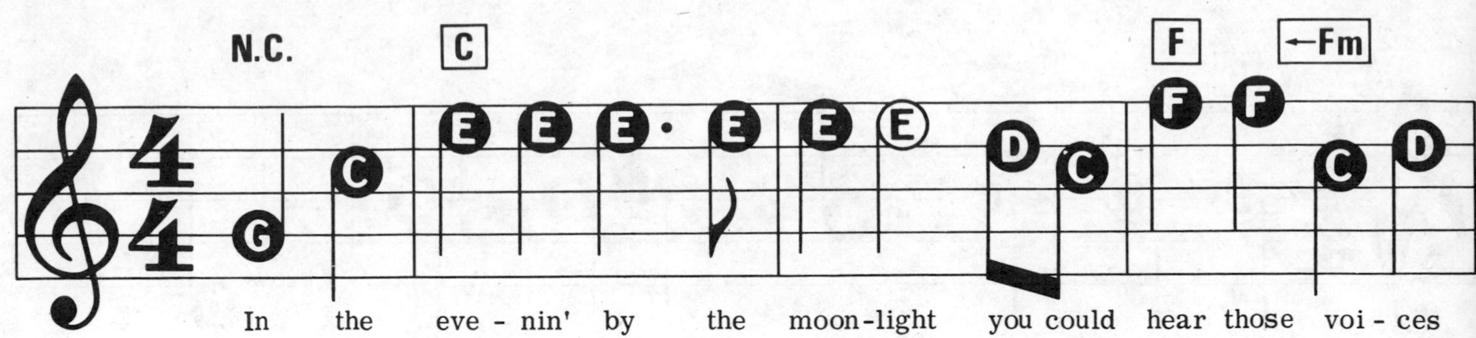

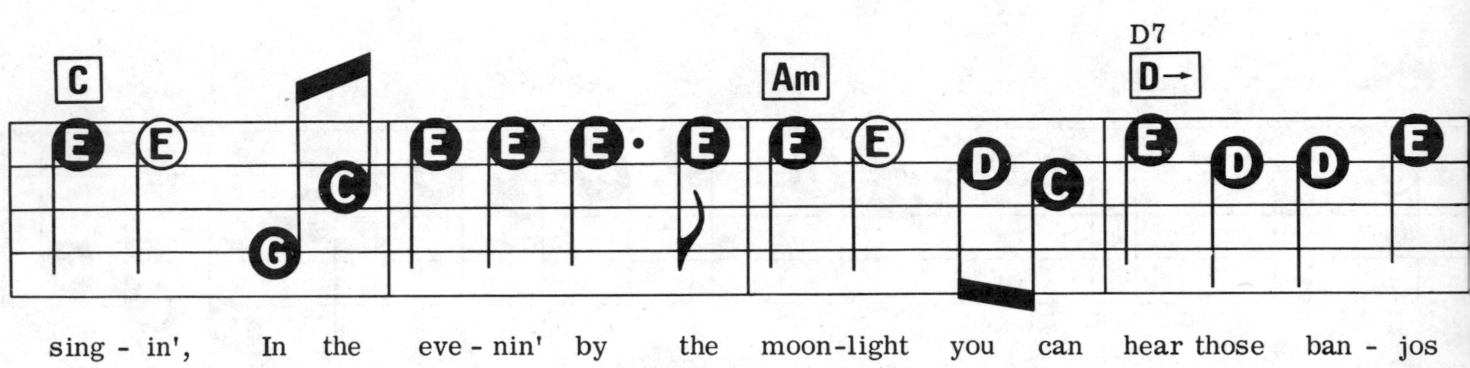

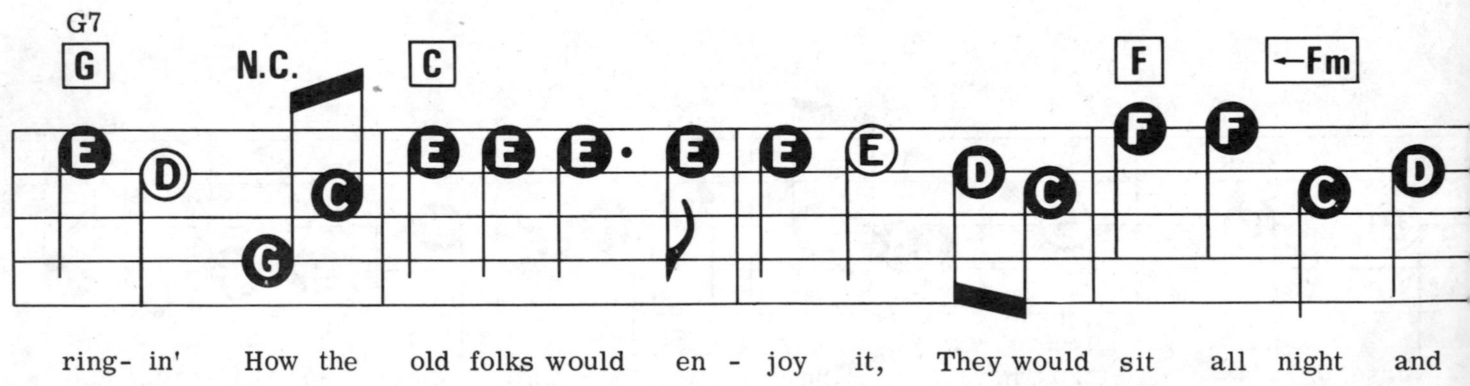

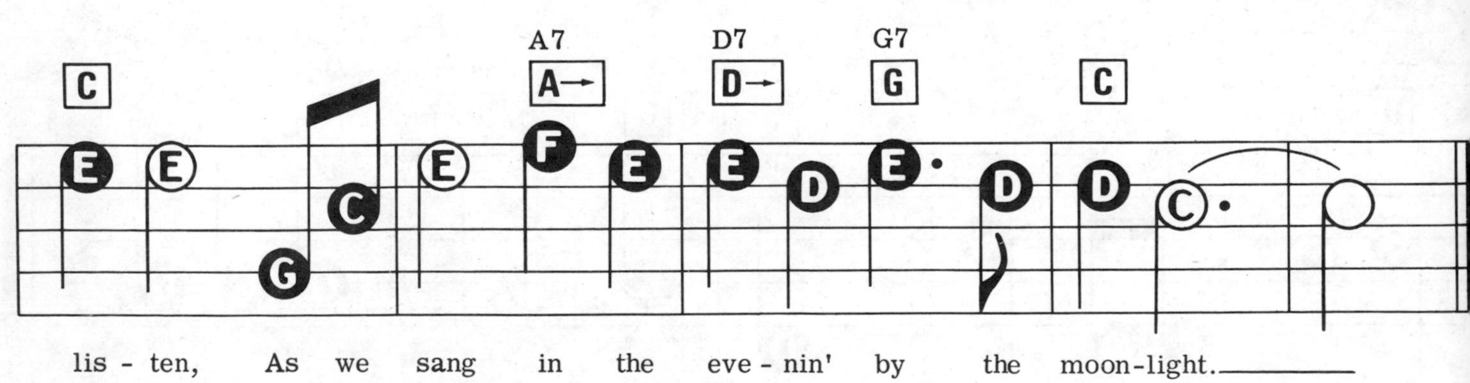

Li'l Liza Jane

Registration 9

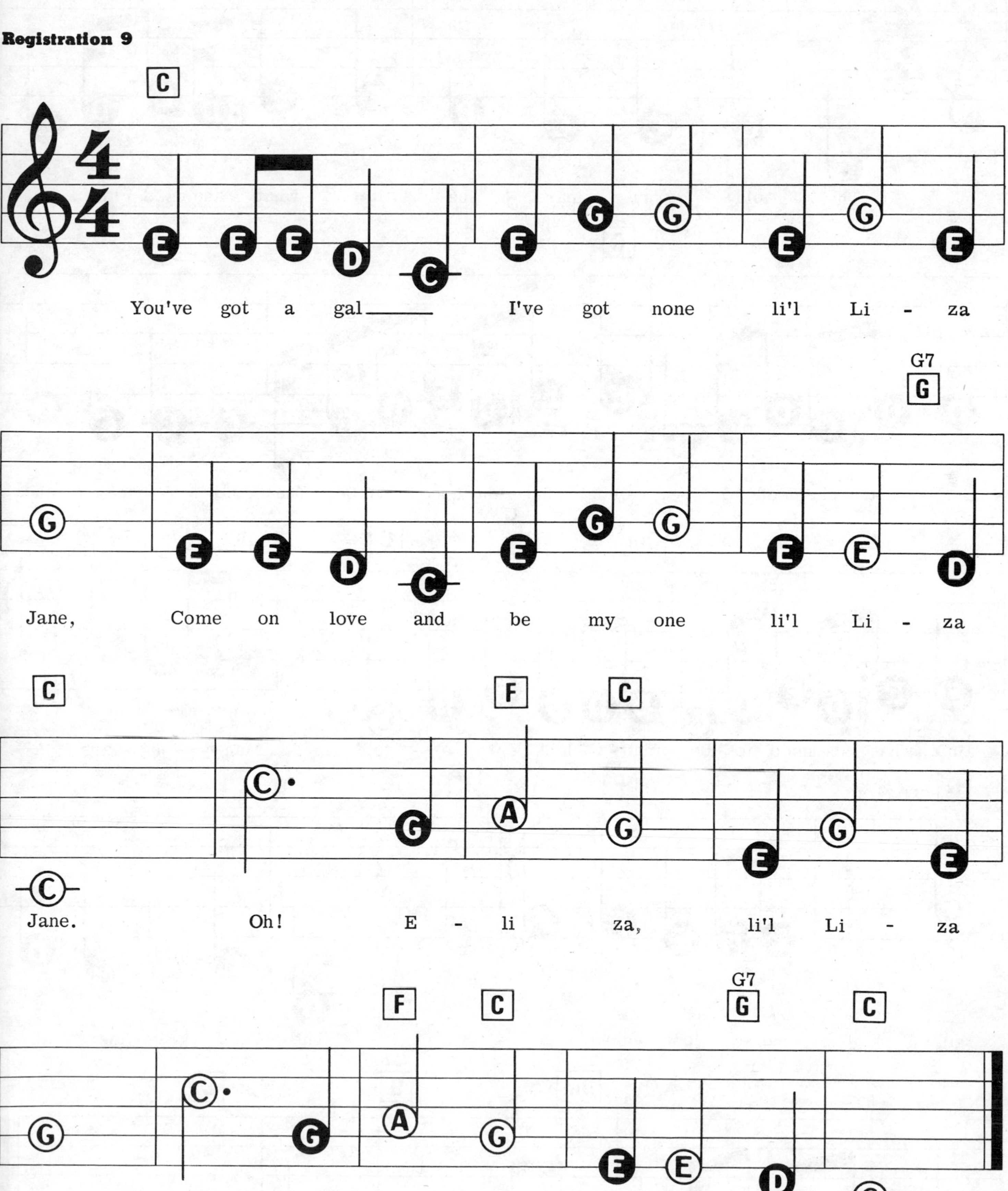

Registration 8

The Old Gray Mare

N.C. C

The old gray mare, she ain't what she used to be,

G7 G C

ain't what she used to be, ain't what she used to be. The old gray mare, she

Dm G7 G C F

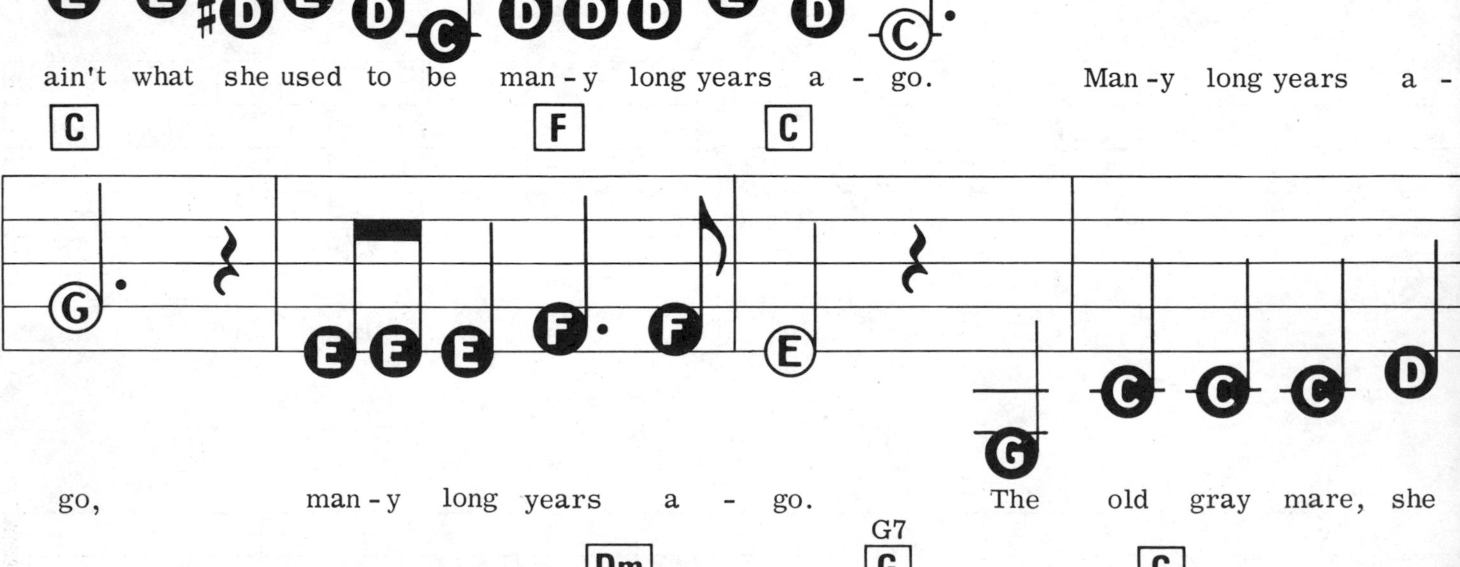

ain't what she used to be man - y long years a - go.

The Old Oaken Bucket

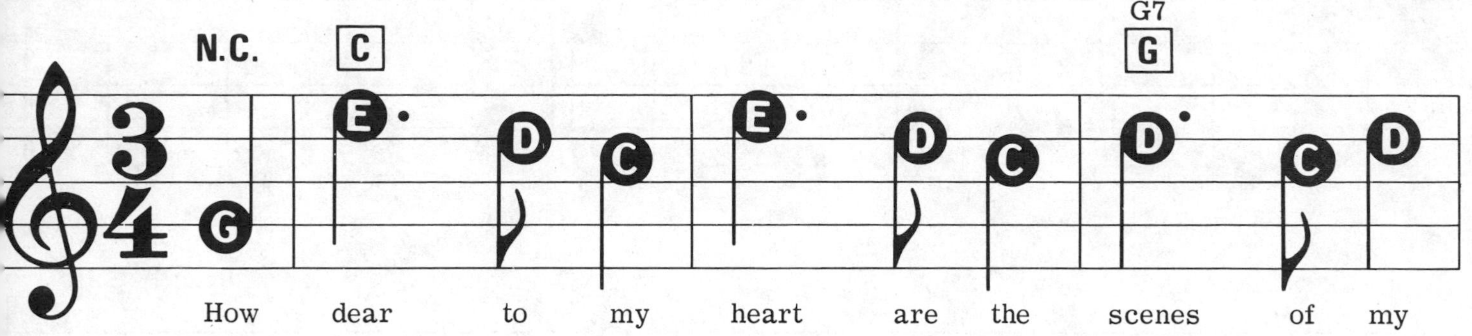

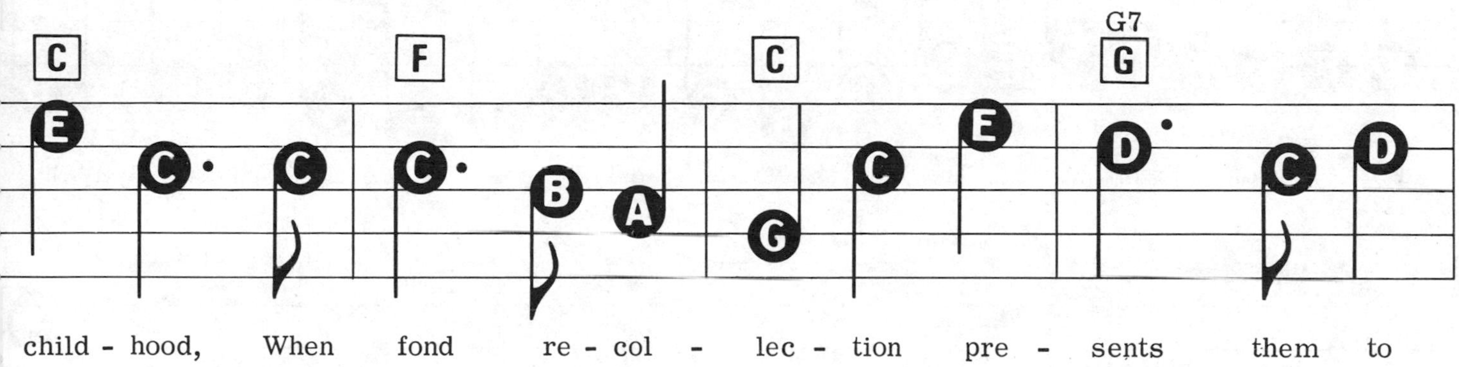

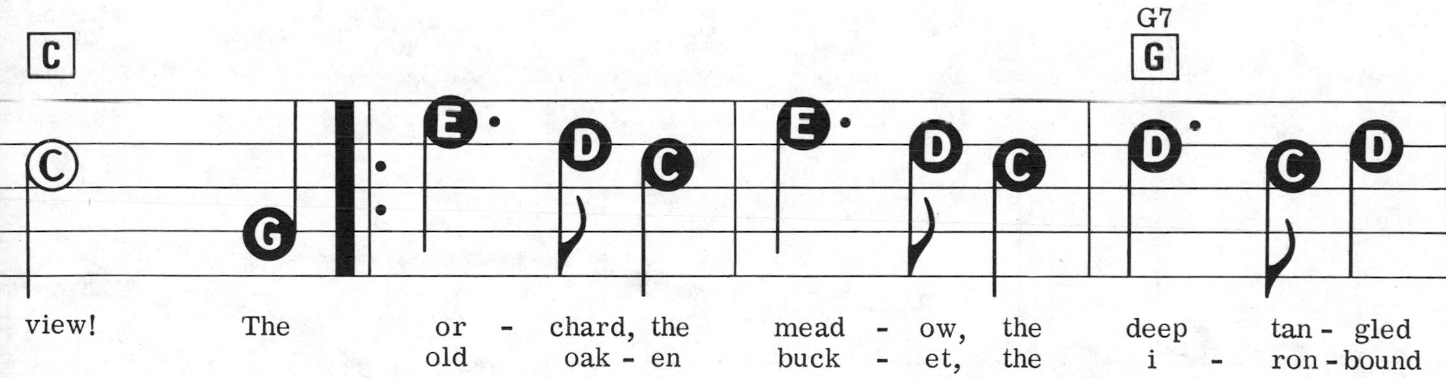

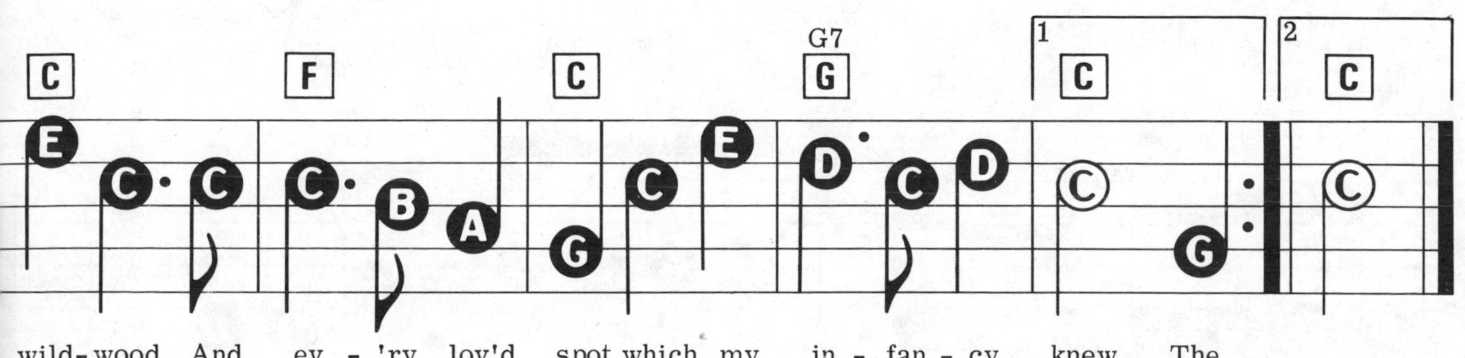

Polly Wolly Doodle

Registration 4

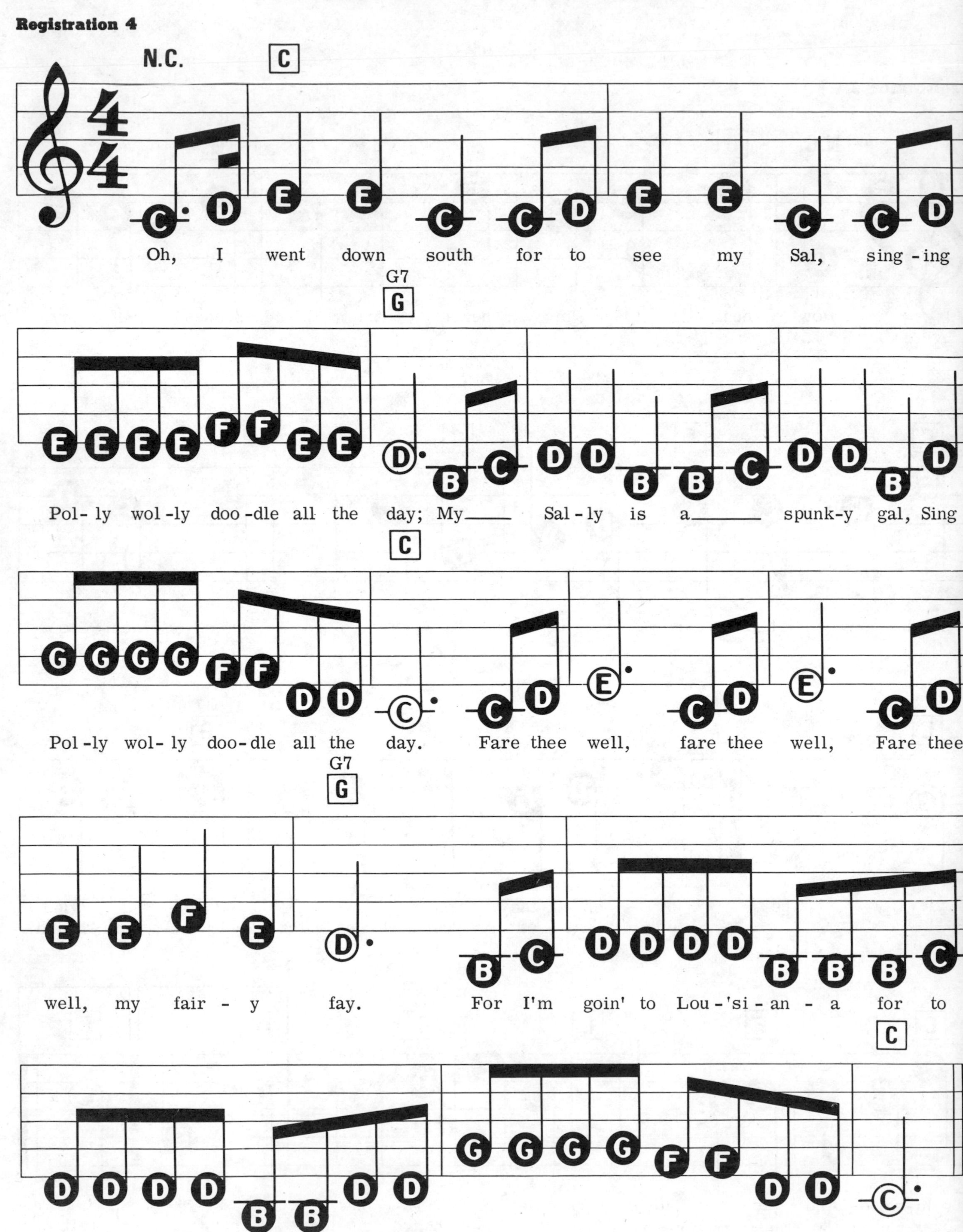

When You Were Sweet Sixteen

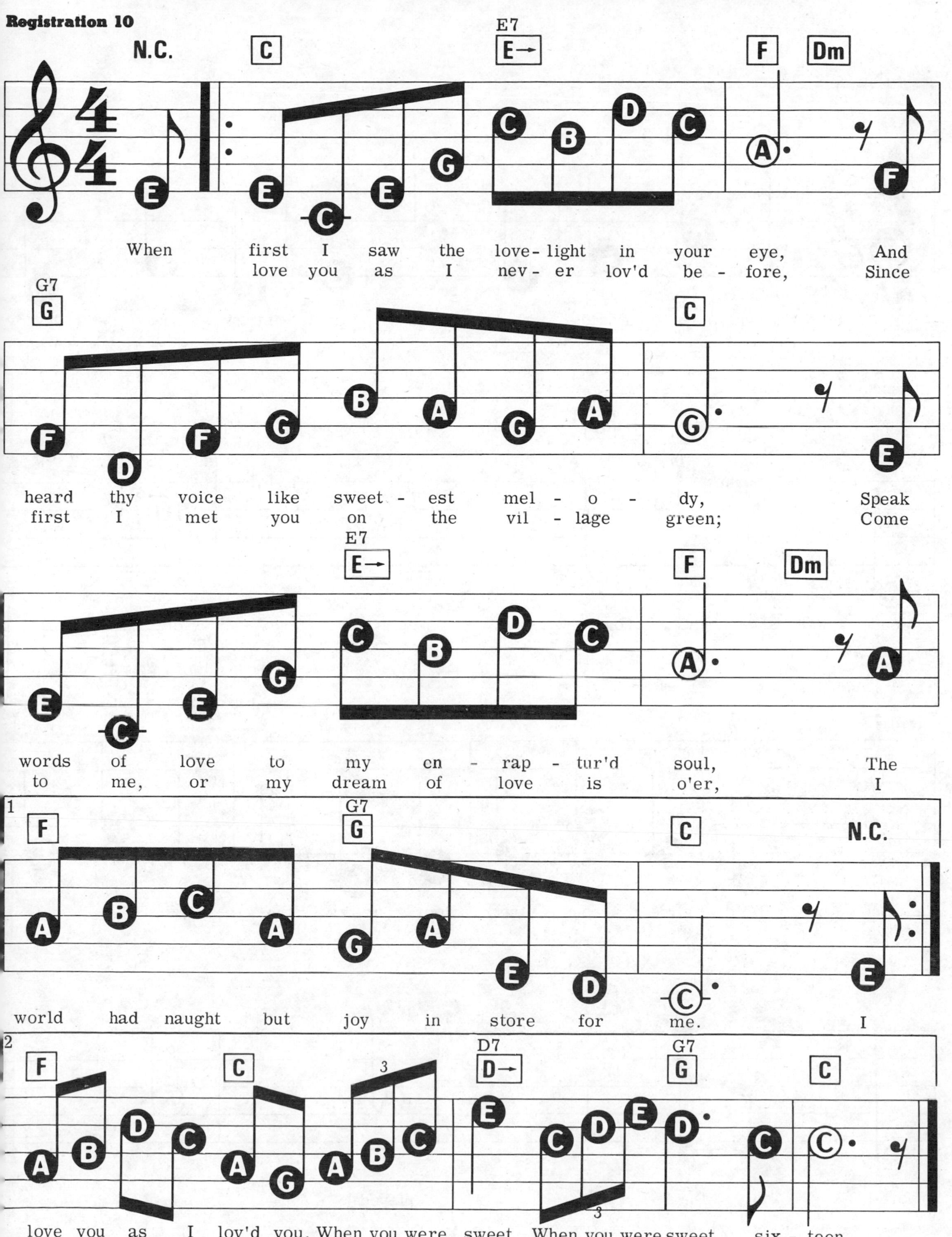

The Band Played On

Registration 5

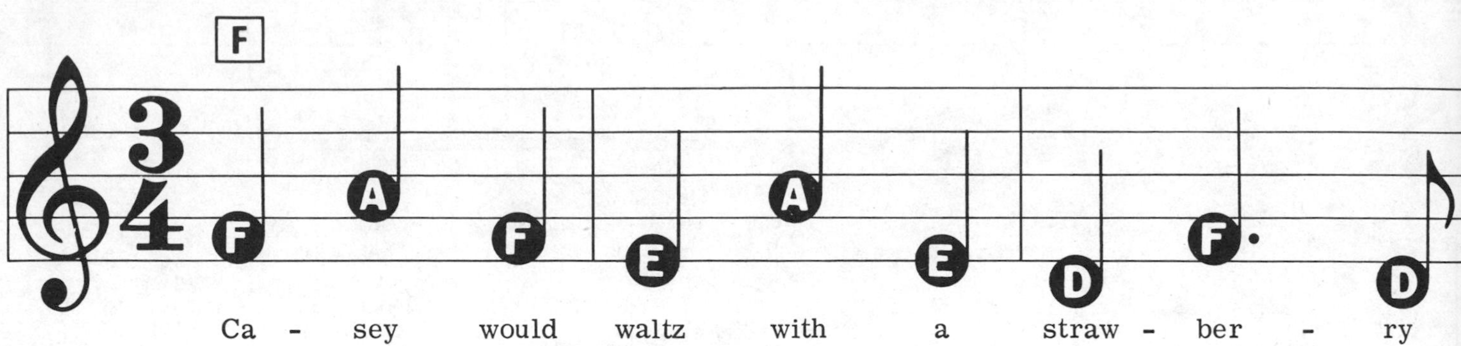

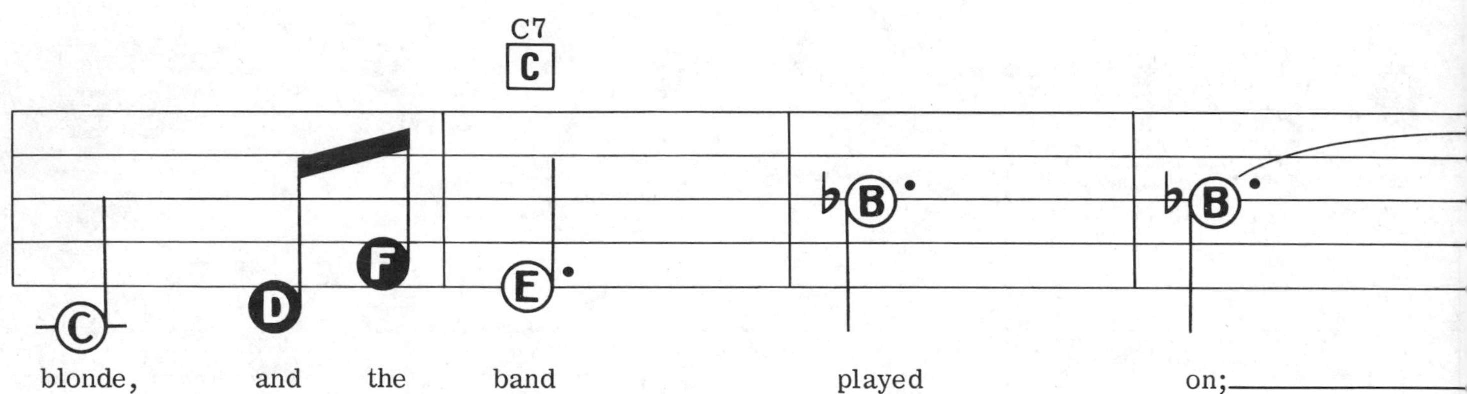

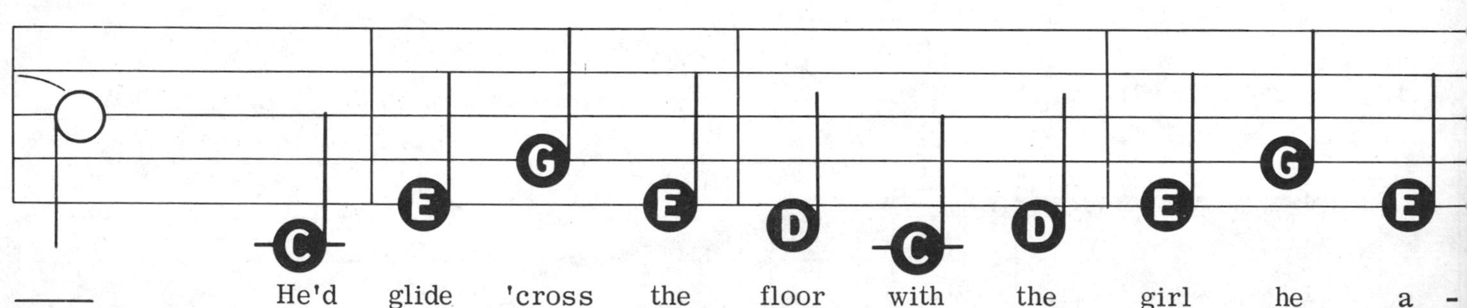

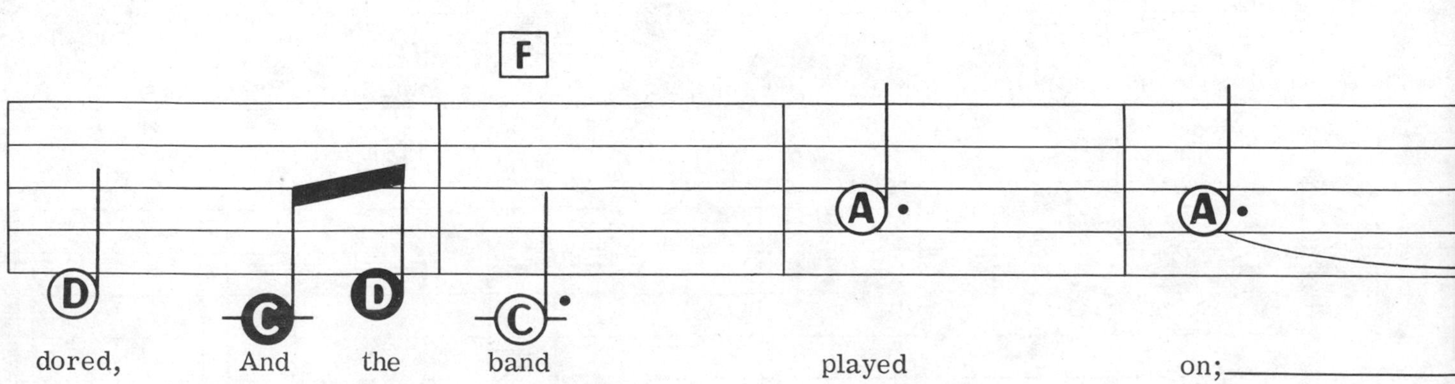

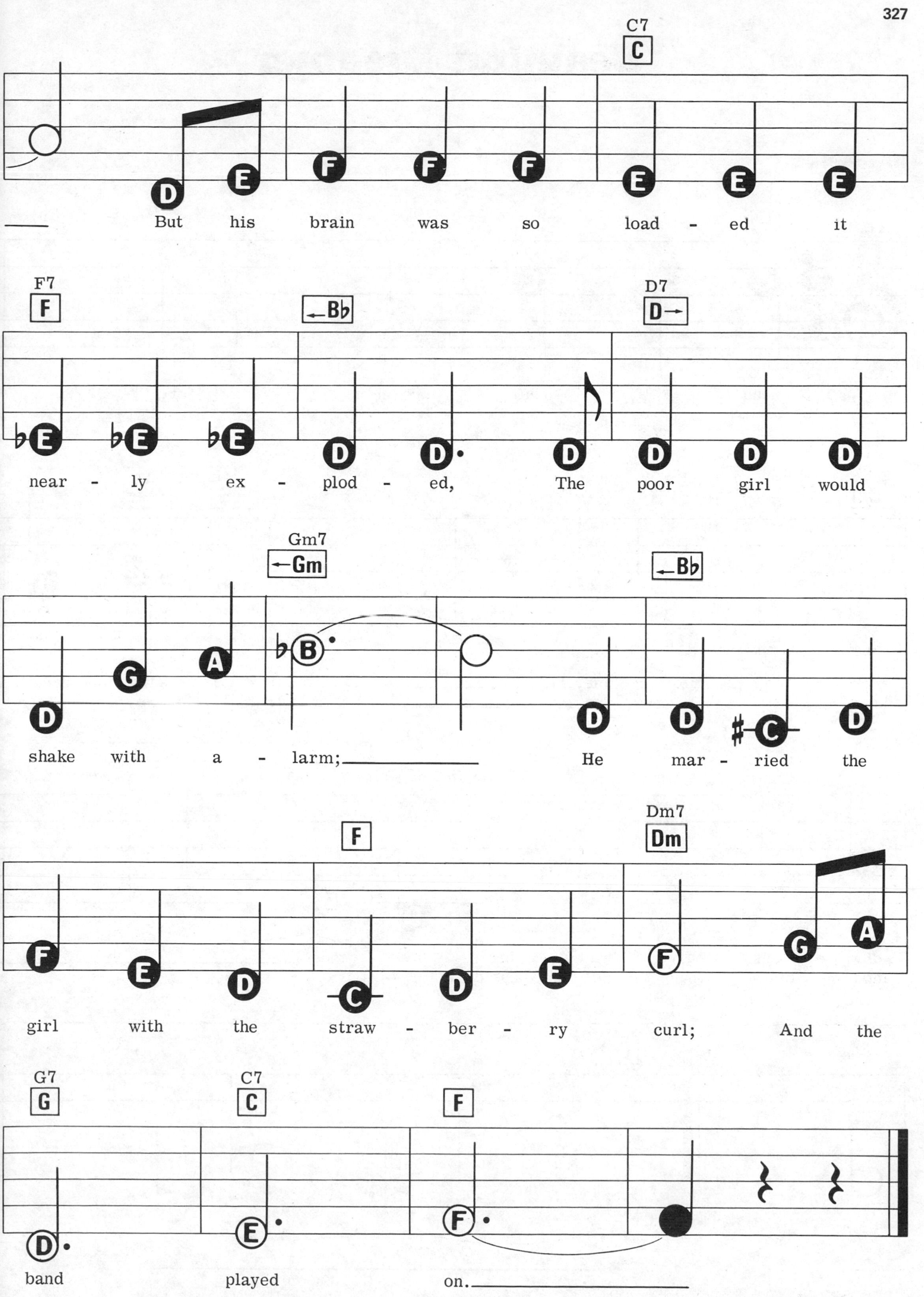
C7
C
D
E
F
F
F
E
E
E
But his brain was so load - ed it
F7
F
←B♭
D7
D→
♭E
♭E
♭E
D
D
D
D
D
D
near - ly ex - plod - ed, The poor girl would
Gm7
←Gm
←B♭
D
G
A
♭B
D
D
♯C
D
shake with a - larm; He mar - ried the
F
Dm7
Dm
F
E
D
C
D
E
F
G
A
girl with the straw - ber - ry curl; And the
G7
G
C7
C
F
D
E
F
band played on.

Beautiful Dreamer

Registration 5

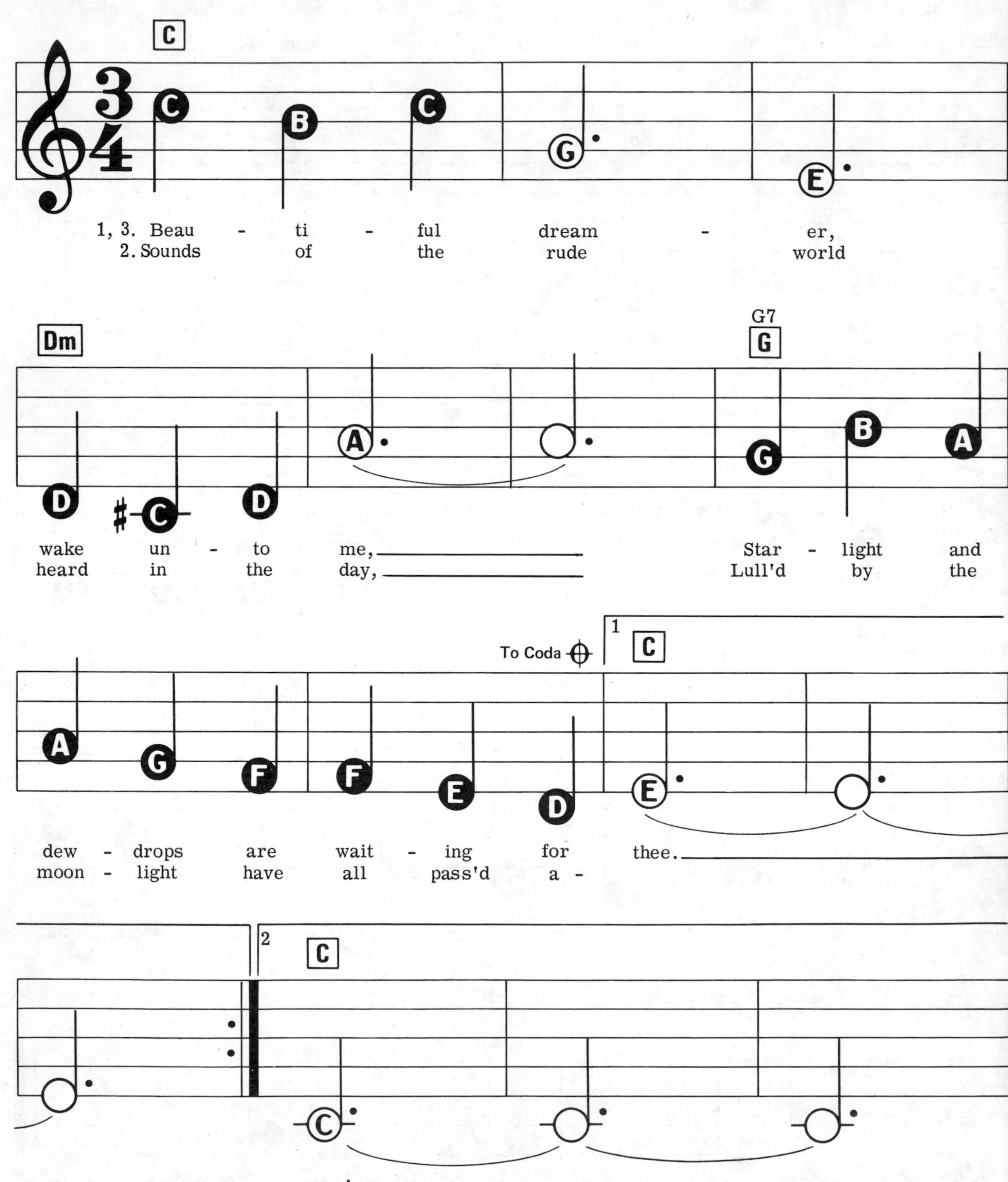

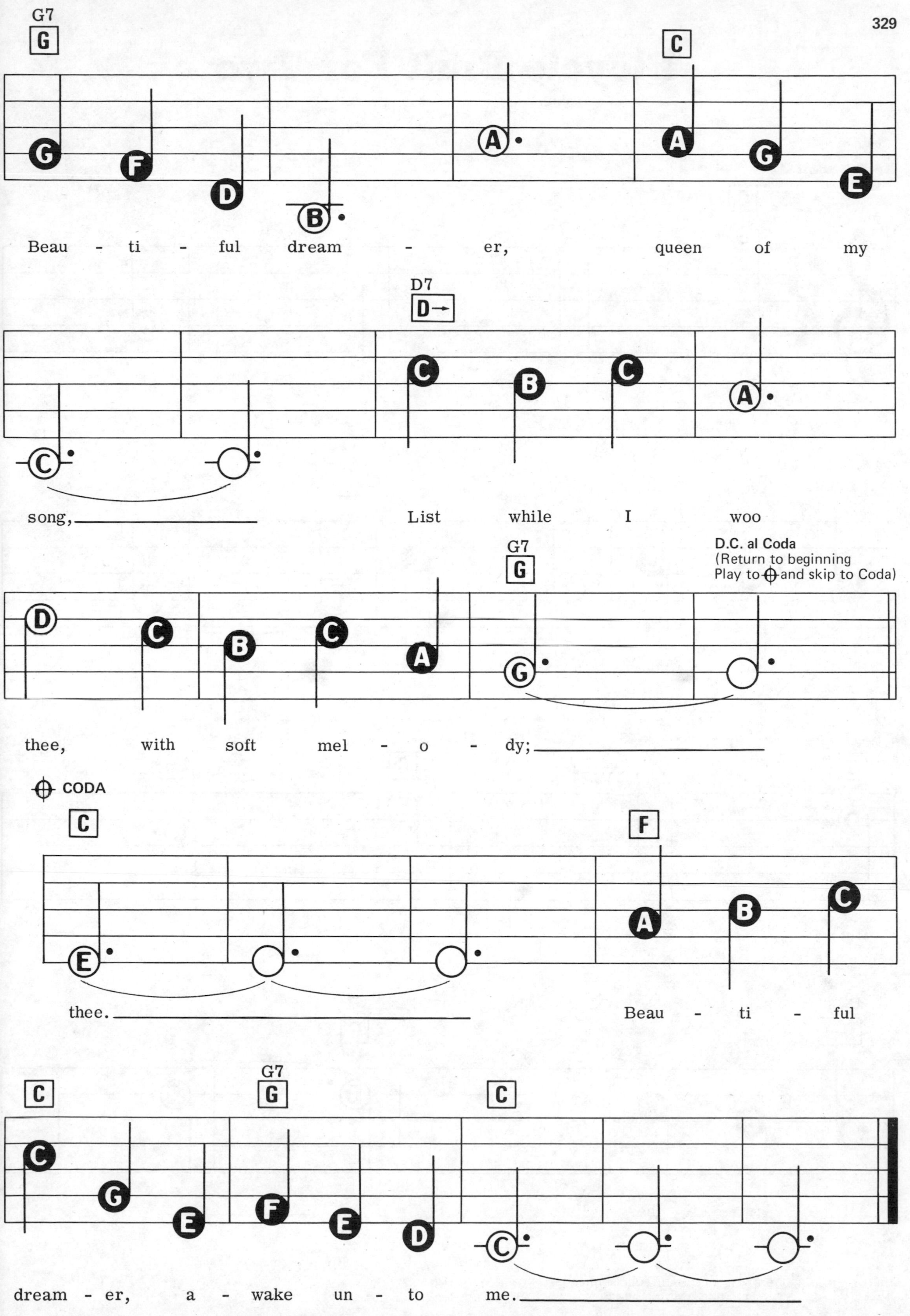
G7
G
C
Beau - ti - ful dream - er, queen of my
D7
D→
song,
List while I woo
G7
G
D.C. al Coda
(Return to beginning
Play to ⊕ and skip to Coda)
thee, with soft mel - o - dy;
⊕ CODA
C
F
thee.
Beau - ti - ful
C
G7
G
C
dream - er, a - wake un - to me.

Bicycle Built For Two

Registration 2

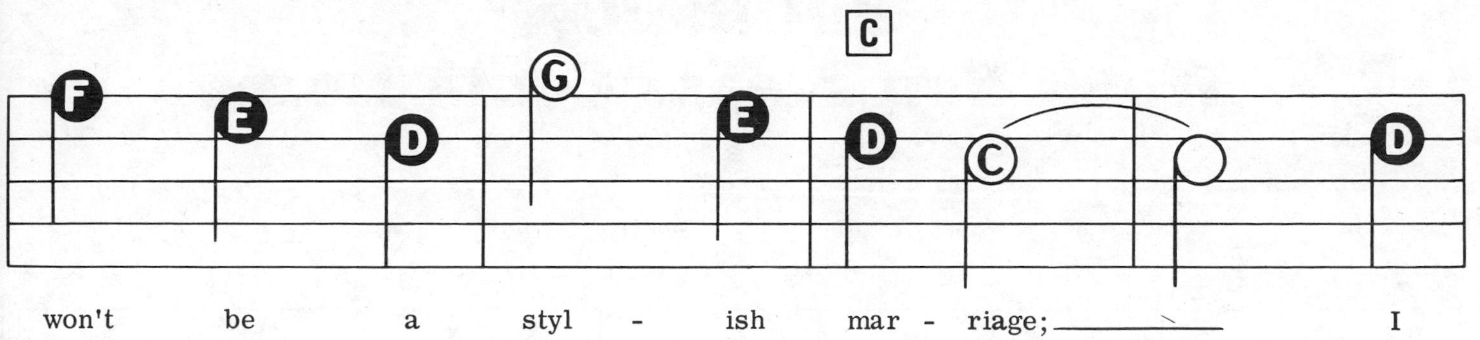
C
F
E
D
G
E
D
C
D
won't be a styl - ish mar - riage;
I

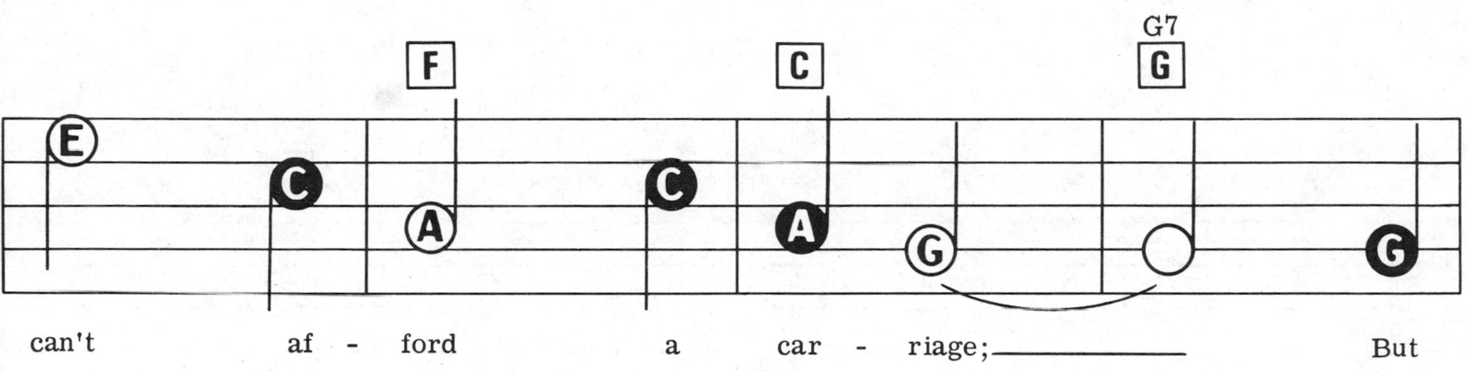
F
C
G7
G
E
C
A
C
A
G
G
can't af - ford a car - riage;
But

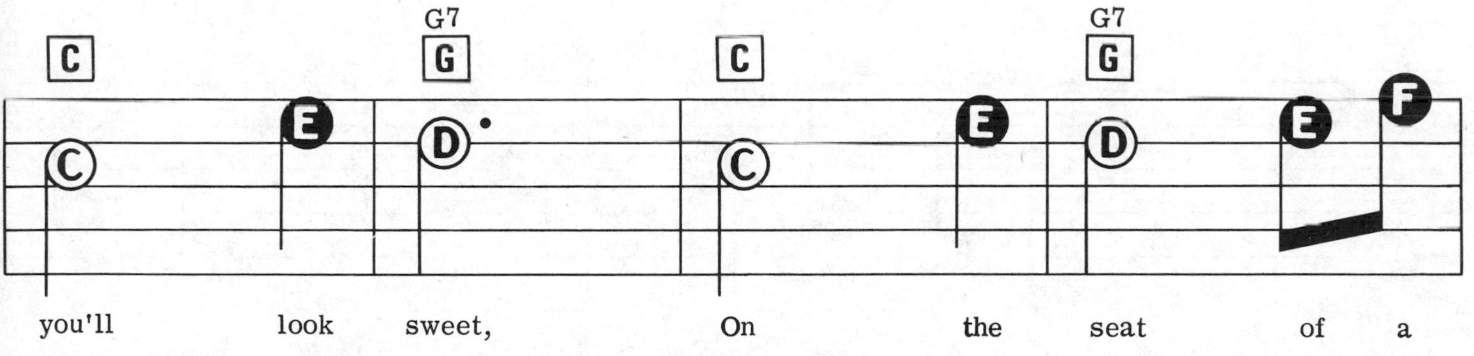
C
G7
G
C
G7
G
C
E
D
C
E
D
E
F
you'll look sweet, On the seat of a

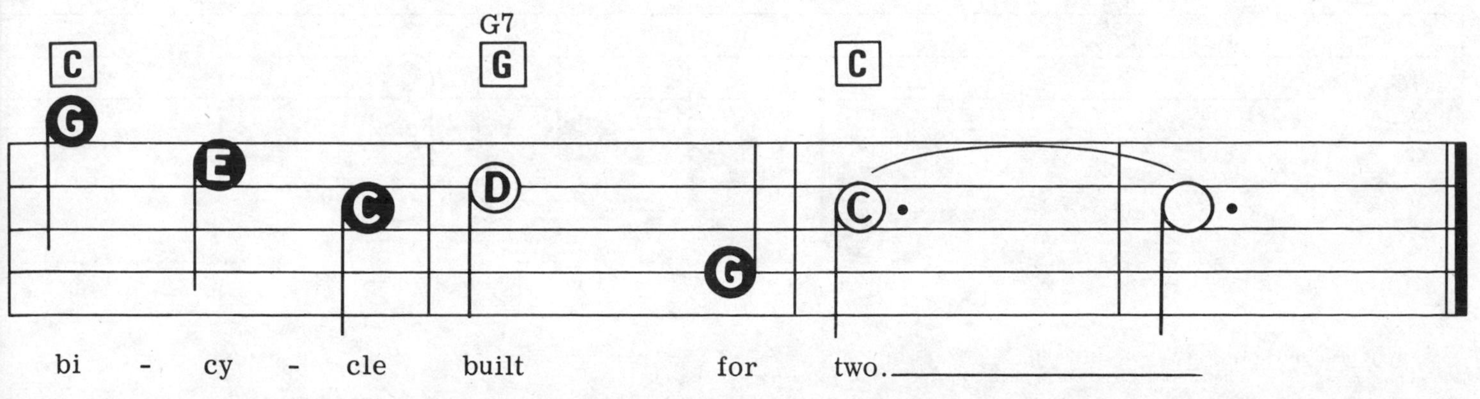
C
G7
G
C
G
E
C
D
G
C
bi - cy - cle built for two.

Bill Bailey, Won't You Please Come Home

Registration 7

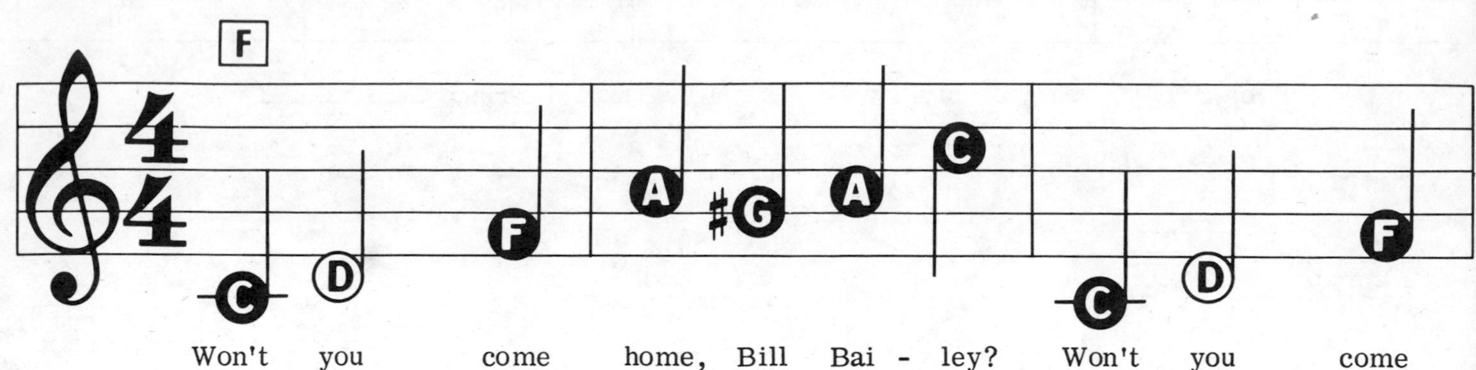

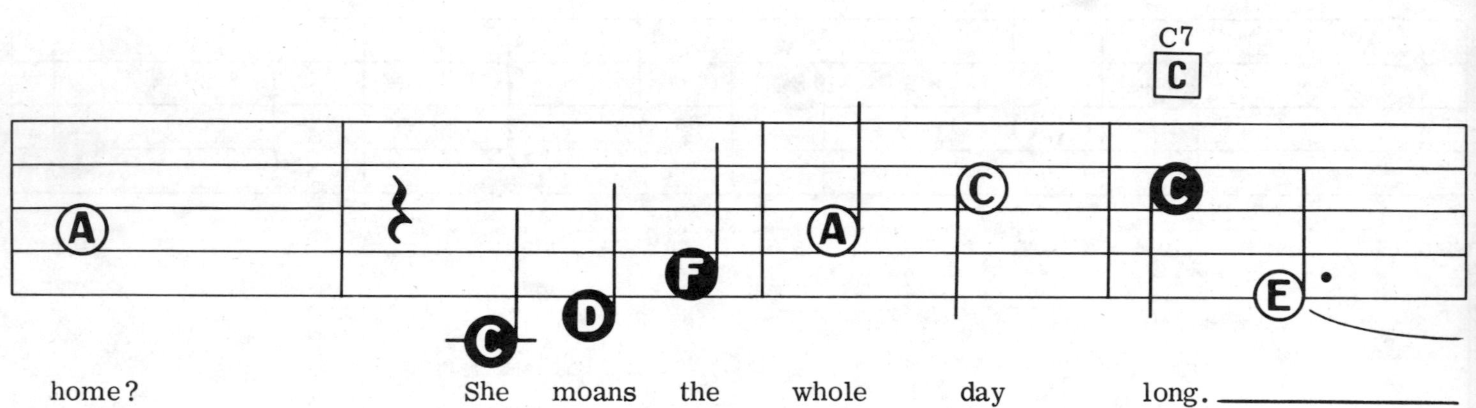

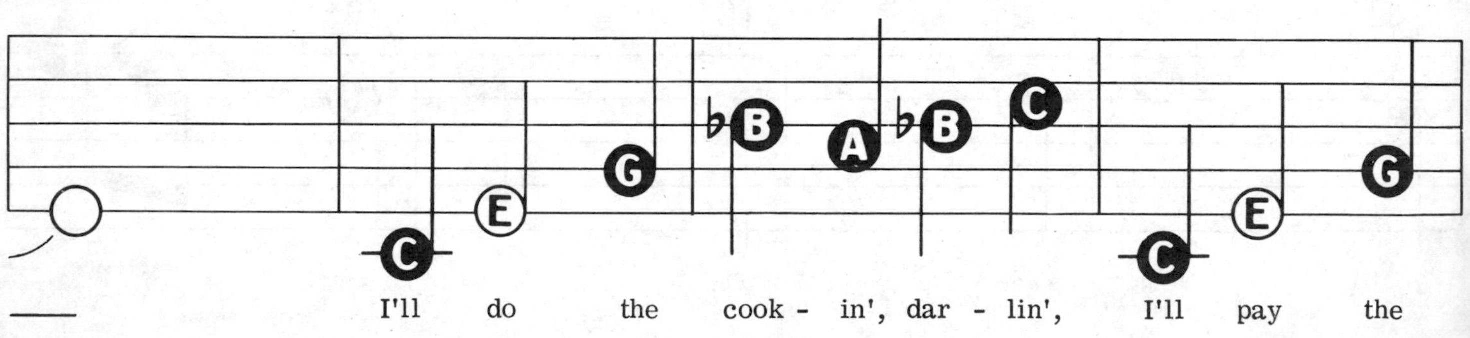

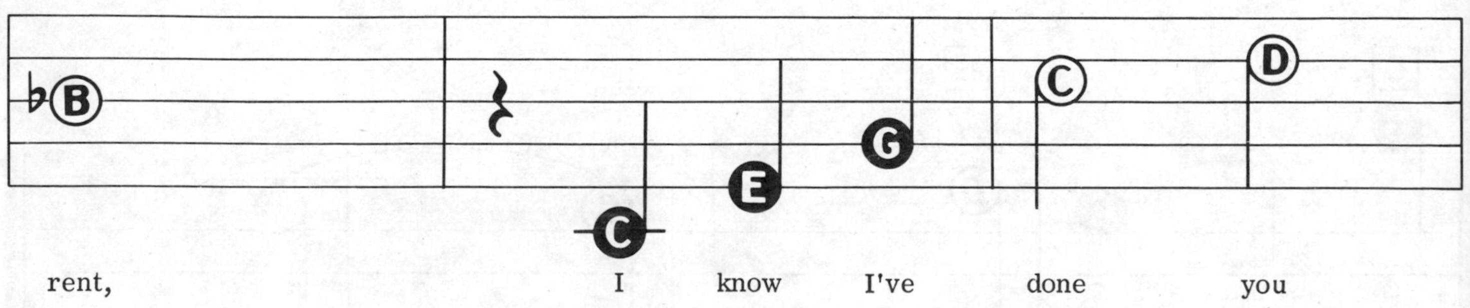

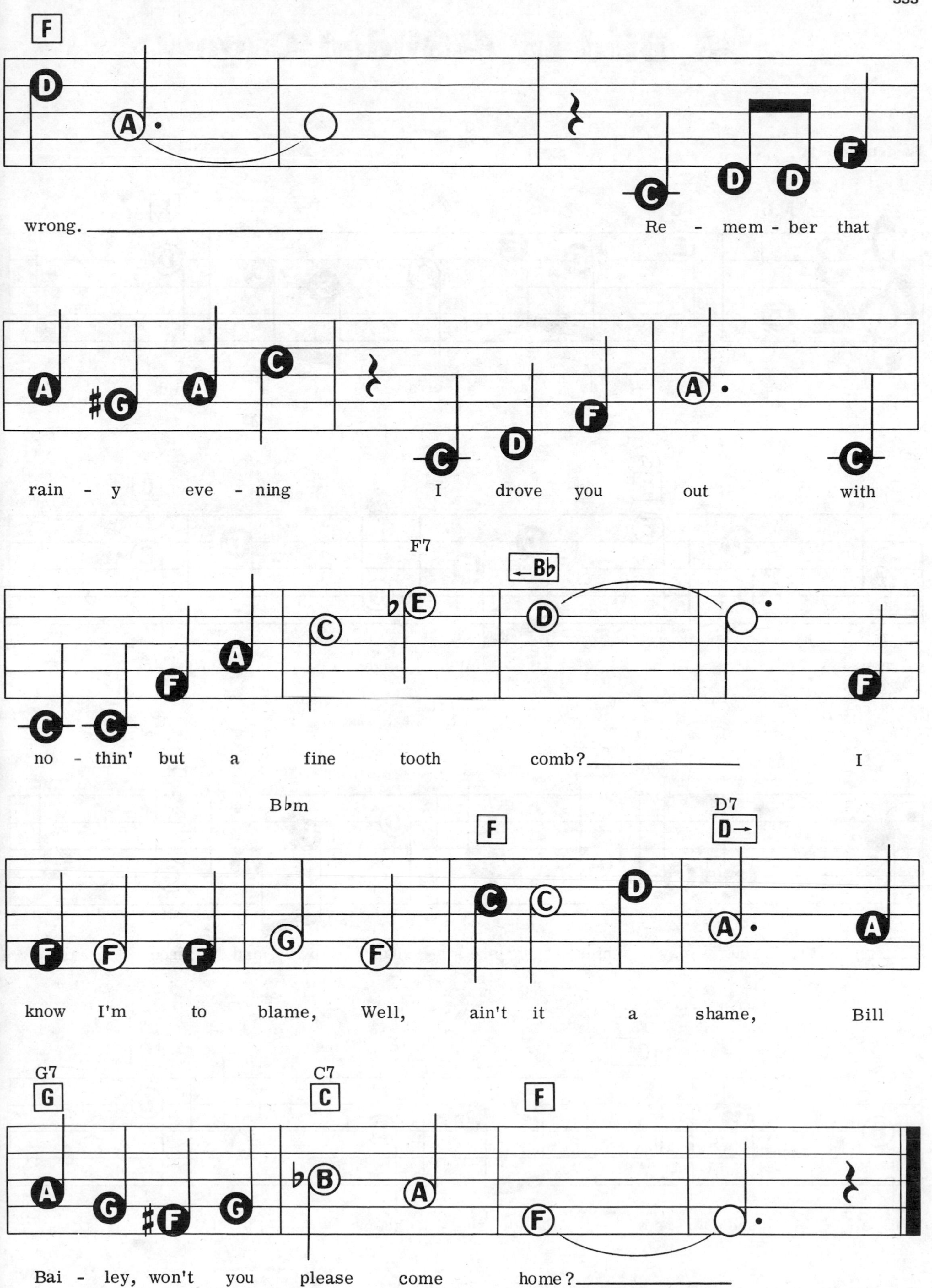
F
wrong. Re - mem - ber that
rain - y eve - ning I drove you out with
F7
←B♭
no - thin' but a fine tooth comb? I
B♭m
F
D7
D→
know I'm to blame, Well, ain't it a shame, Bill
G7
G
C7
C
F
Bai - ley, won't you please come home?

A Bird In A Gilded Cage

Registration 10

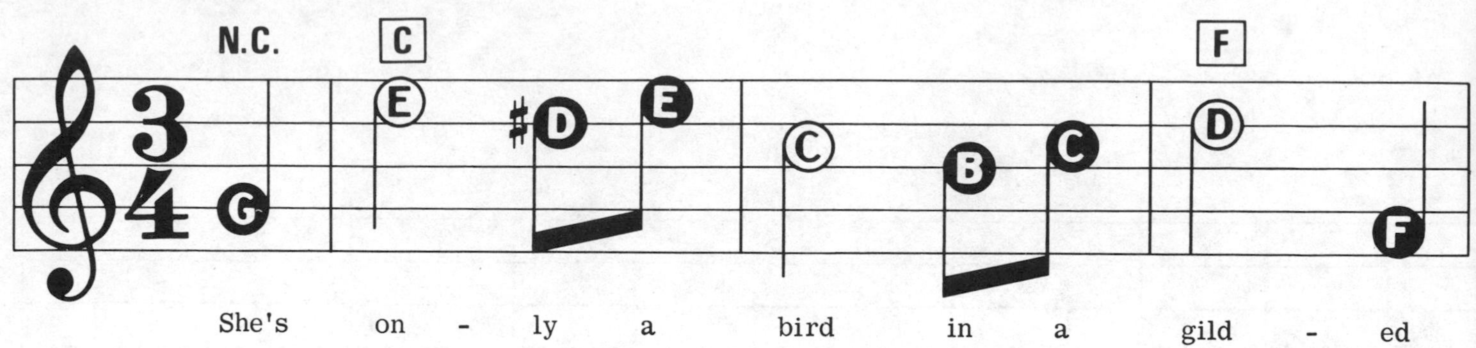

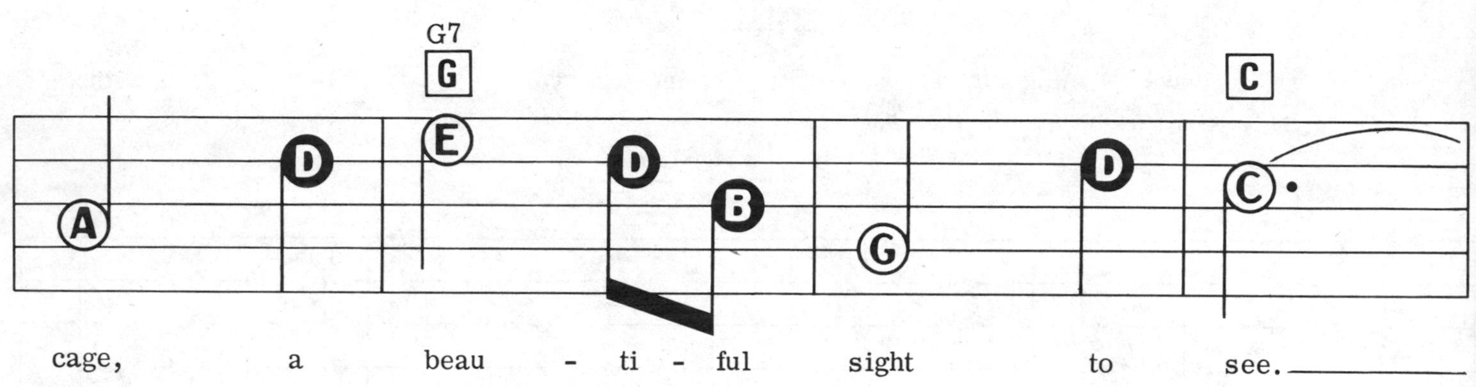

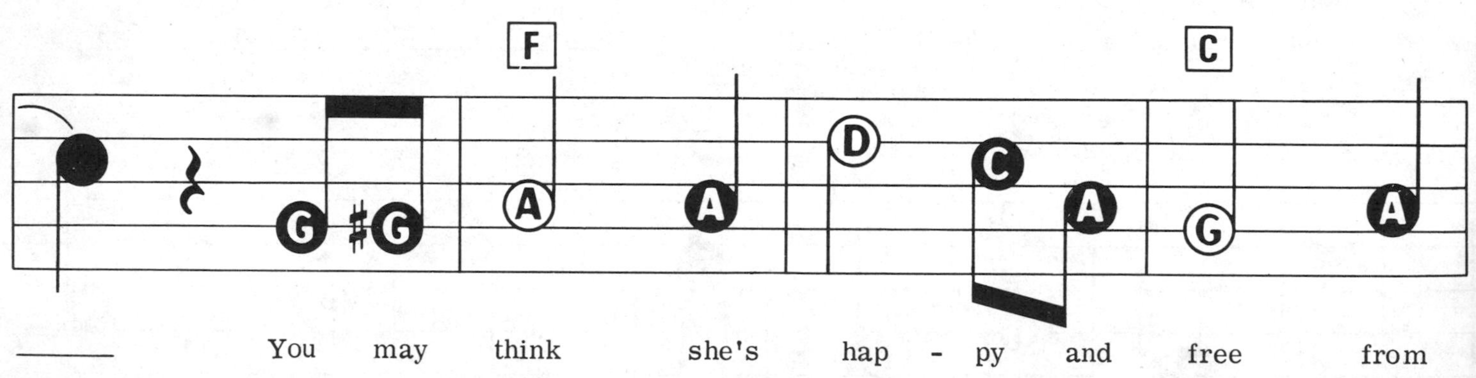

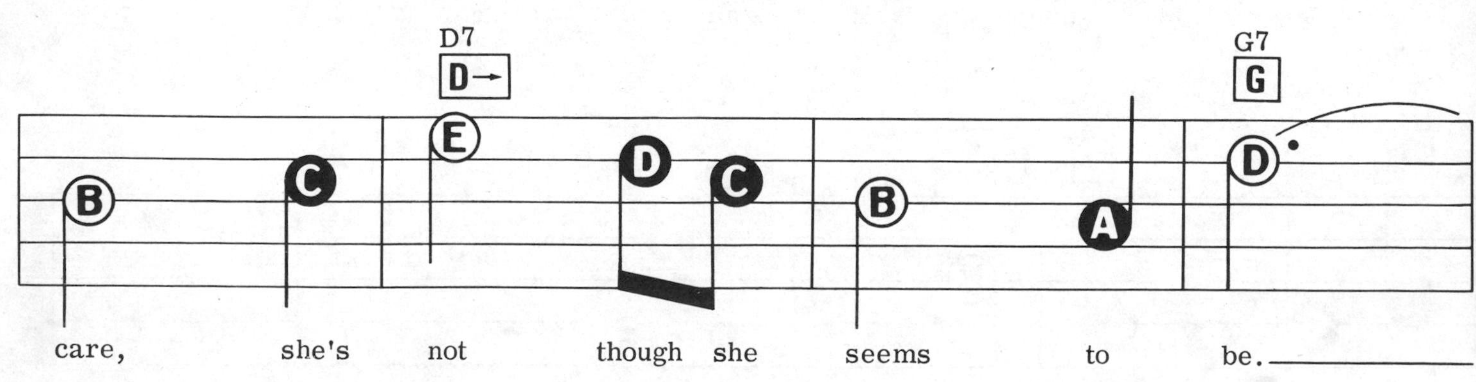

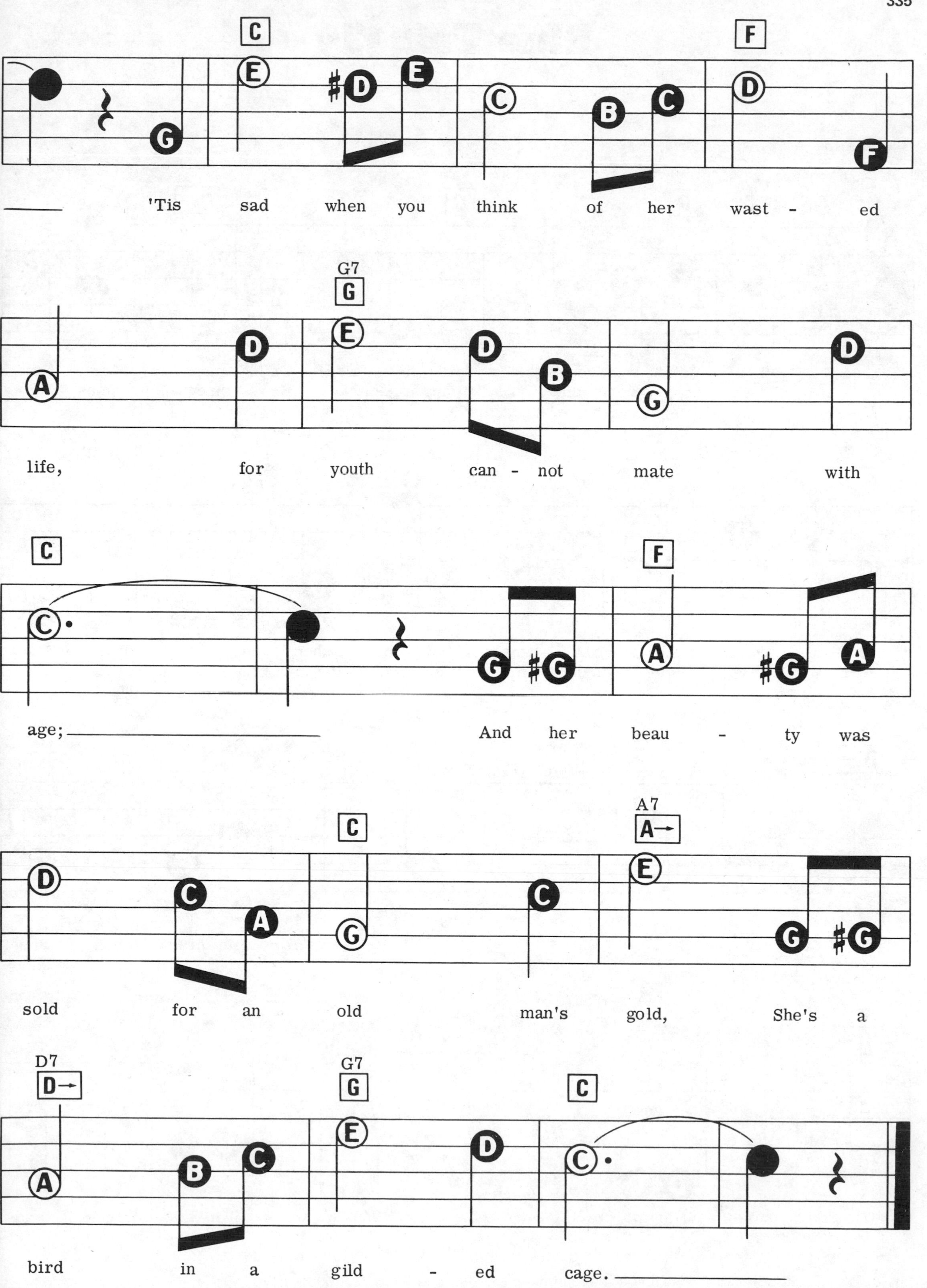
C F
'Tis sad when you think of her wast - ed
G7 G
life, for youth can - not mate with
C F
age; And her beau - ty was
C A7 A
sold for an old man's gold, She's a
D7 D G7 G C
bird in a gild - ed cage.

Blue Tail Fly

Registration 4

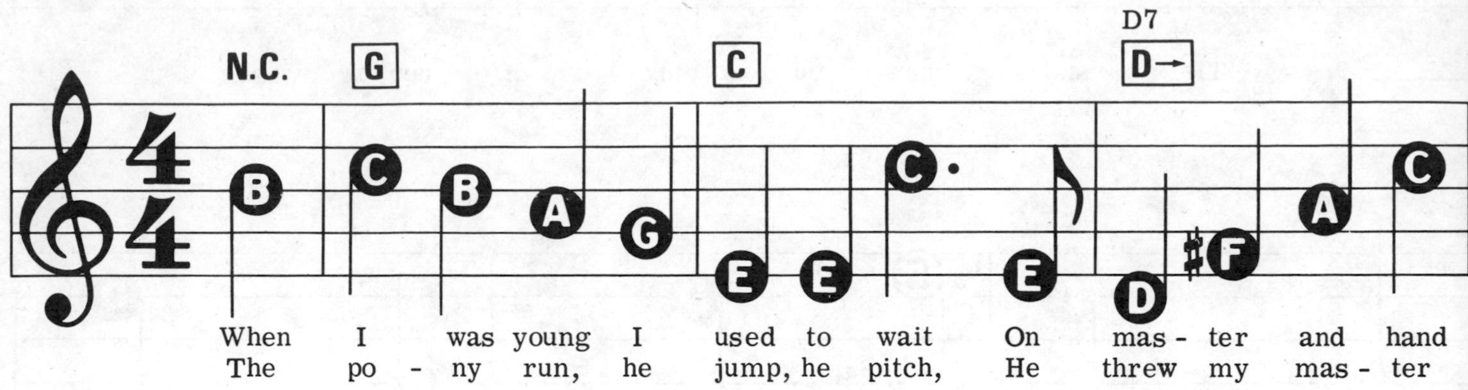

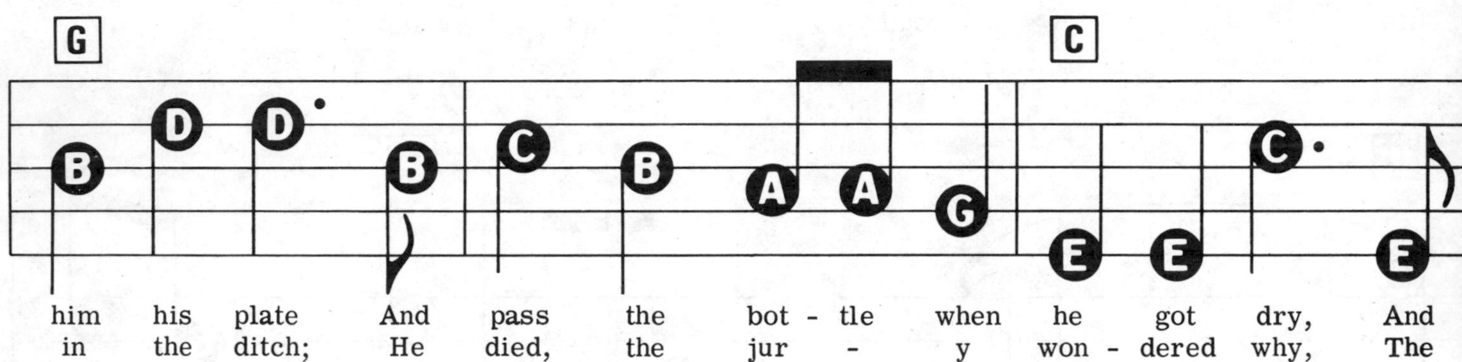

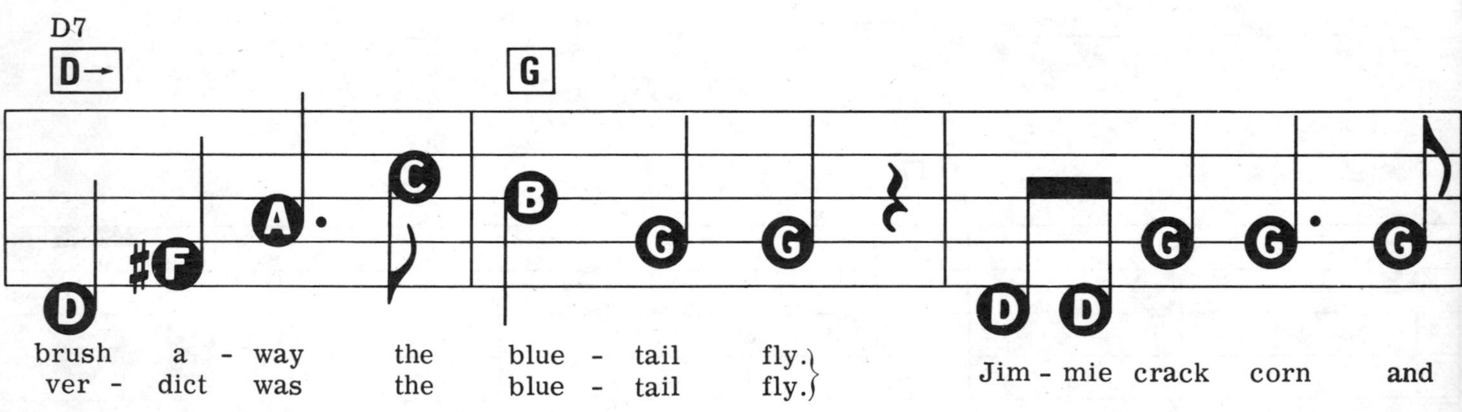

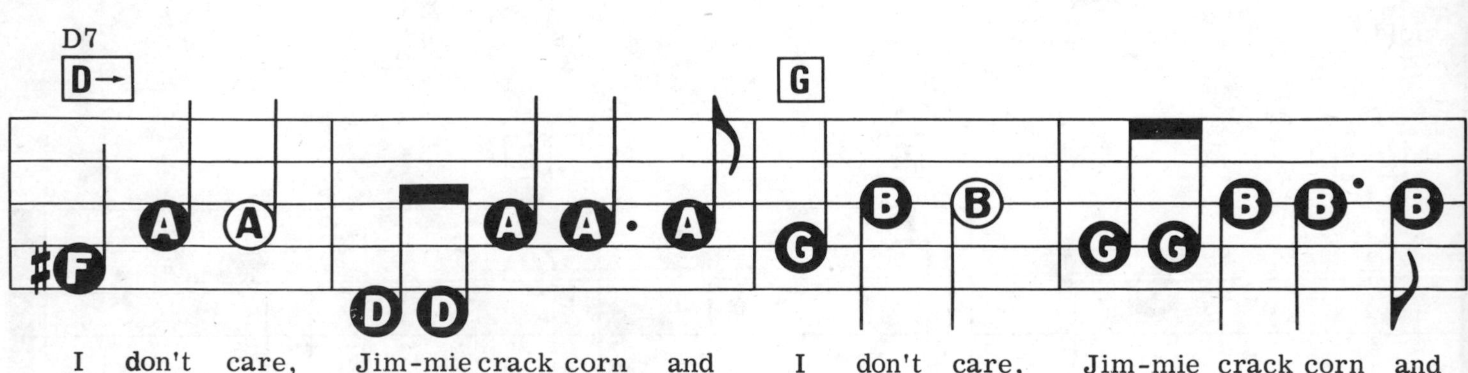

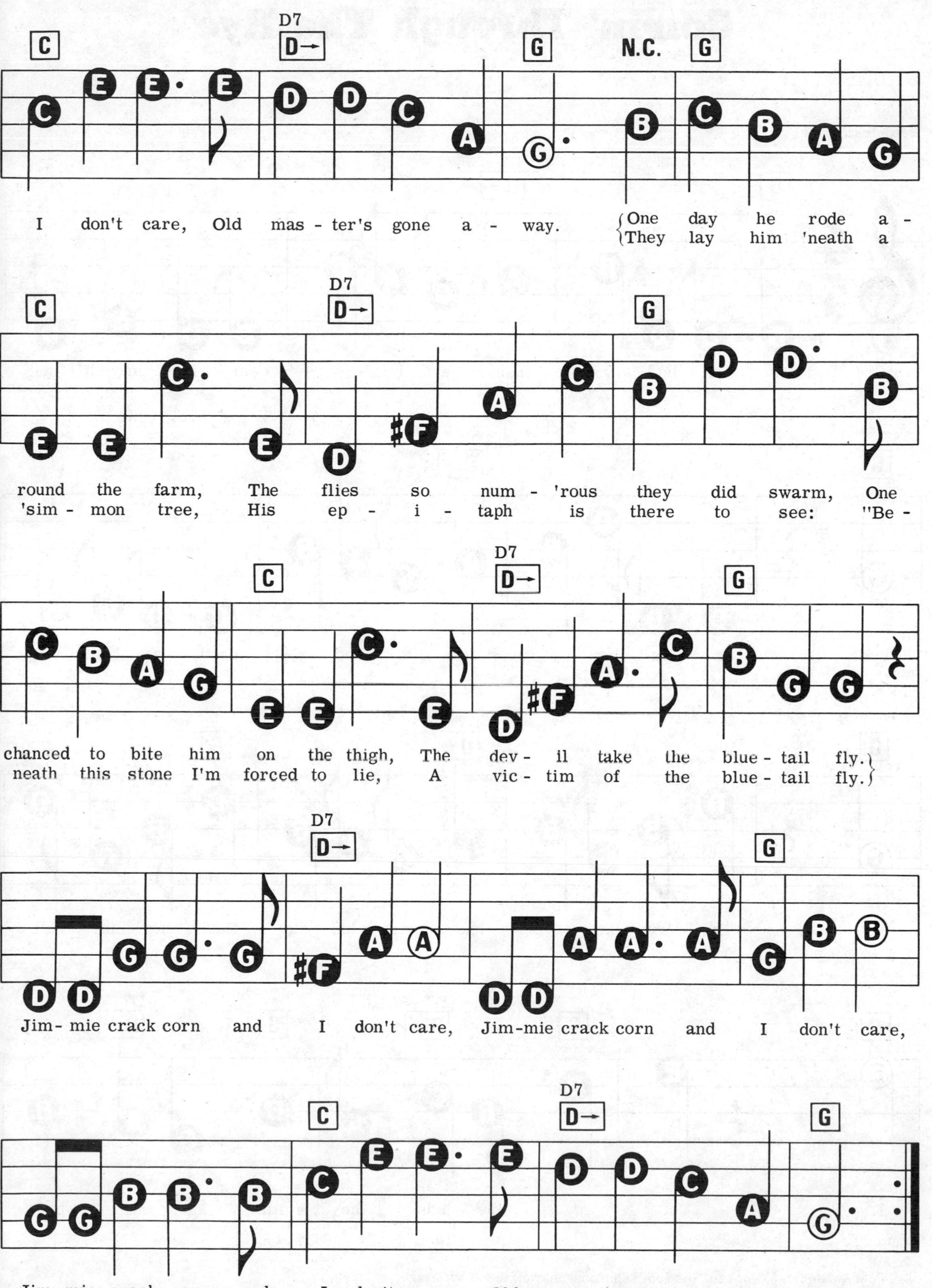
C
D7 D→
G
N.C.
G
I don't care, Old mas - ter's gone a - way.
One day he rode a -
They lay him 'neath a
C
D7 D→
G
round the farm, The flies so num - 'rous they did swarm, One
'sim - mon tree, His ep - i - taph is there to see: "Be -
C
D7 D→
G
chanced to bite him on the thigh, The dev - il take the blue - tail fly.
neath this stone I'm forced to lie, A vic - tim of the blue - tail fly."
D7 D→
G
Jim- mie crack corn and I don't care, Jim-mie crack corn and I don't care,
C
D7 D→
G
Jim- mie crack corn and I don't care, Old mas - ter's gone a - way.

Comin' Through The Rye

Registration 9

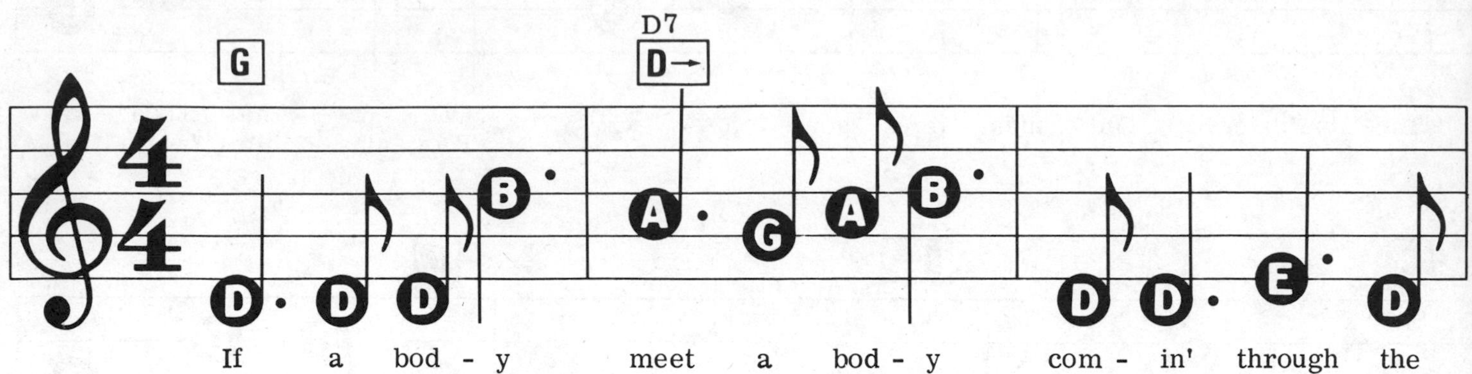

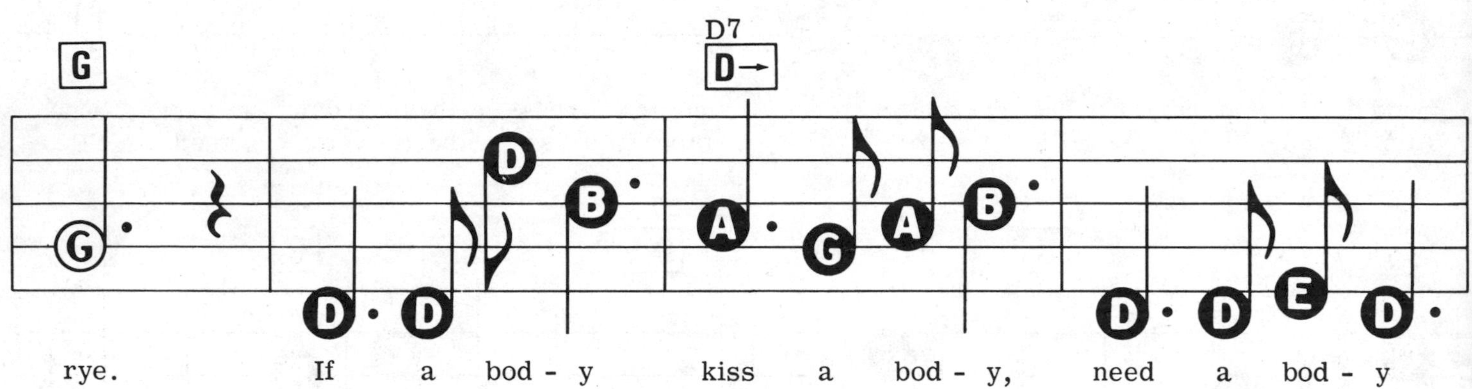

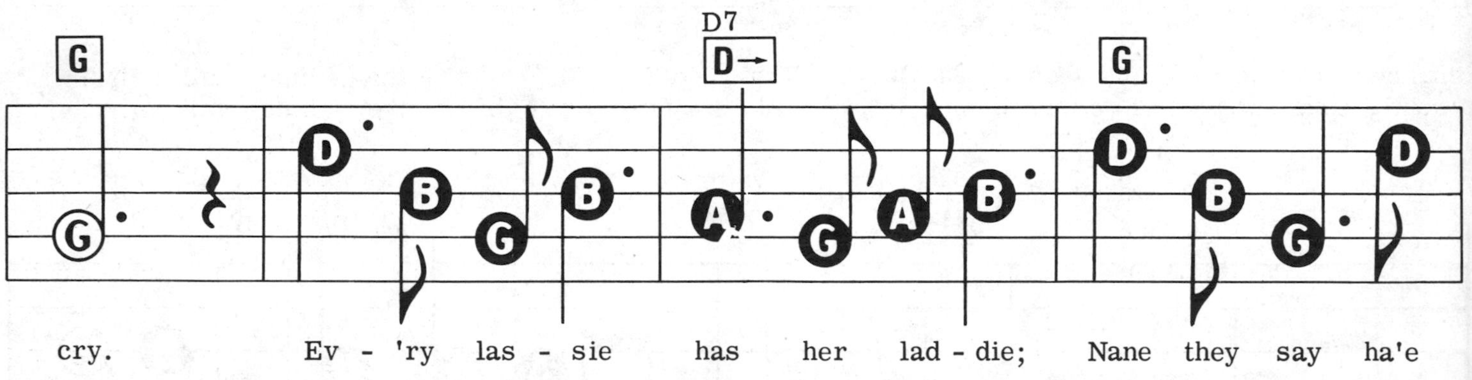

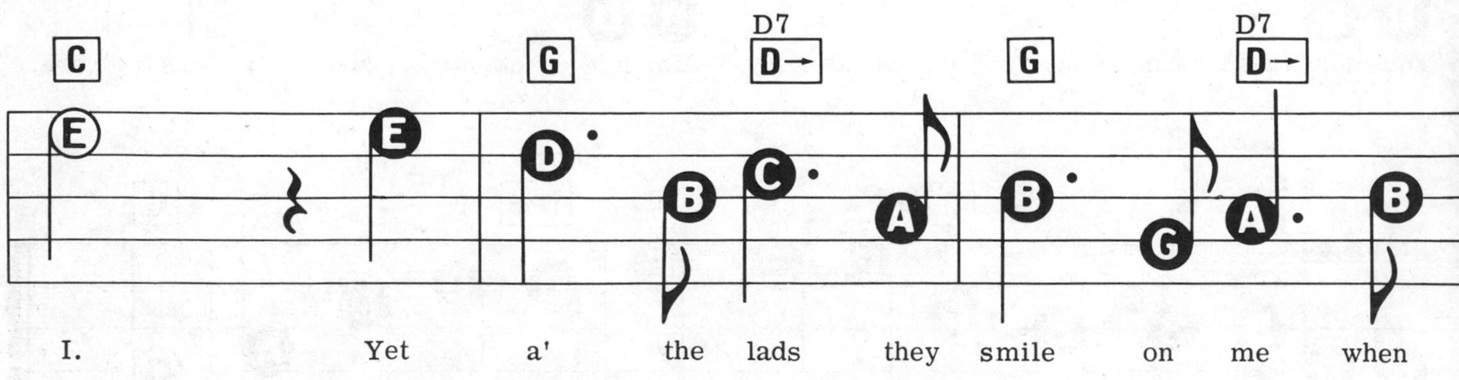

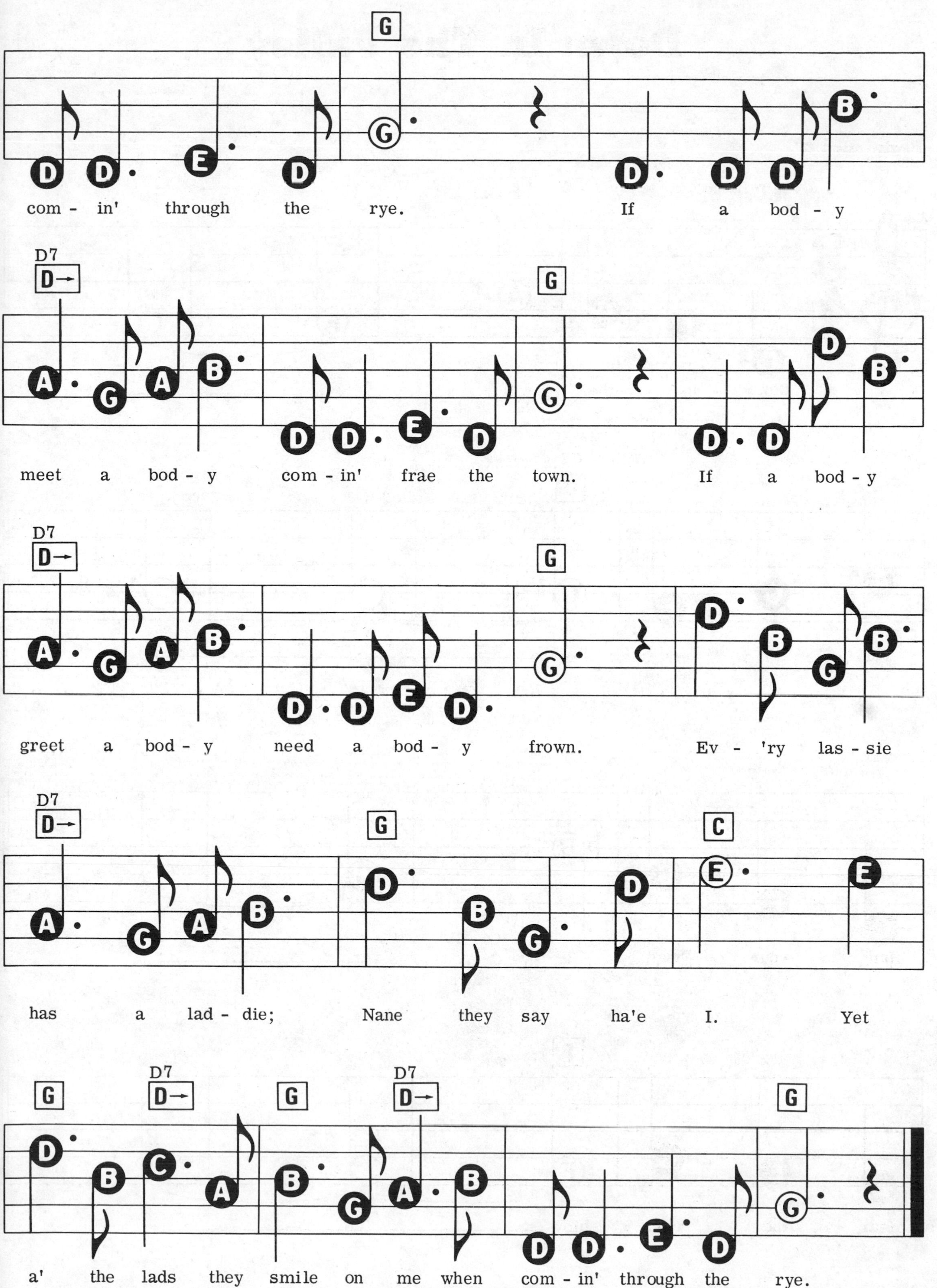
G
com - in' through the rye. If a bod - y
D7 D→ G
meet a bod - y com - in' frae the town. If a bod - y
D7 D→ G
greet a bod - y need a bod - y frown. Ev - 'ry las - sie
D7 D→ G C
has a lad - die; Nane they say ha'e I. Yet
G D7 D→ G D7 D→ G
a' the lads they smile on me when com - in' through the rye.

Down In The Valley

Registration 8

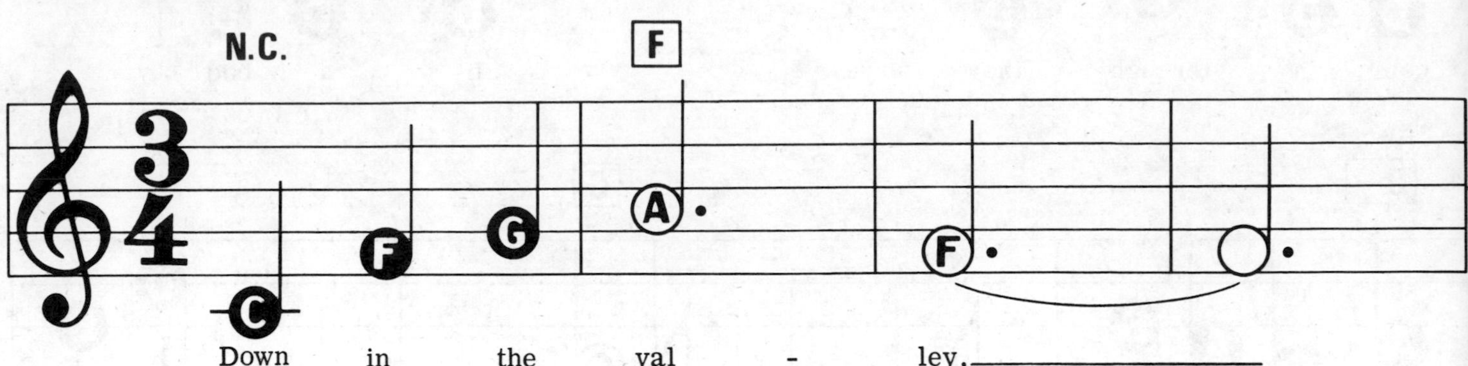

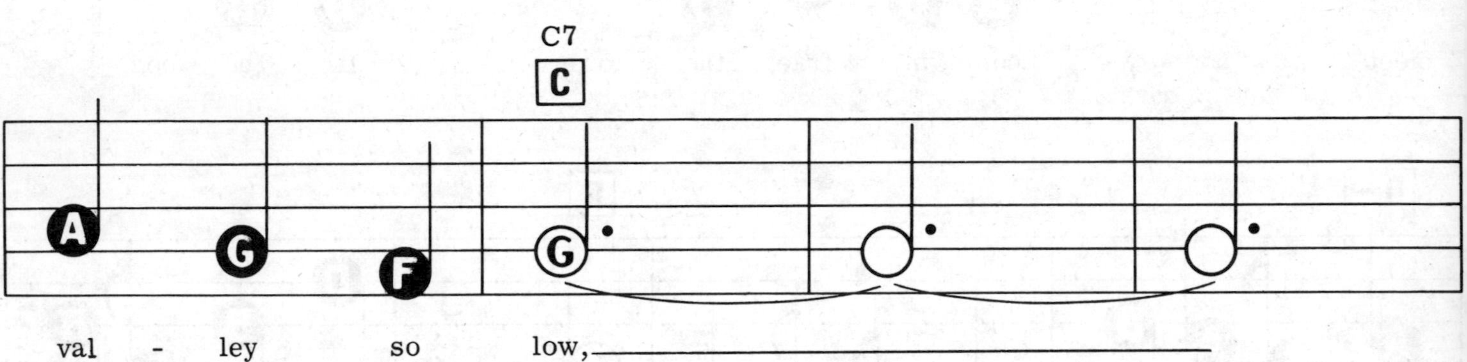

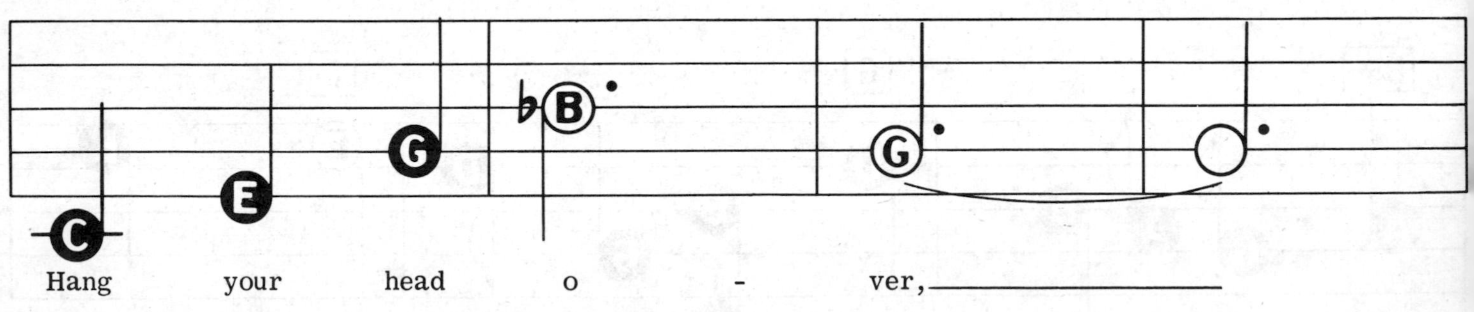

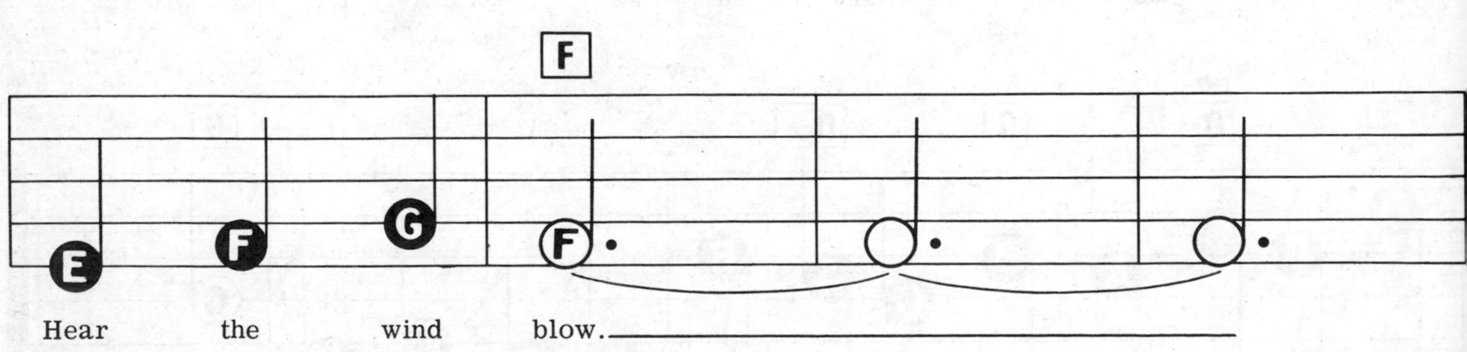

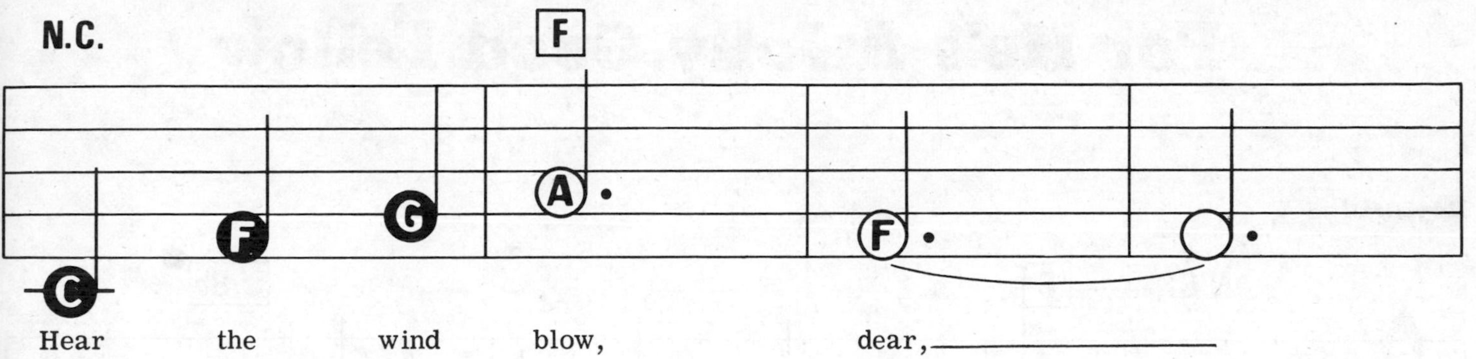
N.C.
F
C
F
G
A
F
Hear the wind blow, dear,

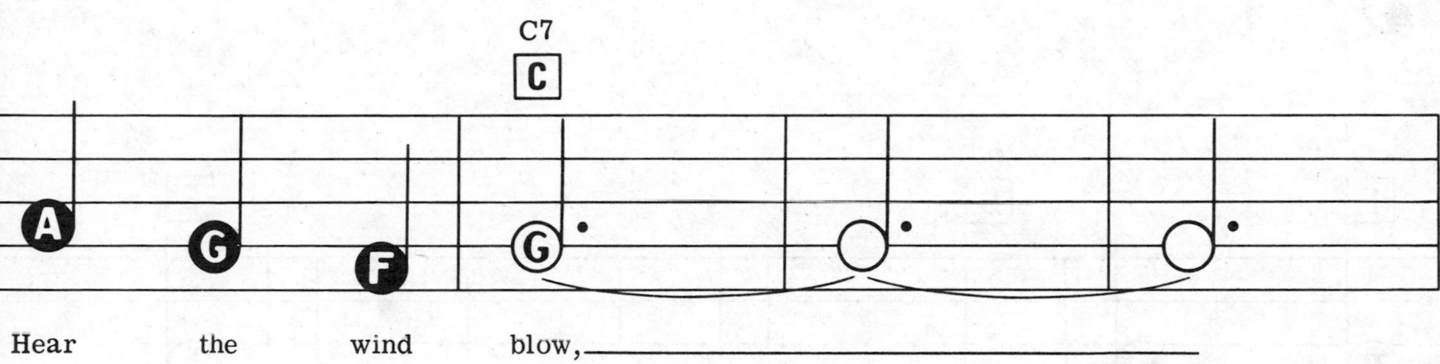
C7
C
A
G
F
G
Hear the wind blow,

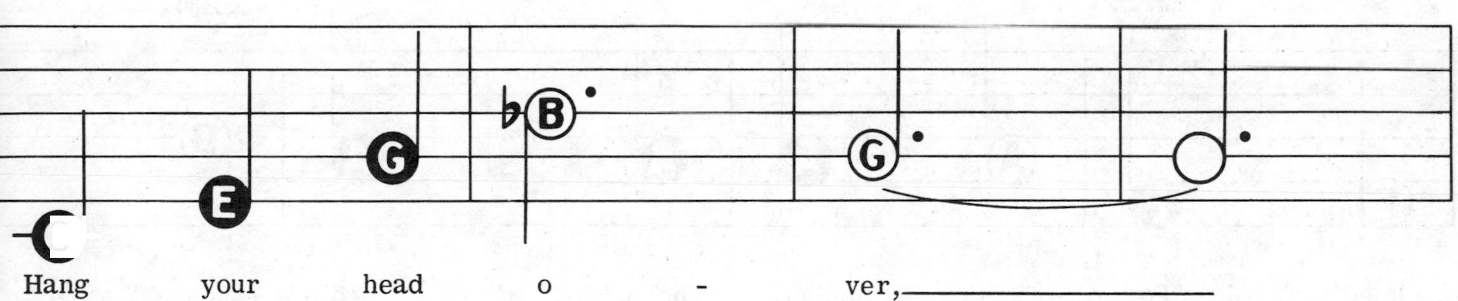
E
G
♭B
G
Hang your head o - ver,

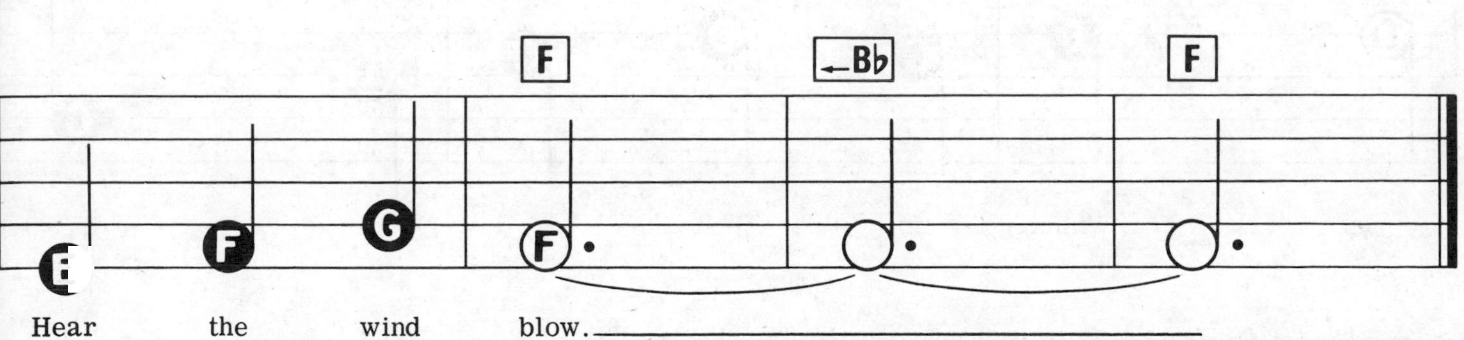
F
←B♭
F
F
G
F
Hear the wind blow.

For He's A Jolly Good Fellow

Registration 4

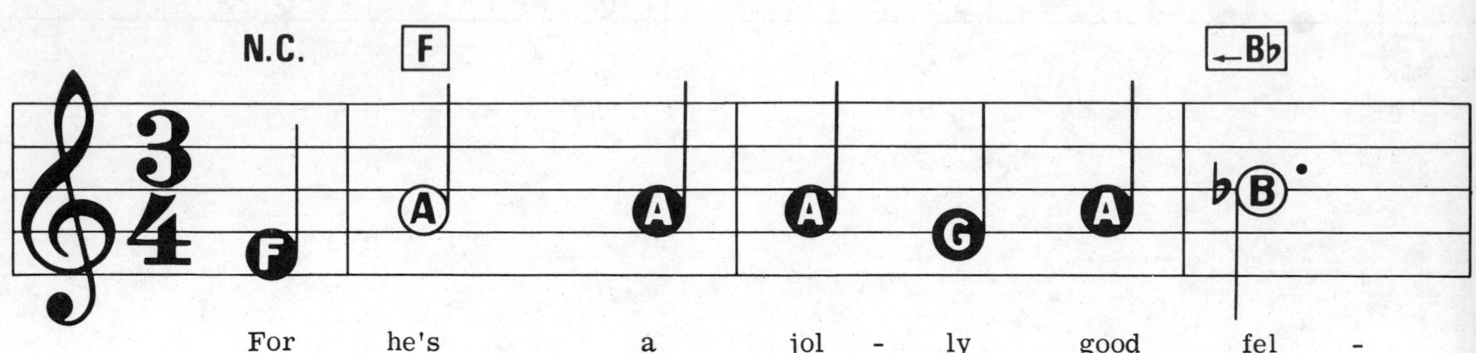

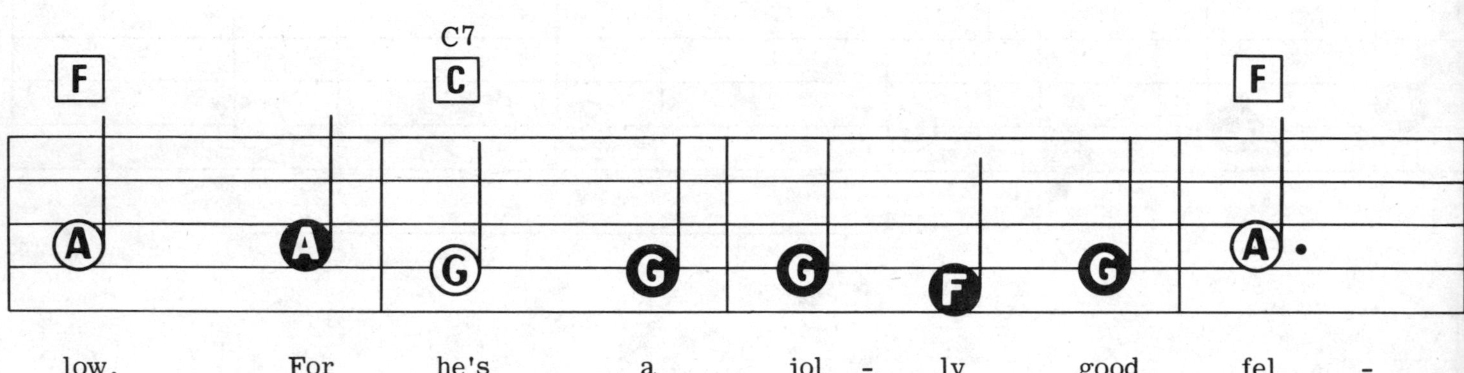

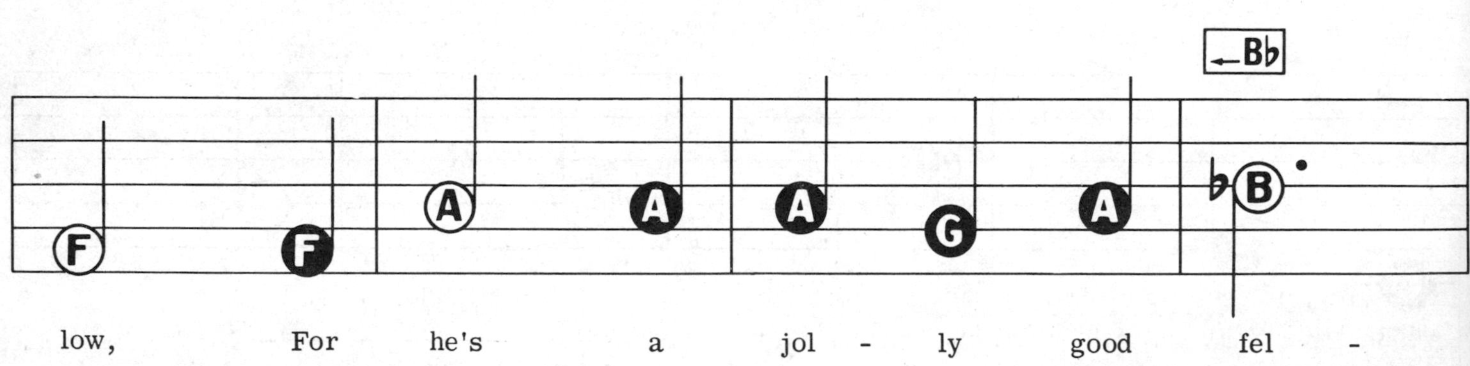

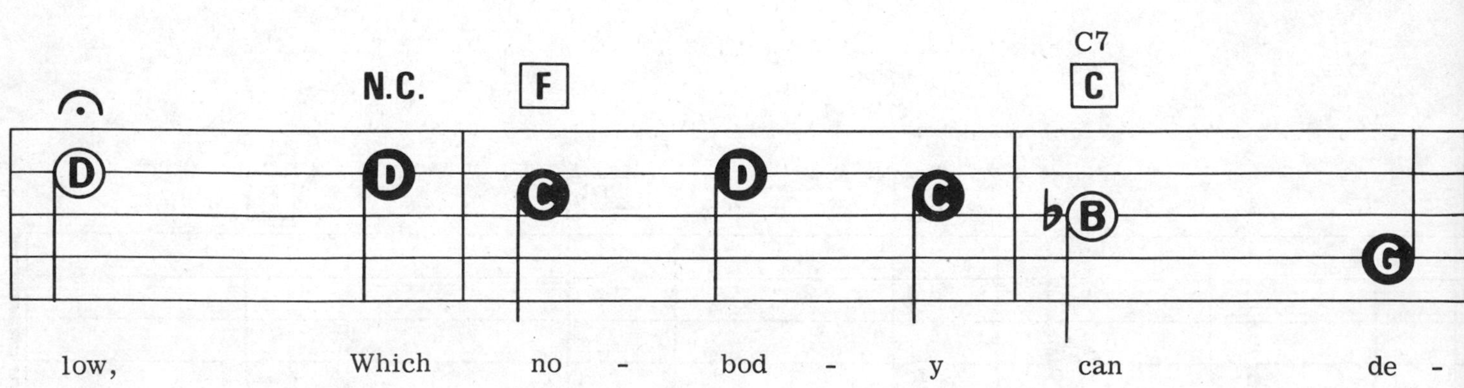

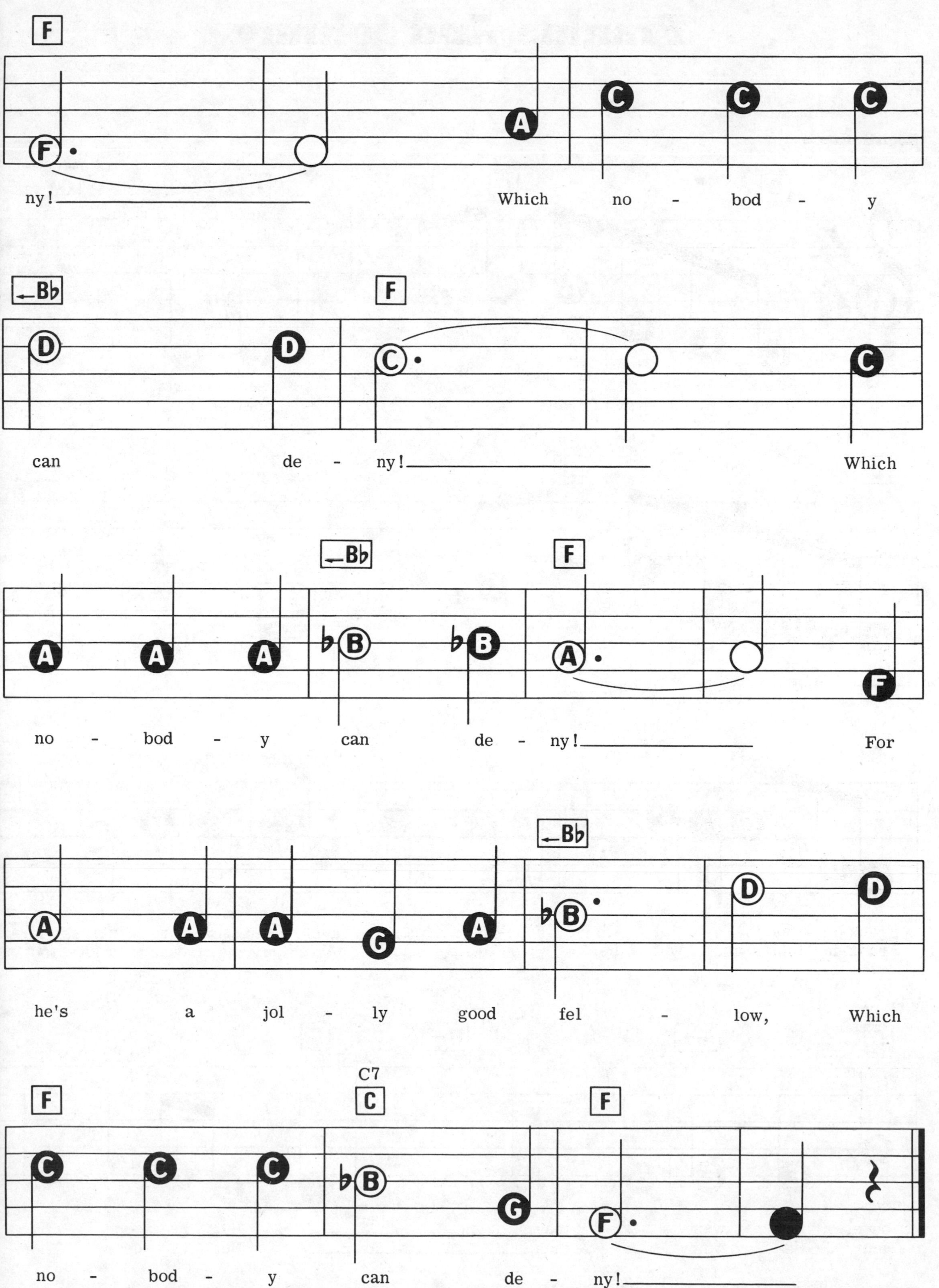
F
ny! Which no - bod - y
←B♭ F
can de - ny! Which
←B♭ F
no - bod - y can de - ny! For
←B♭
he's a jol - ly good fel - low, Which
F C7 C F
no - bod - y can de - ny!

Frankie And Johnny

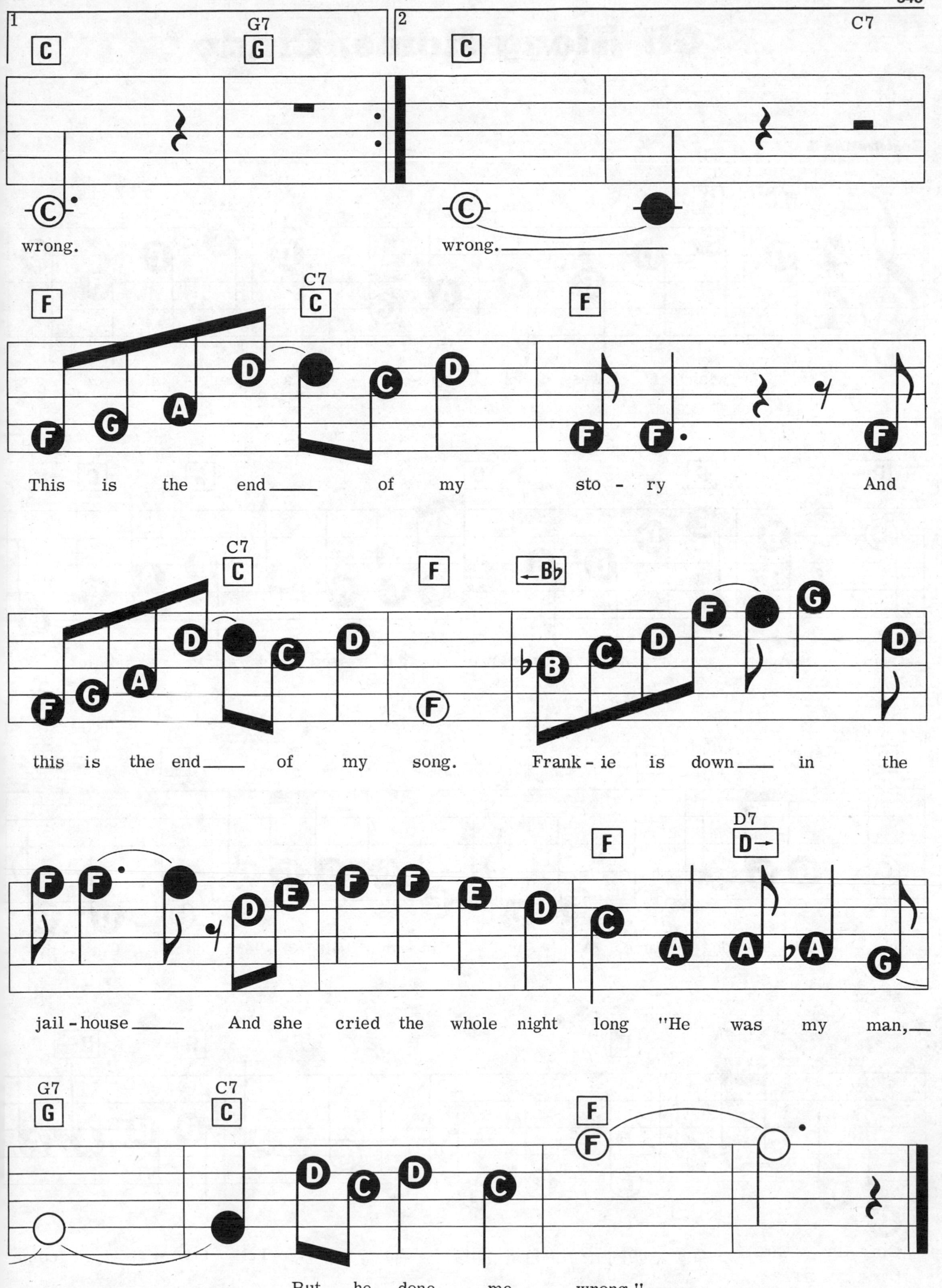
1
G7
C
G
2
C7
C
C
wrong.
C
wrong.
C7
F
C
F
F G A D C D
F F F
This is the end of my sto - ry And
C7
C
F
←B♭
F G A D C D
F
B C D F G D
this is the end of my song. Frank - ie is down in the
D7
F
D→
F F D E F F E D C A A A G
jail - house And she cried the whole night long "He was my man,
G7
G
C7
C
F
D C D C
F
But he done me wrong."

Git Along Home, Cindy

Registration 3

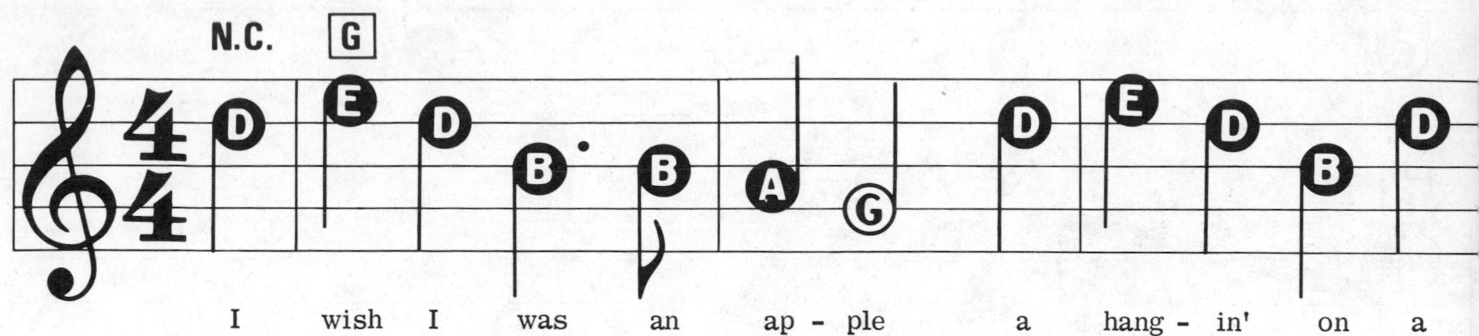

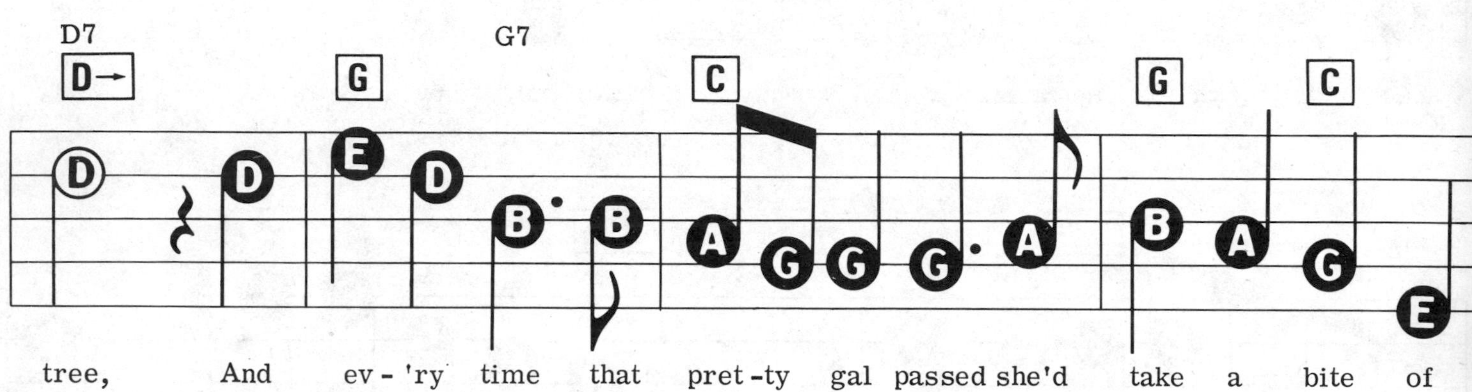

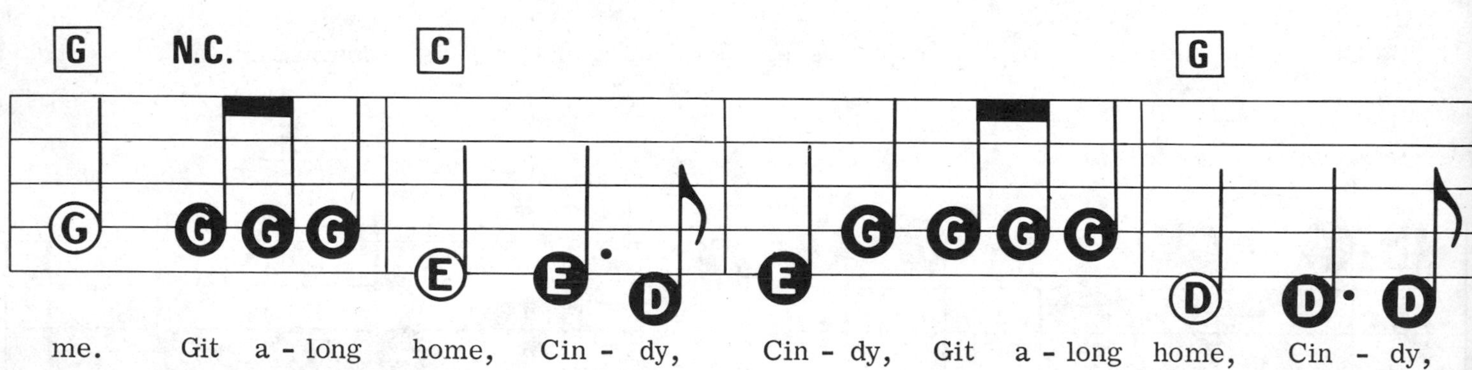

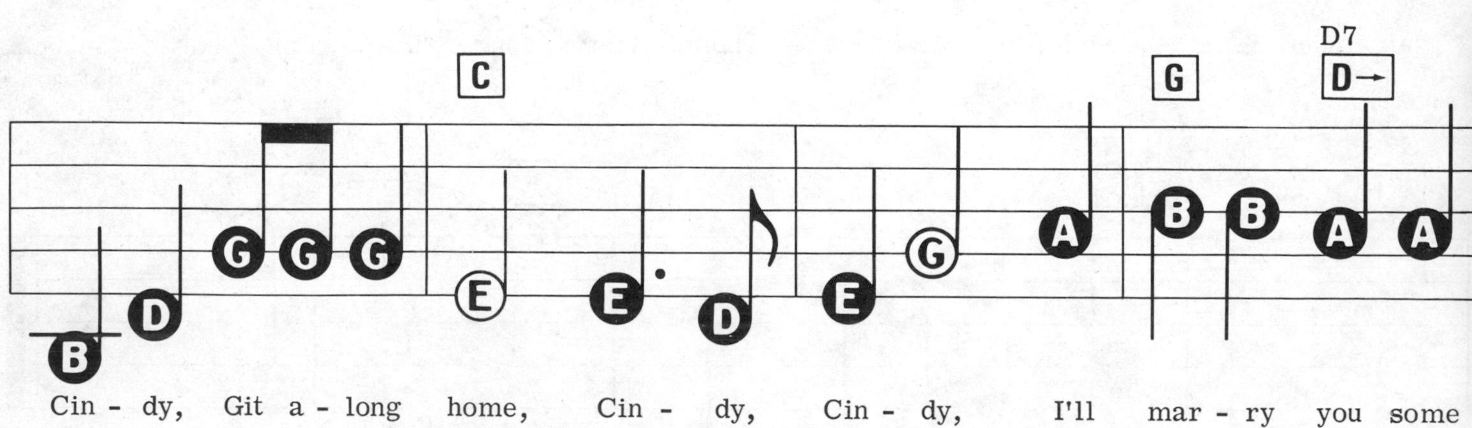

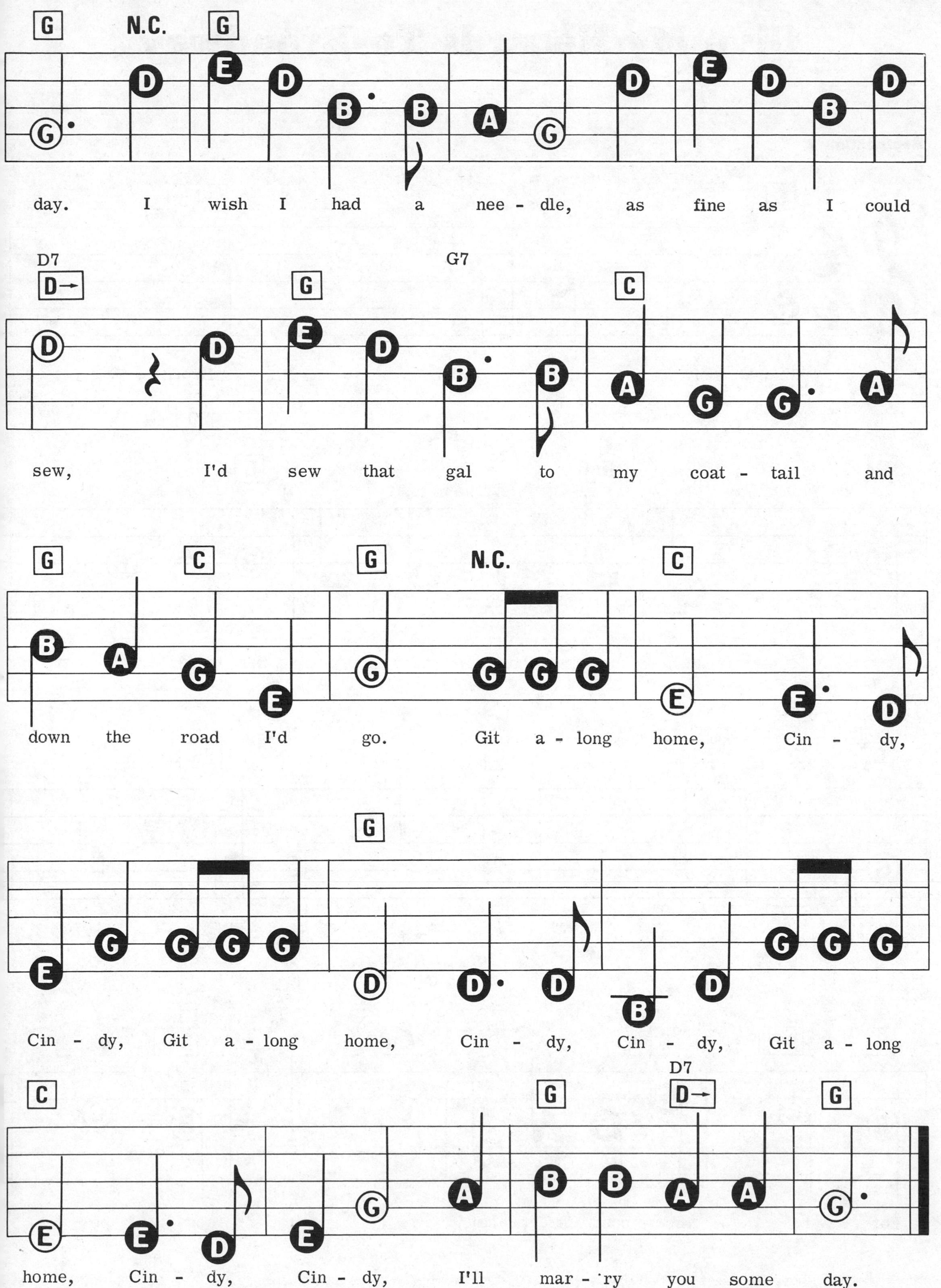
G N.C. G
day. I wish I had a nee - dle, as fine as I could
D7 G7
D→ G C
sew, I'd sew that gal to my coat - tail and
G C G N.C. C
down the road I'd go. Git a - long home, Cin - dy,
G
Cin - dy, Git a - long home, Cin - dy, Cin - dy, Git a - long
D7
C G D→ G
home, Cin - dy, Cin - dy, I'll mar - 'ry you some day.

Give My Regards To Broadway

Registration 2

Words and Music by
George M. Cohan

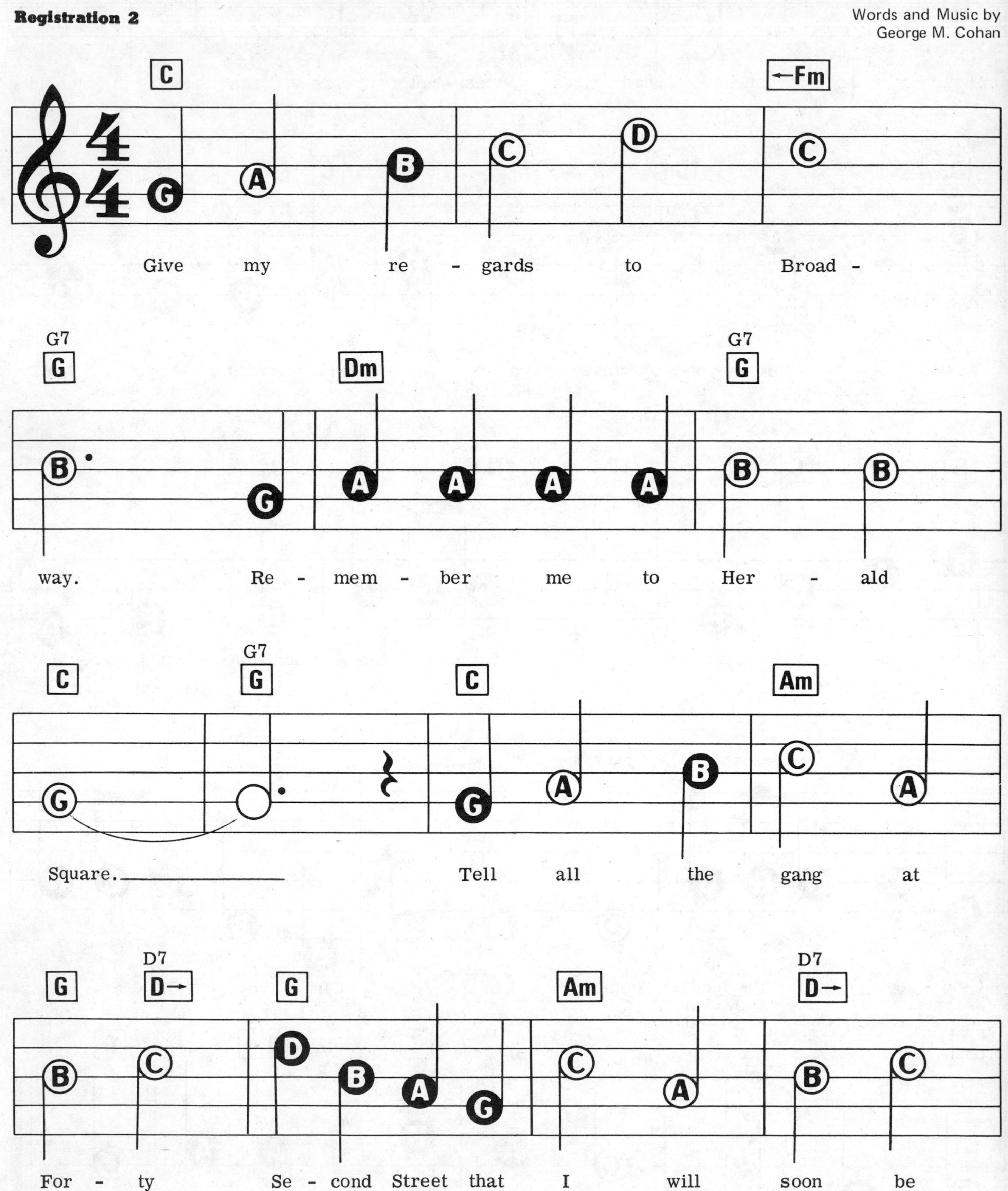

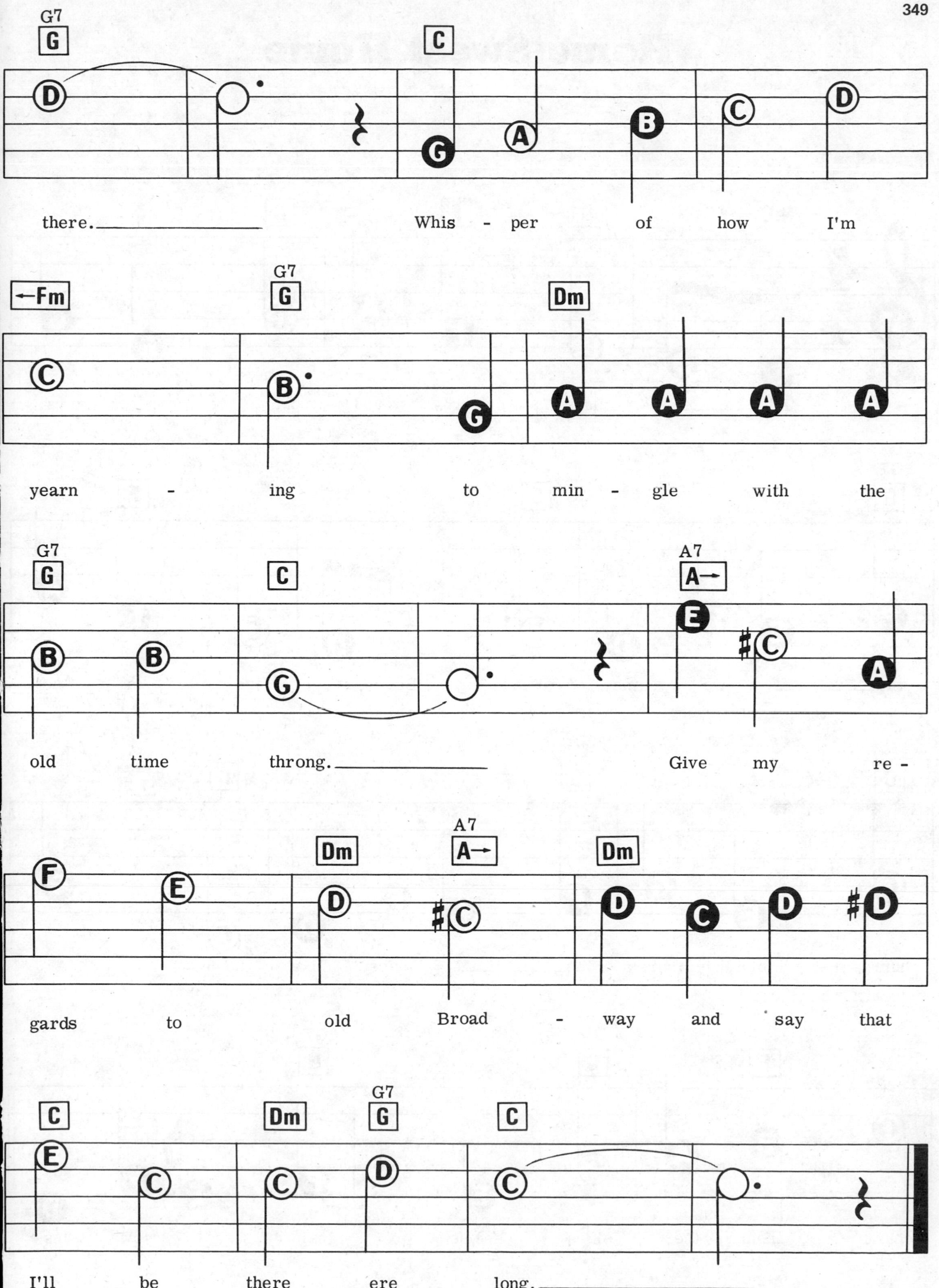
G7
G
C
D
G
A
B
C
D
there.
Whis - per of how I'm
←Fm
G7
G
Dm
C
B
G
A
A
A
A
yearn - ing to min - gle with the
G7
G
C
A7
A→
B
B
G
E
♯C
A
old time throng.
Give my re -
Dm
A7
A→
Dm
F
E
D
♯C
D
C
D
♯D
gards to old Broad - way and say that
C
Dm
G7
G
C
E
C
C
D
C
I'll be there ere long.

Home Sweet Home

Registration 9

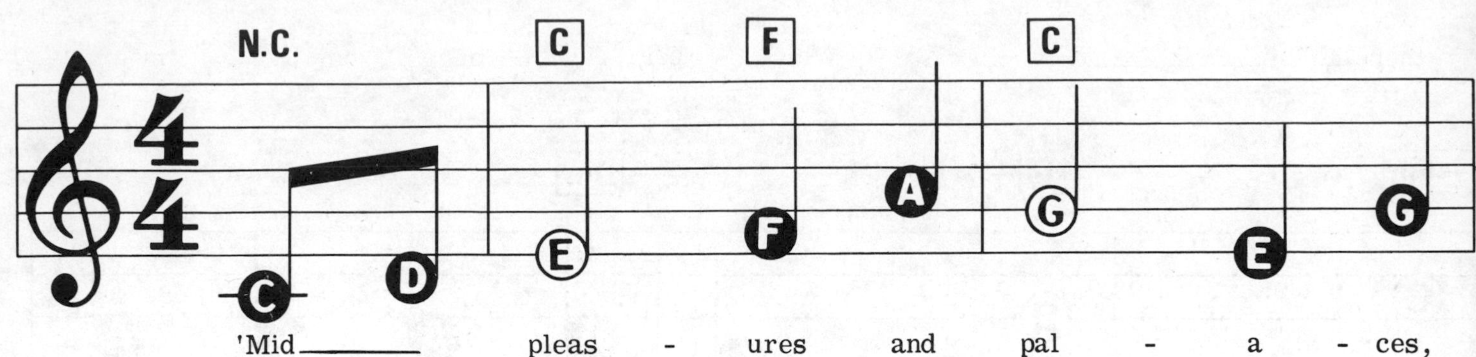

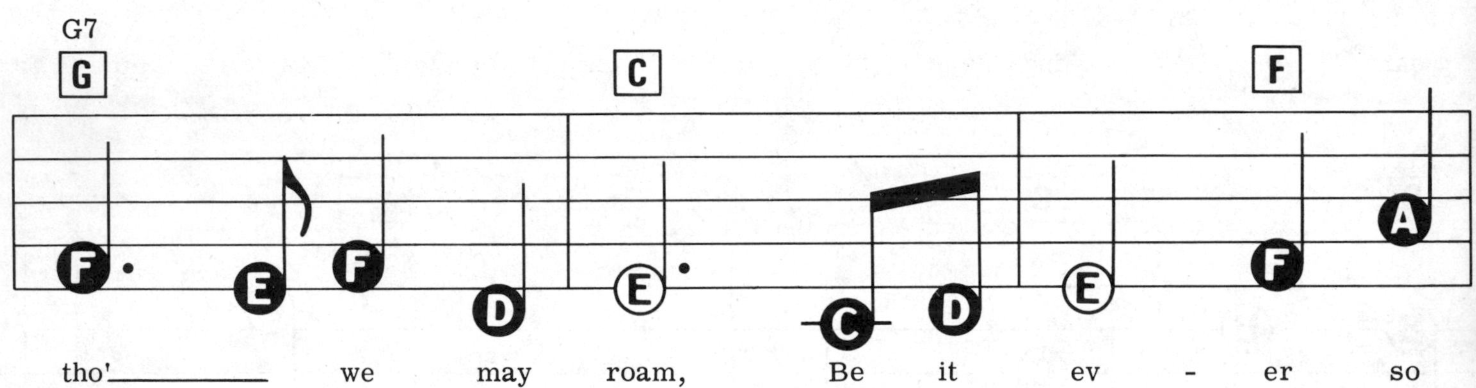

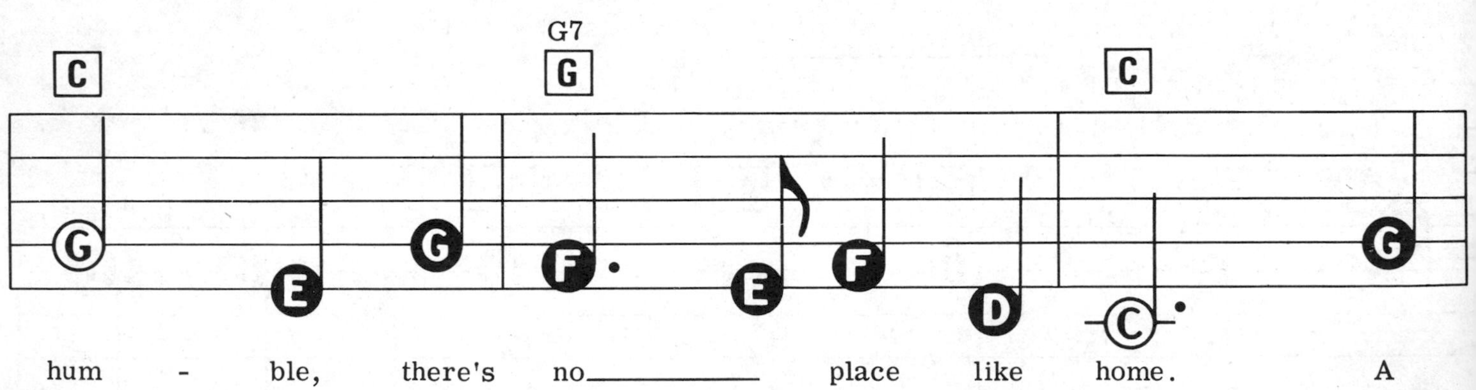

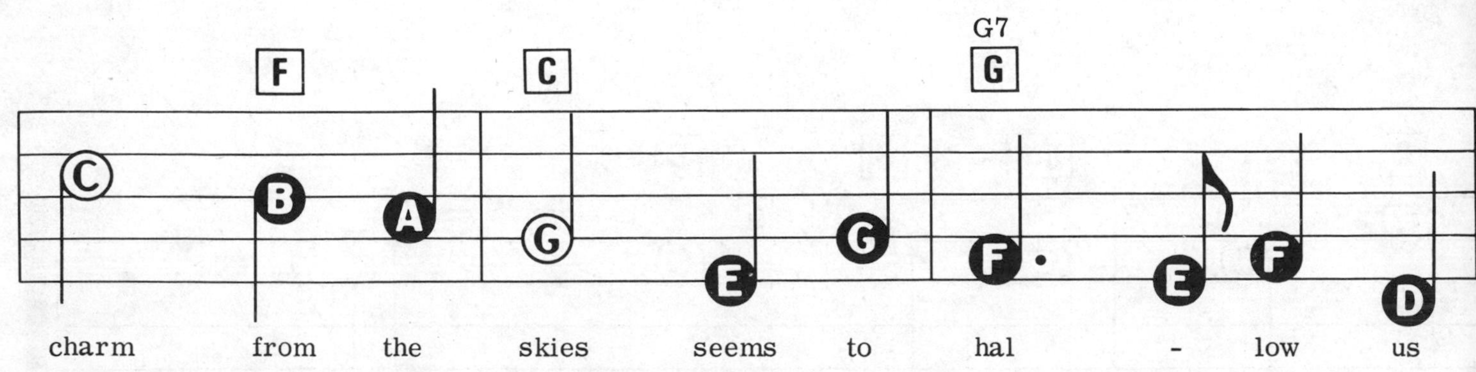

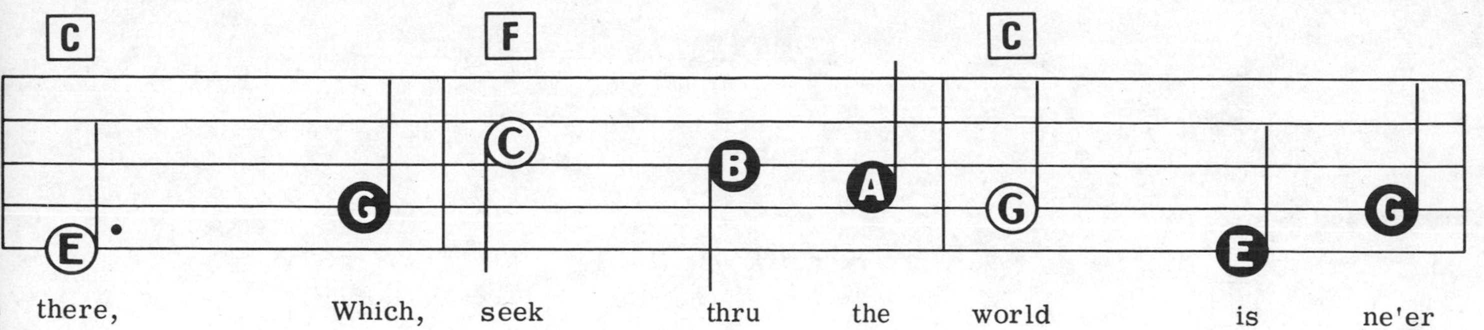
C
F
C
E
G
C
B
A
G
E
G
there,
Which,
seek
thru
the
world
is
ne'er

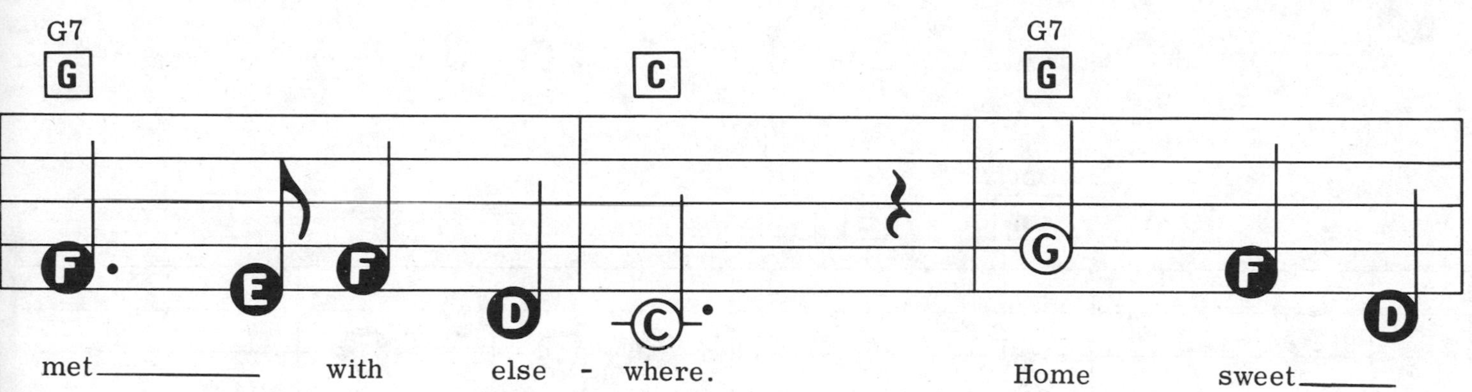
G7
G
C
G7
G
F
E
F
D
C
G
F
D
met
with
else - where.
Home
sweet

C
G7
G
C
F
C
D
E
G
C
B
A
home,
Sweet
home!
There's
no
place
like

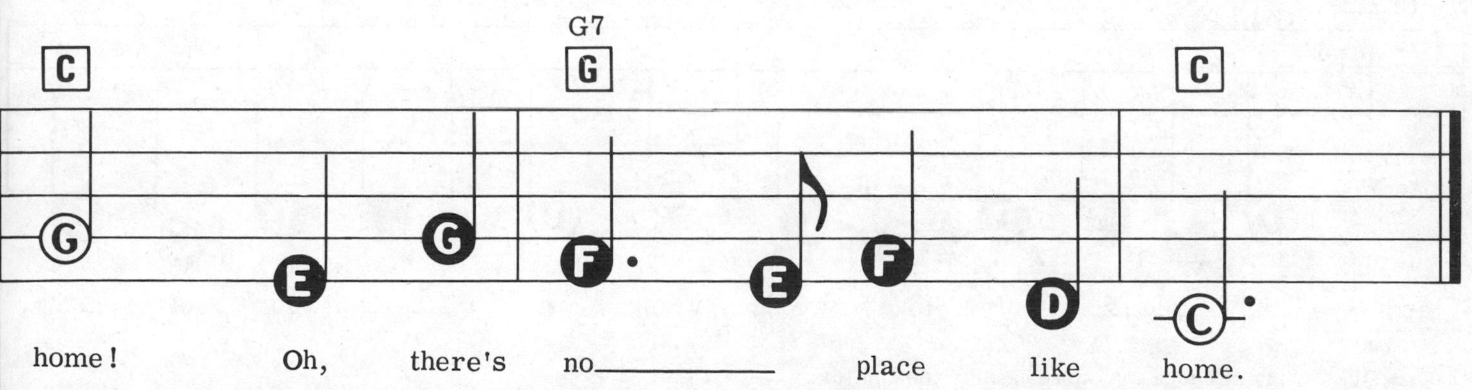
C
G7
G
C
G
E
G
F
E
F
D
C
home!
Oh,
there's
no
place
like
home.

Ida

Registration 3

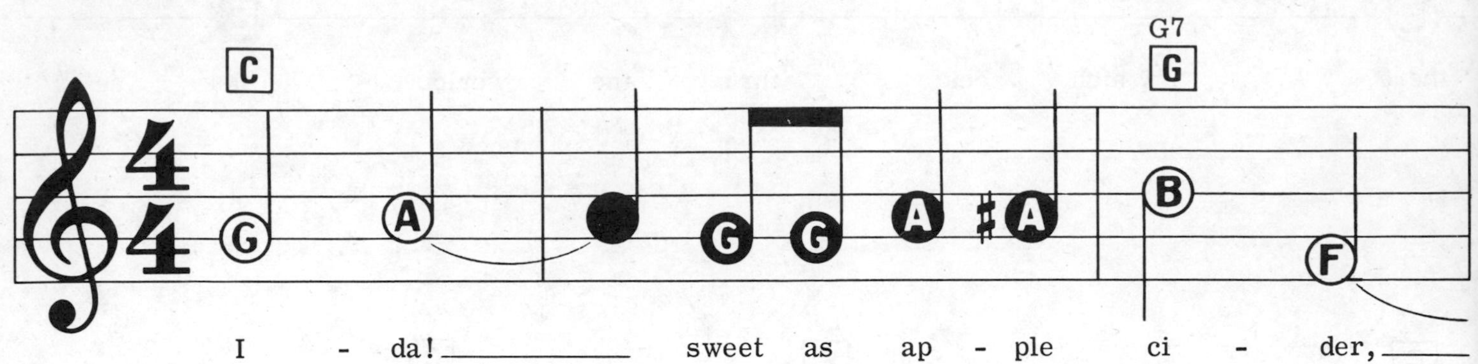

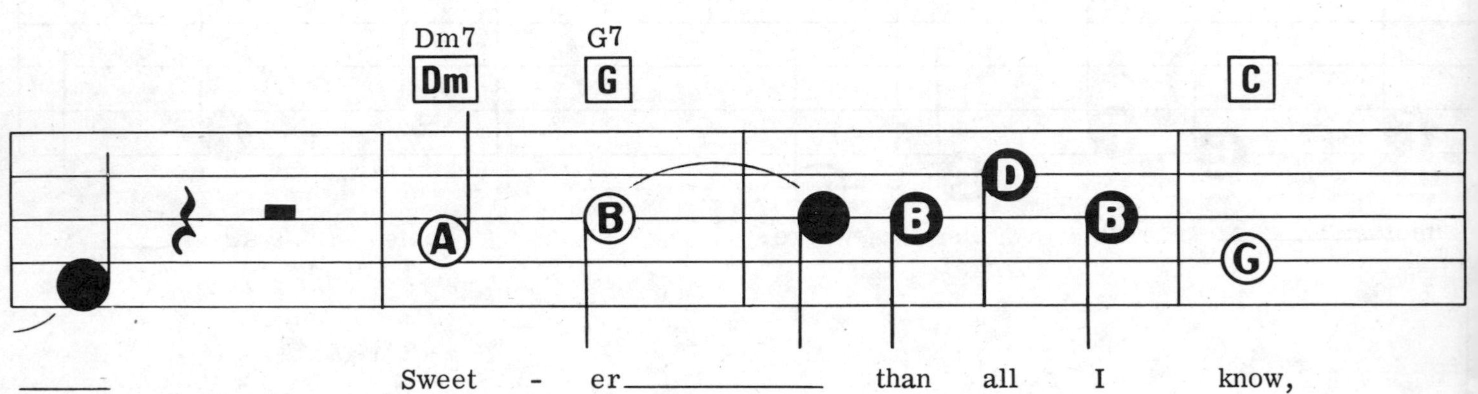

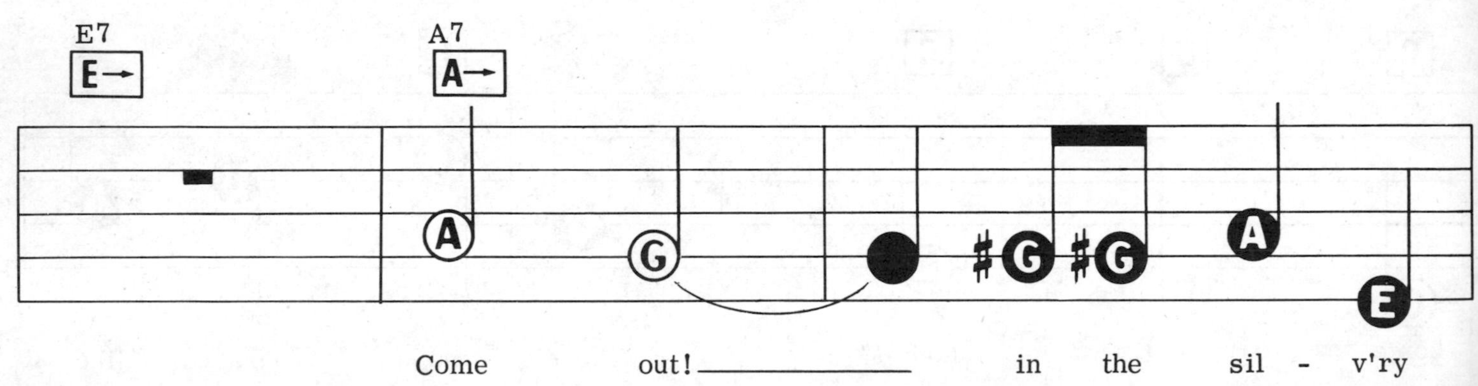

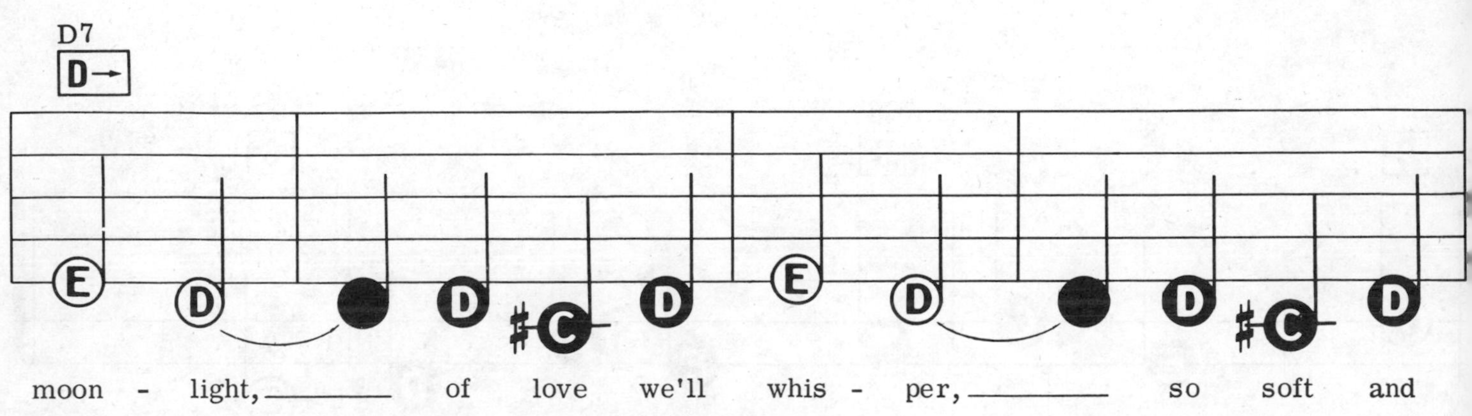

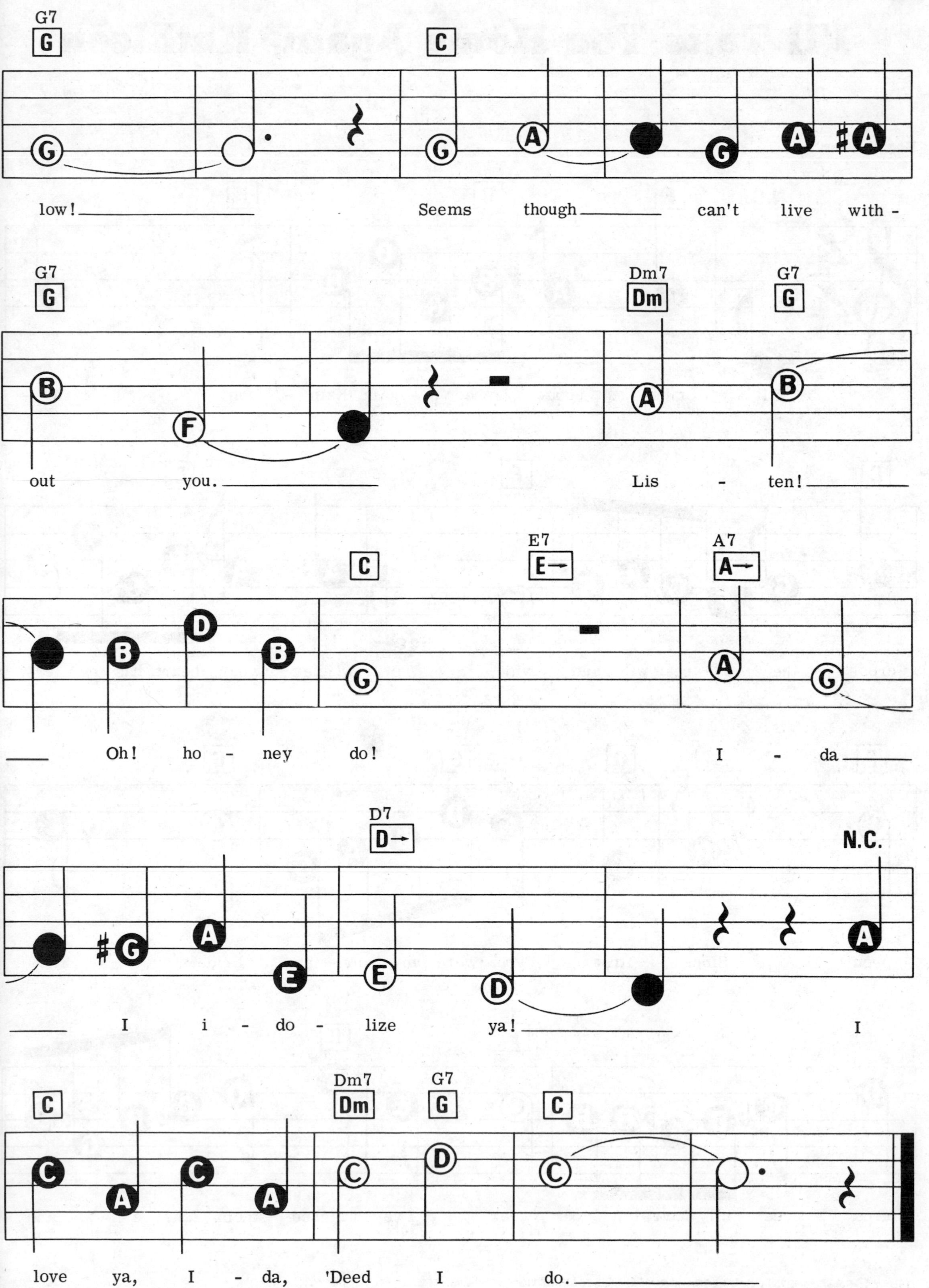
G7 G C
G G A A G A ♯A
low! Seems though can't live with -
G7 G Dm7 Dm G7 G
B F A B
out you. Lis - ten!
C E7 E→ A7 A→
B D B G A G
Oh! ho - ney do! I - da
D7 D→ N.C.
♯G A E E D A
I i - do - lize ya! I
C Dm7 Dm G7 G C
C A C A C D C
love ya, I - da, 'Deed I do.

I'll Take You Home Again, Kathleen

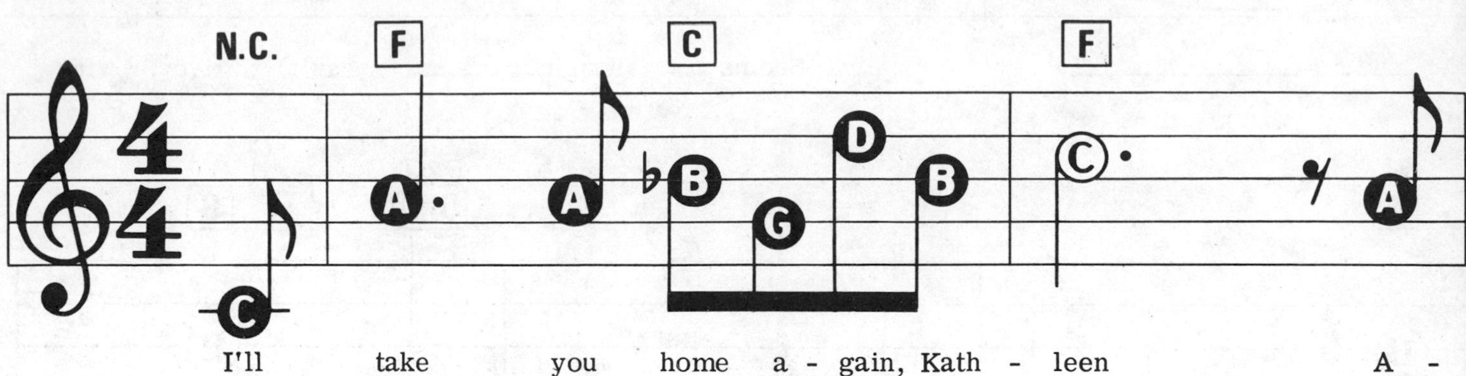

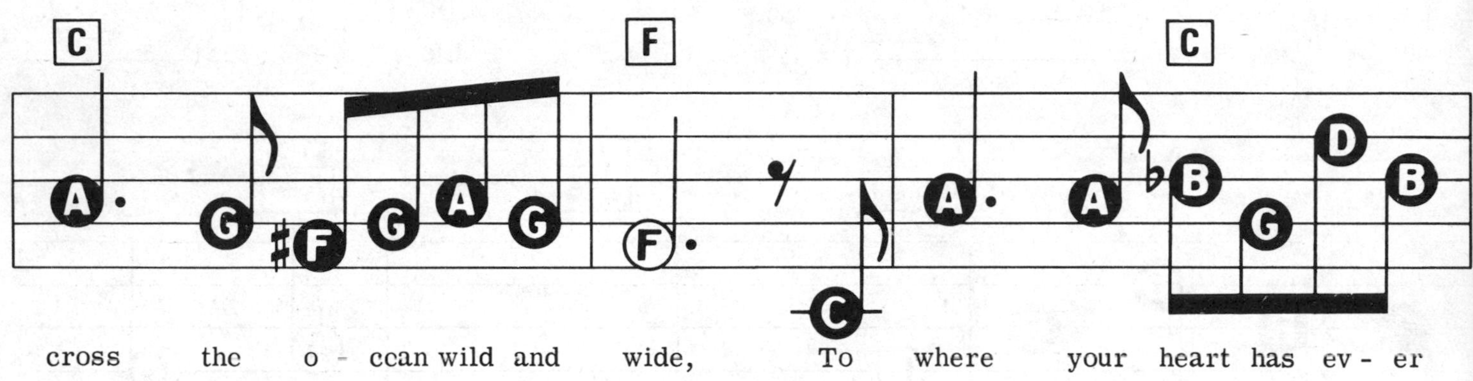

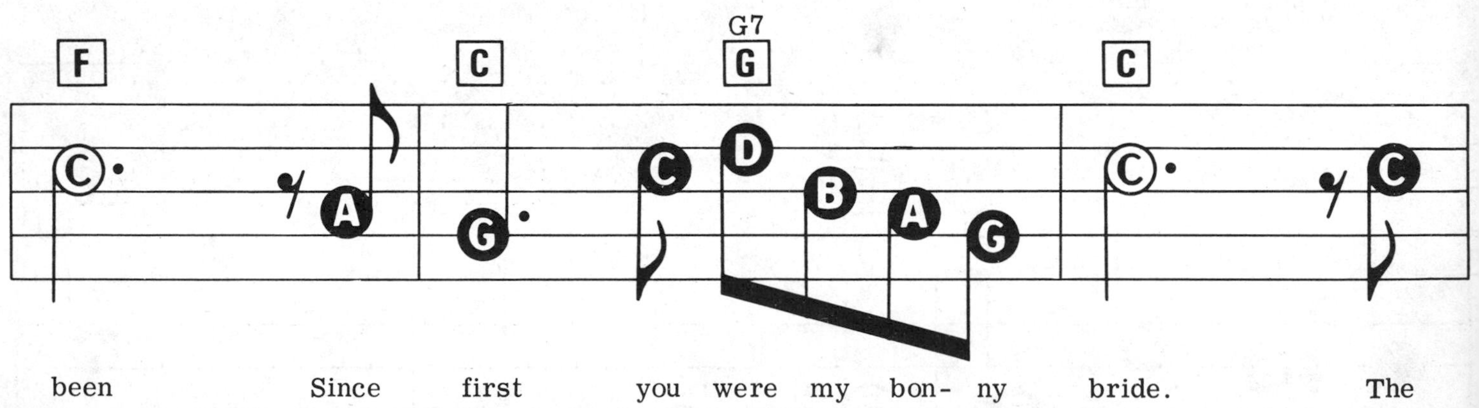

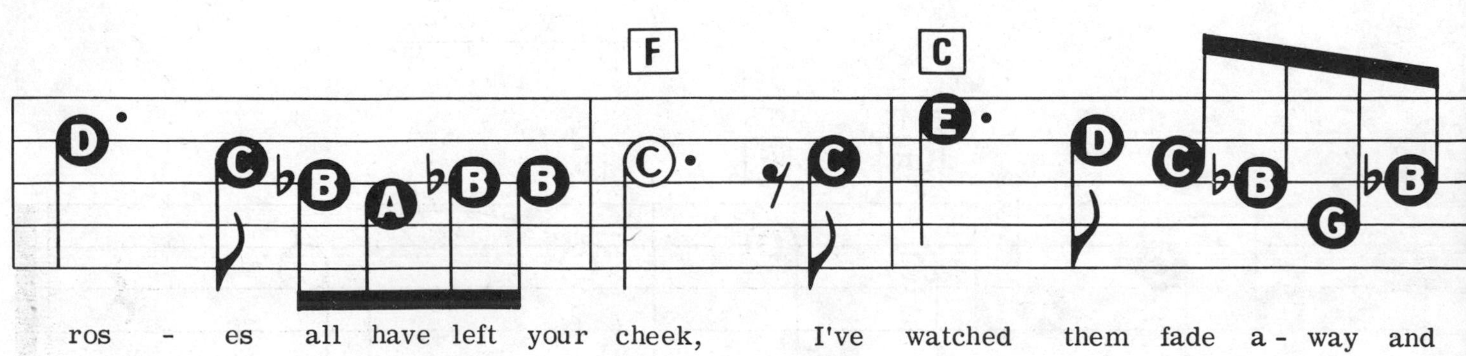

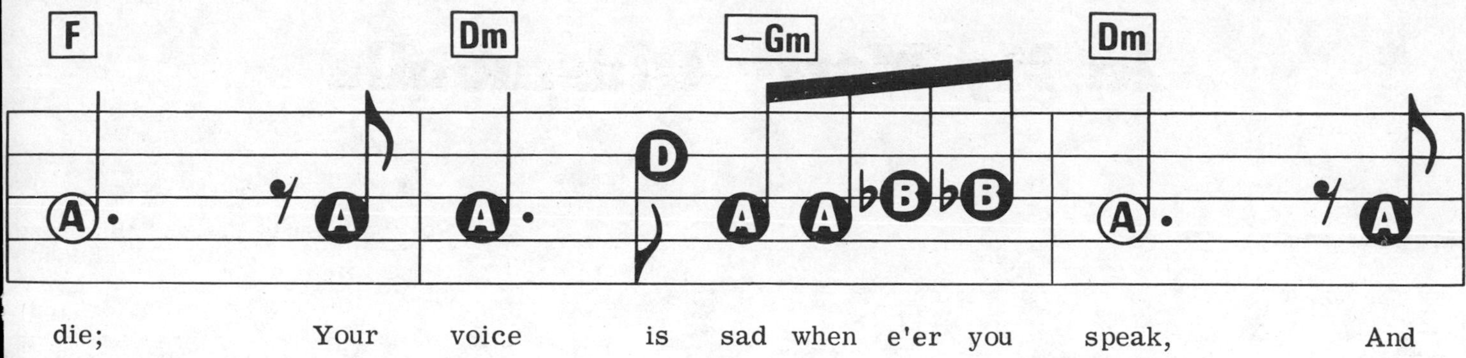
F
Dm
←Gm
Dm
A
A
A
D
A
A
B
B
A
A
die; Your voice is sad when e'er you speak, And

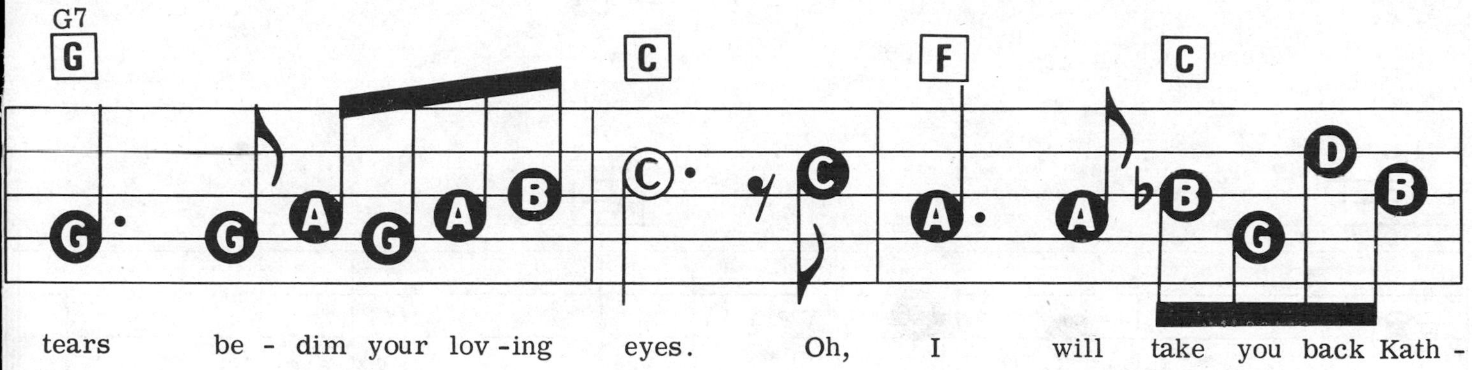
G7
G
C
F
C
G
G
A
G
A
B
C
C
A
A
B
G
D
B
tears be - dim your lov -ing eyes. Oh, I will take you back Kath -

F
C
F
C
A
A
G
F
G
A
G
F
C
leen To where your heart will feel no pain, And

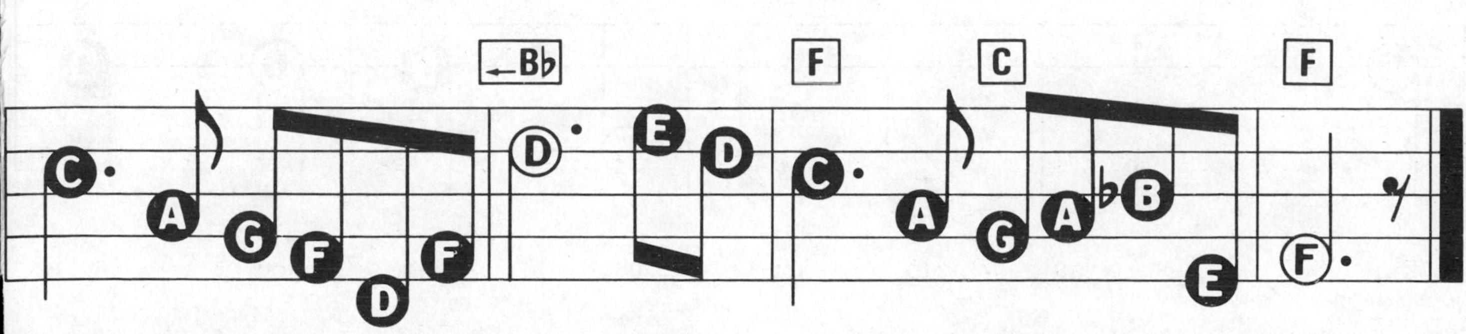
←B♭
F
C
F
C
A
G
F
D
F
D
E
D
C
A
G
A
B
E
F
when the fields are fresh and green, I'll___ take you to your home a - gain.

In My Merry Oldsmobile

Registration 4

Words and Music by Vincent P. Bryan and
Gus Edwards

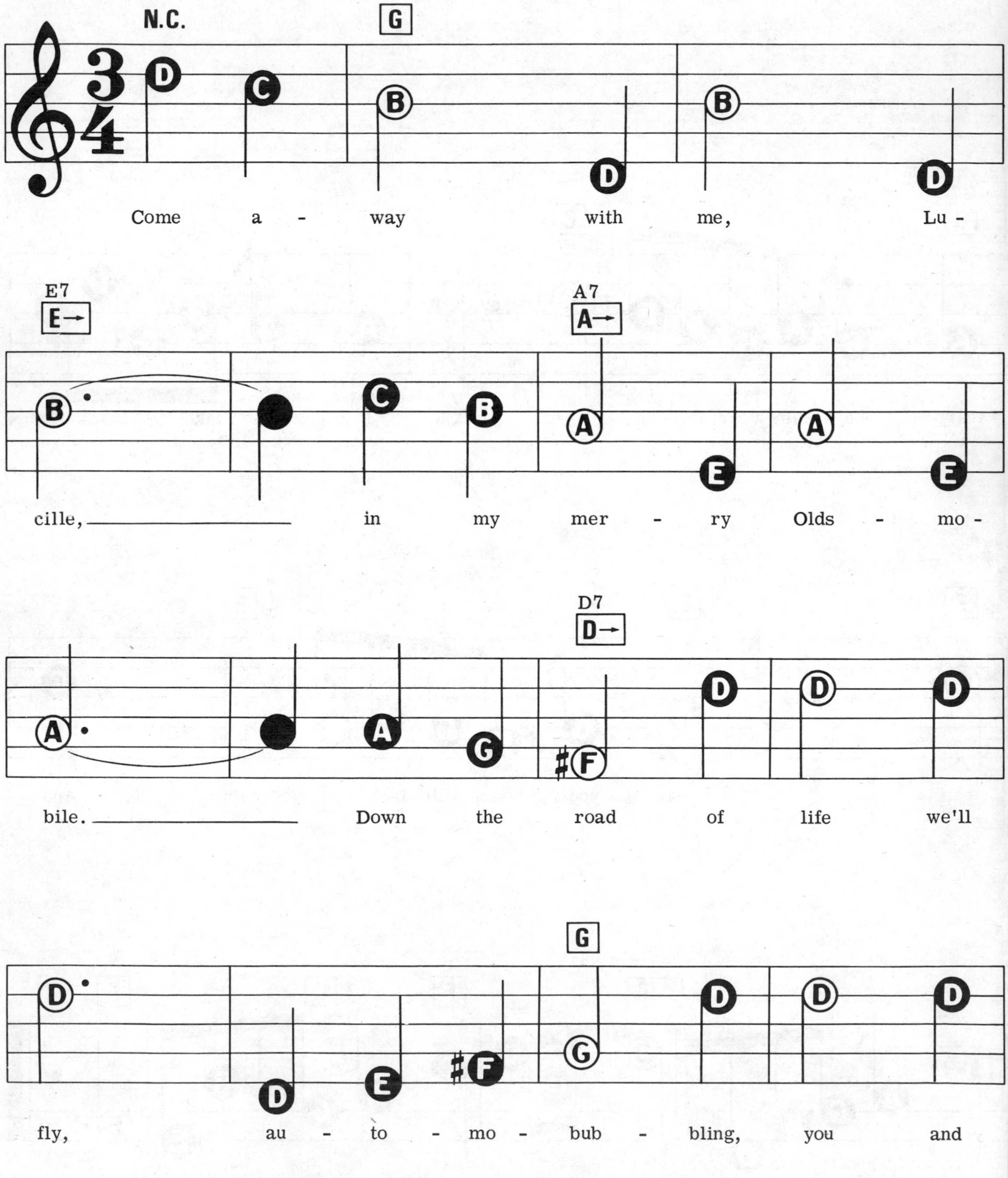

N.C. G

Come a - way with me, Lu -

E7 A7

cille, ___ in my mer - ry Olds - mo -

D7

bile. ___ Down the road of life we'll

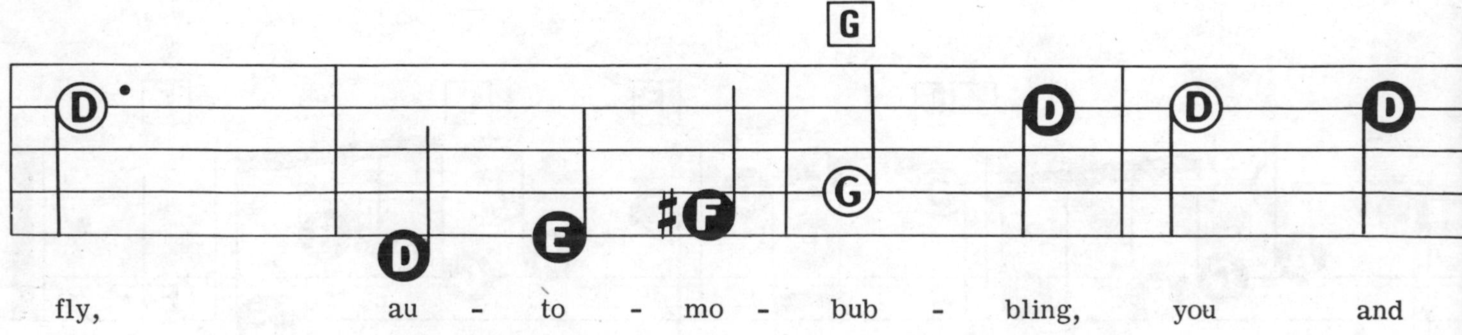

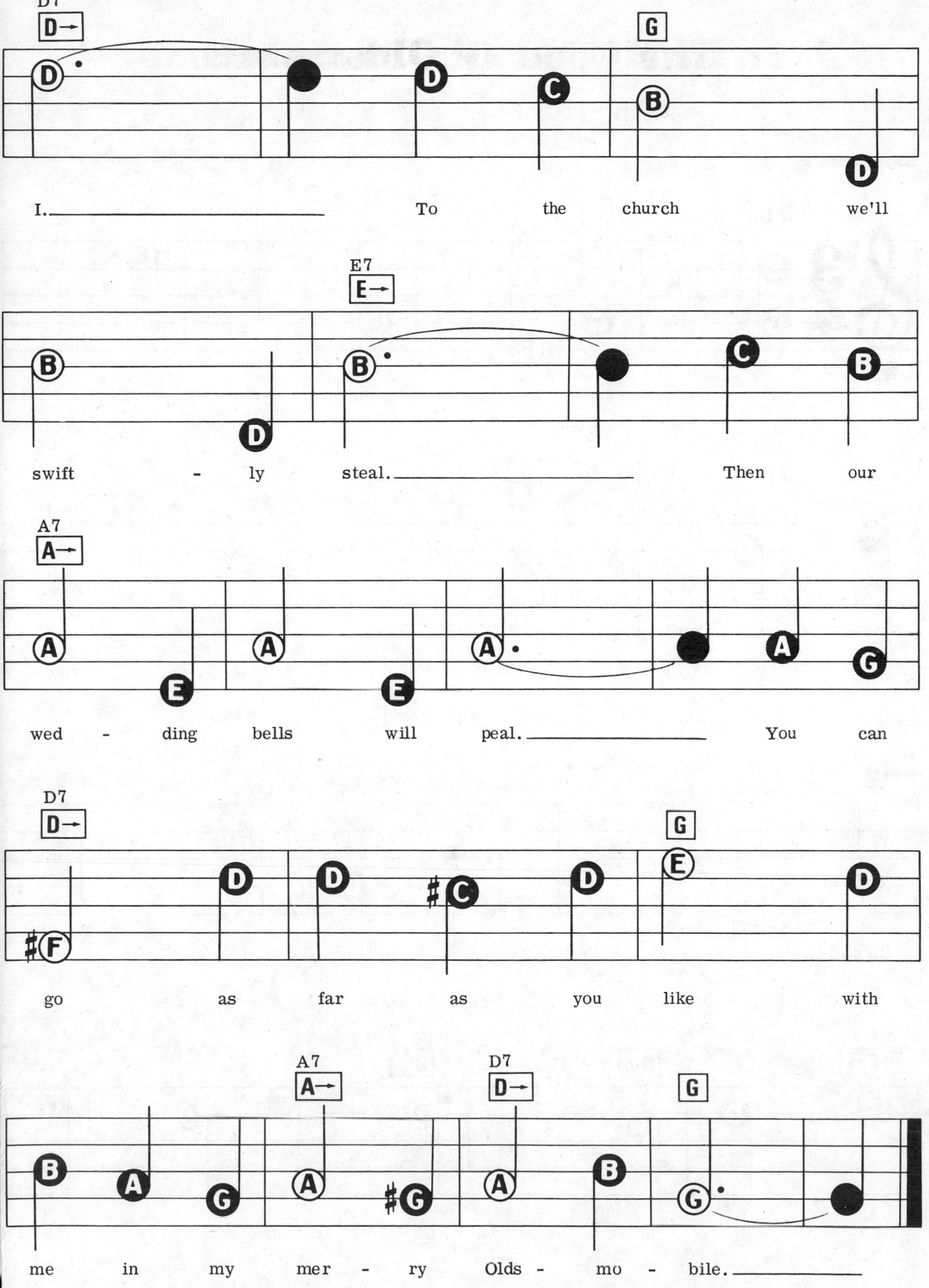
D7
D→
G
D
D
C
B
D
I.
To
the
church
we'll
E7
E→
B
D
B
C
B
swift
- ly
steal.
Then
our
A7
A→
A
E
A
E
A
A
G
wed - ding
bells
will
peal.
You
can
D7
D→
G
♯F
D
D
♯C
D
E
D
go
as
far
as
you
like
with
A7
A→
D7
D→
G
B
A
G
A
♯G
A
B
G
me
in
my
mer - ry
Olds - mo - bile.

In The Good Old Summertime

Registration 5

Words and Music by Ren Shields and George Evans

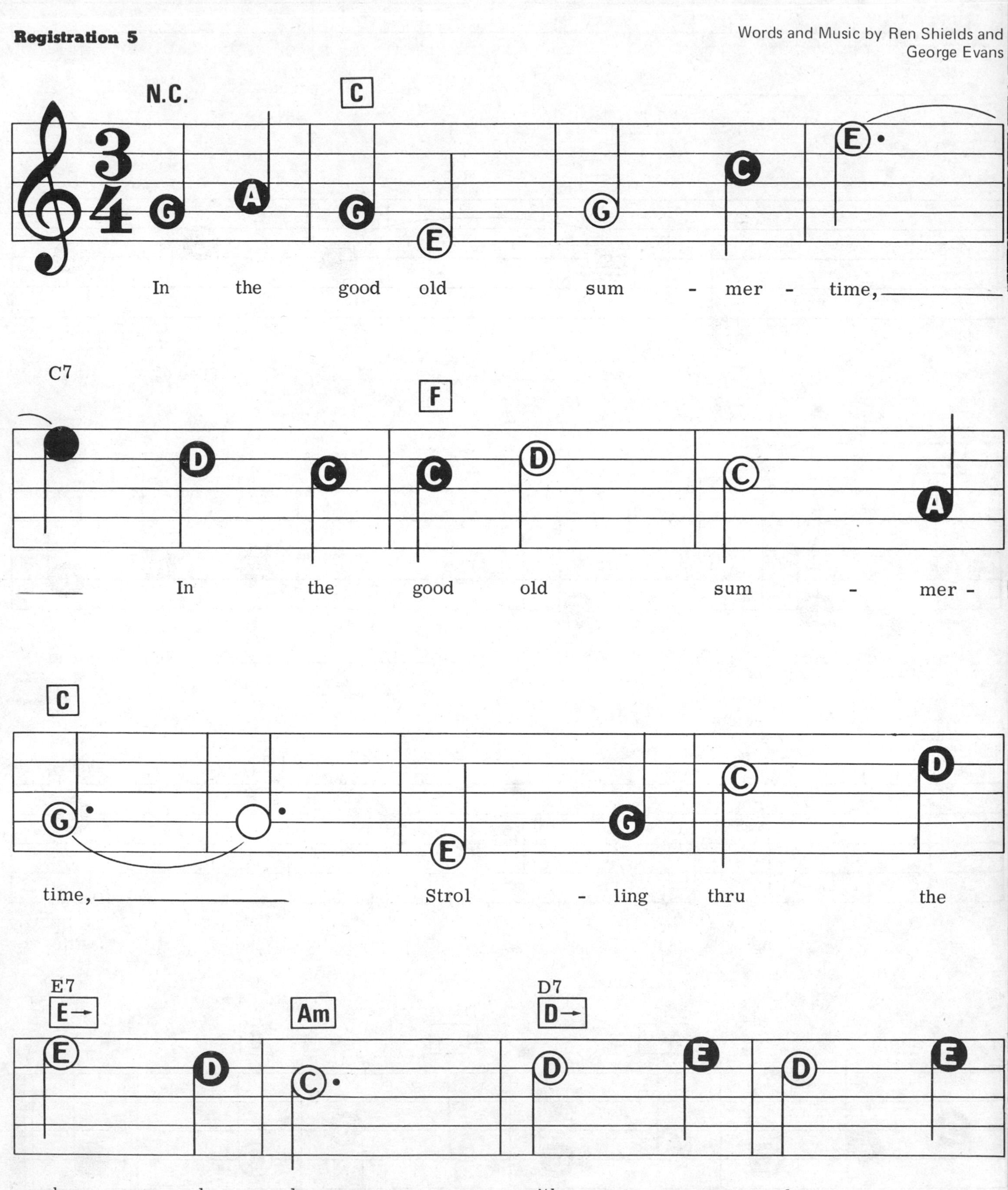

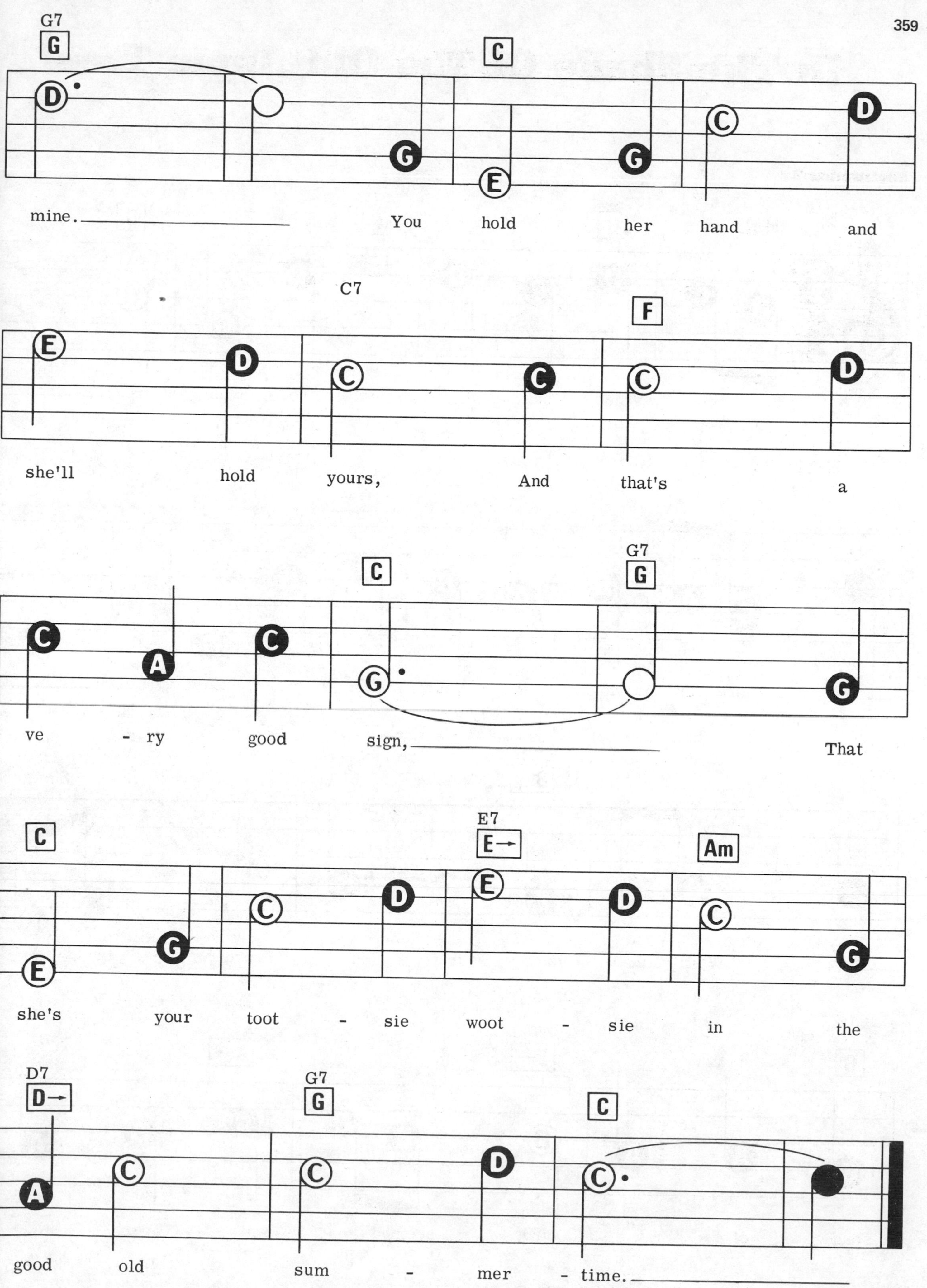
G7
G
C
D
G
E
G
C
D
mine.
You
hold
her
hand
and
C7
F
E
D
C
C
C
D
she'll
hold
yours,
And
that's
a
C
G7
G
C
A
C
G
G
ve
- ry
good
sign,
That
C
E7
E→
Am
E
G
C
D
E
D
C
G
she's
your
toot
- sie
woot
- sie
in
the
D7
D→
G7
G
C
A
C
C
D
C
good
old
sum
- mer
- time.

In The Shade Of The Old Apple Tree

Registration 3

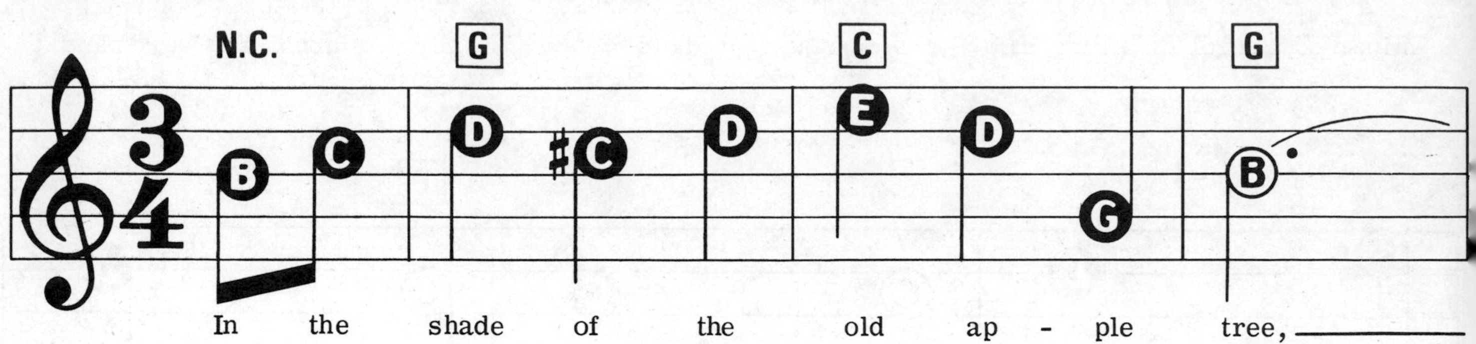

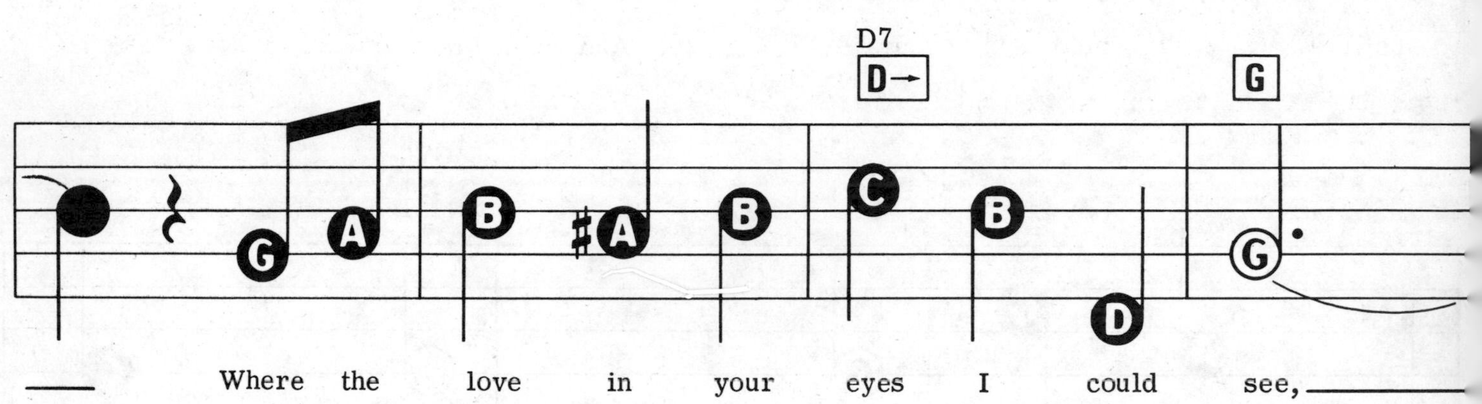

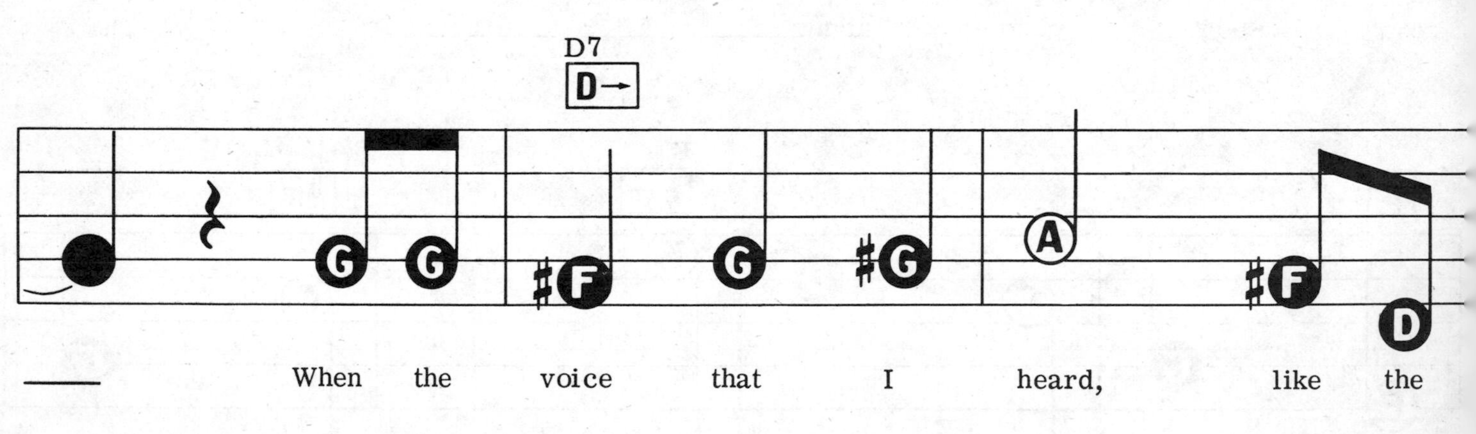

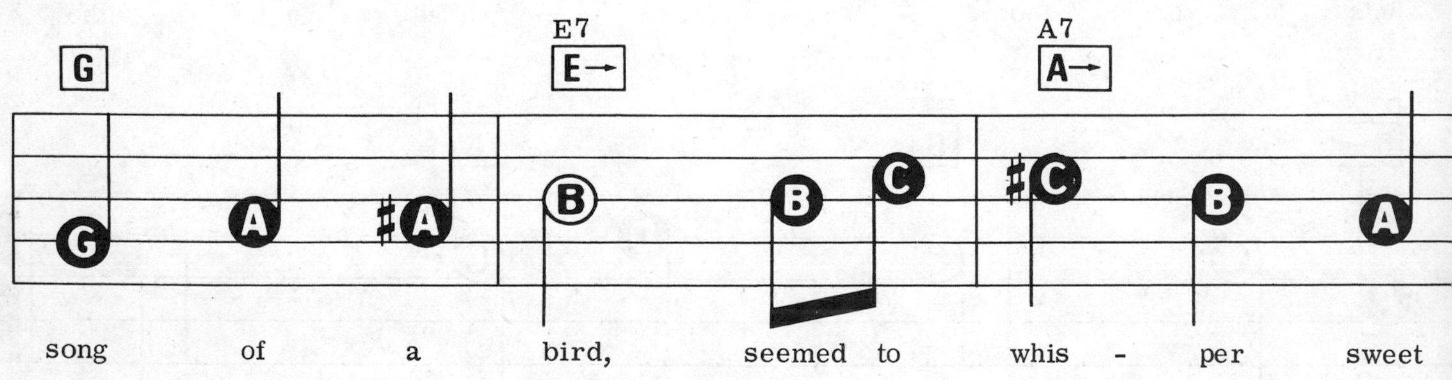

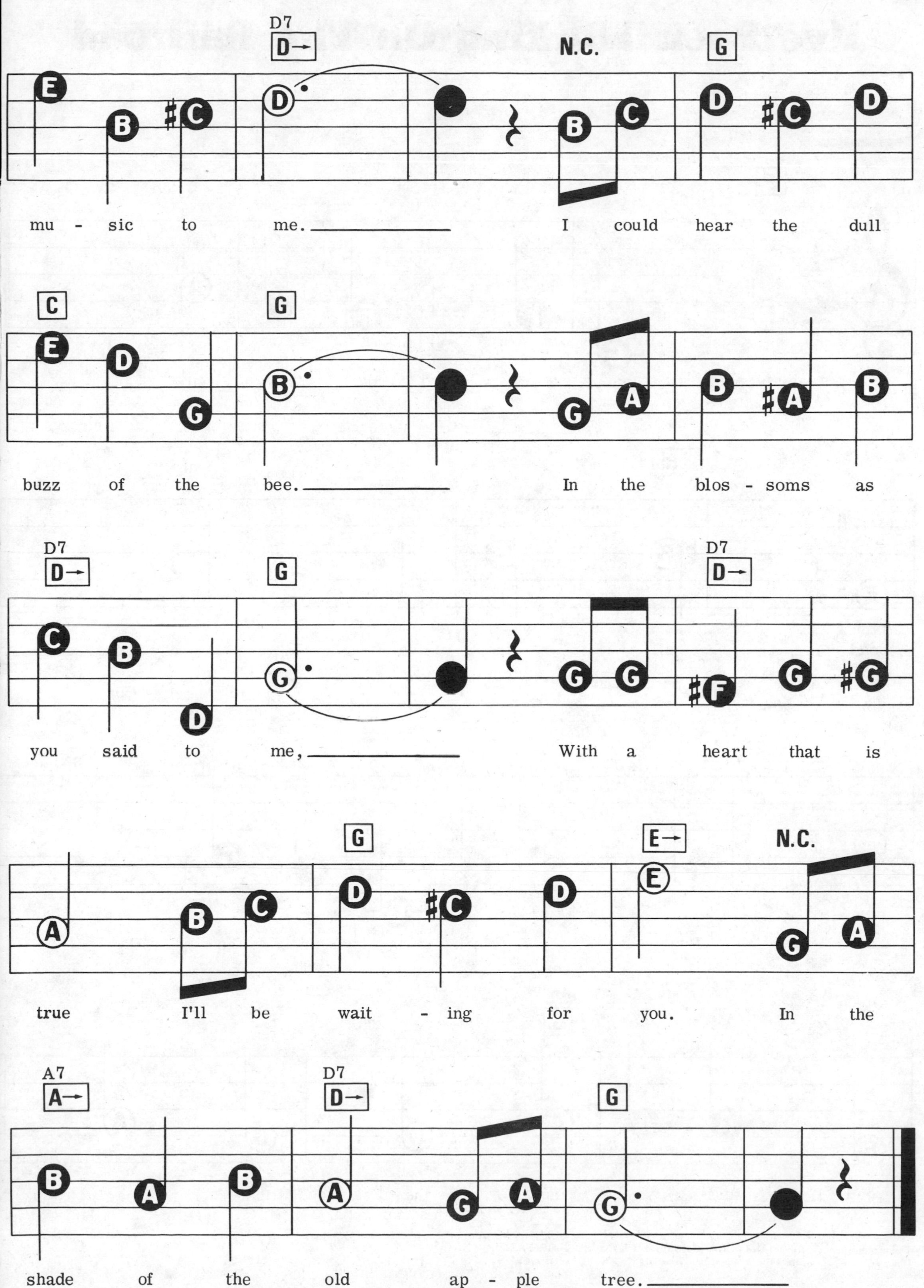
D7
N.C.
G
mu - sic to me. I could hear the dull
C
G
buzz of the bee. In the blos - soms as
D7
G
D7
you said to me, With a heart that is
G
E
N.C.
true I'll be wait - ing for you. In the
A7
D7
G
shade of the old ap - ple tree.

I've Been Working On The Railroad

Registration 5

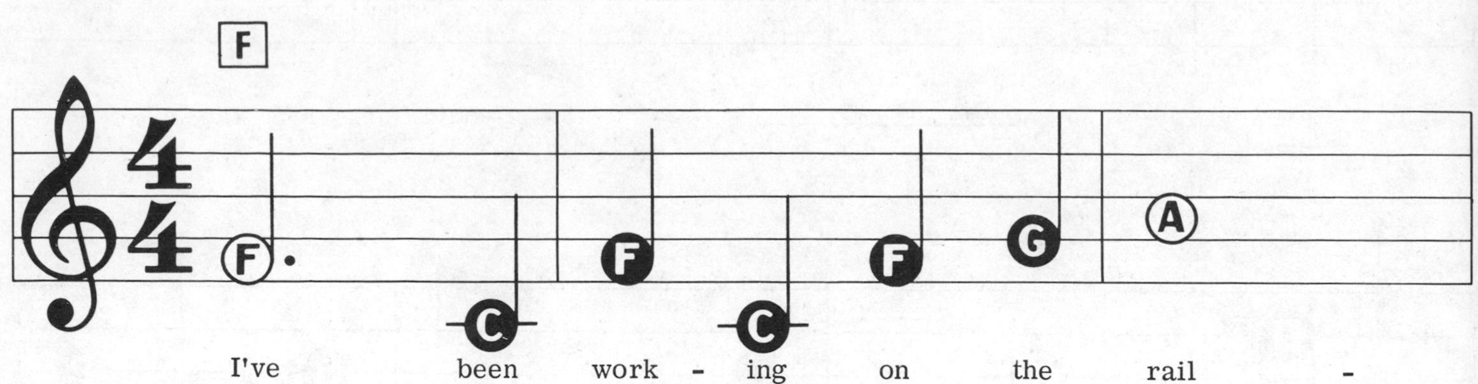

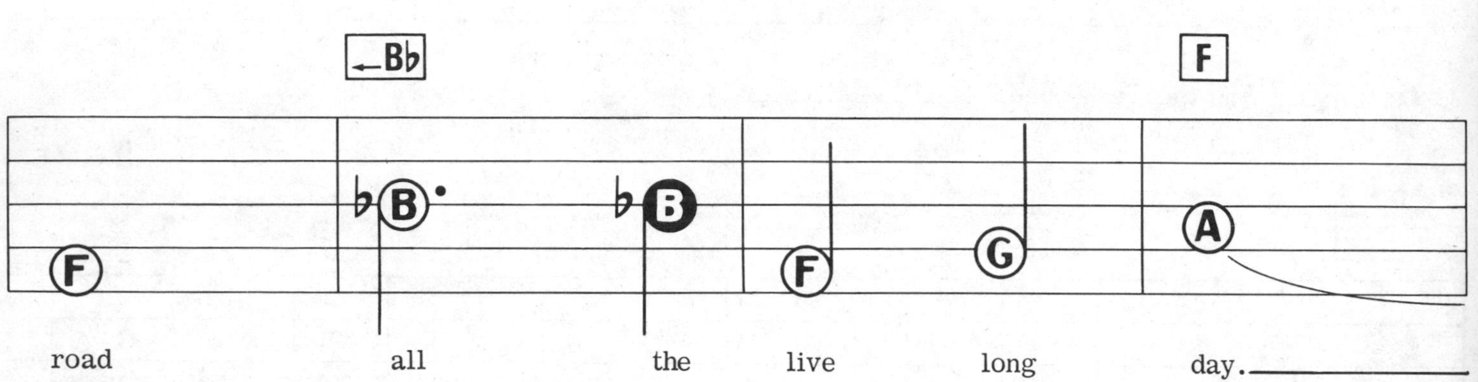

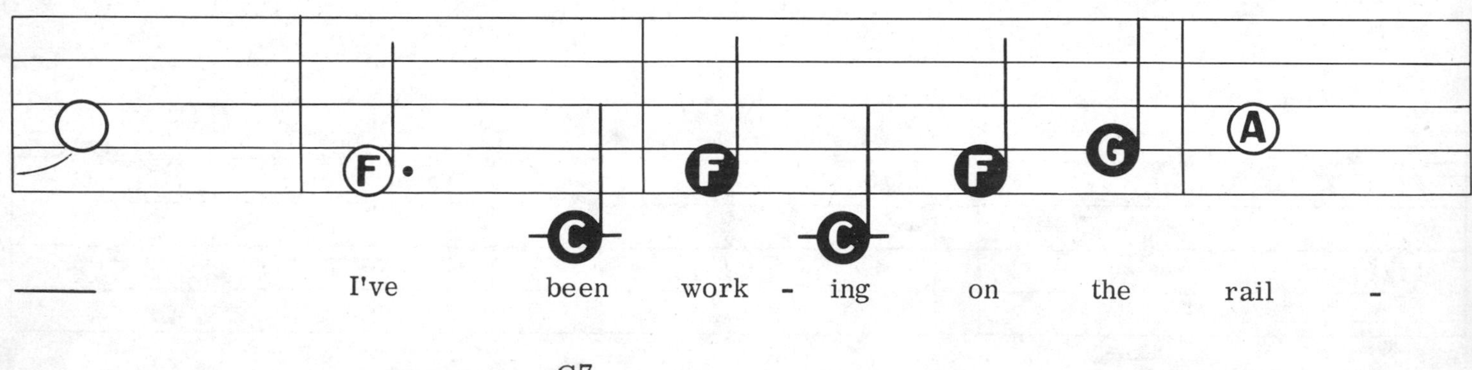

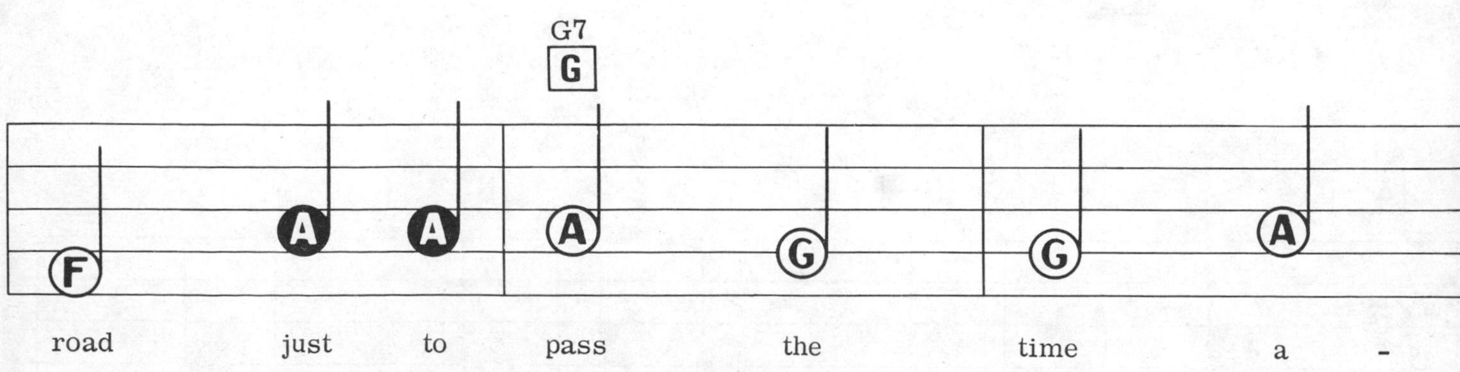

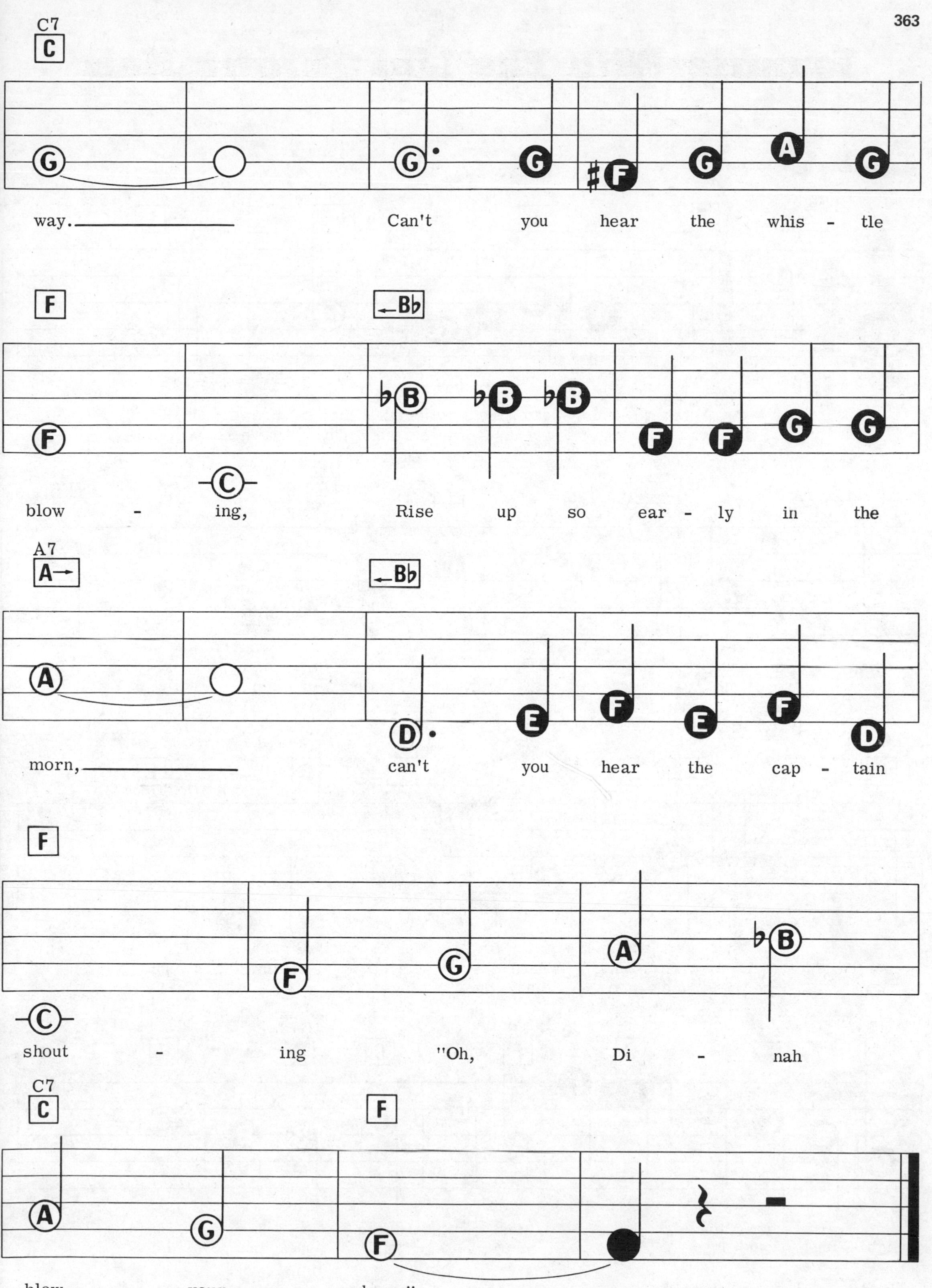
C7
C
G
G
G
♯F
G
A
G
way.
Can't
you
hear
the
whis - tle
F
← B♭
F
C
♭B
♭B
♭B
F
F
G
G
blow - ing,
Rise
up
so
ear - ly
in
the
A7
A →
← B♭
A
D
E
F
E
F
D
morn,
can't
you
hear
the
cap - tain
F
C
F
G
A
♭B
shout - ing
"Oh,
Di - nah
C7
C
F
A
G
F
blow
your
horn."

Jeannie With The Light Brown Hair

Registration 9

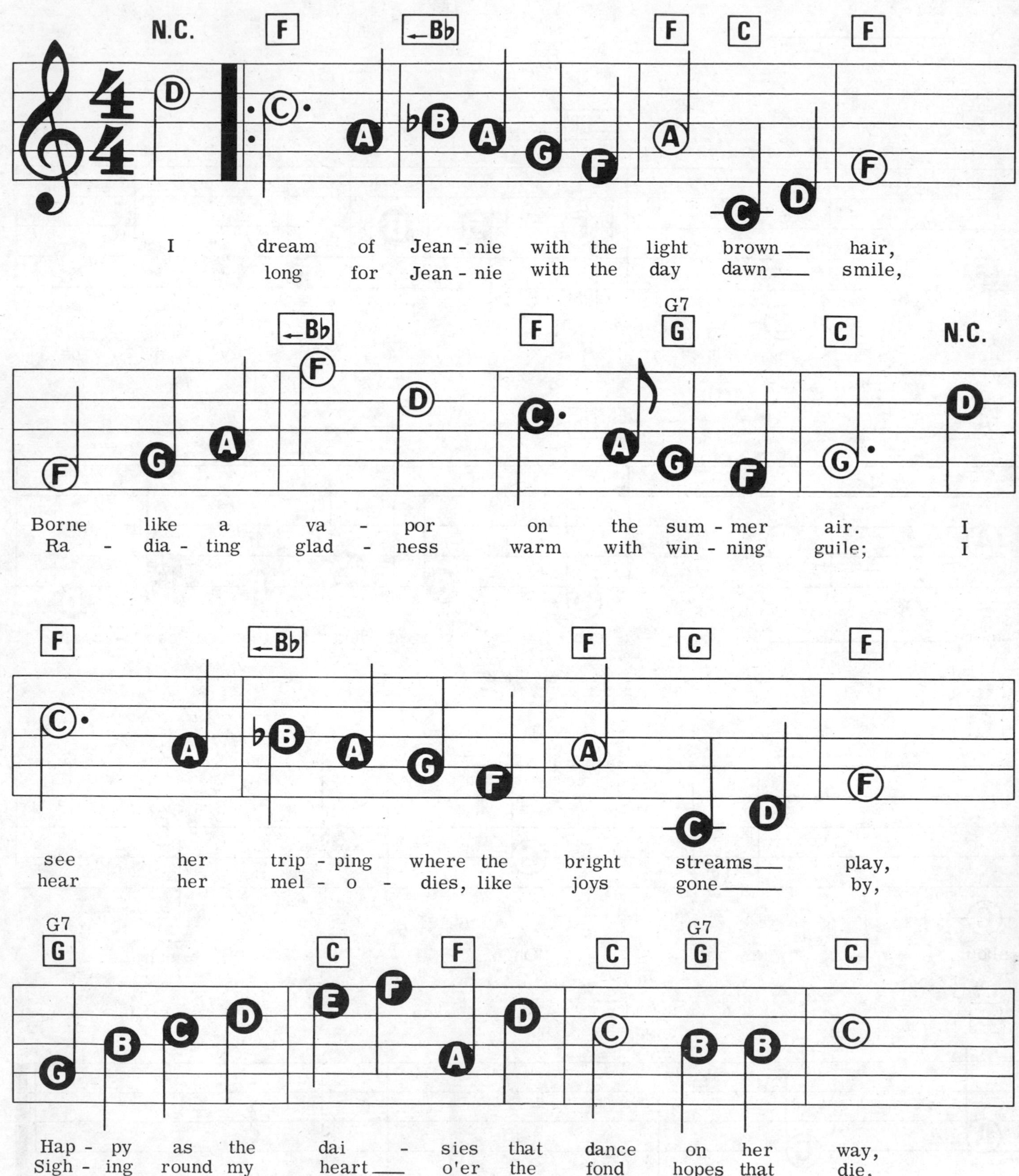

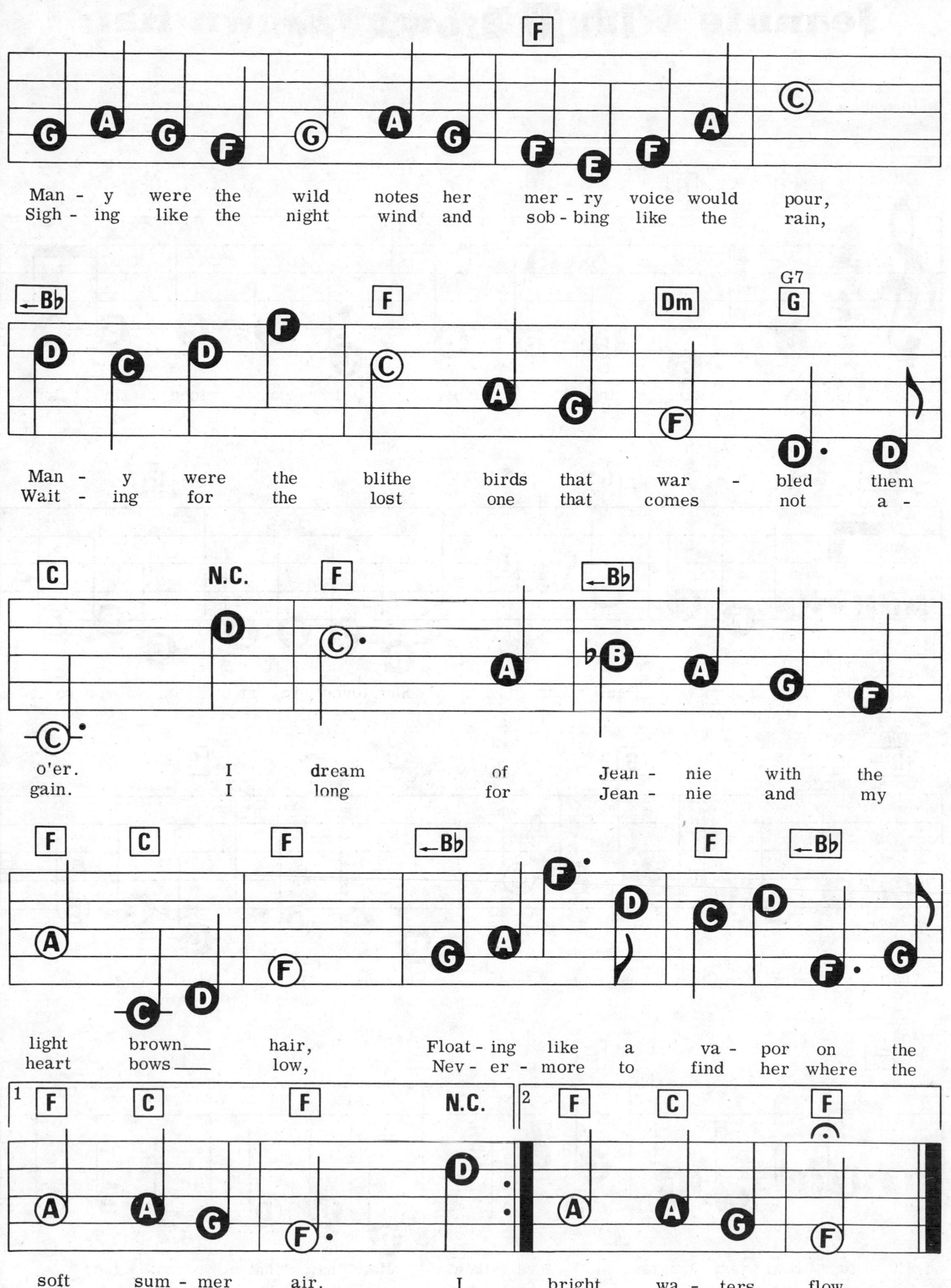
F
Man - y were the wild notes her mer - ry voice would pour,
Sigh - ing like the night wind and sob - bing like the rain,
Bb F Dm G7 G
Man - y were the blithe birds that war - bled them
Wait - ing for the lost one that comes not a -
C N.C. F Bb
o'er. I dream of Jean - nie with the
gain. I long for Jean - nie and my
F C F Bb F Bb
light brown hair, Float - ing like a va - por on the
heart bows low, Nev - er - more to find her where the
1 F C F N.C. 2 F C F
soft sum - mer air. I bright wa - ters flow.

Little Brown Jug

Registration 2

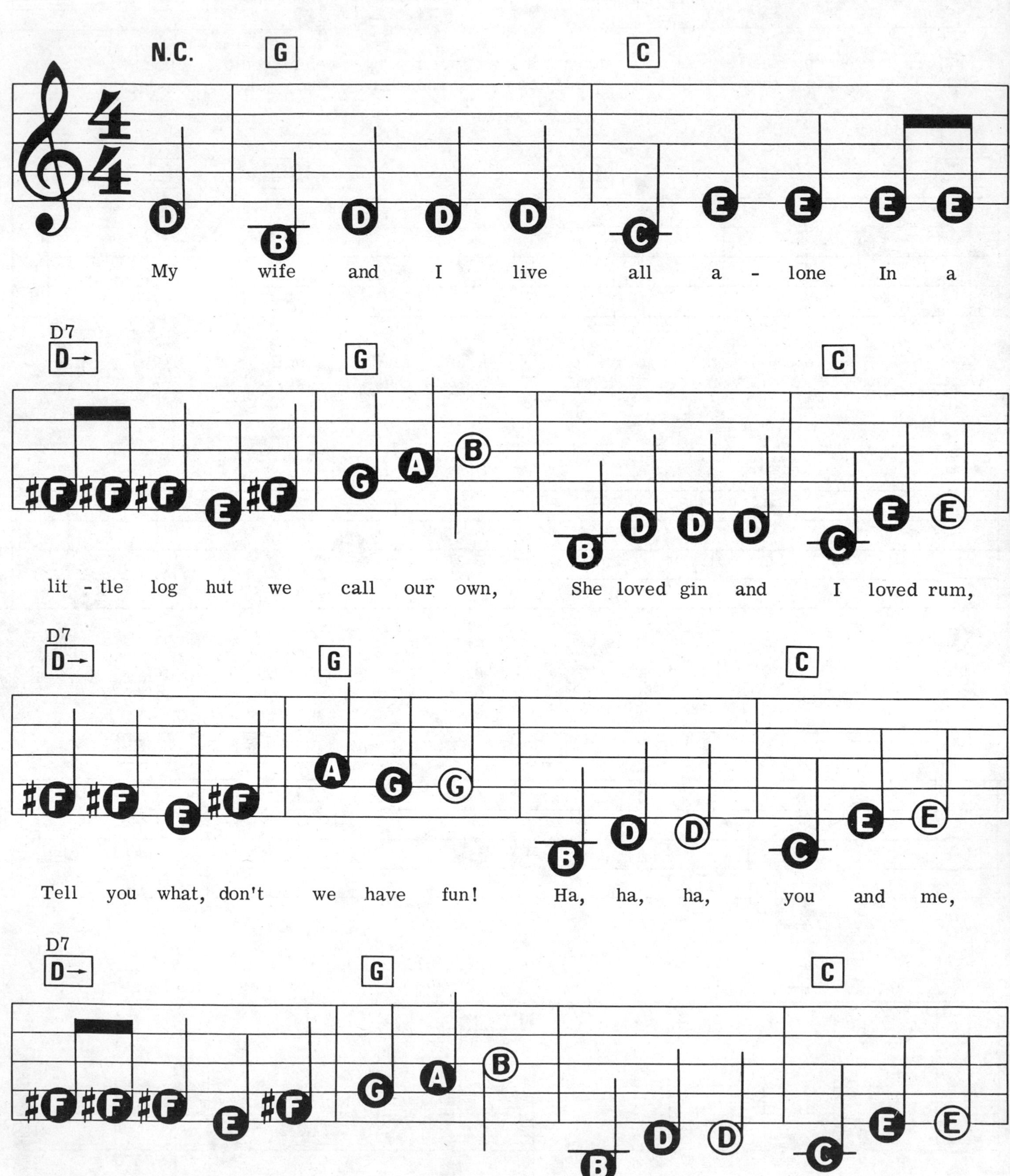

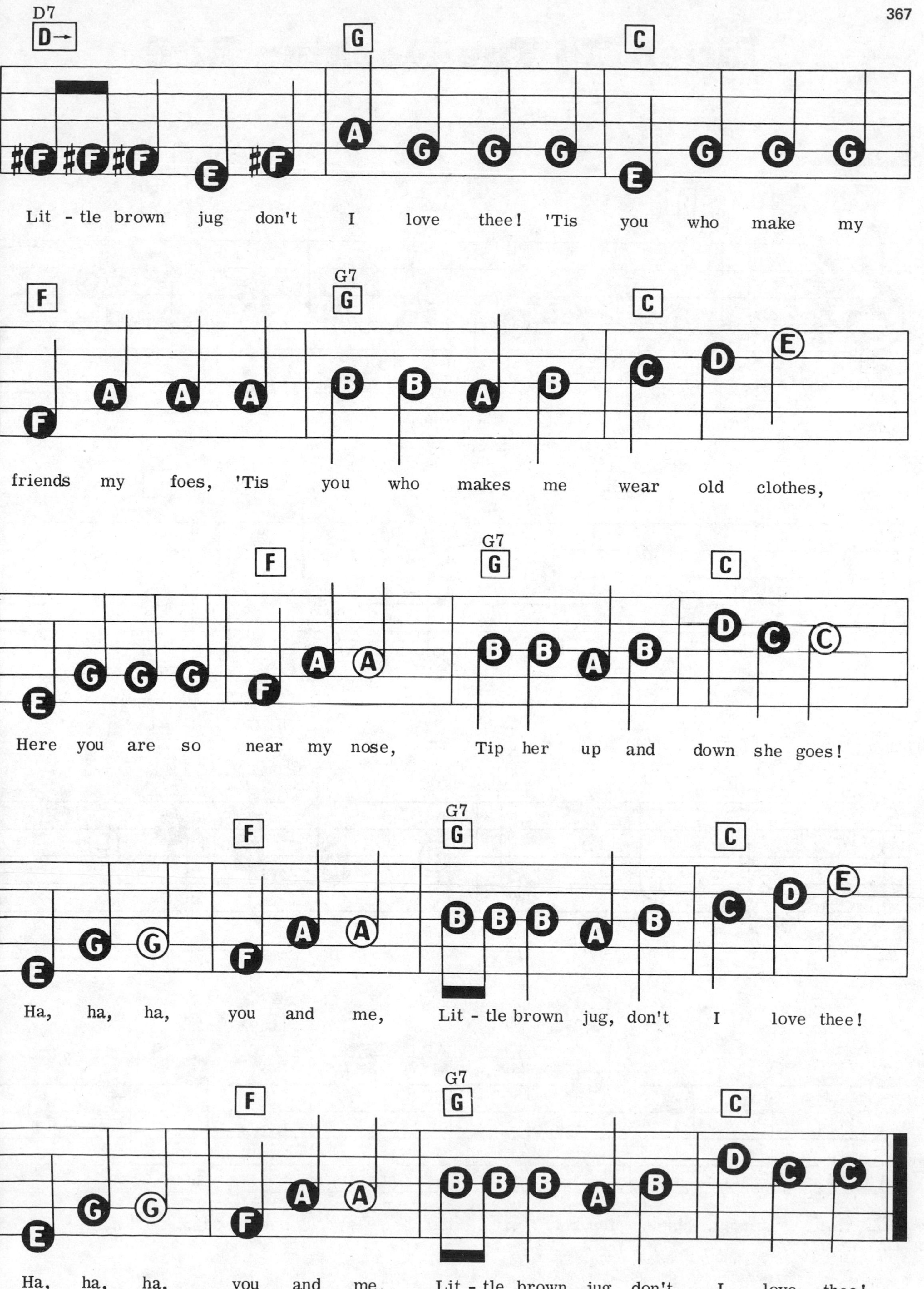
D7
D
G
C
F
G7
G
C
F
G7
G
C
F
G7
G
C
F
G7
G
C
Lit - tle brown jug don't I love thee! 'Tis you who make my
friends my foes, 'Tis you who makes me wear old clothes,
Here you are so near my nose, Tip her up and down she goes!
Ha, ha, ha, you and me, Lit - tle brown jug, don't I love thee!
Ha, ha, ha, you and me, Lit - tle brown jug, don't I love thee!

Listen To The Mocking Bird

Registration 2

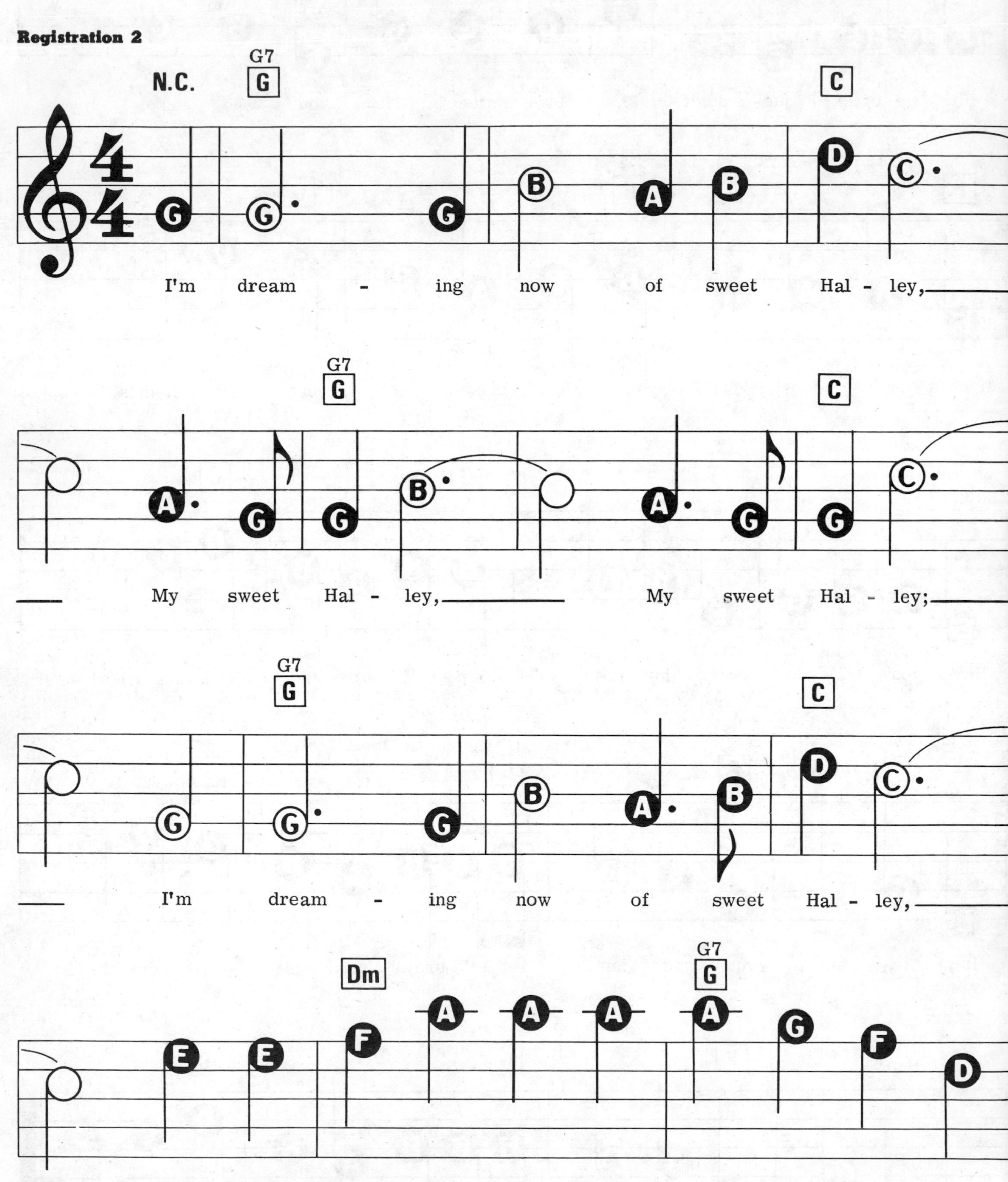

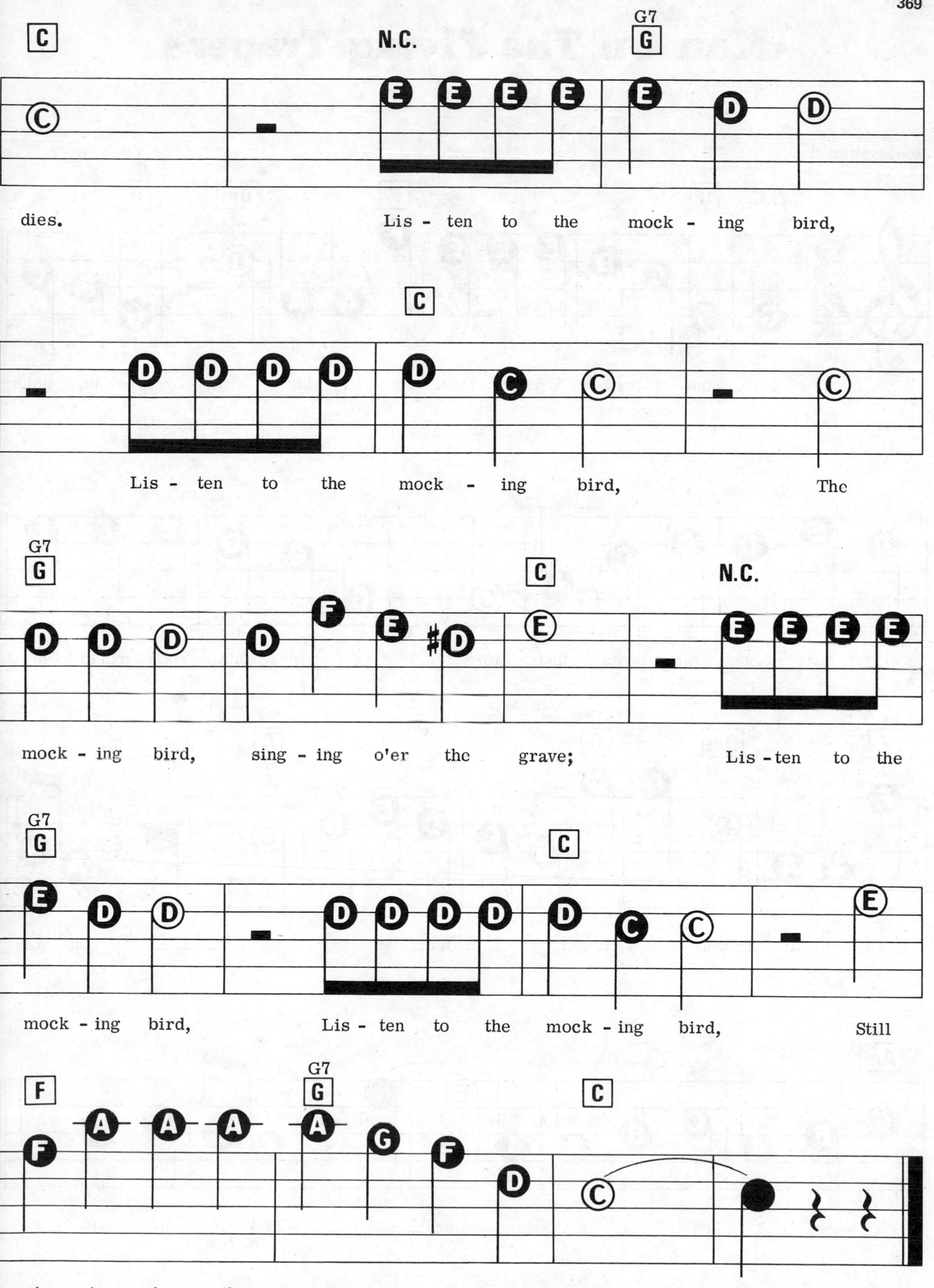
C N.C. G7 G
dies. Lis - ten to the mock - ing bird,
C
Lis - ten to the mock - ing bird, The
G7 G C N.C.
mock - ing bird, sing - ing o'er the grave; Lis - ten to the
G7 G C
mock - ing bird, Lis - ten to the mock - ing bird, Still
F G7 G C
sing - ing where the weep - ing wil - lows wave.

Man On The Flying Trapeze

Registration 5

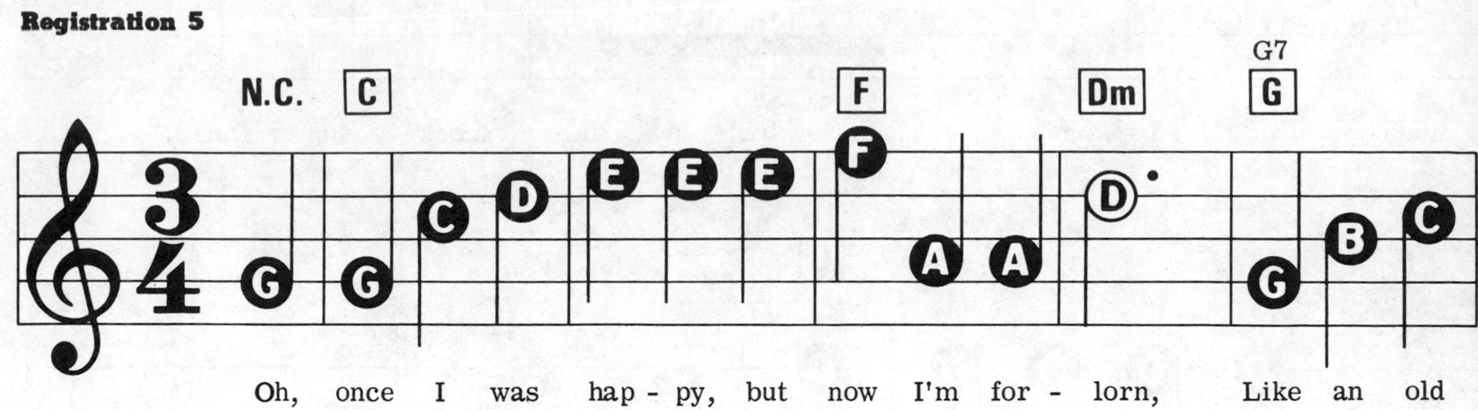

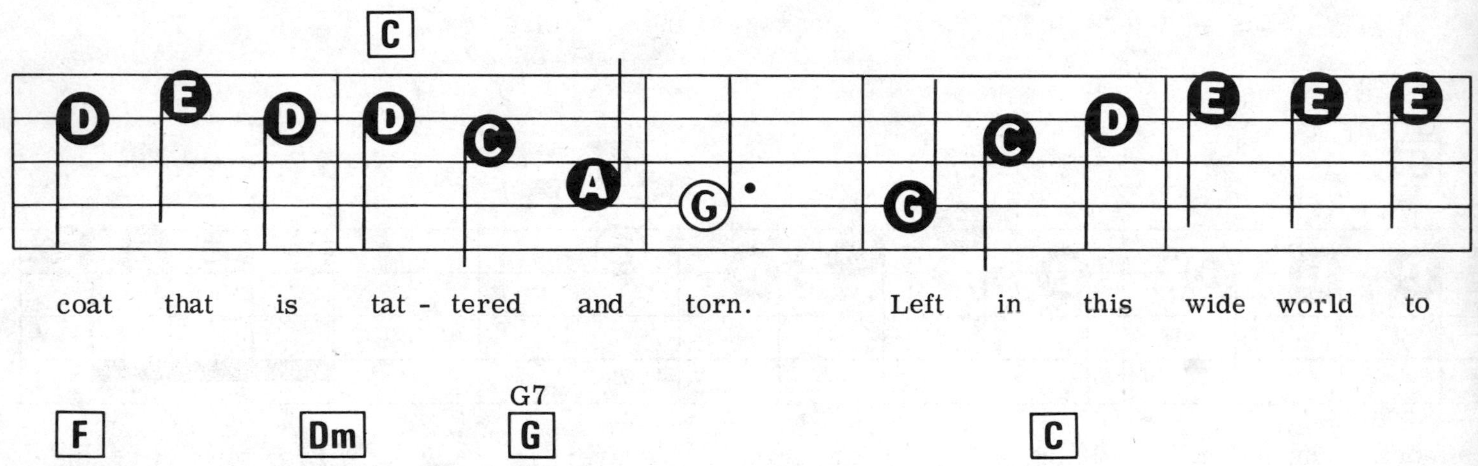

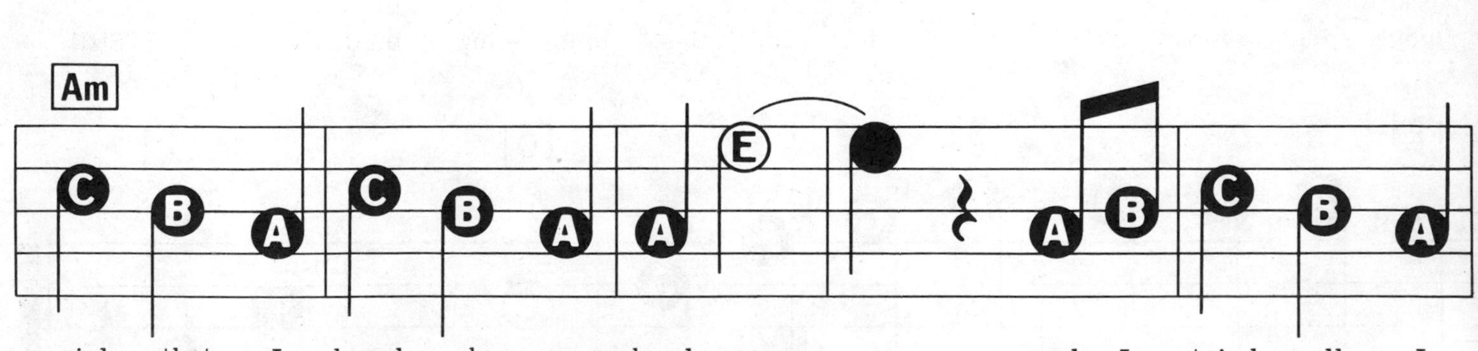

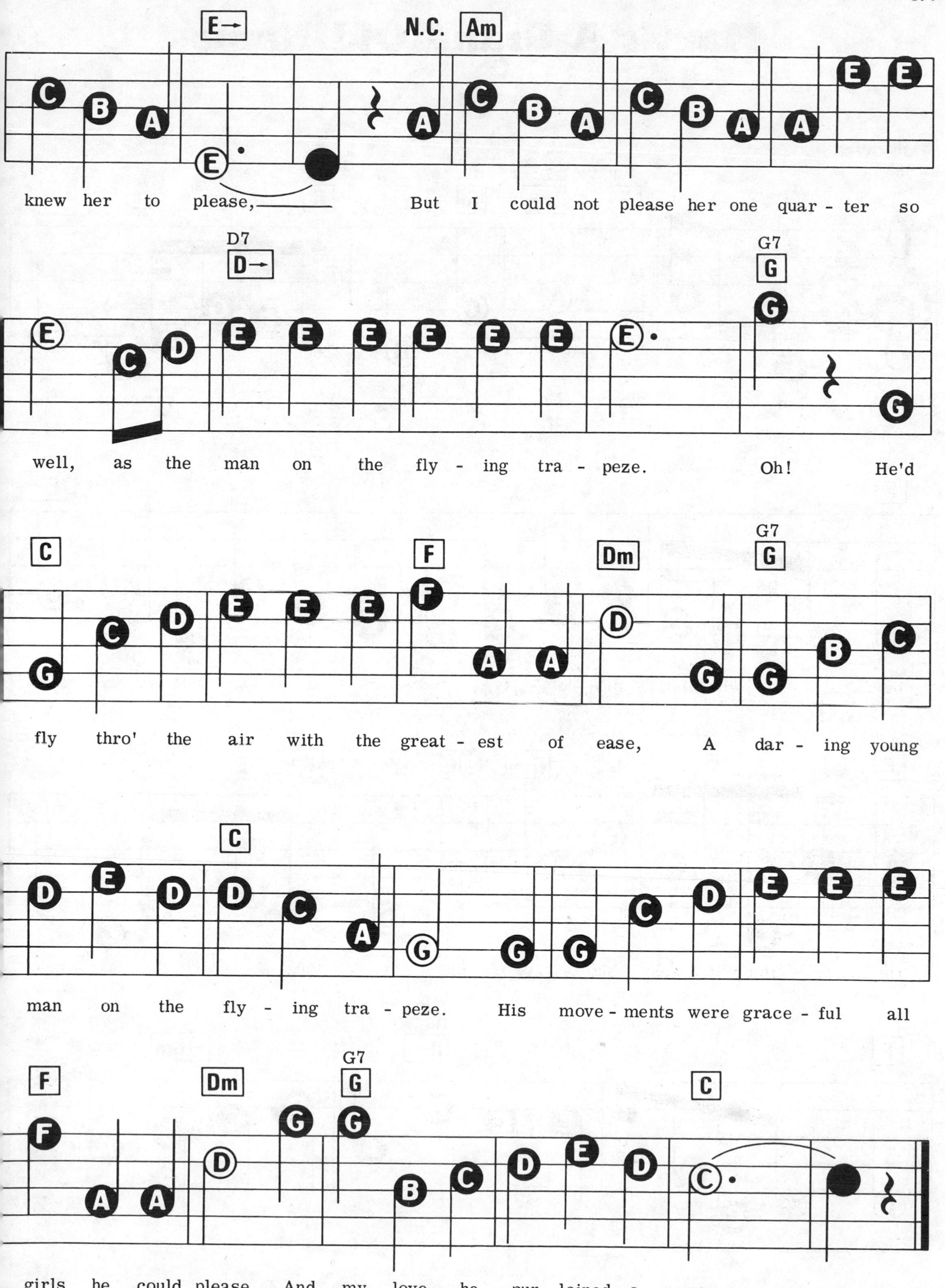
E→ N.C. Am
knew her to please, But I could not please her one quar - ter so
D7 D→ G7 G
well, as the man on the fly - ing tra - peze. Oh! He'd
C F Dm G7 G
fly thro' the air with the great - est of ease, A dar - ing young
C
man on the fly - ing tra - peze. His move - ments were grace - ful all
F Dm G7 G C
girls he could please, And my love he pur - loined a - way.

Mary's A Grand Old Name

Registration 5

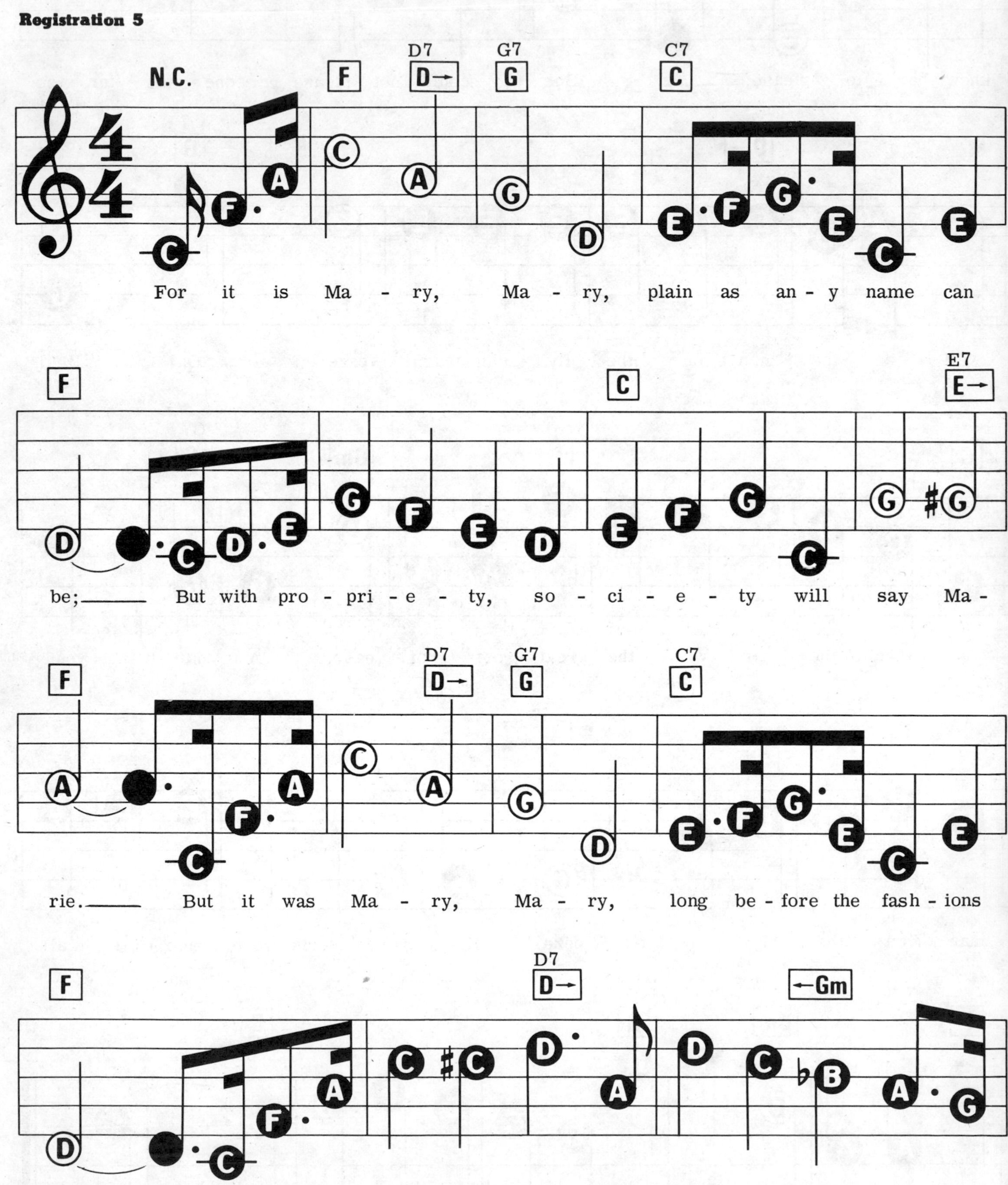

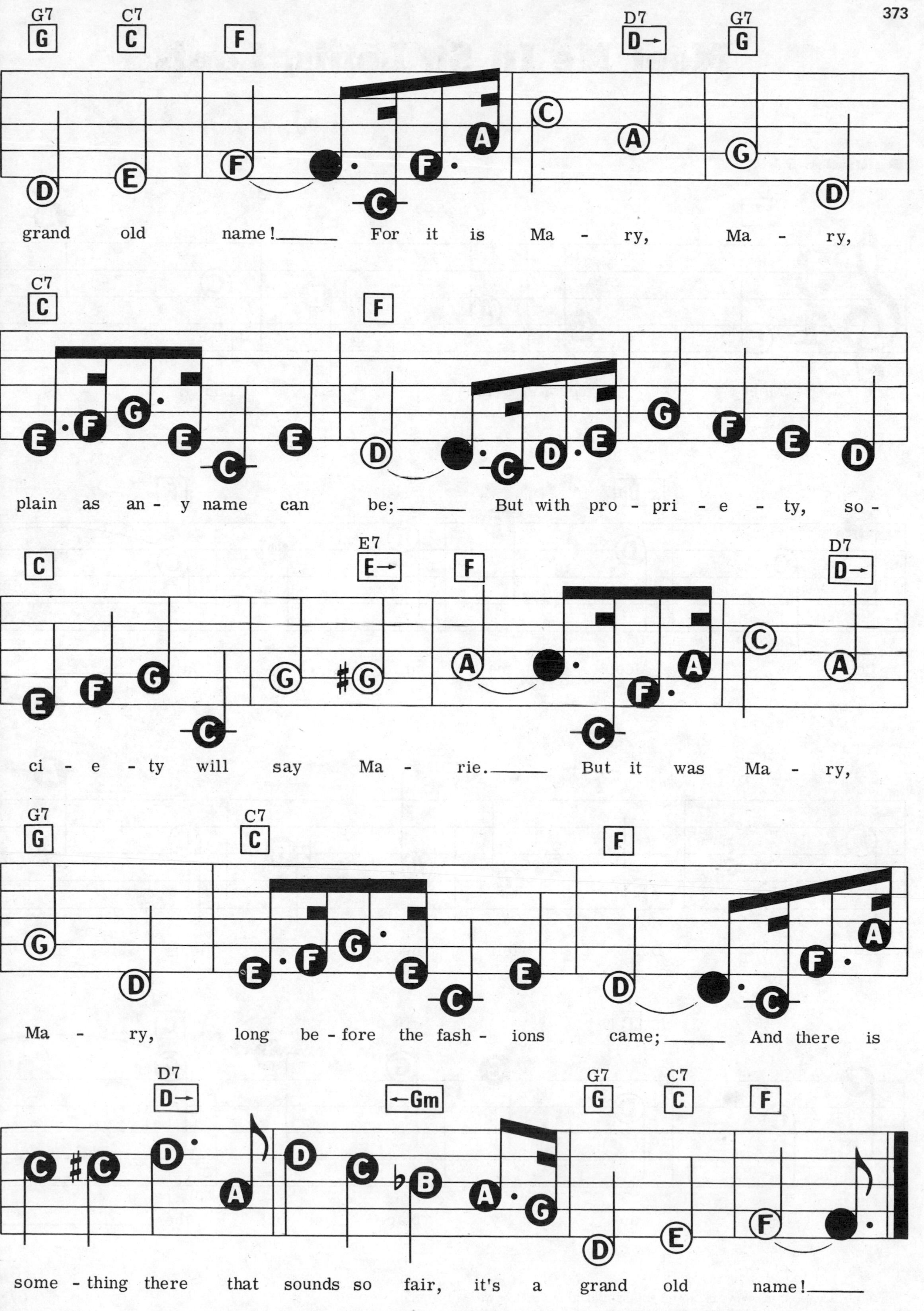
G7 G C7 C F D7 D→ G7 G
grand old name! For it is Ma - ry, Ma - ry,
C7 C F
plain as an - y name can be; But with pro - pri - e - ty, so -
C E7 E→ F D7 D→
ci - e - ty will say Ma - rie. But it was Ma - ry,
G7 G C7 C F
Ma - ry, long be - fore the fash - ions came; And there is
D7 D→ ←Gm G7 G C7 C F
some - thing there that sounds so fair, it's a grand old name!

Meet Me In St. Louis, Louis

Registration 9

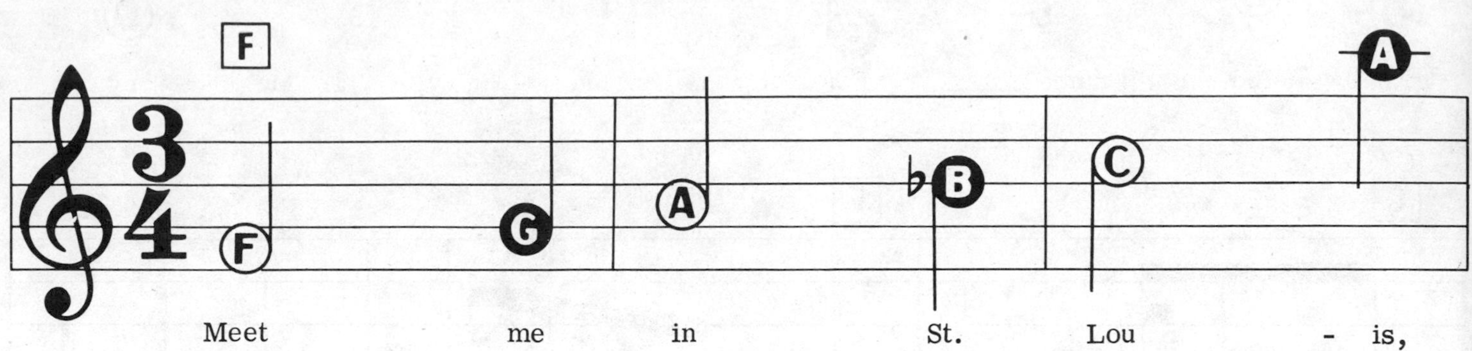

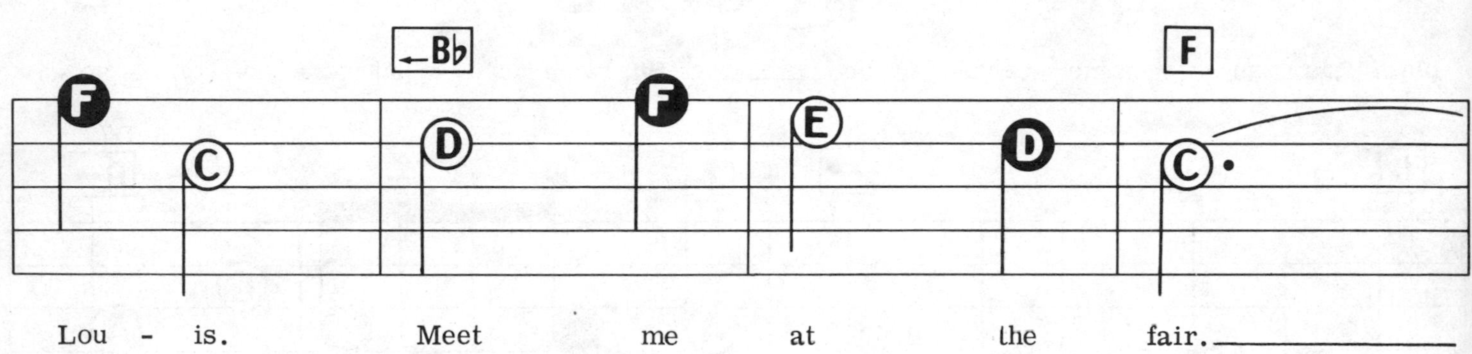

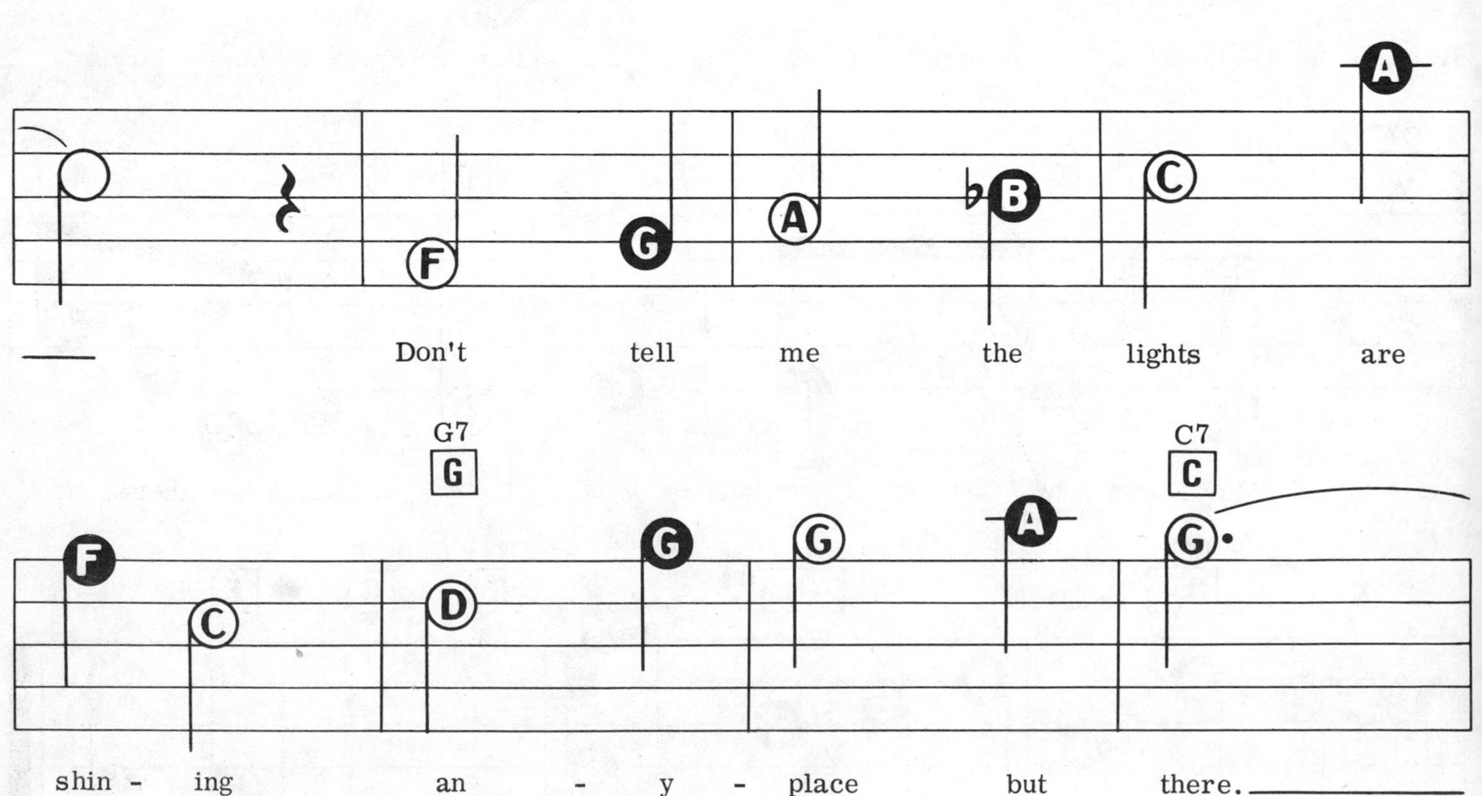

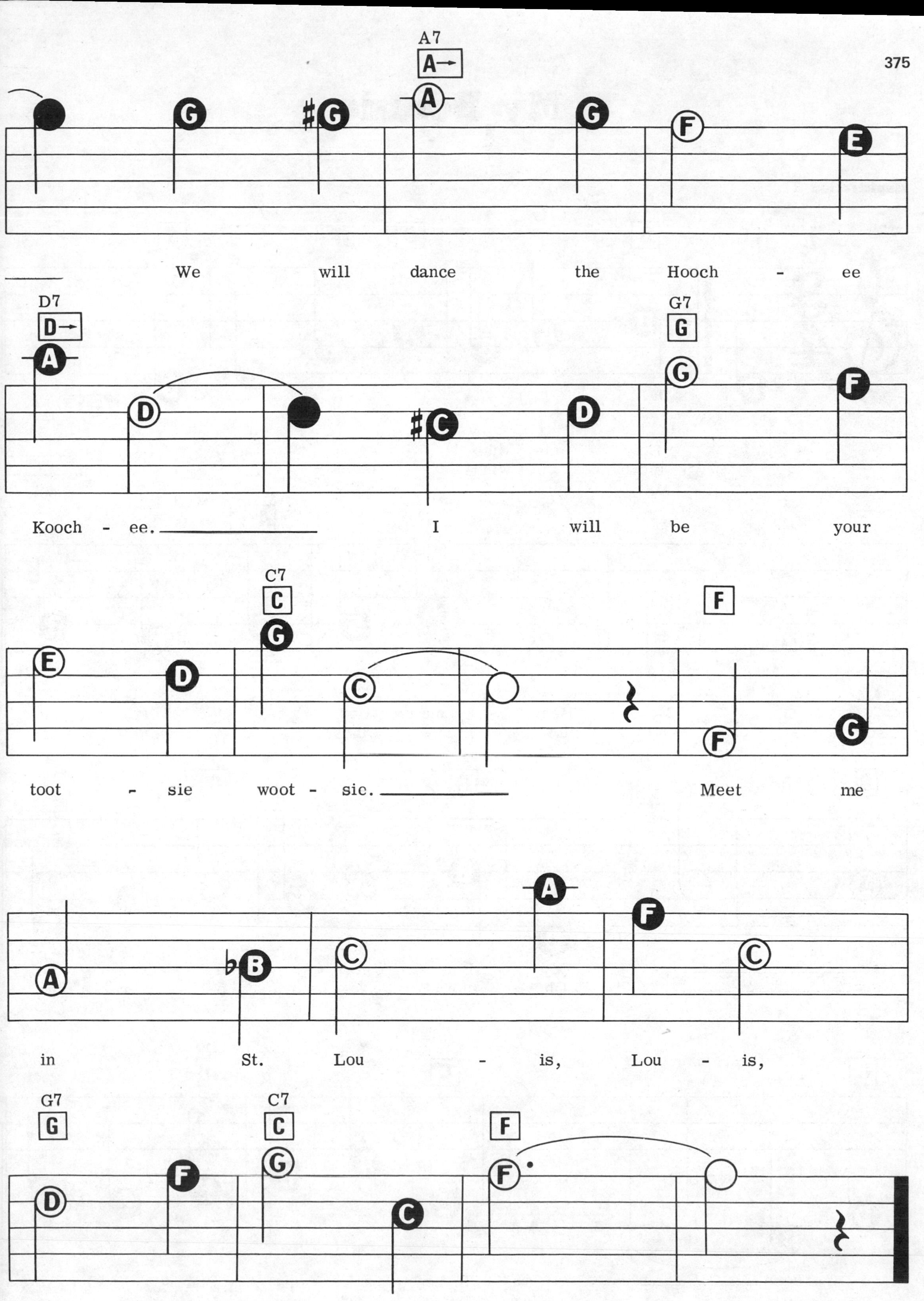
A7
A
G G ♯G A G F E
We will dance the Hooch - ee
D7
D
G7
G
A D ♯C D G F
Kooch - ee. I will be your
C7
C
F
E D G C F G
toot - sie woot - sie. Meet me
A ♭B C A F C
in St. Lou - is, Lou - is,
G7
G
C7
C
F
D F G C F
Meet me at the fair.

My Bonnie

Registration 3

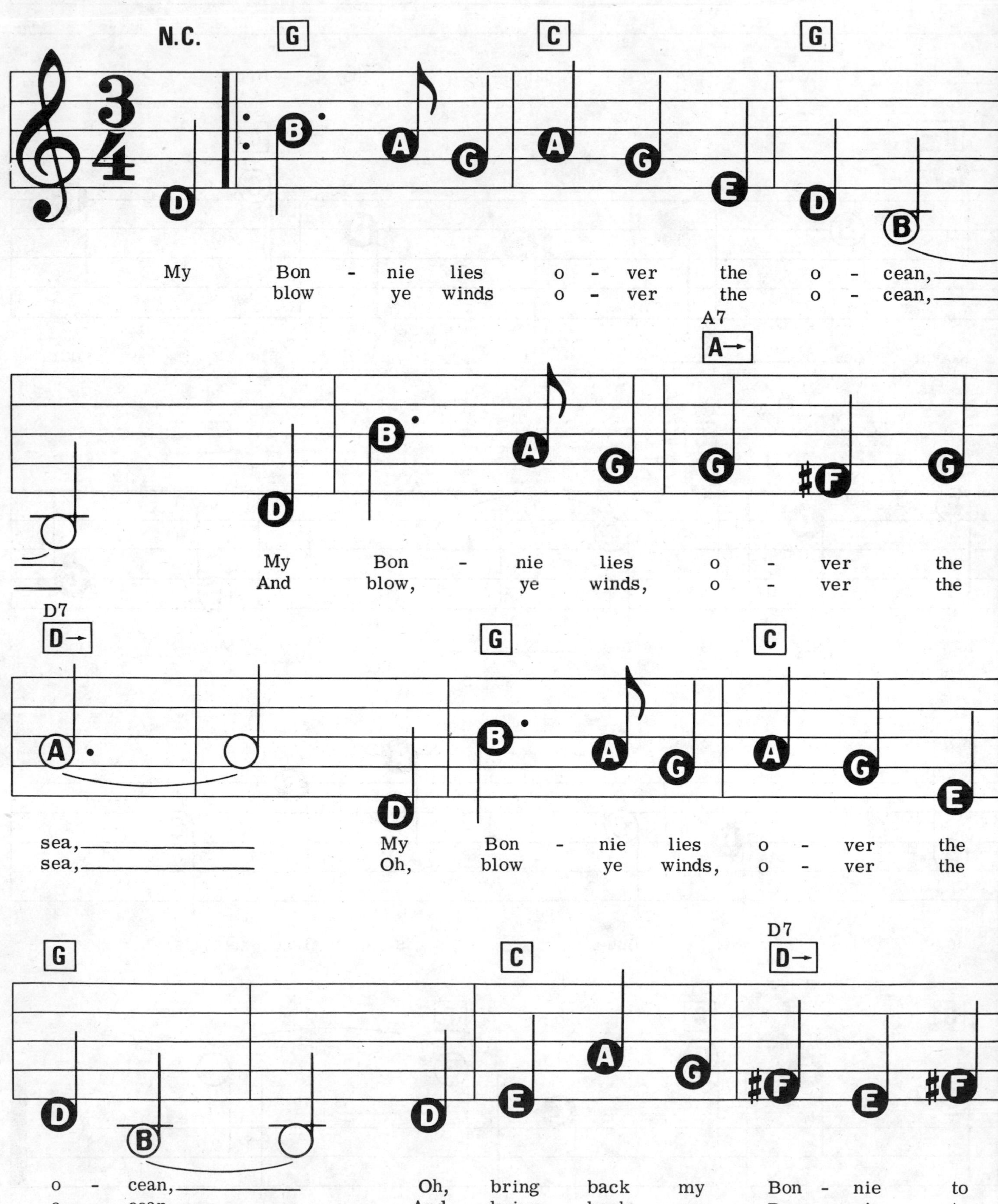

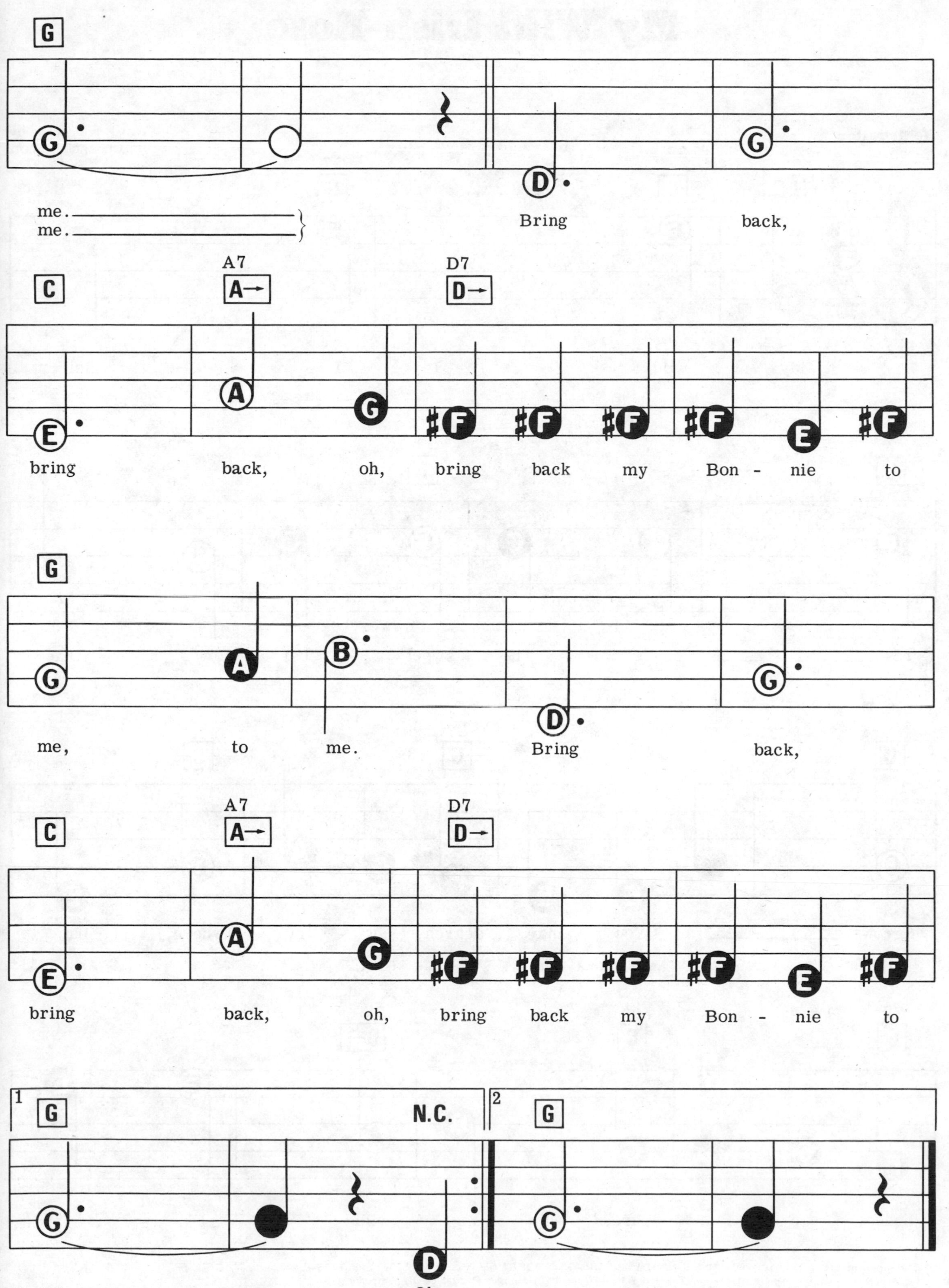
G
me.
me.
Bring back,
C
A7
D7
bring back, oh, bring back my Bon - nie to
G
me, to me. Bring back,
C
A7
D7
bring back, oh, bring back my Bon - nie to
1
G
N.C.
me. Oh,
2
G
me.

My Wild Irish Rose

Registration 2

Words and Music by
Chauncey Olcott

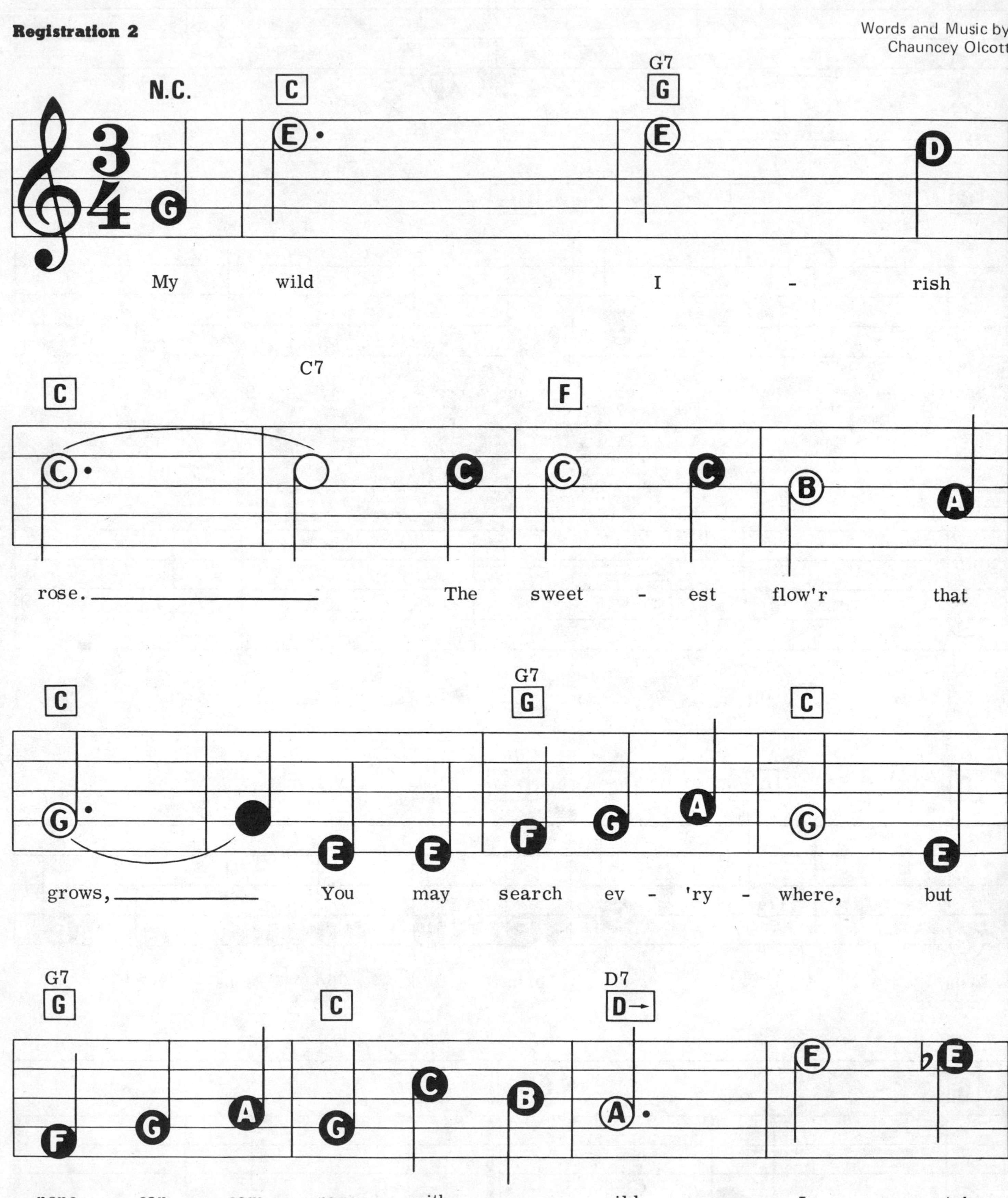

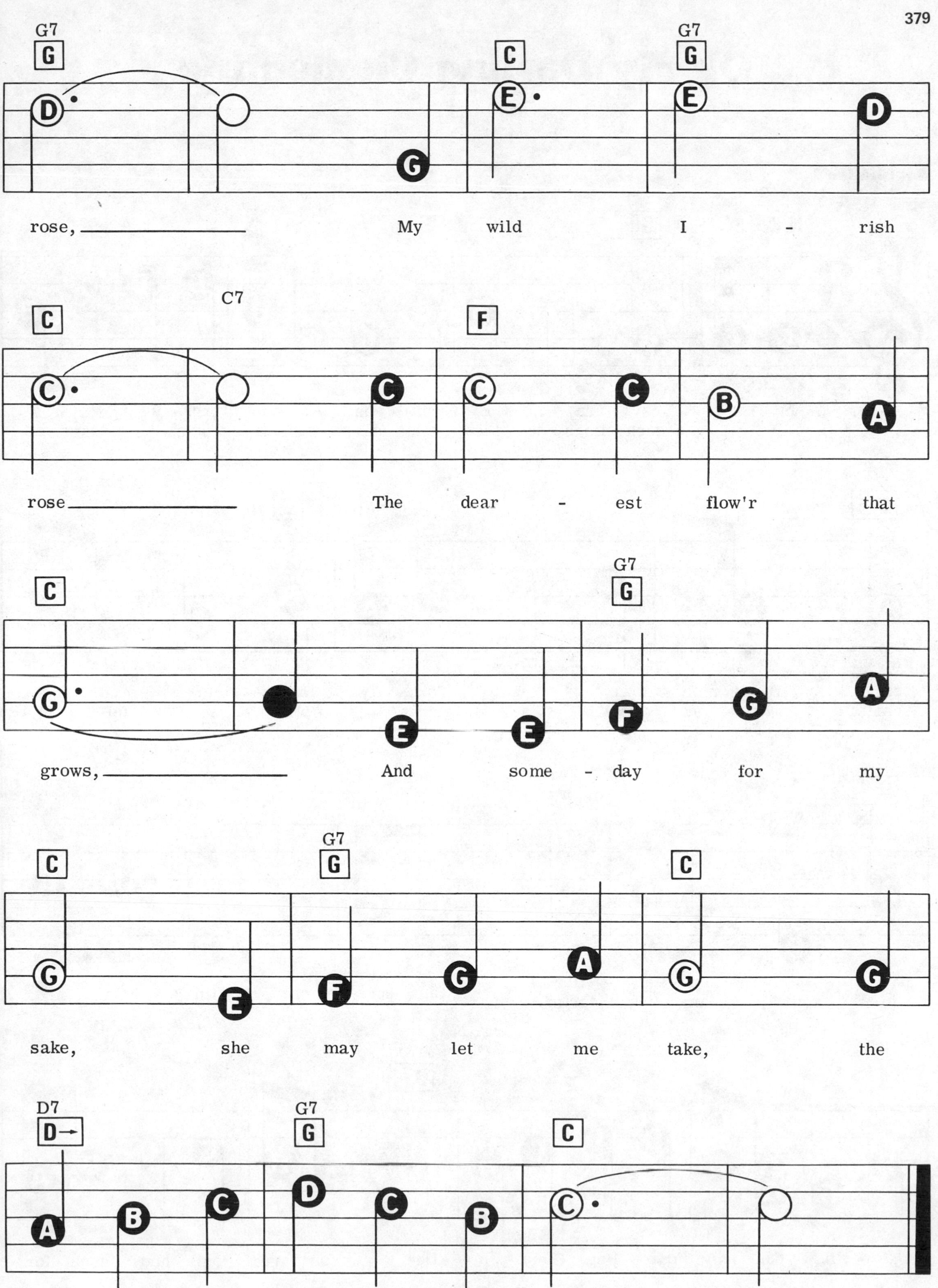
G7
G
C
G7
G
D
G
E
E
D
rose, My wild I - rish
C
C7
F
C
C
C
C
B
A
rose The dear - est flow'r that
C
G7
G
G
E
E
F
G
A
grows, And some - day for my
C
G7
G
C
G
E
F
G
A
G
G
sake, she may let me take, the
D7
D→
G7
G
C
A
B
C
D
C
B
C
bloom from my wild I - rish rose.

Oh My Darling Clementine

Registration 1

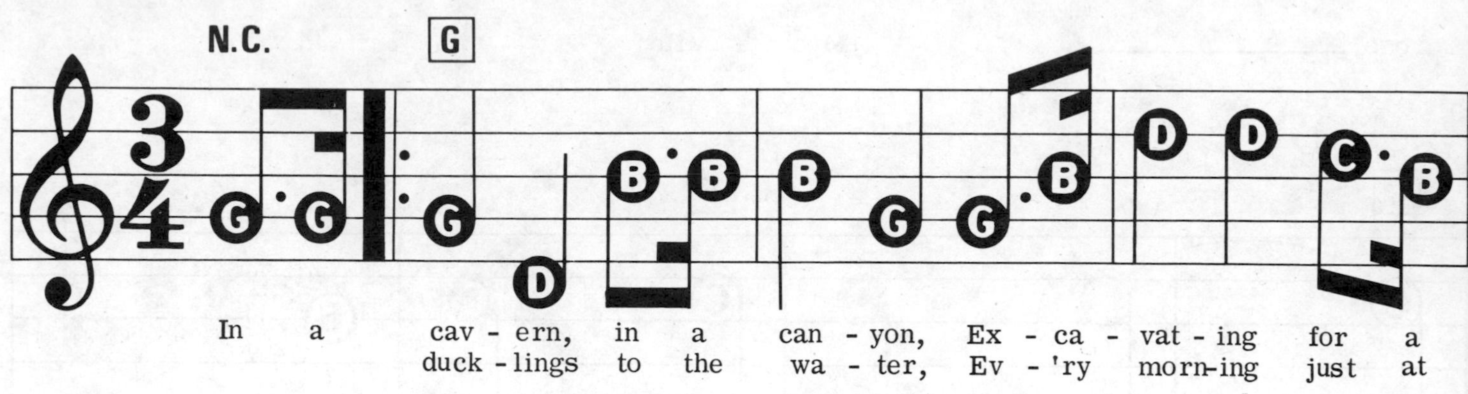

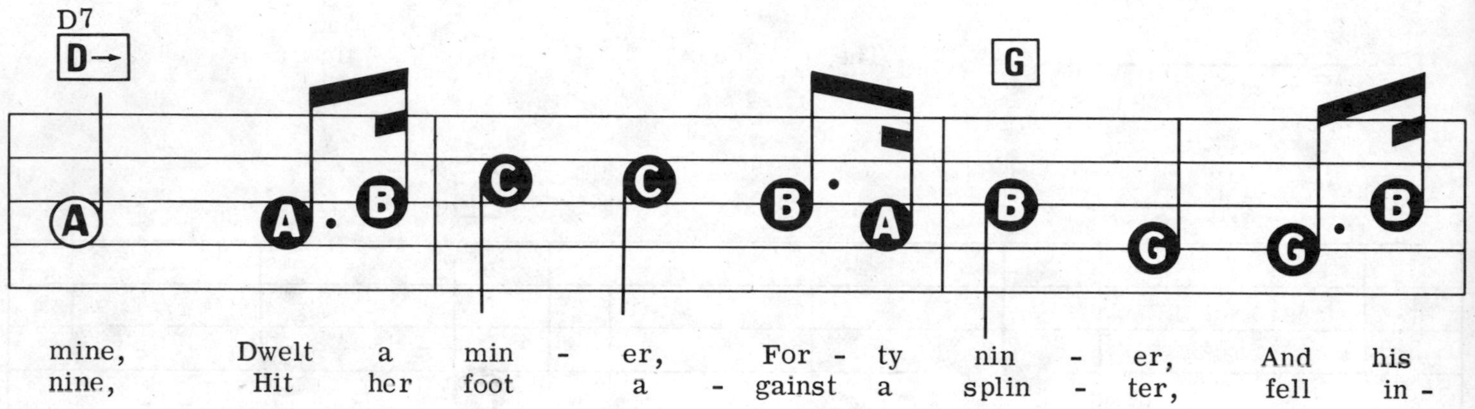

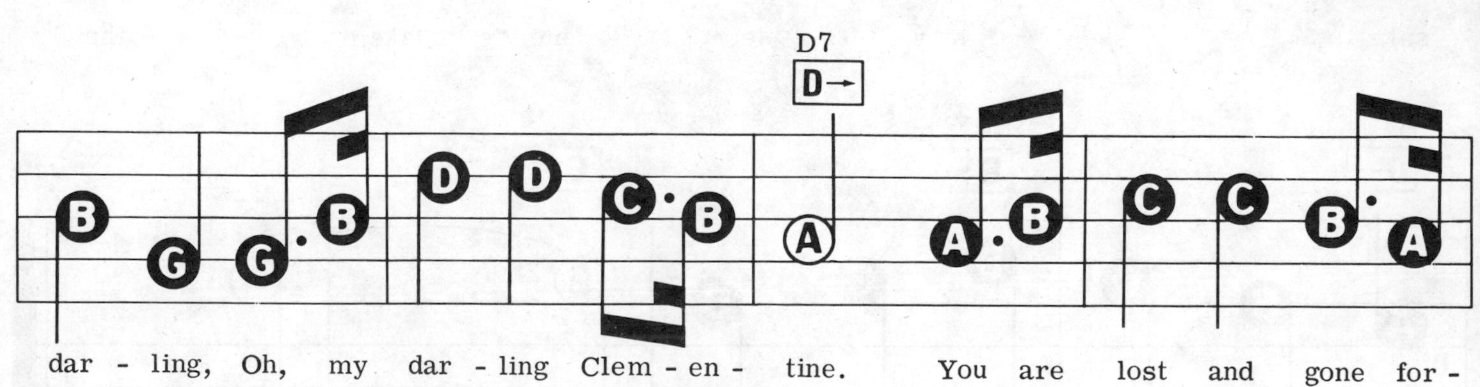

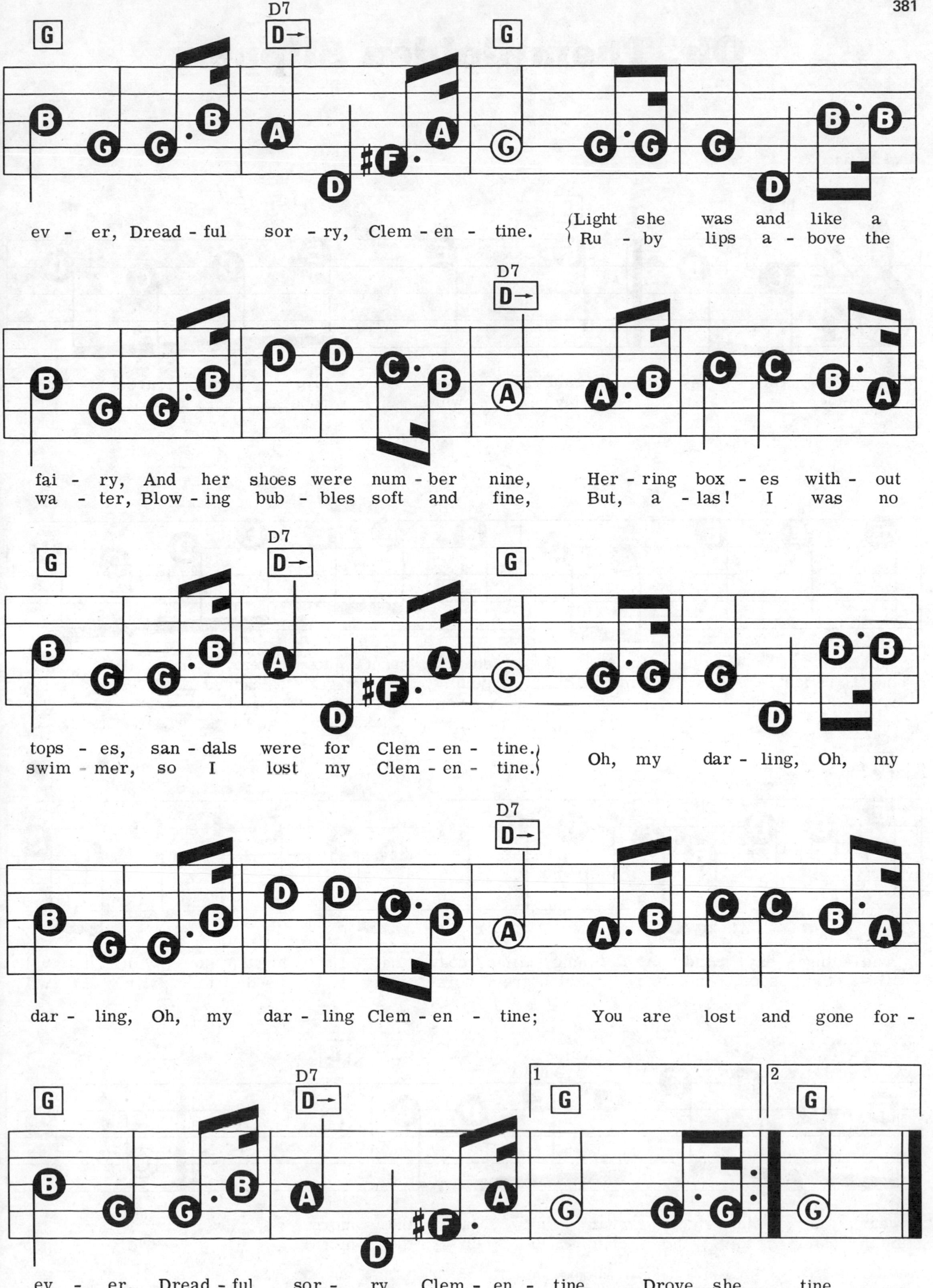
G D7 D→ G
ev - er, Dread - ful sor - ry, Clem - en - tine.
Light she was and like a
Ru - by lips a - bove the
D7 D→
fai - ry, And her shoes were num - ber nine, Her - ring box - es with - out
wa - ter, Blow - ing bub - bles soft and fine, But, a - las! I was no
G D7 D→ G
tops - es, san - dals were for Clem - en - tine.
swim - mer, so I lost my Clem - cn - tine.
Oh, my dar - ling, Oh, my
D7 D→
dar - ling, Oh, my dar - ling Clem - en - tine; You are lost and gone for -
G D7 D→ 1 G 2 G
ev - er, Dread - ful sor - ry, Clem - en - tine. Drove she tine.

Oh, Them Golden Slippers

Registration 7

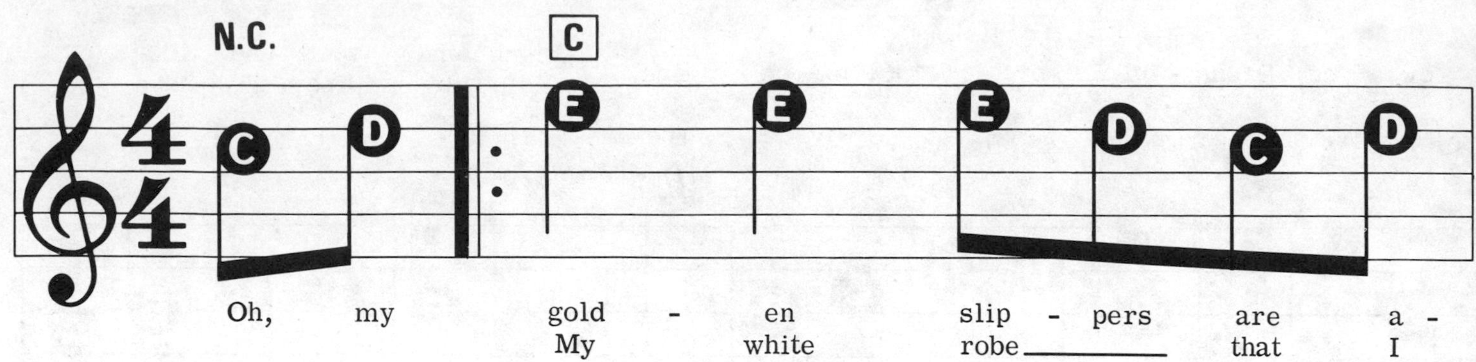

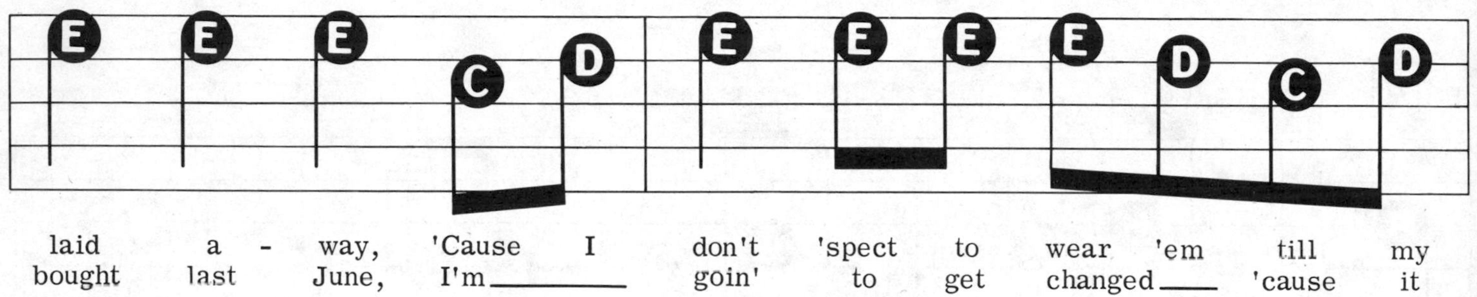

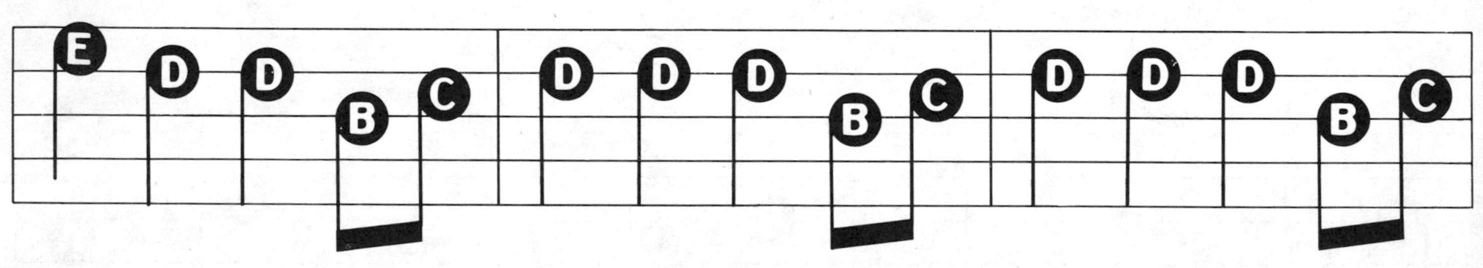

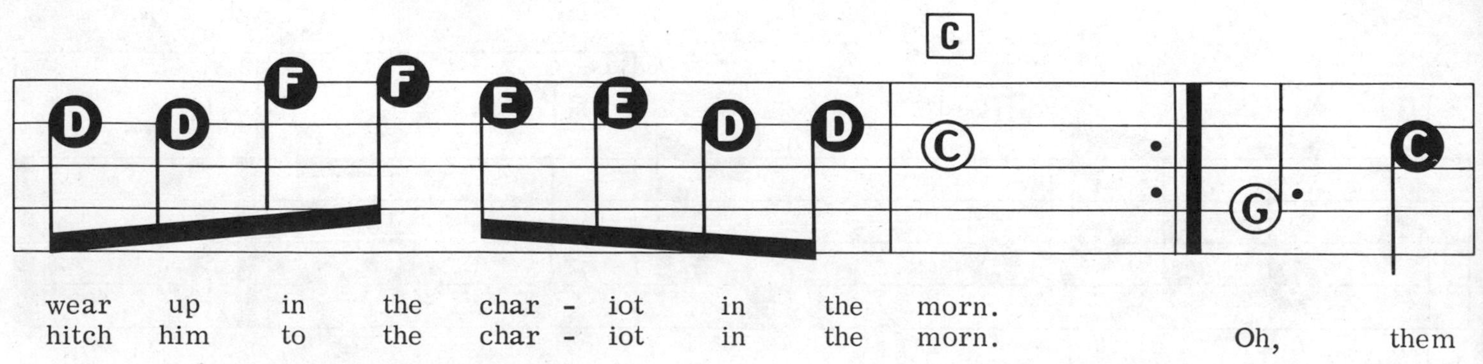

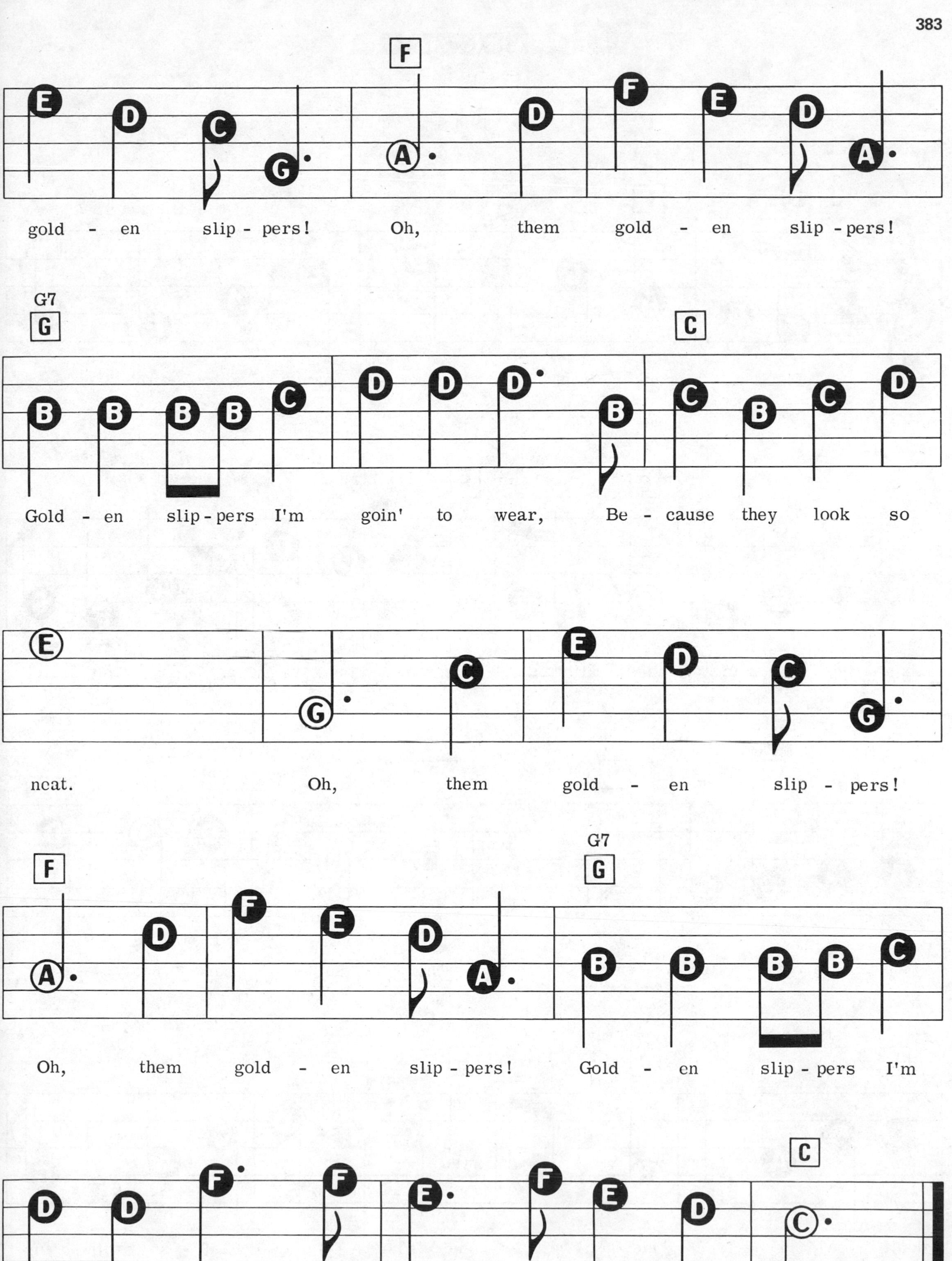
F
gold - en slip - pers! Oh, them gold - en slip - pers!
G7
G
C
Gold - en slip - pers I'm goin' to wear, Be - cause they look so
neat. Oh, them gold - en slip - pers!
F
G7
G
Oh, them gold - en slip - pers! Gold - en slip - pers I'm
C
goin' to wear, To walk the gold - en street.

Oh! Susanna

Registration 3

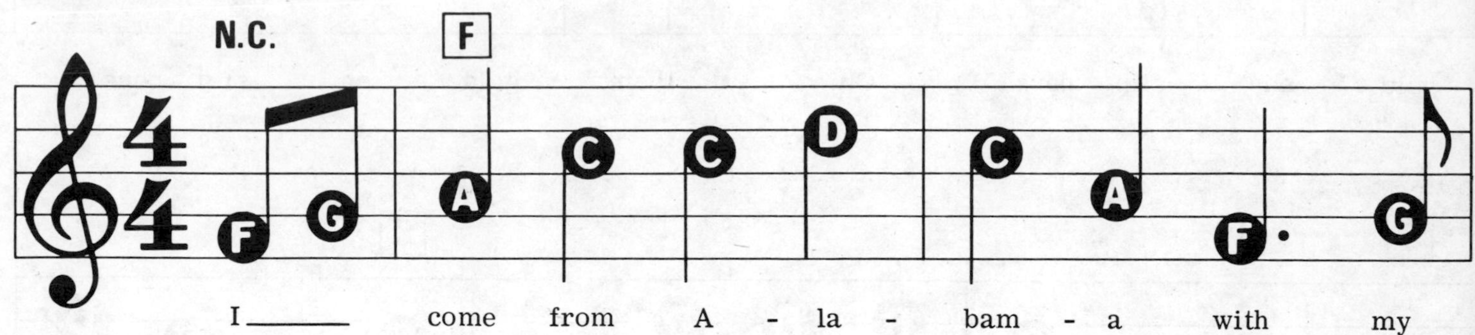

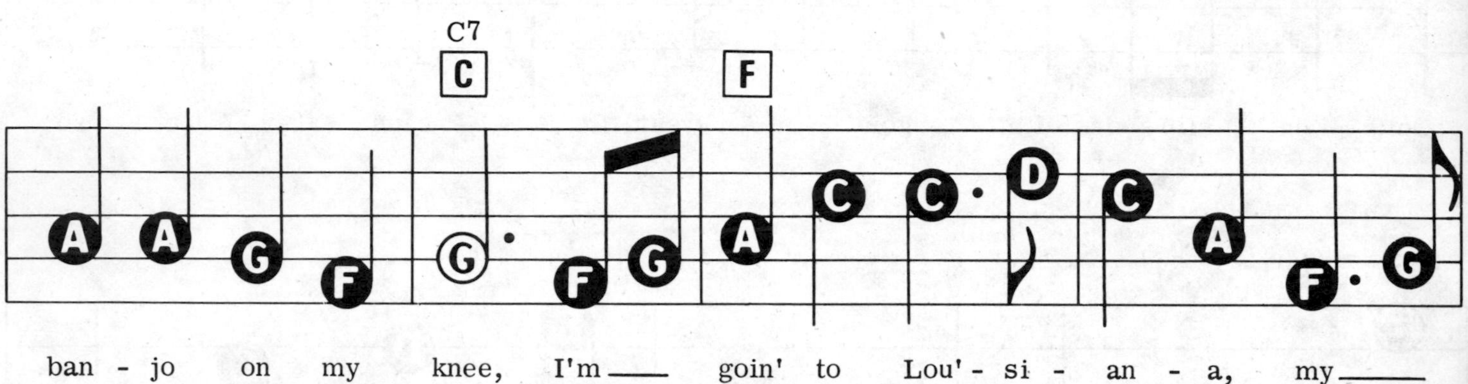

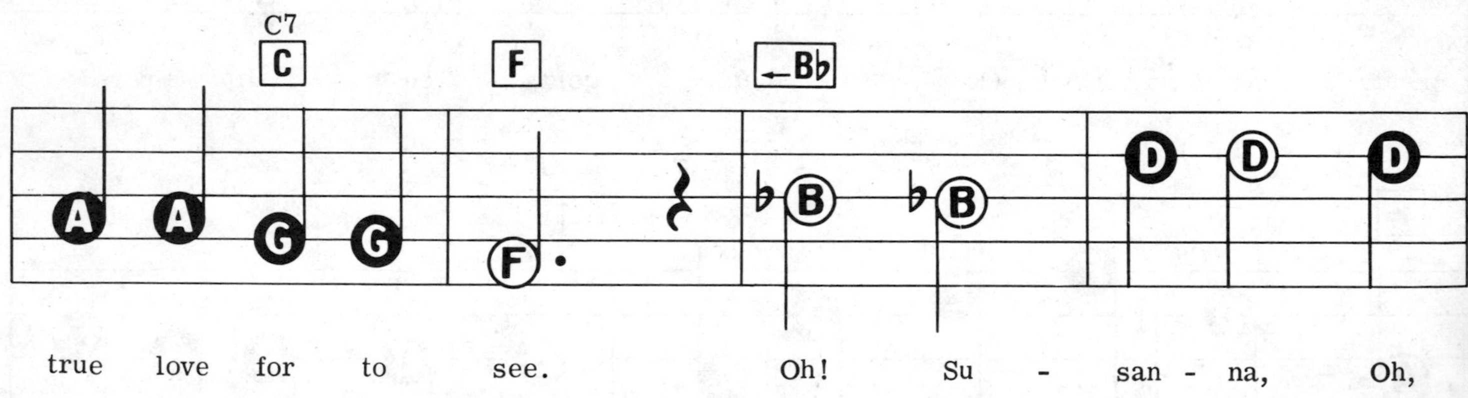

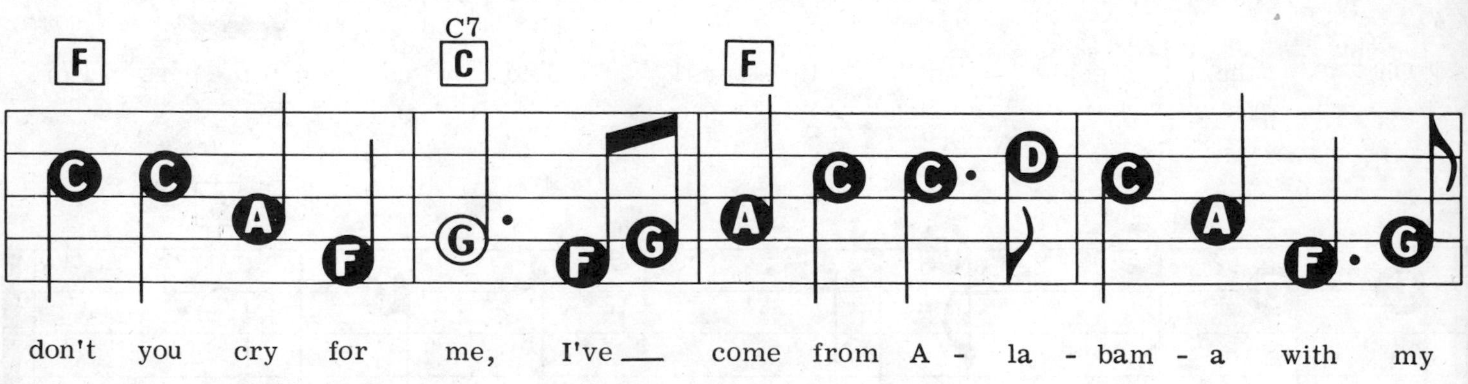

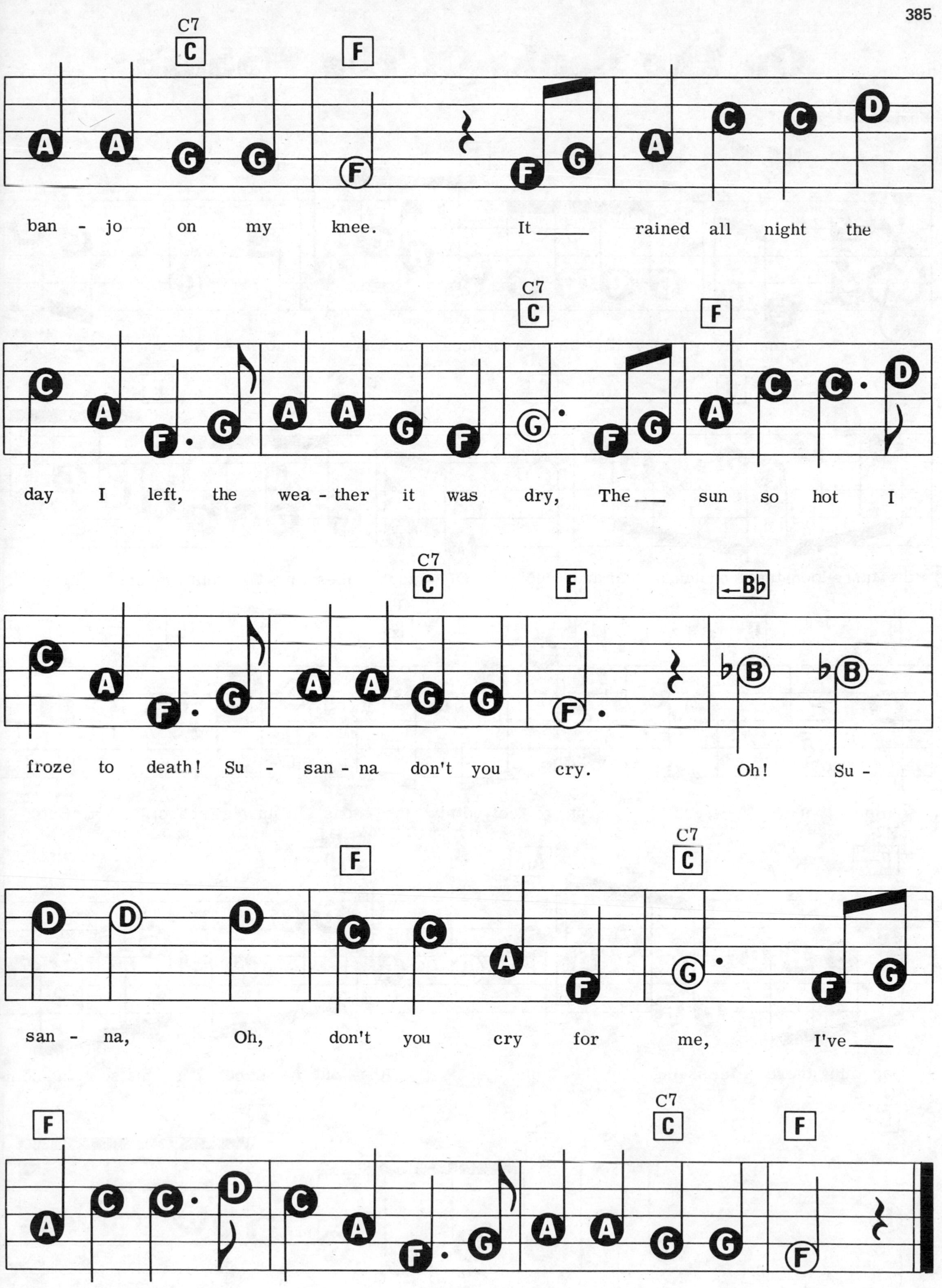
C7
C
F
A A G G F F G A C C D
ban - jo on my knee. It rained all night the
C7
C
F
C A F G A A G F G F G A C C D
day I left, the wea - ther it was dry, The sun so hot I
C7
C
F
←B♭
C A F G A A G G F B B
froze to death! Su - san - na don't you cry. Oh! Su -
F
C7
C
D D D C C A F G F G
san - na, Oh, don't you cry for me, I've
F
C7
C
F
A C C D C A F G A A G G F
come from A - la - bam - a with my ban - jo on my knee.

On The Banks Of The Wabash

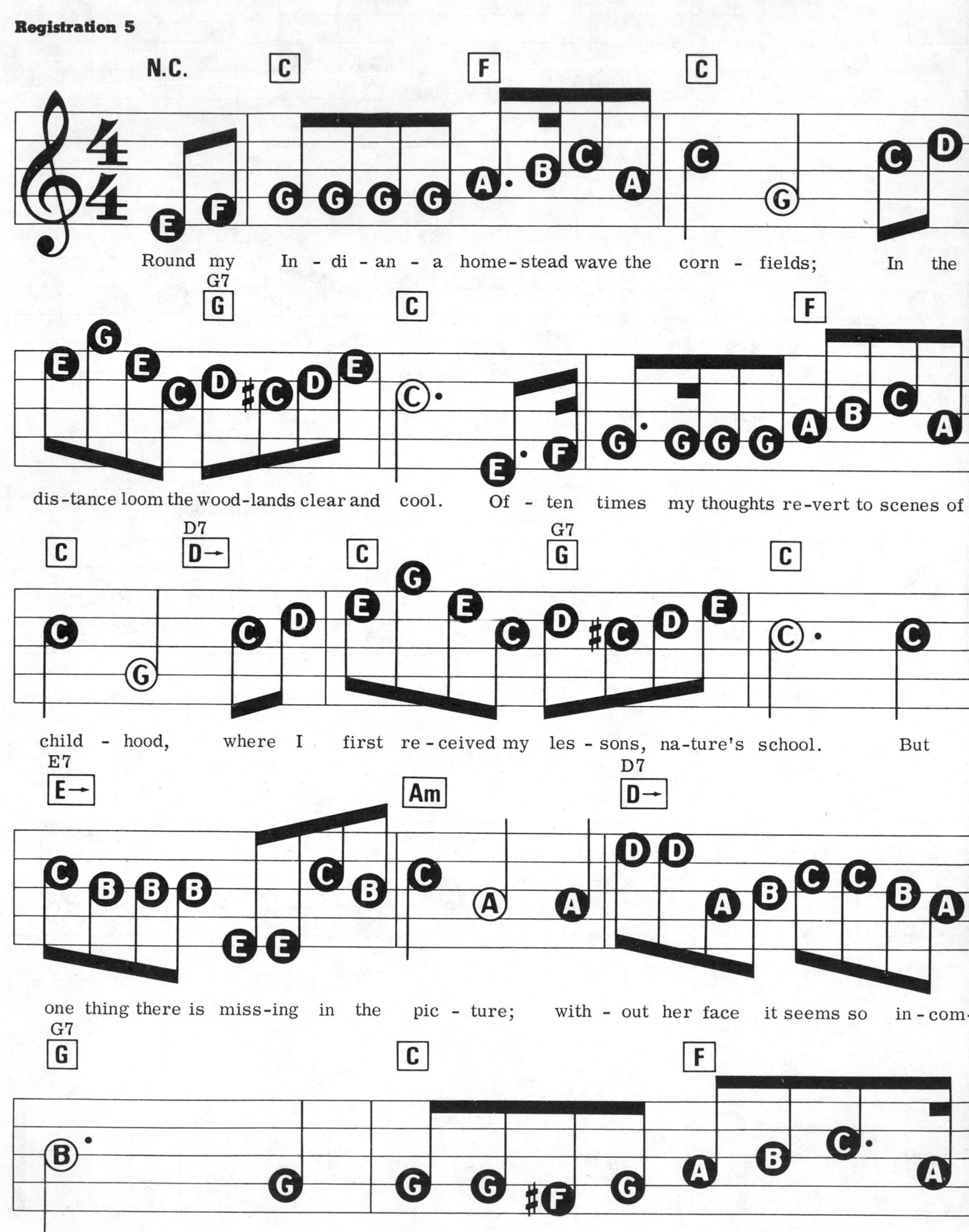

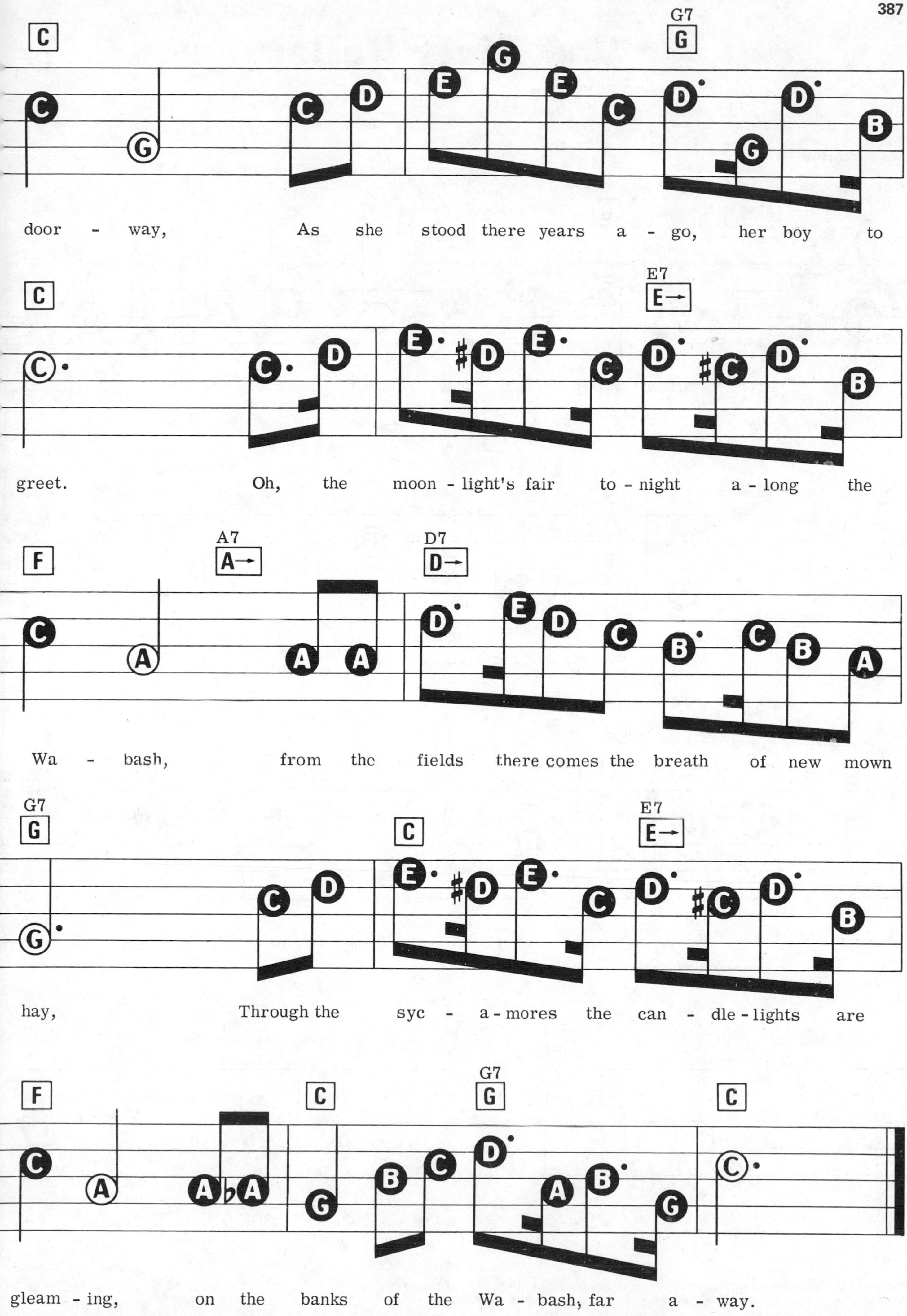

C G7 G

C G C D E G E C D G D B

door - way, As she stood there years a - go, her boy to

C E7 E→

C C D E ♯D E C D ♯C D B

greet. Oh, the moon - light's fair to - night a - long the

F A7 A→ D7 D→

C A A A D E D C B C B A

Wa - bash, from the fields there comes the breath of new mown

G7 G C E7 E→

G C D E ♯D E C D ♯C D B

hay, Through the syc - a - mores the can - dle - lights are

F C G7 G C

C A A ♭A G B C D A B G C

gleam - ing, on the banks of the Wa - bash, far a - way.

Red River Valley

Registration 4

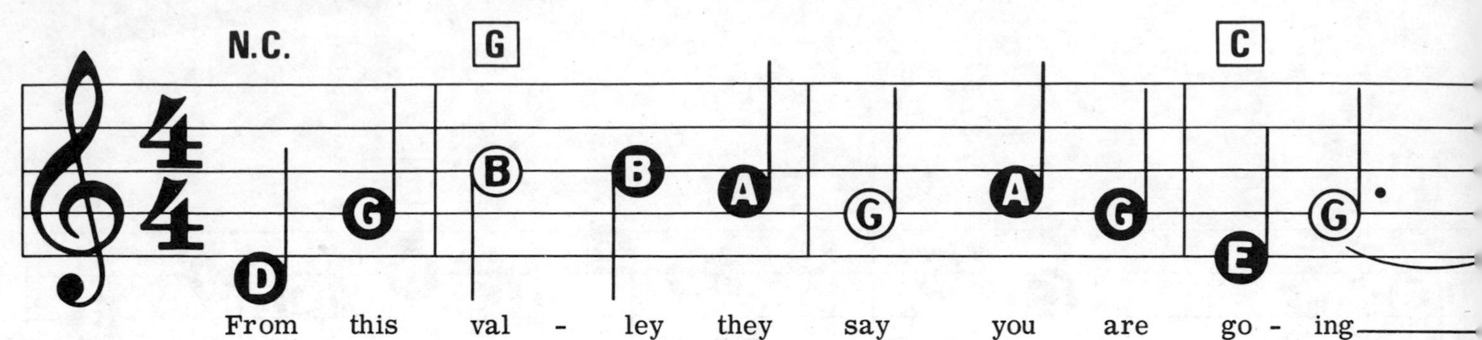

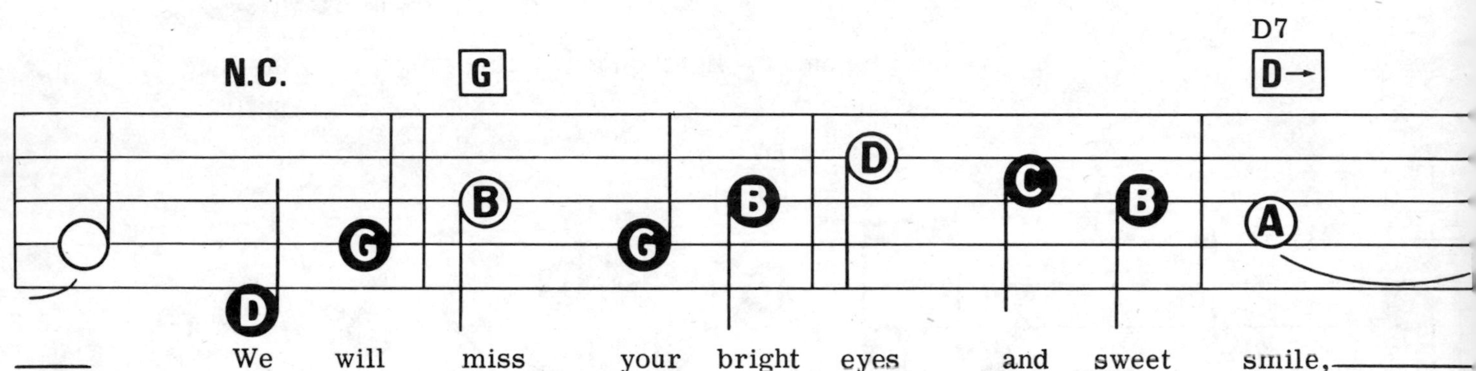

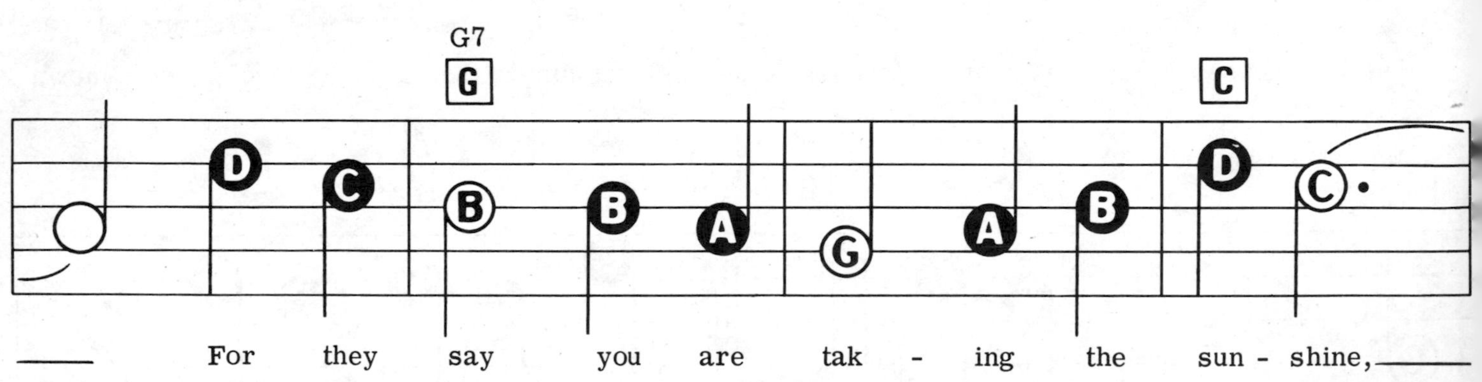

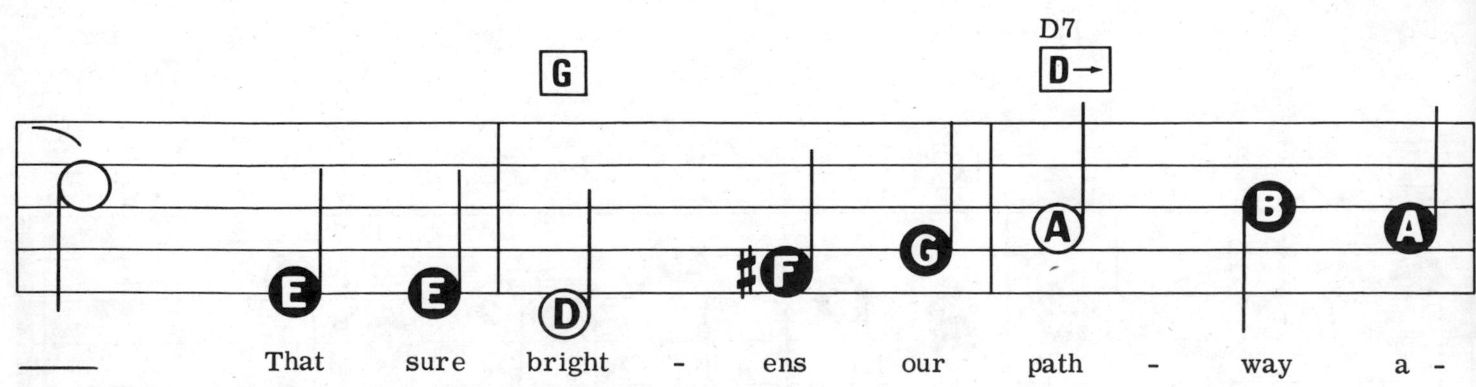

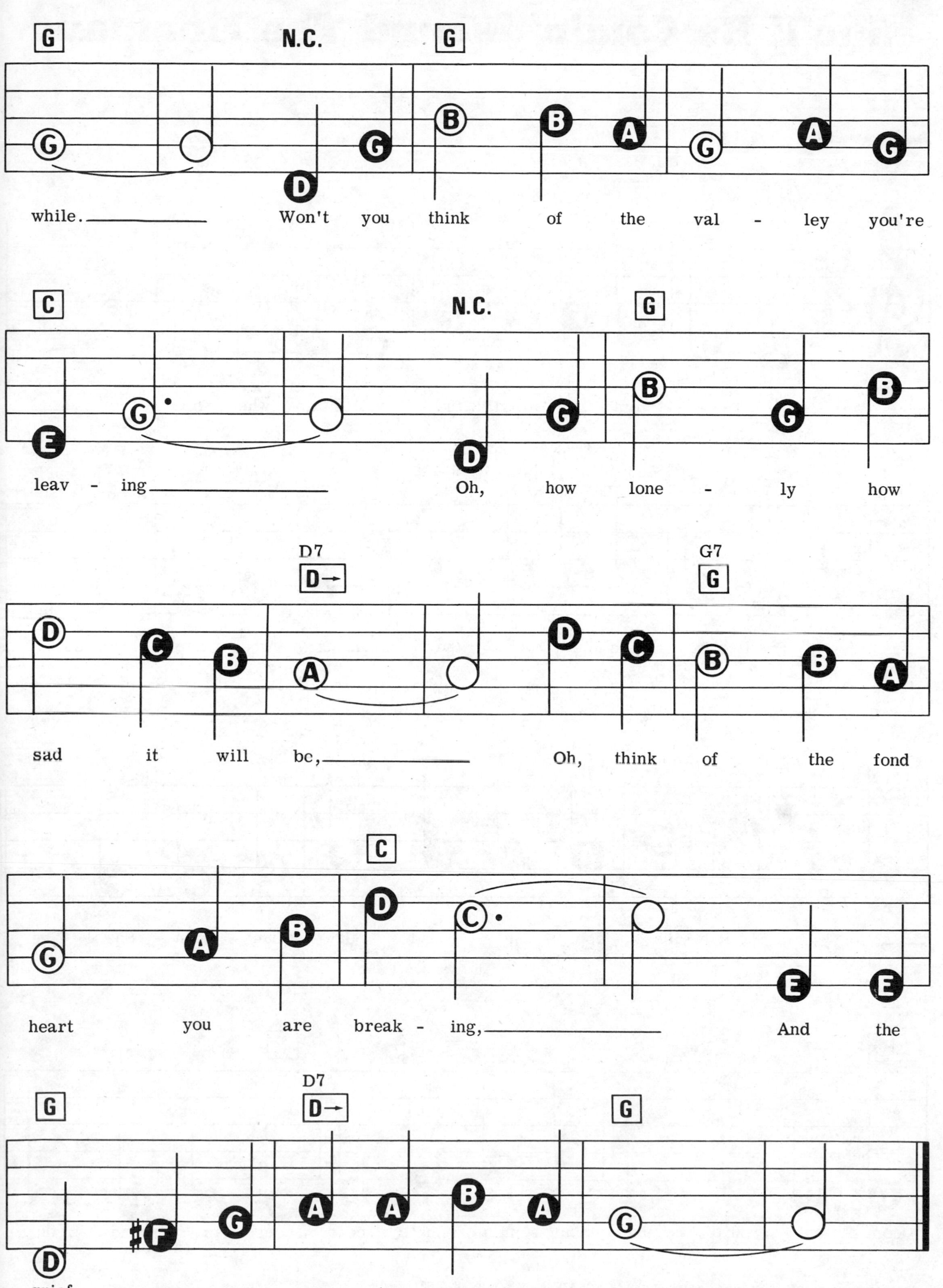
G
N.C.
G
while. Won't you think of the val - ley you're
C
N.C.
G
leav - ing Oh, how lone - ly how
D7
D→
G7
G
sad it will bc, Oh, think of the fond
C
heart you are break - ing, And the
G
D7
D→
G
grief you are caus - ing me to see.

She'll Be Comin' 'Round The Mountain

Registration 8

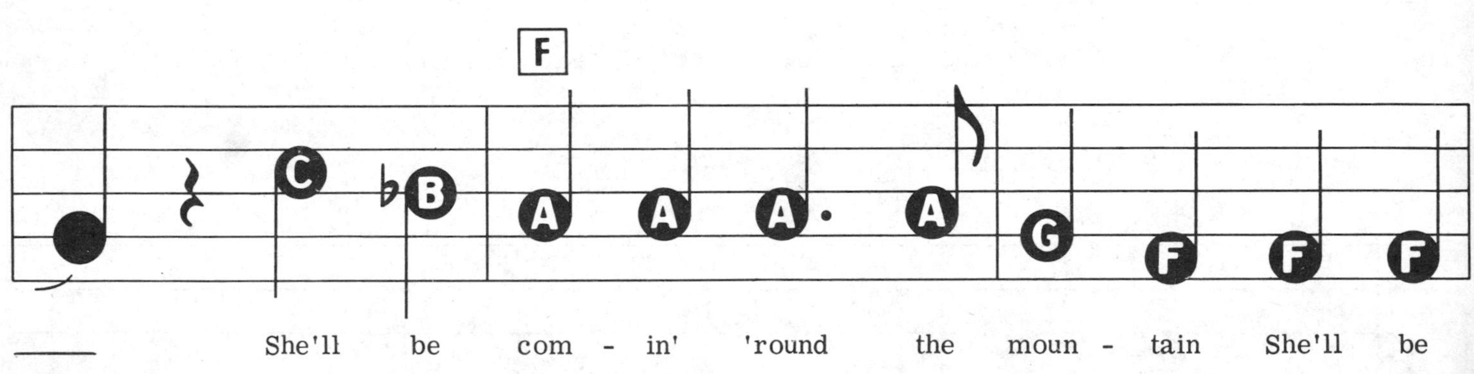

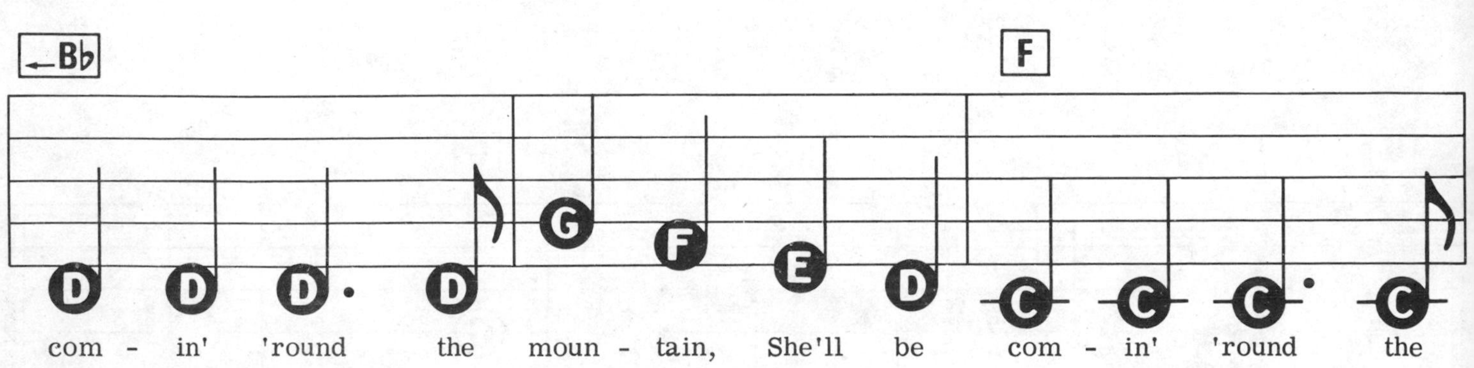

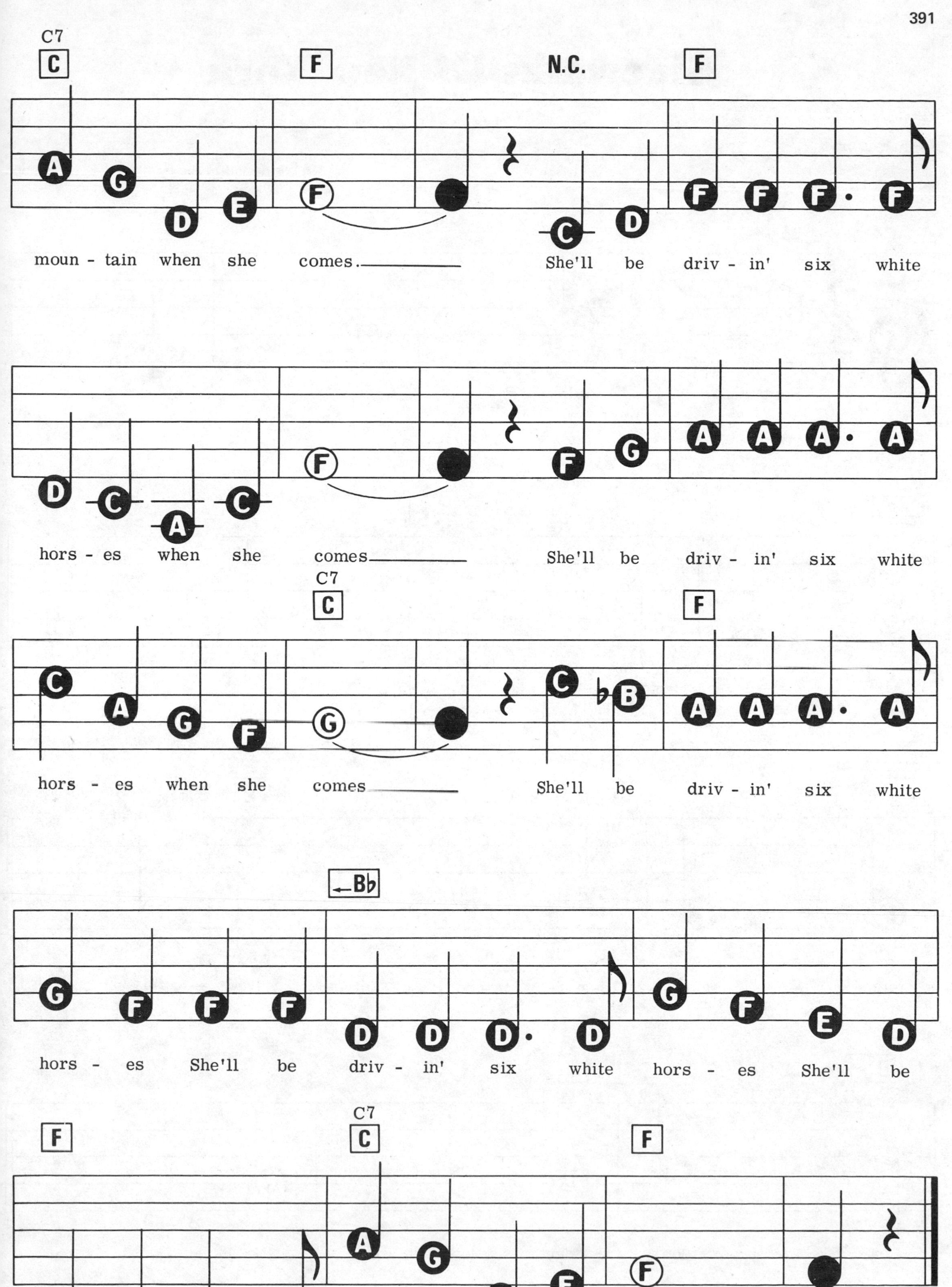
C7
C
F
N.C.
F
mountain when she comes. She'll be drivin' six white
horses when she comes She'll be drivin' six white
C7
C
F
horses when she comes She'll be drivin' six white
Bb
horses She'll be drivin' six white horses She'll be
F
C7
C
F
drivin' six white horses when she comes.

Sidewalks Of New York

Registration 3

Words and Music by Charles B. Lawlor and
James W. Blake

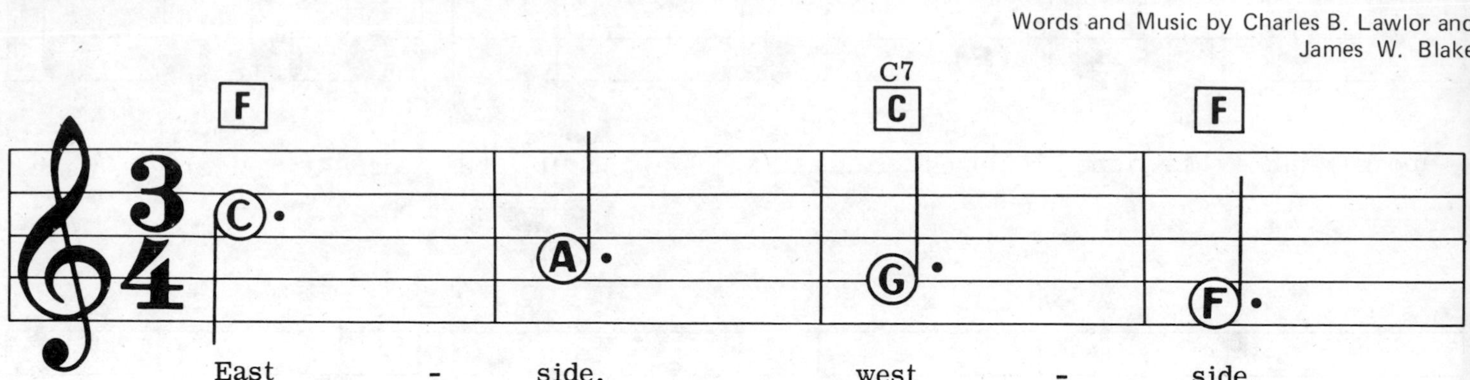

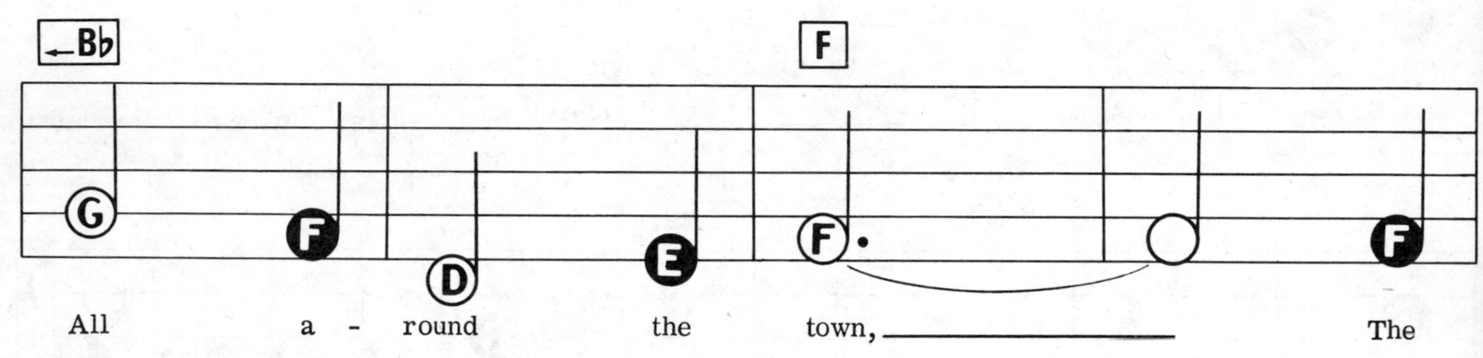

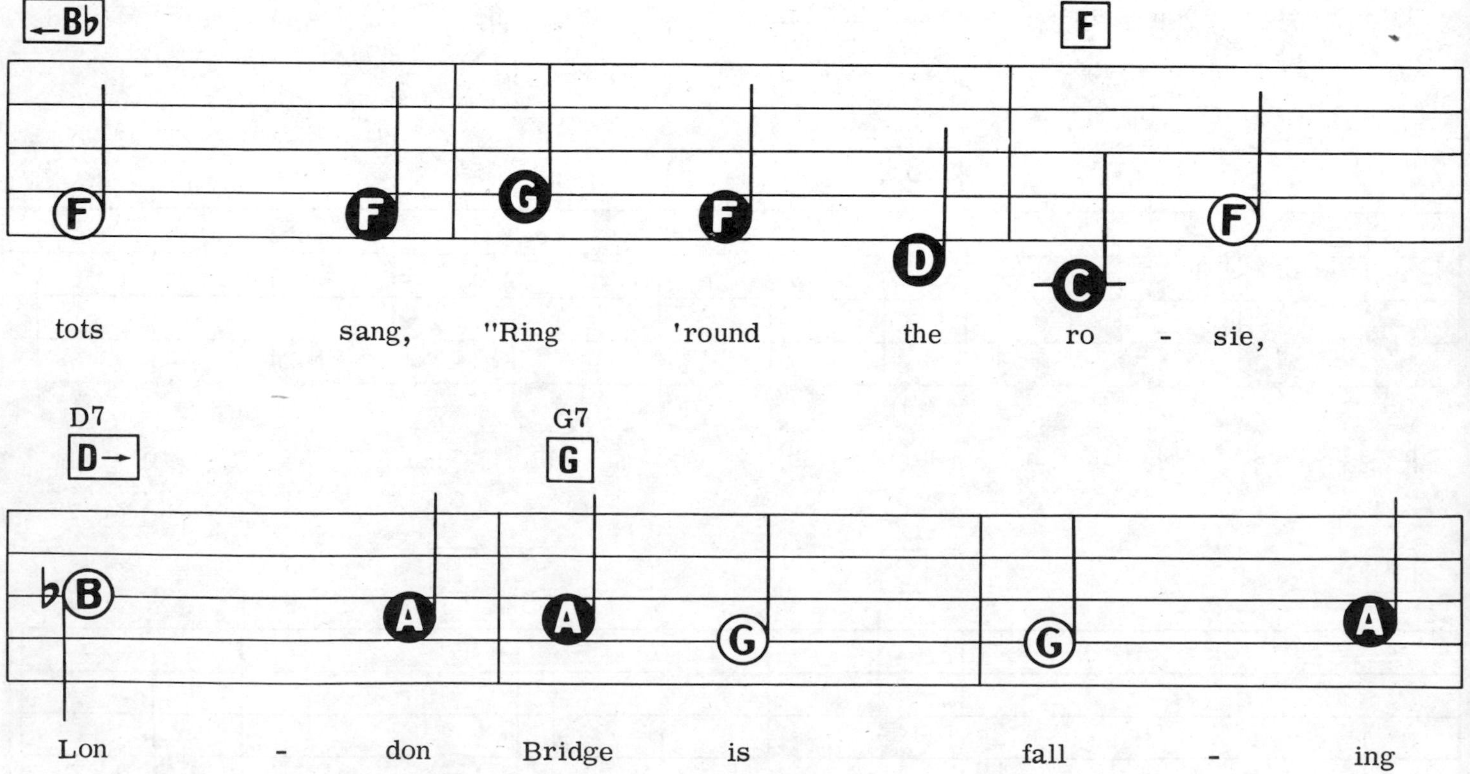

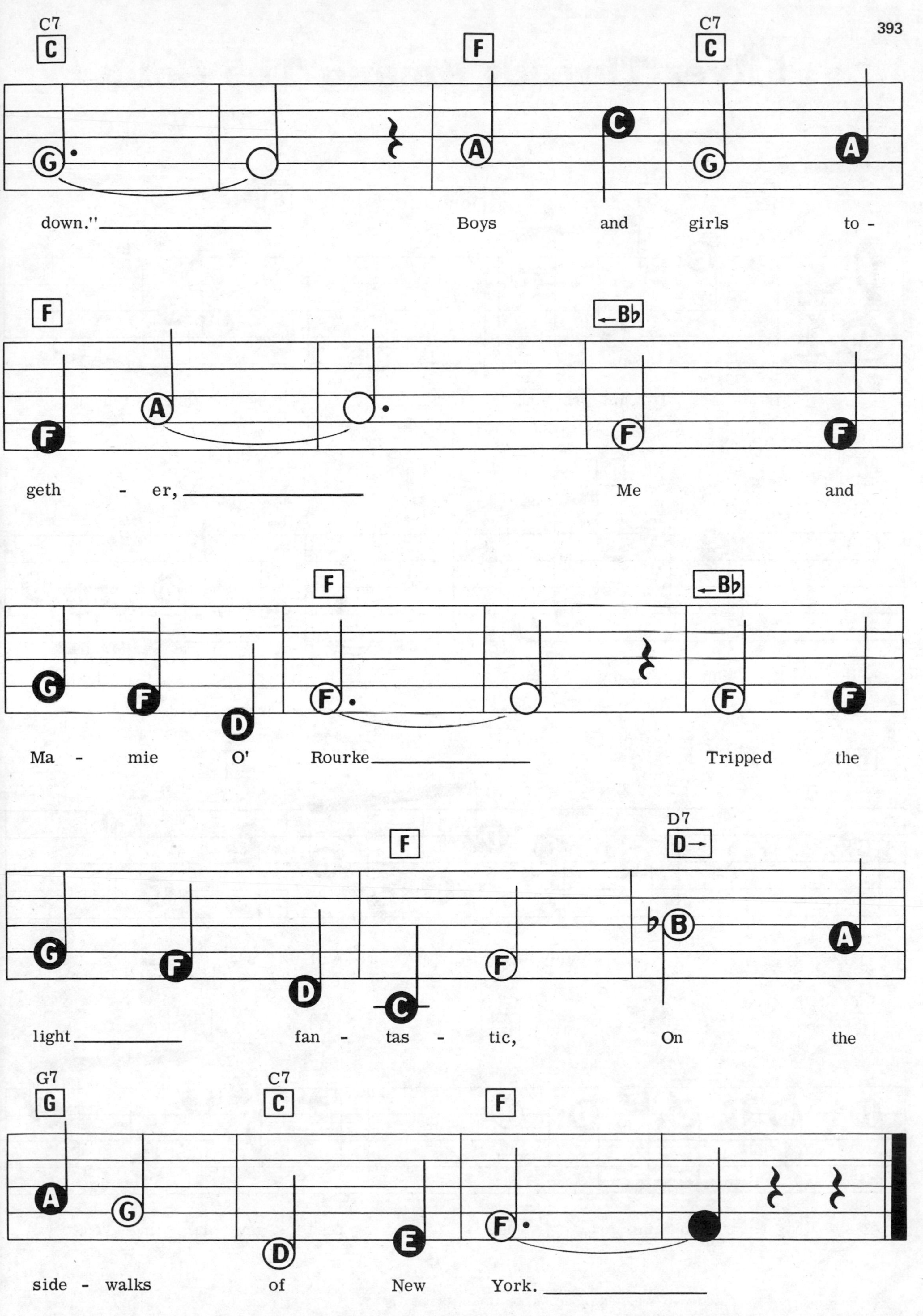
C7
C
F
C7
C
G
A
C
G
A
down." Boys and girls to -
F
←B♭
F
A
F
F
geth - er, Me and
F
←B♭
G
F
D
F
F
F
Ma - mie O' Rourke Tripped the
F
D7
D→
G
F
D
C
F
B
A
light fan - tas - tic, On the
G7
G
C7
C
F
A
G
D
E
F
side - walks of New York.

Silver Threads Among The Gold

Registration 10

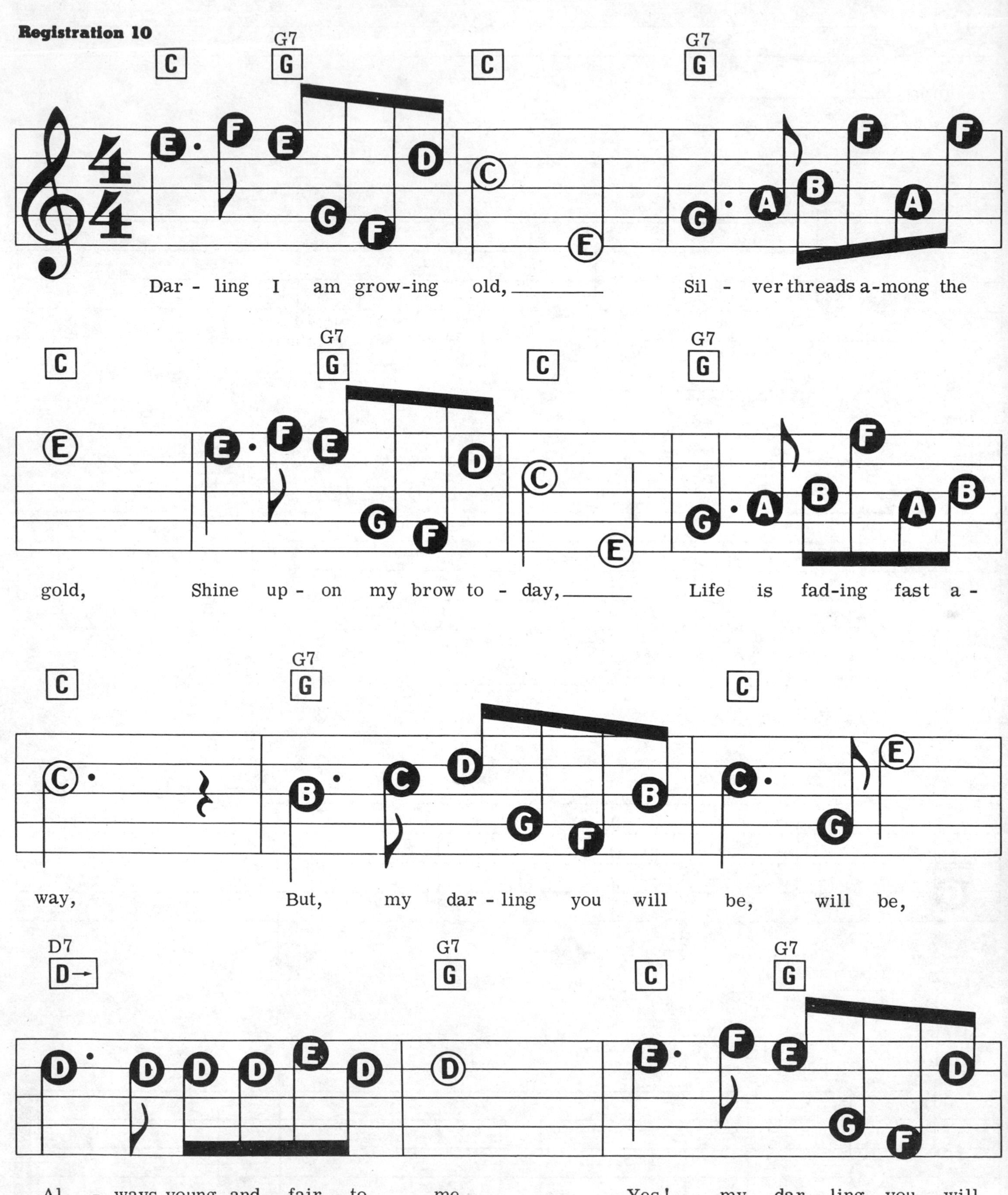

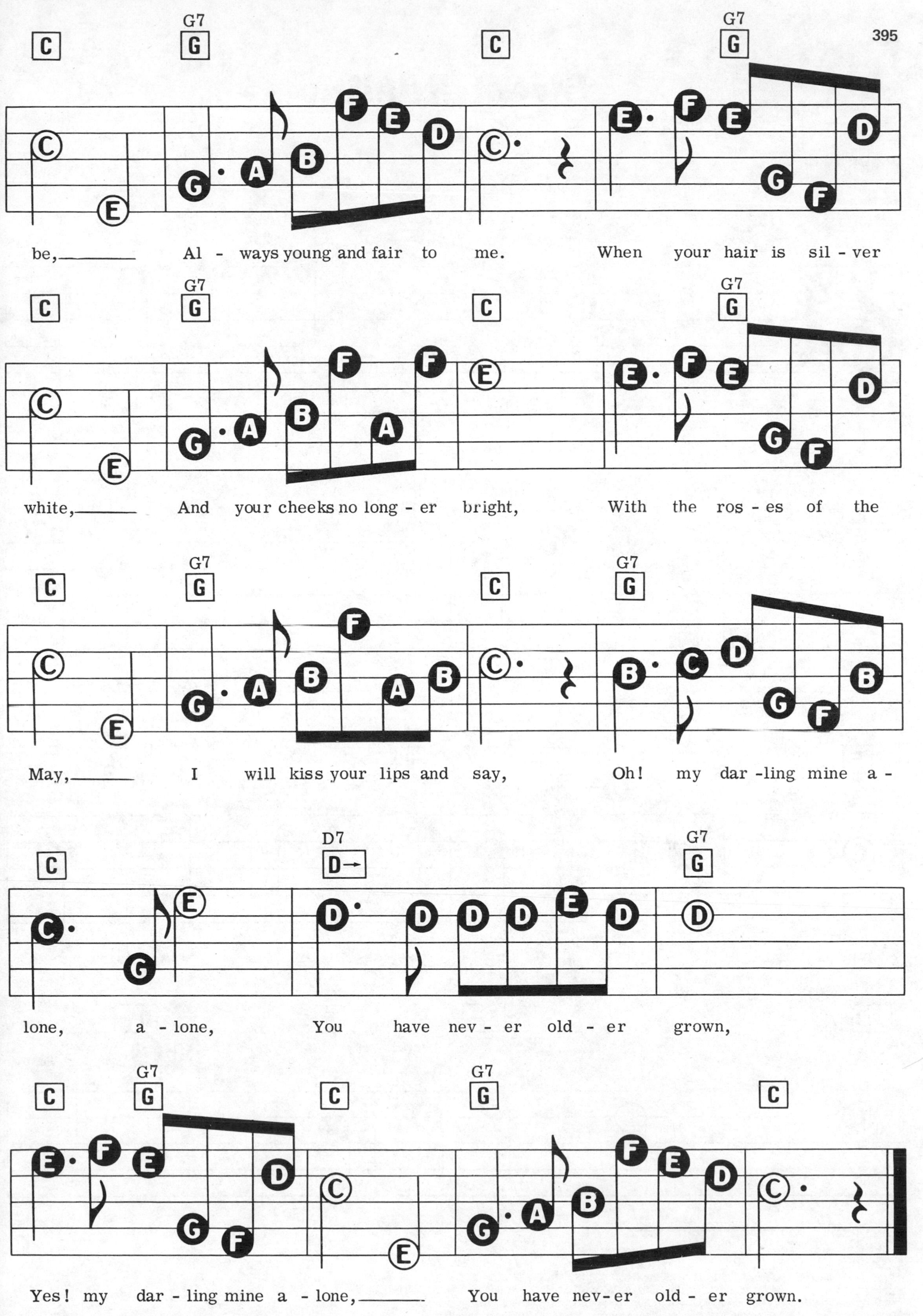
C G7 G C G7 G
be, Al - ways young and fair to me. When your hair is sil - ver
C G7 G C G7 G
white, And your cheeks no long - er bright, With the ros - es of the
C G7 G C G7 G
May, I will kiss your lips and say, Oh! my dar -ling mine a -
C D7 D→ G7 G
lone, a - lone, You have nev - er old - er grown,
C G7 G C G7 G C
Yes! my dar - ling mine a - lone, You have nev-er old - er grown.

Sweet Adeline

Registration 4

Words and Music by Richard H. Gerard and Harry Armstrong

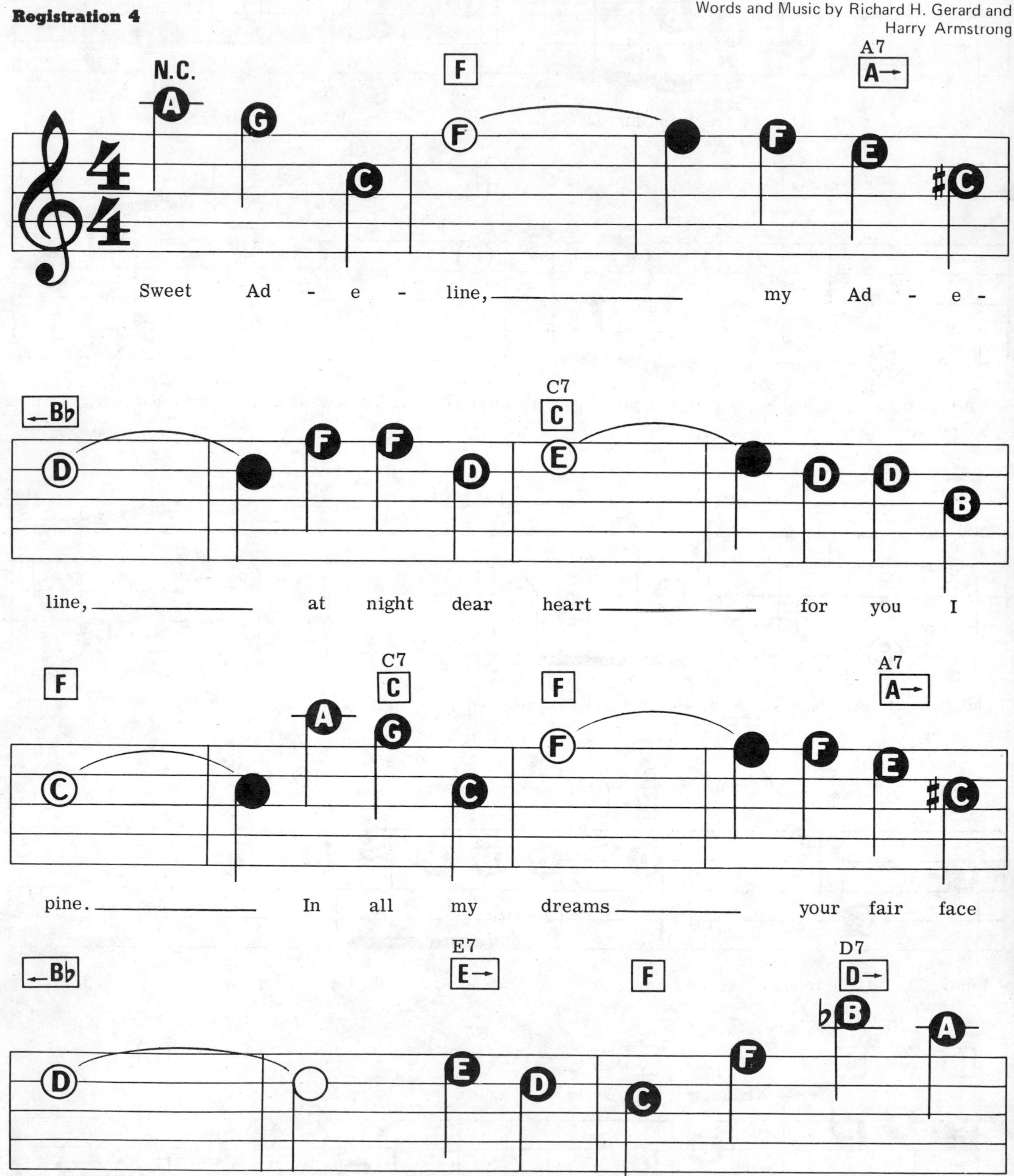

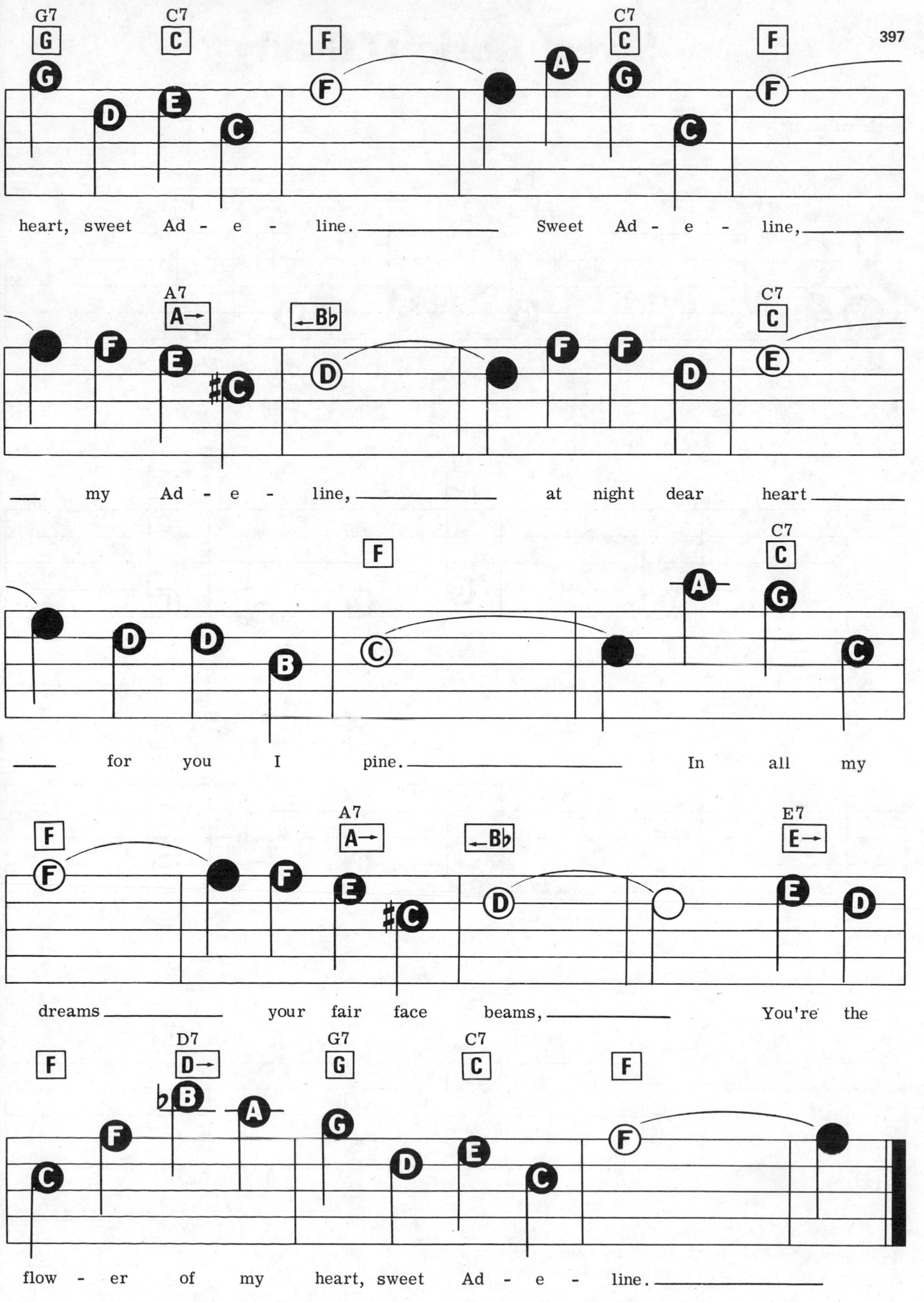
G7 C7 C7
G C F C F
heart, sweet Ad - e - line. Sweet Ad - e - line,
A7 C7
A Bb C
my Ad - e - line, at night dear heart
F C7
C
for you I pine. In all my
F A7 E7
A Bb E
dreams your fair face beams, You're the
D7 G7 C7
F D G C F
flow - er of my heart, sweet Ad - e - line.

Sweet Rosie O'Grady

Registration 10

Words and Music by
Maud Nugent

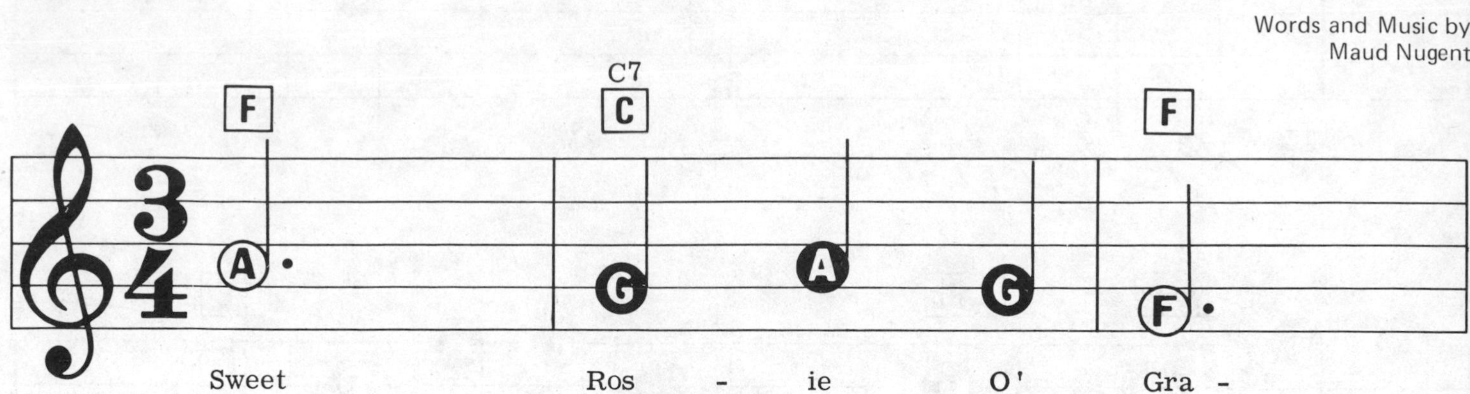

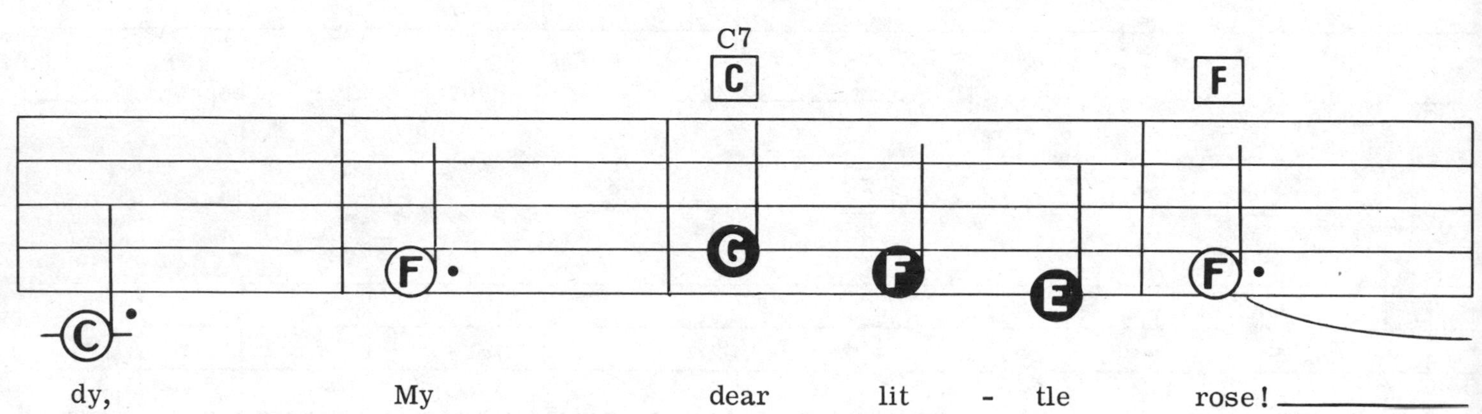

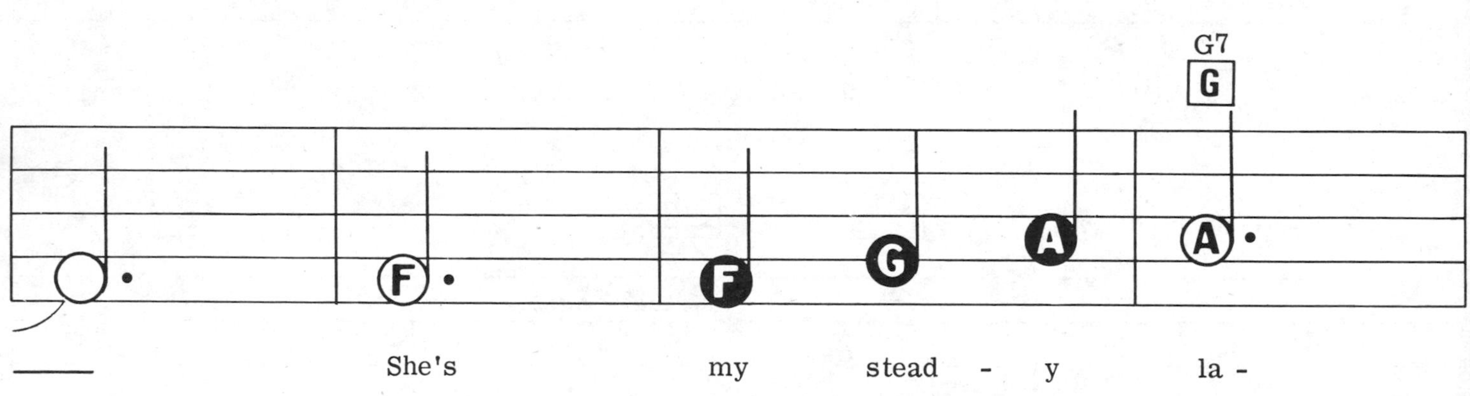

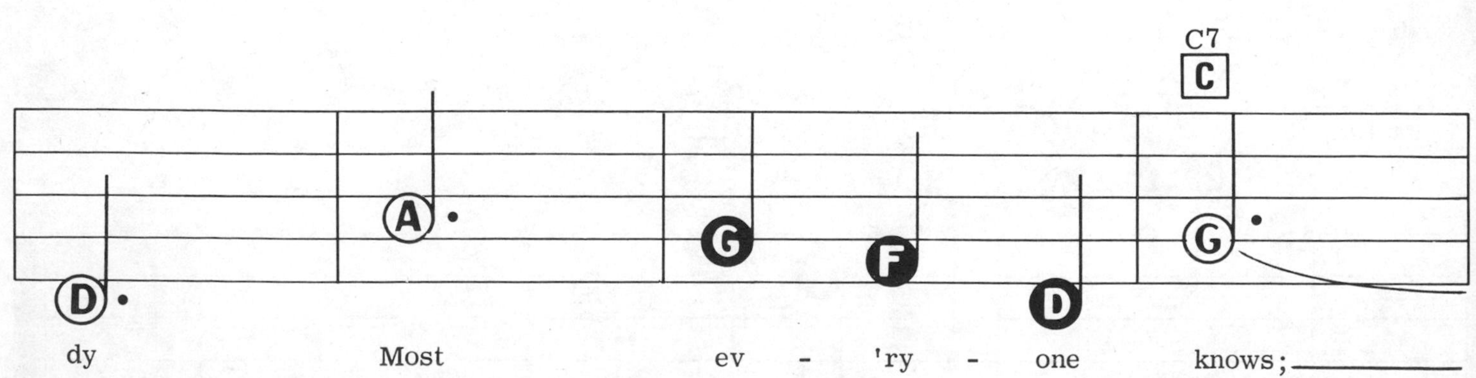

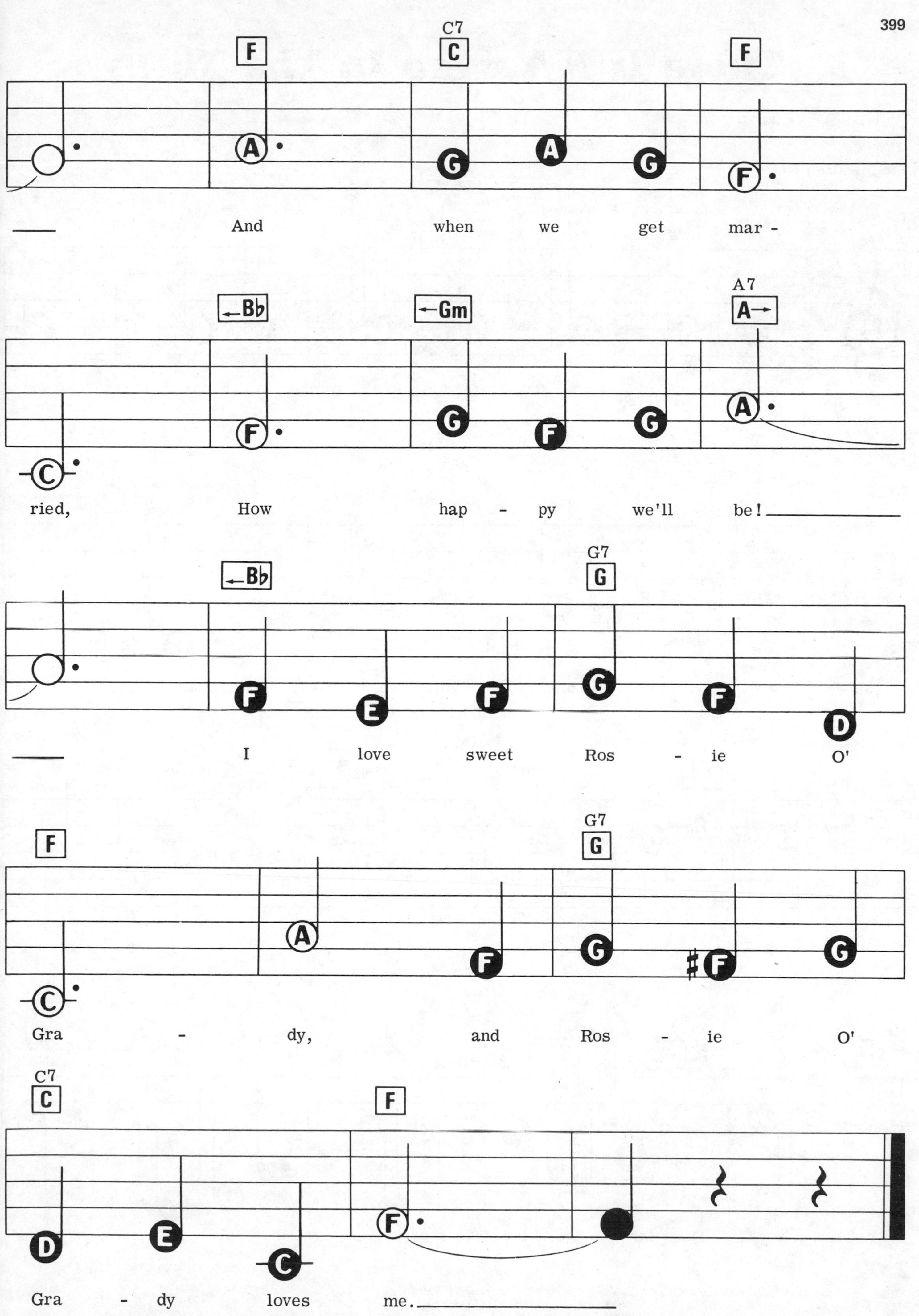
F
C7
C
F
A
G
A
G
F
And when we get mar -
Bb
Gm
A7
A
C
F
G
F
G
A
ried, How hap - py we'll be!
Bb
G7
G
F
E
F
G
F
D
I love sweet Ros - ie O'
F
G7
G
C
A
F
G
F
G
Gra - dy, and Ros - ie O'
C7
C
F
D
E
C
F
Gra - dy loves me.

There Is A Tavern In The Town

Registration 8

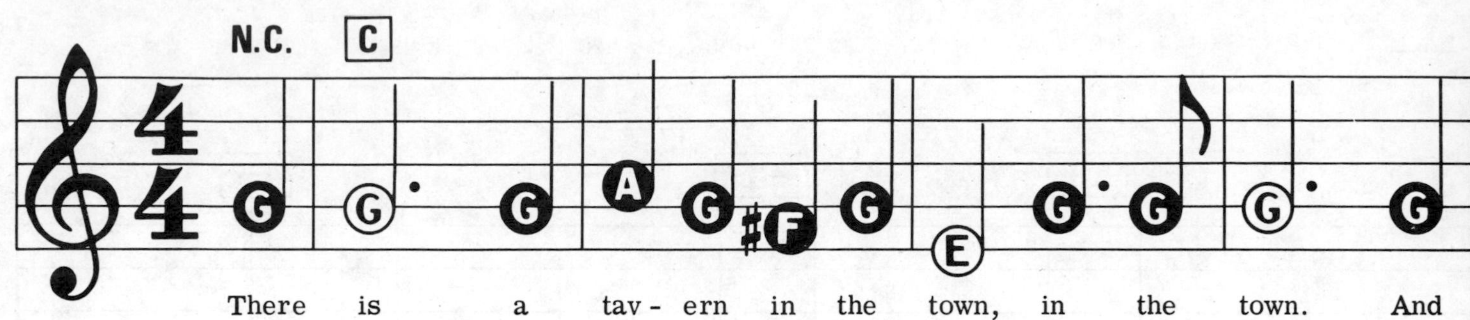

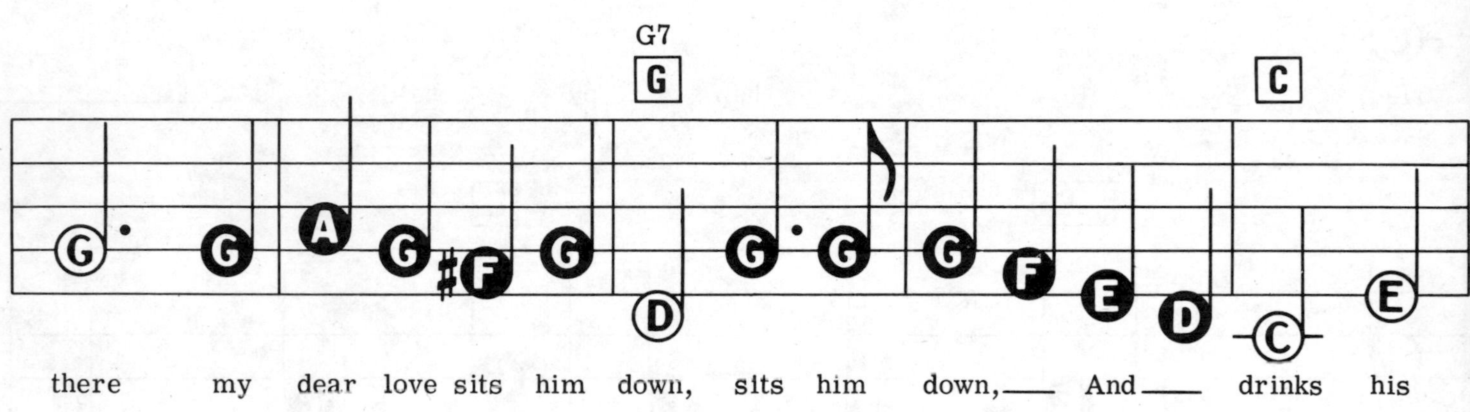

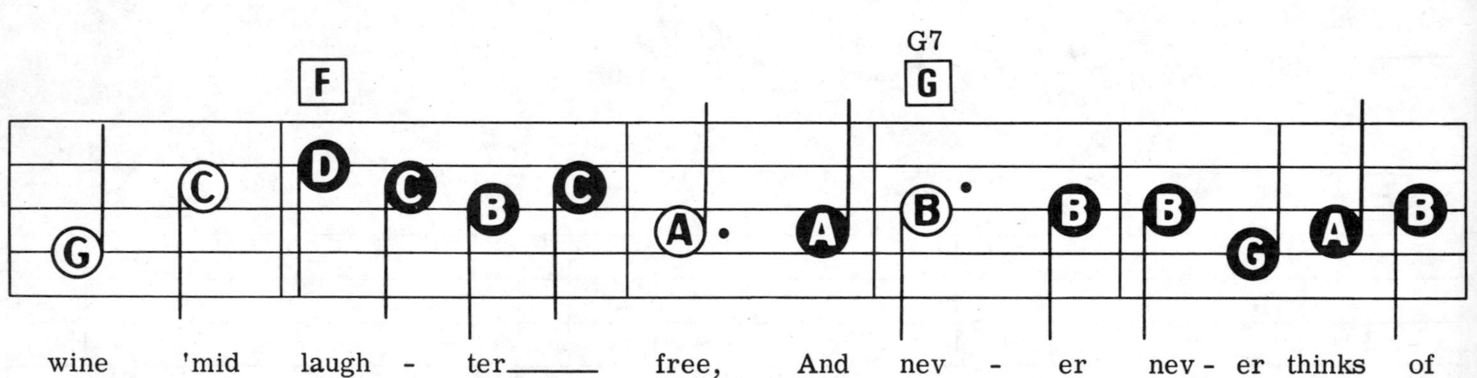

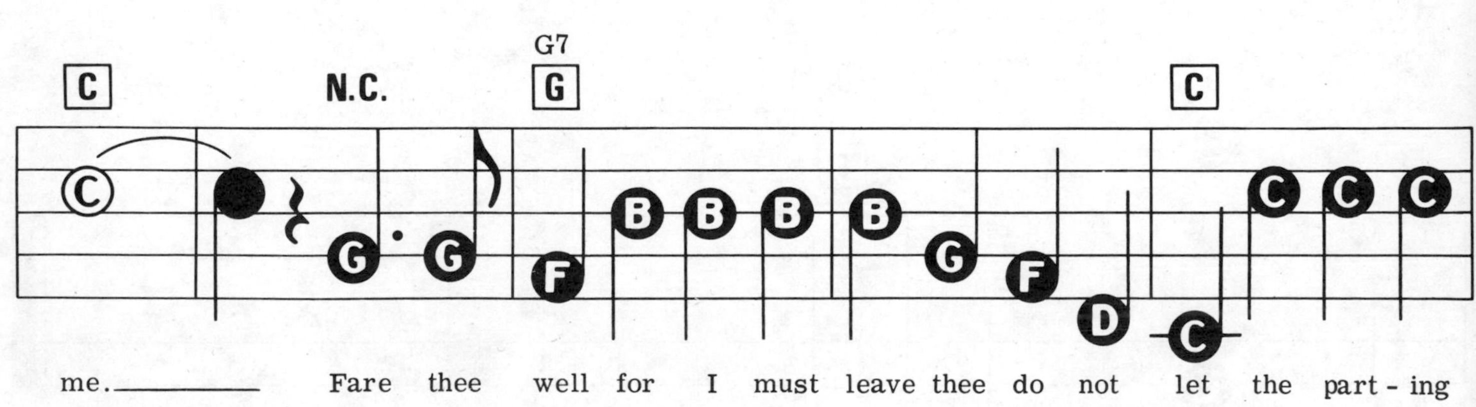

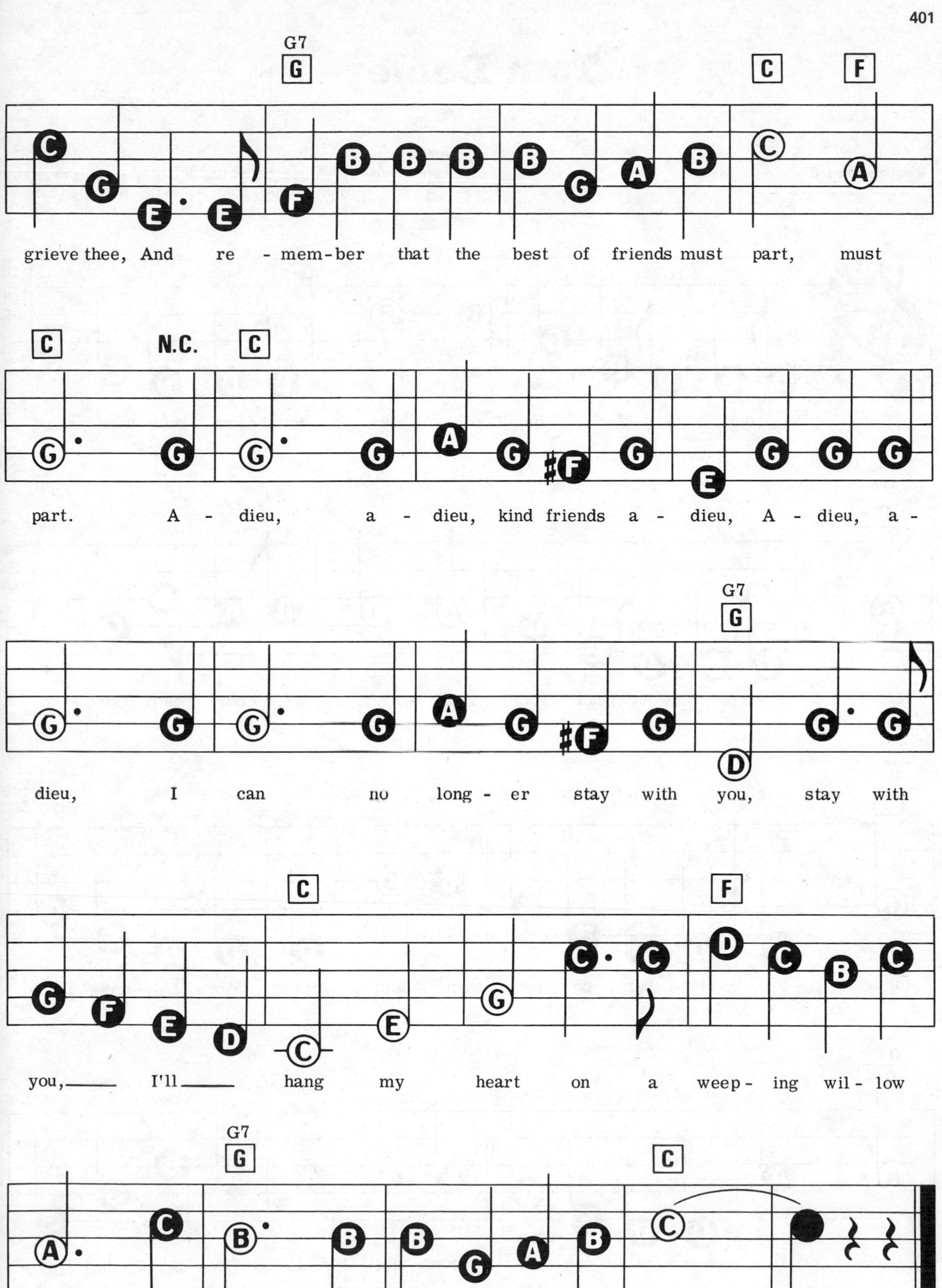
G7 G C F
grieve thee, And re - mem-ber that the best of friends must part, must
C N.C. C
part. A - dieu, a - dieu, kind friends a - dieu, A - dieu, a -
G7 G
dieu, I can no long - er stay with you, stay with
C F
you, I'll hang my heart on a weep - ing wil - low
G7 G C
tree, And may the world go well with thee.

Tom Dooley

Registration 8

Words and Music collected, adapted and arranged by
Frank Warner, John A. Lomax and Alan Lomax

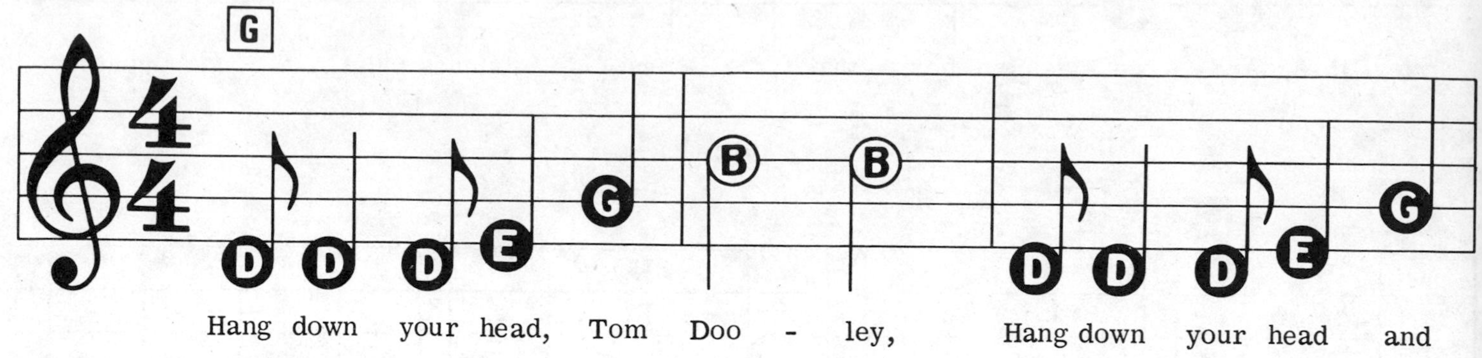

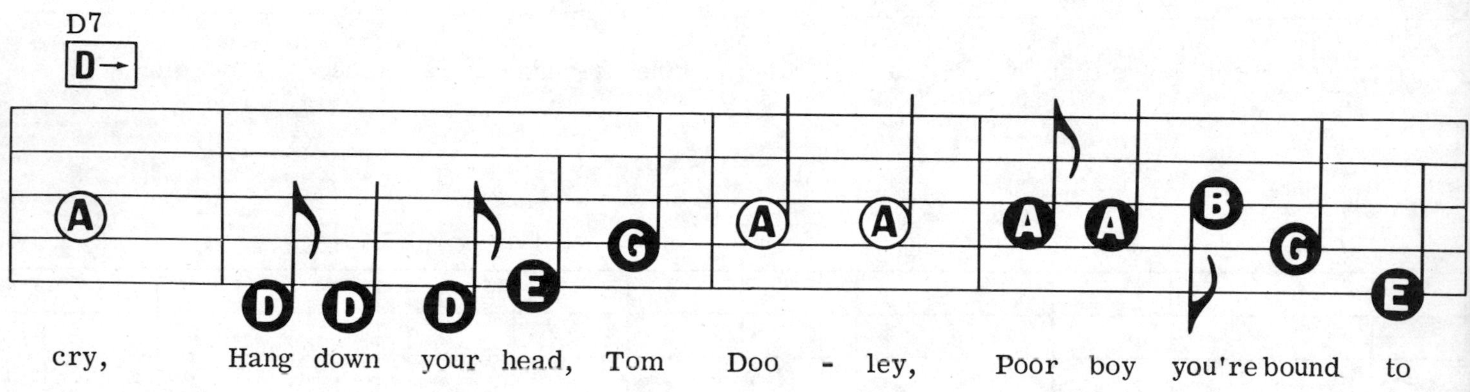

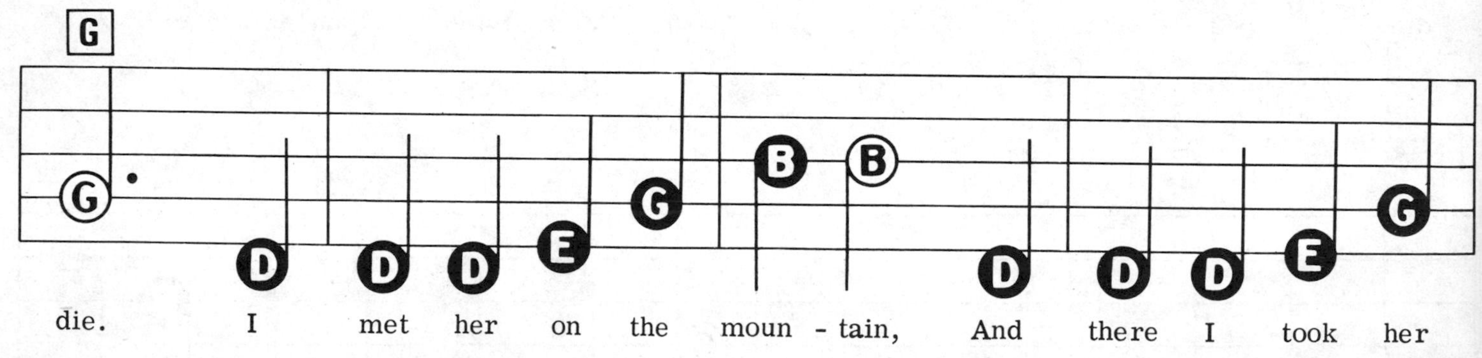

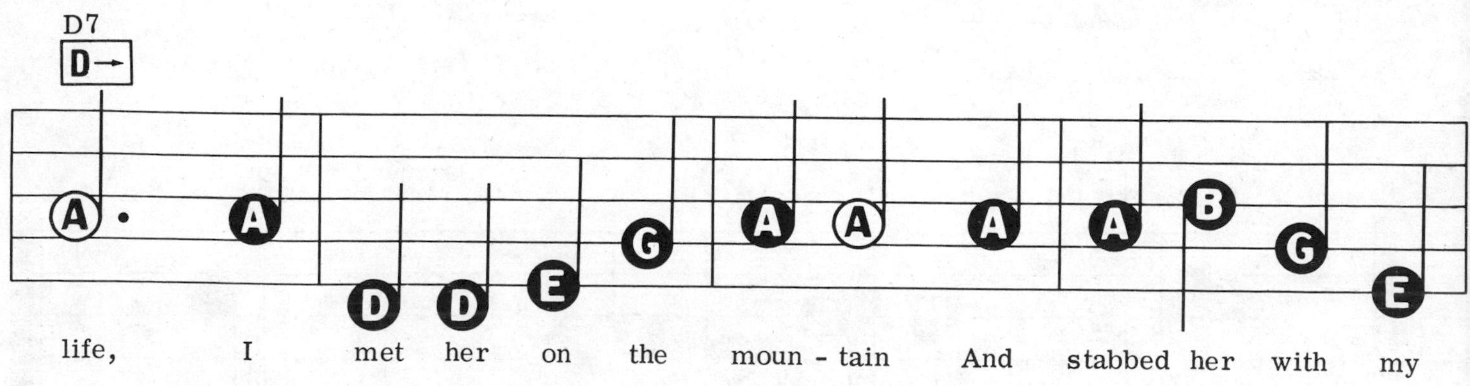

G
knife.
This time to - mor - row Reck - on where I'll
This time to - mor - row Reck - on where I'll
D7
D→
be. If it had - n't - a - been for Gray - son I'd - a
be Way___ down in some lone - some val - ley Hang -in'
G
been in Ten - nes - see.
on a white oak tree.
Hang down your head, Tom
D7
D→
Doo - ley, Hang down your head and cry, Hang down your head, Tom
G
Doo - ley, Poor boy, you're bound to die.

Wait 'Til The Sun Shines, Nellie

Registration 2

Words and Music by Andrew B. Sterling &
Harry Von Tilzer

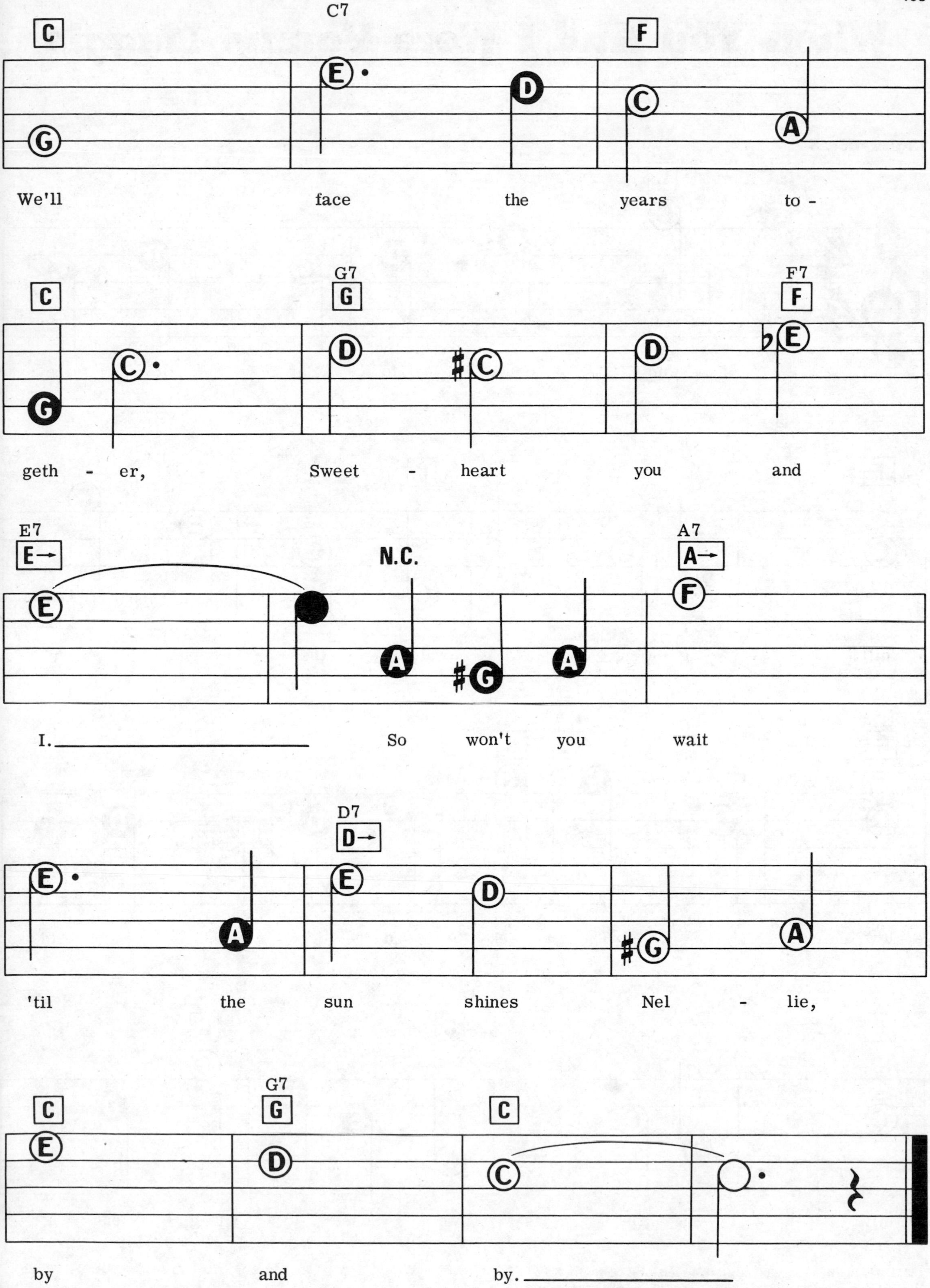
C C7 F
G E D C A
We'll face the years to -
C G7 G F7 F
G C D C D E
geth - er, Sweet - heart you and
E7 E→ N.C. A7 A→
E A G A F
I. So won't you wait
D7 D→
E A E D G A
'til the sun shines Nel - lie,
C G7 G C
E D C
by and by.

When You And I Were Young, Maggie

Registration 5

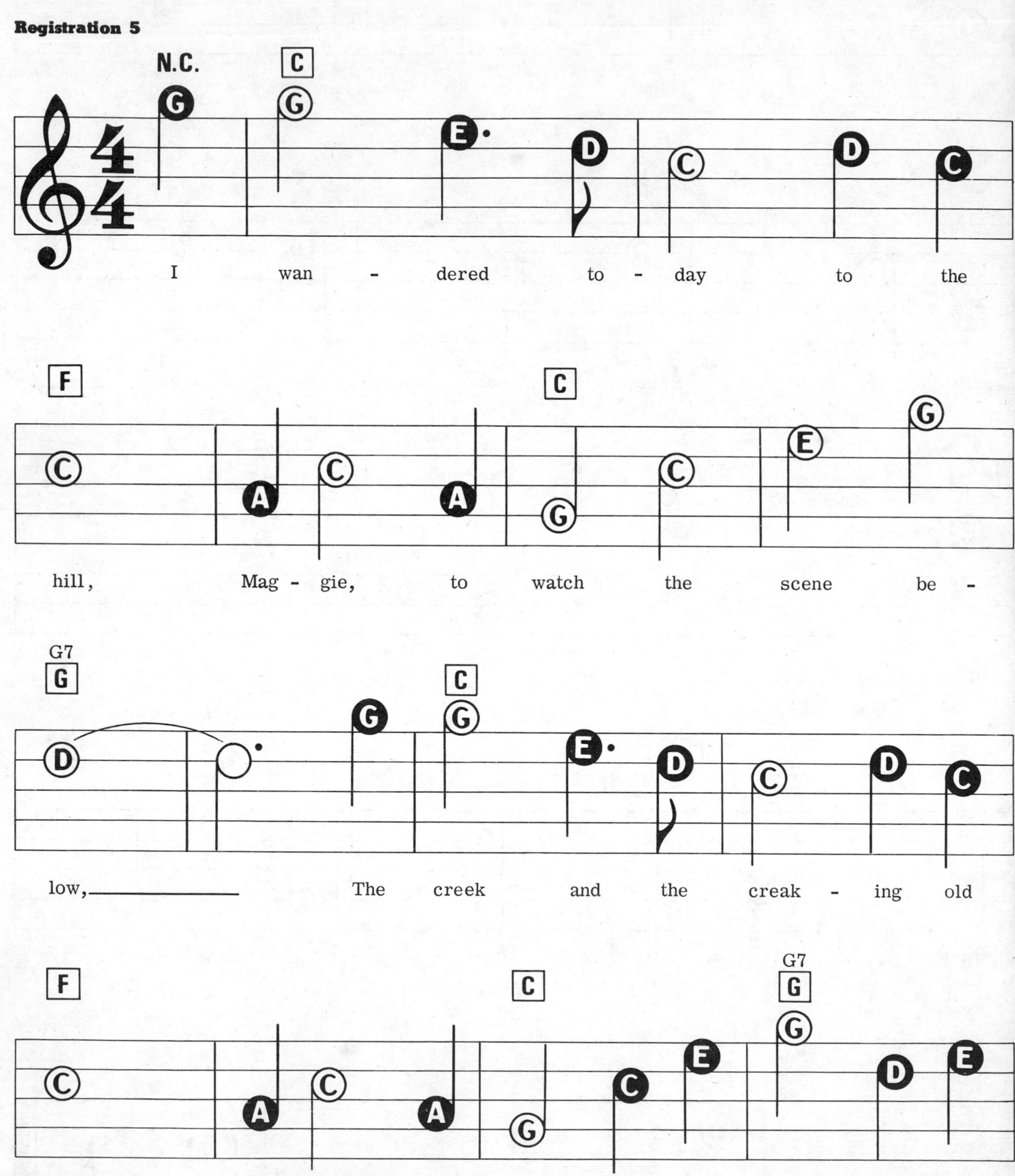

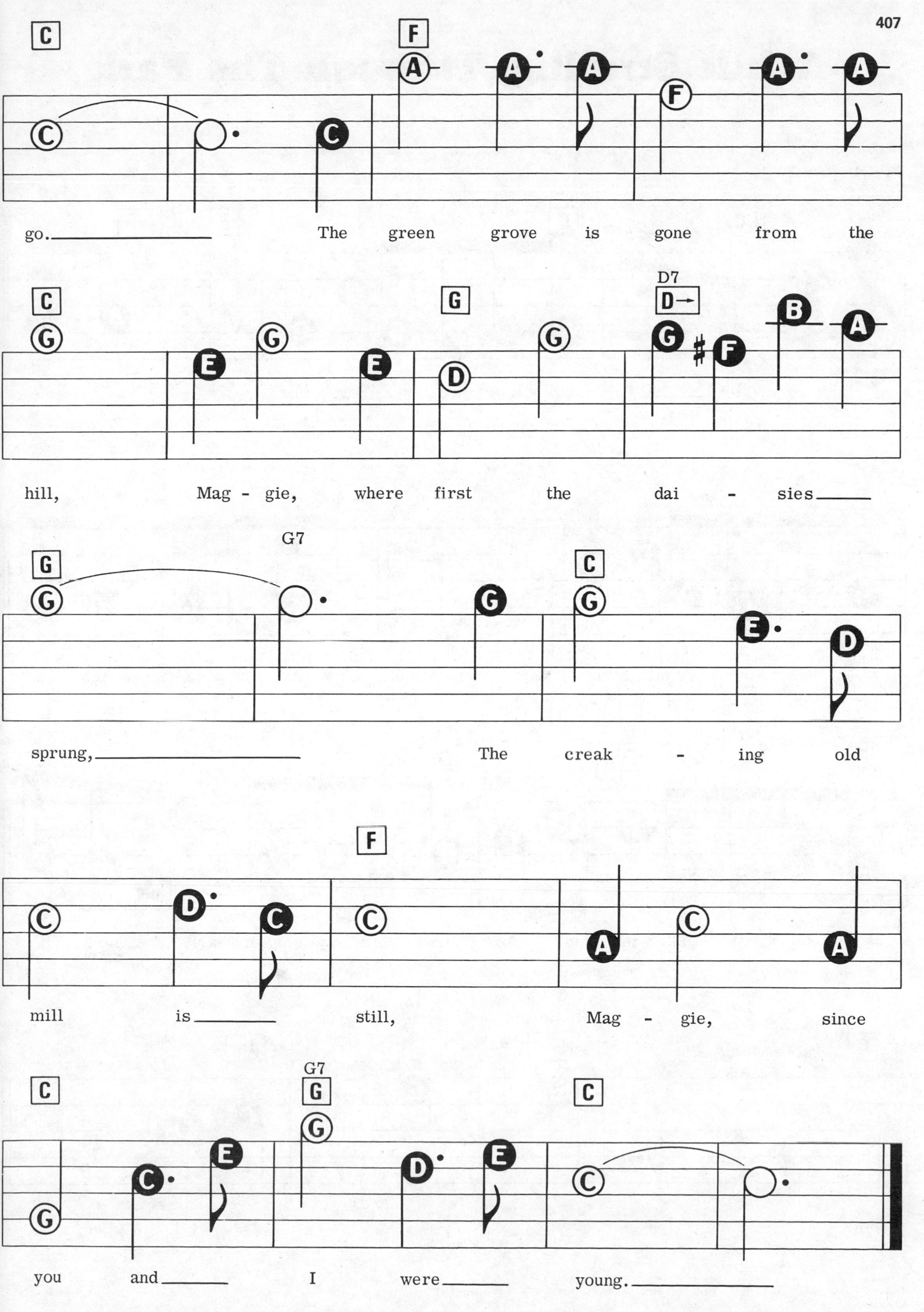
C
F
D7
G
G7
go. The green grove is gone from the
hill, Mag - gie, where first the dai - sies
sprung, The creak - ing old
mill is still, Mag - gie, since
you and I were young.

While Strolling Through The Park

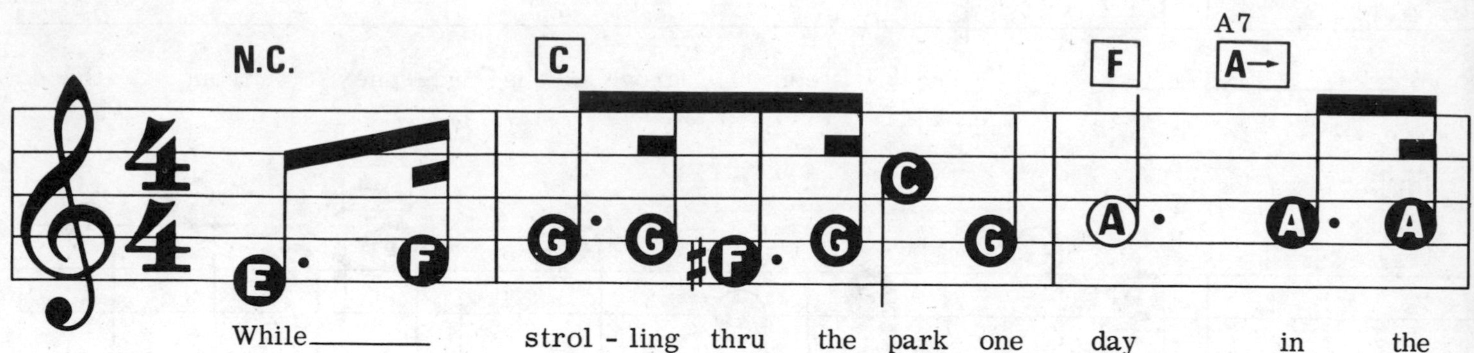

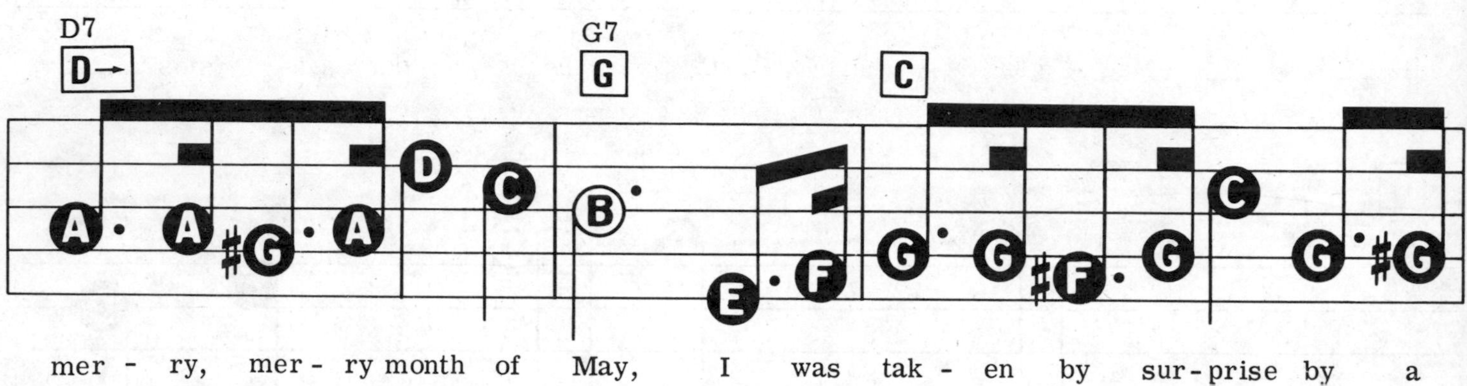

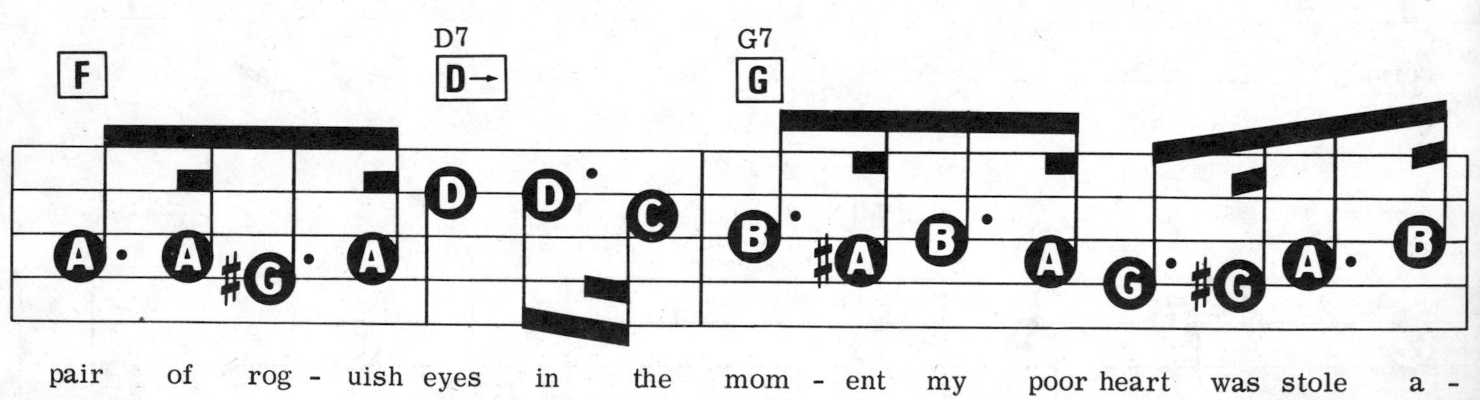

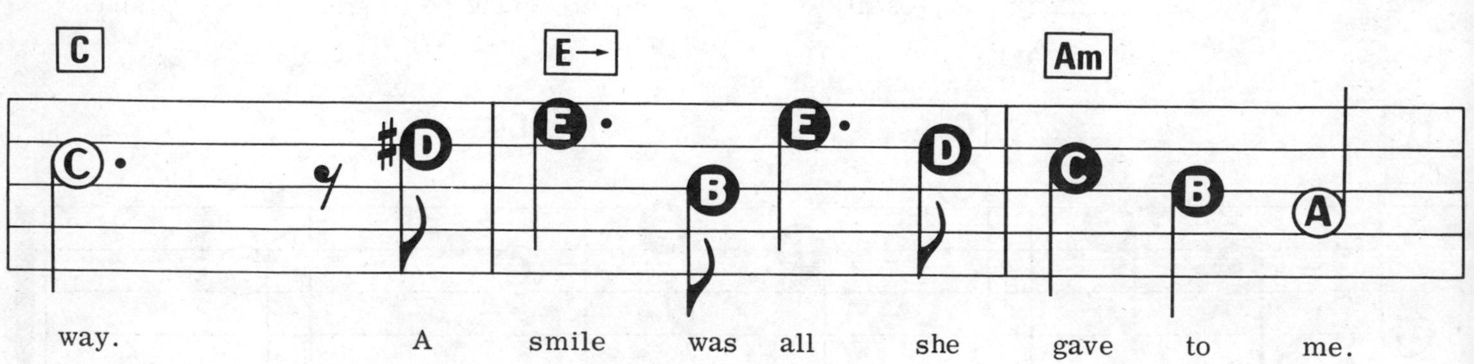

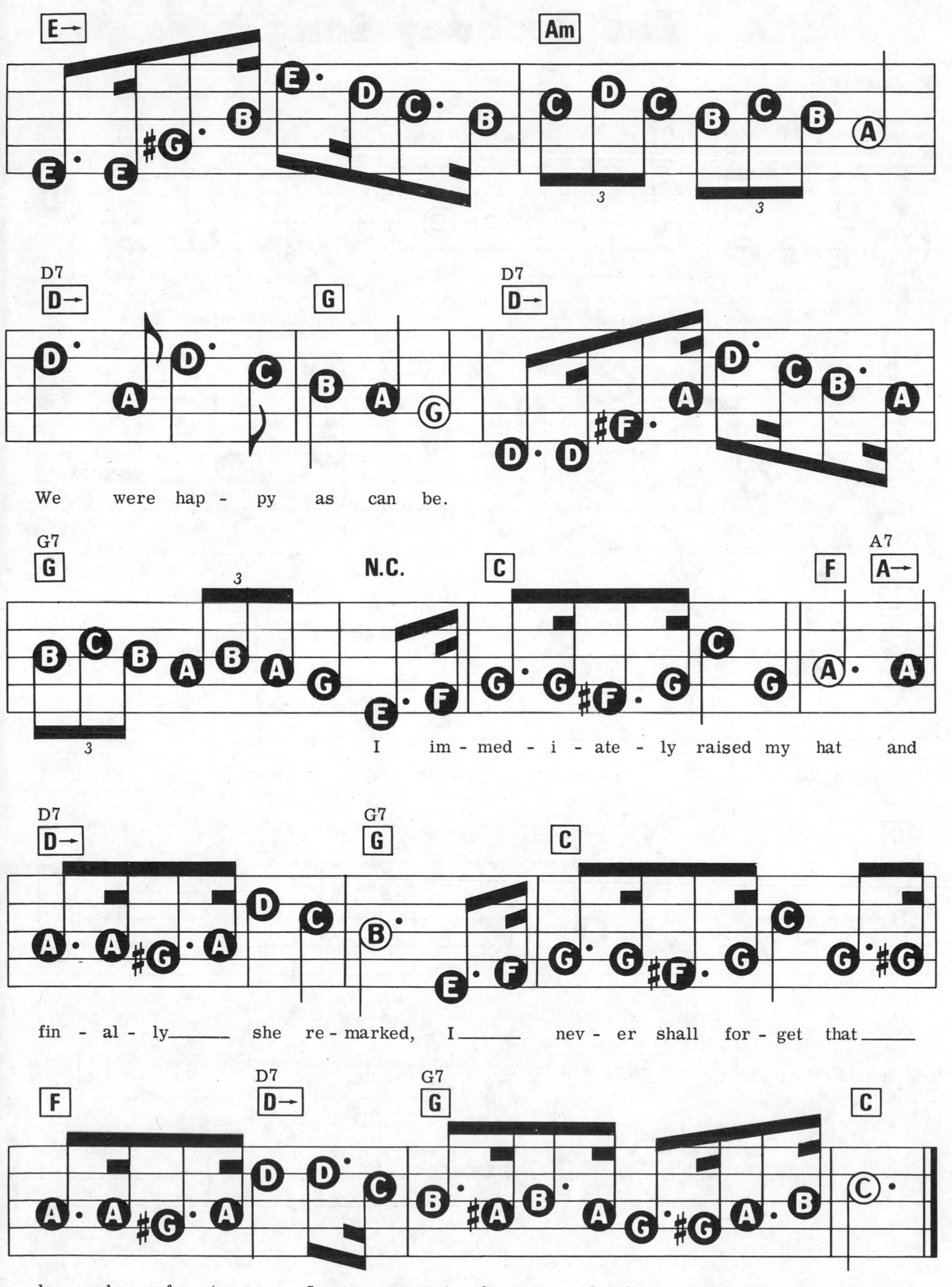
E→
Am
D7
D→
G
D7
D→
We were hap - py as can be.
G7
G
N.C.
C
F
A7
A→
I im - med - i - ate - ly raised my hat and
D7
D→
G7
G
C
fin - al - ly she re - marked, I nev - er shall for - get that
F
D7
D→
G7
G
C
love - ly af - ter - noon I met her at the foun - tain in the park.

The Birthday Song

Registration 5

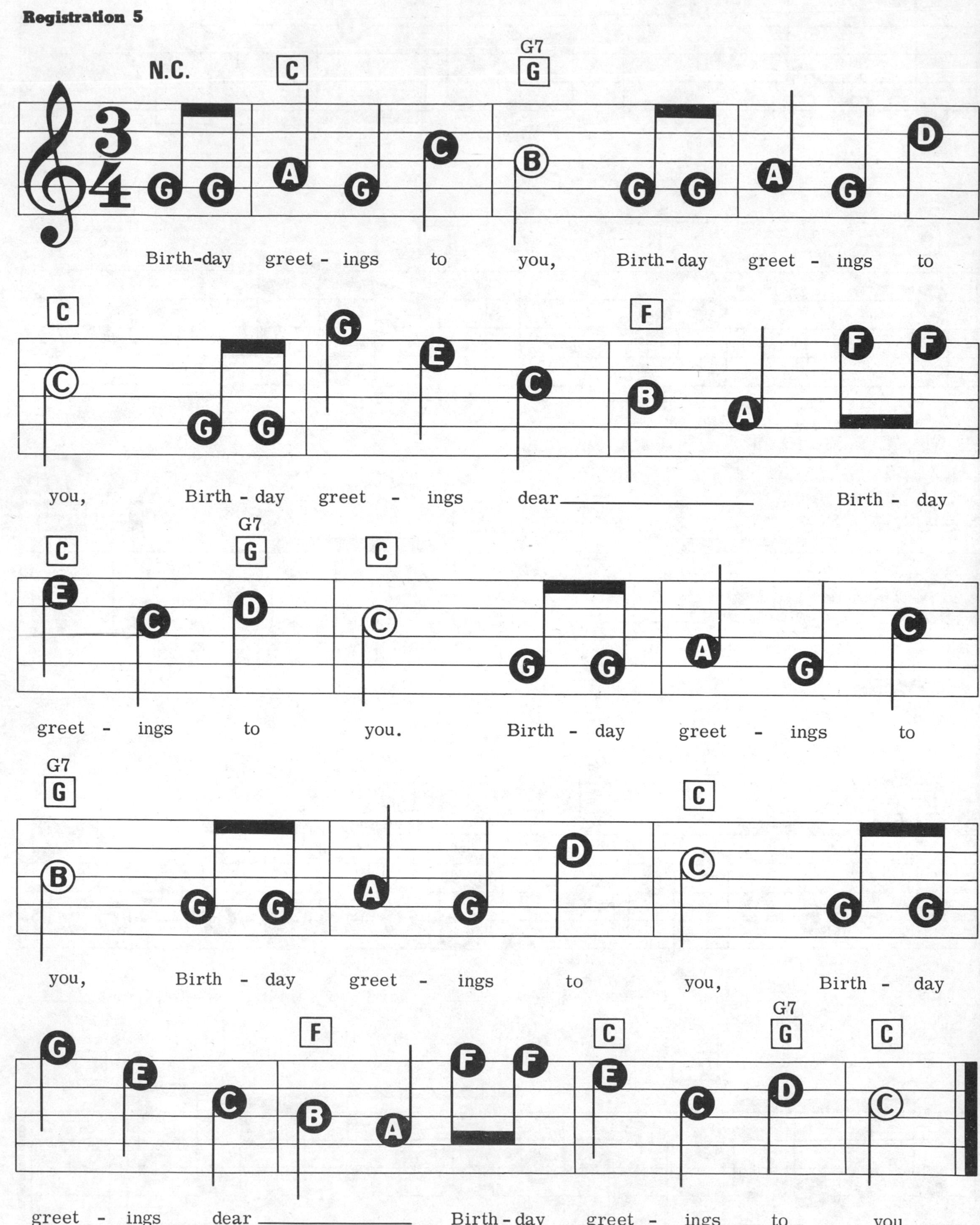

Hickory Dickory Dock

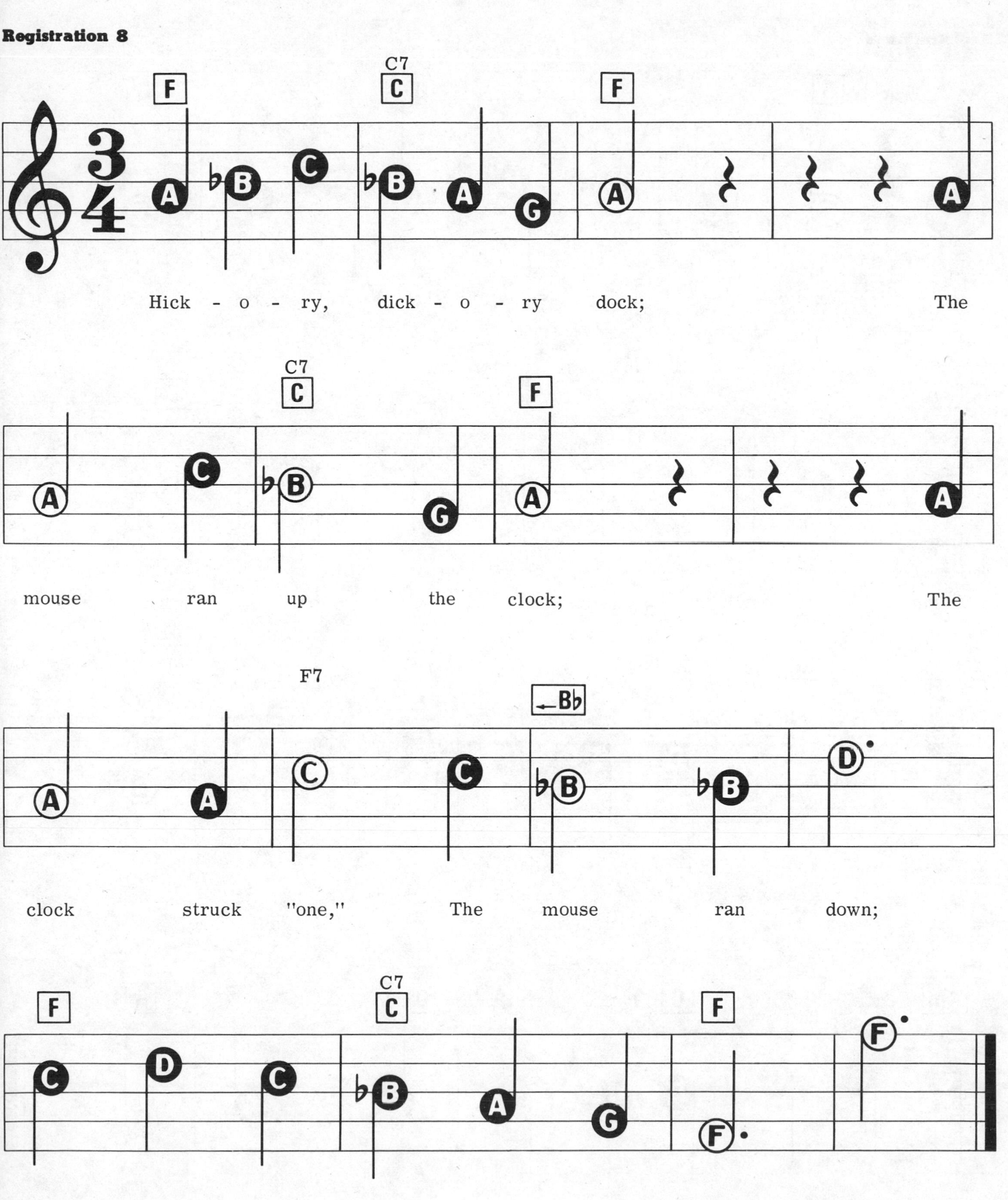

Humpty Dumpty

Registration 2

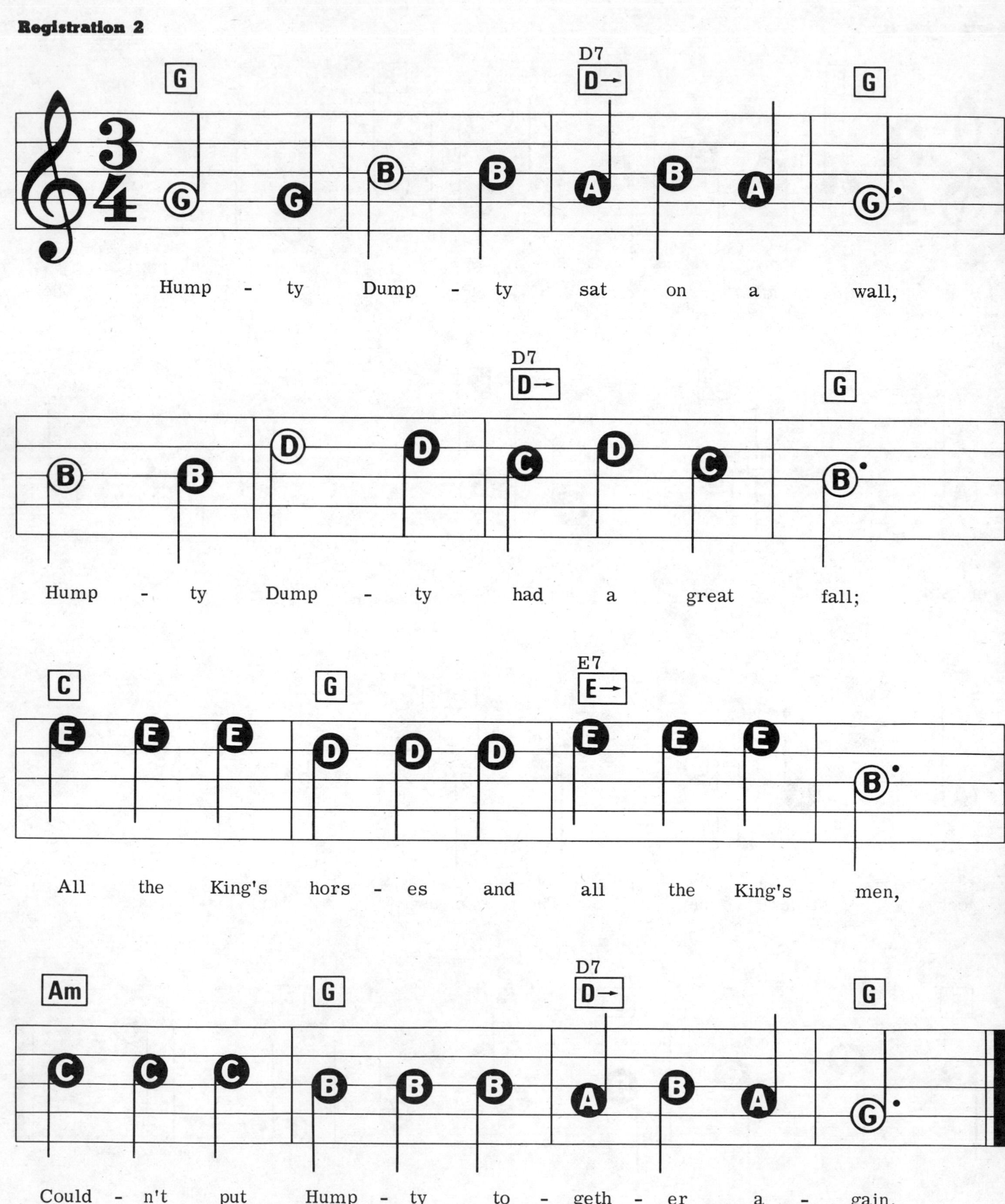

Little Miss Muffet

Registration 8

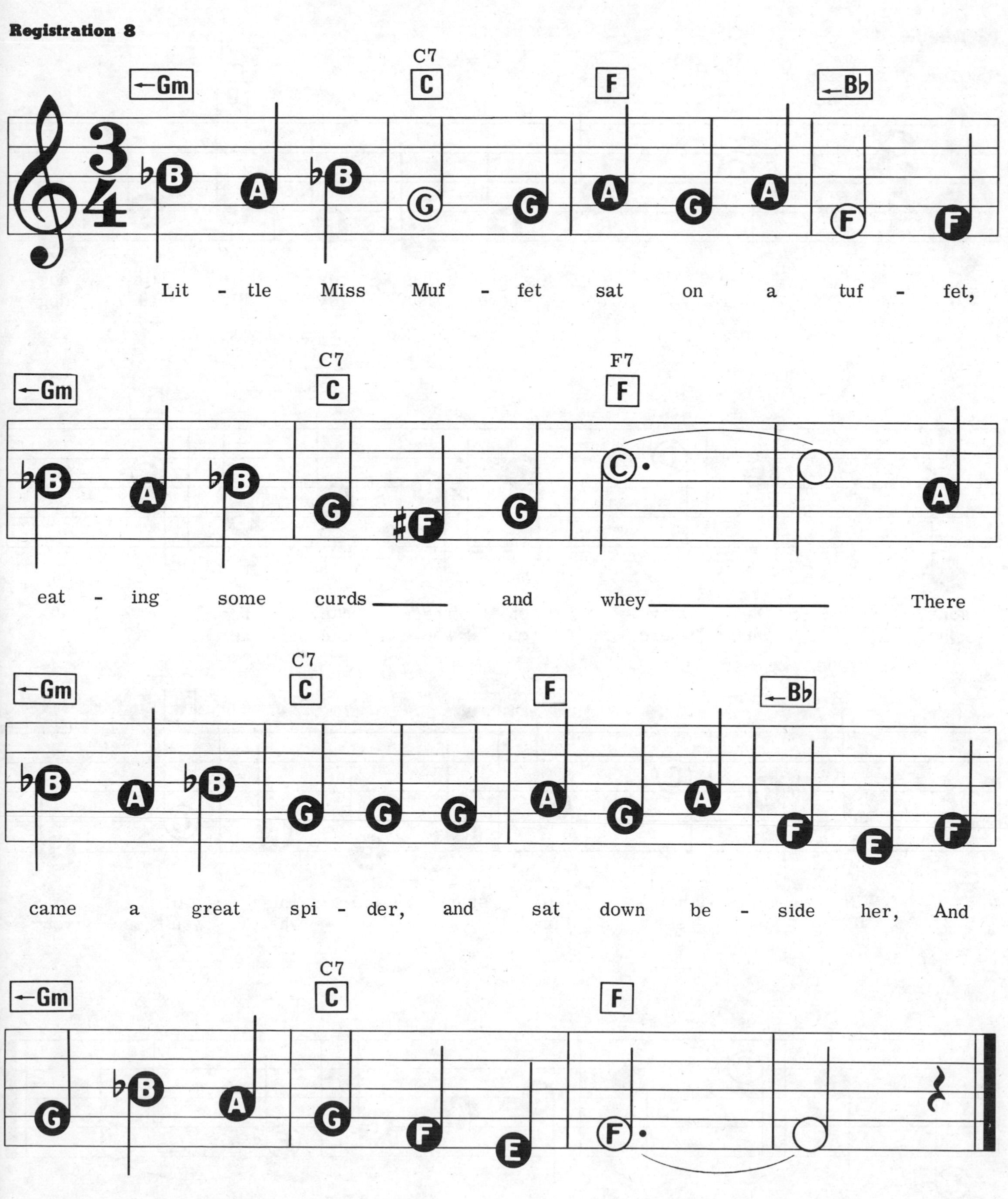

Oh Where Has My Little Dog Gone

Registration 5

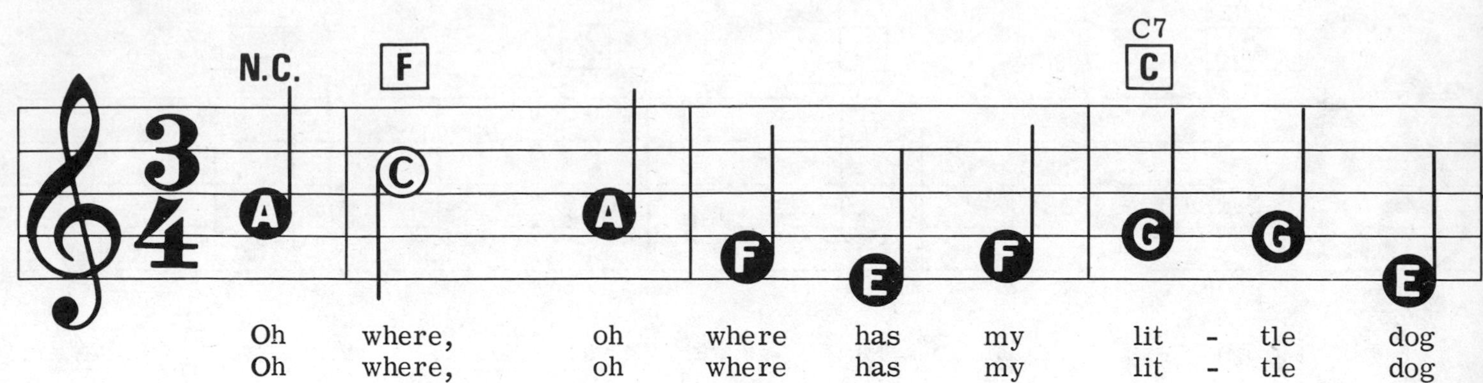

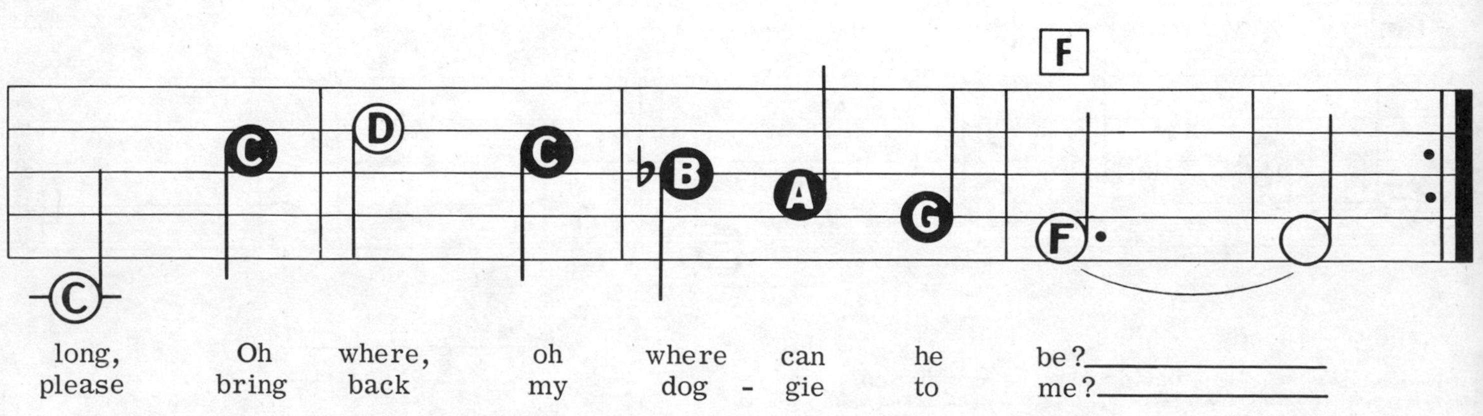

Old King Cole

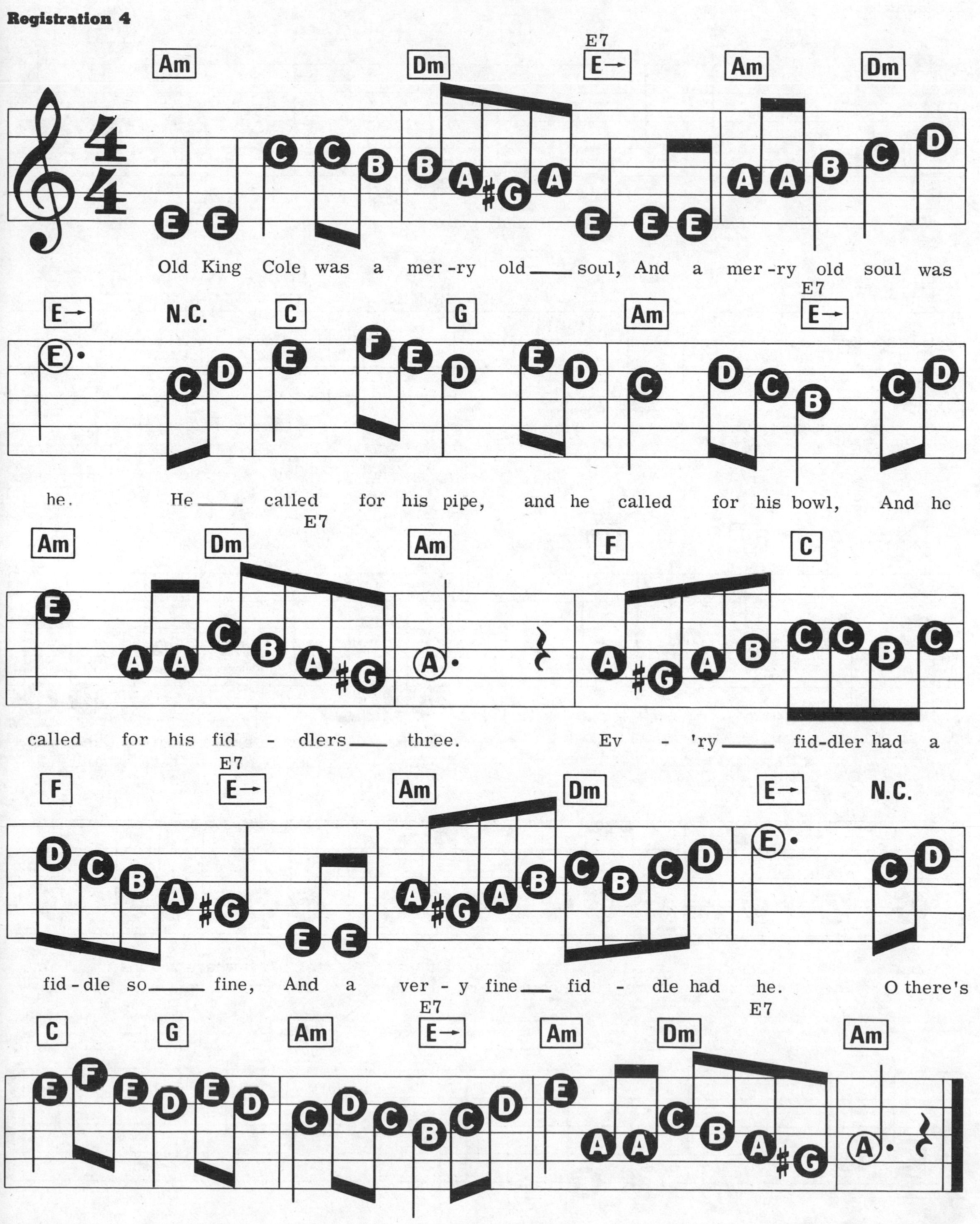

Old MacDonald Had A Farm

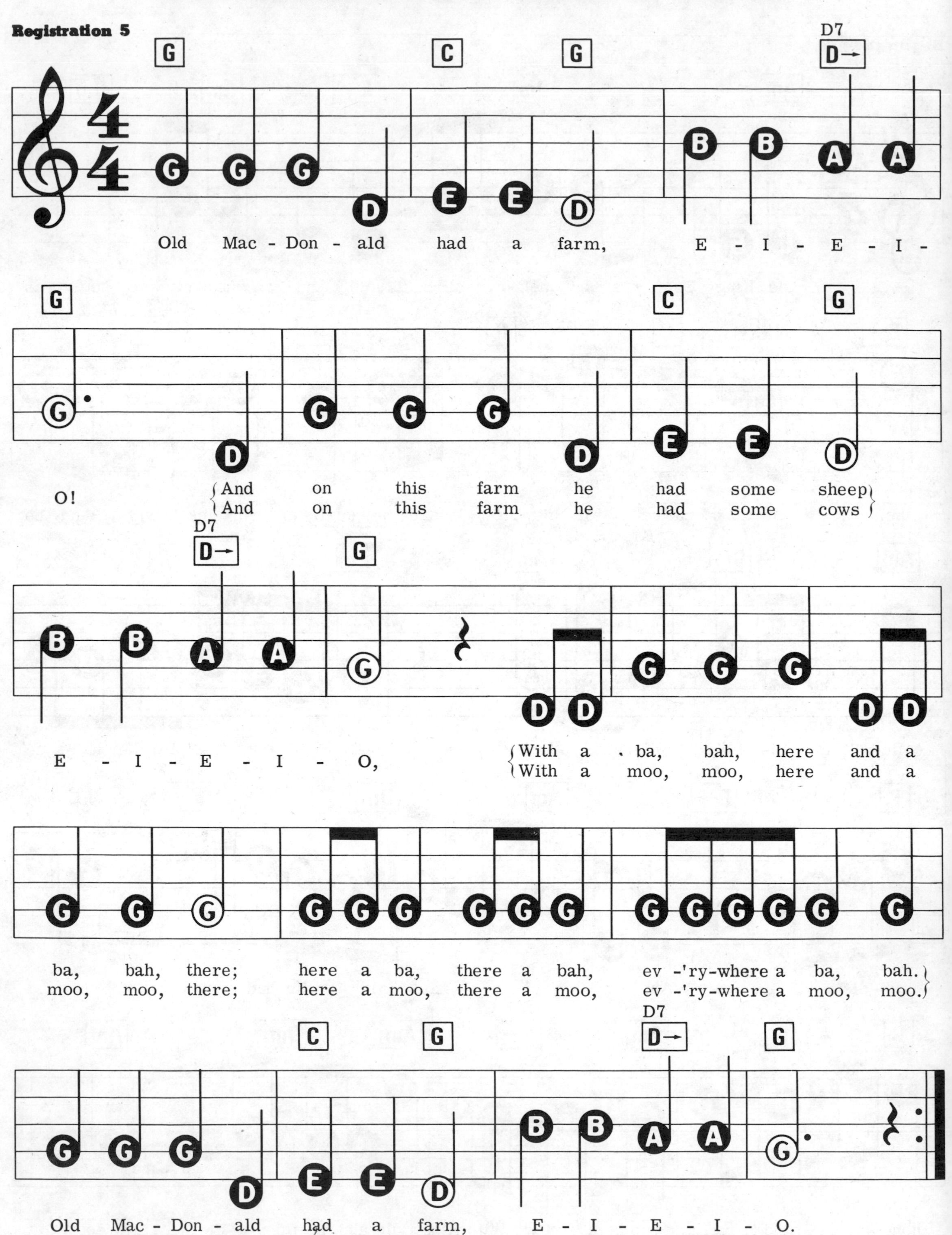

Pop Goes The Weasel

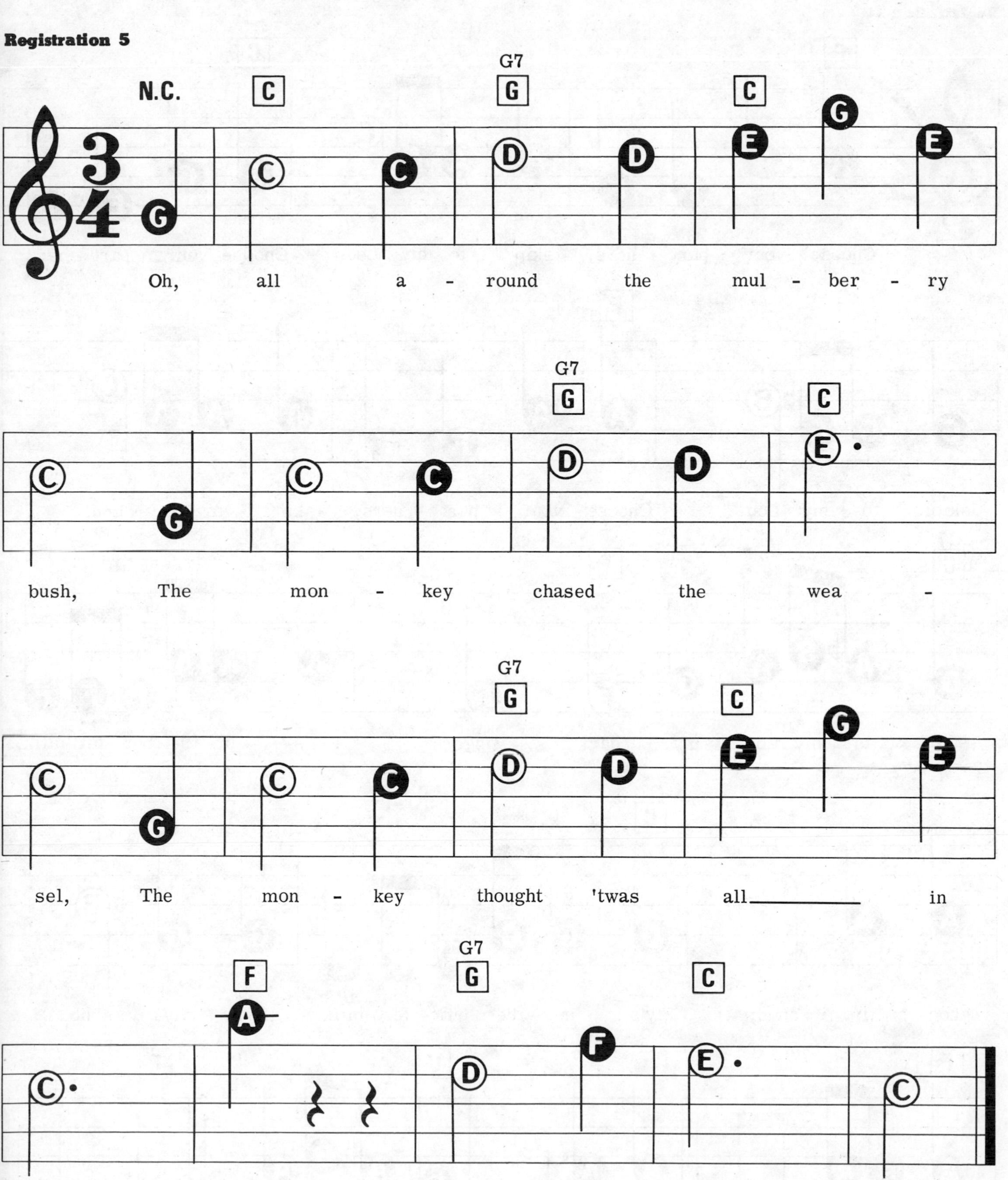

Skip To My Lou

Registration 10

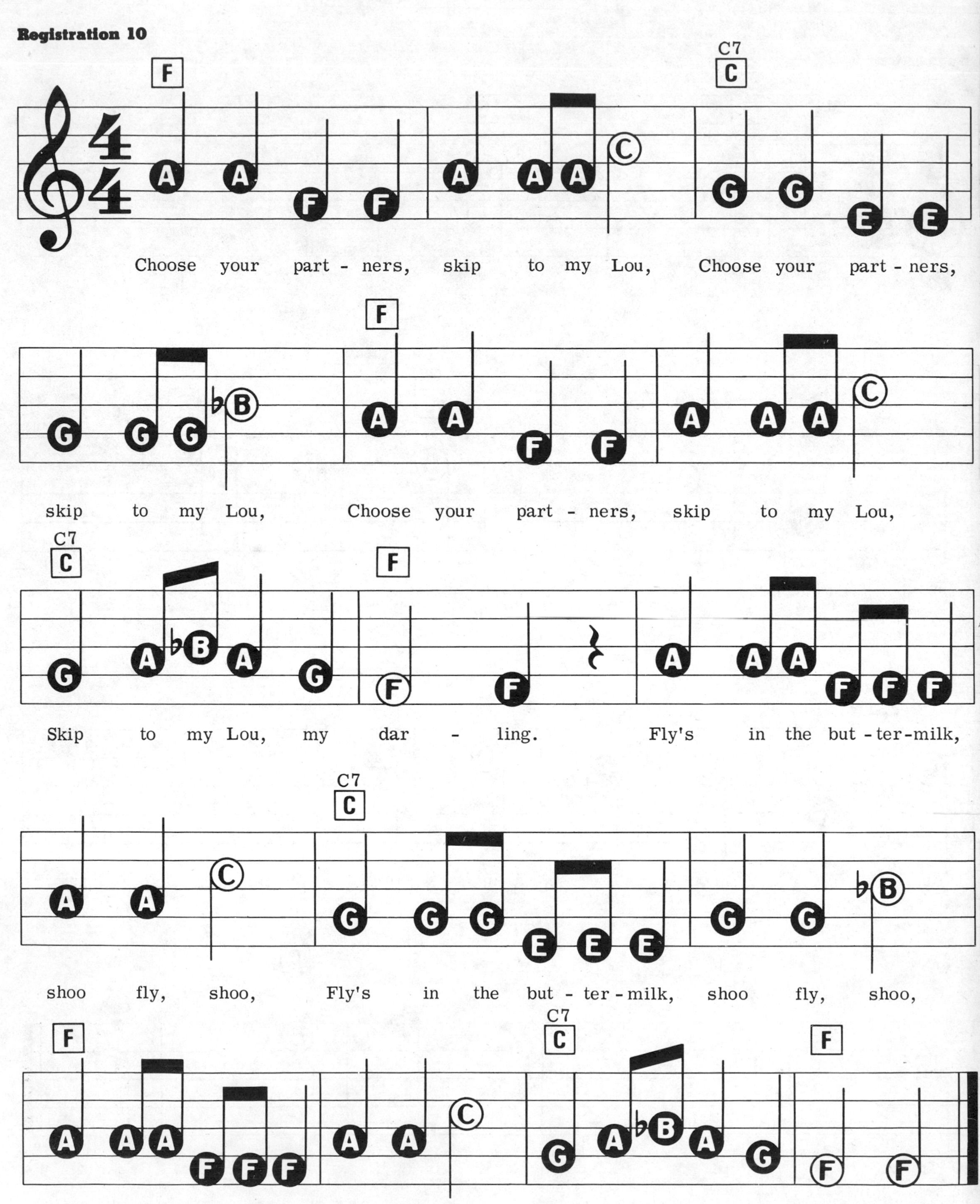

Turkey In The Straw

Registration 3

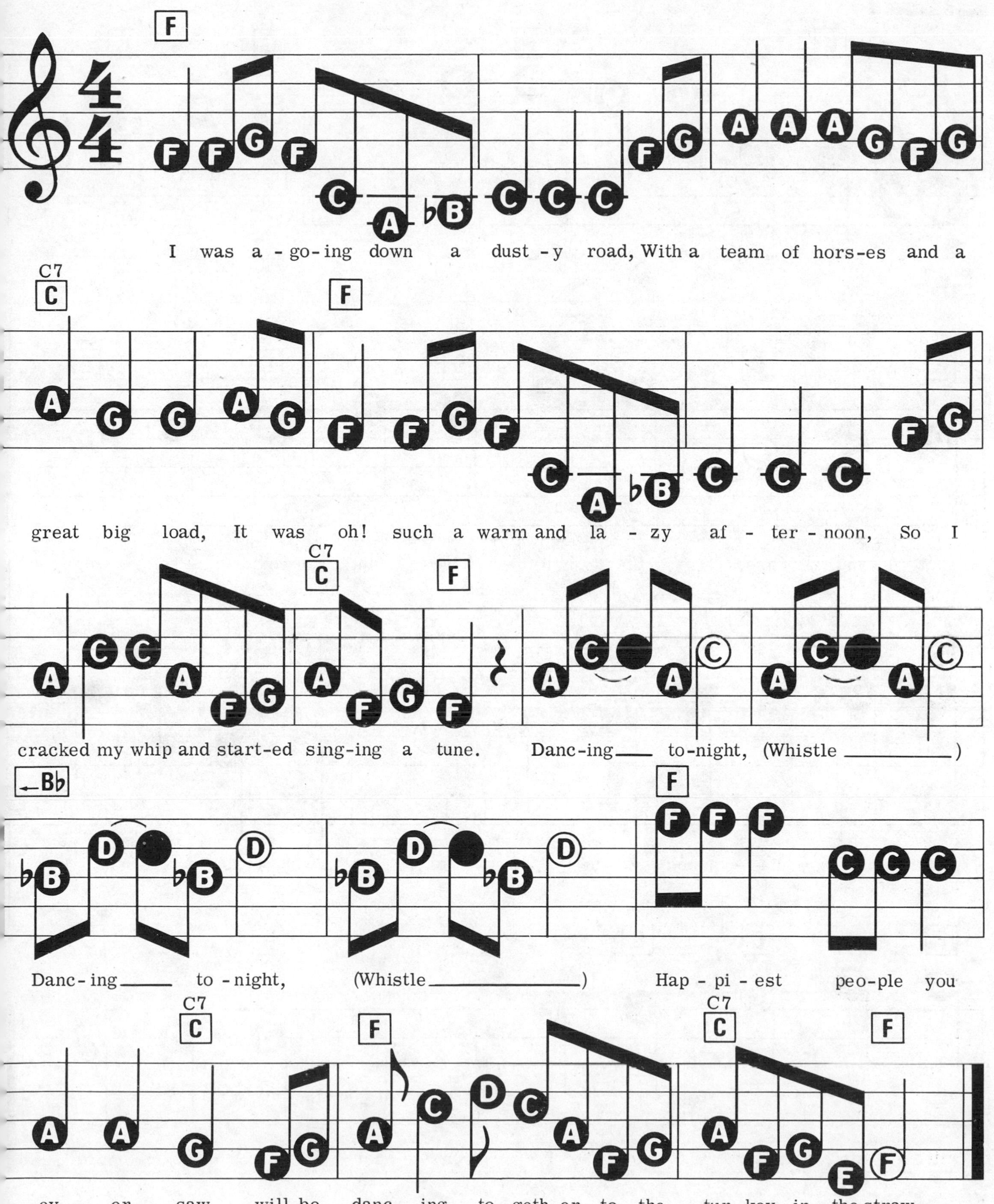

Twinkle, Twinkle, Little Star

Registration 1

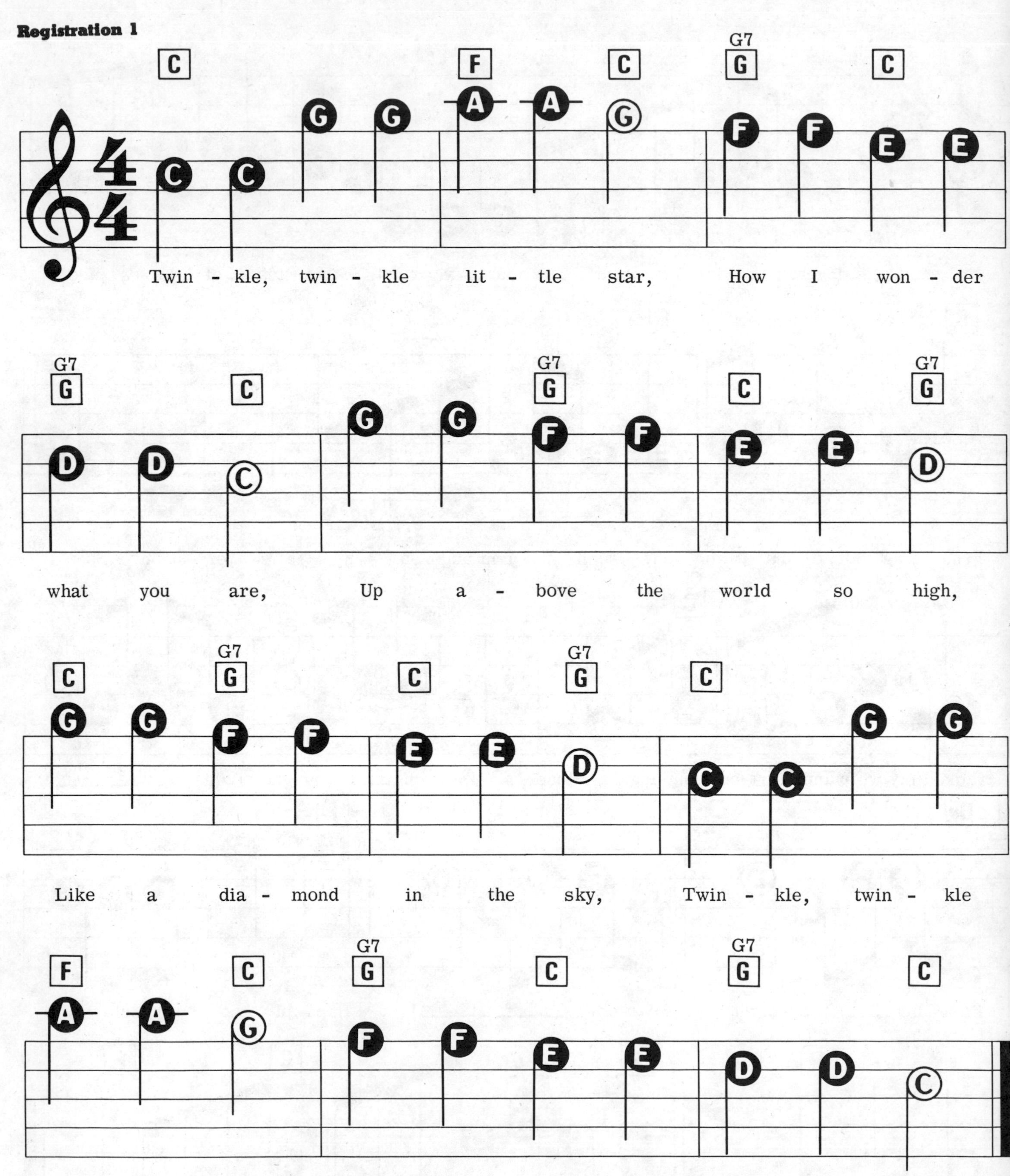

I Heard The Bells On Christmas Day

Registration 6

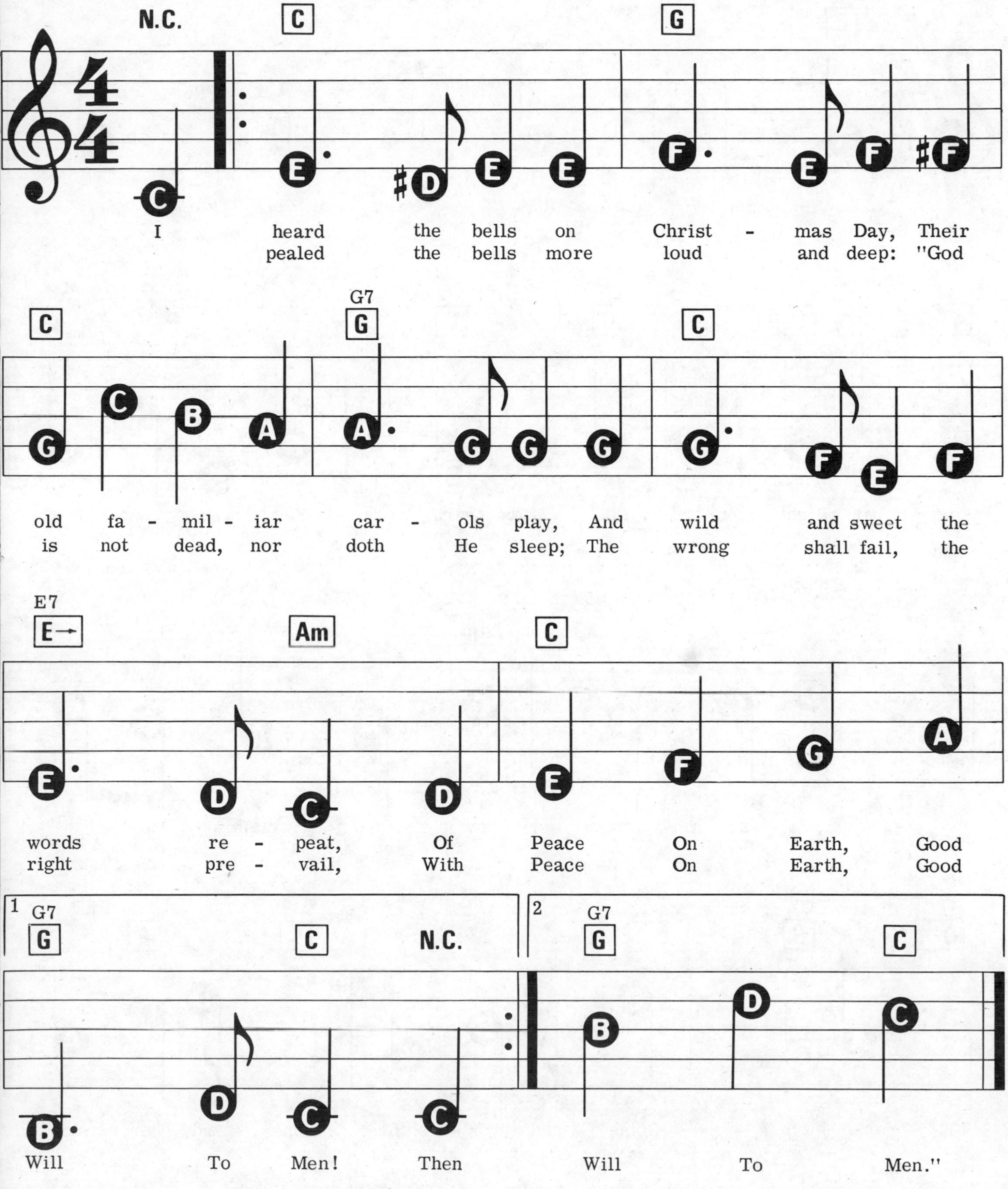

N.C. | C | G

I heard the bells on Christmas Day, Their
pealed the bells more loud and deep: "God

C | G7 (G) | C

old familiar carols play, And wild and sweet the
is not dead, nor doth He sleep; The wrong shall fail, the

E7 (E→) | Am | C

words repeat, Of Peace On Earth, Good
right prevail, With Peace On Earth, Good

1. G7 (G) | C | N.C.

Will To Men! Then

2. G7 (G) | C

Will To Men."

Angels From The Realms Of Glory

Registration 6

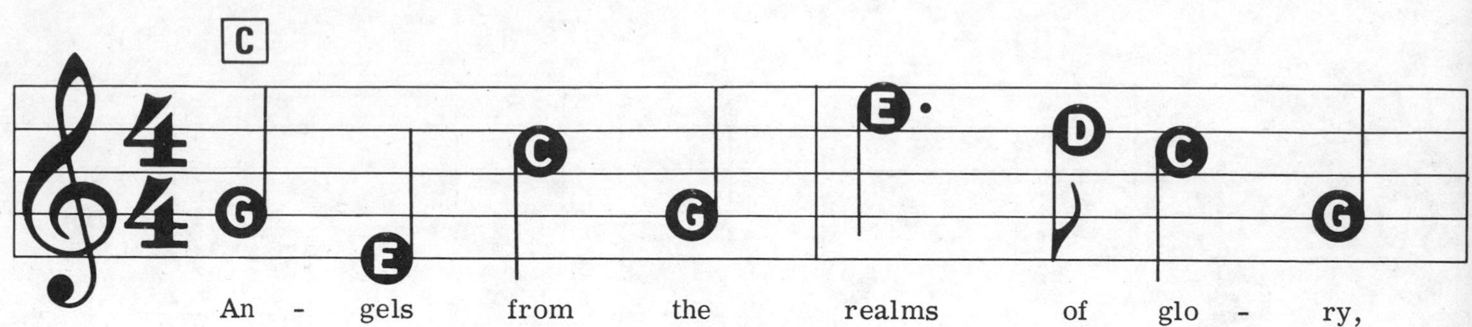

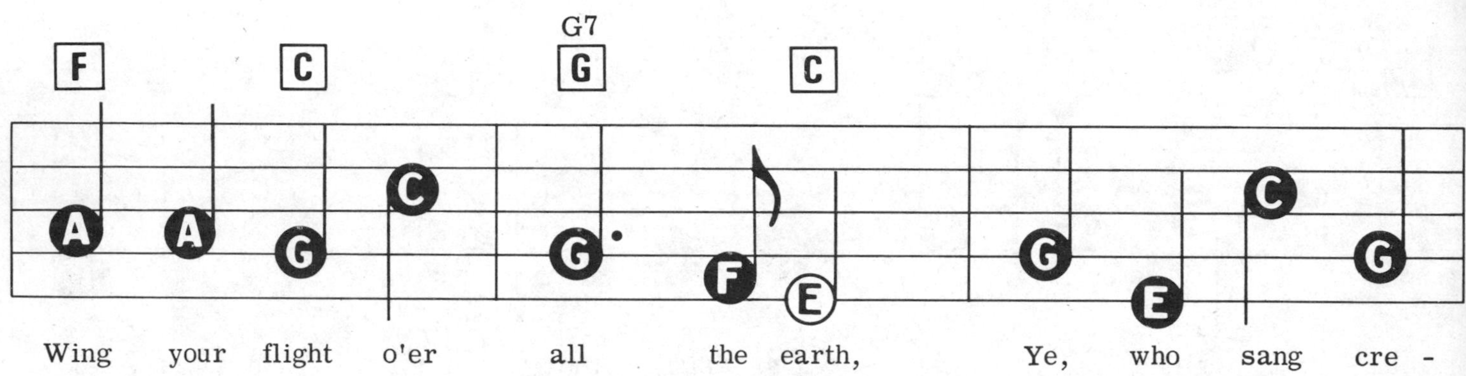

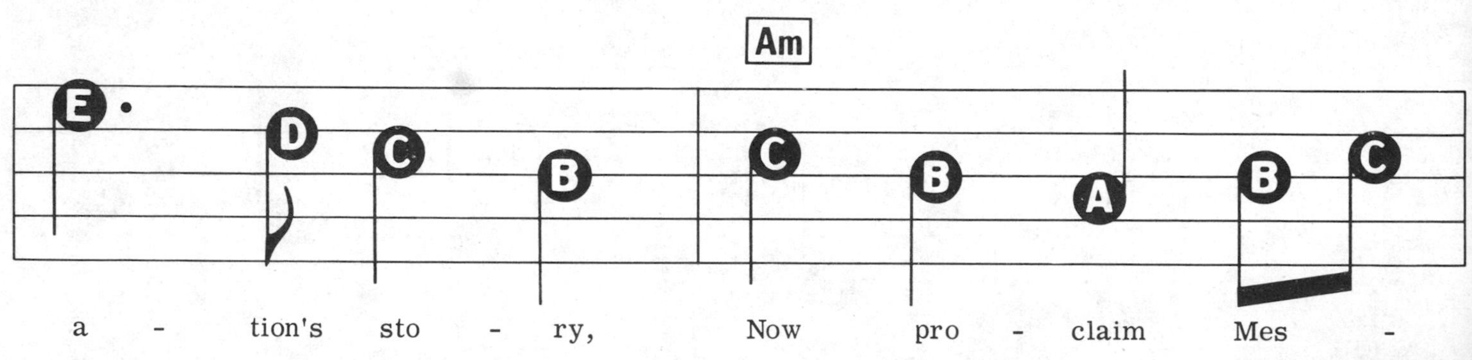

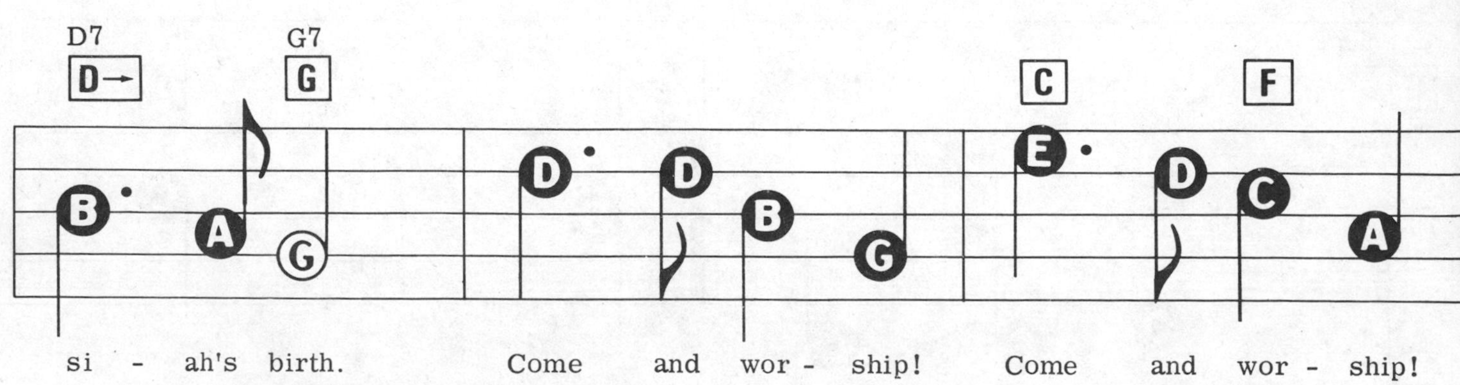

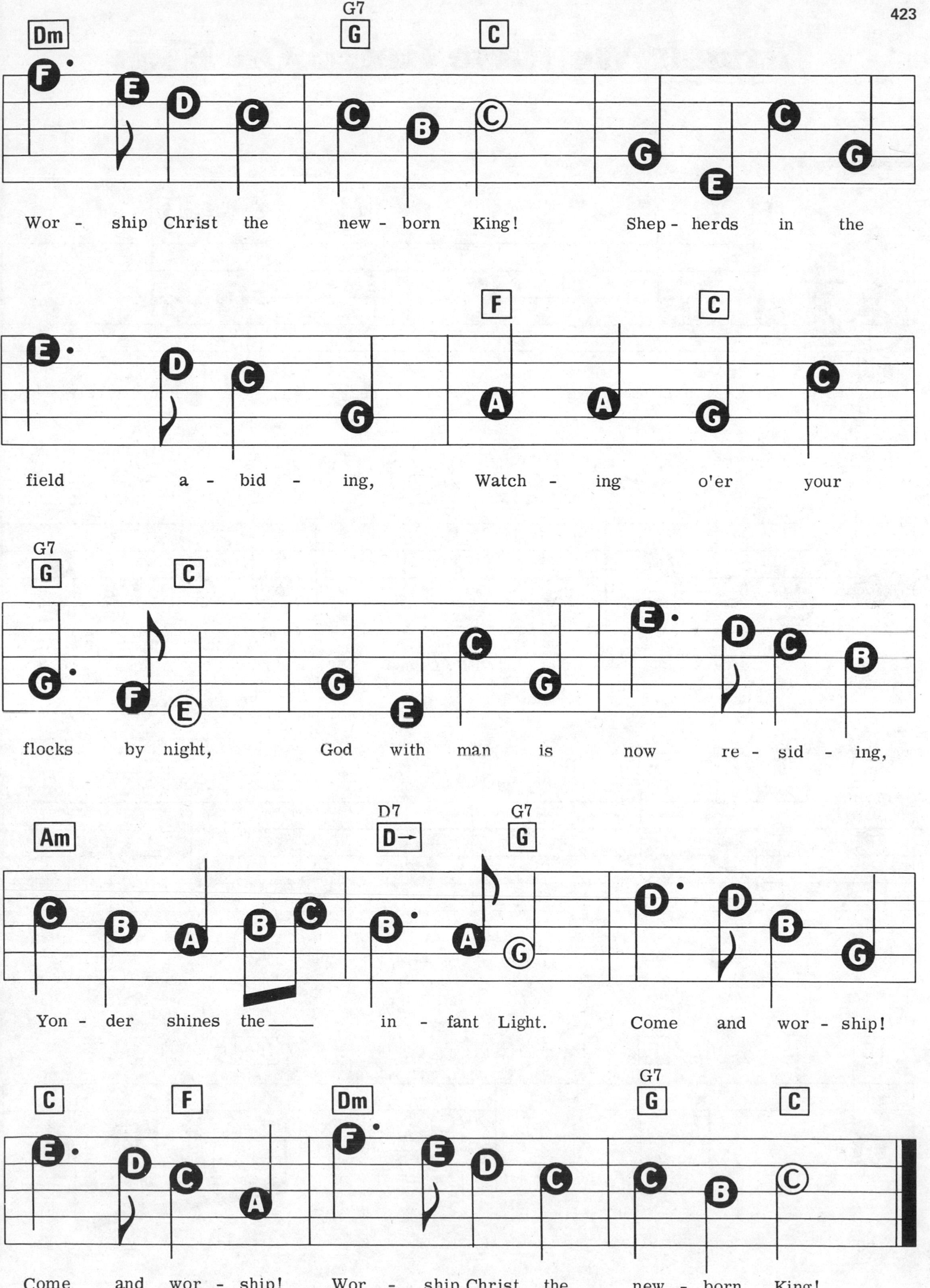
Dm G7 G C
Wor - ship Christ the new - born King! Shep - herds in the
F C
field a - bid - ing, Watch - ing o'er your
G7 G C
flocks by night, God with man is now re - sid - ing,
Am D7 D→ G7 G
Yon - der shines the in - fant Light. Come and wor - ship!
C F Dm G7 G C
Come and wor - ship! Wor - ship Christ the new - born King!

Angels We Have Heard On High

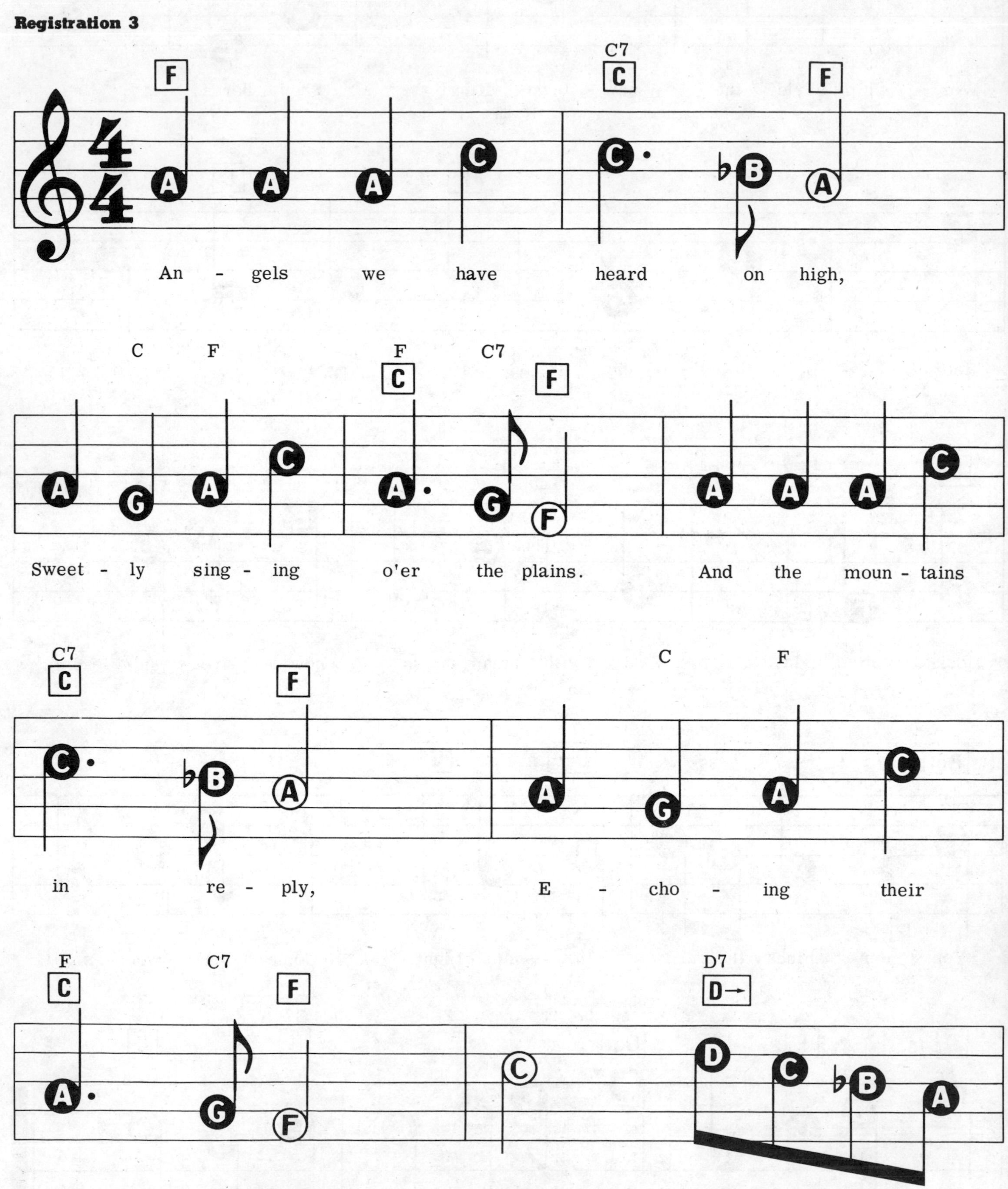

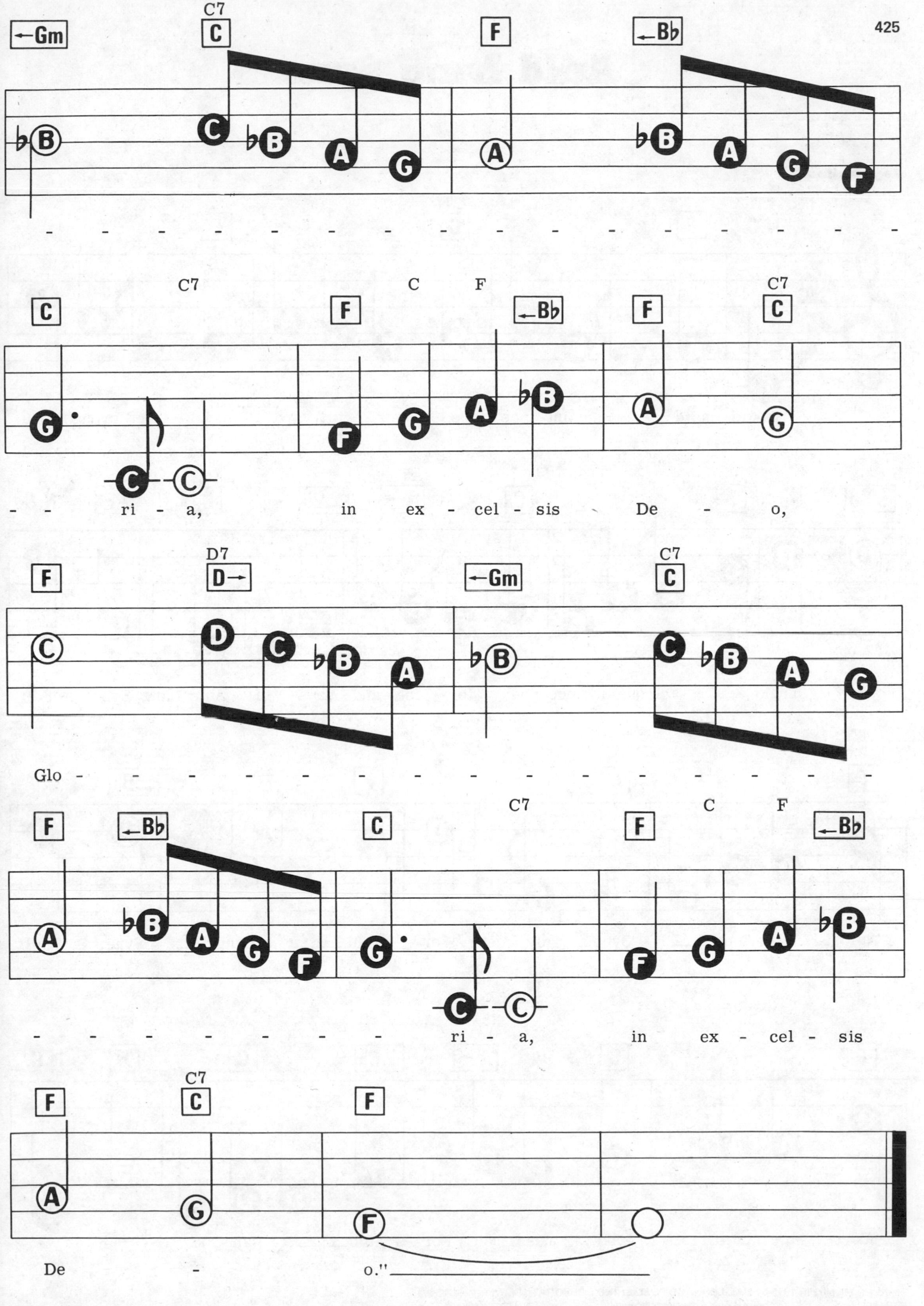
←Gm C7 C F ←B♭
C C7 F C F ←B♭ F C7 C
ri - a, in ex - cel - sis De - o,
F D7 D→ ←Gm C7 C
Glo -
F ←B♭ C C7 F C F ←B♭
ri - a, in ex - cel - sis
F C7 C F
De - o."

Auld Lang Syne

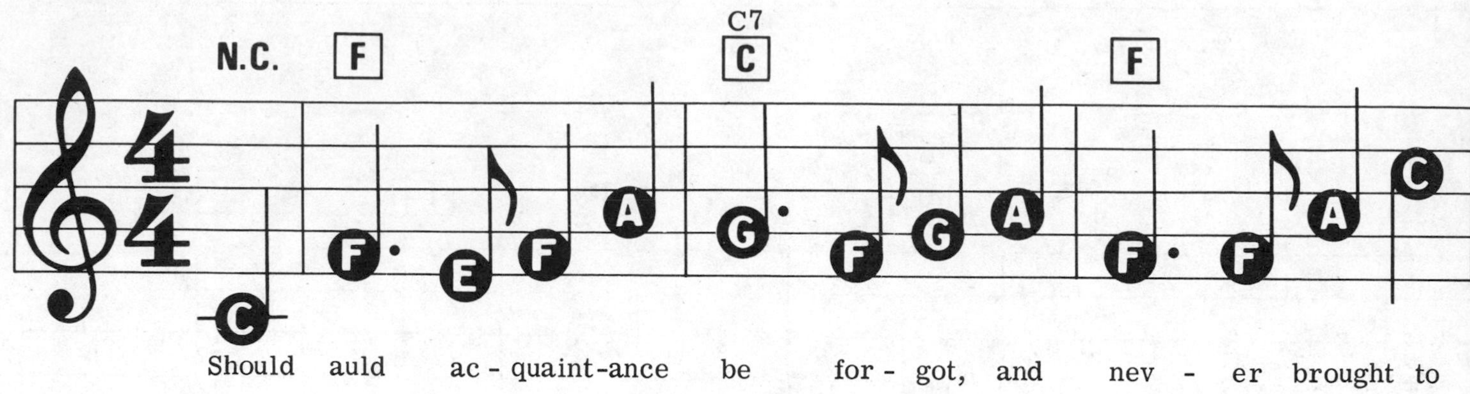

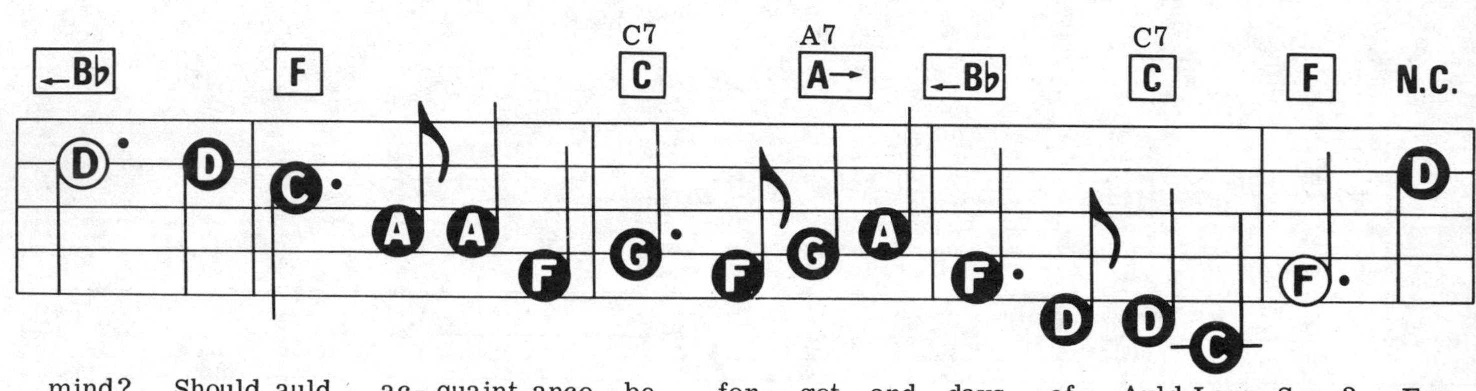

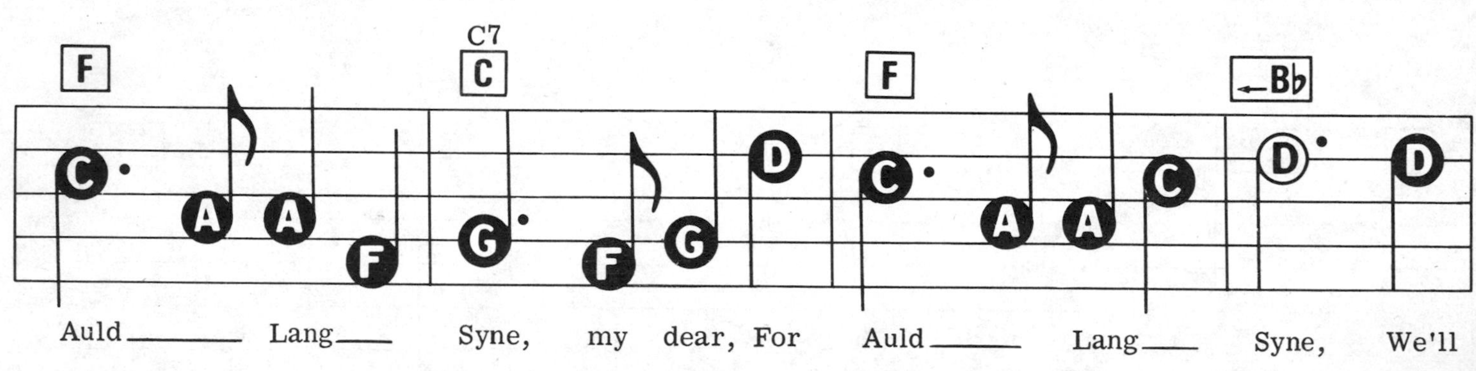

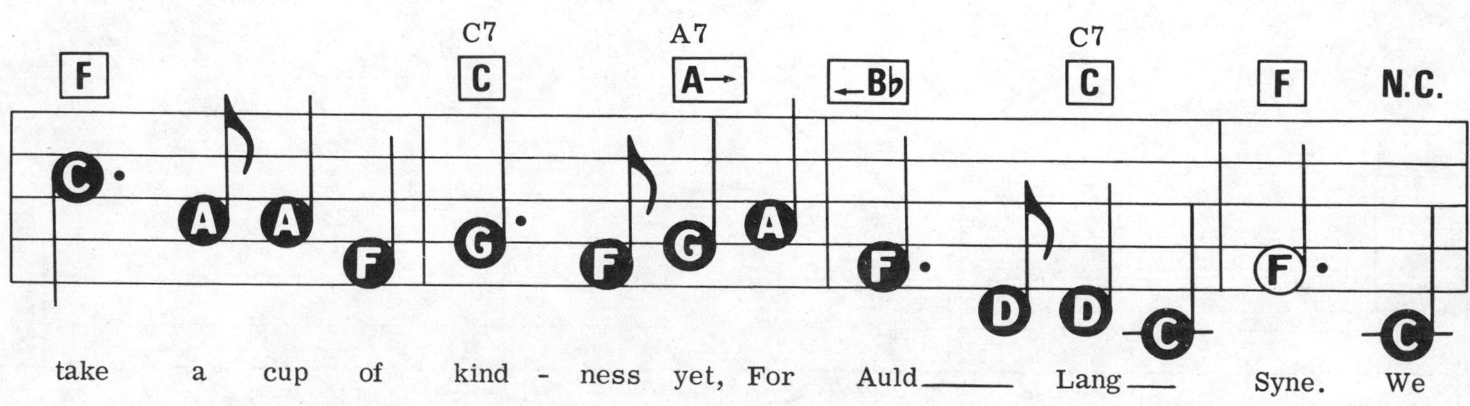

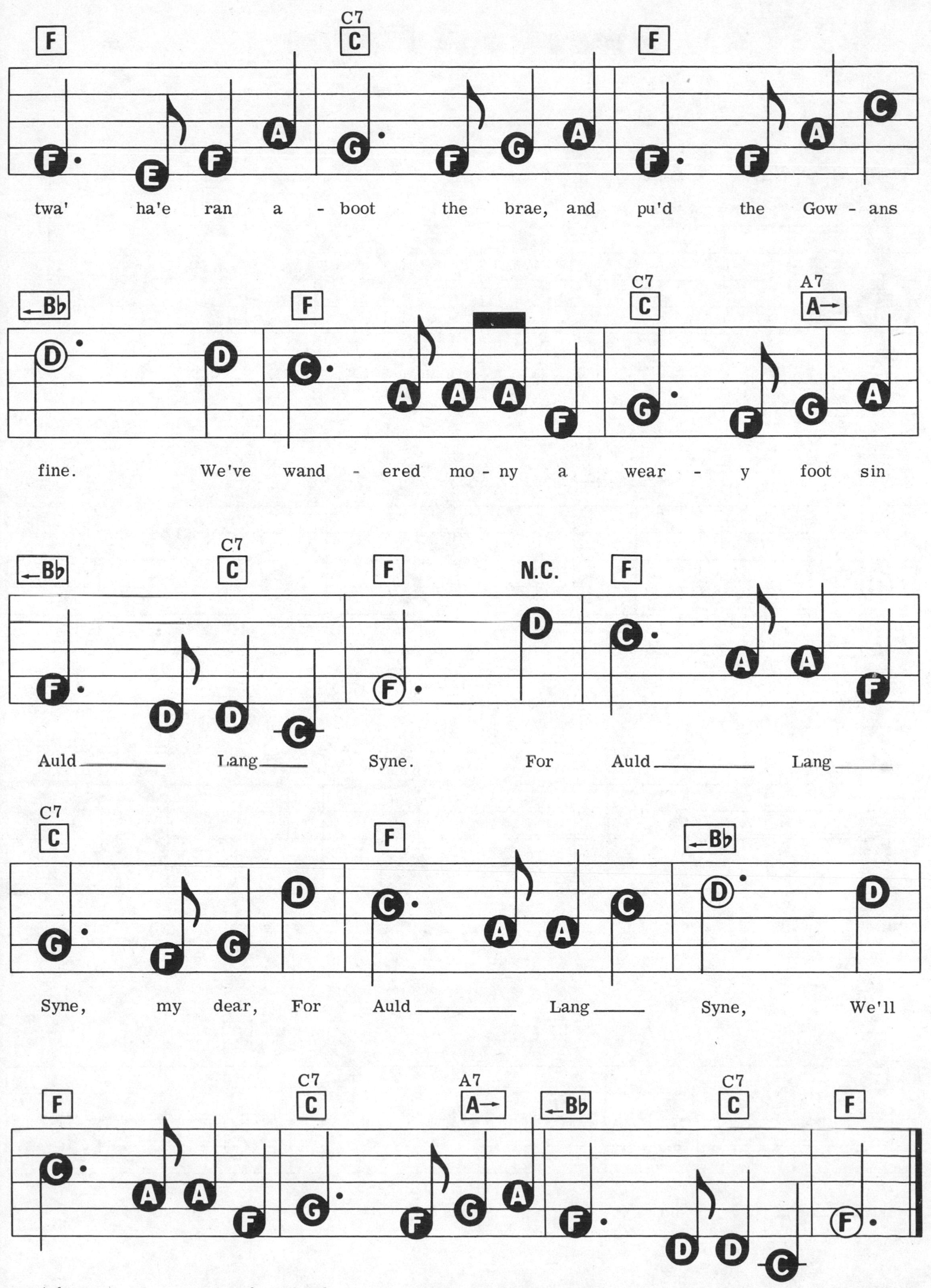
F C7 C F
twa' ha'e ran a - boot the brae, and pu'd the Gow - ans
Bb F C7 C A7 A
fine. We've wand - ered mo - ny a wear - y foot sin
Bb C7 C F N.C. F
Auld Lang Syne. For Auld Lang
C7 C F Bb
Syne, my dear, For Auld Lang Syne, We'll
F C7 C A7 A Bb C7 C F
take a cup of kind - ness yet, for Auld Lang Syne.

Away In A Manger

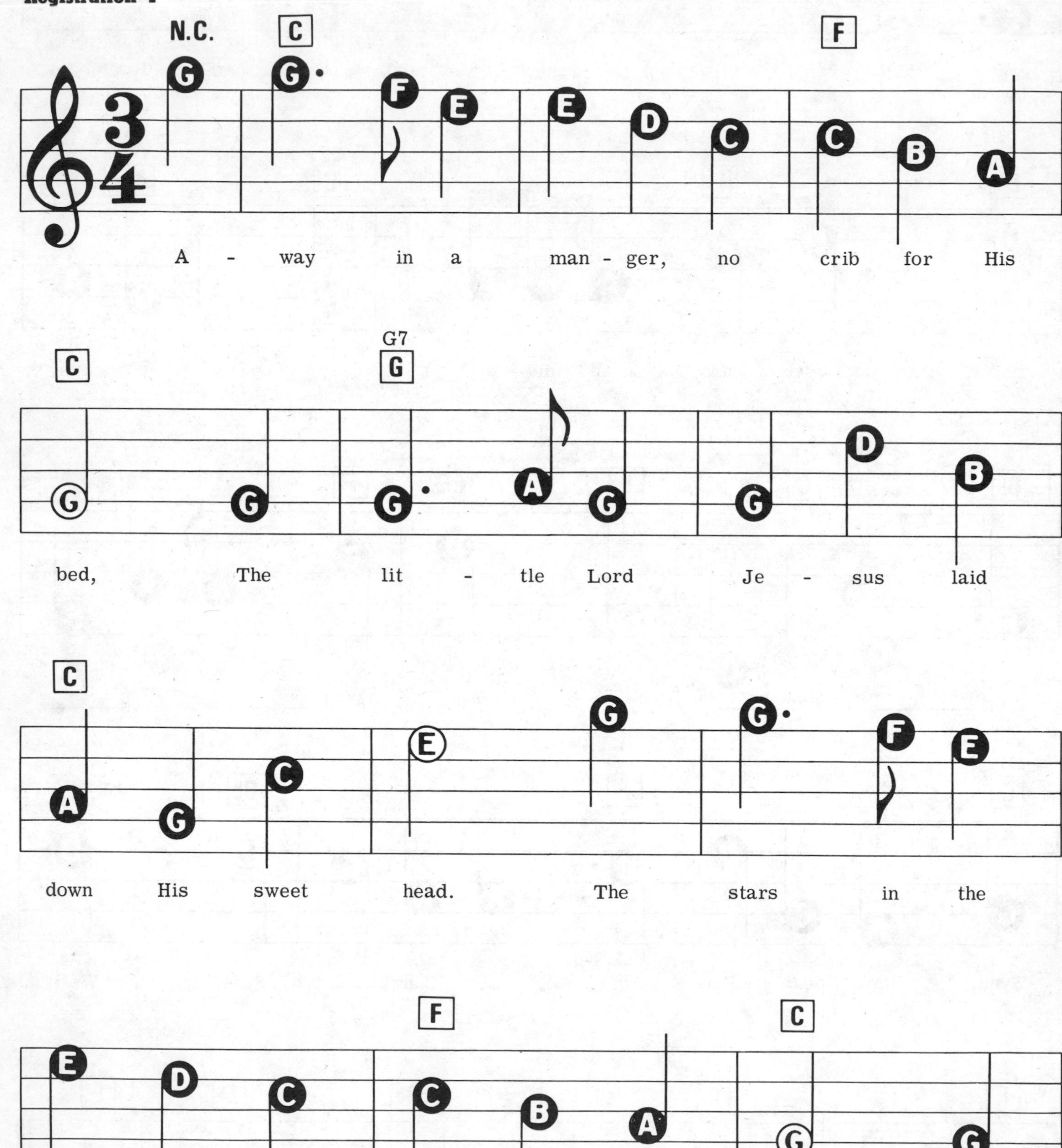

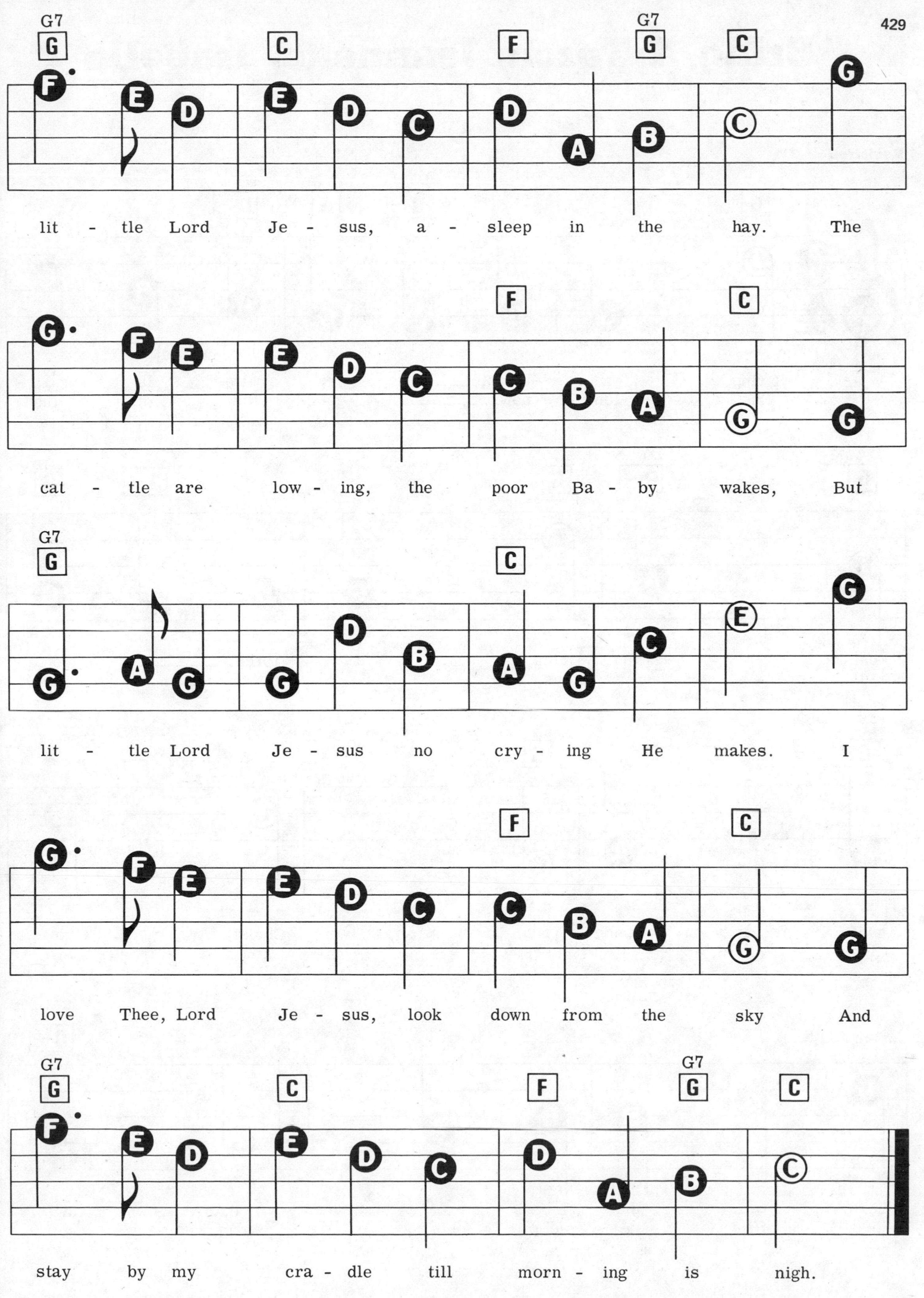
G7 G C F G7 G C
lit - tle Lord Je - sus, a - sleep in the hay. The
F C
cat - tle are low - ing, the poor Ba - by wakes, But
G7 G C
lit - tle Lord Je - sus no cry - ing He makes. I
F C
love Thee, Lord Je - sus, look down from the sky And
G7 G C F G7 G C
stay by my cra - dle till morn - ing is nigh.

Bring A Torch, Jeannette, Isabella

Registration 3

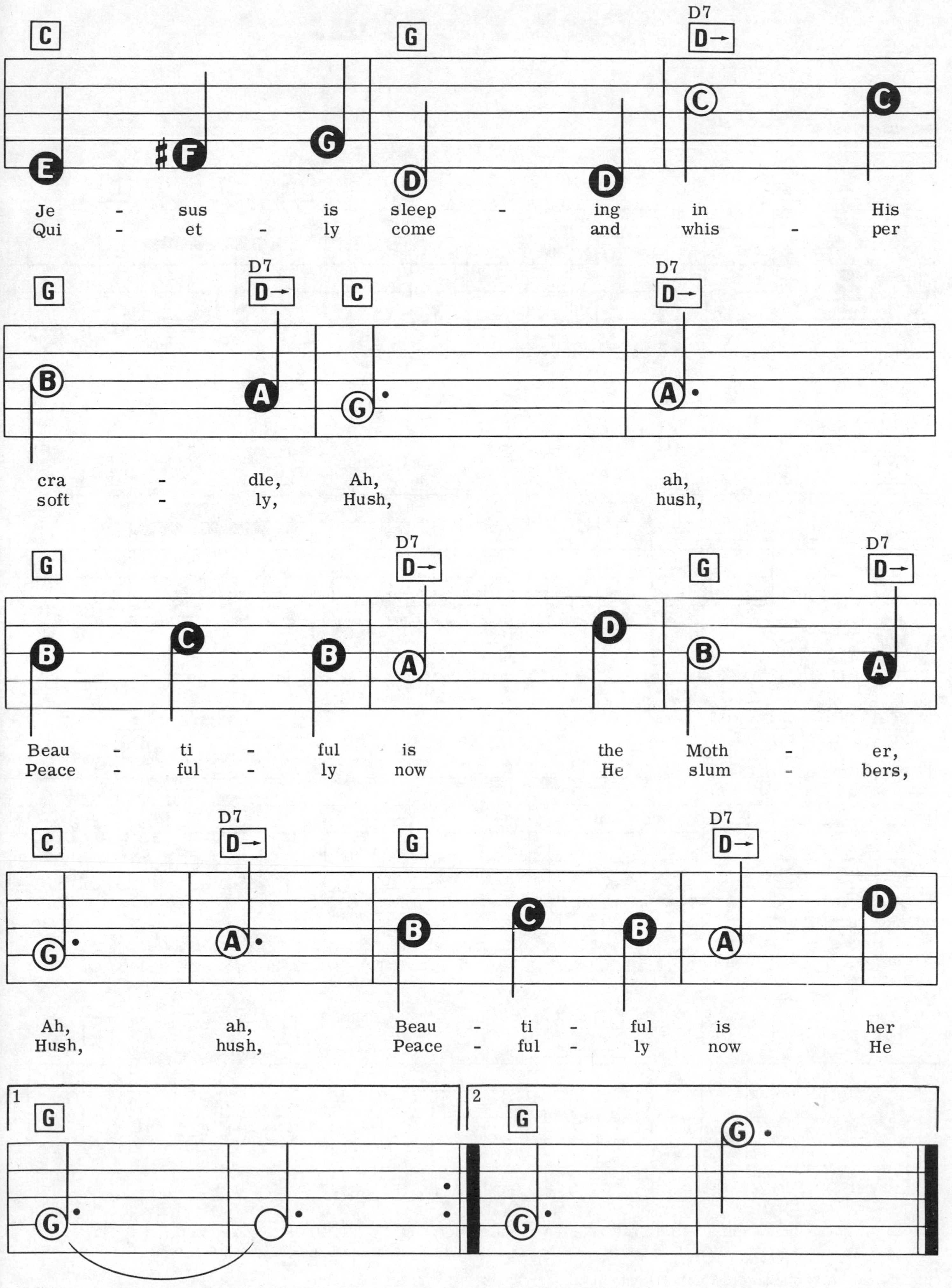
C
G
D7
D→
E
♯F
G
D
D
C
C
Je - sus is sleep - ing in His
Qui - et - ly come and whis - per
G
D7
D→
C
D7
D→
B
A
G
A
cra - dle, Ah, ah,
soft - ly, Hush, hush,
G
D7
D→
G
D7
D→
B
C
B
A
D
B
A
Beau - ti - ful is the Moth - er,
Peace - ful - ly now He slum - bers,
C
D7
D→
G
D7
D→
G
A
B
C
B
A
D
Ah, ah, Beau - ti - ful is her
Hush, hush, Peace - ful - ly now He
1
G
G
2
G
G
G
Son.
sleeps.

Deck The Halls

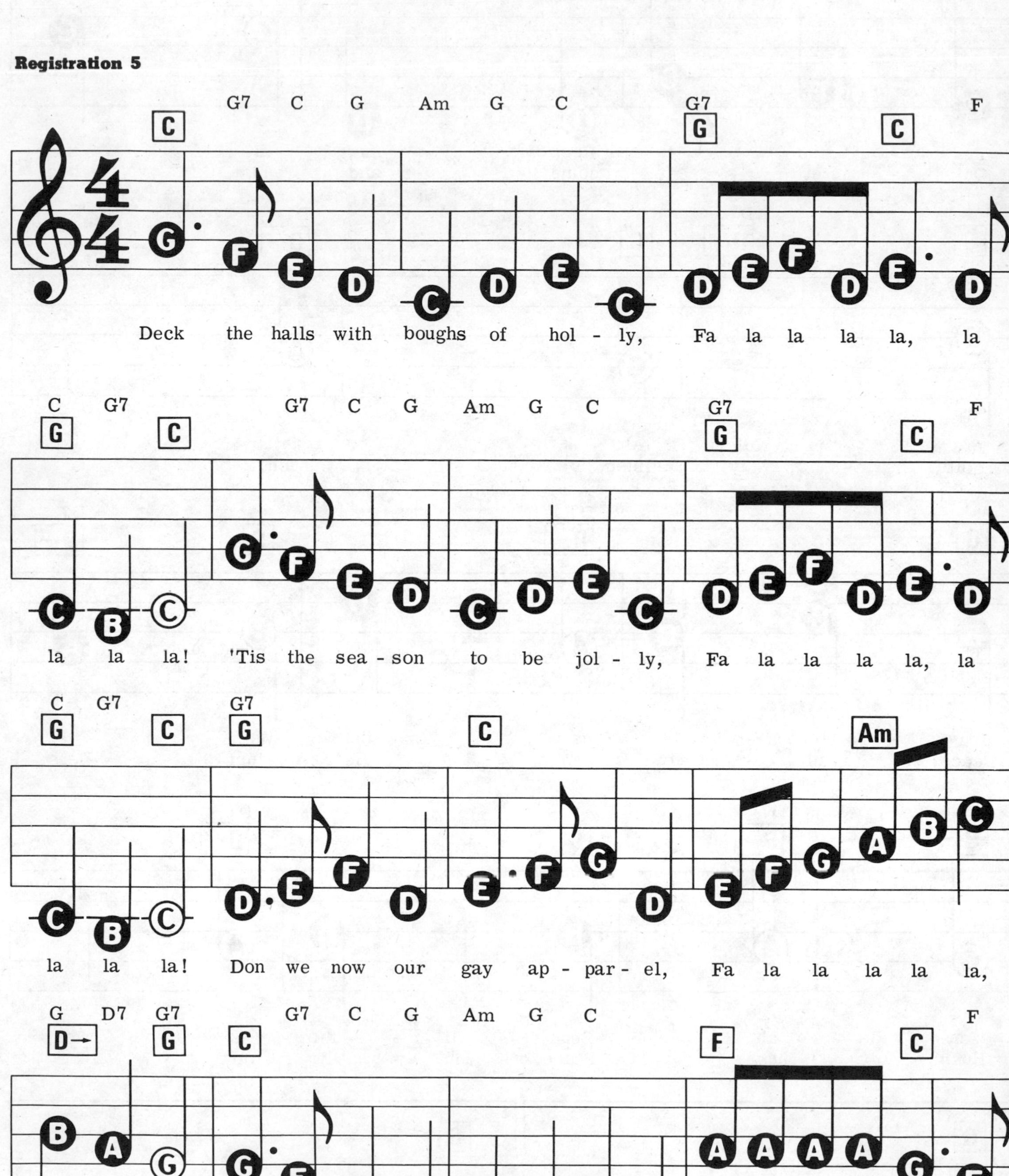

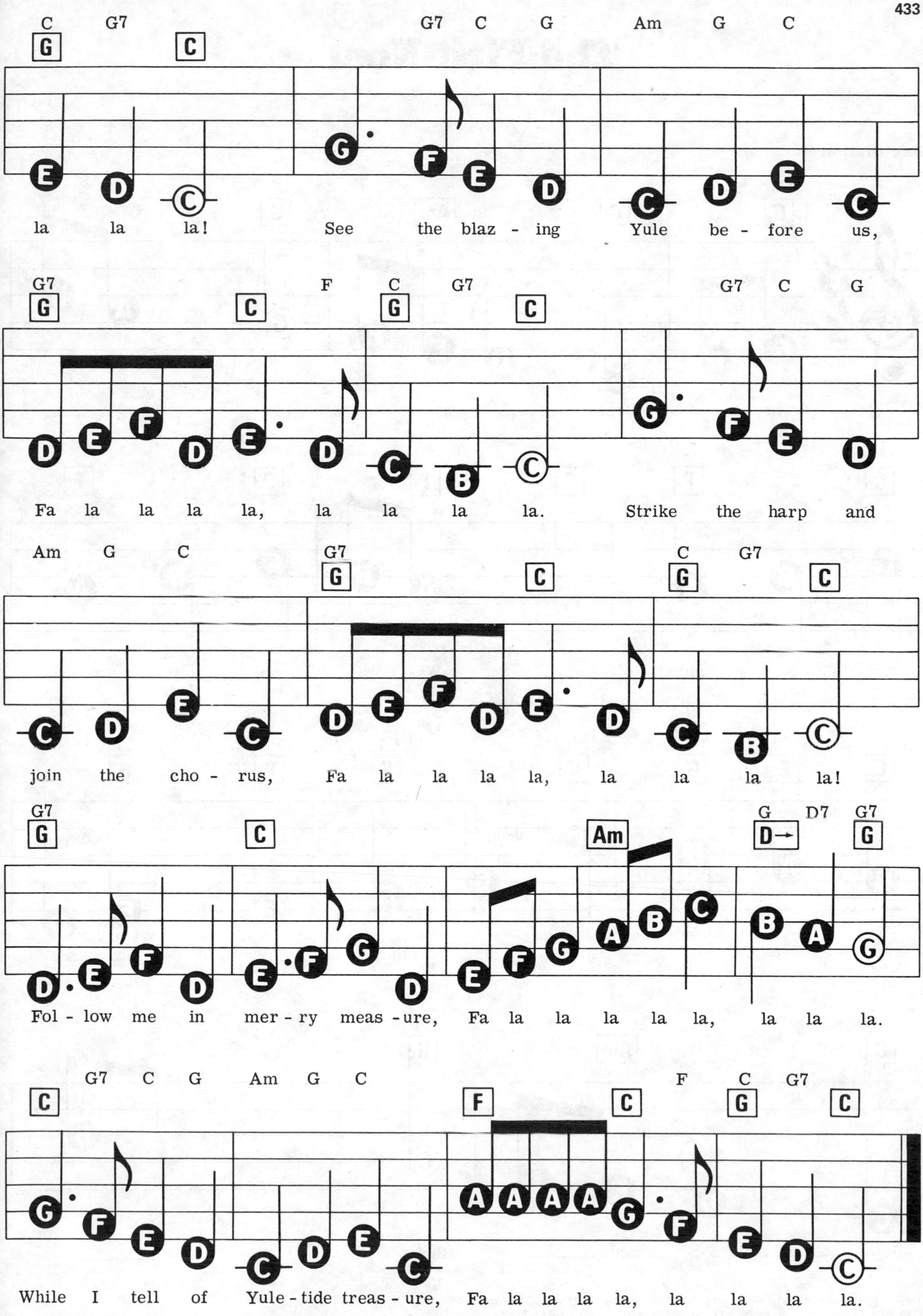

C G7 G7 C G Am G C

la la la! See the blaz - ing Yule be - fore us,

G7 F C G7 G7 C G

Fa la la la la, la la la la. Strike the harp and

Am G C G7 C G7

join the cho - rus, Fa la la la la, la la la la!

G7 G D7 G7

Fol - low me in mer - ry meas - ure, Fa la la la la la, la la la.

G7 C G Am G C F C G7

While I tell of Yule - tide treas - ure, Fa la la la la, la la la la.

The First Noel

Registration 9

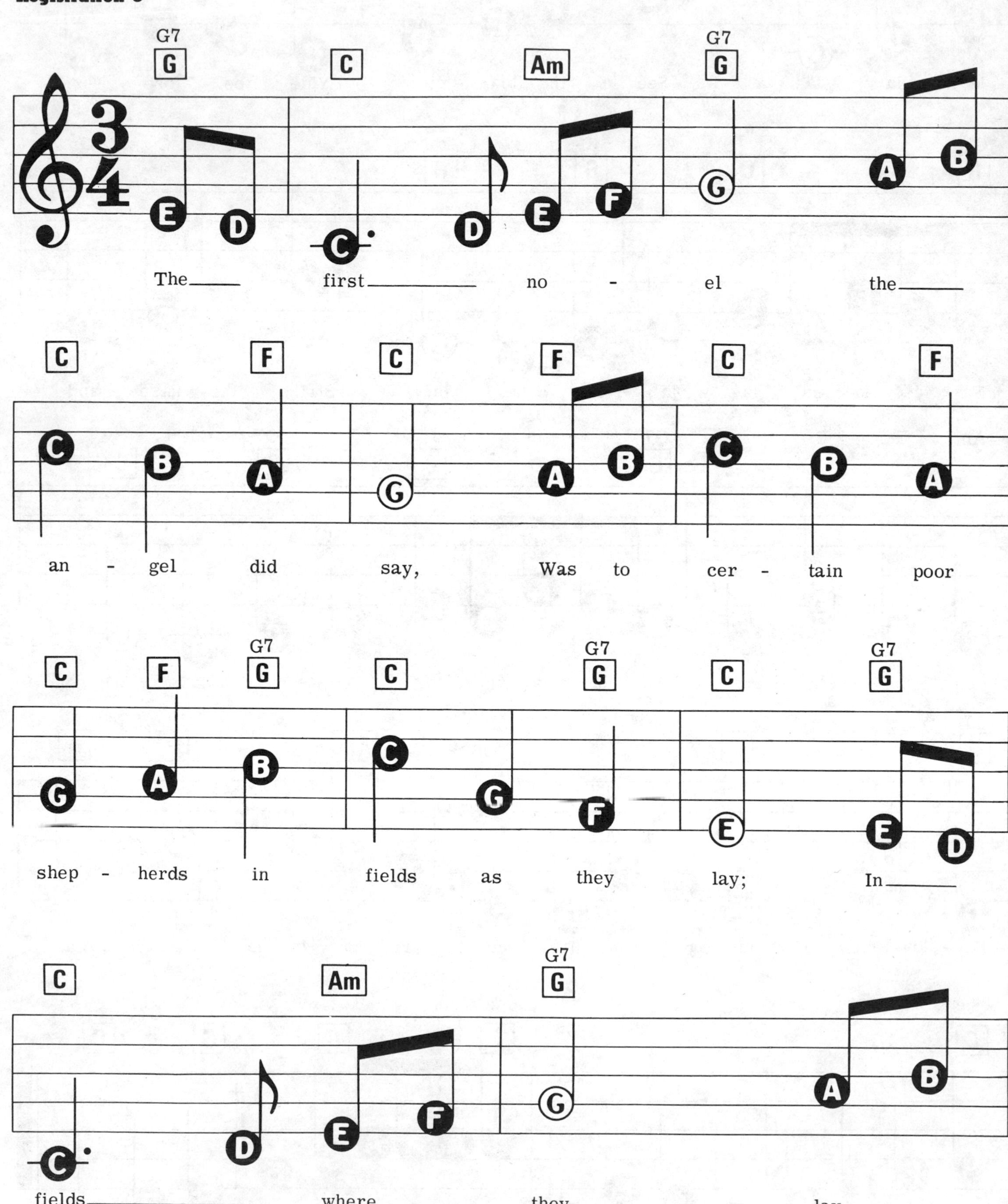

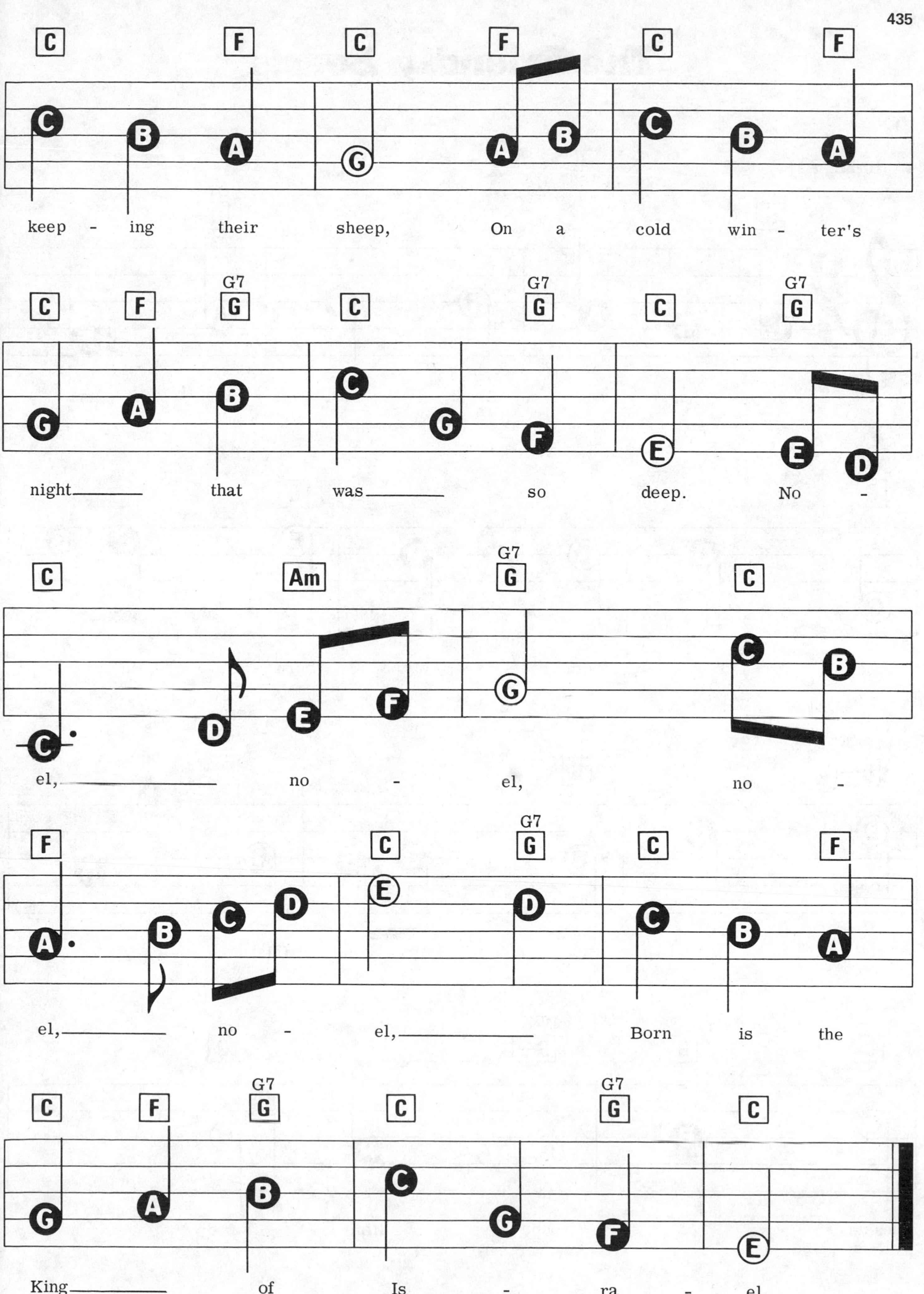
C F C F C F
C B A G A B C B A
keep - ing their sheep, On a cold win - ter's
C F G7 G C G7 G C G7 G
G A B C G F E E D
night that was so deep. No -
C Am G7 G C
C D E F G C B
el, no - el, no -
F C G7 G C F
A B C D E D C B A
el, no - el, Born is the
C F G7 G C G7 G C
G A B C G F E
King of Is - ra - el.

The Friendly Beasts

Registration 3

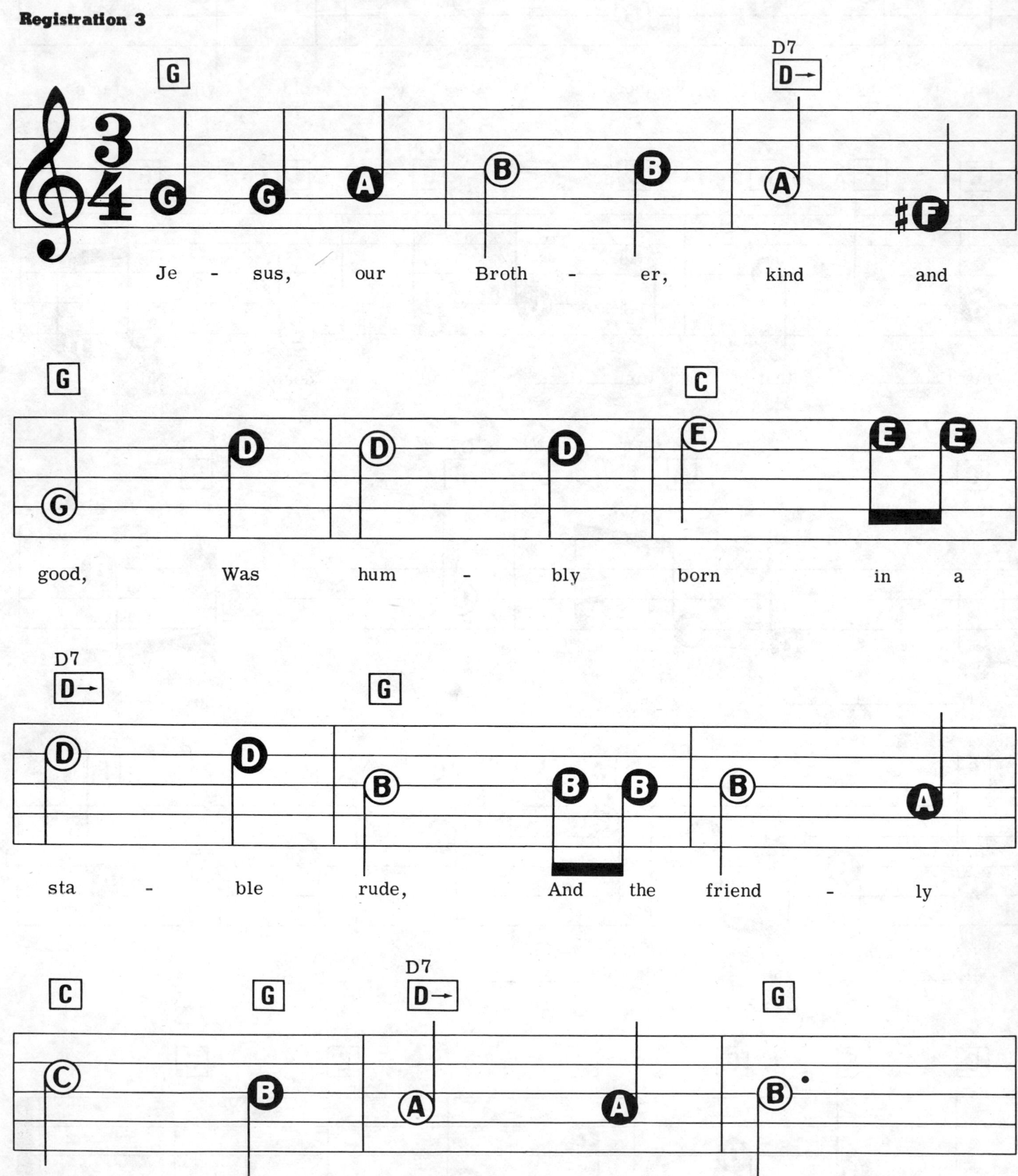

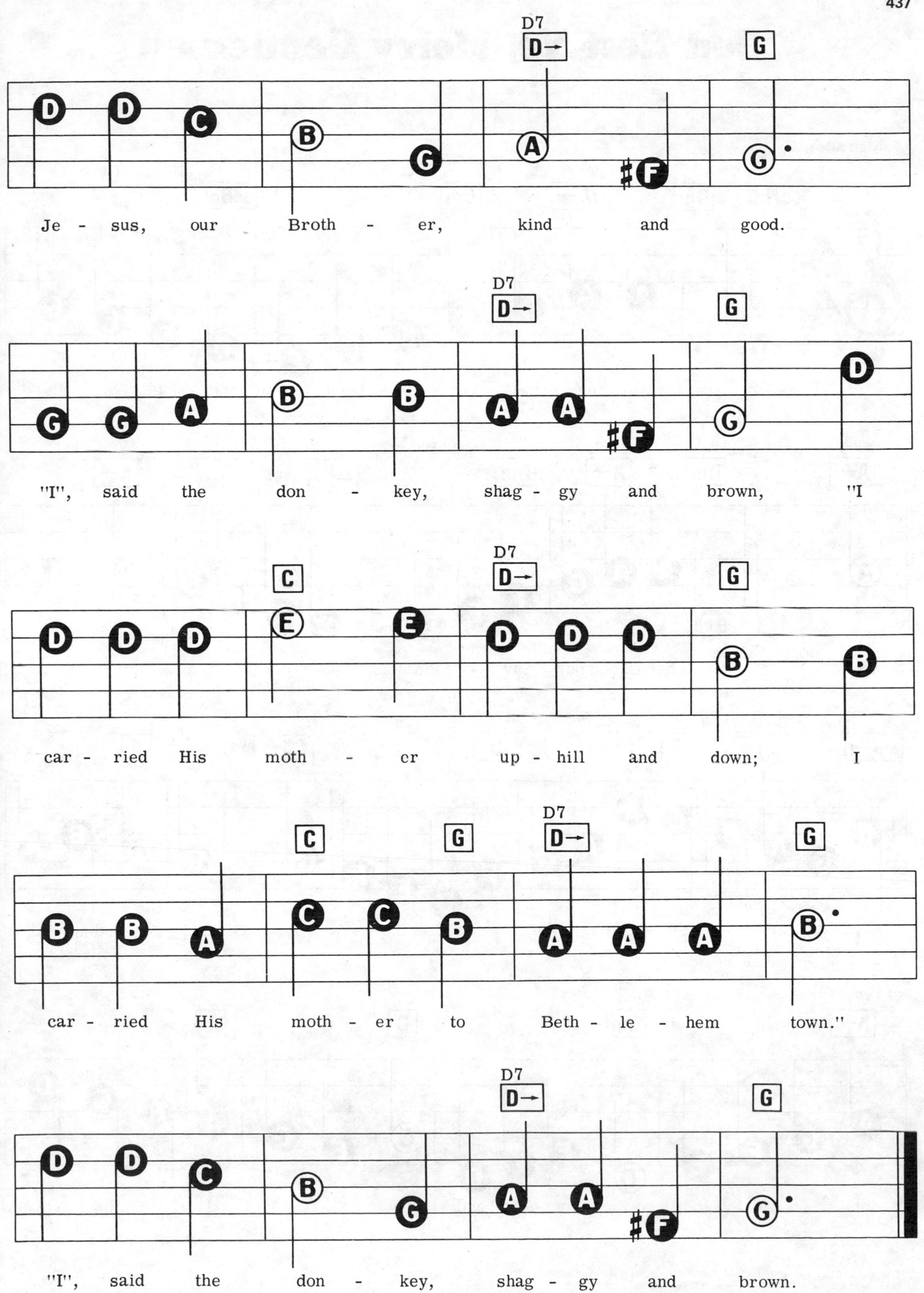
D7
D→
G
D D C B G A ♯F G
Je - sus, our Broth - er, kind and good.
D7
D→
G
G G A B B A A ♯F G D
"I", said the don - key, shag - gy and brown, "I
C
D7
D→
G
D D D E E D D D B B
car - ried His moth - er up - hill and down; I
C
G
D7
D→
G
B B A C C B A A A B
car - ried His moth - er to Beth - le - hem town."
D7
D→
G
D D C B G A A ♯F G
"I", said the don - key, shag - gy and brown.

God Rest Ye, Merry Gentlemen

Registration 6

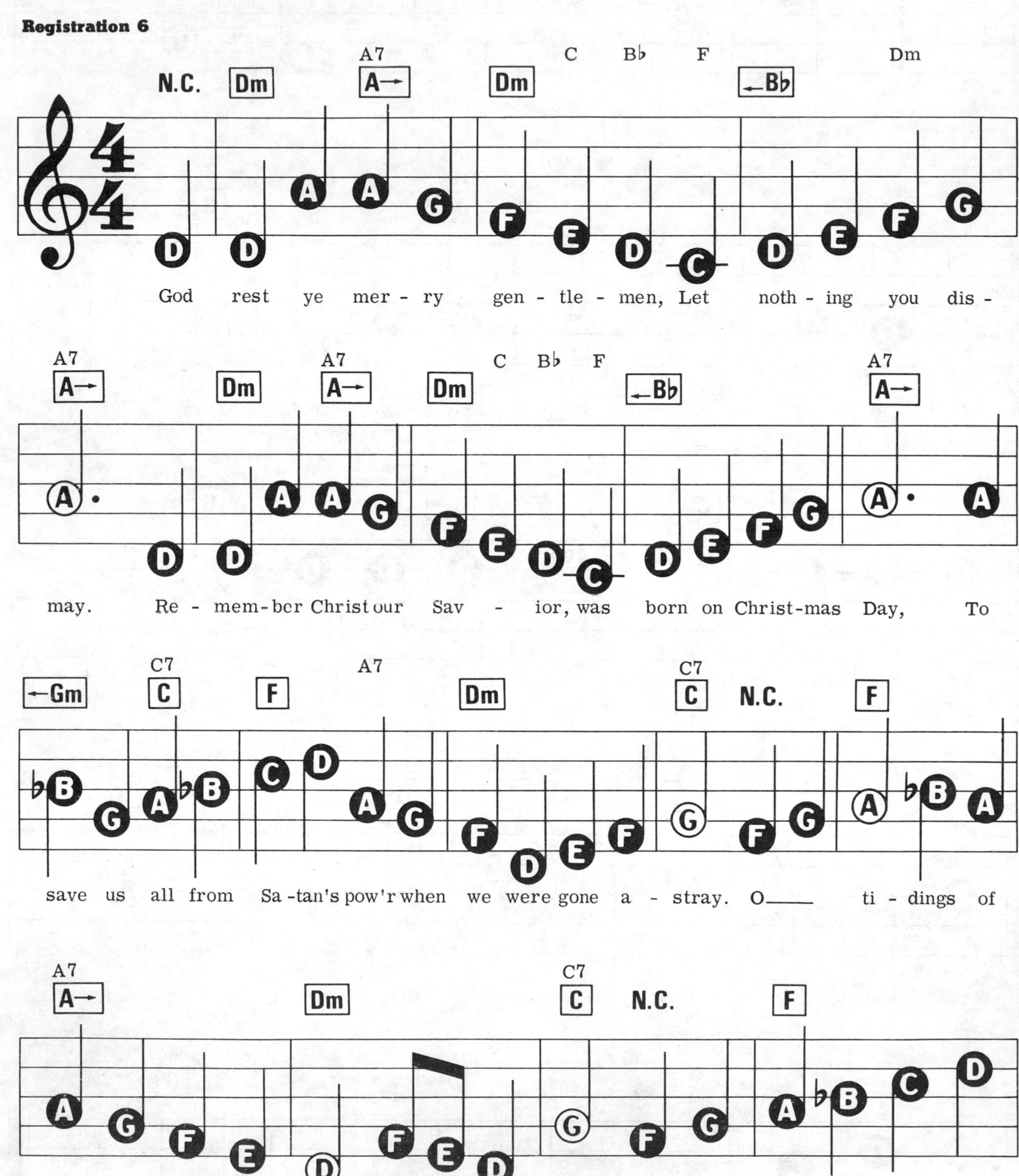

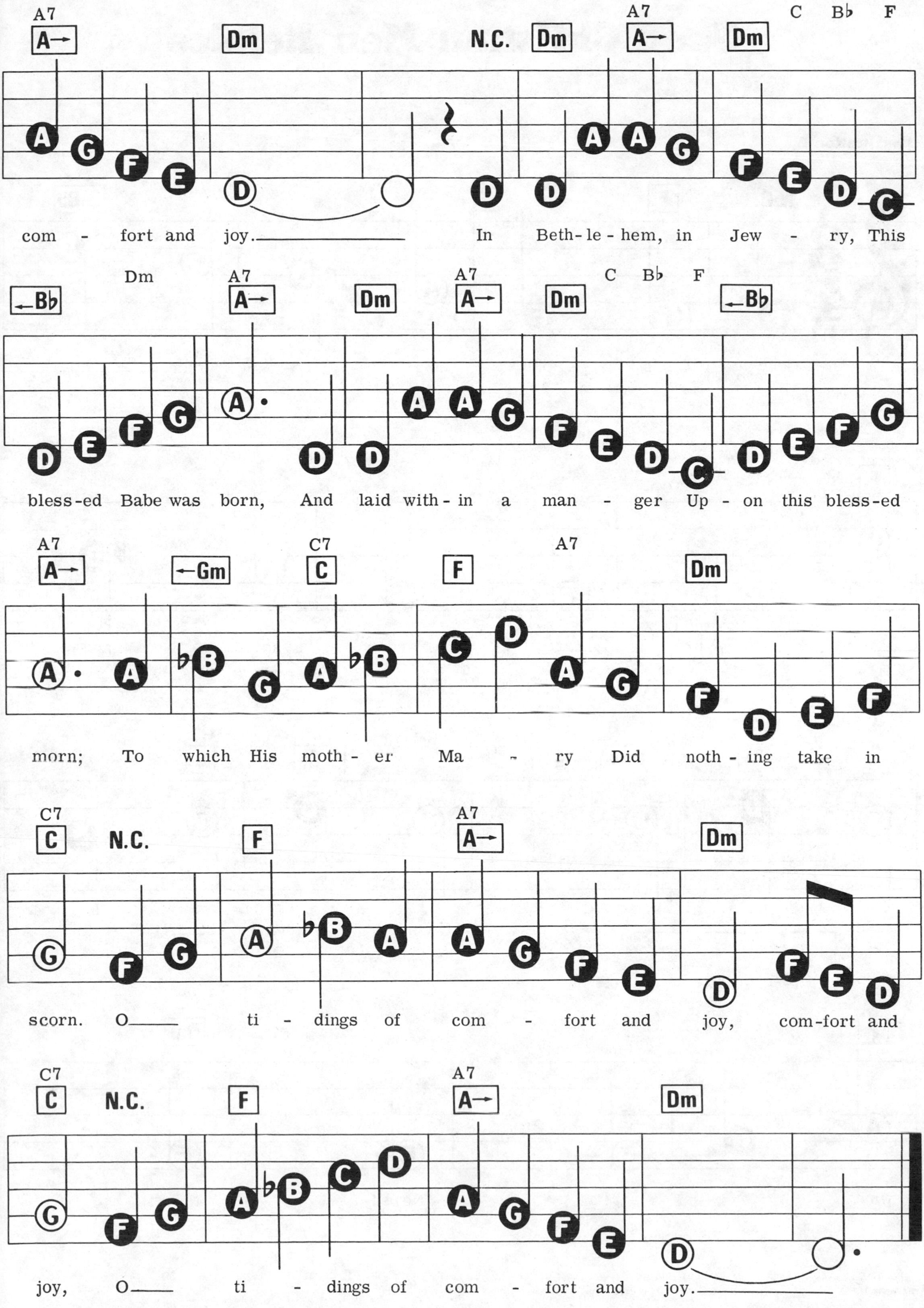

A7 Dm N.C. Dm A7 Dm C B♭ F

com - fort and joy. In Beth-le-hem, in Jew - ry, This

B♭ Dm A7 Dm A7 Dm C B♭ F B♭

bless-ed Babe was born, And laid with-in a man - ger Up - on this bless-ed

A7 Gm C7 F A7 Dm

morn; To which His moth - er Ma - ry Did noth-ing take in

C7 N.C. F A7 Dm

scorn. O ti - dings of com - fort and joy, com-fort and

C7 N.C. F A7 Dm

joy, O ti - dings of com - fort and joy.

Good Christian Men Rejoice

Registration 6

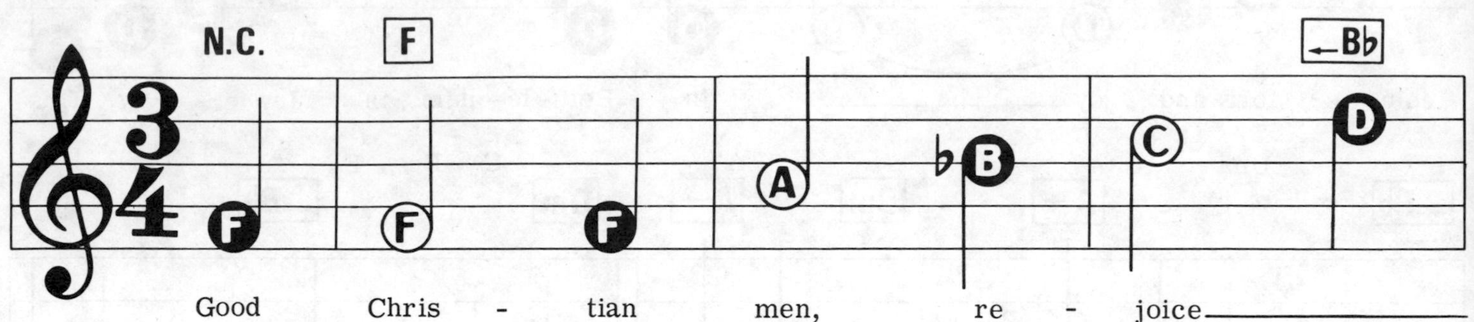

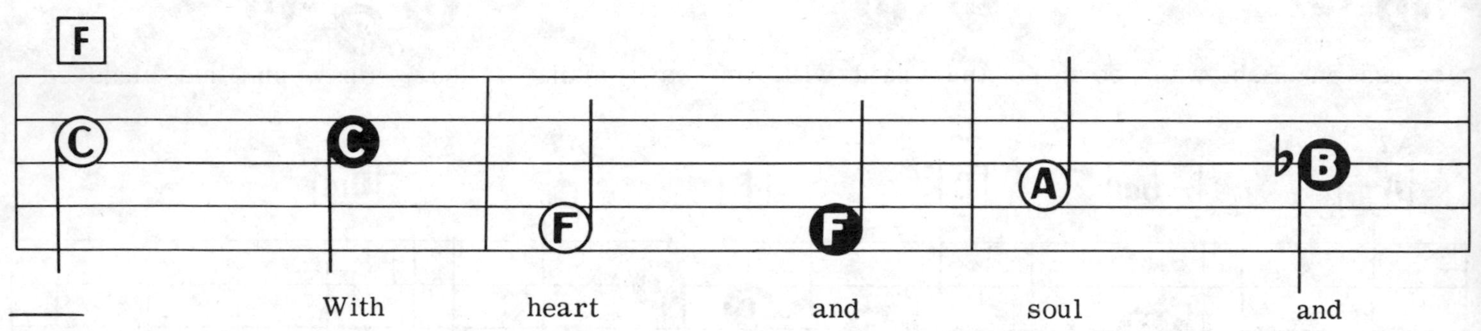

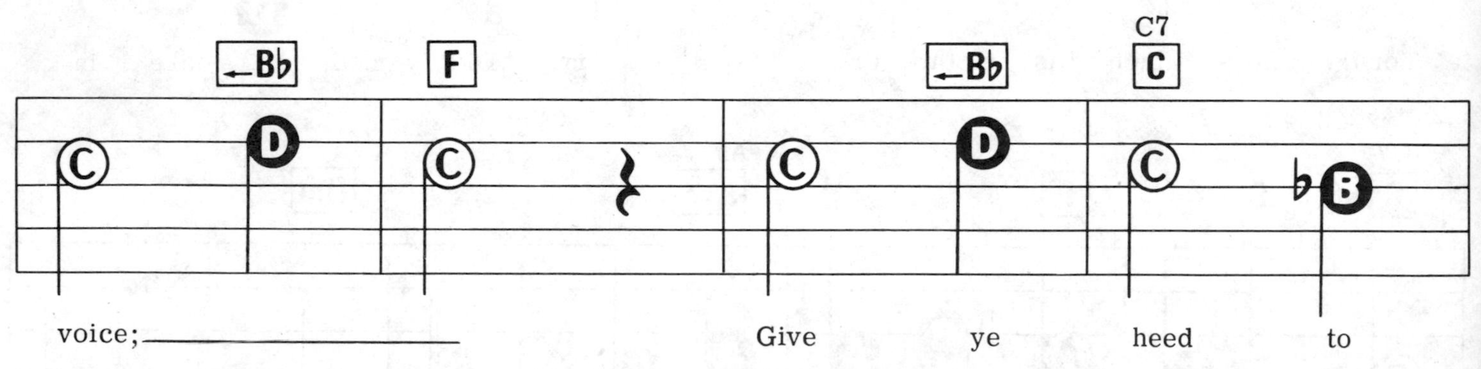

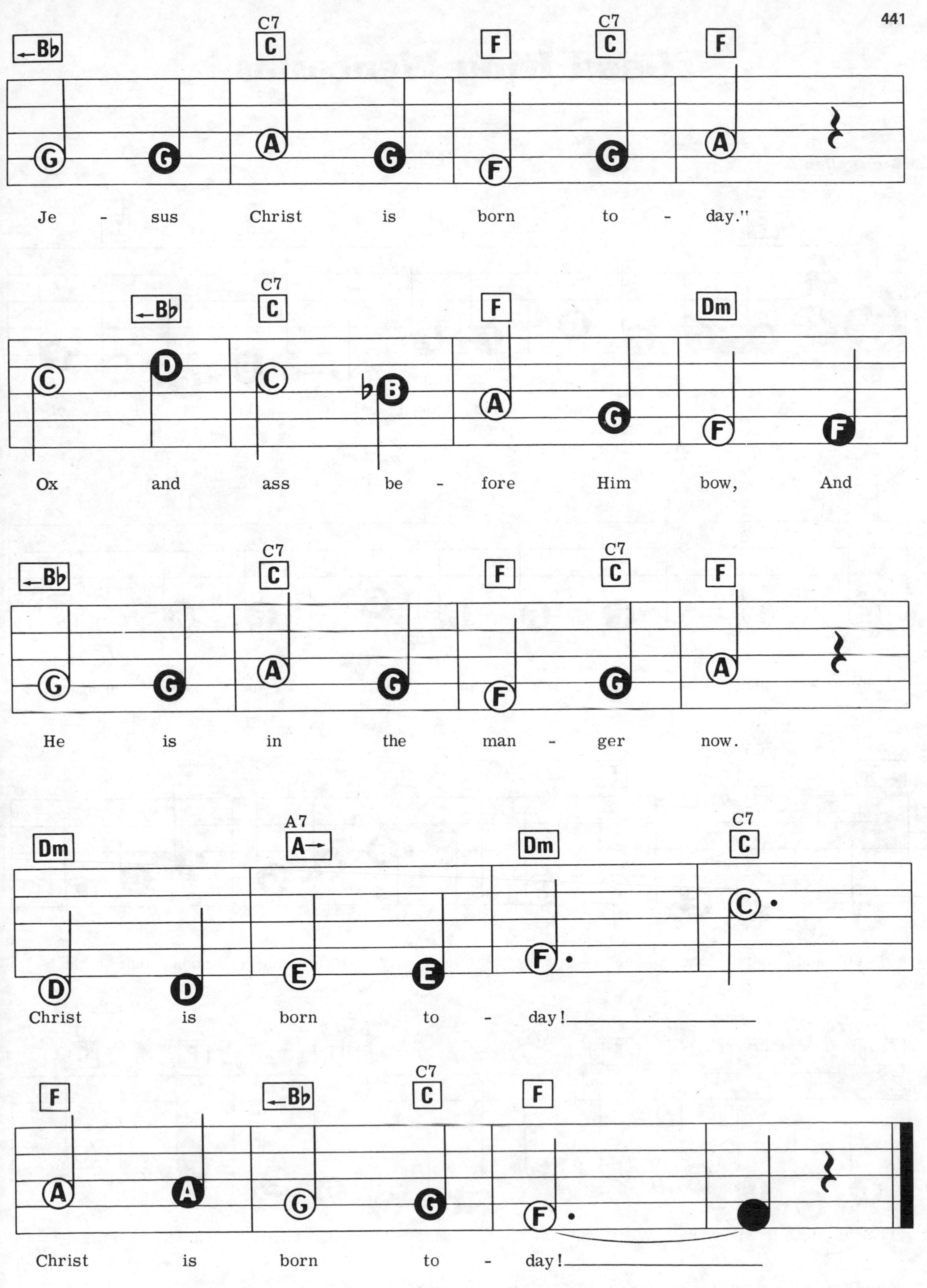
←B♭
C7
C
F
C7
C
F
G
G
A
G
F
G
A
Je - sus Christ is born to - day."
C7
←B♭
C
F
Dm
C
D
C
♭B
A
G
F
F
Ox and ass be - fore Him bow, And
←B♭
C7
C
F
C7
C
F
G
G
A
G
F
G
A
He is in the man - ger now.
Dm
A7
A→
Dm
C7
C
D
D
E
E
F
C
Christ is born to - day!
F
←B♭
C7
C
F
A
A
G
G
F
Christ is born to - day!

Good King Wenceslas

Registration 4

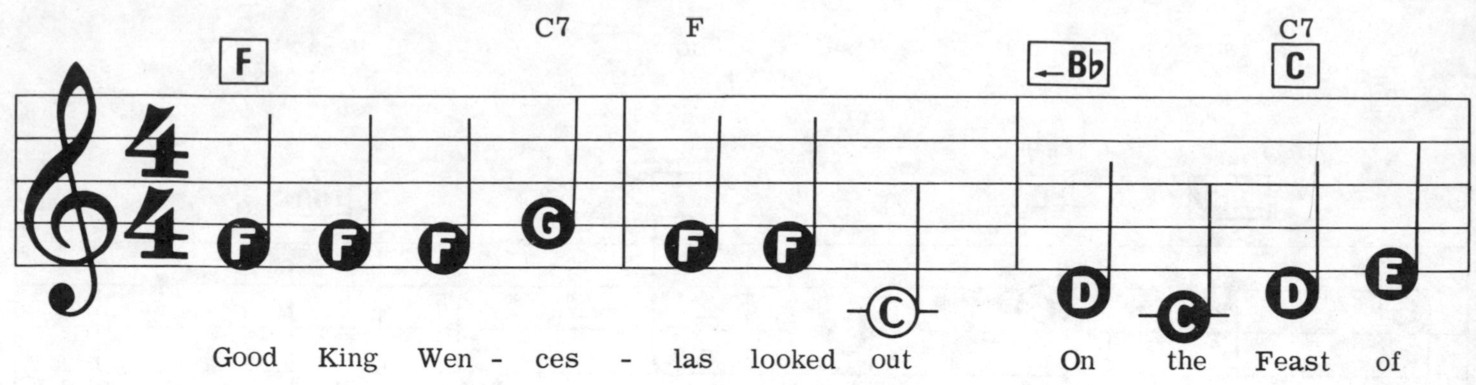

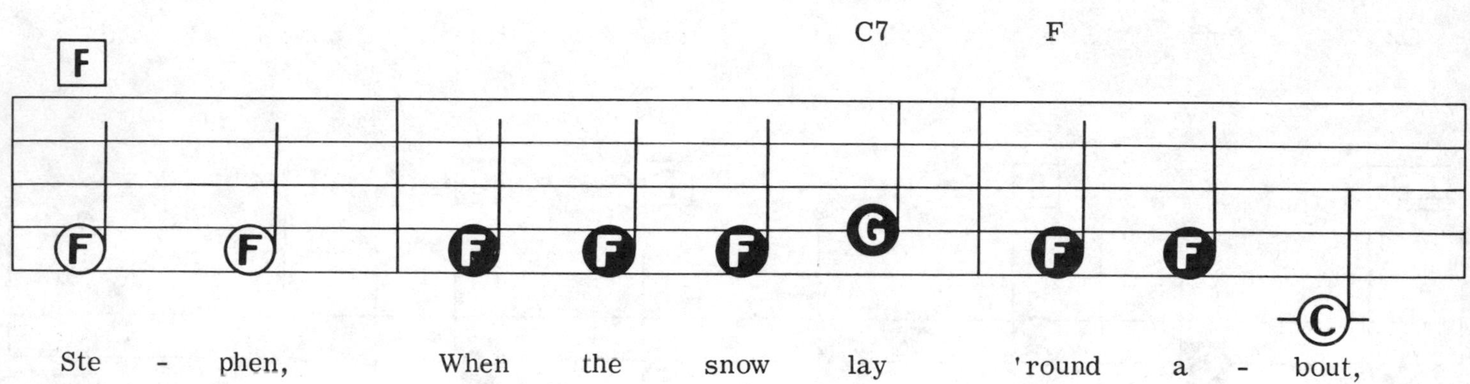

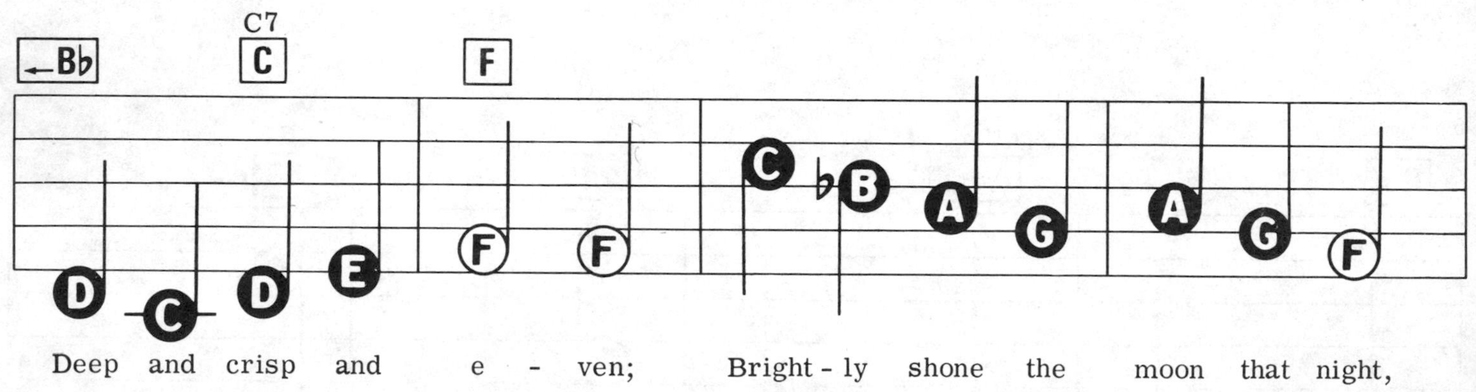

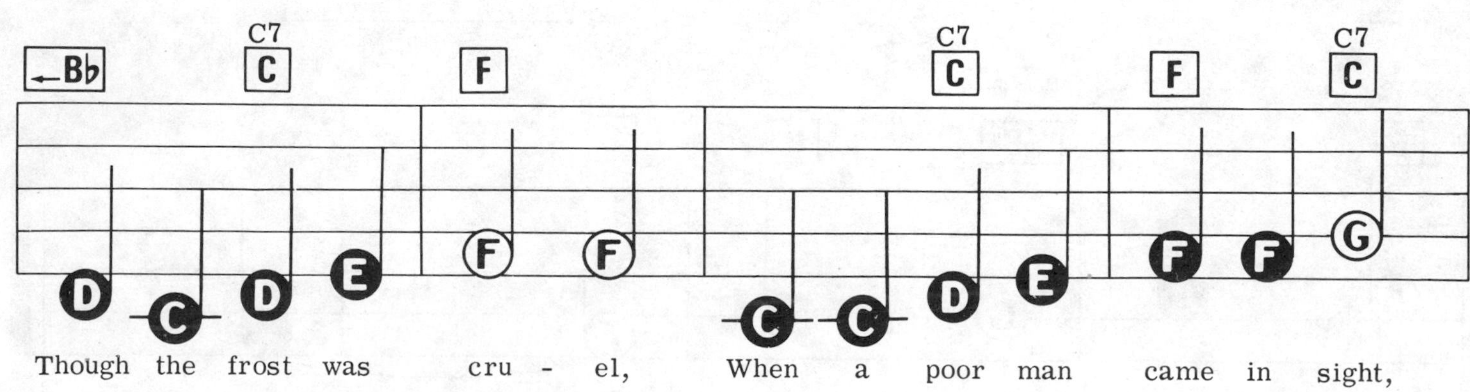

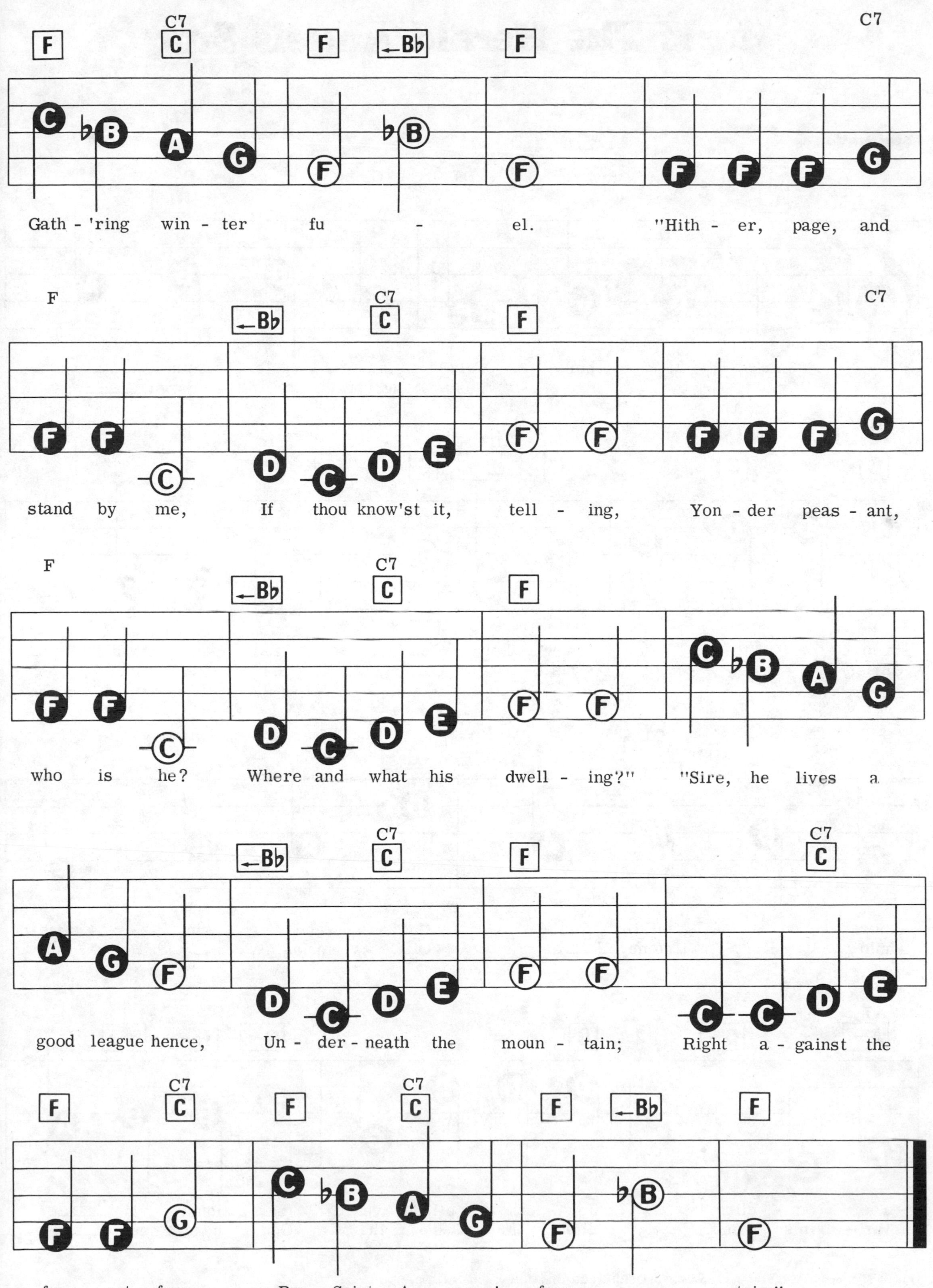
F C7 C F ←B♭ F C7
C B A G F B F F F F G
Gath - 'ring win - ter fu - el. "Hith - er, page, and
F ←B♭ C7 C F C7
F F C D C D E F F F F F G
stand by me, If thou know'st it, tell - ing, Yon - der peas - ant,
F ←B♭ C7 C F
F F C D C D E F F C B A G
who is he? Where and what his dwell - ing?" "Sire, he lives a
←B♭ C7 C F C7 C
A G F D C D E F F C C D E
good league hence, Un - der - neath the moun - tain; Right a - gainst the
F C7 C F C7 C F ←B♭ F
F F G C B A G F B F
for - est fence, By Saint Ag - nes' foun - tain."

Hark! The Herald Angels Sing

Registration 5

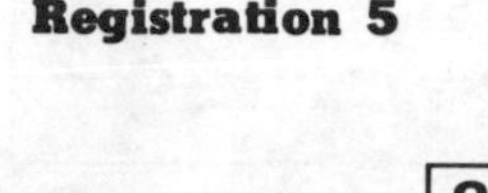

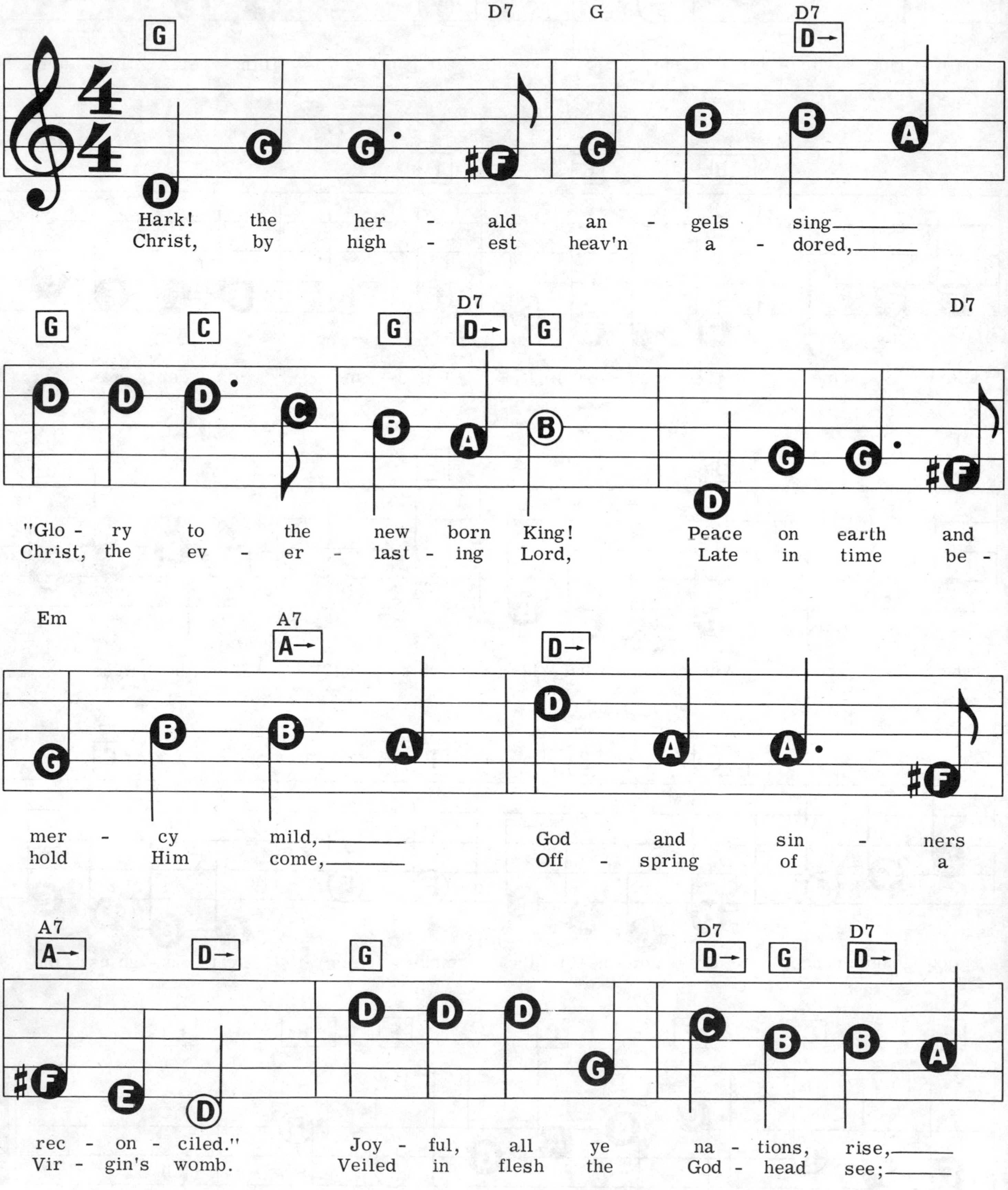

G D7 G D7

Hark! the her - ald an - gels sing
Christ, by high - est heav'n a - dored,

G C G D7 G D7

"Glo - ry to the new born King!
Christ, the ev - er - last - ing Lord,

Peace on earth and
Late in time be -

Em A7

mer - cy mild,
hold Him come,

God and sin - ners
Off - spring of a

A7 G D7 G D7

rec - on - ciled."
Vir - gin's womb.

Joy - ful, all ye na - tions, rise,
Veiled in flesh the God - head see;

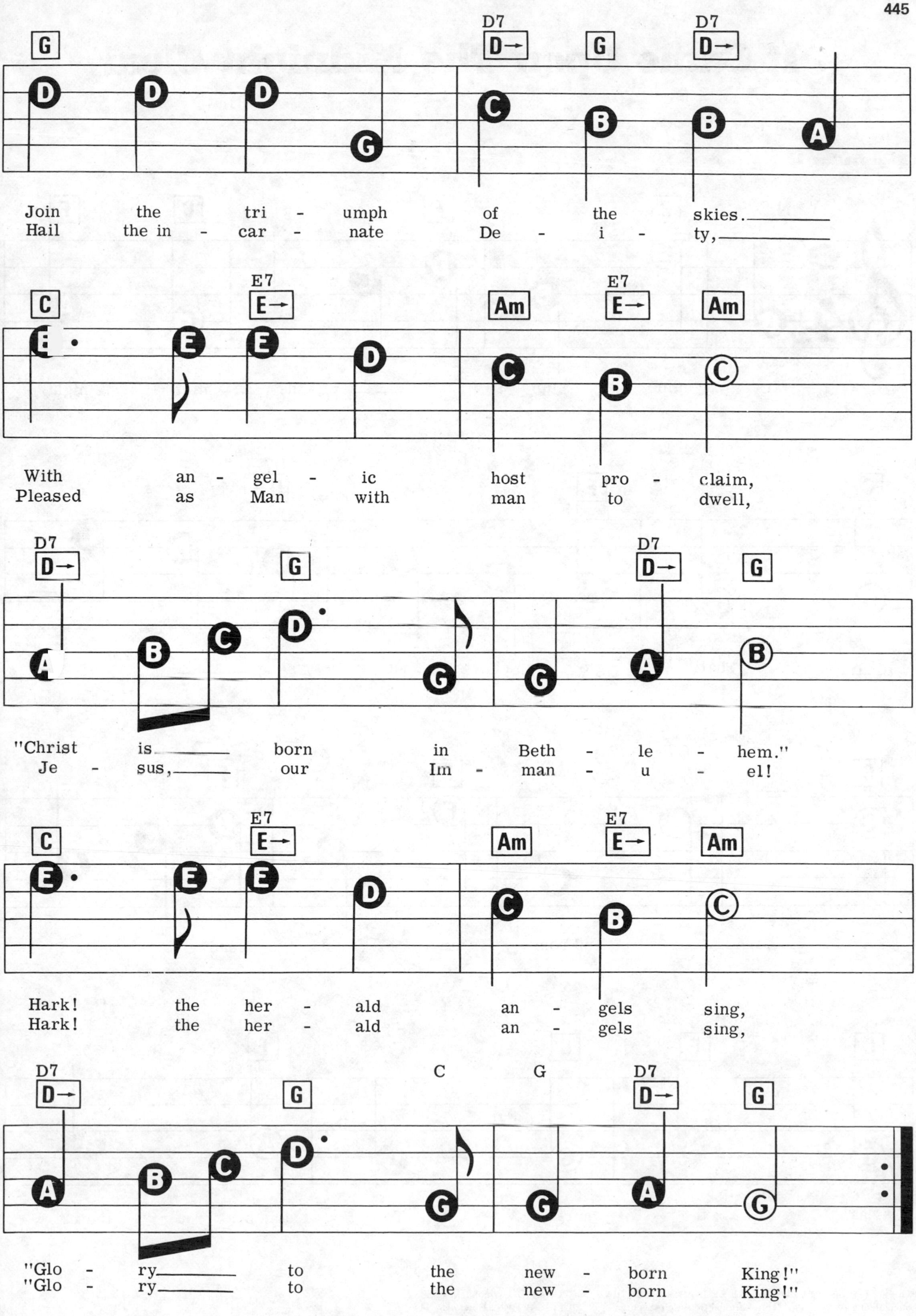

G D7 D→ G D7 D→

D D D G C B B A

Join the tri - umph of the skies. ___
Hail the in - car - nate De - i - ty, ___

C E7 E→ Am E7 E→ Am

E E E D C B C

With an - gel - ic host pro - claim,
Pleased as Man with man to dwell,

D7 D→ G D7 D→ G

A B C D G G A B

"Christ is ___ born in Beth - le - hem."
Je - sus, ___ our Im - man - u - el!

C E7 E→ Am E7 E→ Am

E E E D C B C

Hark! the her - ald an - gels sing,
Hark! the her - ald an - gels sing,

D7 D→ G C G D7 D→ G

A B C D G G A G

"Glo - ry ___ to the new - born King!"
"Glo - ry ___ to the new - born King!"

It Came Upon The Midnight Clear

Registration 1

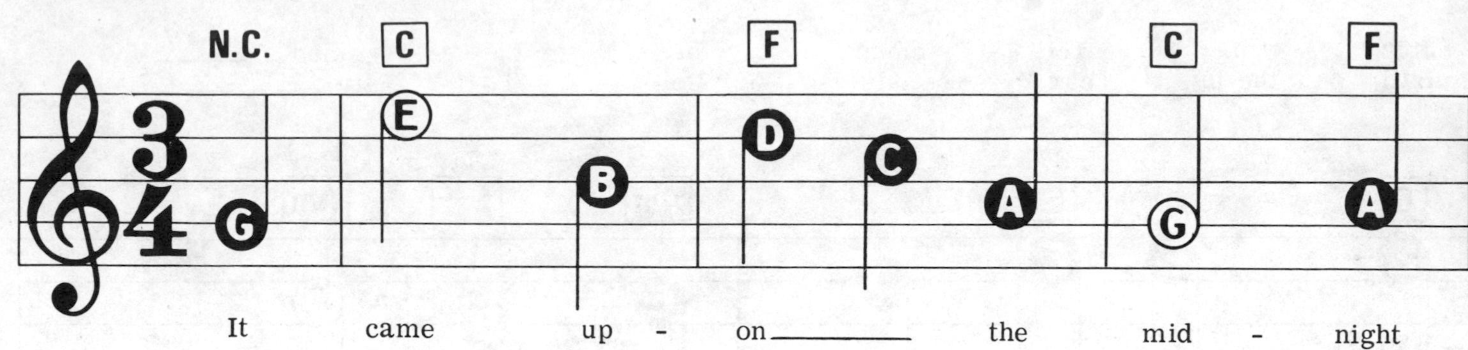

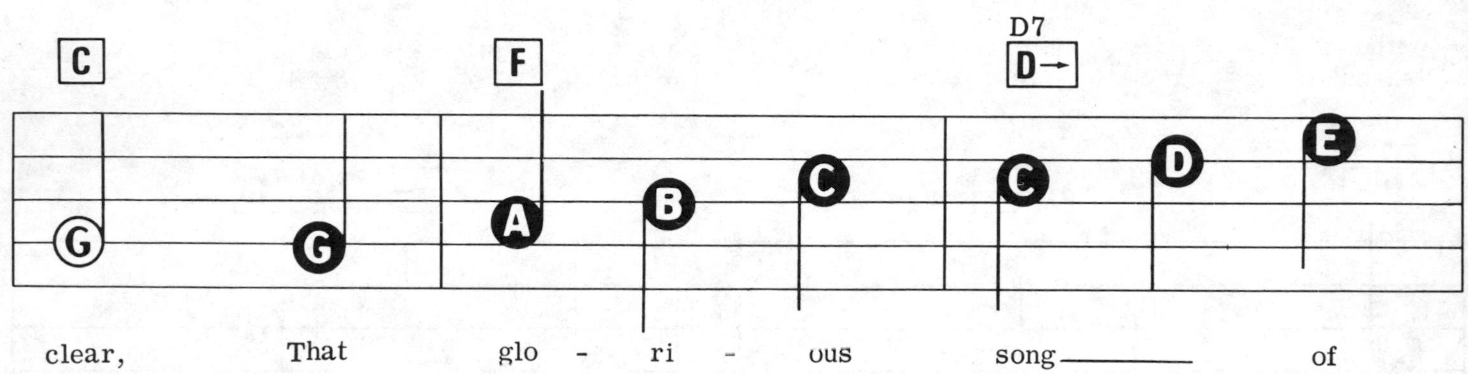

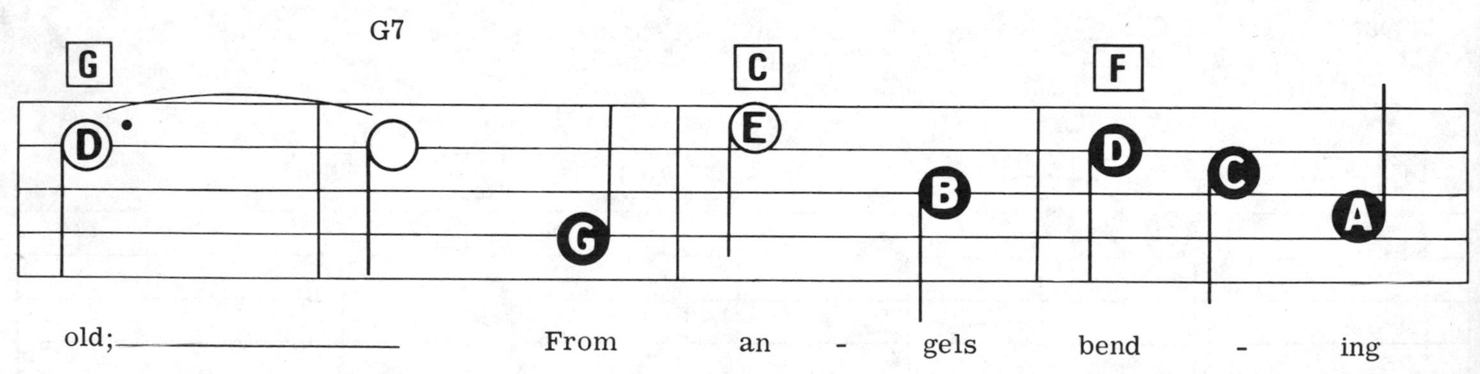

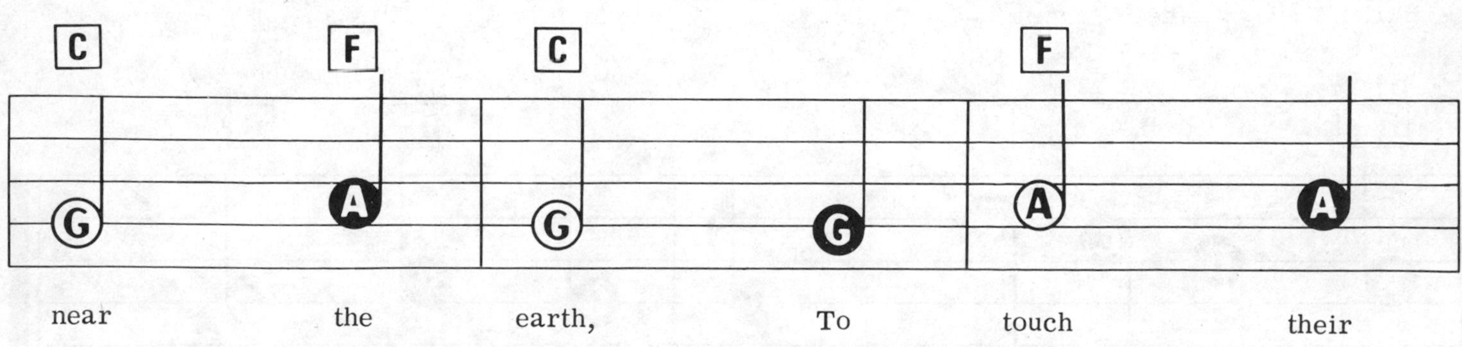

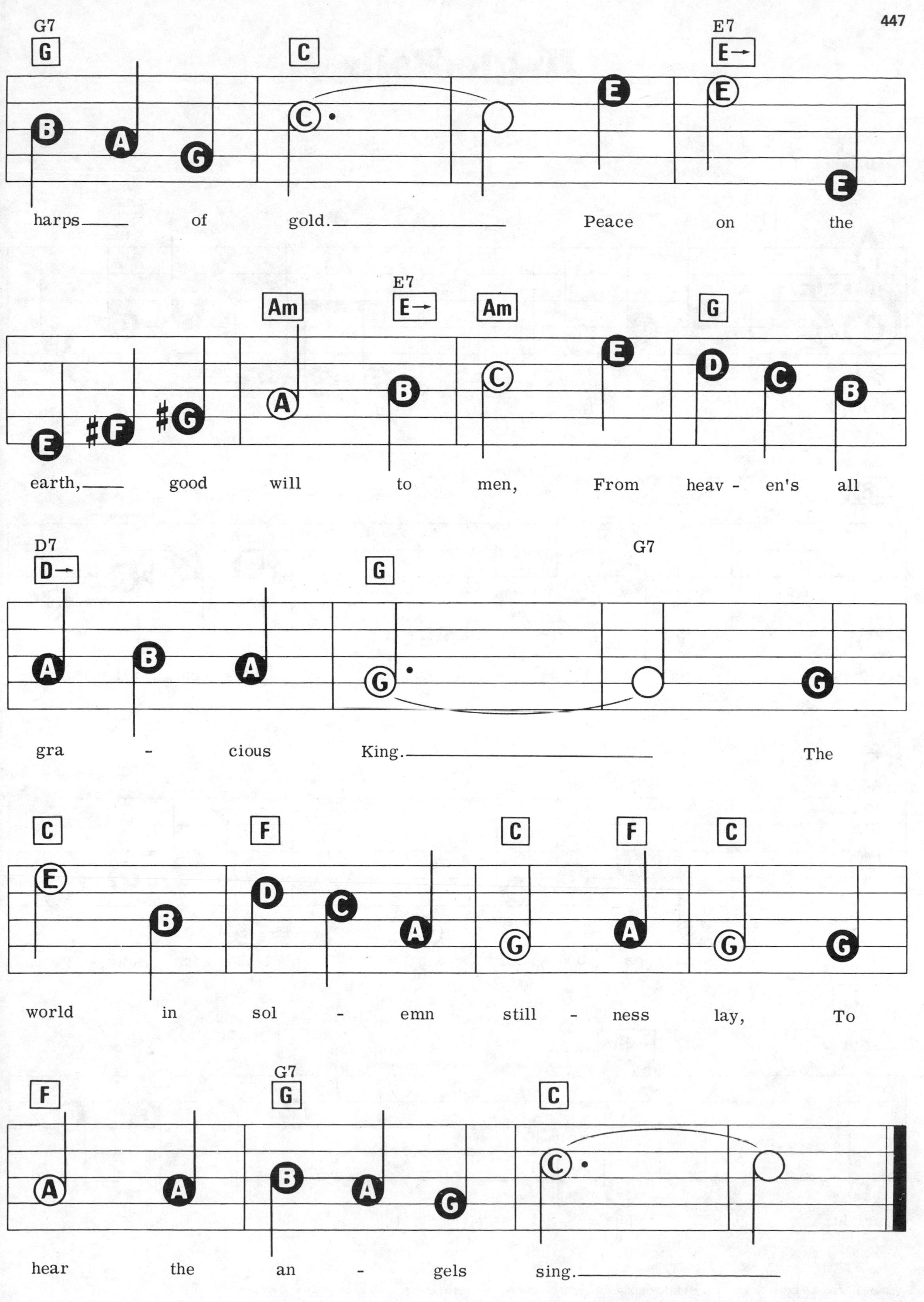
G7 G C E7 E→
harps___ of gold.___ Peace on the
Am E7 E→ Am G
earth,___ good will to men, From heav - en's all
D7 D→ G G7
gra - cious King.___ The
C F C F C
world in sol - emn still - ness lay, To
F G7 G C
hear the an - gels sing.___

Jingle Bells

Registration 5

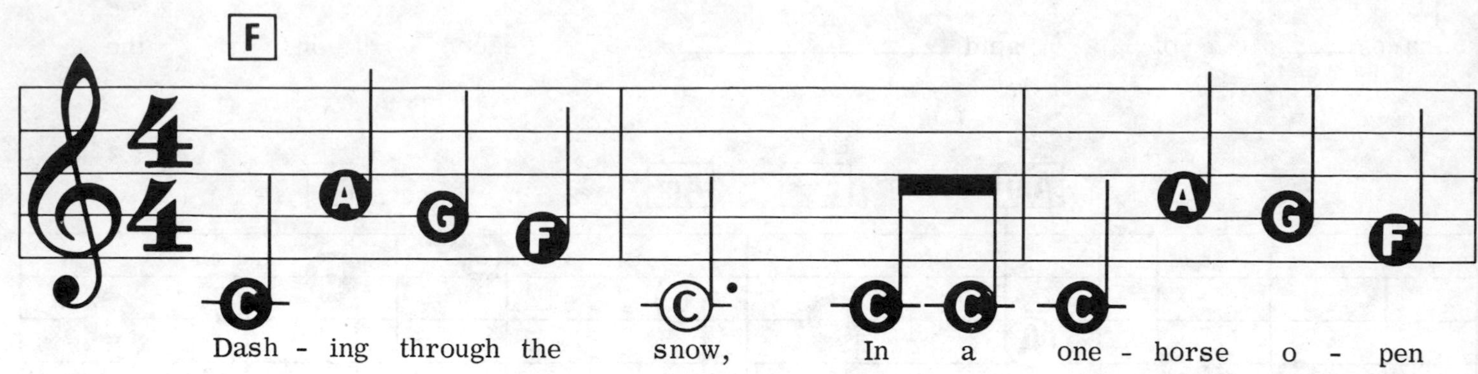

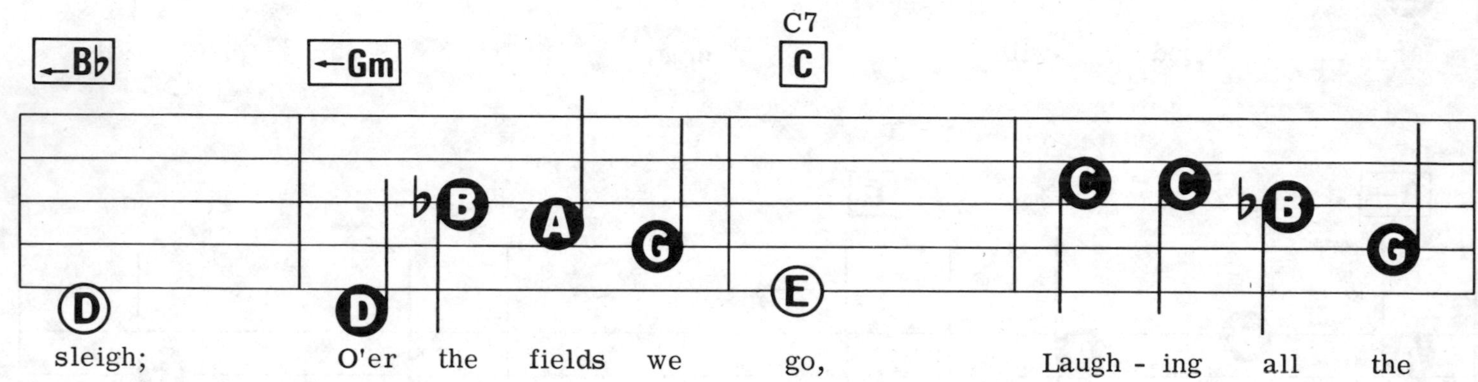

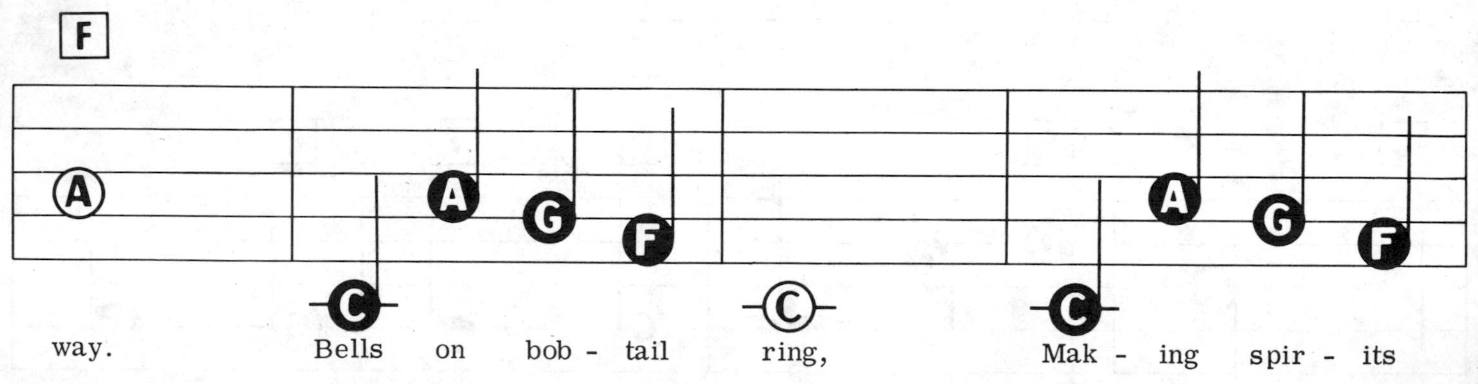

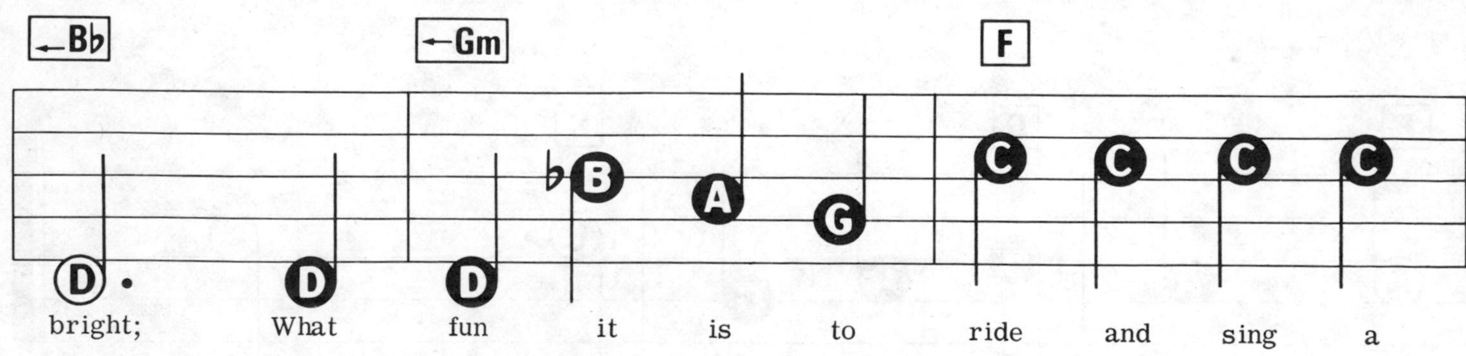

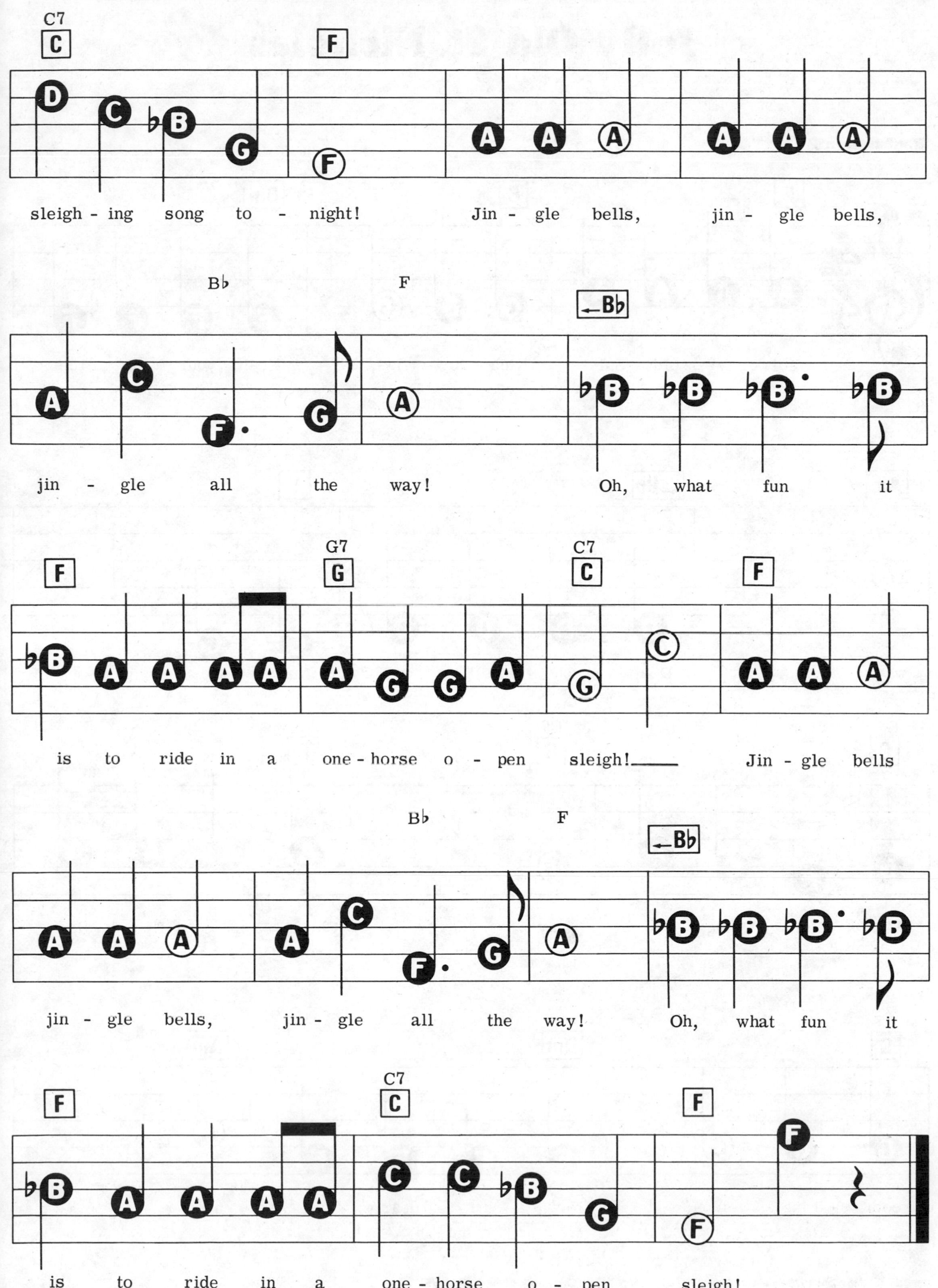
C7
sleigh - ing song to - night!
Jin - gle bells, jin - gle bells,
B♭ F
jin - gle all the way!
Oh, what fun it
G7 C7
is to ride in a one - horse o - pen sleigh!
Jin - gle bells
B♭ F
jin - gle bells, jin - gle all the way!
Oh, what fun it
C7
is to ride in a one - horse o - pen sleigh!

Jolly Old St. Nicholas

Registration 2

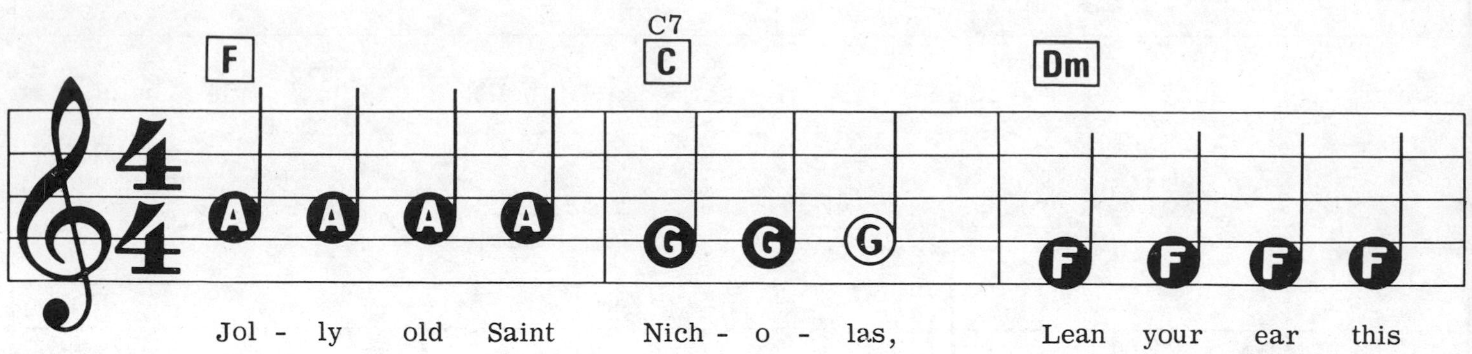

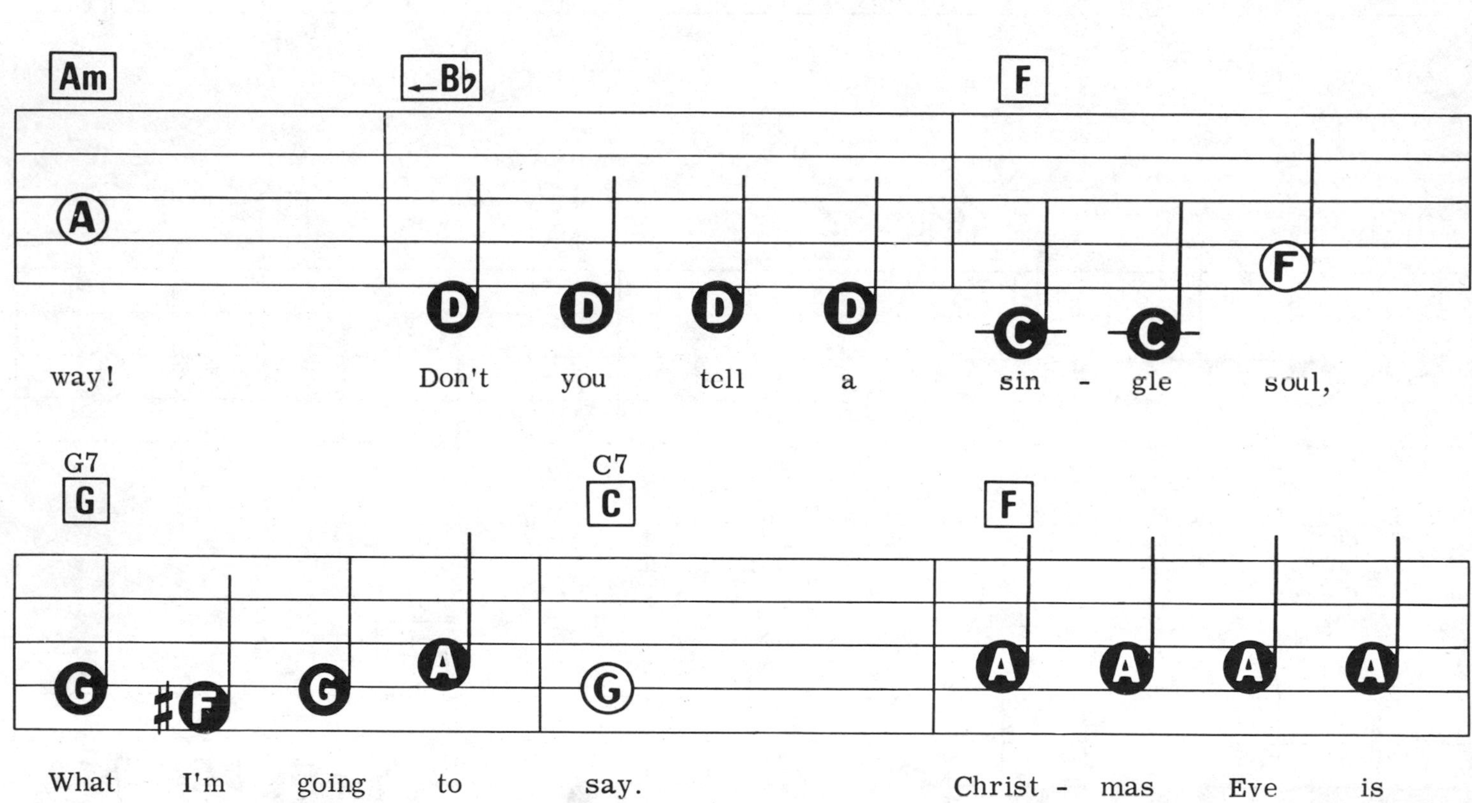

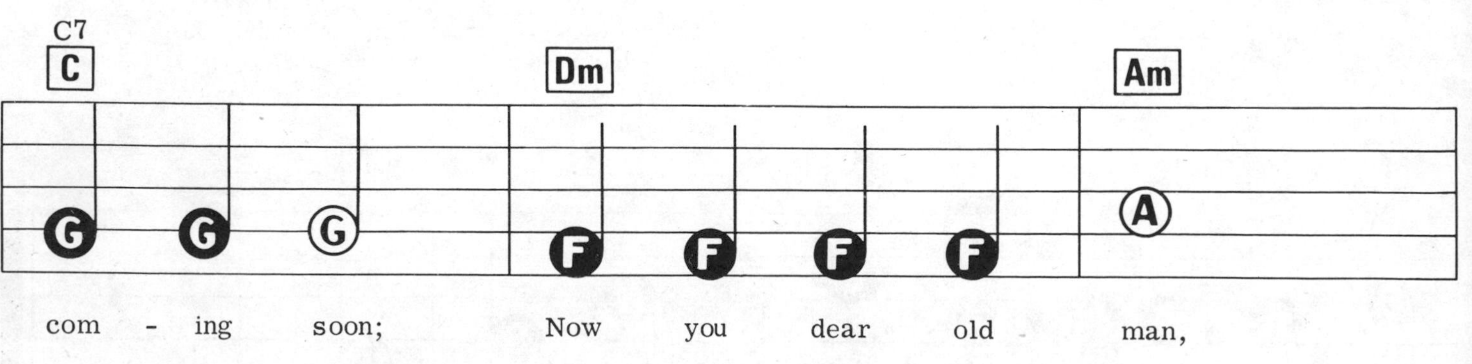

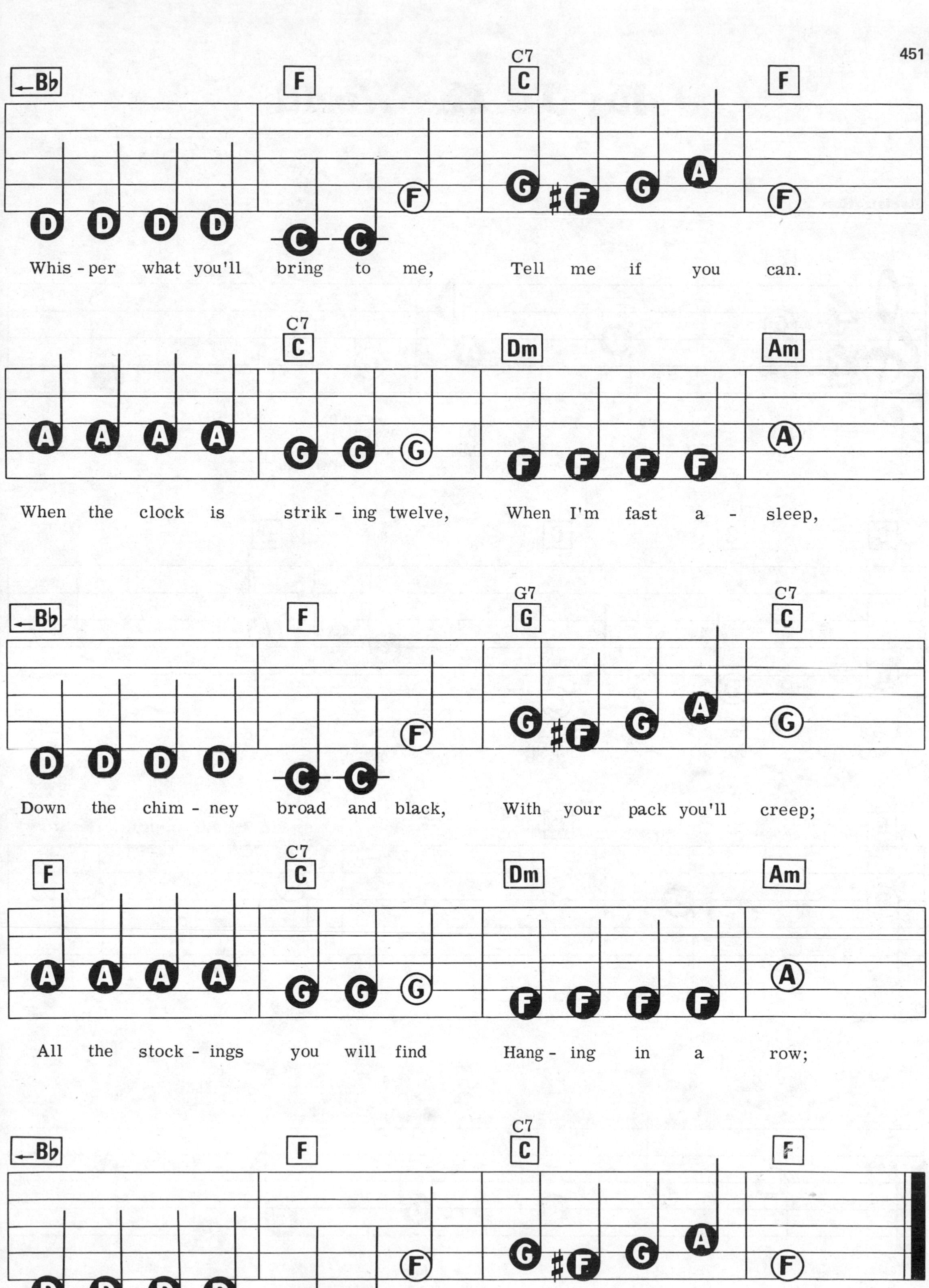
Bb
F
C7
C
F
D D D D C C F G F G A F
Whis - per what you'll bring to me, Tell me if you can.
C7
C
Dm
Am
A A A A G G G F F F F A
When the clock is strik - ing twelve, When I'm fast a - sleep,
Bb
F
G7
G
C7
C
D D D D C C F G F G A G
Down the chim - ney broad and black, With your pack you'll creep;
F
C7
C
Dm
Am
A A A A G G G F F F F A
All the stock - ings you will find Hang - ing in a row;
Bb
F
C7
C
F
D D D D C C F G F G A F
Mine will be the short - est one, You'll be sure to know.

Joy To The World

Registration 2

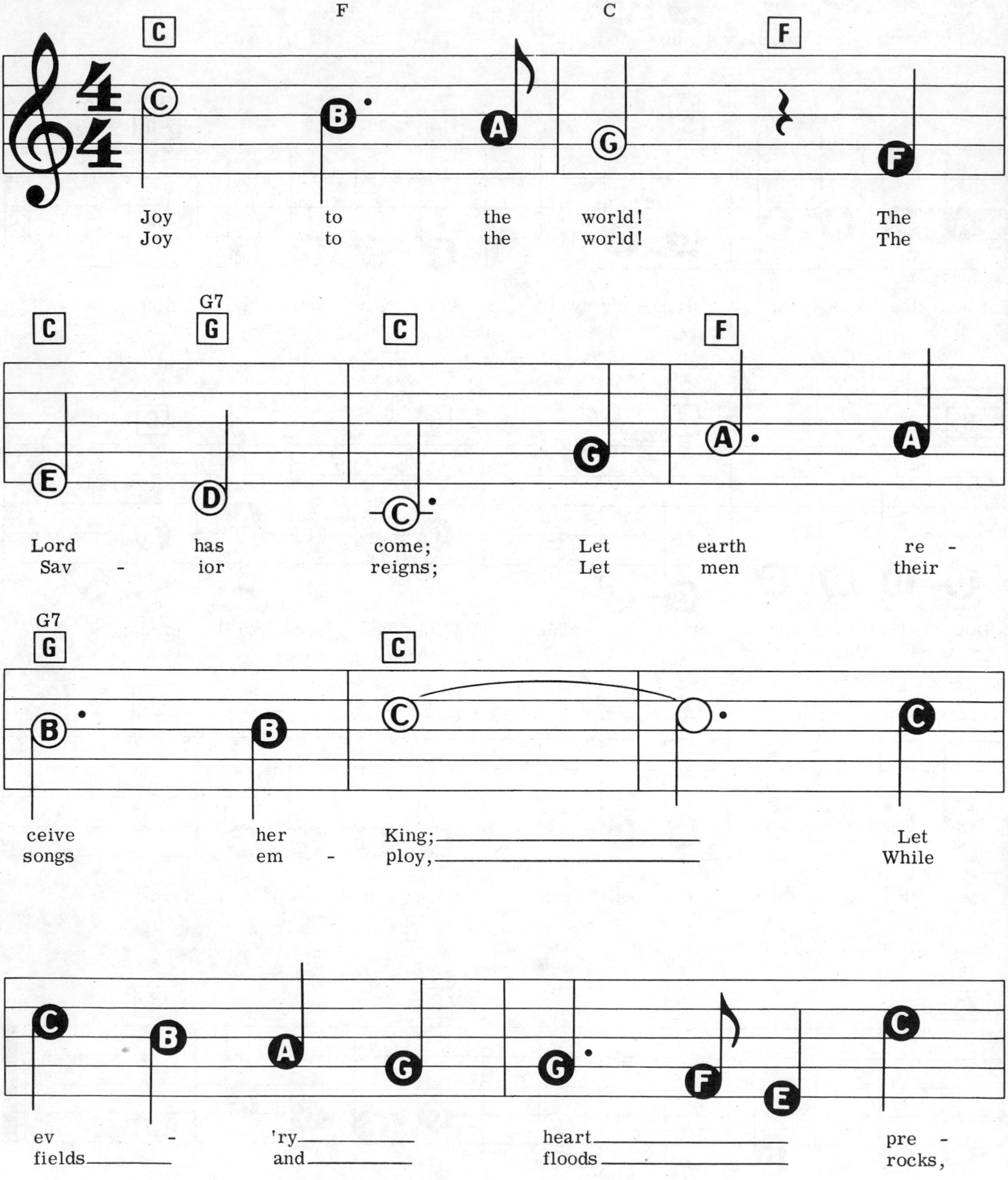

C F C F

C B A G F

Joy to the world! The
Joy to the world! The

C G7 G C F

E D C G A A

Lord has come; Let earth re -
Sav - ior reigns; Let men their

G7 G C

B B C C

ceive her King;
songs em - ploy,

Let
While

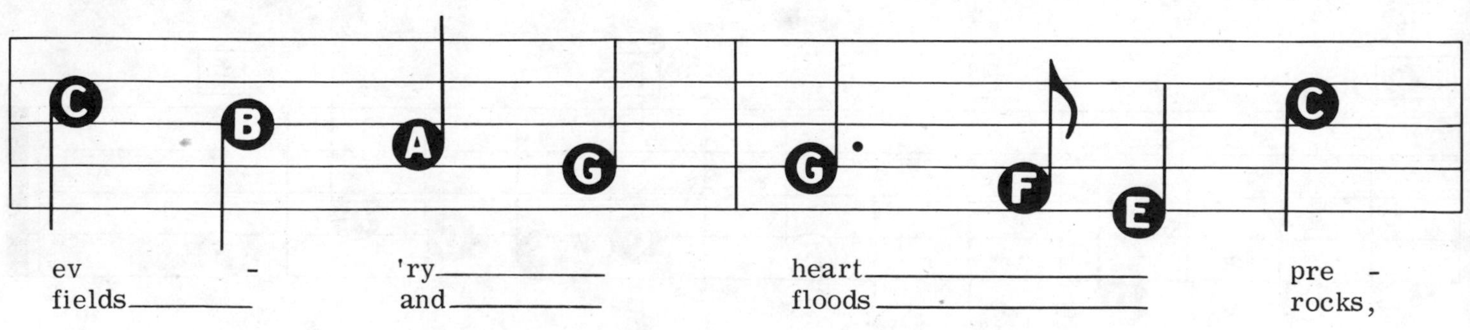

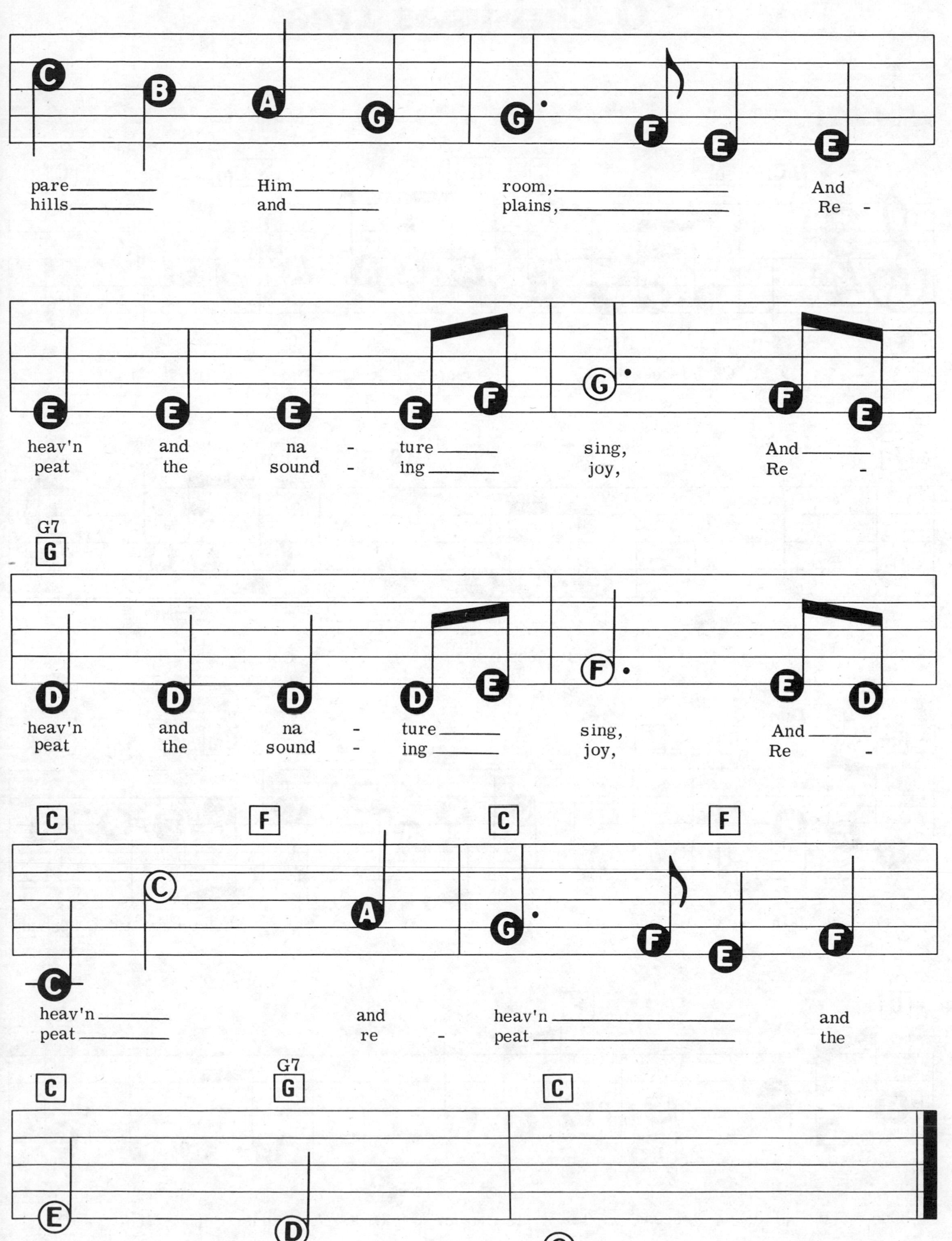
C B A G G F E E
pare hills Him and room, plains, And Re -
E E E E F G F E
heav'n and na - ture sing, And
peat the sound - ing joy, Re -
G7
G
D D D D E F E D
heav'n and na - ture sing, And
peat the sound - ing joy, Re -
C F C F
C C A G F E F
heav'n and heav'n and
peat re - peat the
C G7 G C
E D C
na - ture sing!
sound - ing joy.

O Christmas Tree

Registration 3

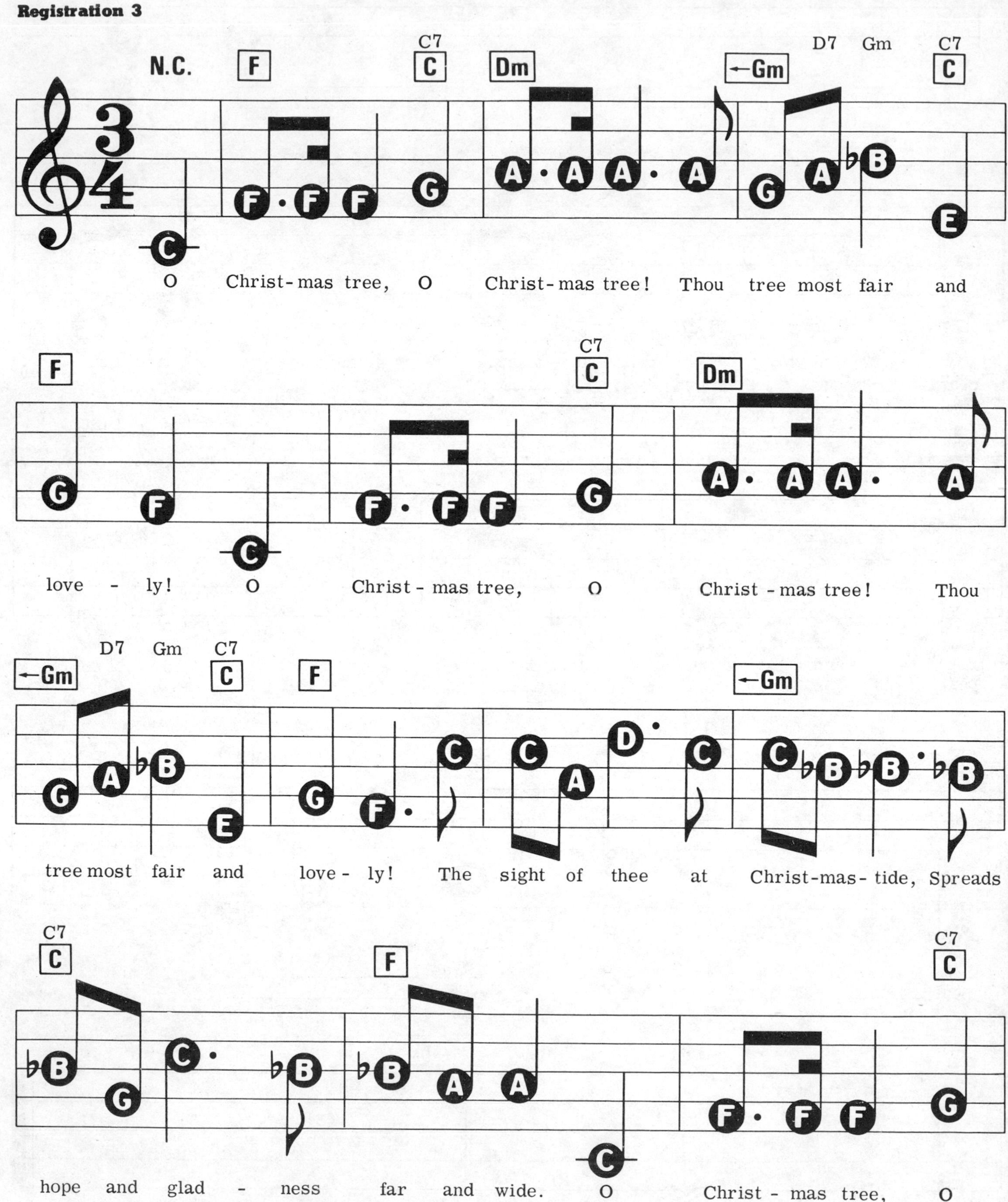

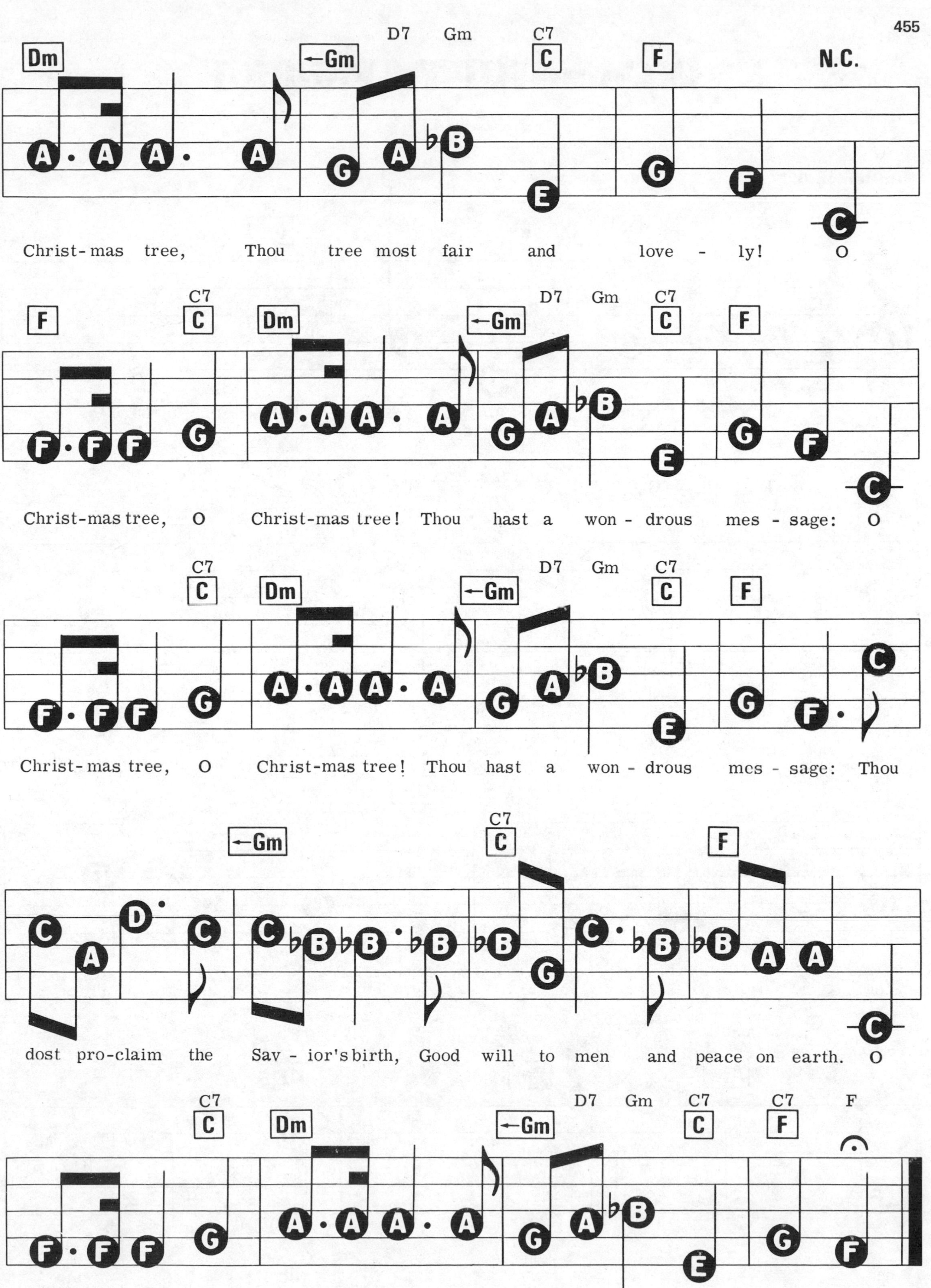
Dm ←Gm D7 Gm C7 C F N.C.
Christ-mas tree, Thou tree most fair and love - ly! O
F C7 C Dm ←Gm D7 Gm C7 C F
Christ-mas tree, O Christ-mas tree! Thou hast a won - drous mes - sage: O
C7 C Dm ←Gm D7 Gm C7 C F
Christ-mas tree, O Christ-mas tree! Thou hast a won - drous mes - sage: Thou
←Gm C7 C F
dost pro-claim the Sav - ior's birth, Good will to men and peace on earth. O
C7 C Dm ←Gm D7 Gm C7 C C7 F F
Christ-mas tree, O Christ-mas tree! Thou hast a won - drous mes - sage.

O Come All Ye Faithful

Registration 6

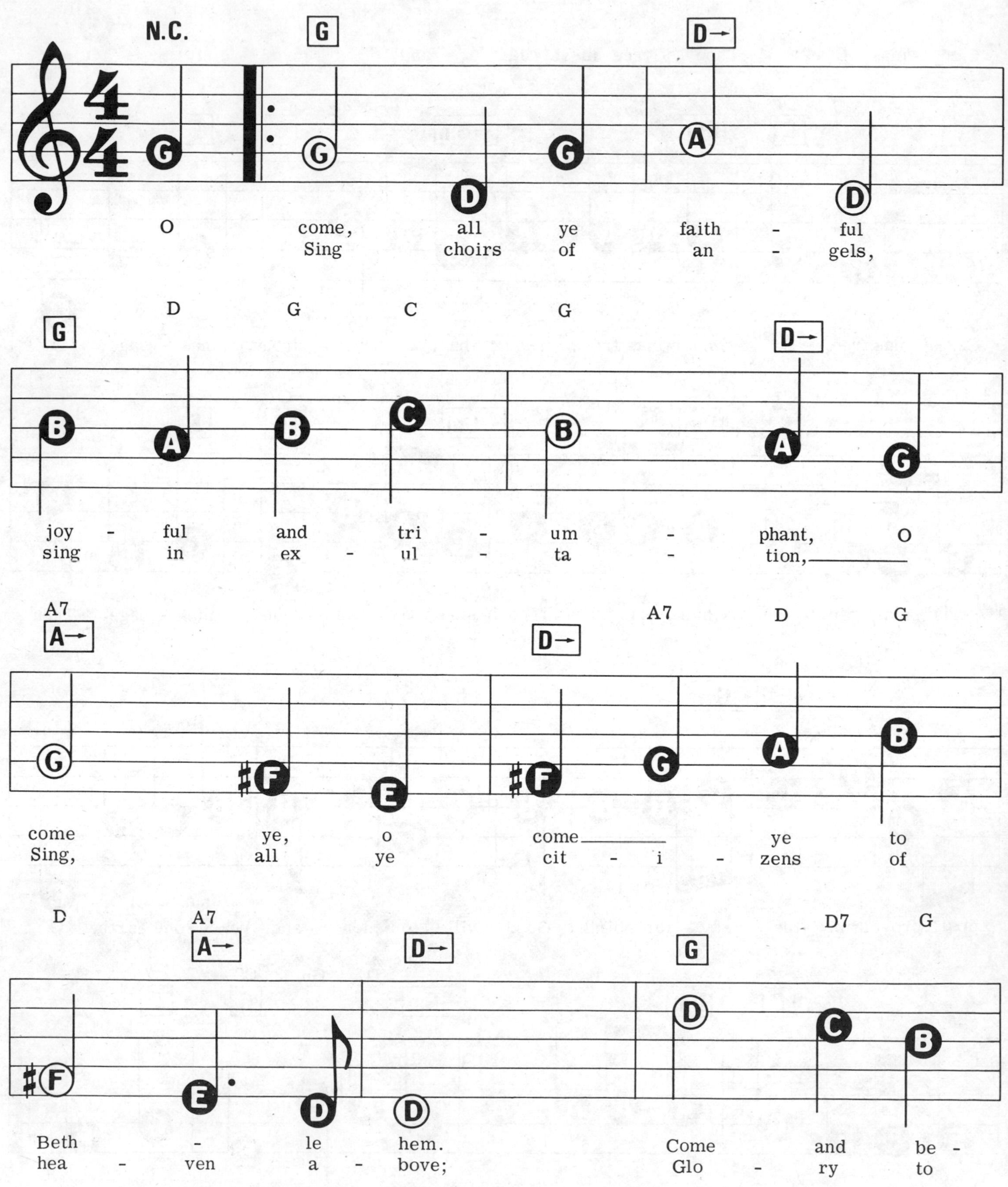

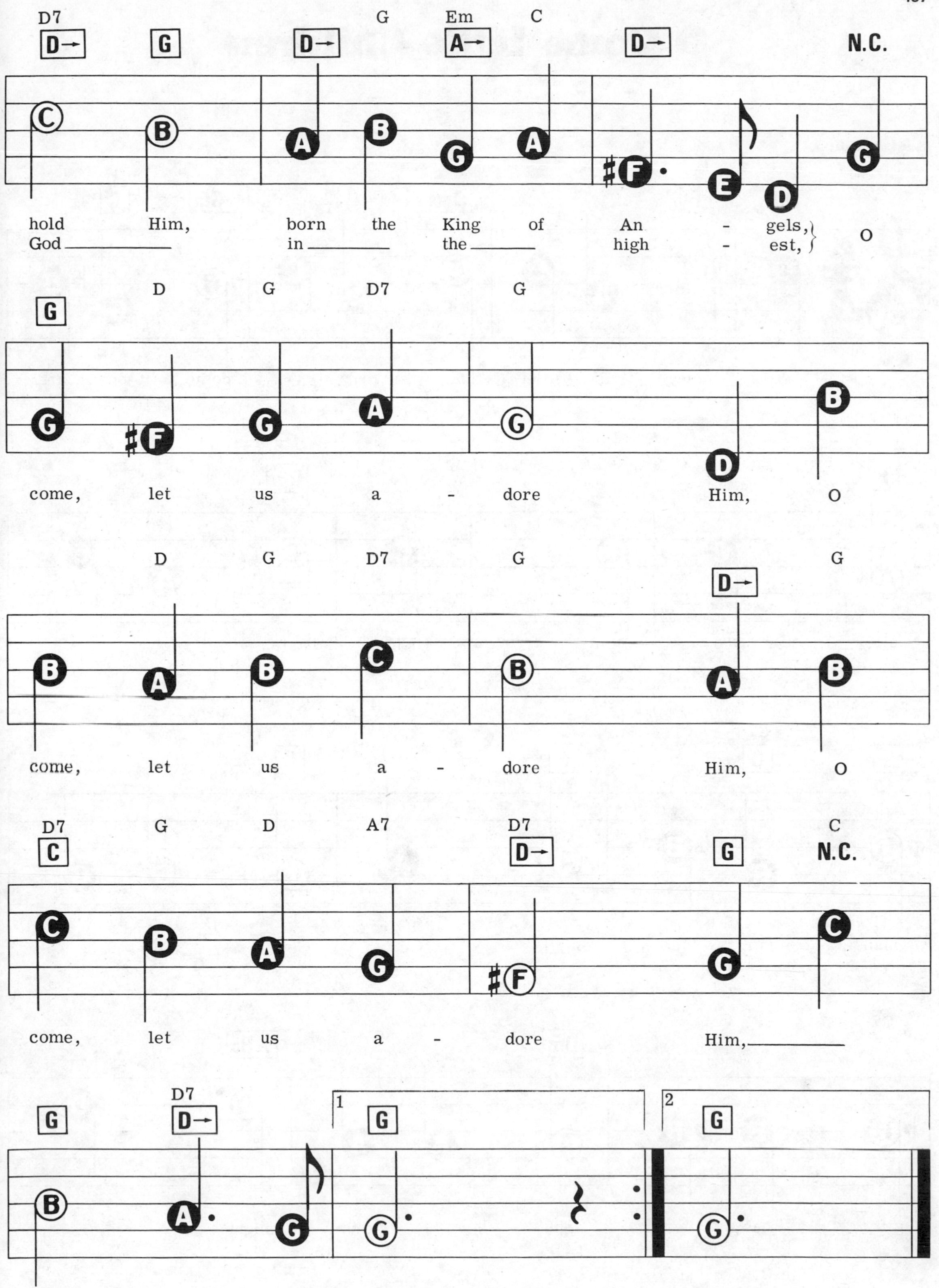
D7 G Em C
D→ G D→ A→ D→ N.C.
hold Him, born the King of An - gels,
God in the high - est,
O
D G D7 G
G
come, let us a - dore Him, O
D G D7 G G
D→
come, let us a - dore Him, O
D7 G D A7 D7 C
C D→ G N.C.
come, let us a - dore Him,
D7
G D→ G G
1 2
Christ the Lord. Lord.

O Come Little Children

Registration 1

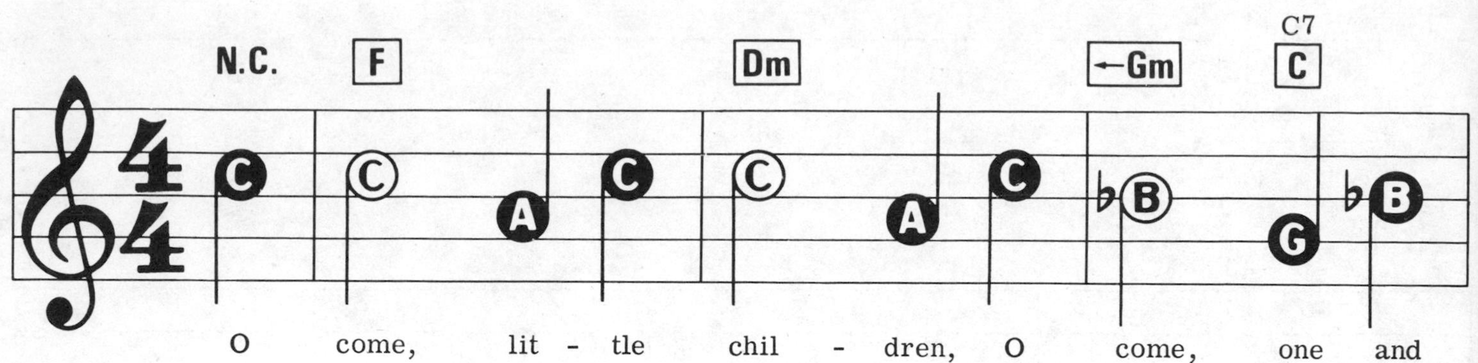

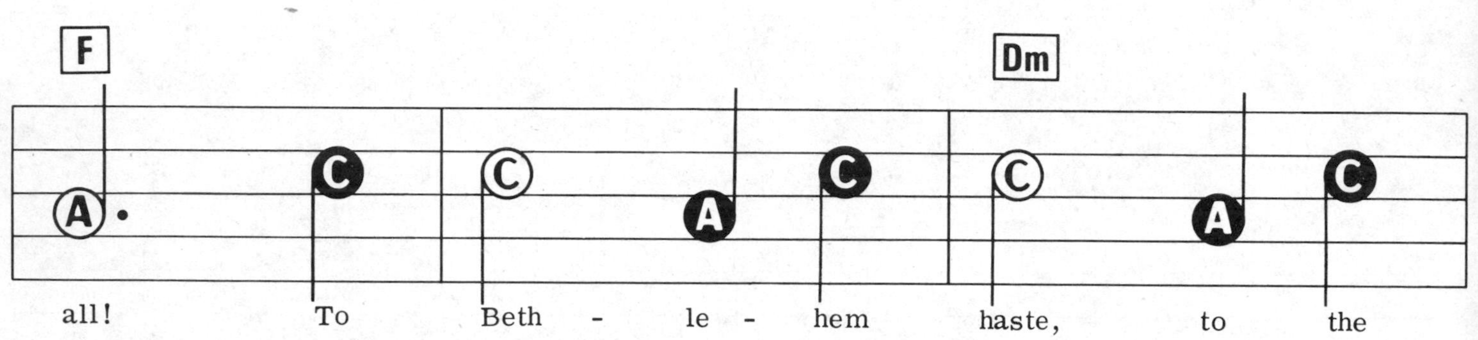

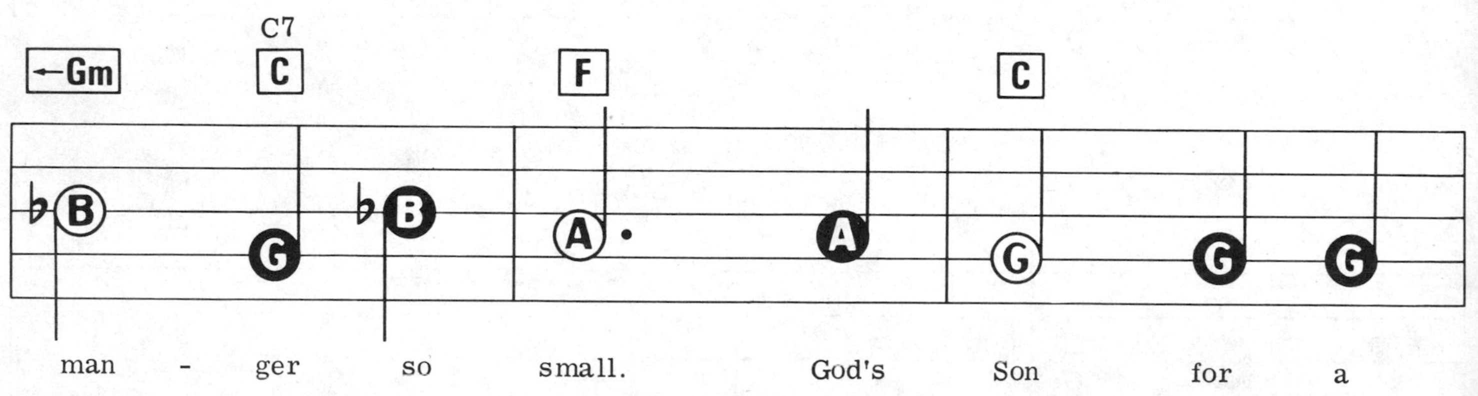

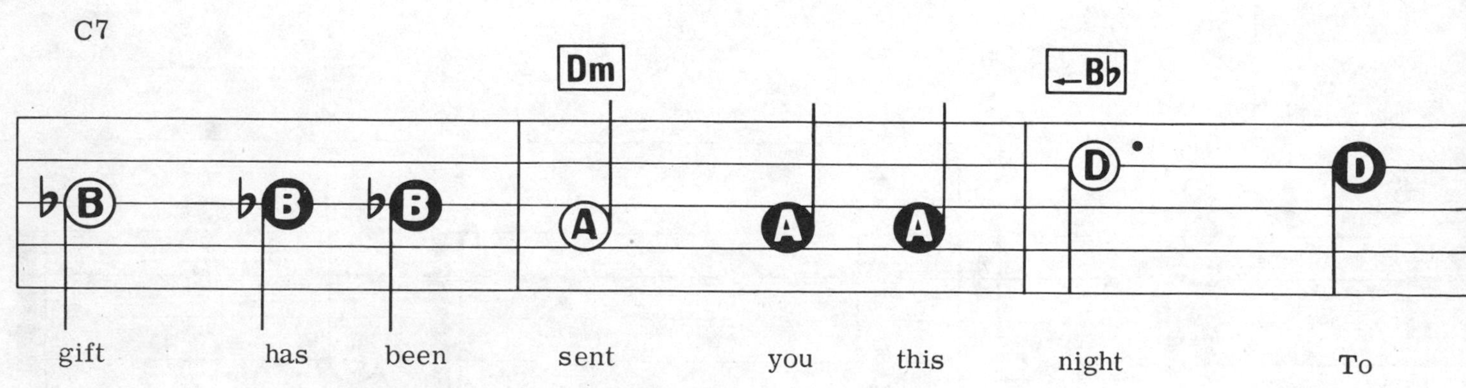

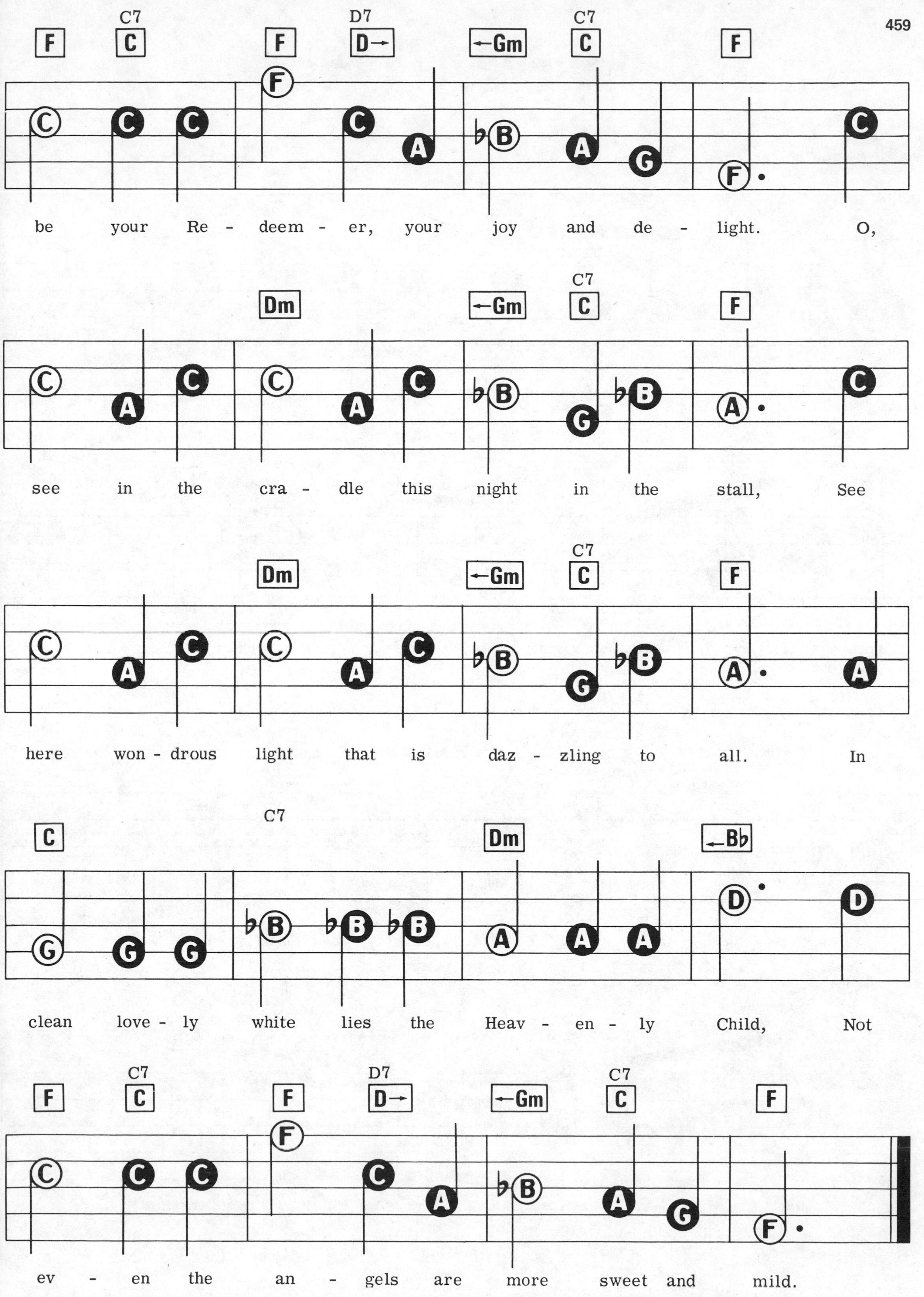
F C7 C F D7 D→ ←Gm C7 C F
be your Re - deem - er, your joy and de - light. O,
Dm ←Gm C7 C F
see in the cra - dle this night in the stall, See
Dm ←Gm C7 C F
here won - drous light that is daz - zling to all. In
C C7 Dm ←B♭
clean love - ly white lies the Heav - en - ly Child, Not
F C7 C F D7 D→ ←Gm C7 C F
ev - en the an - gels are more sweet and mild.

O Holy Night

Registration 6

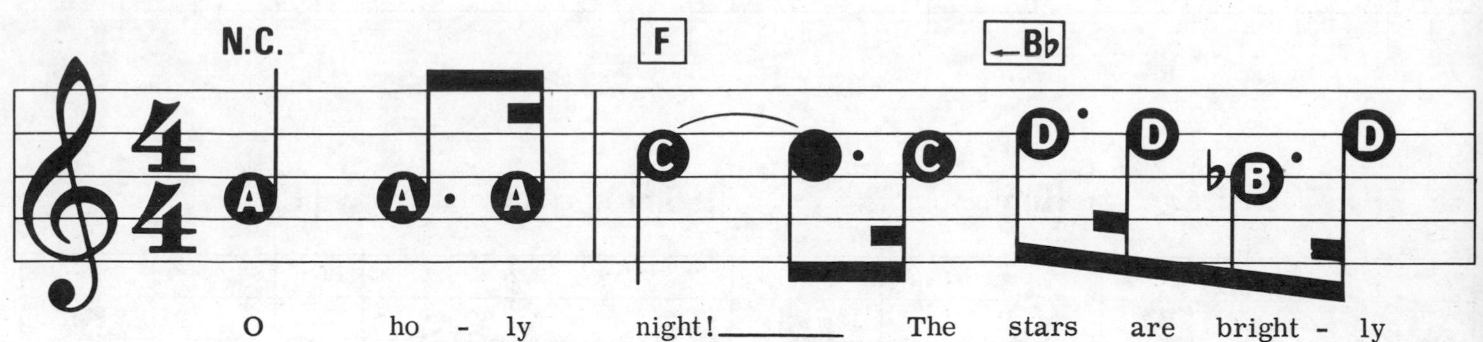

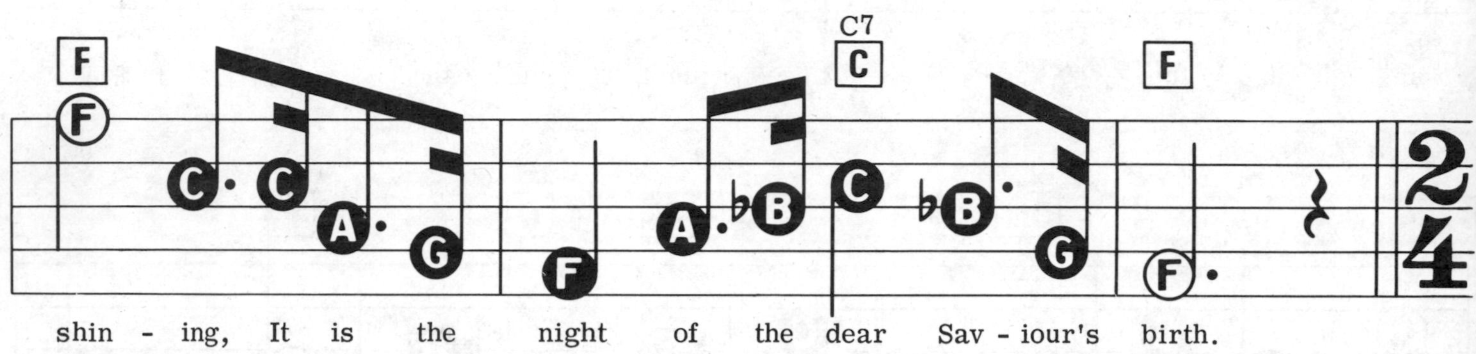

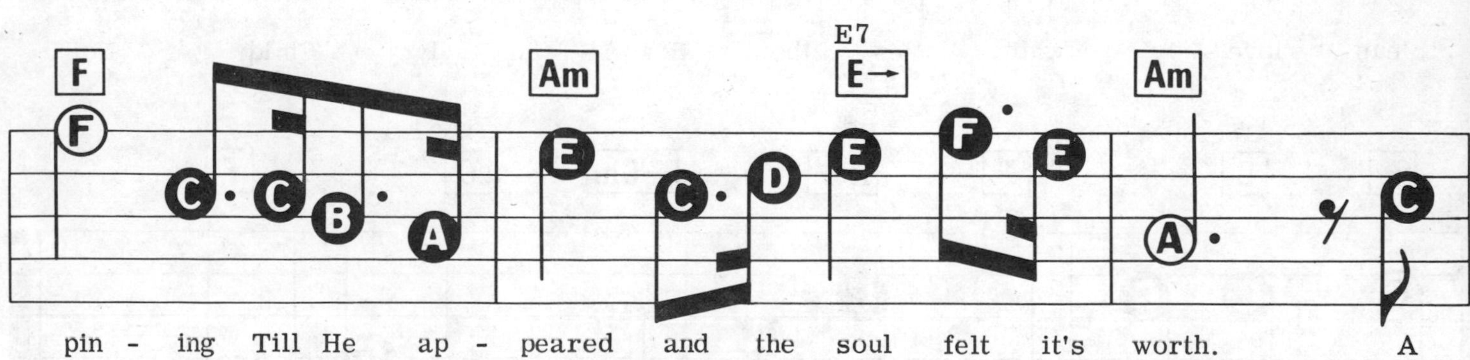

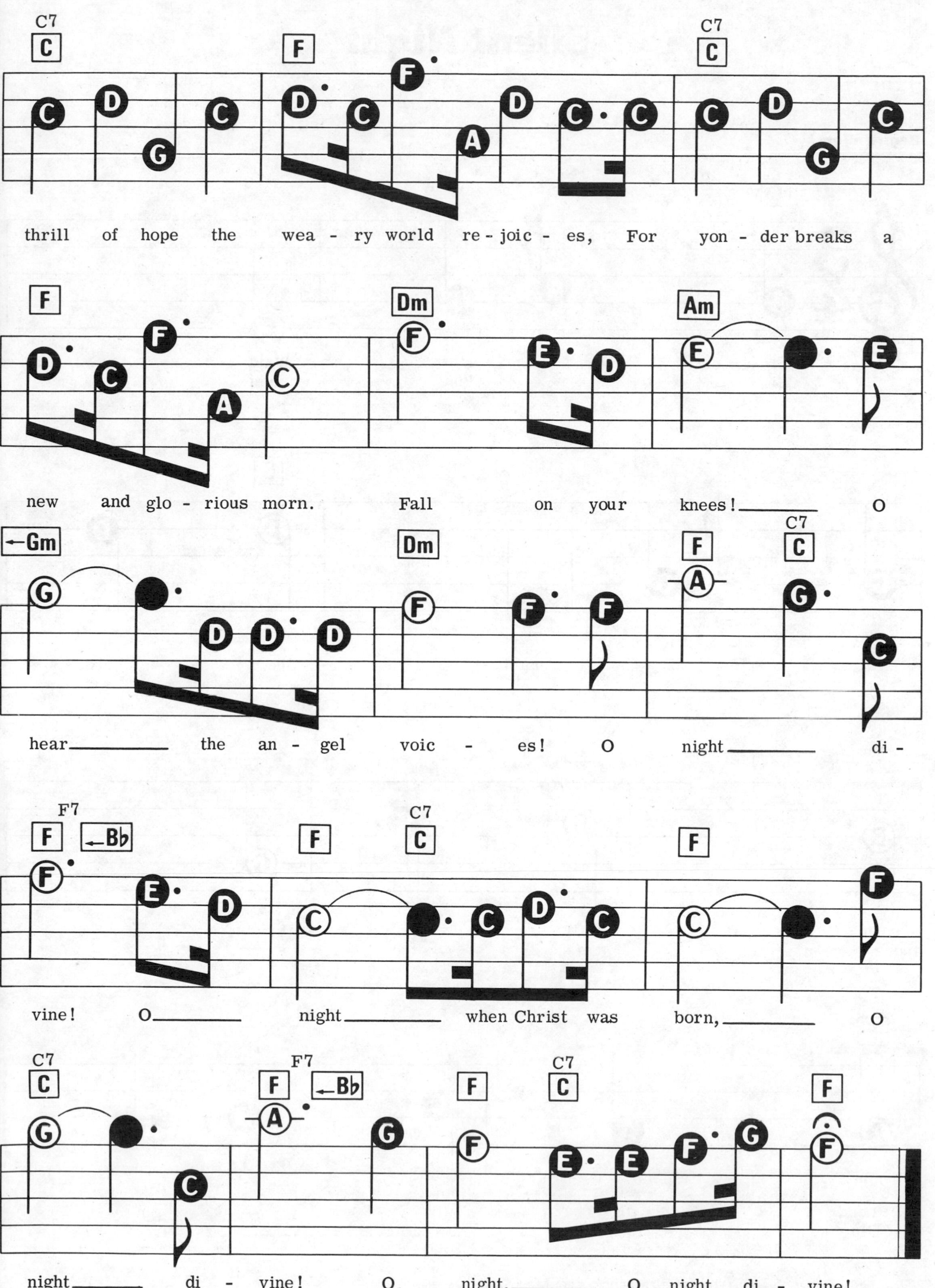
C7
C
F
C7
C
thrill of hope the wea - ry world re - joic - es, For yon - der breaks a
F
Dm
Am
new and glo - rious morn. Fall on your knees! O
←Gm
Dm
F
C7
C
hear the an - gel voic - es! O night di -
F7
F
←B♭
F
C7
C
F
vine! O night when Christ was born, O
C7
C
F7
F
←B♭
F
C7
C
F
night di - vine! O night, O night di - vine!

Silent Night

Registration 1

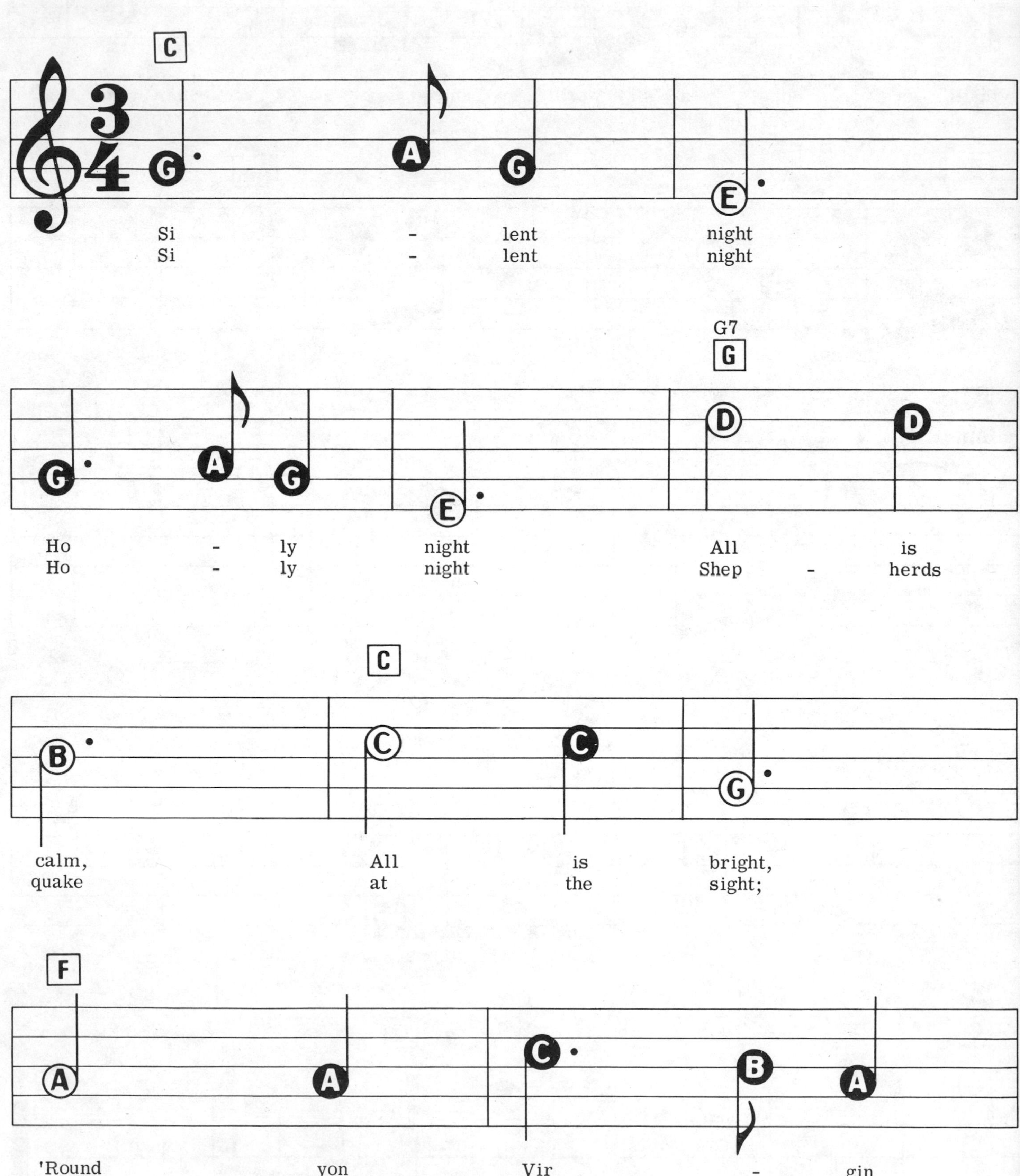

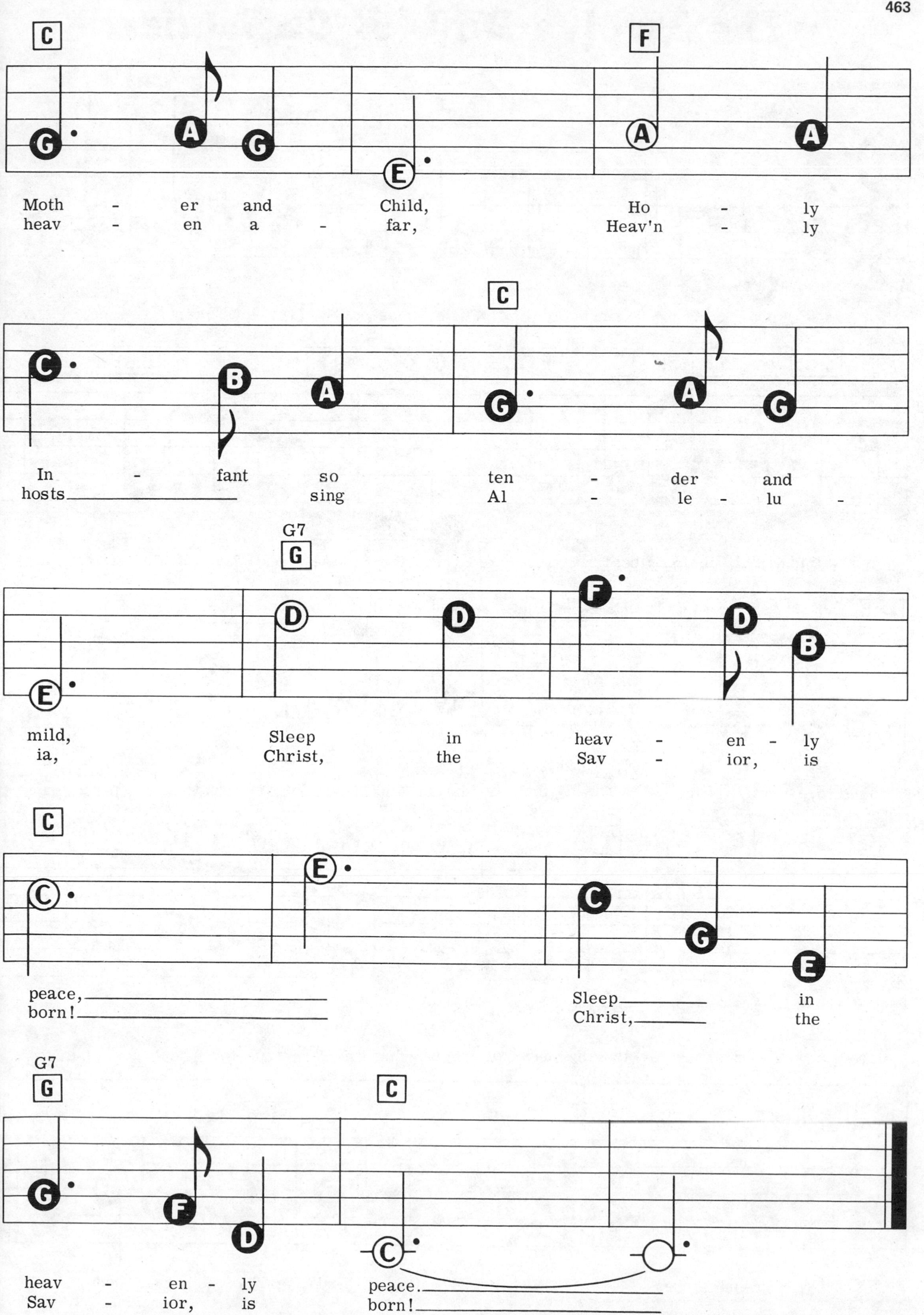
C
F
Moth - er and Child, Ho - ly
heav - en a - far, Heav'n - ly
C
In - fant so ten - der and
hosts sing Al - le - lu -
G7
G
mild, Sleep in heav - en - ly
ia, Christ, the Sav - ior, is
C
peace, Sleep in
born! Christ, the
G7
G
C
heav - en - ly peace.
Sav - ior, is born!

The Twelve Days of Christmas

Registration 5

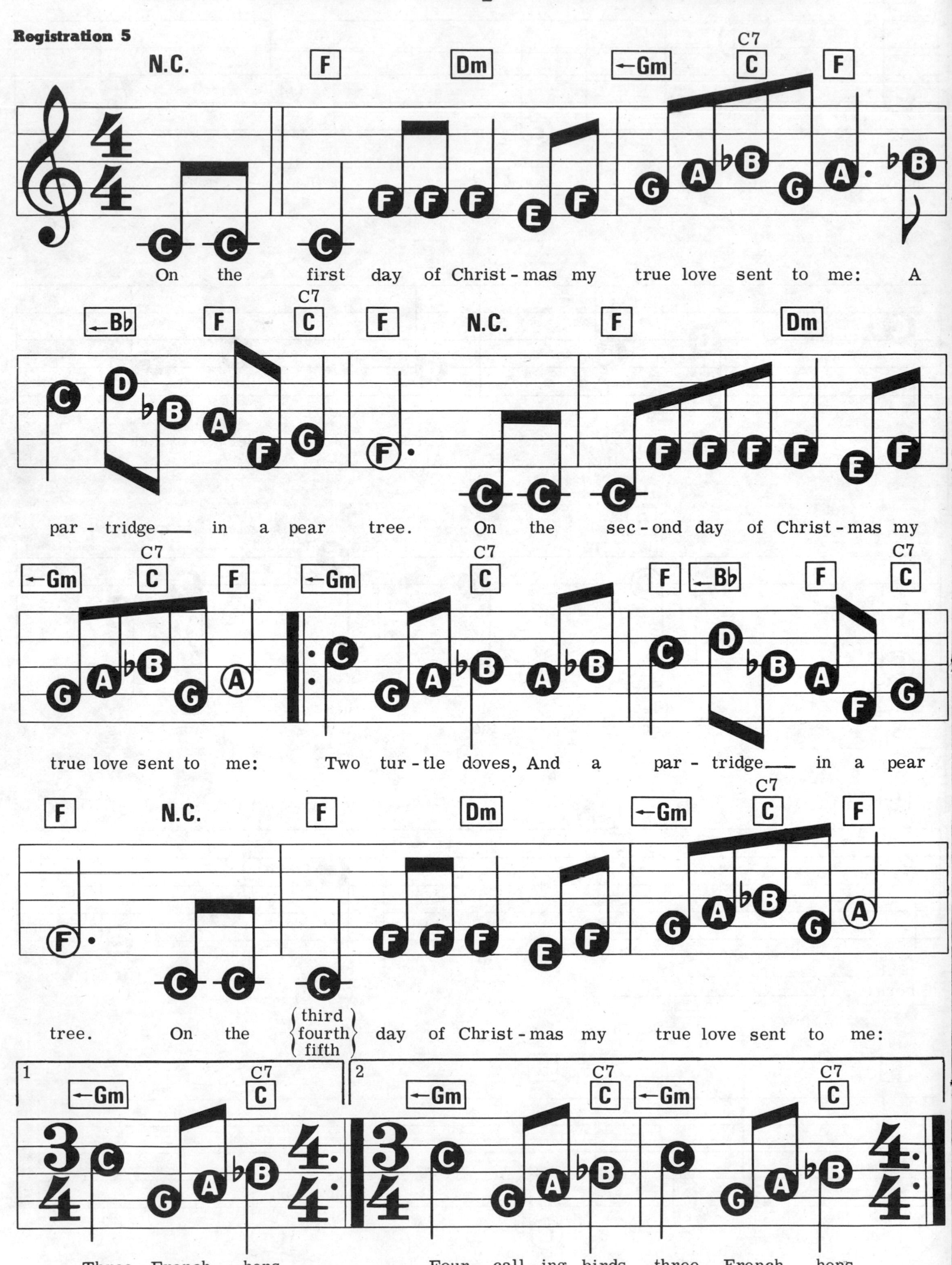

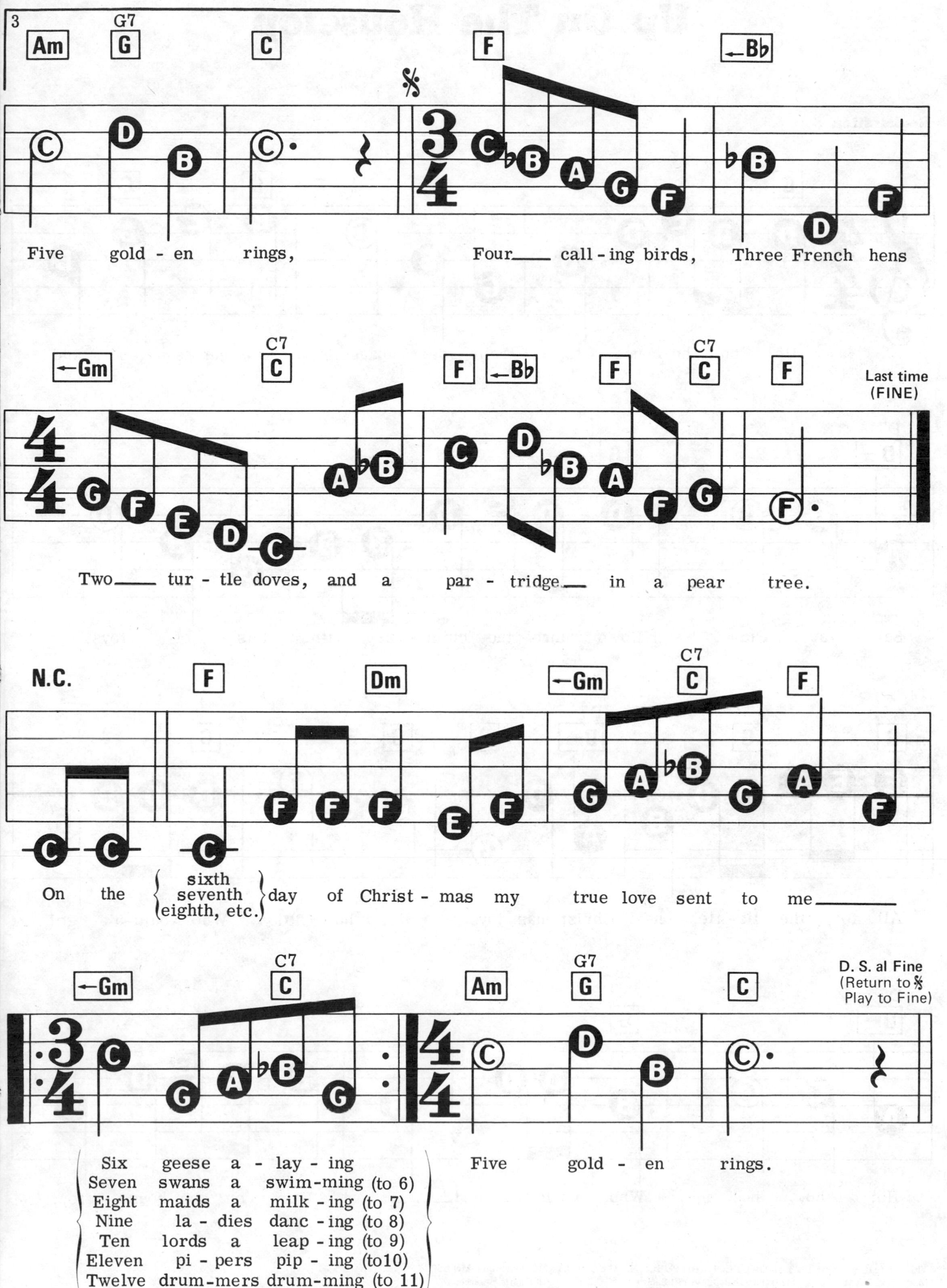
3
Am G7 G C F ←B♭
Five gold - en rings, Four___ call - ing birds, Three French hens
←Gm C7 C F ←B♭ F C7 C F
Last time (FINE)
Two___ tur - tle doves, and a par - tridge___ in a pear tree.
N.C. F Dm ←Gm C7 C F
On the {sixth seventh eighth, etc.} day of Christ - mas my true love sent to me___
←Gm C7 C Am G7 G C
D. S. al Fine (Return to 𝄋 Play to Fine)
Six geese a - lay - ing
Seven swans a swim-ming (to 6)
Eight maids a milk - ing (to 7)
Nine la - dies danc - ing (to 8)
Ten lords a leap - ing (to 9)
Eleven pi - pers pip - ing (to10)
Twelve drum-mers drum-ming (to 11)
Five gold - en rings.

Up On The Housetop

Registration 5

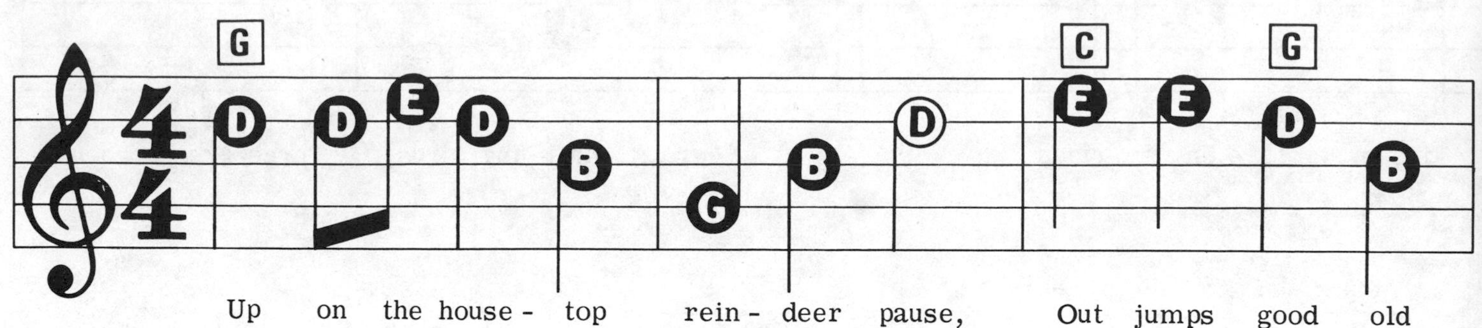

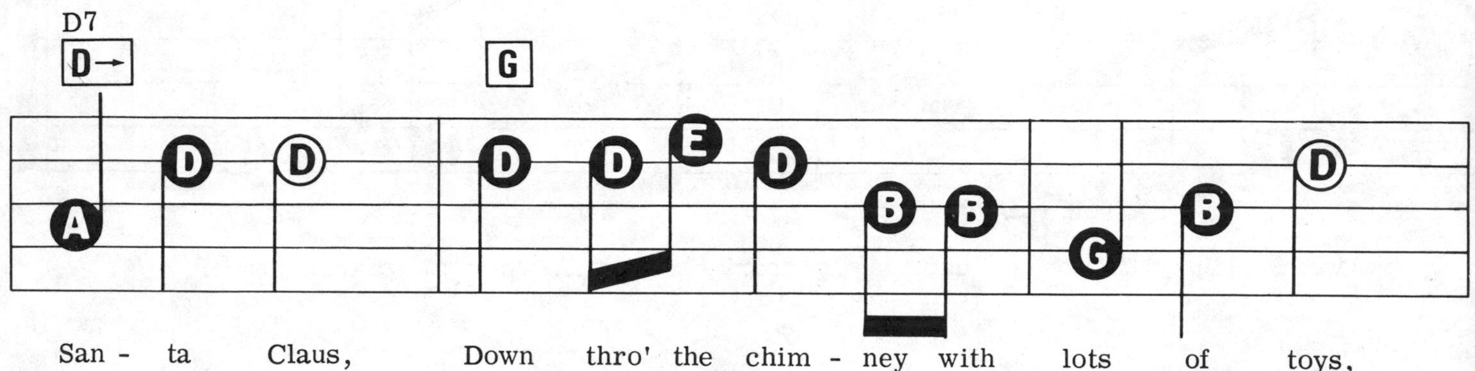

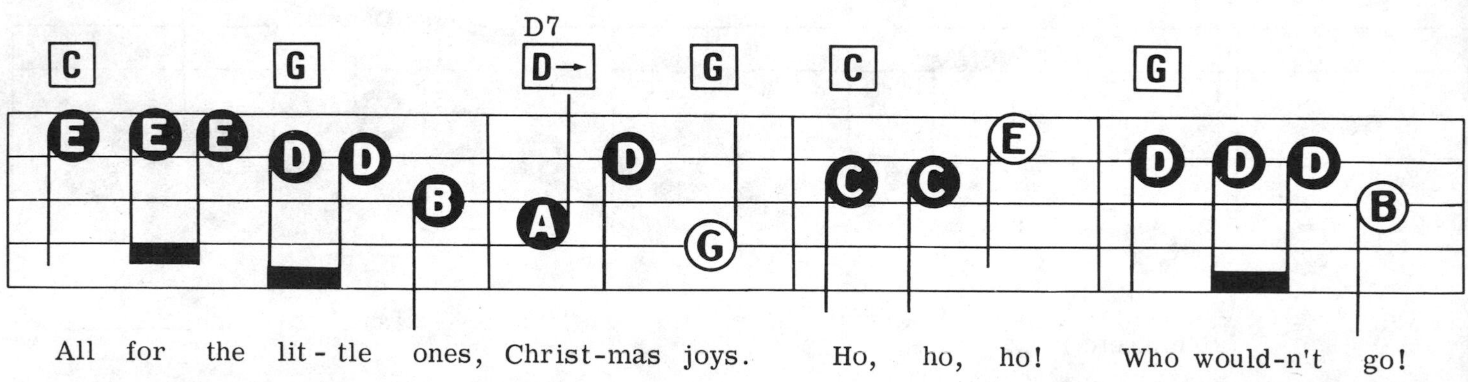

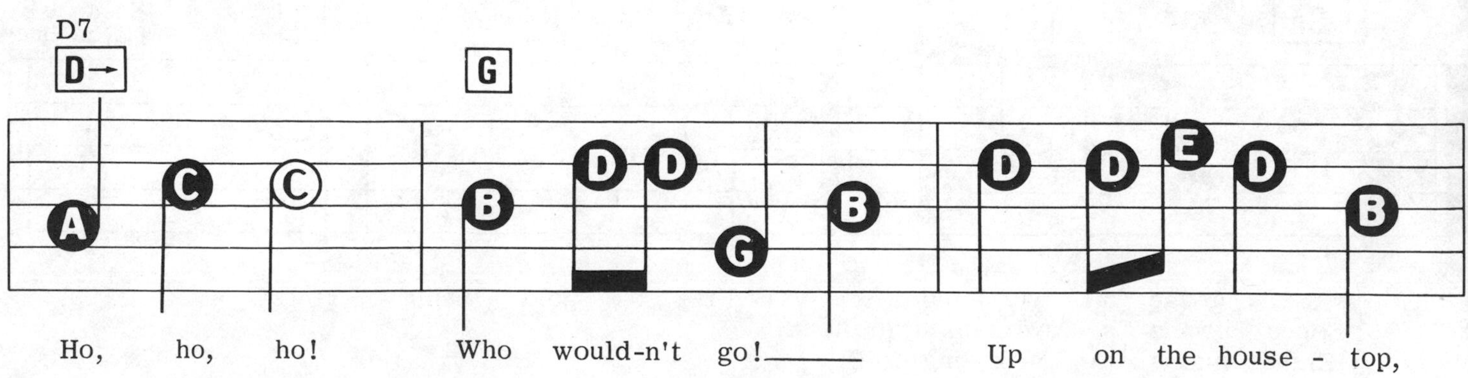

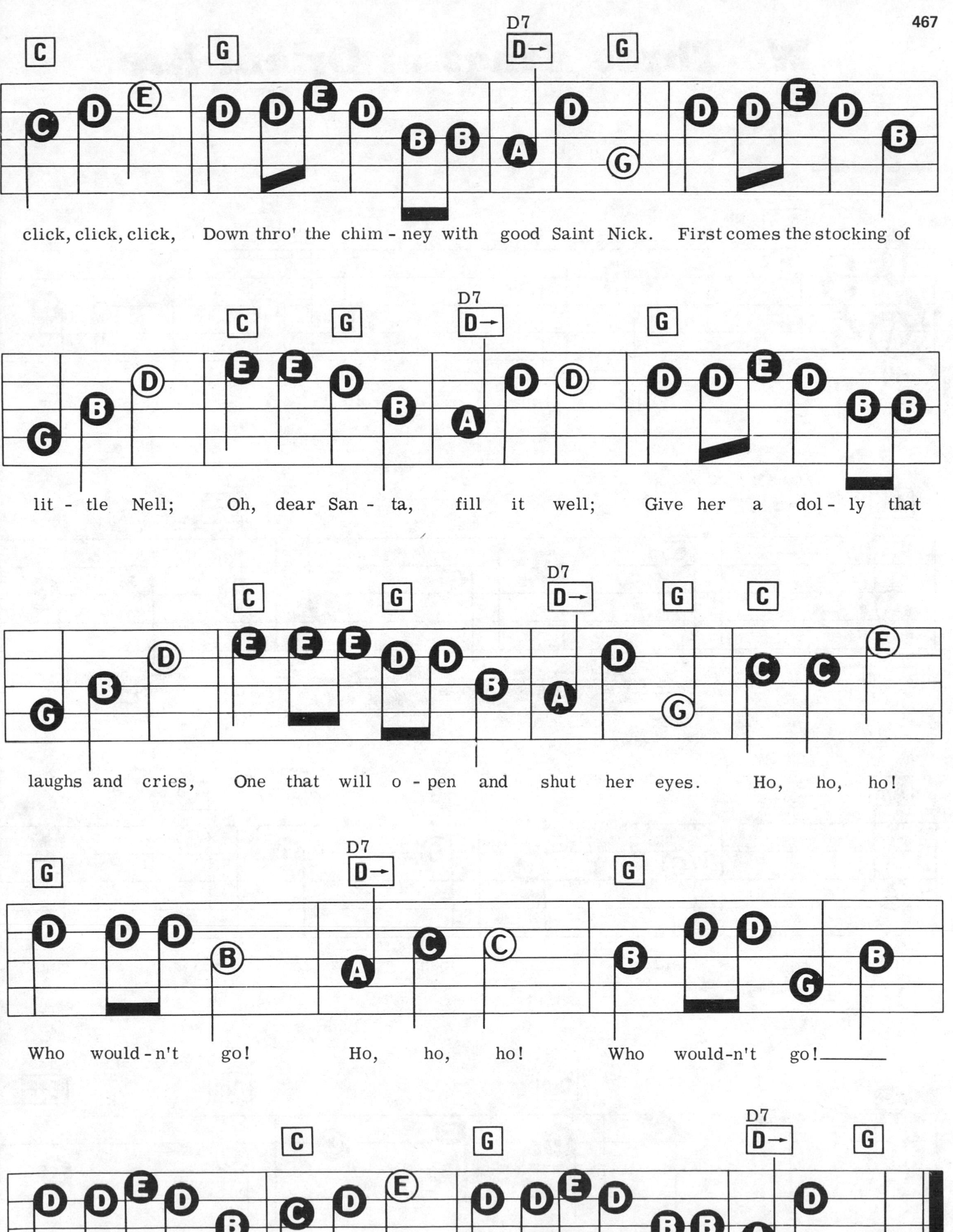
C G D7 D→ G
click, click, click, Down thro' the chim - ney with good Saint Nick. First comes the stocking of
C G D7 D→ G
lit - tle Nell; Oh, dear San - ta, fill it well; Give her a dol - ly that
C G D7 D→ G C
laughs and cries, One that will o - pen and shut her eyes. Ho, ho, ho!
G D7 D→ G
Who would-n't go! Ho, ho, ho! Who would-n't go!
C G D7 D→ G
Up on the house - top click, click, click, Down thro' the chim -ney with good Saint Nick.

We Three Kings of Orient Are

Registration 9

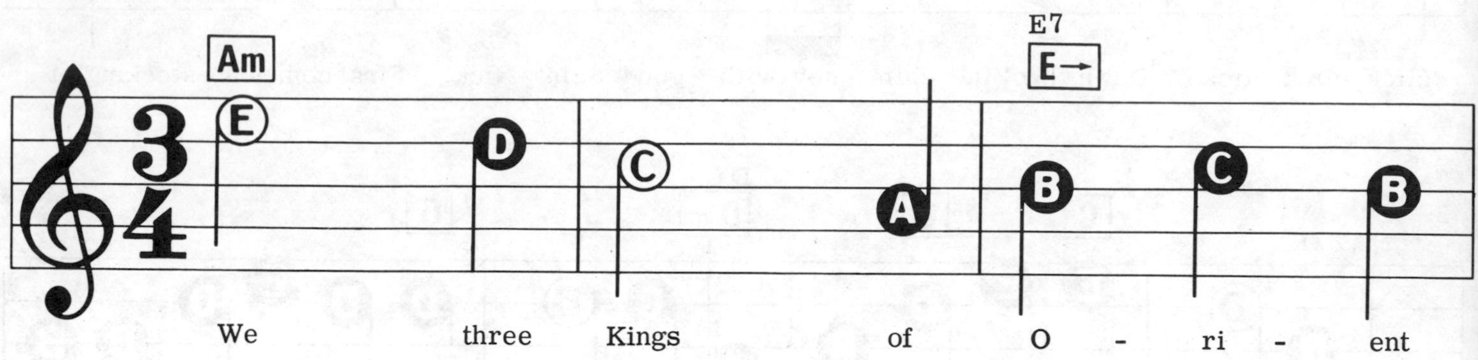

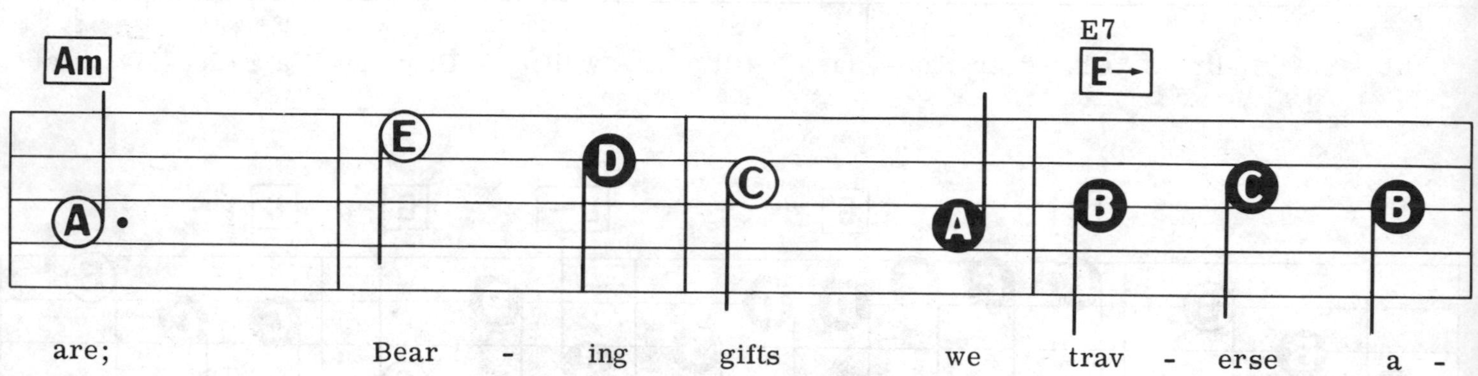

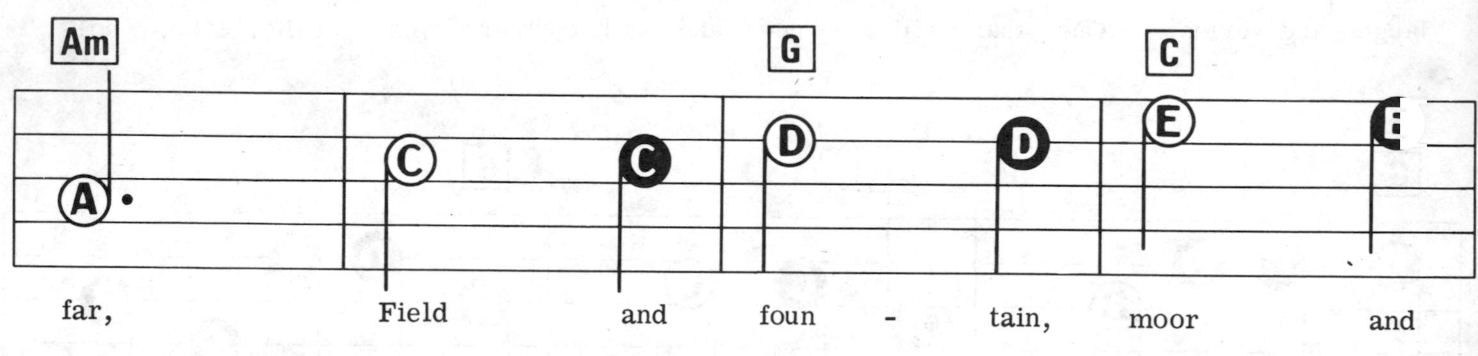

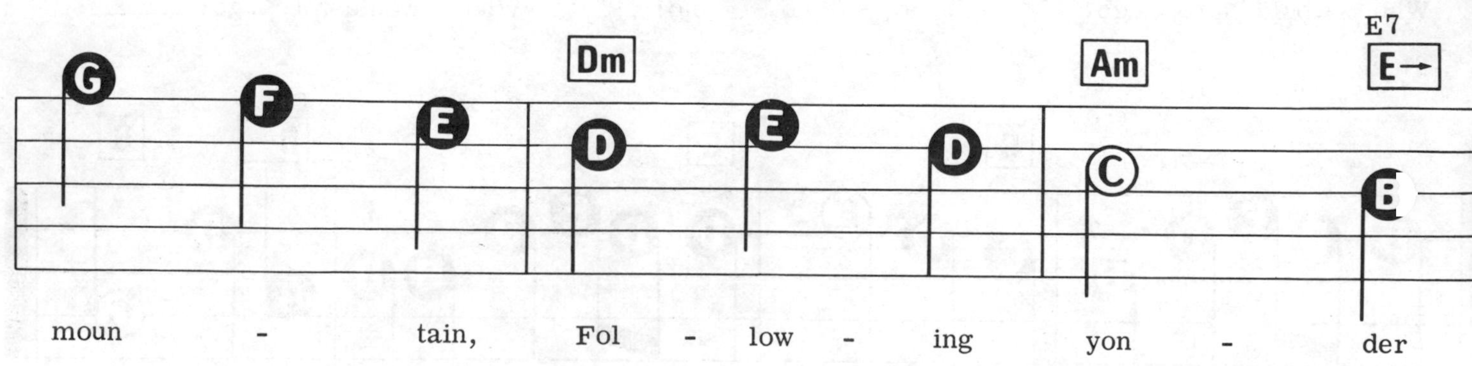

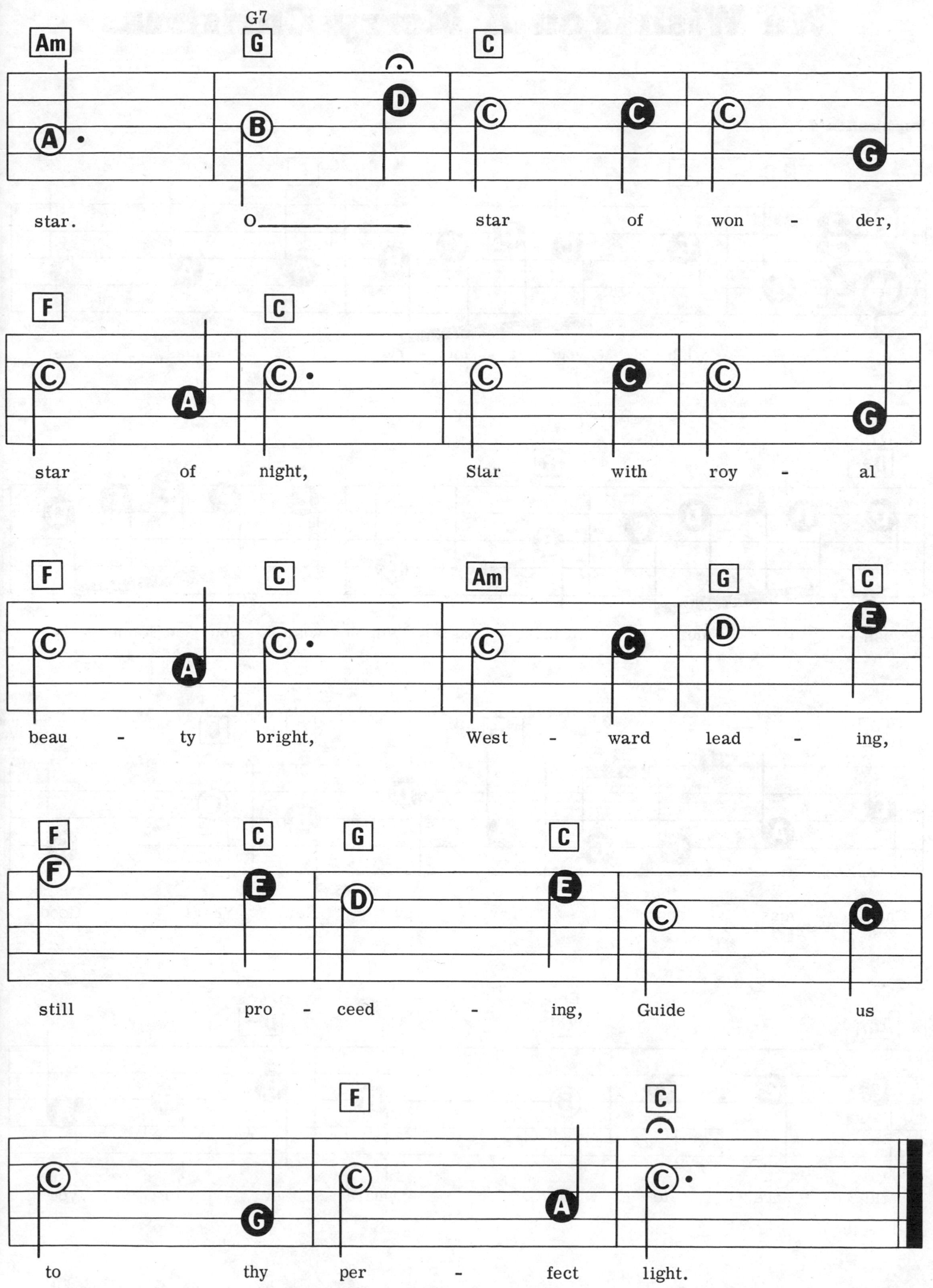
Am
G7
G
C
star.
O
star
of
won - der,
F
C
star of night,
Star with roy - al
F
C
Am
G
C
beau - ty bright,
West - ward lead - ing,
F
C
G
C
still pro - ceed - ing,
Guide us
F
C
to thy per - fect light.

We Wish You A Merry Christmas

Registration 4

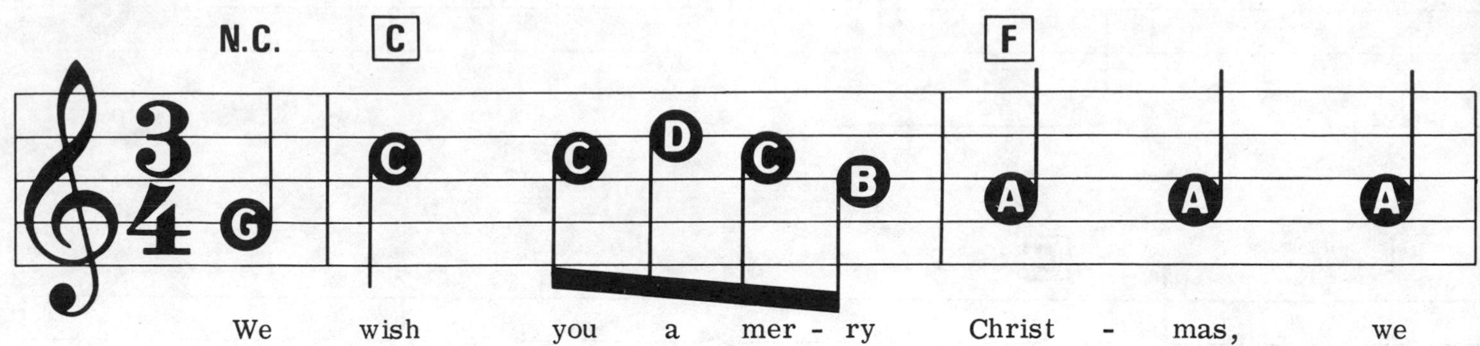

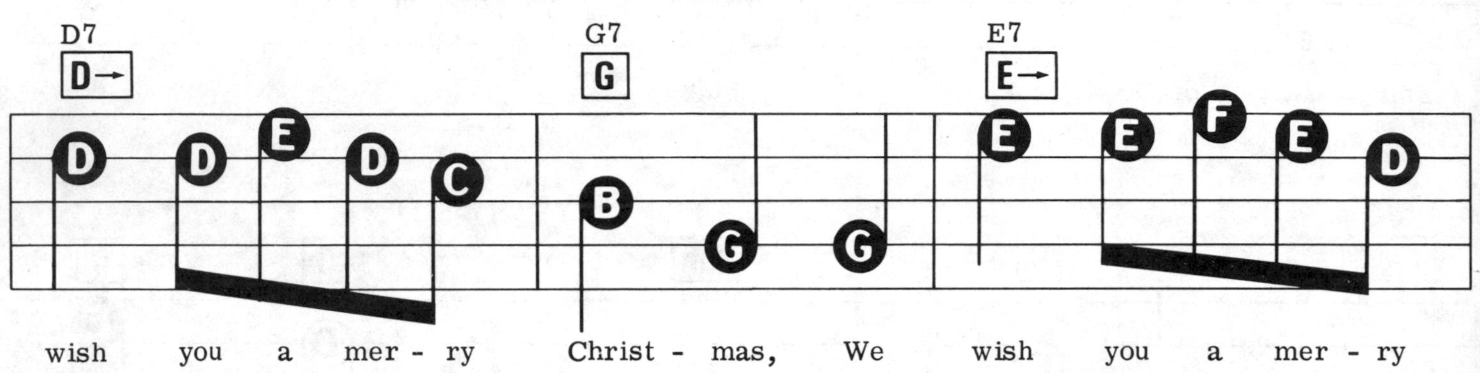

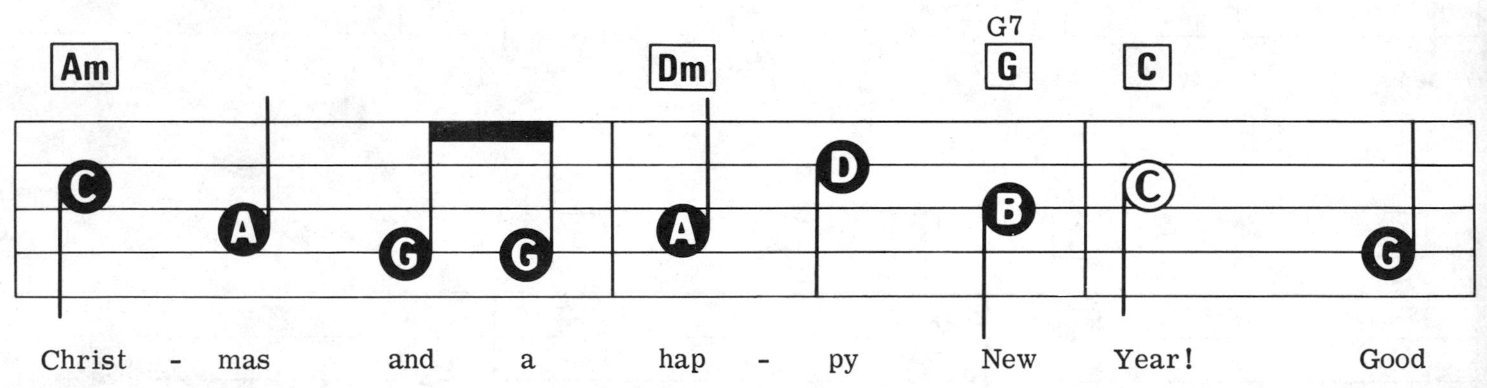

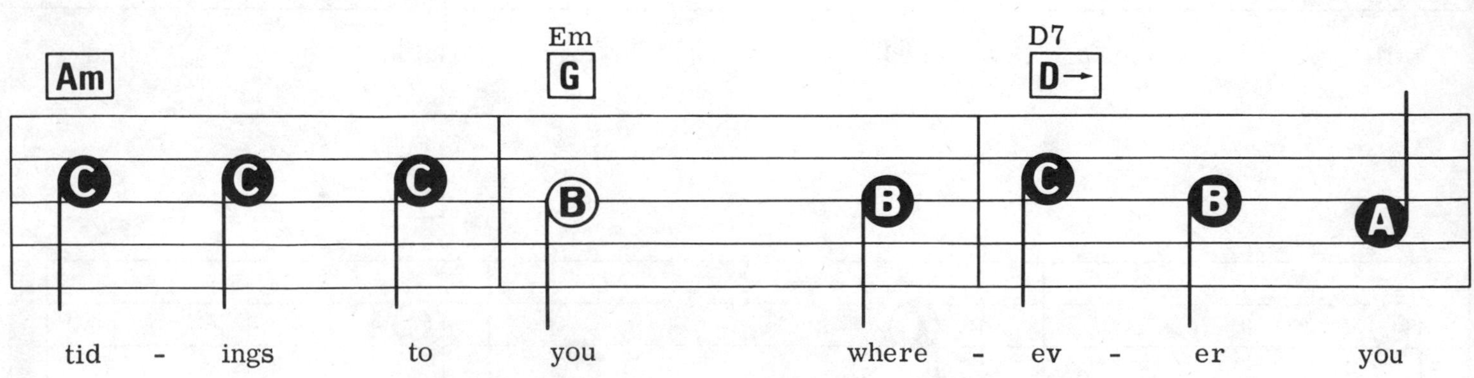

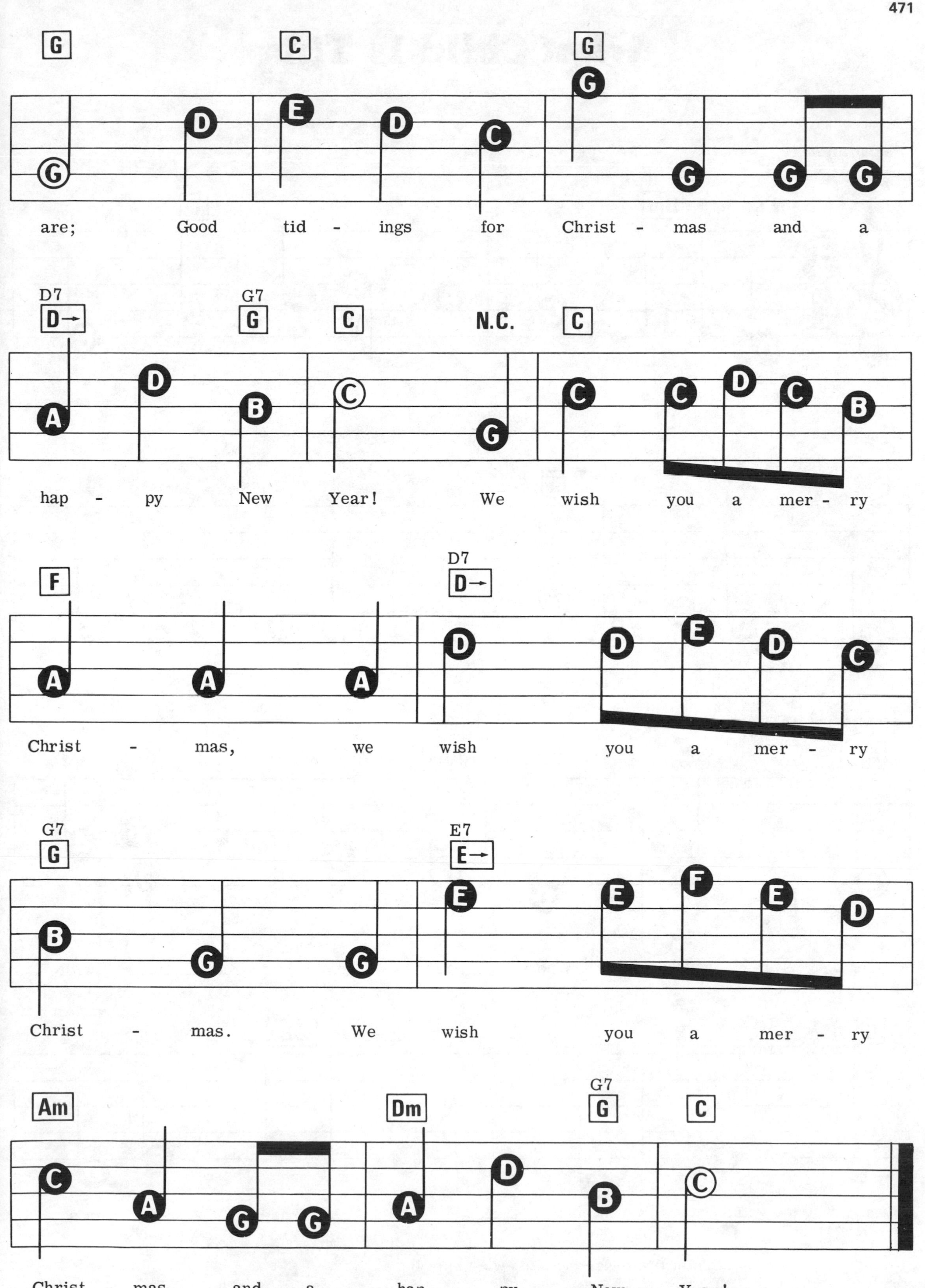
G
C
G
G
D
E
D
C
G
G
G
G
are; Good tid - ings for Christ - mas and a
D7
D→
G7
G
C
N.C.
C
A
D
B
C
G
C
C
D
C
B
hap - py New Year! We wish you a mer - ry
F
D7
D→
A
A
A
D
D
E
D
C
Christ - mas, we wish you a mer - ry
G7
G
E7
E→
B
G
G
E
E
F
E
D
Christ - mas. We wish you a mer - ry
Am
Dm
G7
G
C
C
A
G
G
A
D
B
C
Christ - mas and a hap - py New Year!

What Child Is This

Registration 10

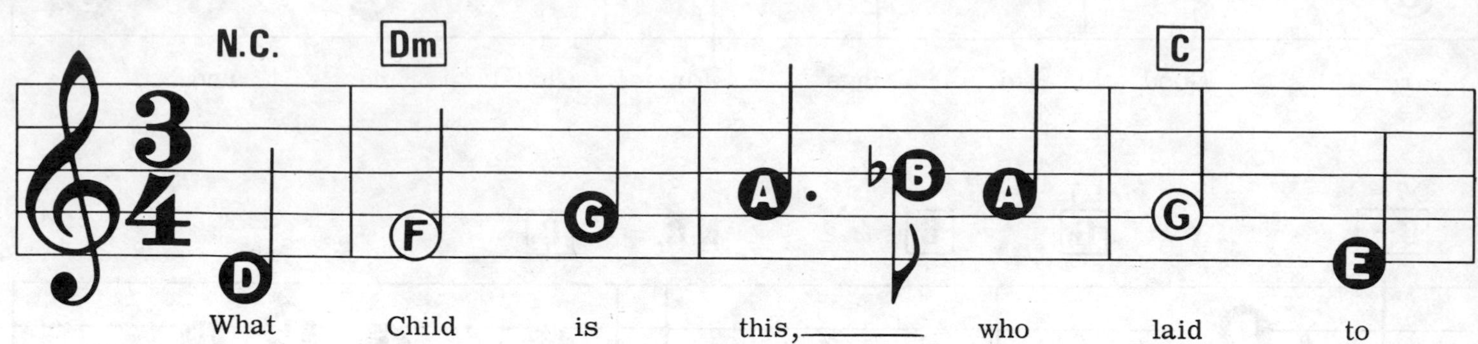

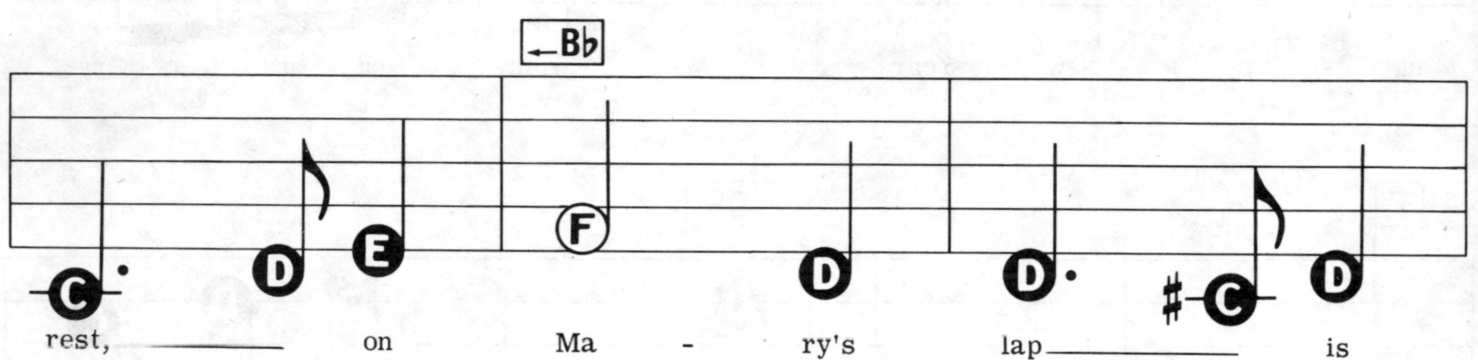

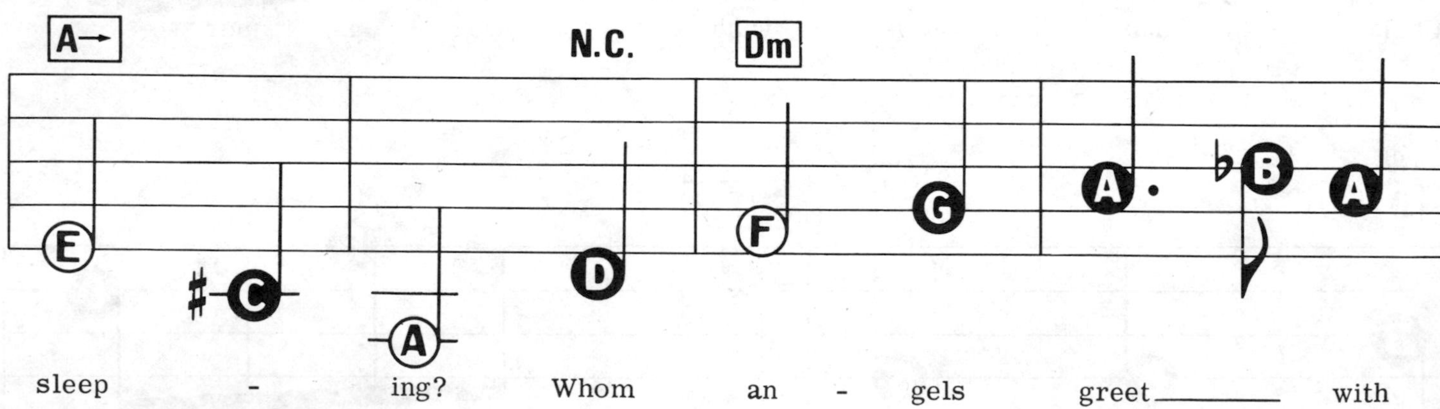

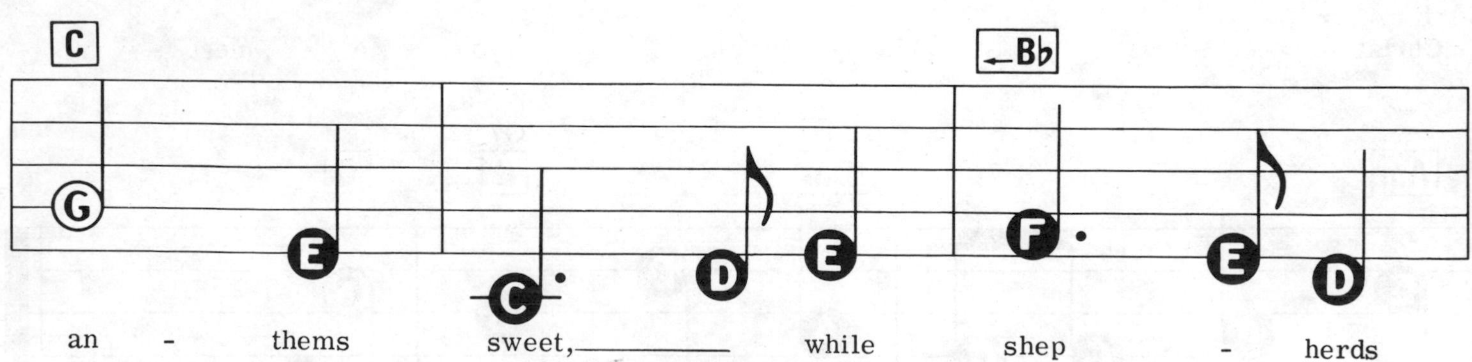

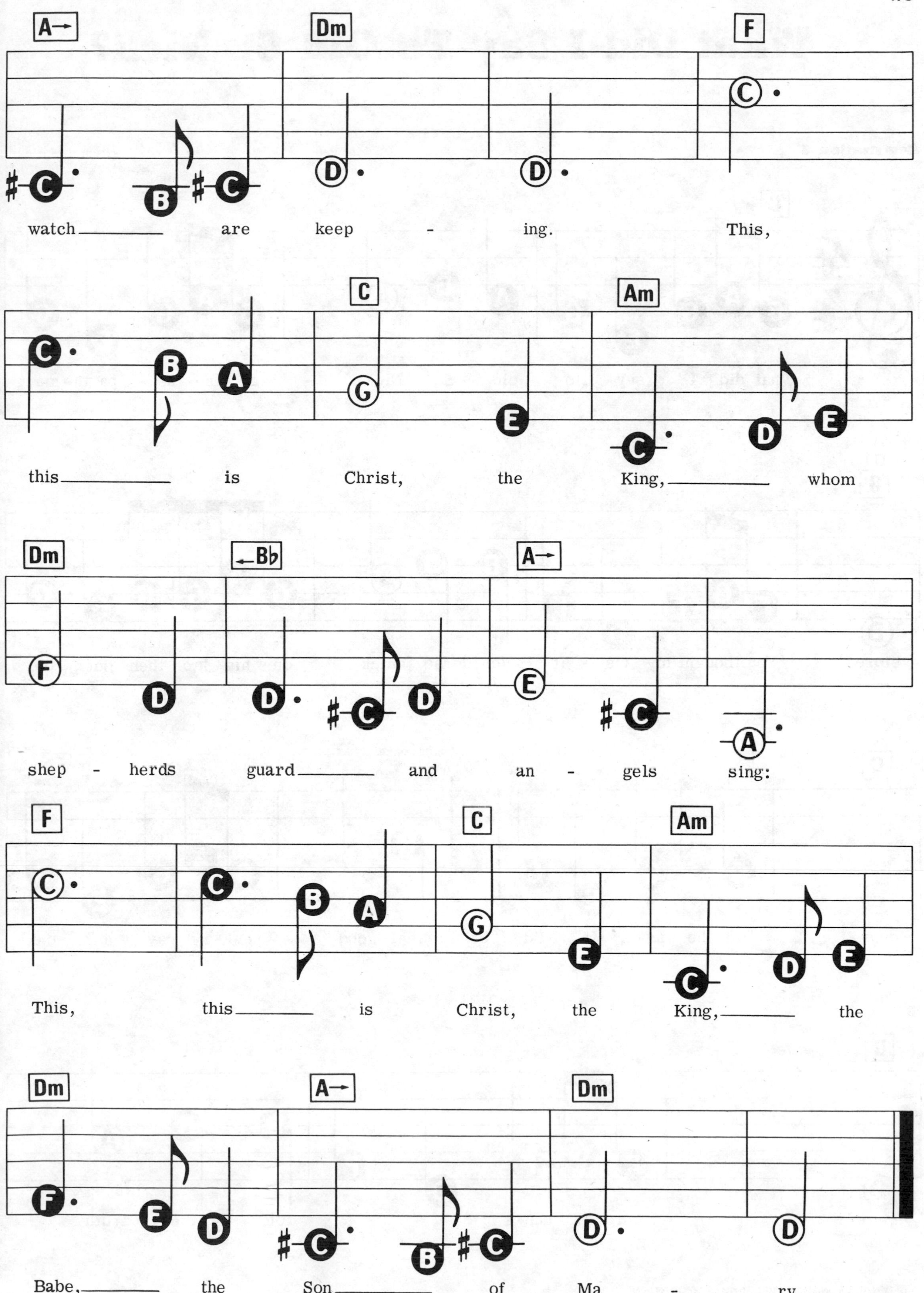
A→
Dm
F
watch are keep - ing. This,
C
Am
this is Christ, the King, whom
Dm
←B♭
A→
shep - herds guard and an - gels sing:
F
C
Am
This, this is Christ, the King, the
Dm
A→
Dm
Babe, the Son of Ma - ry.

What Did I Say To Old St. Nick?

Registration 4

Words and Music by
Jim Cliff

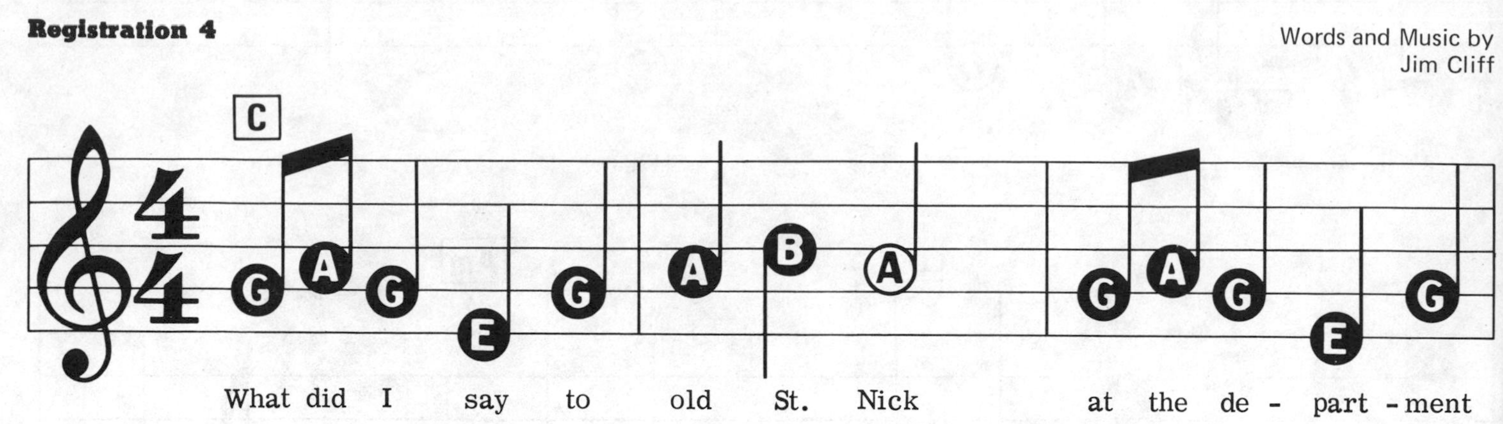

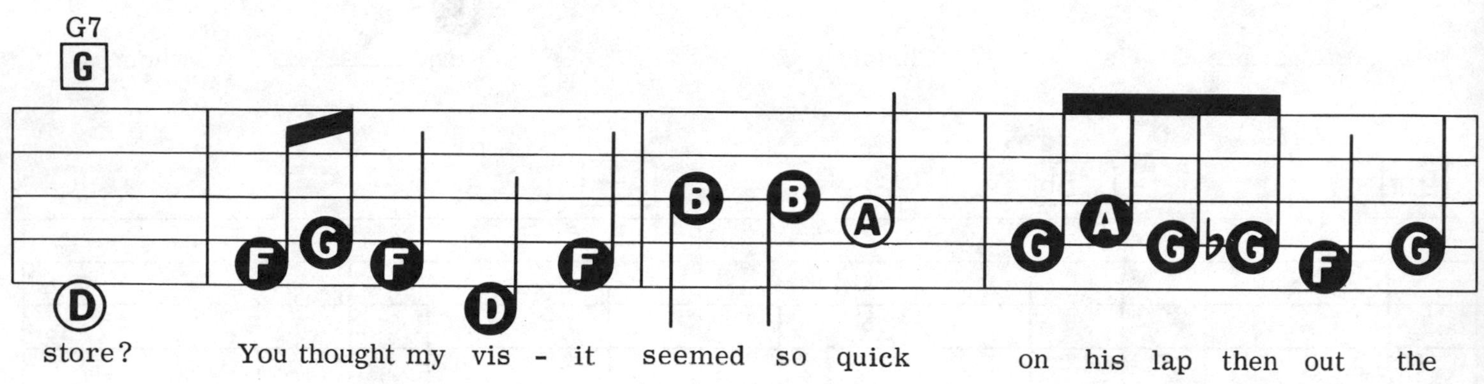

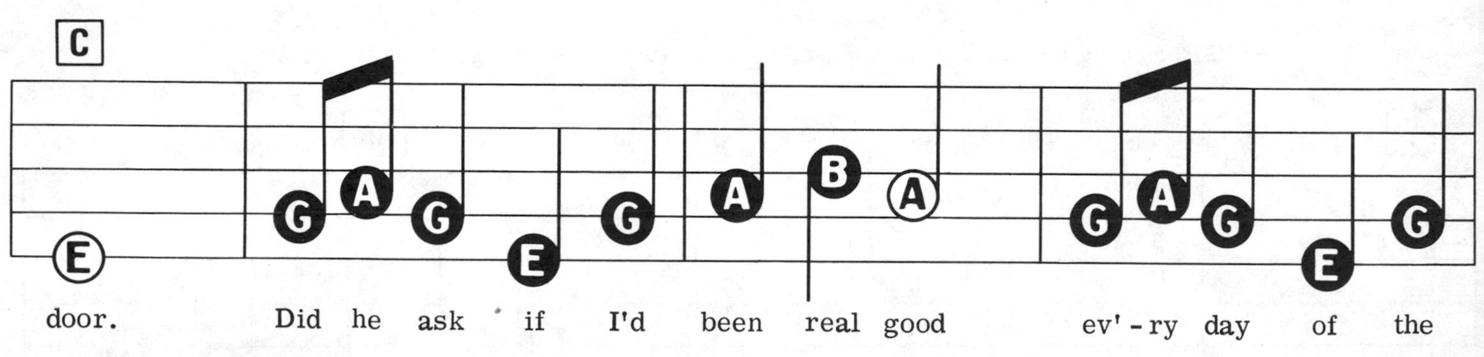

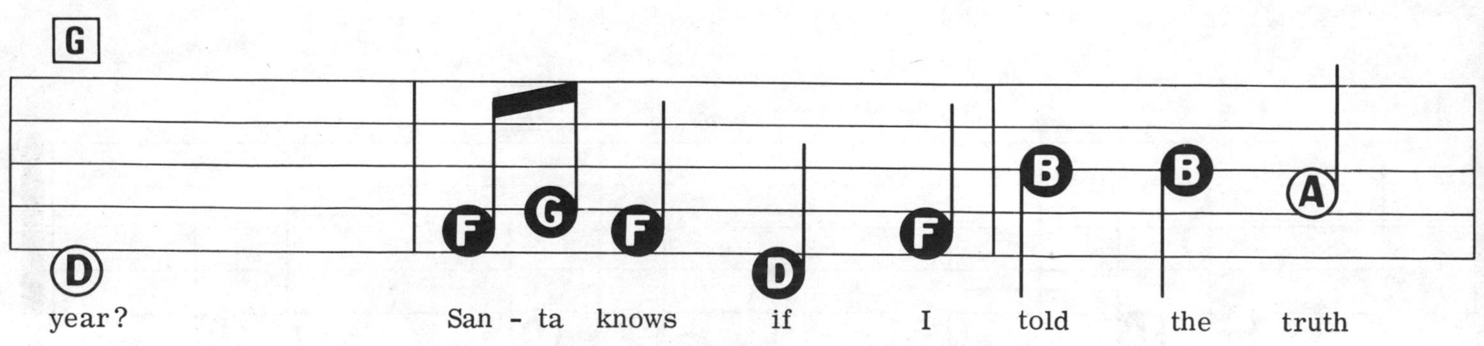

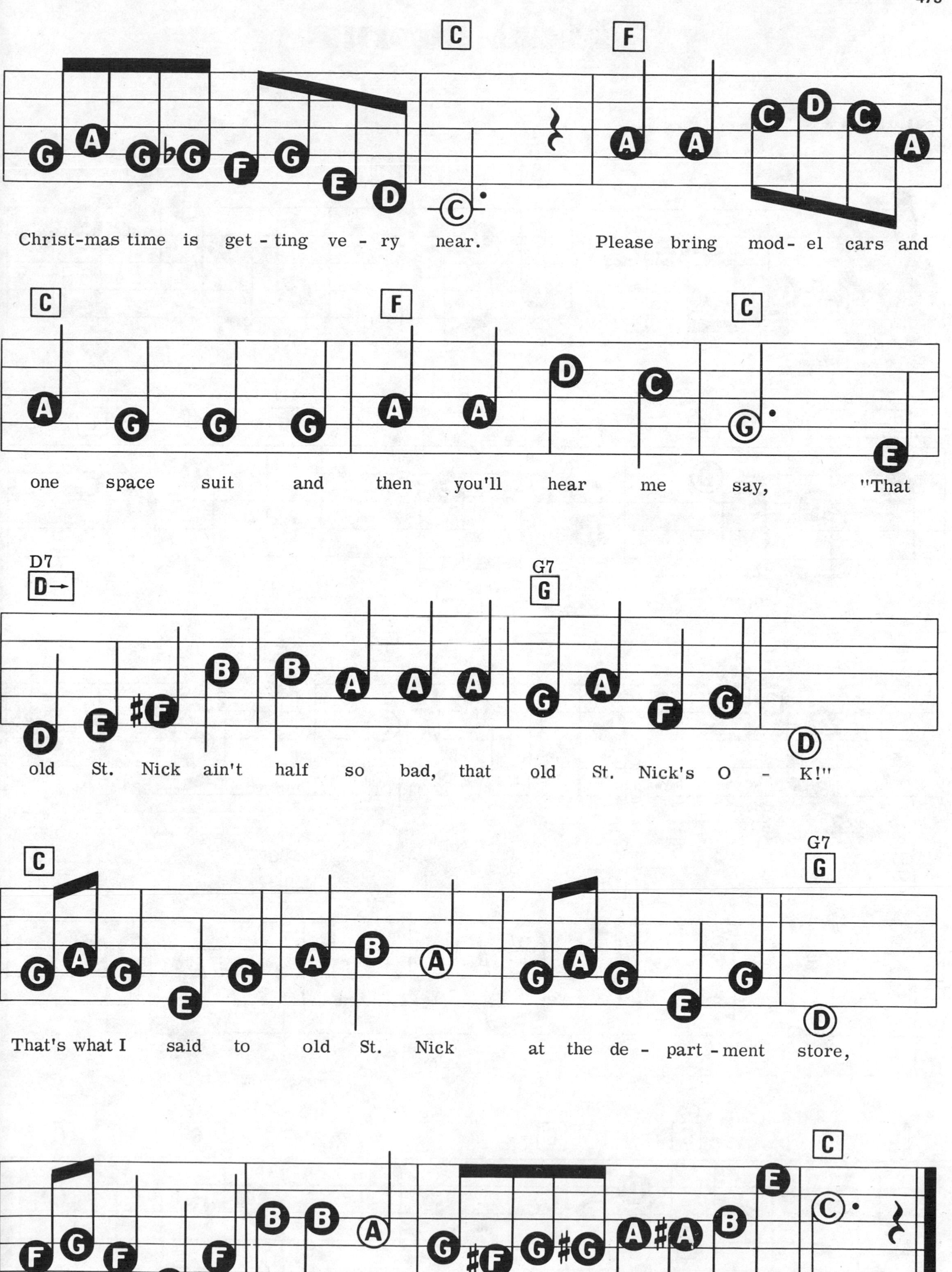
C F
Christ-mas time is get - ting ve - ry near. Please bring mod - el cars and
C F C
one space suit and then you'll hear me say, "That
D7 G7
old St. Nick ain't half so bad, that old St. Nick's O - K!"
C G7
That's what I said to old St. Nick at the de - part - ment store,
C
Did he say that he'd bring some toys? Ask me Christ-mas Day, I'll tell you more.

Bridal Chorus

Registration 6

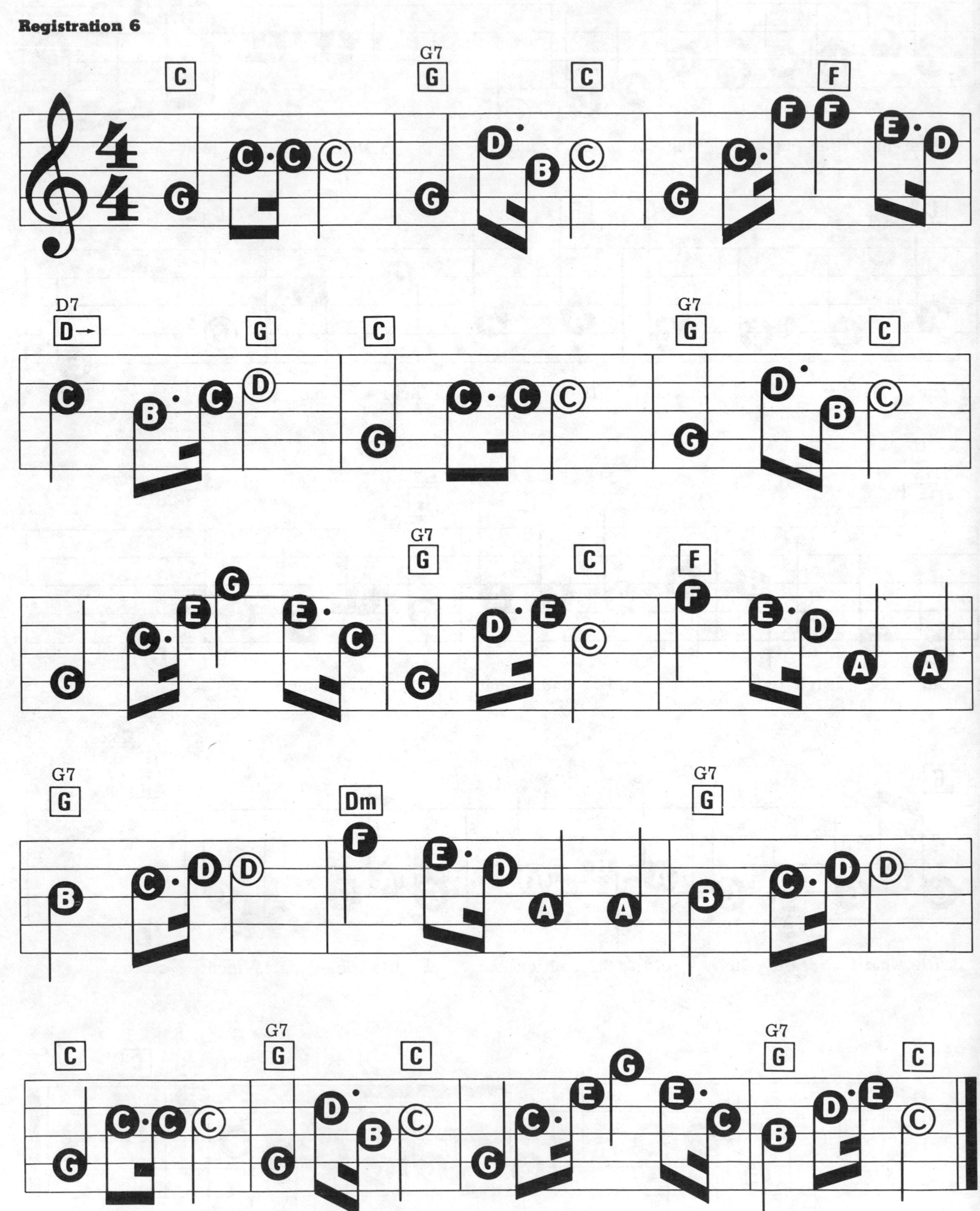

Ich Liebe Dich

(I Love Thee)

Registration 10

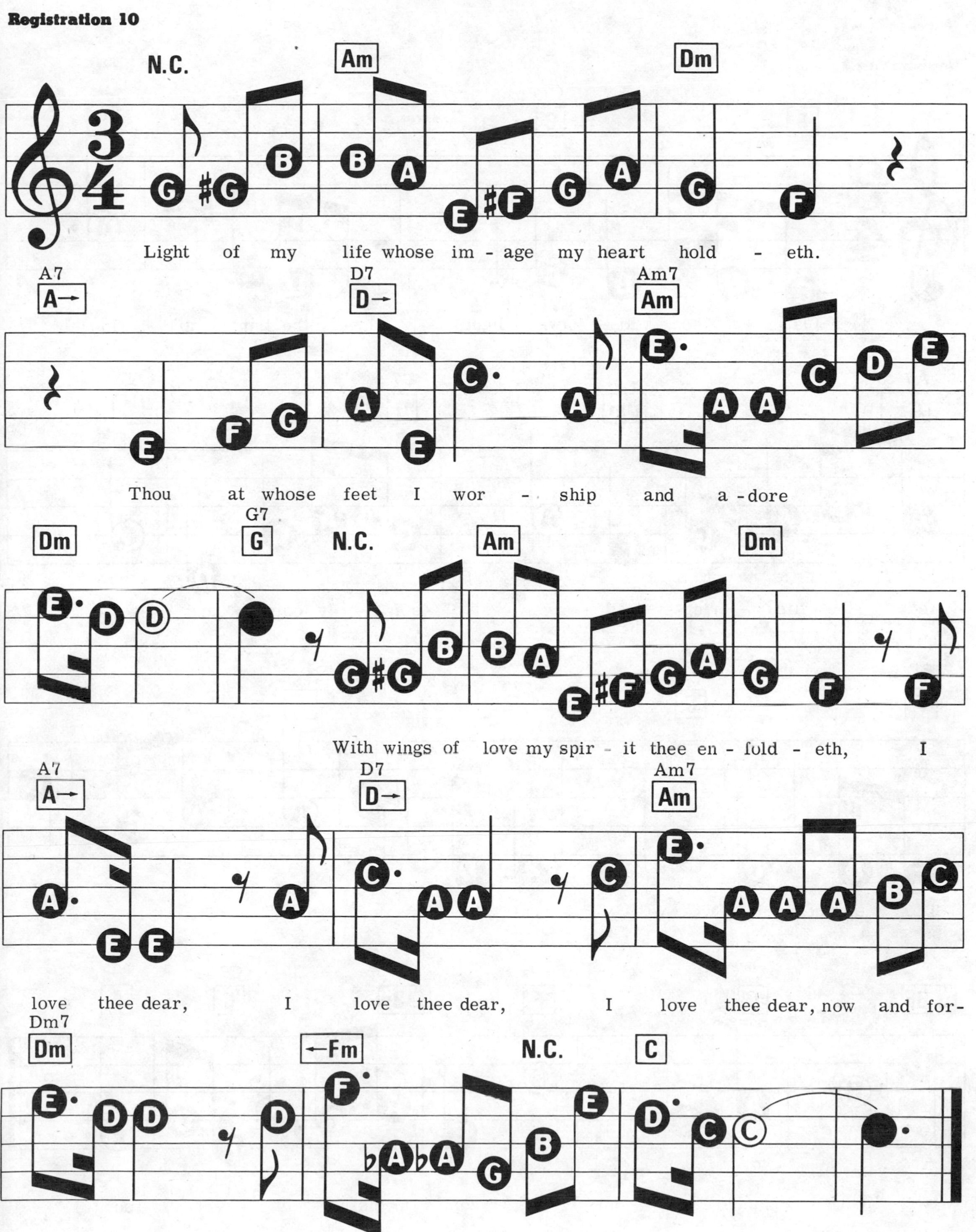

Just A Song At Twilight

Registration 1

Wedding March

Registration 5

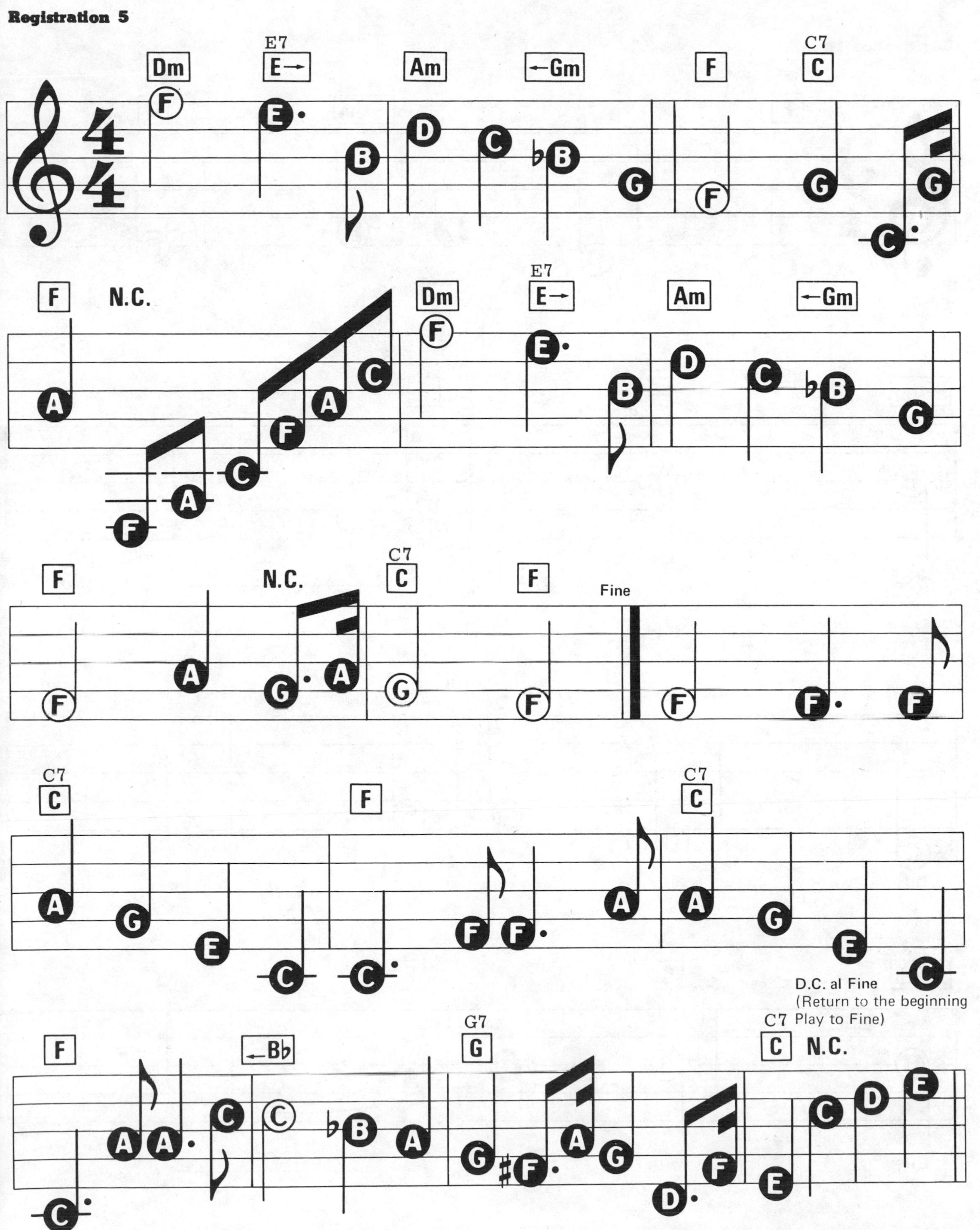

I Love You Truly

Registration 10

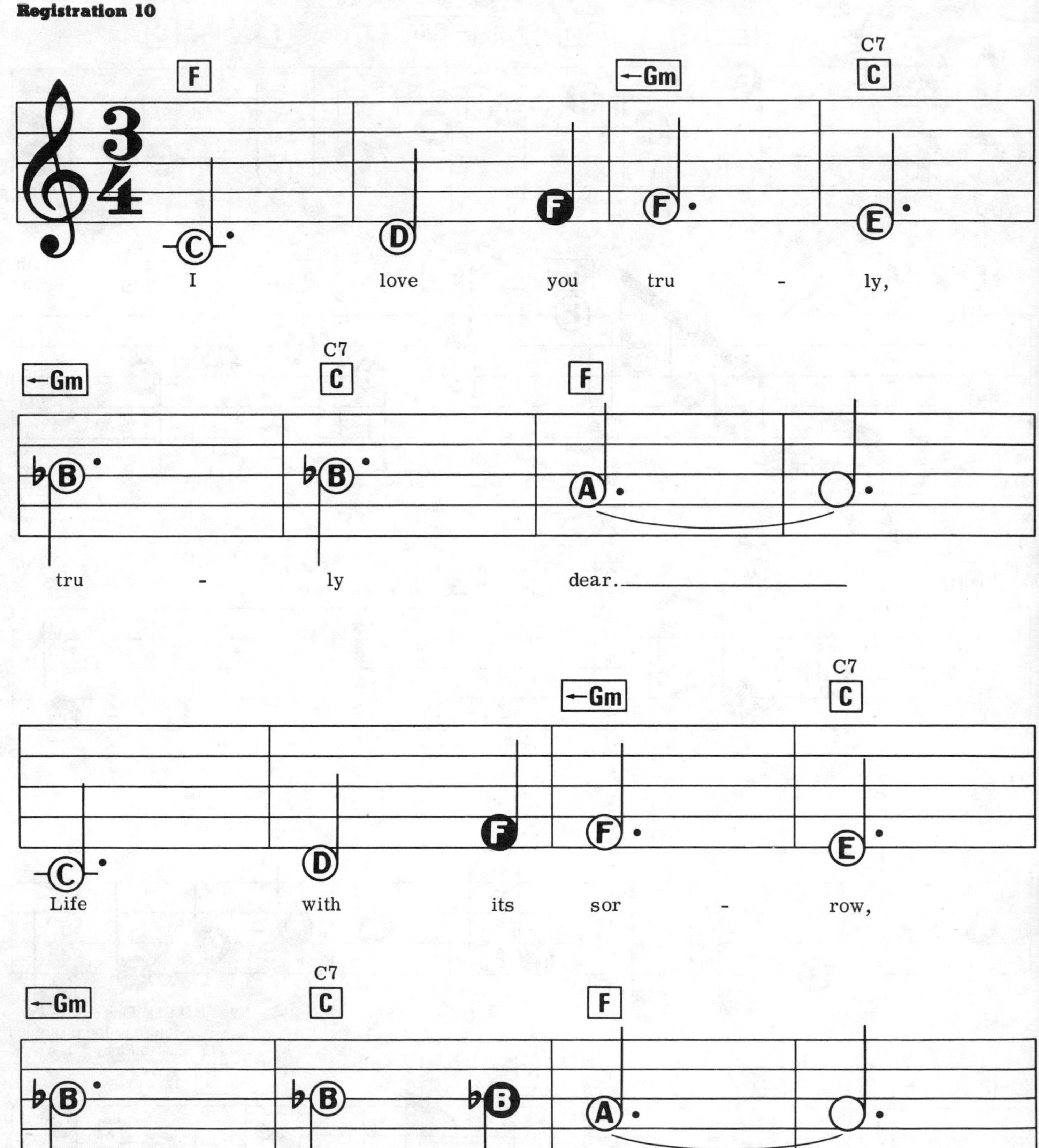

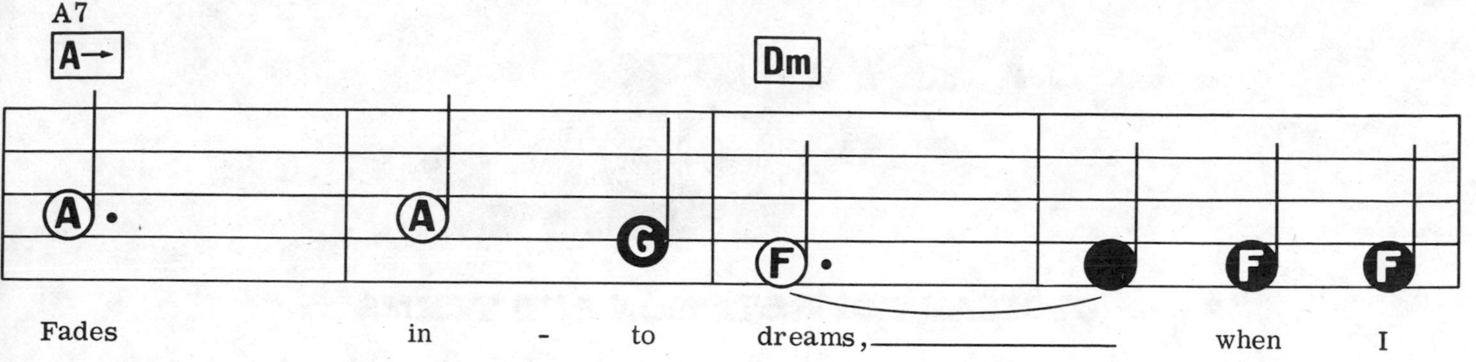
A7
A
Dm
A
A
G
F
F
F
Fades in - to dreams, when I

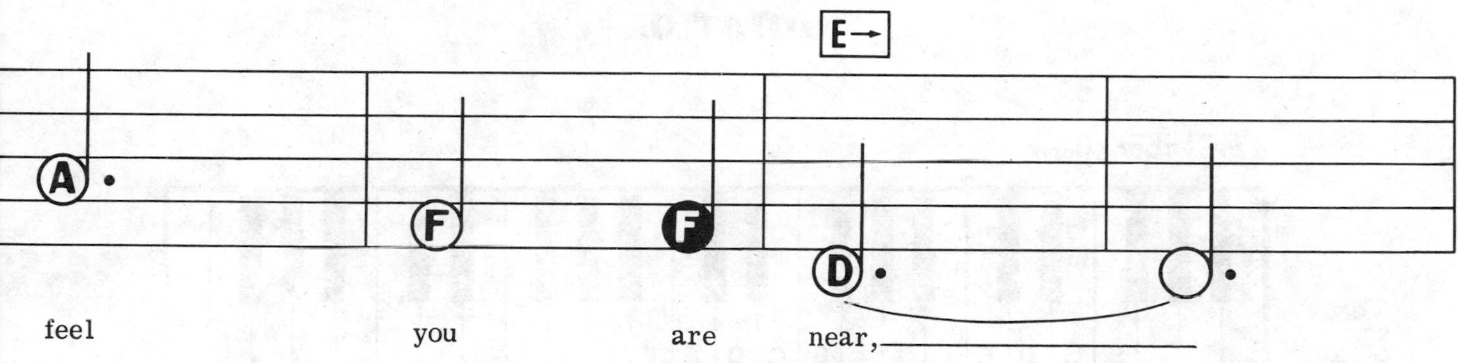
E
A
F
F
D
feel you are near,

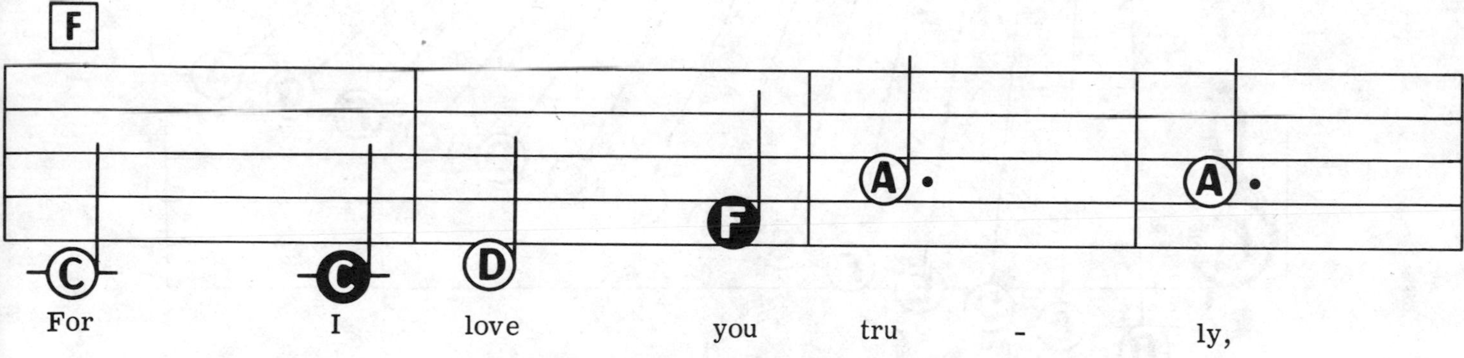
F
C
C
D
F
A
A
For I love you tru - ly,

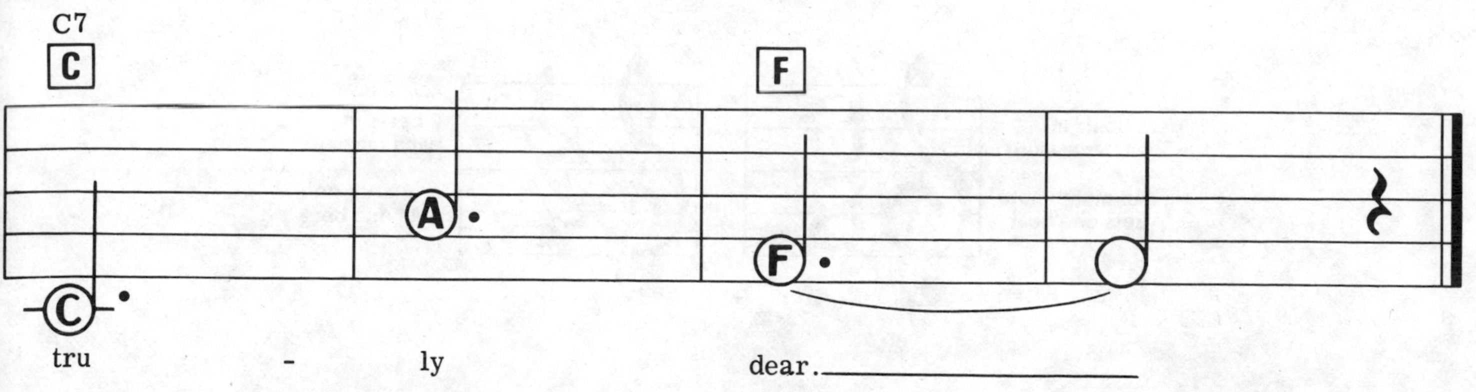
C7
C
F
C
A
F
tru - ly dear.

GLOSSARY OF NOTATION AND TERMS

The following Glossary of Notation and Terms has been included for your reference. Some additional music fundamentals have been included which you may encounter in other songbooks in the E-Z Play TODAY music series.

NOTATION

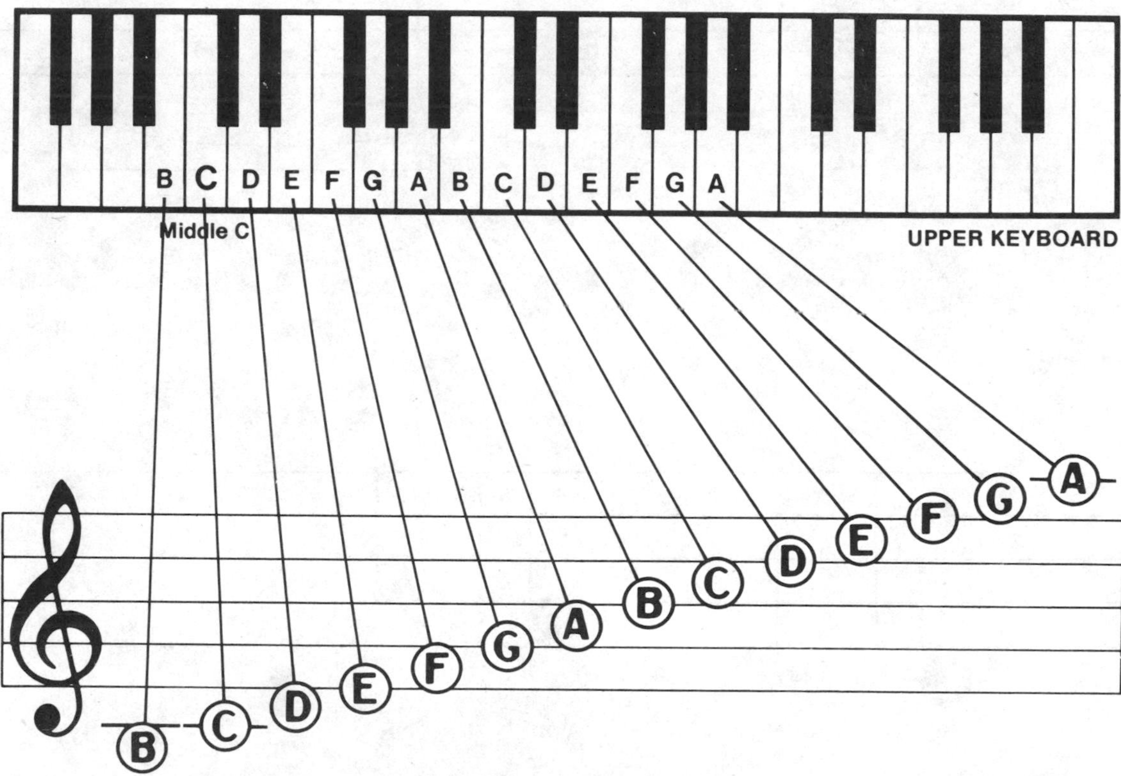

Time Signatures

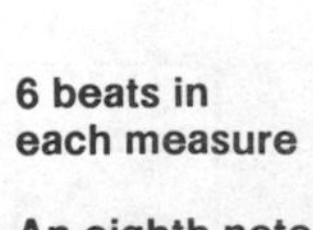

2 beats in each measure

A quarter note gets one beat

Note Values

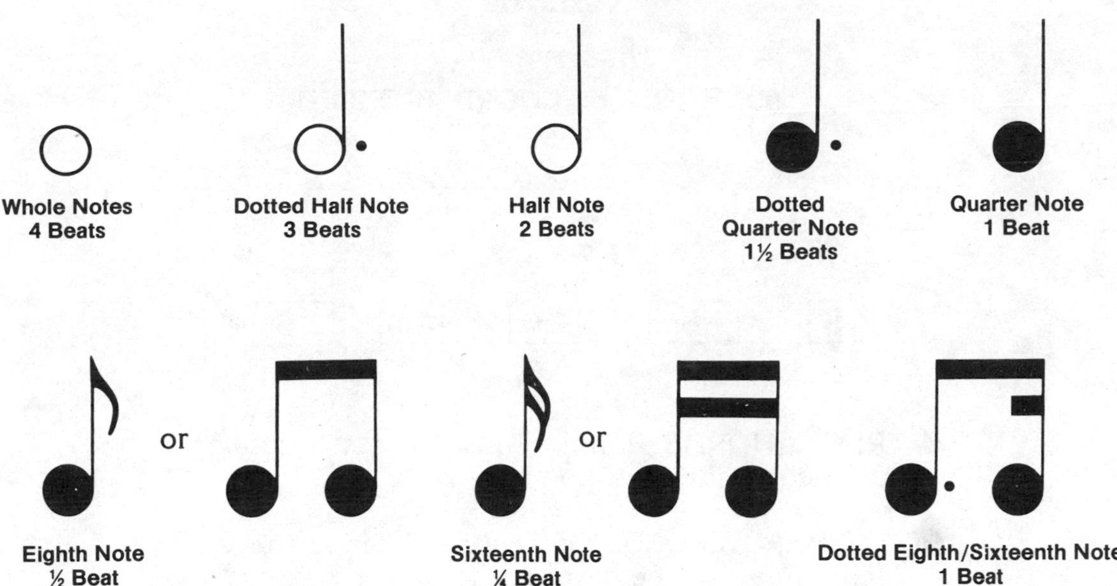

A "triplet" is a group of three notes played in the same amount of time as two notes of the same time value. A triplet is indicated by the number 3 above or below the notes.

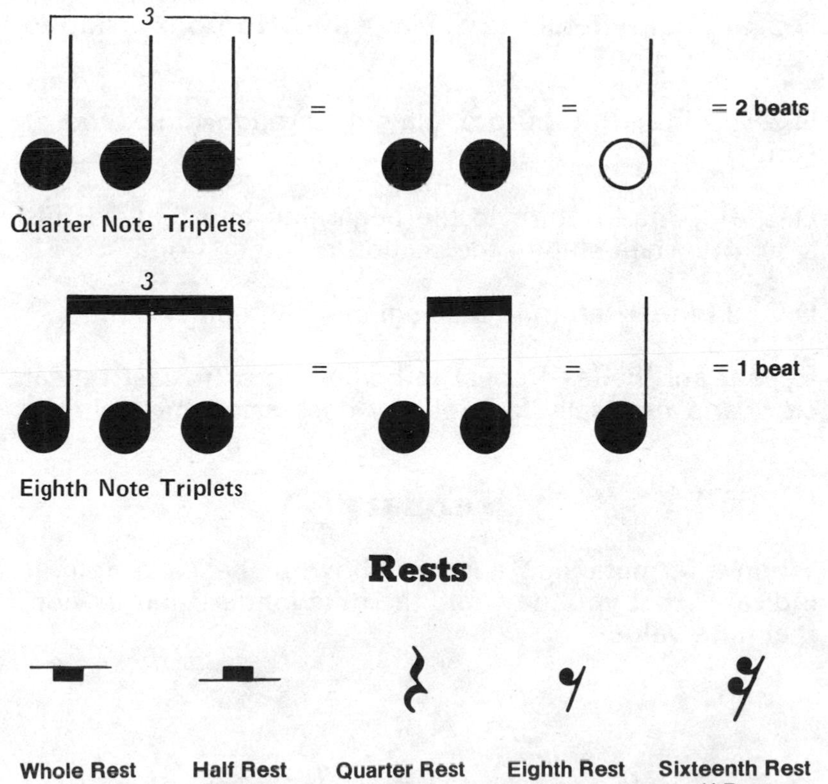

Chords

(ONE KEY or CHORD BUTTON)

C D→ Dm E→ F ←Fm

G ←Gm A→ Am ←B♭

- TRIAD CHORDS—Form all new chords according to the method introduced on page 6.
- STANDARD CHORD POSITIONS—Refer to the Chord Speller Chart on the next page for playing chords used in the E-Z Play TODAY music arrangements.

TERMS

Repeat Signs

D.S. al Coda—Return to 𝄋, play up to "To Coda," skip to "Coda" section.

D.S. al Fine—Return to 𝄋, play up through Fine (end of song).

D.C. al Coda—Return to the beginning and play to this sign 𝄌. Then skip to the section marked "Coda."

D.C. al Fine—Return to the beginning and play to Fine.

Repeat and Fade—Repeat to beginning or to last repeat sign, and gradually fade out by decreasing the volume.

Fermata 𝄐

When a fermata sign appears above or below a note, it indicates that you may hold the note longer than its normal time value.

N.C.

This is an abbreviation for No Chord. Do not play a chord or pedal until the next chord symbol appears.

Chord Speller Chart

of Standard Chord Positions

For those who play standard chord positions, all chords used in the E-Z Play TODAY music arrangements are shown here in their most commonly used chord positions. Suggested fingering is also indicated, but feel free to use alternate fingering.

CHORD FAMILY Abbrev.	MAJOR	MINOR (m)	7TH (7)	MINOR 7TH (m7)
C	5 2 1 G-C-E	5 2 1 G-C-E♭	5 3 2 1 G-B♭-C-E	5 3 2 1 G-B♭-C-E♭
D♭	5 2 1 A♭-D♭-F	5 2 1 A♭-D♭-E	5 3 2 1 A♭-B-D♭-F	5 3 2 1 A♭-B-D♭-E
D	5 3 1 F♯-A-D	5 2 1 A-D-F	5 3 2 1 F♯-A-C-D	5 3 2 1 A-C-D-F
E♭	5 3 1 G-B♭-E♭	5 3 1 G♭-B♭-E♭	5 3 2 1 G-B♭-D♭-E♭	5 3 2 1 G♭-B♭-D♭-E♭
E	5 3 1 G♯-B-E	5 3 1 G-B-E	5 3 2 1 G♯-B-D-E	5 3 2 1 G-B-D-E
F	4 2 1 A-C-F	4 2 1 A♭-C-F	5 3 2 1 A-C-E♭-F	5 3 2 1 A♭-C-E♭-F
F♯	4 2 1 F♯-A♯-C♯	4 2 1 F♯-A-C♯	5 3 2 1 F♯-A♯-C♯-E	5 3 2 1 F♯-A-C♯-E
G	5 3 1 G-B-D	5 3 1 G-B♭-D	5 3 2 1 G-B-D-F	5 3 2 1 G-B♭-D-F
A♭	4 2 1 A♭-C-E♭	4 2 1 A♭-B-E♭	5 3 2 1 A♭-C-E♭-G♭	5 3 2 1 A♭-B-E♭-G♭
A	4 2 1 A-C♯-E	4 2 1 A-C-E	5 4 2 1 G-A-C♯-E	5 4 2 1 G-A-C-E
B♭	4 2 1 B♭-D-F	4 2 1 B♭-D♭-F	5 4 2 1 A♭-B♭-D-F	5 4 2 1 A♭-B♭-D♭-F
B	5 2 1 F♯-B-D♯	5 2 1 F♯-B-D	5 3 2 1 F♯-A-B-D♯	5 3 2 1 F♯-A-B-D

Guitar Chord Chart

To use the E-Z Play TODAY Guitar Chord Chart, simply find the **letter name** of the chord at the top of the chart, and the **kind of chord** (Major, Minor, etc.) in the column at the left. Read down and across to find the correct chord. Suggested fingering has been indicated, but feel free to use alternate fingering.

	C	D♭	D	E♭	E	F
MAJOR						
MINOR (m)						
7TH (7)						
MINOR 7TH (m7)						

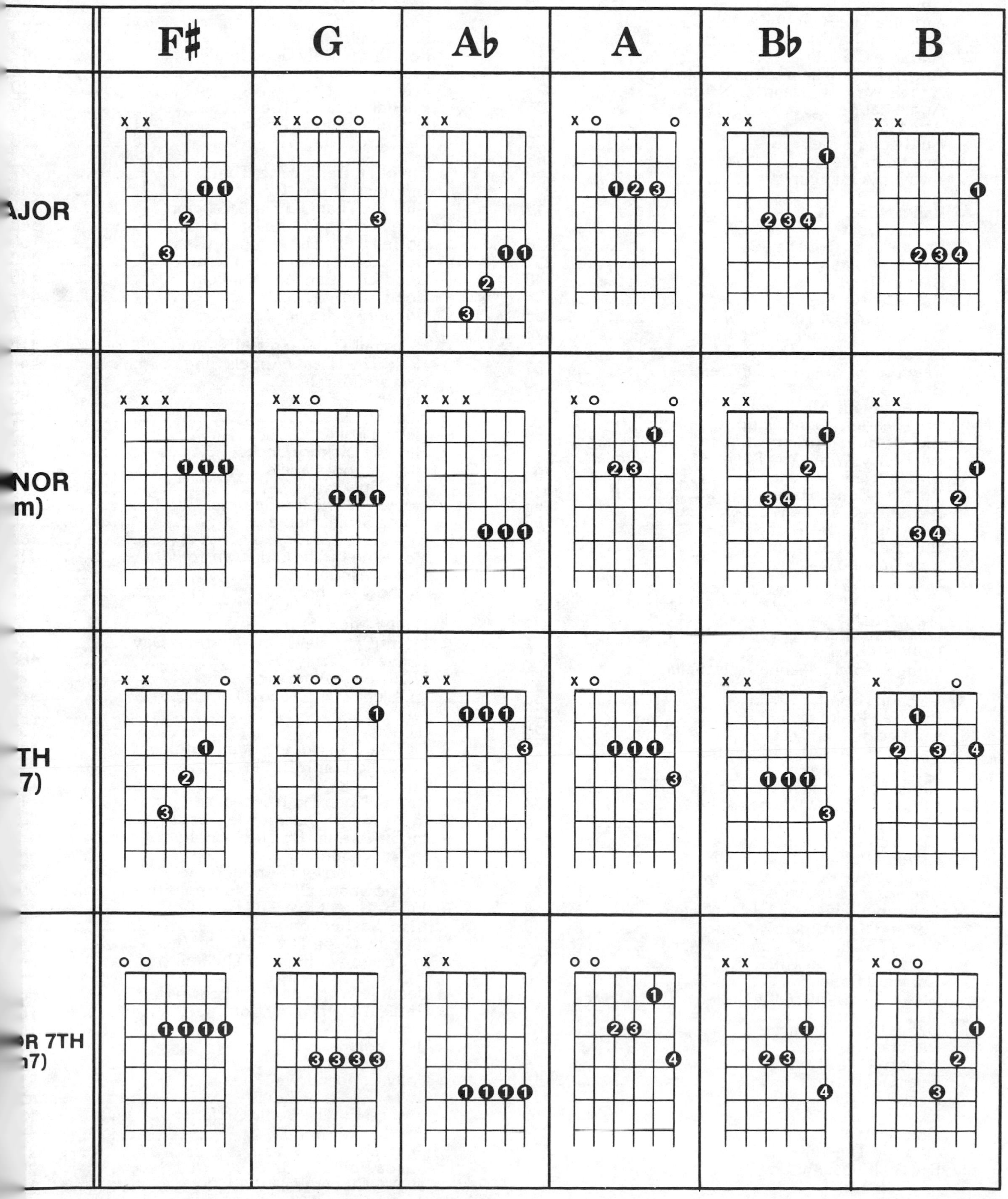

	F♯	G	A♭	A	B♭	B
AJOR						
NOR m)						
TH 7)						
R 7TH n7)						

ALPHABETICAL INDEX